chan

FOURTH EDITION

BSCS Biology

A Human Approach

BSCS

Kendall Hunt
publishing company

Acknowledgments

Fourth Edition Contributors

Content Reviewers

Dr. Amy Angert, Colorado State University, Ft. Collins, CO

Dr. Andrew Ray, Oregon Institute of Technology, Klamath Falls, OR

Dr. Doug Dransfield, Cape Elizabeth, ME

Francoise Benay, University of Colorado, Boulder, CO

Dr. Scott Gilbert, Swarthmore College, Swarthmore, PA

Dr. Katharine Semsar, University of Colorado, Boulder, CO

Dr. Kevin Middleton, California State University, San Bernardino, San Bernardino, CA

Kim Nichols, Biological Sciences Initiative, Boulder, CO

Ronald LaCoss, University of Colorado, Boulder, CO

Dr. Ann Mackenzie, Miami University, Oxford, OH

Dr. Maureen Munn, University of Washington, Seattle, WA

Dr. Chris Ray, University of Colorado, Boulder, CO

Dr. Sam Donovan, University of Pittsburgh, Pittsburgh, PA

Tammy A. Maldonado, University of Colorado, Boulder, CO

Advisors

Joshua Adams, Raymond S. Kellis HS, Glendale, AZ

Margaret Aguilar, Deer Valley USD, Phoenix, AZ

Joni Lee Bartholomew, Raymond S. Kellis HS, Glendale, AZ

Jessica LaNae Batty, Sunrise Mountain, Peoria AZ

Alan Chintis, Mountain View HS, Tucson, AZ

Geraldine Fisher, Desert View HS, Tucson, AZ

Sylvia Janie Garcia-Lohr, Flagstaff HS, Flagstaff, AZ

Joni Giacomino, Buena HS, Bisbee, AZ

Mary Frances Giannola, Flagstaff HS, Flagstaff, AZ

Amanda Lee Grunden, Boulder Creek HS, Anthem, AZ

Erik Hanchett, Safford HS, Safford, AZ

Carolyn Sue Harris, Bisbee HS, Bisbee, AZ

Seth Hoopingarner, Peoria Transition Center, Peoria, AZ

Barry Horst, Douglas HS, Douglas, AZ

Judith Hughes, Peoria HS, Peoria, AZ

Kristen Lee Kaus, Cactus HS, Glendale, AZ

Jeffrey Landers, Page HS, Page, AZ

David Richard Lanning, Page HS, Page, AZ

Stephen Joseph Murray, Catalina Magnet HS, Tucson, AZ

Dwight Rawlings, Raymond S. Kellis HS, Glendale, AZ

Tom Reeder, Ironwood HS, Glendale, AZ

Eric Matthew Regh, Deer Valley USD, Phoenix, AZ

Donna Savill, Douglas HS, Douglas, AZ

Michele Marie Schiff, Ironwood HS, Glendale, AZ

David Serafin, Cactus High School, Glendale, AZ

David Edwin Simmons, Page HS, Page, AZ

William M. Sorensen, Cactus HS, Glendale, AZ

Erin Stuart, Boulder Creek HS, Anthem, AZ

Kelly Neil Thomas, St. Johns HS, St. Johns, AZ

Wendy West, Desert Ridge HS, Gilbert, AZ

Brooke Nicole White, Cactus HS, Glendale, AZ

Howard Yauney, Desert Ridge HS, Gilbert, AZ

Patricia Pauline Zint, Ironwood HS, Glendale, AZ

Second Edition Contributors

Pedagogical Advisors

Scott Charleton, Lebanon High School, Lebanon, OH

Frank Girolami, Mason High School, Mason, OH

Barbara Grosz, Pine Crest Preparatory School, Fort Lauderdale, FL

Melanie Hardel, Hartford Union High School, Hartford, WI

Terry Houchens, Joliet Central High School, Joliet, IL

Mary McClellan, Seattle School District, Seattle, WA

Kimberly Noethen, Cornell University, Ithaca, NY

Eugene O'Brien, Hartford Union High School, Hartford, WI

Members of the BSCS-Human listserv

Content Reviewers

Dr. John G. Bailey, College of Veterinary Medicine, Mississippi State, MS (Chapter 7)

Dr. Marvin Druger, Syracuse University, Syracuse, NY (Chapter 1)

Dr. Diane Ebert-May, Michigan State University, East Lansing, MI (Chapter 9)

Reviewers

Douglas Allchin, University of Texas, El Paso, TX; Tom Anderson, University of Illinois, Champaign, IL; James Botsford, New Mexico State University, Las Cruces, NM; Robert A. Bouchard, College of Wooster, Wooster, OH; Jack Carter, Prof. Emeritus, The Colorado College, Colorado Springs, CO; Frank Cassel, Prof. Emeritus, North Dakota St. University, Fargo, ND; Angelo Collins, Vanderbilt University, Nashville, TN; Robert Cook-Degan, Institute of Medicine, Washington, DC; David Corbin, Monsanto Company, Chesterfield, MO; Jorge Crisci, Museo de La Plata, Argentina; Mary Ann Cutter, University of Colorado, Colorado Springs, CO; Hans Dethlefs, The Neighborhood Health Center—South, Omaha, NE; Edward Drexler, Pius XI High School, Milwaukee, WI; James Ebersole, The Colorado College, Colorado Springs, CO; Diane Ebert-May, Northern Arizona University, Flagstaff, AZ; Philip R. Elliott, The Colorado College, Colorado Springs, CO; Michael Fatone, United States Air Force Academy, CO; Kim Finer, Kent State University,

Canton, OH; Steven Fleck, United States Olympic Center, Colorado Springs, CO; Geoff Gamble, Washington State University, Pullman, WA; Barbara Grosz, Pine Crest School, Fort Lauderdale, FL; Topper Hagerman, Steadman-Hawkins Sports Medicine Foundation, Vail, CO; Jerry Harder, NOAA Aeronomy Laboratory, Boulder, CO; Jeff Hays, United States Air Force Academy, CO; Werner Heim, Prof. Emeritus, The Colorado College, Colorado Springs, CO; Barry Hewlett, Washington State University, Pullman, WA; Michael Hoffman, The Colorado College, Colorado Springs, CO; Michael Keelan, Medical College of Wisconsin, Milwaukee, WI; Rich Kulmacz, University of Texas Health Science Center, Houston, TX; Linda Lundgren, Bear Creek High School, Lakewood, CO; Thomas Manney, Kansas State University, Manhattan, KS; Cheryl Mason, San Diego State University, San Diego, CA; Jeffry Mitton, University of Colorado, Boulder, CO; Adrian Morrison, University of Pennsylvania, Philadelphia, PA; Jamie Nekoba,

Waiákea High School, Hilo, HI; Gene O'Brien, Hartford Union High School, Hartford, WI; John Opitz, Montana State University, Helena, MT; Carl Pierce, Harrington Cancer Center, Amarillo, TX; Tracy Posnanski, University of Wisconsin, Milwaukee, WI; Ken Rainis, Ward's Natural Science Establishment, Inc., Rochester, NY; Barbara Saigo, Saiwood Biology Resources, Montgomery, AL; Orwyn Sampson, Brigadier General Retired, United States Air Force Academy, CO; James Short, Packer Collegiate Institute, Brooklyn, NY; James Siedow, Duke University, Durham, NC; Fran Slowiczek, San Diego City Schools, San Diego, CA; Susan Speece, Fresno City College, Fresno, CA; Sam Stoler, National Institutes of Health, Washington, DC; Richard Storey, The Colorado College, Colorado Springs, CO; Gordon E. Uno, University of Oklahoma, Norman, OK; Jeff Velten, New Mexico State University, Las Cruces, NM; Mariana Wolfner, Cornell University, Ithaca, NY

Field Test Site Centers and Coordinators

Arizona

Northern Arizona University, Flagstaff, AZ: Diane Ebert-May, Julie McCormick, Brownie Sternberg

Colorado

BSCS, Colorado Springs, CO: Laura J. Laughran, Randall K. Backe

University of Northern Colorado, Greeley, CO: April Gardner, Alan Lennon, Brenda Zink

Florida

University of South Florida, Tampa, FL: Barbara Spector, Leslie Brackin, Craig Holm

Kansas

Kansas State University, Manhattan, KS: Gail Shroyer, Carol Arjona

Ohio

Miami University, Oxford, OH: Jane Butler Kahle, Rick Fairman

Washington

University of Washington, Seattle, WA: Carole Kubota, Claire McDaniel Orner

v

Field Test Schools and Teachers

Colombia, South America

Haydée Bejardno de Cadena, Marcela Melendez, Monica Sarmiento, Colegio Los Nogales, Bogotá

Arizona

Marcia Fisher, Arcadia High School, Scottsdale; Doug Davis, Dub Manis, Dee Schwartz, Chinle High School, Chinle; Geri Fisher, Jo Quintenz, Desert View High School, Tucson; Kathy Thayer, Ray High School, Ray; Clyde Christensen, Scott Greenhalgh, Ray Pool, Mary Southall, Elizabeth Stone, Tempe High School, Tempe; Willie Long Reed, Tuba City High School, Tuba City; Jack Johnson, Williams High School, Williams; Carlos Estrada, Karen Steele, Window Rock High School, Fort Defiance

Colorado

Don Born, Peggy Wickliff, Air Academy High School, United States Air Force Academy; Linda Lynch, Douglas County High School, Castle Rock; Doug Hewins, Liberty High School, Colorado Springs; Barbara Andrews, Mitchell High School, Colorado Springs; Rata Clarke, Ray Coddington, Jean Orton, Jim Snare, Palmer High School, Colorado Springs; Rod Baker, Michele Girard, Peyton High School, Peyton; Kathy Dorman, Malcom Hovde, Ponderosa High School, Parker; Ann Pollet, Deborah Walters, Pueblo County High School, Pueblo; Glen Smith, Sabin Junior High School, Colorado Springs; Jeff Cogburn, B.J. Stone, Valley High School, Gilcrest; Bill Bragg, Wasson High School, Colorado Springs; Larry Jakel, Doug Steward, Weld Central High School, Keenesburg; Jay Matheson, West Center for Intergenerational Learning, Colorado Springs; Christy Beauprez, Glenn Peterson, Windsor High School, Windsor

Florida

James Happel, Constance Hopkins, Manatee High School, Bradenton; Scott MacGregor, Joe Martin, Palmetto High School, Palmetto; Barbara Grosz, Pine Crest School, Fort Lauderdale

Hawaii

Jamie Nekoba, Waiákea High School, Hilo; Jennifer Busto, Maryknoll Schools, Honolulu

Illinois

Shelly Peretz, Thornridge High School, Dolton

Kansas

J.D. Hand, Chuck Mowry, Gina Whaley, Junction City Senior High School, Junction City

Minnesota

Clyde Cummins, St. Paul Academy Summit School, St. Paul

Missouri

David Jungmeyer, California R-1 High School, California

New Jersey

Judith Jones, Saint John Vianney High School, Holmdel; Margaret Sheldon, West Morris Central High School, Chester; Karen Martin, West Morris Mendham High School, Mendham

Ohio

Barbara Blackwell, Susan Keiffer-Barone, Aiken High School, Cincinnati; Scott Popoff, Sycamore High School, Cincinnati

Texas

Peter Mariner, Francis Mikan, Dean Mohlman, Tom Stege, St. Stephen's Episcopal School, Austin

Washington

Kathleen Heidenrich, Vicky Lamoreaux, River Ridge High School, Lacey; Larry Bencivengo, Mary Margaret Welch, Mercer Island High School, Mercer Island; Mary Ketchum, Jeannie Wenndorf, Lindberg High School, Renton; Gro Buer, Carol Nussbaum, B.E.S.T. Alternative School, Kirkland; Connie Kelly, Diane Lashinsky, Patrick Taylor, Shorecrest High School, Seattle

Wisconsin

Gene O'Brien, Hartford Union High School, Hartford

Contents

Being a Scientist — Engage   2

Evolution: Change in Living Systems — Unit 1   24

Homeostasis: Maintaining Dynamic Equilibrium in Living Systems   204

Unit 2

Ecology: Interaction and Interdependence in Living Systems   758
Unit 6

Thinking Like a Biologist   818
Evaluate

Appendices

Dear Learners:

The staff at BSCS developed *BSCS Biology: A Human Approach* for students first. Not all of the programs you use are developed this way. But we feel that focusing on the student is the only way to provide you with the best biology learning experience possible. As you glance through this book, notice that this is not a passive, encyclopedic approach to biology. You will not sit day after day in lectures. Instead, this program's print and digital tools help you learn biology through active involvement.

BSCS cares about the quality of its programs because we care about students and teachers. We are a nonprofit organization where scientists and educators are dedicated to improving science education. *BSCS Biology: A Human Approach* is the result of BSCS's study of the research in biology and learning. We think it is a better way to help students learn biology. When we defined the word "better," we decided that a better high school biology program would mean the following:

- More emphasis on the big concepts of biology and less emphasis on vocabulary words
- More connections between biological concepts and your life
- More opportunities to conduct investigations that you design
- More ways to gain an understanding of how science works
- More learning strategies to help you get the most out of your work

In the program overview on the next several pages, you can read about how we put these differences into practice in *BSCS Biology: A Human Approach*. The overview describes the key features of the program that we think make it noticeably different from and better than other texts. To make sure our ideas worked in classrooms, we spent 2½ school years testing our ideas in classrooms with approximately 80 teachers and 5,000 students. Then, after students and teachers used our program for several years, we took all the feedback we received from classrooms around the nation. We combined that with current research on how people learn and used that information to improve the program. In addition, many biologists and educators reviewed the materials to make sure they were accurate and current at the time we published. We list these contributors and reviewers at the front of the book.

Hundreds of people work together to create one new BSCS program. This process never ends as long as the program is active. If you read something that you think is confusing or inaccurate, or if you have suggestions for improving an activity, please write to us or email us at info@bscs.org. We will consider your comments when we revise the program in later editions. Our mailing address is

BSCS Biology: A Human Approach Revision Team
BSCS
5415 Mark Dabling Boulevard
Colorado Springs, CO 80918-3842
info@bscs.org

We hope you enjoy learning biology in this new way. We enjoyed putting this program together for you because learners are the most important people in schools.

Sincerely,
The Project Staff

Program Overview

The letter from the project staff states that *BSCS Biology: A Human Approach* is a better way to learn biology. Six key features of the program help explain why we think this program is better. We describe each feature below.

I. Unifying Themes

We organized the program into three sections and six core units. The three sections are the Engage, Explain, and Evaluate Sections. They come at the beginning, middle, and end of the program and are described under the *Instructional Model* heading. We organized the six core units around six major biological concepts. These concepts are recurring themes that unify all of biology. Although you will see these themes in every unit, we focus on one theme in each unit.

Evolution: Change in Living Systems

How do organisms, including humans, change through time? This is the central question of Unit 1. You will assess the unique qualities of humans and the diversity of life while trying to place humans in the scheme of living systems. Then you will consider how evolution provides an explanation for the adaptations organisms display and the existence of great biological diversity on Earth. Unity, diversity, common ancestry, and evolution, including cultural evolution, are the major conceptual themes in Unit 1.

Homeostasis: Maintaining Dynamic Equilibrium in Living Systems

Unit 2 explores the controlled internal environment that all organisms require to function well. You will use familiar examples to develop an understanding of the concepts of response, regulation, and feedback. Then you will examine the division between internal and external conditions. You will look at the processes by which internal conditions are maintained in spite of changes in external conditions. In the final chapter of the unit, you will expand these concepts by analyzing the way health and disease affects both the individual human and society as a group.

Energy, Matter, and Organization: Relationships in Living Systems

Unit 3 begins by letting you explore the requirements of physical performance and consider the effects of fitness, drugs, and alcohol on performance. You will develop an understanding of the relationship between structure and function. You also will explore the interplay between energy and matter. You will do this by studying metabolic processes such as photosynthesis and cellular respiration as well as through interactions in a community. Finally, you will consider the role of producers, consumers, and decomposers in the flow of energy and cycling of matter in a community.

Continuity: Reproduction and Inheritance in Living Systems

Unit 4 focuses on reproduction, the role of genes and DNA in inheritance, and patterns of inheritance. The discussion of human sexual reproduction includes reproductive systems and cycles, reproductive behavior, and ethical issues, such as contraception and sexually transmitted diseases. You will consider how genes are a source of coded information and study the dynamics of gene expression and replication at a molecular level. This provides a basis for understanding genetic engineering. Finally, you will investigate how genetics can explain patterns of inherited traits in humans and other organisms.

Development: Growth and Differentiation in Living Systems

As Unit 5 begins, you will consider development as a process that involves cell division and cell differentiation and that requires regulation. You will explore patterns of development in a variety of organisms, including humans. Development is affected by evolutionary history and provides opportunities for evolutionary change. Finally, you will consider human development across all stages of life. You will look at genetically influenced events as well as the cultural environment in which they take place.

Ecology: Interaction and Interdependence in Living Systems

Unit 6 centers on ecological concepts and environmental issues. You will learn about interactions among populations, resources, and environments, and dilemmas that often arise from these interactions. You will examine the concepts involved in population dynamics. This sets the stage for studying the interactions between humans and their environment. Next, you will focus on how human actions can modify the environment, especially by using technology. The final emphasis is on how humans can work together to generate policies that guide the use of common resources.

II. Subthemes

Two subthemes, or background ideas, are woven through the entire program. They help to establish connections between biology and your life. They improve your reasoning ability. The Science as Inquiry subtheme refers to the discovery process by which information is obtained and evaluated. It also refers to the changing body of knowledge that characterizes scientific understanding. This theme systematically exposes you to the processes of science. This includes making observations, making inferences, assembling evidence, developing hypotheses, designing experiments, collecting data, analyzing and presenting results, and communicating and evaluating conclusions.

The Science and Humanity subtheme makes your study of biology more relevant and approachable. It does this by incorporating the critical elements of human culture; the history of science; the place of ethics, ethical analysis, and decision making in a world that is increasingly shaped by science and technology; and the importance of human technology as a way of adapting. We define technology as the use of knowledge to achieve a practical solution to a perceived problem. We also recognize that the ultimate effects of the technological process or product on society and the biosphere may extend beyond the intended effects.

III. Instructional Model

We organized the instruction of major concepts in this book around a model of learning that recognizes how individuals build or construct new ideas. This model is known as the BSCS 5E Instructional Model. The program is organized around five phases of learning that we best can describe using words that begin with E: Engage, Explore, Explain, Elaborate, and Evaluate. The entire book is shaped by this model. You will get an overview of the program by completing the *Engage* Section. Units 1 to 3 let you *explore* the big ideas of scientific inquiry. The *Explain* Section then sets you up to conduct your own scientific inquiry. Units 4 to 6 are designed to help you *elaborate* your understanding of the processes of science. The *Evaluate* Section provides several opportunities for you to evaluate your progress in learning biology.

Furthermore, each chapter of the book uses the BSCS 5E Instructional Model as a framework. Each chapter begins with an activity which helps you *engage* the big idea of the chapter and articulate any initial ideas you have around the chapter's topics of study. Next, you will take part in activities that help you *explore* concepts and information related to the chapter. In the middle of the chapter, you will encounter an activity that will give you the opportunity to construct an *explanation* of what you have been learning. Later activities in the chapter are designed to help you *elaborate* your learning by either broadening your knowledge to include new examples, or deepening your understanding of the explanation you have developed. In each chapter, the final activity helps you bring together all of the learning you have done and *evaluate* your understanding.

IV. Cooperative Learning

Cooperative learning is an educational strategy that helps you increase your responsibility for your own learning. Cooperative learning also models the processes that scientists use when collaborating. It helps you develop the working relationship skills necessary for today's workforce.

V. Assessment

Assessment opportunities allow you to evaluate your progress. These activities are embedded throughout the program, and the assessments themselves are learning experiences. The following assessment strategies are included in the program:

- Assessments of your performance, such as experiments
- Written tests that have a variety of short-answer and essay questions
- Assessments of cooperative learning skills
- Presentations, both by teams and by individuals
- Written assignments, both by teams and by individuals
- Journal assignments that include short-term and long-term work
- Projects, both ongoing and one-time
- An ongoing activity about an organism you "adopt"
- Opportunities for self-assessment and peer assessment
- Discussions, both by teams and by the whole class

VI. Educational Technology

Educational technology is integral to the program. It is used as a tool to enhance learning and understanding. *BSCS Biology: A Human Approach* now provides access to many electronic tools through **Flourish,** Kendall Hunt's new learning network.

Flourish is a one-stop location for:

- The interactive **eBook** version of your textbook
- Point-of-use links to **video clip segments, readings,** and **interactive animations** and **simulations**
- Quick click **English** and **Spanish** audio and text
- **SciLinks®** Internet sites which provide information and activities specific to topics in the program

In addition where appropriate, you will find instructions for using **Probe ware,** and options for computer-based laboratory work.

Symbols Used in This Program*

 Science Notebook

 Audio and text available online

 Poison

 Flourish Learning Network

 Caution

 Lab Apron

 SciLinks

 Irritant

 Lab Gloves

 Audio available online

 Flammable

 Safety Goggles

* Refer to the need to know in appendix A, Safety Symbols Used in This Program.

FOURTH EDITION

BSCS Biology

A Human Approach

> *The whole of science is nothing more than a refinement of everyday thinking.*
>
> Albert Einstein

When faced with a problem or a puzzle, how do you figure things out? You might answer, "I think about them." But are you aware of *how* you think? *BSCS Biology: A Human Approach* focuses on science as one of the important ways humans understand and explain their world. The activities throughout this program encourage you to think as a scientist does. This short section is titled *Engage* because it engages you in the type of experiences that you will have in this course. In this section, you will begin to use some of the same techniques scientists use to carry out their work.

Chapter organizers help you remember what you have learned and where you are headed. They also help you recognize the most important concepts to learn in a chapter. Look at the chapter organizer every day. Think about where you are in the flow of the chapter. The organizer provides a way to compare what you know now with what you knew a week ago. You can use the chapter organizer to help you map your learning and monitor your progress. Then you can look back and see what you have accomplished.

GOALS FOR THE SECTION

In the *Engage* section, you will work to gain an understanding of these ideas:

✔ Scientific inquiry can be used to study questions about living systems.

✔ Science is a part of many aspects of life outside the science classroom.

To help you develop this understanding, you will carry out the following activities.

ENGAGE	Cooperating like a Scientist
EXPLORE	Communicating like a Scientist
EXPLAIN	Thinking as a Scientist Thinks
ELABORATE	Recording Data in Your Science Notebook
EVALUATE	You and the Science of Biology

ENGAGE

Cooperating like a Scientist

Key Idea: Cooperation plays an important role in doing science.

Linking Question:
How do scientists communicate with one another when they work together?

Engage

MAJOR CONCEPTS

✔ Cooperation and communication are necessary skills when doing science.

✔ Doing science involves asking questions, gathering evidence, and proposing explanations.

✔ Graphing is a method for clearly and accurately reporting information.

✔ Science is relevant to life.

✔ Biology can be organized into six big ideas.

EXPLORE

Communicating like a Scientist

Part A: Your Science Notebook: Recording Your Thoughts and Observations

Part B: Using Drawings to Record Observations

Part C: Using Words to Record Observations

Key Idea: Scientists can communicate about their work through speaking, writing, and drawing.

Linking Question:
What role do observations play in a scientific experiment?

EVALUATE

You and the Science of Biology

Key Idea: Thinking scientifically helps people make informed decisions and choices.

Being a Scientist

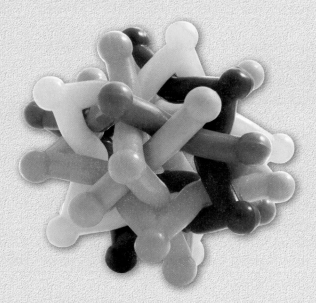

Linking Question:
How do I link the skills I have learned about science to my life?

ELABORATE

Recording Data in Your Science Notebook

Key Idea: Graphing is a way for scientists to report information clearly and accurately.

Linking Question:
How can a scientist report his or her results to others?

EXPLAIN

Thinking as a Scientist Thinks

Key Idea: Scientists ask questions, gather information, use reasoning, and develop explanations when they carry out their work.

ENGAGE

Cooperating like a Scientist

Imagine a scientist at work. Do you see a man in a white coat working alone? Scientists come in all shapes and sizes—men and women from all cultures—and they rarely work in isolation. Usually, two or more scientists work cooperatively to make scientific breakthroughs possible. In this Engage activity, *Cooperating like a Scientist*, you will look at the role that cooperation plays in science.

Materials

items needed to play the radar game
different-colored pens or pencils

PROCESS AND PROCEDURES

1. Work with a partner to "brainstorm" a list in response to this question: "What is science?" Write down your best ideas in your science notebook.
2. Exchange lists with another team of 2 and discuss the similarities and differences among your ideas.
3. Join another pair of lab partners as directed by your teacher so that you have a team of 4 together at 1 table. Your new team will play the radar game.
4. Choose 2 people to be "blinds" (persons wearing blindfolds) and 2 people to be "helpers."
5. Have the 2 students who will be the blinds sit on the same side of the table. Helpers sit on the opposite side of the table.
6. Read the rules for the radar game in the need to know, *Game Rules*. Follow these rules for the rest of the game.
7. Obtain a clean blindfold from your teacher. Helpers blindfold their blinds. Blinds must stay blindfolded and remain seated for the entire activity.

CAUTION: Be sure to stay seated anytime you are wearing a blindfold.

8. Follow the instructions given by your teacher, and proceed with the radar game.
9. Participate in a class discussion of your success with the radar game. Answer the following questions.
   a. How close did you come to accomplishing the task?
   b. What surprised you about this activity?
   c. How did you feel during the game?
   d. Why did you feel the way you did?
   e. If you could change the rules of the radar game, how would you change them?
   f. How does this game relate to the work that scientists do?

NEED TO KNOW

ENGLISH SPANISH

Game Rules

1. Helpers may not touch any materials or the blinds. (If a blind drops something, however, helpers may retrieve the material and give it back to the blind.)

2. Helpers may not talk. They may not talk to the teacher, their blinds, or helpers or blinds from other teams. Helpers may not speak to answer a question even if a blind asks. Helpers pretend that they are completely mute. Helpers cannot make any sounds using their voices.

3. Helpers and blinds may not use any materials other than those your teacher instructed you to get after the blindfolds are in place.

4. Blinds *may* talk. They may talk to each other, to the teacher, to their helpers, and to helpers and blinds from other teams.

5. Blinds may touch the materials.

10. Look back at the list you wrote in step 1. Using a different-colored pen or pencil, revise your list to include the role that communication plays in doing science.

> You will frequently be asked to revise what you have written throughout this program. Each time, you will use a different-colored pen or pencil. This process will help you stay aware of how your thinking changes over time, which is an important part of learning.

Communicating like a Scientist

EXPLORE

The radar game required cooperation. You will continue to develop and use cooperation skills throughout this program. You will also develop other skills of working like a scientist, such as strong communication habits. One of the most important tasks of a scientist is to accurately record ideas and data to share with other scientists and the public. In this Explore activity, *Communicating like a Scientist*, you will practice the different ways scientists can record ideas.

Materials

Part A (per student)
1 spiral or composition notebook

Part B (per student)
1 unknown object
1 soft pencil (no. 2)
blank drawing paper
1 ruler

Part C (per team of 2)
1 termite
1 small paintbrush or cotton swab

PROCESS AND PROCEDURES

Part A   Your Science Notebook: Recording Your Thoughts and Observations

1. Examine the following list of ways that you will use your science notebook in this class.
   a. Recording data
   b. Responding to questions
   c. Taking notes
   d. Keeping track of your questions
   e. Keeping track of your responsibilities
   f. Using your science notebook during assessment

2. Read appendix B1, *How to Use the Science Notebook*. As you read, list the important points that you need to remember about each way of using the science notebook.

3. Obtain a *Science Notebook Techniques Rubric* from your teacher to help you evaluate your science notebook techniques. Read and discuss the rubric with your partner. Record any questions you have about science notebook evaluation.

   > A rubric is a guide that you and your teacher will use to determine how well you accomplished the goals of an assignment or task. You should be able to read a rubric and understand exactly what you need to do to be successful.

4. Participate in a class discussion about science notebook techniques. Think about the following questions.
   a. What are the differences between keeping a science notebook and writing a laboratory report?
   b. What do you think sounds the most interesting about keeping a science notebook?
   c. What part of keeping a science notebook sounds the most challenging?

HOW TO

© Dreamstime/Michelle Milliman

Part B   Using Drawings to Record Observations*

"A picture is worth a thousand words." This familiar saying can be true when you are recording scientific observations. In your science notebook, you must carefully describe the observations that you make, and a drawing can be an excellent way to describe an object. In this activity, you will work on the art of making careful observations. You do not need any drawing skills to be able to learn to sketch what you see.

Observing and Describing

1. Decide which person will be the observer. The other person will identify an object without seeing or touching it.
2. The observer will select an object in the room without showing it to his or her partner.
3. Sit back-to-back with your partner. The observer holds the selected object.
4. The observer will describe the object to his or her partner but can only describe the object with the art terms listed in the need to know, *Art Terms*.

NEED TO KNOW ENGLISH SPANISH

Art Terms

- **Line:** A line can be horizontal, vertical, diagonal, broken, wavy, and so forth. Length is the most important dimension of line.
- **Space:** Space is the area between, around, above, below, or within.
- **Shape:** Shapes can be geometric or lack a specific form. Shape is the length and width of an object.
- **Form:** There are five fundamental forms in nature: sphere, cube, cone, pyramid, and cylinder.
- **Texture:** Texture is the surface quality of an object. It can either be a real texture that you can feel or a visible texture that you see. It is the look and feel of the surface of an object.
- **Value:** Value is the relative lightness or darkness of areas.
- **Color:** Color is composed of three distinct properties:
  a. Hue: The name of a color
  b. Value: The lightness (tint) or darkness (shade)
  c. Intensity: The quality of brightness or dullness

---

* Brian C. Dempsey and B.J. Betz, authors. Adapted from *The American Biology Teacher* with permission from the National Association of Biology Teachers.

5. After the partner has correctly identified the object, switch roles and obtain a new, unknown object for the second observer to describe.
6. Record in your science notebook the 3 art terms you found the most useful for describing the object. Explain which terms you found the most difficult to use.

Experimenting with the Pencil Line

For this task, you will use your pencil and 1 sheet of paper and will work individually. You will have 3 minutes to make a variety of marks on the paper. Be imaginative and feel free to experiment (figure En.1). Use the point and the side of the pencil to create lines of varying length, thickness, and shape and to create shading effects. Your objective is to become familiar with the pencil and the various effects you can create with it.

**Figure En.1
Experiment with your pencil.**

Making a Detailed Drawing

A detailed drawing records accurate information about the material. In this type of drawing, keep your interpretation to a minimum. The goal is to draw only what is visible and to select those details that are the most important observations to capture in a drawing.

1. Work individually to draw the object that your partner described to you.
2. Begin by making a simple line drawing that accurately captures the basic shape, size, and proportion of the object.
3. Add details to your line drawing using some of the effects that you developed in your pencil-line experimentation.
4. How long did it take to make your drawing as accurate as possible?
   When you think about how long you should take to make a drawing in your science notebook, remember your detailed drawing. Any drawing that you make to accurately record your observations will take time and concentration.
5. When your drawing is complete, label it to indicate the relative size of the drawing to the real object (for example, one-half actual size or 10× magnification).
6. Attach your completed drawing to a page in your science notebook.

Part C   Using Words to Record Observations

Sometimes it is more useful to describe what you see, rather than using a picture to record observations. One example where words may be helpful is when you are describing the behavior of an organism. In this activity, you will make observations about the behavior of termites.

Termites are social insects that live in colonies. A typical colony contains workers, soldiers, and reproductive individuals. Termites feed on dead plant material, such as wood. Although they are not in their natural setting in a classroom, you may still use them to make observations about how they move and behave.

1. Obtain a termite and a paintbrush or cotton swab (figure En.2).
2. With your team, spend several minutes carefully observing your termite. You might try to answer questions such as these.
   a. What are the characteristics of the termite's body?
   b. How do the legs of the termite coordinate with one another?
   c. How does the termite respond to a paintbrush or cotton swab placed in its path?

   > Termites are soft-bodied insects and must not be pinched. Use the soft bristles of the paintbrush or a cotton swab to block your termite and redirect it. *Do not* try to pick up your termite with your fingers or push it around with the paintbrush.

3. In your science notebook, write down at least 5 observations about your termite.

   > When you are making observations, remember to only write those things you can see. Do not try to assign meaning to the organism's behavior. For example, saying that the termite ran away because it was afraid of being crushed is not an objective observation. A good observation might be that the termite moved quickly in the opposite direction of the cotton swab.

4. Share your observations with your partner and discuss whether they are good observations.

Figure En.2
To move the termite without harming it, block the termite's path without touching it.

Analysis

Use the following questions to help you think about scientific observations. Work individually unless otherwise instructed.

1. Answer the following questions in your science notebook.
   a. How did your drawings differ when your partner described the object to you and when you were looking at the object?
   b. Based on this experience, what advice would you give to someone about how to communicate effectively?
2. Explain whether or not you think scientific observations are completely objective. Provide an example to illustrate your point of view.
3. Read the following paragraphs about the importance of science notebooks. When you have finished reading, brainstorm with your partner about examples of information that might be important for a scientist to record in his or her science notebook.

   > Like a scientist, you will keep a science notebook throughout this course. The accuracy with which you describe events in your science notebook is important. This will allow you to compare your observations with those of others. For example, your records should show important information about what might have caused differences in investigations that you and your classmates do in your classroom. Keeping an accurate science notebook is also a vital way to keep track of your ideas. You can look back and see how your thinking has changed.

   > A science notebook also helps scientists communicate with others about their work so that their peers and the public may review the work.

Accurate record keeping makes it possible for scientists to repeat experiments and see whether they obtain the same results. This process of repeating experiments is essential in order for other people to trust a scientist's work.

Your classmates will depend on you to keep accurate records of your investigations so that your class can analyze results effectively. In addition, your teacher will evaluate your science notebook. It is important for your science notebook to be well organized and to represent your work thoroughly so that your teacher can give you credit for your accomplishments.

Thinking as a Scientist Thinks

To think as a scientist thinks, you need to

- ask questions,
- gather information,
- use logical reasoning, and
- apply your creativity to develop predictions and explanations that are based on the evidence that you collected.

You will practice these skills in this Explain activity.

Scientists are often inspired by an event that happens while they are doing something else. Hundreds of years ago, people thought that maggots (immature flies) spontaneously came to life from meat. They thought this because when meat was left at room temperature for several days, maggots began to crawl out of the meat. In 1668, however, a biologist named Francesco Redi *questioned* whether it was possible for life to come from nonliving matter. He *gathered information* by making careful observations and experimenting. Redi placed some meat under gauze and left some uncovered. He found that only the uncovered meat developed maggots. After analyzing his careful observations and data, Redi *reasoned* that flies were laying eggs on the uncovered meat. This meant that maggots came from the fly eggs, not the rotting meat. In this way, Redi used scientific inquiry to *explain his observations* and questions about the natural world. Scientists propose explanations based on evidence.

In the activity, *Thinking as a Scientist Thinks*, imagine that something happened while you were writing in your science notebook that caused you to ask questions. You will use this situation to learn about the basic processes of science. You will collect relevant evidence and use logical reasoning to propose explanations that are based on that evidence. Throughout the year, you will continue to build your understandings and abilities to conduct scientific inquiries. This will continue until you can design and conduct your own independent investigations.

Materials (per team of 2)

1 termite
1 small paintbrush or cotton swab
1 set of different-colored ballpoint pens
blank white paper

PROCESS AND PROCEDURES

1. Listen to or read to yourself the scenario, *Late One Night*.
2. Pick up 1 set of materials for you and your partner.
3. Using your colored pens, create a simple line diagram on a sheet of paper like the one that might have been found in the scientist's notebook (see figure En.3). Observe your termite's behavior.

   Remember to use the soft bristles of the paintbrush or the cotton swab to block your termite and redirect it. *Do not* try to pick up your termite with your fingers or push it around with the paintbrush.

4. The first step in thinking scientifically is to identify the questions you are trying to answer. Begin this process by thinking about the

SCENARIO

Late One Night

You are a scientist who works with termites, and you were working late last night. You drew a diagram in different colors of ink that looked similar to the drawing in figure En.3. You realized that you were late for dinner, so you quickly tidied up the area and left your science notebook open on your work space.

When you returned the next morning, you found there was a termite in the middle of the diagram. You watched the termite's response to the ink on the page, and it made you wonder. Next, you called in your friend, who is also a scientist. Together you made a prediction about what the termite was doing. Questions about the termite and its behavior led you to start experimenting and making careful observations to see whether your prediction was correct.

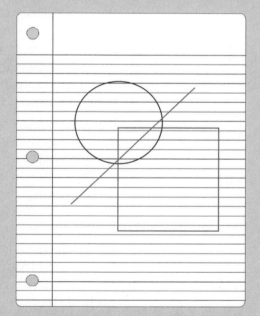

Figure En.3 A simple line diagram.

questions that come to mind as you watch your termite on the diagram. Identify 3 questions you have about the termite's behavior and record them in your science notebook.

5. Work with your partner to select 1 question about the termite's behavior. Choose a question that you think you can answer by testing with the supplies available.

6. Make a prediction in your science notebook about an answer to your question. Explain briefly why you think your prediction is reasonable.

7. Discuss with your partner how you will design an experiment and make observations to learn more about your question. Briefly outline your plan in your science notebook.

8. Conduct your experiment within the time allotted. Save all test diagrams that you use and record your observations in your science notebook.

9. Make a claim based on the results of your experiment and write it in your science notebook.

   Your claim should make an assertion or state a conclusion that addresses your question. It should be based on evidence from your experiment.

10. What evidence from your experiment supports your claim? List the evidence under your claim.

Analysis

The following questions will help you understand more about how scientists think about their work.

1. Participate in a class discussion by sharing your experimental question, the way you carried out your experiment, and your claims about termite behavior.

2. Can you make any new claims about termite behavior based on the experiments from other teams in the class?

3. Read the following terms and add 2 terms of your own that are important in describing the way scientists think:
   • Explanation
   • Evidence
   • Prediction
   • Reasoning

4. Examine figure En.4, which summarizes the process of scientific inquiry. Write a paragraph in your science notebook to summarize how you participated in scientific inquiry in this activity. Include the 4 terms from question 3 and the 2 terms that you added.

5. In your science notebook, explain whether you agree or disagree with each of the following statements.

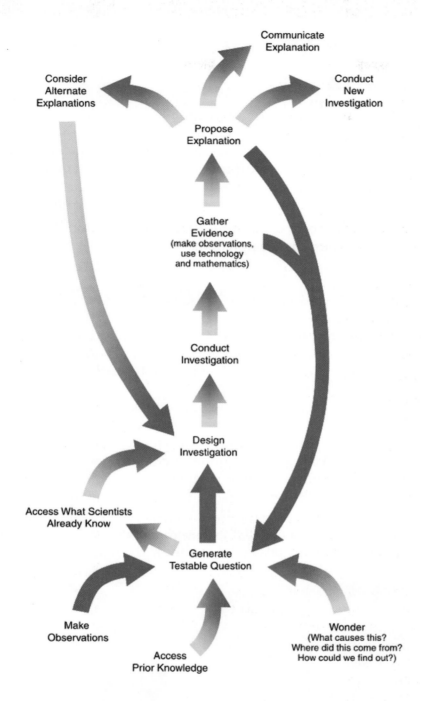

Communicate
Explanation

Consider
Alternate
Explanations

Conduct
New
Investigation

Propose
Explanation

Gather
Evidence
(make observations,
use technology
and mathematics)

Conduct
Investigation

Design
Investigation

Access What Scientists
Already Know

Generate
Testable Question

Make
Observations

Access
Prior Knowledge

Wonder
(What causes this?
Where did this come from?
How could we find out?)

Figure En.4
Scientific inquiry is a dynamic process used to study nature. How did you use this process in your investigation?

a. Scientists observe without making any judgments; scientific observations are objective and value free.
b. If 2 scientists run the same experiment and have similar observations, they will develop the same explanation for the results.

Recording Data in Your Science Notebook

Scientists communicate information and ideas through speaking and writing. It is important for scientists to report the results of their work in a way that is easily understood by their peers and the public. Graphs are one way for scientists to report information clearly and accurately. Because you will be designing your own investigations in this course, you also will need to work as a scientist to design appropriate graphs. In this Elaborate activity, *Recording Data in Your Science Notebook*, you will learn how to create your own graphs.

PROCESS AND PROCEDURES

1. Turn to a partner and discuss the following questions.
   a. What are some of the most effective ways you have seen data recorded on Web sites, in newspapers, in math class, or in other places besides science class?
   b. What types of graphs do you like to make?

2. Read appendix D3, *How to Create Graphs*. As you read, begin a personal glossary in the back of your science notebook, like the one in figure En.5. Your glossary should include any word that is important to graphing or that is unfamiliar to you. See appendix B8, *How to Develop a Personal Glossary*, for more information about developing a glossary.

   Begin your glossary about 25 pages from the end of your science notebook. Write the title of the chapter at the top of the page. Add the

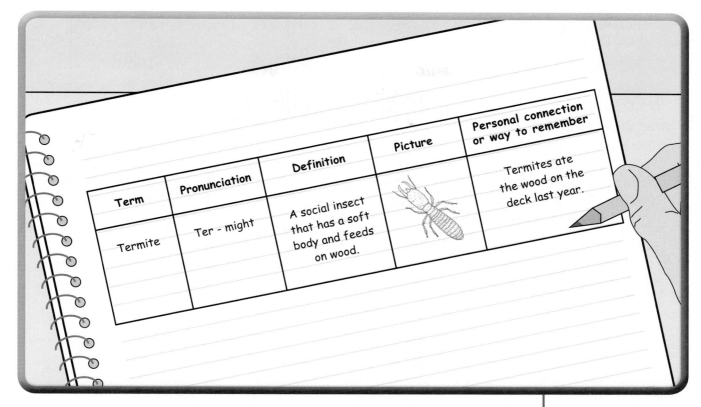

Figure En.5 Personal glossary. A personal glossary will help you learn and retain words that are important or unfamiliar to you.

   headings shown in figure En.5, then complete each column for any word
   that is important to graphing or that is unfamiliar to you.

3. Follow the instructions in appendix D3, *How to Create Graphs*, to
   practice measuring and graphing.
4. Read the scenario, *Which Way?*
5. What type of graph would be best to show these results?
6. Create a graph based on these results. Include all the steps you
   learned in your practice graphs.
7. Use the highlight comments strategy to help make sense of your
   graph.

   Although being able to make a graph is important, it is not very helpful
   unless you also know how to interpret your graph. One easy way to do
   this is to look for differences in the graph, then write what you see that
   has changed and what you think each change means. These are the
   steps of the highlight comments strategy.

   a. Look for changes, trends, or differences on your graph. Draw an
      arrow to each of these that you notice.
   b. Write "What I see" followed by a short phrase describing what
      you notice. Be concise and write only the *highlights* of what
      you see.

SCENARIO

ENGLISH SPANISH

Which Way?

Your friend wanted to perform another experiment on the termites. She was interested to see if the termites were more likely to go straight or turn to the right or left when following a line. She drew a "+" and placed termites, one at a time, at the base of it. She then recorded which direction the termite went when it reached the intersection of the lines.

The results of the experiment are shown in figure En.6. Help your friend interpret these results by following the directions given.

Number of termites turning:		
Straight	**Right**	**Left**
14	5	6

Figure En.6 Results of an experiment to determine which direction termites follow at an intersection.

HOW TO

c. Interpret what you see, 1 observation at a time. Write "What it means" below your "What I see" phrase and describe what you think the observation means.

For more information on using this strategy, see appendix B6, *How to Write Highlight Comments and Captions.*

8. Answer the following questions based on what you learned from your graph.
   a. Do the termites seem to go straight, turn to the right, or turn to the left when they follow a line?
   b. What evidence do you have from the graph that supports your answer?

Analysis

Answer the following questions individually and then participate in a class discussion about the importance of graphing.

1. What do you find is the hardest decision that you have to make when you construct a graph? Why is it difficult to decide?
2. Write a paragraph about why graphs are important for accurate scientific communication.

3. Participate in a class discussion about how you and your classmates will make graphs to clearly and accurately report results to one another and to your teacher. Consider the following questions.

    a. What are the terms in graphing that are important to understand?

    b. Why is it important for your class to agree to use the same terms when you describe data in graphs, conclusions, analysis questions, and presentations?

    c. Why is it useful for scientists to have a particular format, or set of characteristics, that is always used when making graphs?

    d. What is useful about having standard formats for data in a high school biology class?

    e. What graph formats will be standardized in your class?

You and the Science of Biology

In this Evaluate activity, *You and the Science of Biology*, you will think about how the information you learn in science class applies to society. Imagine yourself doing one or more of the following:

- Understanding the choices a doctor offers for treatment of an illness
- Deciphering nutritional information on a food package label
- Voting on an issue involving science and technology
- Serving on a jury that has to listen to an expert describe DNA evidence
- Deciding whether or not to support the construction of a new dam

These are examples of actions that happen in the United States. Will you be one of the people making informed decisions and choices because you have learned to think scientifically? Or will you be one of the people who act and hope for the best, despite a lack of information and understanding? By participating in this biology program, you are taking a big step toward joining the first group of knowledgeable people.

In this course, we use six main ideas to organize your study of biology. They are listed in the box in the essay, *A Human Approach to Biology*. We also integrate these ideas with opportunities for you to think about and use the methods of science. As a result, you can learn how to think scientifically while you learn biology, and you will use scientific thinking when making decisions in your everyday life.

PROCESS AND PROCEDURES

Read the essay, *A Human Approach to Biology*. As you read, record in your science notebook at least 1 reason why each of the following is relevant.

    a. The study of biology now

    b. The study of biology in the future

A Human Approach to Biology

Bring to mind an image of a scientist. Did you imagine someone wearing a white lab coat and looking through a microscope? While this image is commonly used to represent scientists and science, there are many ways people apply the methods of science in everyday life. Consider the activities shown in figure En.7 and think about the activities listed at the beginning of this Evaluate activity, *You and the Science of Biology*. Two activities are making choices in the doctor's office and voting, for example.

Biology is a way of explaining what living organisms do and how they do it. There are other ways to look at life. You could describe living things in poetry, in paintings, or in a written story. These activities have great value and add

an important dimension to human life. These ways of describing life, however, would not be a scientific approach. In a scientific approach, explanations are based on questions that can be answered by collecting evidence and then logically analyzing what we know. (See the summary of the processes of science in figure En.8.) In this program, you will be practicing "Science as Inquiry" when you learn and use the processes of science.

This program is called *BSCS Biology: A Human Approach* because we have focused your activities around human interactions. You will experience this human approach in several ways. You will complete experiments that involve yourself. Because living things also share some very important characteristics, you will read and experience

© Dreamstime/Robert Mizerek

© iStockphoto/sjlocke

© Dreamstime/Simone Van Den Berg

Figure En.7 How are these people applying the methods of science to their lives?

- Asking questions
- Gathering information
- Proposing explanations

Figure En.8   The processes of science.
The processes of science help you learn more about biology.

examples of the unifying principles that point out the connection between humans and evolution; homeostasis; matter, energy, and organization; continuity; development; and ecology.

Furthermore, you will learn about living things as they relate to the levels of organization of matter. There is increasing complexity and organization of matter, starting with atoms as the least complex and leading to the biosphere as the most complex. Look at figure En.9. Each level is dependent on the one below it. Where along this scale would you draw a line to distinguish between living things and nonliving things?

This program will also help you understand "Science and Humanity" through a variety of experiences. You will see highlights of how humans use technology to help solve problems. This helps improve our ability to survive in the future. You will also experience the differences in technology from culture to culture and across time. You will learn how science is affected by cultural and historical contexts. You will also learn about ethical analysis, which helps humans make decisions on how to apply scientific findings.

As you study biology in this course, you will learn about living systems. If you can understand how you learn, you will further enjoy the process of learning and be more successful at it. In order to learn, a learner first must be engaged in an idea. Then the learner must explore the idea. Next, the learner develops an explanation of the idea. Finally, the learner elaborates his or her understanding and is able to evaluate what he or she has learned. As you look through this book, you will notice the use of those same five words that start with the letter *E*. This program uses these "E-words" to organize the instructional flow in each chapter and emphasize the step in the learning process that you will be completing. The instructional flow is designed to help you construct an understanding of each big idea in biology.

The essays found throughout the chapters give you a place to gather information, but they are intended to be only one resource of the many resources available to you. For example, you may supplement your research with other books, magazines, and the Web. We also think you should have continual opportunities to evaluate your understanding and growth, so you will notice frequent chances to monitor and reflect on your own learning.

Levels of Biological Organization

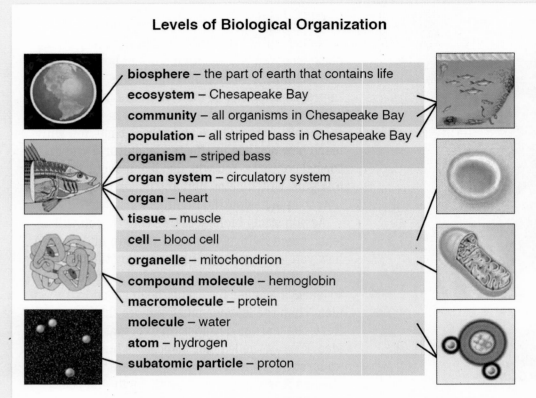

biosphere – the part of earth that contains life
ecosystem – Chesapeake Bay
community – all organisms in Chesapeake Bay
population – all striped bass in Chesapeake Bay
organism – striped bass
organ system – circulatory system
organ – heart
tissue – muscle
cell – blood cell
organelle – mitochondrion
compound molecule – hemoglobin
macromolecule – protein
molecule – water
atom – hydrogen
subatomic particle – proton

Figure En.9 **Levels of structure in the biosphere and specific examples.** Matter in the biosphere is characterized by increasing levels of organization and complexity. Each higher level of order is dependent on the one below it. Where would you draw a line to distinguish between life and nonlife?

Unifying Principles of Biology

Evolution: Change in Living Systems

Homeostasis: Maintaining Dynamic Equilibrium in Living Systems

Energy, Matter, and Organization: Relationships in Living Systems

Continuity: Reproduction and Inheritance in Living Systems

Development: Growth and Differentiation in Living Systems

Ecology: Interaction and Interdependence in Living Systems

Unifying principles of biology. These six big ideas are one way to organize the discipline of biology. These ideas are also the titles of the six units in *BSCS Biology: A Human Approach*.

Analysis

Use your experiences from the activities you have just completed and your general life experiences to answer the following questions. In your science notebook, leave room below each answer to revise your response after a class discussion of the questions.

1. What role does biology play in your life now? What role will it play in the future?
2. Choose 1 of the actions listed at the beginning of this activity. How does the process of cooperating, communicating, and thinking like a scientist relate to that action?
3. Are there limits to what biology can discover?
4. How can biology help you make decisions about yourself, your lifestyle, your community, and your planet?
5. How do the decisions that we make today influence future generations, generations that could include your children and grandchildren?

©Dreamstime/Les Watts

Earth is teeming with life. You are probably familiar with many common types of living things such as large animals and plants. However, there are a large number of living species that you have probably never seen. Microbes like the bacteria in the unit opener collage are by far the most numerous organisms on Earth. Other organisms like the gulper eel live in the ocean at depths of a mile or more. These eels have a large jaw and an organ that emits light on the end of their tails. The fly agaric mushroom looks harmless but carries a lethal poison. The titan arum plant has a very large flower and is sometimes called the corpse plant. This name comes from the smell given off by the flower when it blooms. During that time, the flower smells like decomposing flesh. Biologists use the term *diversity* to refer to the wide range of different types of organisms.

How did Earth come to have such a great diversity of organisms? On the other hand, what do the organisms living on Earth have in common with one another? Can we learn anything about humans from our knowledge of these diverse organisms?

These questions do not have simple answers. Scientists and philosophers have been asking these questions for thousands of years. Biologists study the diversity found in living systems by looking for patterns of evidence. For example, they study the patterns in the information, sequences of events, and chemical and physical structures of living things. Biologists also try to understand the processes that lead to the formation of diversity. Understanding these processes helps us address questions about the diversity of life and how it came to be. Scientists learn about these patterns and processes by asking questions, gathering information, and proposing explanations. Through scientific inquiry, scientists have developed evolutionary theory, which provides an explanation for why life is so diverse yet shares a set of fundamental characteristics. These analyses also help us understand some things about humans.

© Dreamstime/Joan Kerrigan

Evolution:
Change in Living Systems

In unit 1, you will explore change in living systems from a scientific viewpoint. The following goals will help you learn the big ideas in this unit. By the end of unit 1, you should be able to

- ✔ explain how humans are both similar to and distinct from other organisms,

- ✔ demonstrate your understanding of how evolution explains the unity and diversity of life, and

- ✔ use evidence to develop explanations about the living world.

UNIT CONTENTS

1 **The Human Animal**

2 **Evolution: Change Across Time**

3 **Products of Evolution: Unity and Diversity**

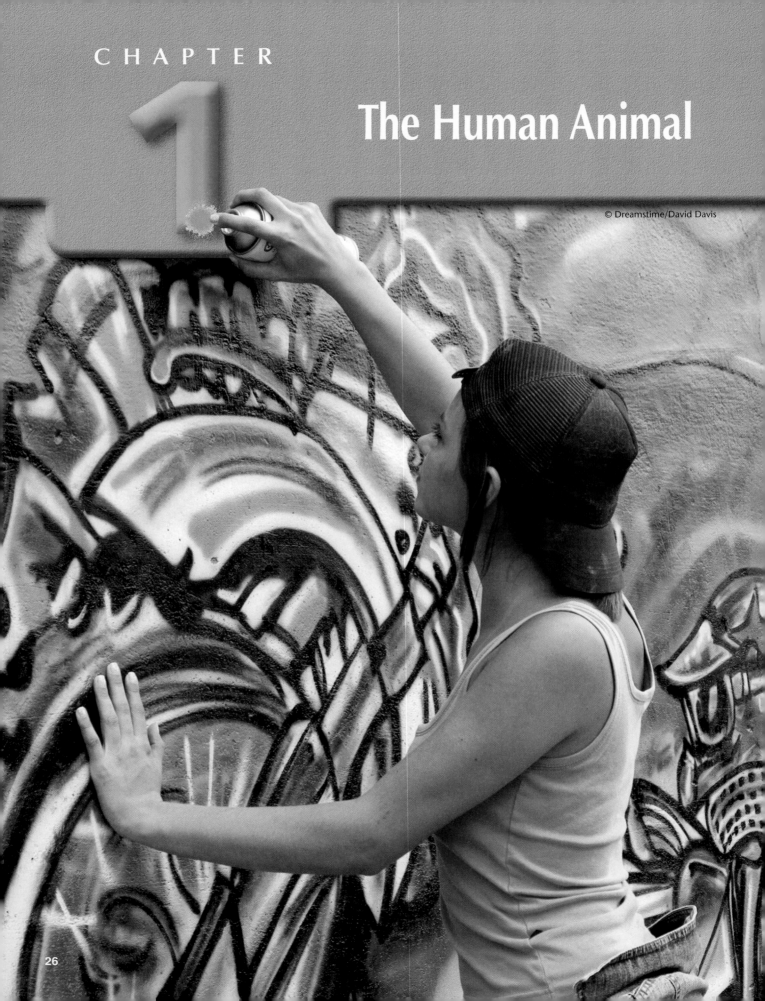

1

The Human Animal

And this is the weaving of human living:
of whose fabric each individual is a part.

James Agee and Walker Evans

Consider for a moment the differences among humans. We differ in height, the shape of our eyes, the texture of our hair, and the color of our skin. We differ in our ways of living, the languages that we speak, the foods that we grow and eat, and our concepts of the universe. In other words, humans are diverse in physical appearance and cultural behavior. Yet all humans have common bonds, and we see some of ourselves reflected in each of a thousand other faces.

As you begin the first chapter of this unit, you will look at humans in a way that may be new to you. You will look at humans the way scientists do. To do this, you will build a range of knowledge and skills to help you make scientific observations and explanations. You will examine physical characteristics that humans share with primates. Primates are the group of animals that includes humans, apes, and monkeys. You will also examine the ways in which humans are different from the rest of the primates. This chapter also explores humans as social and cultural animals that use language and have a great capacity for learning. Your experiences in these activities will help you begin to develop a scientific understanding of the human animal.

GOALS FOR THE CHAPTER

Throughout chapter 1, *The Human Animal*, you will work to gain an understanding of the following concepts:

✔ Humans share many characteristics, in varying degrees, with other organisms.

✔ A combination of characteristics distinguishes humans from other animals. Scientists' views of human uniqueness have changed over time.

✔ Scientific studies pose questions that can be tested with specific measurements and available resources.

✔ Scientific studies use evidence and logic to develop explanations.

To help you develop these understandings, you will complete the following activities.

ENGAGE	How Different Are We?
EXPLORE	Primates Exploring Primates
EXPLORE	A Cold, Hard Look at Culture
EXPLAIN	Explaining Humankind
ELABORATE	How Similar Are We?
EVALUATE	What Does It Mean to Be Human?

ENGAGE

How Different Are We?

Key Idea: Humans have distinctive characteristics.

Linking Question:
What can I learn from observations about the similarities and differences between humans and other primates?

Chapter 1

EXPLORE

Primates Exploring Primates

Part A: Get a Grip!
Part B: All Brains on Board
Key Idea: Humans share many physical features with other primates, but their hands, feet, ways of moving, and brains are distinctive.

Linking Question:
How do scientists use evidence and inference to understand the distinctive characteristics of an ancient human?

MAJOR CONCEPTS

✔ Humans share many characteristics, in varying degrees, with other organisms.

✔ A combination of characteristics distinguishes humans from other animals. Scientists' views of human uniqueness have changed over time.

✔ Scientific studies pose questions that can be tested with specific measurements and available resources.

✔ Scientific studies use evidence and logic to develop explanations.

EXPLORE

A Cold, Hard Look at Culture

Key Idea: Evidence can be used to draw inferences about the life and culture of ancient humans.

Linking Question:
How do distinct physical and cultural characteristics combine to explain humankind?

28

EVALUATE

What Does It Mean to Be Human?

Key Idea: Humans share many features with other organisms, but we have distinct physical, behavioral, and cultural characteristics.

The Human Animal

Linking Question:
Given humans' similarities to and differences from other life-forms, what does it mean to be human?

ELABORATE

How Similar Are We?

Key Idea: Human similarities with other organisms can be extended to include diverse forms of life.

Linking Question:
What features of humans are shared with organisms that look very different from them?

EXPLAIN

Explaining Humankind

Part A: A Long Childhood
Part B: Portraying Humankind

Key Idea: A combination of distinct human characteristics, including a long period of development and learning, contributes to the complexity of human behavior and culture.

ENGAGE

How Different Are We?

In the previous *Engage* section, *Being a Scientist,* you began to explore science as a way of learning about the natural world. Remember, before you began your experiments with termites you made careful observations and thought about termite behavior to gain a sense of what the termite was doing. These processes—observing and thinking—always precede experimental work. Careful observations help you collect information about the world around you. Thinking about those observations helps you make sense of the information that you have gathered. Thoughtful observations also tend to point to other questions.

To begin your study of humans, you will make preliminary observations and think about what those observations mean. As you complete this Engage activity, *How Different Are We?,* reflect on the focus question, "What evidence do you have that humans are unique?"

Materials (per team)

flip chart paper
felt-tipped markers

PROCESS AND PROCEDURES

1. Conduct a brainstorming session with the team that your teacher assigns. In your session, consider the question, "What is it about humans that makes us unique?"

   Imagine that you are describing a human to an alien in outer space. How would you describe humans biologically, so that the alien could tell them apart from other animals?

2. Write your team's responses on a large piece of paper and post it in the front of the room.

3. Write the following questions in your science notebook, leaving several lines of space between them.
   a. What common ideas do all teams have?
   b. What ideas are unique to each team?
   c. Examine the characteristics that the teams listed as being unique to humans. What other animals show the same characteristics?

4. Participate in a class discussion by sharing the responses from your team and listening carefully to other teams. As you listen, record in your science notebook your answers to the discussion questions from step 3.

5. Choose at least 6 characteristics that all teams agree make humans different from other organisms, based on the class discussion. Record this list of 6 characteristics in your science notebook.

6. Consider the 6 human characteristics you listed in step 5 as you read the scenario, *Chimps at Gombe.* For each characteristic, record in your science notebook whether or not you think that the chimpanzees

also possess the characteristic. Record this by writing "chimp" next to those characteristics that are shared.

Chimps at Gombe describes Dr. Jane Goodall's observations of a family of chimpanzees at the Gombe Stream Chimpanzee Reserve in Tanzania, Africa. Jane Goodall is a British scientist who began studying chimpanzees in the wild in the 1960s (figure 1.1). If you would like to learn more about Jane Goodall, read the sidebar, *The Chimp Scientist*.

7. Discuss with your team the thoughts that crossed your mind as you read *Chimps at Gombe*. Record your ideas in your science notebook. Focus your discussion on the following questions.

   a. Were you surprised by anything that Dr. Jane Goodall observed? If so, what?

   b. Did you find yourself reflecting more on the similarities or on the differences between humans and chimps? Explain your response.

   c. If you had been Goodall observing this group of chimpanzees, what questions would you now have about these animals? Record in your science notebook at least 2 questions that you would like to research if you were Goodall.

Analysis

Use the following tasks to analyze your list from step 5 of the 6 characteristics that make humans different from other animals. Record your responses in your science notebook.

1. For each characteristic you listed in step 5, identify and describe a nonhuman animal that you think may also display that characteristic to some degree.

2. Do you think there is any single characteristic that sets humans apart from all other animals? Explain your answer.

Figure 1.1 Jane Goodall. As Goodall studied chimpanzees in the wild, she recorded as many movements, interactions, gestures, and grunts as she could observe.

SCENARIO

ENGLISH   SPANISH

Chimps at Gombe

Gombe Stream Chimpanzee Reserve, Tanzania, Africa

1980: Nope and Pom, two wild chimpanzees, are feeding quietly. Suddenly, a chimp screams in the distance. Pom stares toward the sound, turns to Nope, and grimaces. Then the screams break out again. Now at least two chimps are screaming, and one is an infant. Above the screams, the observer can hear male barks and whoops of attack. Instantly, Pom leaps to her feet and charges toward the sounds of battle. By the time the observer arrives, it is quiet again, and Pom and her mother, Passion, are grooming each other intently. Pom's little brother, Pax, is close beside them. Both Passion and Pax have fresh, bleeding wounds, but the family is safe and together.

1981: On a blustery morning, Pom's new baby clings tightly to her hair. As the wind starts to die down, he begins to play, venturing out on the limb that he and his mother are sharing. Just then, a violent gust sweeps through the tree and his little body falls spread-eagle through the air. The observer hears a thud and then nothing but silence. Pom looks down at her infant son. Slowly she climbs out of the tree and gathers the tiny form into her arms. For the next two hours, she grooms and nurses him. He leans against her body with his eyes closed. Finally, she carries his battered body away. Three days later, he is dead.

1982: Pom is 17 and her brother Pax is still a youngster when their mother, Passion, dies. Passion has been ill for weeks, and now she trembles with every movement. One morning, she is dead. She must have fallen in the night; her body hangs in a tangle of vines. Pom and Pax sit staring at their mother's body. Little Pax repeatedly approaches her and tries to nurse from her cold breasts. Then he starts to scream and pull at her dangling hand. So frantic are his efforts that finally he succeeds in pulling her loose. As Passion sprawls lifeless on the wet ground, her children inspect her body many times. Pax cries softly. At last, just before darkness, Pom and Pax move off together.

1983: Having lost both her baby and her mother, a weak and listless Pom finally leaves the community and is not seen at Gombe again. Pax, on the other hand, attaches himself to an older brother, Prof, who provides the care that a mother chimpanzee would. One day, Pax sneezes loudly. Before the astonished observer can get out the camera, Prof hurries over to Pax and stares at his runny nose. Then, picking up a handful of leaves, Prof carefully wipes the mess away.

3. Chimps and humans share many characteristics. Write down your best ideas about why you think these 2 species share so many characteristics.

> It is OK not to know the right answer at this point. Just as it is important for a scientist to reflect on his or her observations, it is important for you to reflect back frequently on your own understanding. When you connect new information to what you already know, learning becomes easier. Frequent reflection helps you spend less time to learn more effectively. You will have a chance to revisit your answer at a later point.

Further Challenges

To learn more about Jane Goodall, check your library for the many books that she has written and look for information at the Jane Goodall Institute Web site. You also may be interested in other scientists who have done or are doing similar work. The American Society of Primatologists maintains a Web site with links to many interesting research projects, scientists, and general information about primates.

SIDEBAR

ENGLISH SPANISH

The Chimp Scientist

. . .I have often wondered exactly what it was I felt as I stared at the wild country that so soon I should be roaming. Vanne [Goodall's mother] admitted afterward to have been secretly horrified by the steepness of the slopes and the impenetrable appearance of the valley forests. And David Anstey [a game warden in Tanzania] told me several months later that he had guessed I would be packed up and gone within six weeks. . . What had I, the girl standing on the government launch [landing dock] in her jeans, to do with the girl who in a few days would be searching those very mountains for wild chimpanzees?

Jane Goodall

Jane Goodall began to observe and study the chimpanzees of Gombe Stream in Tanzania about 50 years ago (figure 1.2). At that time, some people thought that it was not scientific to talk about an animal's mind or personality. However, Goodall's careful and detailed observations and evidence changed many people's minds. Today, her work stands as one of the great contributions to science made during the 20th century.

In the past, some people thought of science only as experiments that men in white coats conducted in laboratories. Indeed, some people still have that mistaken image today. As you have been discovering, however, science is a particular way of knowing and learning about the world.

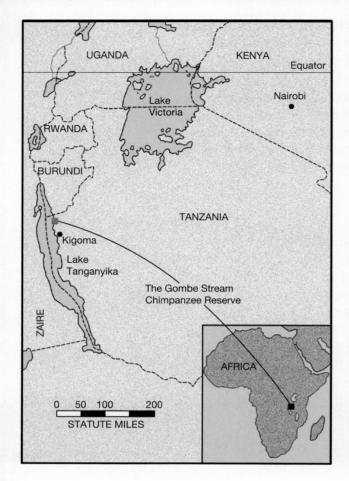

Figure 1.2 The Gombe Stream Chimpanzee Reserve. The Gombe Stream Chimpanzee Reserve is located near Kigoma, on Lake Tanganyika in Tanzania.

Each of us can learn the methods of science and put them into practice.

Goodall's work is a great example of the role of observation and reflection, two key aspects of science. The notes pictured in figure 1.3 are copied from a page of Goodall's field journal. Like your science notebook, her notebook documents her observations. The notes recorded on the page reveal the value of careful organization for keeping accurate records. Can you tell what Goodall's notes mean? She made detailed observations while she kept careful watch on her chimpanzee subjects. She designed her own abbreviations and note-taking style to make it easy to write quickly and understand later.

To learn about how chimpanzees behave in the wild, you have to go into nature and observe them across long periods of time.

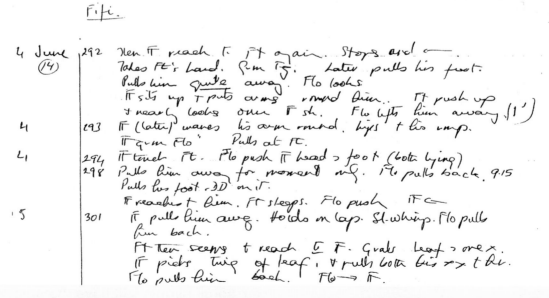

Figure 1.3 Jane Goodall's field notes. These notes were taken while observing Flo and her children, Fifi (FF) and Flint (Ft). Can you imagine the scene as Fifi tried to take her baby brother, Flint, from Flo? Flo had at least five children in her lifetime and was an exceptional mother.

It took Goodall close to four years to collect a significant amount of information. The chimpanzees were hard to find and resisted her presence for the first several years. But eventually they came to trust her—this itself was a key observation. Goodall carefully recorded their every move, interaction, gesture, and grunt. She found that chimpanzees are caring, clever, and capable of lasting attachments. Through years of observations, she also learned that some individuals are capable of extreme aggression, even cannibalism.

Scientists used to think that humans were the only toolmaking animals and generally assumed that humans were the only organisms that could think or have emotions. Today, due to the work of Goodall and other scientists in related fields, we recognize that many intellectual abilities once thought to be unique to humans are present in other animals. For instance, Goodall observed the problem-solving ability of chimpanzees. They recognized a need for tools, planned ahead of time to prepare tools, made the tools, and used the tools. One such observation involved a chimp named Mike (see figure 1.4). He finally solved the problem of how to get a banana that Goodall held out to him. Apparently too nervous to take the banana from her hand, he finally used a stick to knock it to the ground. Only then did he grab it and run.

Jane Goodall's long-term studies and careful observations resulted in important pieces of evidence about chimpanzee

Figure 1.4   Mike bangs kerosene cans together. Although Mike was not the largest or strongest male, he made his way to the top by creating frightful noises with these empty cans.

behavior. This knowledge is important because the chimpanzee is the closest living relative of the human species. Accurate information about chimpanzees helps us come to a better understanding of what it means to be human.

EXPLORE

Primates Exploring Primates

In the Engage activity, *How Different Are We?*, you read and thought about observations that someone else made. You also considered your own ideas about how humans are similar to and different from other animals. Now you will have a chance to explore these ideas in more depth and to make observations of your own. You will observe humans and other related animals as they move about and use tools. You also will compare human brains with those of other animals. Remember, your goal is to look at humans in the way scientists do. In this Explore activity, *Primates Exploring Primates*, you will gather evidence about the characteristics that set humans apart from other animals and the characteristics that they share with other animals.

Materials (per team of 2)

Part A
online resource
assortment of objects to grip
1 padlock and key
1 stopwatch (optional)
masking tape (optional)

Part B
2 pairs of latex gloves (if using sheep brains)
1 sheep brain (optional)
online resource

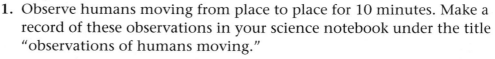
PROCESS AND PROCEDURES

Part A   Get a Grip!

1. Observe humans moving from place to place for 10 minutes. Make a record of these observations in your science notebook under the title "observations of humans moving."

   Record your observations with descriptive words and drawings. For example, after watching someone jog by, you might write: "When humans jog, they take short steps quickly. Slower runners tend to have their heel strike first and then they push from their toes." In contrast, writing "People jog" is not as good an observation because it is not descriptive. What do you think about the comment "He is jogging because he wants to lose weight"? This is an interpretation because it attaches meaning to an action, rather than being an objective description. Try to make all your observations as objective as you can. Take the time to notice all the different types of strides that are possible and the differences in the way humans use their arms, legs, and feet.

2. Observe the different ways that humans hold and use the objects. Record your observations in detail in your science notebook under the title "observations of how humans hold and use objects."

CAUTION: Do not swing, throw, drop, or fool around with any of the objects in a way that might harm you or your classmates.

Make observations about what parts of the hand and arm your partner uses to hold objects. For example, after examining how your partner turns the pages of a book, you might write: "When humans are reading a book, they use the tip of the thumb and forefinger to pick up a page, and then they rotate the forearm to turn the page." In contrast, writing "Humans use their fingers to turn pages" is not as good an observation because it is less descriptive.

Topic: scientific investigation
Code: human4E37

3. With your partner, discuss the different ways humans use and hold objects.

4. Insert a chart like the one in figure 1.5 into your science notebook. Title the chart "observations of primates moving." You will be assigned to observe either arms and hands or legs and feet. Write column headings appropriate to the observations you are assigned.

Online Resource

5. Watch the video segment, "Observing Primates," while recording your observations in your chart. Be sure to make objective, descriptive observations for each primate in the same way you did for humans.

Record as much detail as you can in your table. As you observe humans in this video segment, add any new observations to those that you made in steps 1 and 2. If you are observing hands, pay particular attention to how each primate uses its fingers and thumbs so that you can compare those motions with the human grip observations you made earlier.

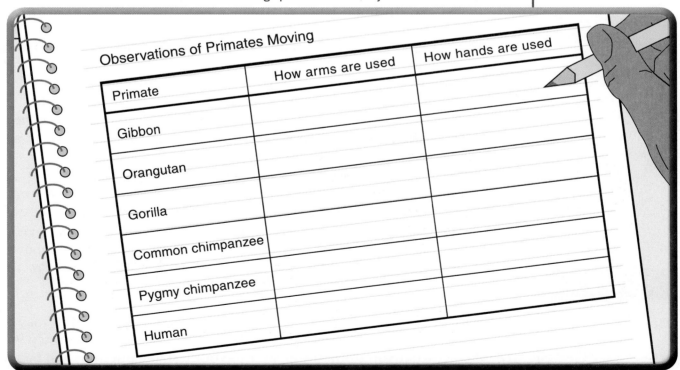

Observations of Primates Moving

Primate	How arms are used	How hands are used
Gibbon		
Orangutan		
Gorilla		
Common chimpanzee		
Pygmy chimpanzee		
Human		

Figure 1.5 Sample table of observations of primates moving. A table similar to this one will help you organize your observations.

6. Switch science notebooks with your partner and review his or her observations. Ask your partner to clarify any observation that you do not fully understand. Use your partner's questions to refine the wording of the observations in your chart.

7. Discuss the following questions with your partner and record answers in your science notebook.
   a. How is human movement and posture different from that of other primates?
   b. In what ways do primates (other than humans) use their thumbs?
   c. In what ways does human thumb use differ from that of other primates?

8. Brainstorm with your partner all the questions that come to mind about how primates move about and use their hands to grip and manipulate objects. Include at least 1 question that relates to how different primates could use a key to unlock a padlock. Record this list in your science notebook.

   Come up with at least five questions. If you have trouble coming up with questions, or if you would like to learn more about the ways that humans use their hands, read the sidebar, *Do You Have a Grip on That?*

9. Discuss with your partner which of the following 2 questions meets the criteria for a testable question, as described in the need to know, *Testable Questions*. In your science notebook, explain the reasons for your choice. This will help you gain a clearer sense of the nature of testable questions.
   a. What is the importance of an opposable thumb for the ways in which humans use their hands?
   b. How does using an opposable thumb affect the time it takes to use a key to open a lock?

10. Reexamine the questions you wrote with your partner in step 8 by using the think-share-advise-revise (TSAR) strategy. Then, place an asterisk by the questions that you and your partner agree are testable.

   As you read each of the criteria, *think* about whether or not the questions you generated in step 8 are testable or not testable. Then *share* your ideas with your partner and *advise* each other for possible corrections in your thinking. Finally, *revise* your ideas based on your discussion.

   It may be helpful for you to look back to the questions you tested using termites in the Explain activity, *Thinking as a Scientist Thinks*, from the *Engage* section. For more information about using the TSAR strategy, see appendix B3, *How to Use the Think-Share-Advise-Revise (TSAR) Strategy*.

HOW TO

11. With your partner, choose the question you would like to test. It may be 1 of your own questions or 1 of the 2 questions presented in step 9.

12. Predict what you think the answer to your testable question will be. Record your prediction in your science notebook and explain why you have made this prediction.

NEED TO KNOW

Testable Questions

Science begins with observing and asking questions about the natural world around us. Then it moves to a stage in which we begin to answer those questions by using a combination of further observation and experimentation. Scientists often have many questions that they would like to answer, but science is limited to answering questions that are testable in the natural world.

1. A question is likely to be testable if it uses question words like "whether," "when," "where," "what," "how many," "how much," and "how often," rather than question words like "why."

   For example, the question, "How many fingers does a gorilla have on its right hand?" is easy to answer. Yet the question, "Why does a gorilla have four fingers on its right hand?" is not.

2. If the specific issue to be tested is stated in your question and you list the specific items that will be involved, then your question is likely to be testable.

   The question, "How much do gorillas eat?" is not easily tested. A more easily tested version of this question is, "How many pounds of bananas do adult male gorillas eat?"

3. A question is likely to be testable if it describes the conditions under which to conduct the test.

   An even better version of the gorilla and banana question would be, "How many pounds of bananas do the three adult male gorillas in the National Zoo eat in one week?" This question specifies the conditions that interest us; we are not asking how many pounds of bananas this gorilla would eat in the wild or during his lifetime.

4. A question is likely to be testable if it describes the criteria that will be used to judge the outcome of the test.

   Does a half-eaten banana count as having been eaten? How about a banana that is three-quarters eaten? Can you phrase this gorilla and banana question so that it is easier to test than the other questions listed above?

5. A question is likely to be testable if it can be tested using available resources and procedures.

   In the end, questions about gorillas and bananas, although they may be testable by some people in some parts of the world, are not testable questions for us in the classroom. All researchers (students and teachers alike) are limited by the resources that they have available.

Do You Have a Grip on That?

Tying a shoe, threading a needle, throwing a baseball, taking notes, or carrying a bucket. Think of all the tasks—large and small—that humans accomplish with their hands every day. Have you ever thought about the amazing number of ways in which humans can use their hands to grip things?

Scientists have studied the different grips of primates for some time. They have more than one way of classifying what they have observed. One school of thought divides grips into two major categories: power grips and precision grips. You use the power grip when you grasp an object with your palm and then curve your fingers around it. The power from the power grip comes as you apply pressure with your whole hand. This power is made possible by the muscles of your palm that are located at the base of your thumb. These muscles are responsible for moving your thumb. The power grip requires the full grip of the hand—when you use a hammer or open a tightly closed jar, for example. The precision grip is a more intricate grip that requires a specific alignment of the thumb with one or more fingers. The thumb applies pressure against another finger or fingers in order to accomplish a precise motion, such as picking up a coin. Sometimes it lets you make a precise motion that also requires strength, such as placing a key in a lock and turning it.

Another school of thought subdivides the power and precision grips into as many as 12 categories by defining the grip according to the exact placement of the palm, fingers, and thumb. Figure 1.6 shows seven of the 12 grips.

Cylindric grasp. The palm is used to grasp a cylindrical object; the thumb opposes all of the fingers.

Fist grasp. The fingers are wrapped around a narrow or small object; the thumb opposes the fingers, lying on top of them and securing the grip.

Figure 1.6 Types of grips. These photographs show seven of the 12 ways humans can grip objects. Which grips did you see the primates use in the video segment, "Observing Primates"? Which grip did you test in the Explore activity, *Primates Exploring Primates*?

Hook grasp. The fingers are used as a hook; the thumb is not used.

Spheric grasp. The palm is used to grasp a spherical object; the thumb opposes the fingers.

Tip prehension. The tip of the thumb and one or more of the fingers are used like tweezers to pick up small objects; the thumb opposes one or more fingers.

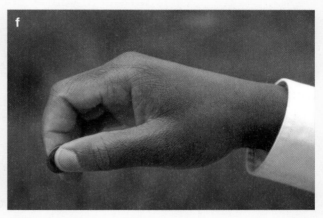

Palmar prehension. The flat surface of the thumb is pressed against the flat surface of the finger or fingers. This grip is similar to the way the tip of a pair of pliers holds an object.

Lateral prehension. The thumb presses against the side of the index finger with other fingers providing additional support. Another type of lateral grip involves the sides of two fingers pressing against each other.

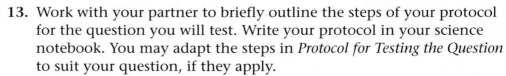
PROTOCOL

HOW TO

13. Work with your partner to briefly outline the steps of your protocol for the question you will test. Write your protocol in your science notebook. You may adapt the steps in *Protocol for Testing the Question* to suit your question, if they apply.

> Although you may be testing your own question during your experiment, this protocol will give you an idea of the detailed steps that are included in a protocol. It is important that protocol steps be followed carefully and in order.

> If you are designing your own investigation, you may wish to review the guiding questions in *How to Design an Investigation*, in appendix C2.

14. As you carry out your protocol, be sure to record your observations and data in your science notebook.

15. Use your results to answer the question you tested. Record your answer in your science notebook.

PROTOCOL

Protocol for Testing the Question

A protocol is a plan or procedure for a basic investigation that can answer a testable question. The protocol also serves as a standard for controlling variables. When you construct a more challenging or creative testable question, you can modify the standard protocol to collect the data you need to answer or better understand your question.

1. Obtain a lock, a key, and masking tape as your teacher directs.
2. Decide who will carry out the task first and who will keep track of the time and record observations.
3. Be certain that the lock is locked. Place the lock and the key on the table in front of you and your partner.
4. When the person responsible for keeping track of the time says "begin," the person performing the task will pick up the key and attempt to unlock the lock.

> This task lasts 30 seconds. The timer-recorder should keep track of the time and record whether or not the person was successful.

5. Switch places and repeat steps 3 and 4.
6. Use the masking tape to tape 1 partner's thumbs to the side of each hand, as shown in figure 1.7.
7. Repeat steps 3 and 4 with the hands taped.
8. Switch places and have the second person tape his or her thumbs. Repeat steps 3 and 4 once more.
9. In your science notebook, record any results from your team's experiment that you haven't yet documented.

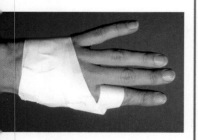

Figure 1.7 Ask your partner to help you tape your thumbs to the sides of your hands, as shown. You should not be able to use your thumb at all, but you should be able to move and use each of your other fingers.

16. Write a few sentences to explain the connection between the results and your answer to the question.

17. With your partner, discuss the limits, exceptions, or alternative interpretations of your results. Record your ideas in your science notebook.

18. Share your results with the rest of the class.

19. Reflect on all the steps of this activity, starting with your observations of humans moving. Write a statement in your science notebook about what aspects of inquiry you engaged in during this activity.

> Use the scientific inquiry diagram (see figure En.4 in the Explain activity, *Thinking as a Scientist Thinks*, of the *Engage* section) to review all the steps of inquiry and identify those you were engaged in during this activity.

Part B   All Brains on Board

In part A of this activity, you observed primates by using scientific techniques similar to the ones that Jane Goodall used. You may have noticed that chimpanzees and other primates have some behavioral similarities to humans. In part B of this activity, you will observe the brains of various organisms and examine their similarities and differences. You will use drawings and the video segment, "Comparing Brains," for your observations and comparisons. Continue to work with your partner through-out this part of the activity. If your teacher provides them, you will need to share sheep brains with other teams.

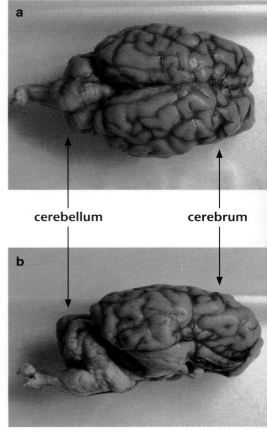

cerebellum   cerebrum

Figure 1.8   Sheep brain (a) top view, (b) side view. What do you think these two regions of the brain might do?

1. In your science notebook, draw a sketch of the sheep brain. Refer to the preserved brain, if your teacher provides one, or the pictures in figure 1.8. Draw the brain from different perspectives

CAUTION: Be sure to wear gloves if you handle the preserved brain and to wash your hands thoroughly at the end of class.

> To get different perspectives on the brain, draw it as you see it from the top and side.

2. Study the cerebellum and cerebrum of the sheep brain (figure 1.8). You will learn the definition for these terms later. Locate the same 2 regions on the sheep brain that you are examining, if your teacher provides one. Label their location on your drawing from step 1.

3. Read the essay, *Mapping the Brain,* to learn general information about the brain. Add the heading "chapter 1" to your personal glossary in the back of your science notebook. As you read, add any words that are important or unfamiliar to you to your glossary.

> For more information on completing a personal glossary, see the information in the Elaborate activity, *Recording Data in Your Science Notebook*, of the *Engage* section or *How to Develop a Personal Glossary* in appendix B8.

HOW TO

Mapping the Brain

In the mid-1800s, an engineer named Phineas Gage made a spark while tapping a metal rod. This action set off a charge of dynamite. In that instant, his whole life changed. The charge exploded, and the metal rod shot up with enormous force. The rod passed right through his cheek, eye, and the front part of his brain. He fell backward. The other workers thought he was dead. Remarkably, he survived. It seemed that his only lasting injury would be the loss of sight in one eye. Unfortunately, his loss of sight was only a small part of the lasting effect. As time passed, people who worked with Gage found him to have an entirely different personality. His friendly nature was a thing of the past. Instead, he was a foulmouthed, rude, and untrustworthy person.

For more than 100 years, the strange effects of Gage's remarkable injury and recovery remained a mystery. But in the 1990s, scientists used new techniques and the remains of Gage's skull to learn more. The scientists found that the accident damaged both sides of the front part of Gage's brain. These areas are called frontal lobes and they are a part of the brain's cerebrum. The **cerebrum** influences social behavior (see figure 1.9).

This dramatic story shows how the brains of animals have specialized regions. Each region controls different activities. For instance, the victim of a motorcycle accident who sustains a severe brain injury may continue to breathe and to have a regular heartbeat. Yet he or she may have no conscious thoughts and no voluntary control over the body. In a situation like this, the family members, the physicians, and the legal experts are faced with a difficult question. Is this patient a living person, even though there is no higher-level thought and the body can stay alive only through artificial feeding? This dilemma raises many complex ethical questions. But it also shows an important biological fact. The brain has

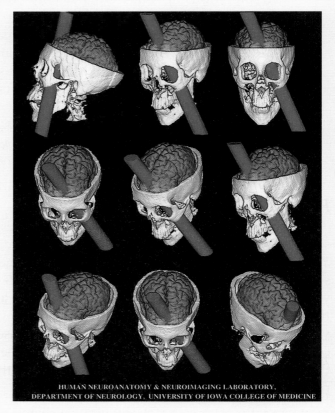

HUMAN NEUROANATOMY & NEUROIMAGING LABORATORY,
DEPARTMENT OF NEUROLOGY, UNIVERSITY OF IOWA COLLEGE OF MEDICINE

Figure 1.9 Gage's skull. In 1994, scientists at the University of Iowa used measurements from Gage's skull along with modern neuroimagery technology to revisit the accident and determine the likely location of damage to the brain. Hanna Damasio created this series of digital images taken from different angles, which show the results of their work.

specialized functions, and these functions often can be mapped to specific regions of the brain.

The drawing in figure 1.10 shows only some of what we know about the different functions of various regions of the brain. The large upper part of the brain, the cerebrum, is responsible for complex reasoning, thought, language, voluntary movement, and the initial processing of sensations.

The structure at the back of the brain, which in certain views looks like a clamshell, is called the

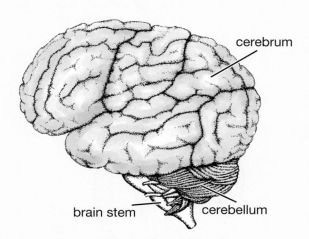

cerebrum

brain stem   cerebellum

Figure 1.10   Regions of the brain. The cerebrum is responsible for conscious thought, language, and voluntary movement. The cerebellum is responsible for balance and posture.

cerebellum. It controls posture and balance. The **brain stem** directs critical, life-sustaining activities such as breathing and heartbeat. This part of the brain evolved long ago, and it occurs in one form or another in most animals. In the example of the victim of the motorcycle accident, the brain stem may have been uninjured. But the cerebrum may have been damaged so that the victim would be unable to think.

Have your parents ever accused you of not using your brain? Recent research indicates that the human cerebrum continues to develop well into a person's 20s. Even though teenagers may look and often act like adults, their developing cerebrums appear to react to stress differently than those of adults. In particular, new studies of the brain suggest that under stress, areas of the frontal lobes (the portion damaged in Phineas Gage) work much harder in teenagers than in adults. The data suggest that under these conditions the cerebrum may be overloaded with activity. This means it may be more difficult for teens to make good decisions quickly.

Some researchers have questioned the data, noting that all of the sampled teens were from the United States. They would like the study to be repeated with teens from different cultures. However, the researchers make a strong argument that frontal lobe overload helps explain why teenagers are more likely to be involved in car accidents. Driving may be stressful for new drivers, and when faced with a decision on how to react, teenagers may have a hard time making a good decision. Researchers also note it could explain why teens have difficulty controlling impulses, and why they have more trouble than adults with resisting peer pressure. Does knowing this make you more likely to keep your developing brain in mind the next time you are under stress?

4. Compare the cerebellum and cerebrum of the sheep brain to the color-coded brains of 8 additional organisms. In your science notebook, record your observations of the similarities and differences among the brains.

Online Resource

Use the drawings in figure 1.11 and the images of brains in the video segment, "Comparing Brains," to make these comparisons. Compare the relative sizes, shapes, and textures of the different regions of the brains. Also record any unique or distinguishing characteristics that you observe. Making a table to record your observations will help you make comparisons more easily.

Figure 1.11
Comparing brains. The drawings on these two pages show the brains of a variety of animals from the top view. Side views of the human, macaque, and chimpanzee brains are included to show the cerebellums. All the brains are life size. In addition to the cerebellum (in yellow) and the cerebrum (in blue), the optic lobes and olfactory bulbs are labeled on some drawings. The optic lobes are associated with the sense of sight. The olfactory bulbs are associated with the sense of smell.

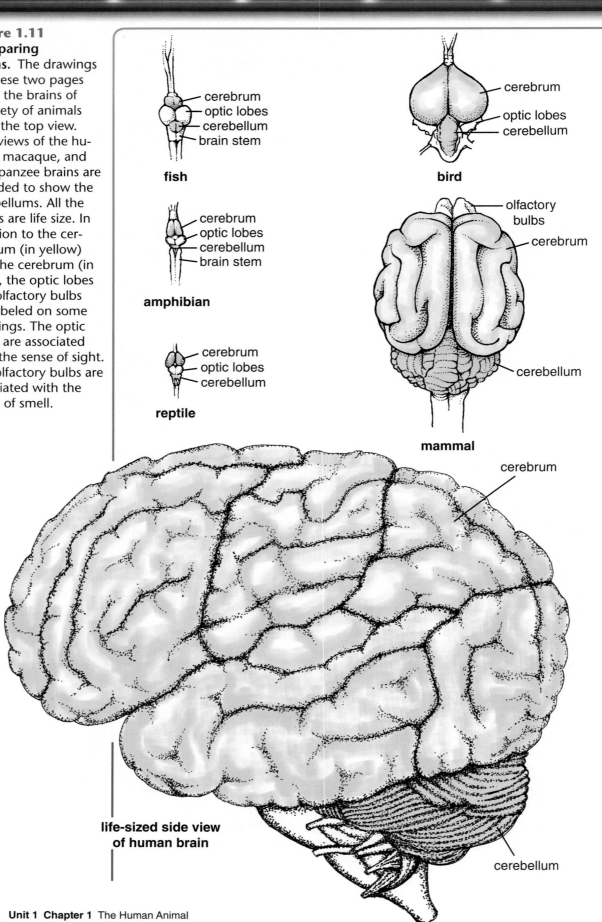

cerebrum
optic lobes
cerebellum
brain stem

fish

cerebrum
optic lobes
cerebellum

bird

cerebrum
optic lobes
cerebellum
brain stem

amphibian

olfactory bulbs
cerebrum
cerebellum

mammal

cerebrum
optic lobes
cerebellum

reptile

cerebrum

cerebellum

life-sized side view of human brain

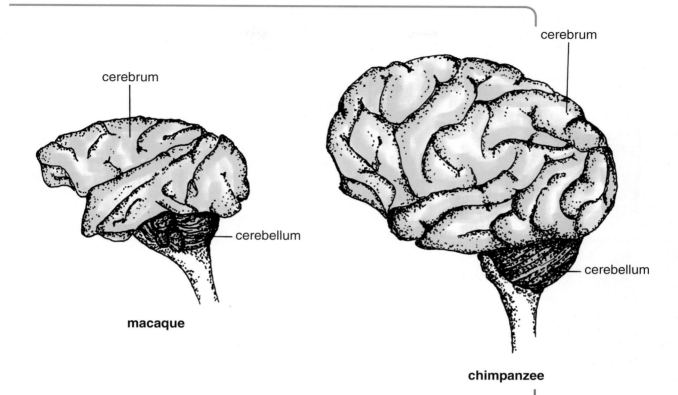

cerebrum

cerebellum

macaque

cerebrum

cerebellum

chimpanzee

5. Participate in a class discussion of the following questions by listening to your classmates and contributing your own ideas. Use your observations of the various brains and the insights from your classmates to answer these questions in your science notebook.

   a. Consider the sheep brain. Which brain of those that you have studied is most like the sheep brain?

   b. Write down the evidence or reasoning you used to answer step 5a.

   c. Why do you think some brains are similar?

       Use the information you collected in step 4. Make sure you can explain your choices.

   d. Consider the cerebrum of each animal. What do you observe about the human cerebrum that makes it distinctive from the others?

   e. How are the functions of the cerebrum in humans distinctive?

       You learned about the function of the cerebrum in the essay, *Mapping the Brain*.

   f. Consider the cerebellum of each animal. Which animals would you expect to have well-developed cerebellums and why?

   g. Consider the other observations you made about the brains. What inferences might you make about an animal that has a brain with very large optic lobes or olfactory bulbs?

Analysis

Discuss the following with your partner, and then record your own answers in your science notebook.

1. Different animals show very different behaviors. How might these differences be related to the differences in their brains? Explain your answer.

   To answer this question, use what you know about the behavior of fish, amphibians, reptiles, birds, sheep, other nonhuman mammals, and humans. Think about what you have learned from the observations that you made during this activity.

2. List 2 additional questions that you have about the brain as a result of your observations and readings in this activity.

© Dreamstime/Justin Yamada

Further Challenges

1. Read the sidebar, *Brains and More Brains,* to find out more information about the functions of the brain. Create a way to visually represent the different functions of the different parts of the brain.
2. Visit a zoo and make detailed observations of the way various primates or other animals move. You could record your observations in writing, drawings, or video.
3. Develop an experiment designed to answer another 1 of your testable questions from this activity.

SIDEBAR

ENGLISH SPANISH

Brains and More Brains

Think hard! Add 235 and 25, and then divide by two. Now, which part of the cerebrum did you use? The left half of your cerebrum was probably the most active. On the other hand, if you imagine how to draw a picture, you would probably use more of the right half of your brain. We are just starting to unravel the mysteries about how the brain works. Scientists called **neurobiologists** study the different regions of the brain and work to learn more about how they function and what they control.

Not only are the physical structures of the brain specialized, but also within each of the structures there is further specialization. The cerebrum has two distinct parts, or sides, called the left and right hemispheres (see figure 1.12). The hemispheres individually control certain behaviors. Sensory and movement functions on the left side of the body are controlled by the right hemisphere of the cerebrum and vice versa. The specific area of the cerebrum that controls the movements of your body is called the motor cortex. The specific area of the cerebrum that lets you feel sensations from your body is called the **sensory cortex** (see figure 1.13).

Scientists have been able to map many sites on the motor cortex to a particular part of the human body. They have been able to do the same for the sensory cortex. That is, when you move a certain part of your body, scientists know what part of your motor cortex is making that movement possible. When you smell a rose, scientists know what part of your sensory cortex is allowing you to experience that fragrance.

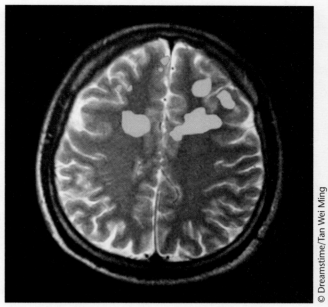

Functional magnetic resonance image of the brain of a person smelling something. The image is a virtual cross section of the brain, showing a bird's-eye view.

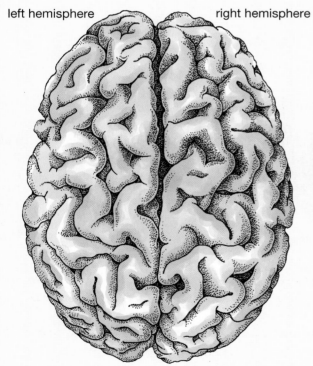

left hemisphere   right hemisphere

Figure 1.12   Top view of human brain (approximately 65 percent of life size). The human cerebrum is split into halves, or hemispheres.

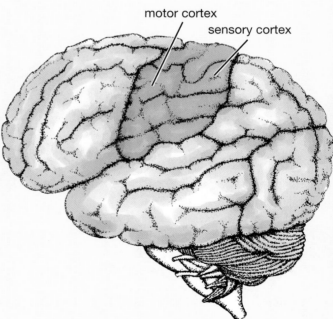

motor cortex

sensory cortex

Figure 1.13   Side view of human brain. In humans, the motor cortex and the sensory cortex are located alongside each other, across both hemispheres of the cerebrum. The cortex is the top layer of the cerebrum.

Figure 1.14 shows the results of this mapping process. The figure of the person looks distorted because the size of the area that is mapped to a particular part of the body is not related to the actual size. Rather, it is related to the amount of precision required for that part of the body to do its job. A larger area in the brain means that body part requires relatively more precision. In humans, a good deal of space is dedicated to the face, tongue, and hands. Why do you think that is so?

In most individuals, the left hemisphere of the human brain controls language and speech, as well as mathematical and other analytical abilities. The right hemisphere is responsible for visual and spatial processing. Many functions, including various aspects of those mentioned above, are controlled jointly by both hemispheres. Communication between the two hemispheres is possible because a bundle of nerve fibers, called the **corpus callosum,** connects them.

Evidence suggests, however, that the brain can process information in more than one way. In addition, certain functions that are normally performed by one region of the brain can sometimes be taken over by other regions. This is particularly true when the individual is young. For instance, when young children suffer strokes (a blood clot that damages the brain), they tend to recover more quickly than older individuals. For example, if the stroke damaged a child's right hemisphere, instead of the child losing some or all of his or her language ability, the left hemisphere often takes over this function.

Another example of different regions of the brain taking over for a damaged region takes place when input from one of the

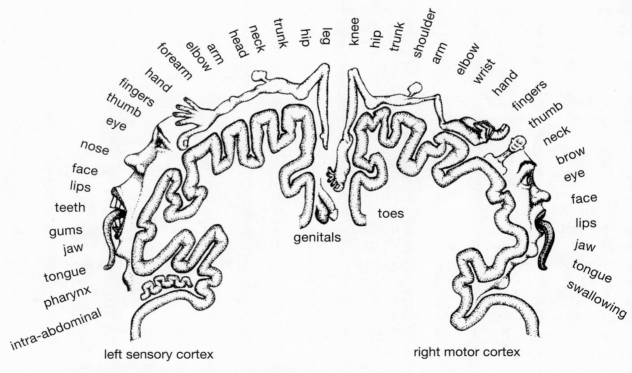

Figure 1.14 **Parts of the human body mapped to the motor and sensory cortices.** The resulting figure looks distorted because the area of the cortex that is devoted to a particular body part is not related to the actual size of that part. It is instead related to the amount of precision required to control it. In this drawing, only the left sensory cortex and the right motor cortex are shown.

senses is impaired, for example, when an individual loses his or her sight. In this case, input from another sense will make up for the loss. For these reasons, the brain often is said to be plastic—that is, it can change in response to certain events and experiences. It is a good thing that the brain can change—that is what learning is all about.

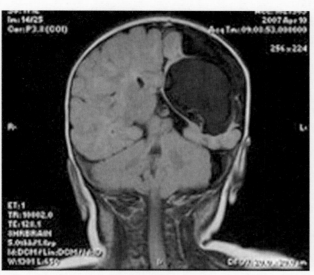

Recovery from brain damage. This young girl had a stroke while still in the womb, which caused half her brain to stop developing. Magnetic resonance imaging (MRI) shows the extent of the damage. However, other parts of her brain have compensated for the damage. She is able to move, sense, and learn fairly normally.

A Cold, Hard Look at Culture

EXPLORE

In the last activity, you compared human hands, feet, physical movement, and brains with those of other animals in order to pinpoint some truly distinctive characteristics. But do these physical characteristics capture the essence of what it means to be human? Take a moment to review the class's brainstorming results of distinctive human features from the Engage activity, *How Different Are We?* How many of the features on that list are not clearly physical characteristics?

Perhaps the class's list included such notable human characteristics as using language to communicate, creating art and music, and participating in ceremonies. Humans have an exceptional ability to develop behaviors and technologies that permit us to cope with new situations. For example, we can minimize the effects of an extremely hot environment by using the technology of air-conditioning to modify part of that environment. This ability is called **cultural adaptation**, and it is one of the distinguishing characteristics of humans.

Unlike physical characteristics, cultural adaptations are not inherited. Think about the development of new words as an example. When did you first hear the word "blog"? It is unlikely that your parents ever used this word before you were born, but it has quickly become a part of modern culture. The transmission of information and values from person to person and generation to generation happens through cultural communication and learning. In this Explore activity, *A Cold, Hard Look at Culture*, you will explore the question, "How is human culture related to the distinctive physical characteristics of humans?"

You and your teammates will take on the role of anthropologists in order to pursue this question. A scientific society has asked your team to help its members study a human who died more than 5,000 years ago and the cultural artifacts found with the human. Because he was buried in ice and snow high in the Italian Alps, his body and his belongings were unusually well preserved. Your assignment is to infer whatever you can about his life and his culture.

Materials

online resource
different-colored pens or pencils

PROCESS AND PROCEDURES

1. Consider the question, "How do scientists study events that occurred 5,000 or more years ago?" Take notes as you participate in a class discussion of this question. Write your best answers in your science notebook.

2. Read the following paragraphs by yourself:

A man died high in the Alps, above tree line. His body was frozen into a glacier and remained there for more than 5,000 years. Then, in 1991, some hikers discovered the well-preserved corpse. They assumed that it was a modern hiker who was killed the previous winter, and they notified

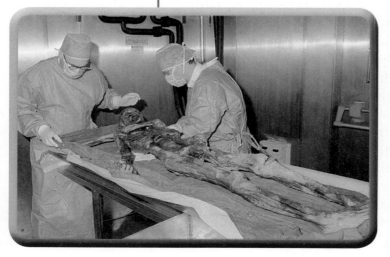

authorities. Because the authorities did not realize that they were dealing with something very old, they removed the body from the ice carelessly. Unfortunately, this carelessness resulted in the loss of valuable evidence.

Imagine their surprise when it was discovered that the body was ancient, probably 5,300 years old. He was male, stood 165 cm tall, weighed about 38 kg, and was about 45 years old at the time of his death. He had a series of blue markings on his skin. This included several sets of blue parallel lines on his lower back, stripes on his right ankle, and a cross behind his left knee. His hair was medium length and had been cut. His physical features were similar to those of humans today. His final meal had been eaten about eight hours before he died. This meal included a crackerlike bread, some green plant material, and some meat. X-rays and CAT scans revealed that before his death, he received a blow to his head as well as an arrow wound through his back left shoulder, which punctured an artery.

The Iceman and his possessions are among the most valuable anthropological evidence ever found. Usually, the types of evidence that are preserved from humans who lived 5,000 years ago are hard substances, such as teeth, bones, or metal parts of tools. Soft tissues such as skin, hair, plant materials, and leather generally are destroyed by decay. In this case, however, many unusual material remains were recovered with the Iceman. These remains are called artifacts.

Scientists often draw logical conclusions about things they cannot directly observe. For example, scientists come up with ideas about the skin and outward appearance of a dinosaur from its fossil remains. In the same way, scientists come up with ideas about the appearance or culture of early humans from artifacts that are preserved.

3. Use the information found in the table in figure 1.15 to help you imagine what the Iceman was wearing and carrying when he died.

Topic: iceman
Code: human4E53
www.scilinks.org

Artifact	Comment
Grass cape	The cape is carefully stitched together; isolated repairs were made with grass thread.
Arrows and leather quiver (carrying case for arrows)	This is the oldest leather quiver ever found; some arrows have flint arrowheads, other arrows are unfinished.
Very long bow	The bow is unstrung.
Pouch with worked bits of flint	Flint is a type of stone that flakes easily into sharp pieces.
Clothing and boots	The clothing and boots are made of leather; grass is stuffed inside boots.
Copper-bladed axe with wooden handle	This is one of the oldest axes of its type and the first with handle intact; it is attached by leather ties and glue; it has a copper blade.
Mushrooms strung on a leather strip	These mushrooms are a type of fungus with medicinal (antibiotic) properties.
Flint dagger and grass sheath	The worked flint blade is on a wooden handle; this is the first sheath of this age recovered.
Bone needle	
Grass rope	
Stone disk threaded with a leather strap	
Bits of a primitive wheat and wheat pollen	This type of wheat grew only at low altitudes.

Figure 1.15 **Artifacts recovered with the Iceman.**

4. Watch the video segment, "A Glimpse of the Iceman." As you watch, take notes on ideas that come to mind about what the Iceman's life and culture were like.

5. Think about questions you have about the Iceman's life and culture. In your science notebook, record 3 testable questions that you think evidence from the Iceman could help answer.

   Reflect on all the evidence from the reading in step 2, the table in figure 1.15, and your notes from the video segment as you think about questions that scientists could test. If needed, review the need to know, *Testable Questions*, in part A of the Explore activity, *Primates Exploring Primates*.

6. To prepare for a team discussion, construct a table titled "evidence and ideas about the Iceman" in your science notebook. The table should look like figure 1.16.

Figure 1.16
Table of evidence and ideas about the Iceman. Write down evidence in the left column and your ideas in the other two columns.

Evidence	What it might indicate about the Iceman	What it might indicate about the Iceman's culture

7. With your team, discuss each piece of evidence from the Iceman's body and possessions. Contribute your ideas about what each observation may indicate about the Iceman and his culture. Record all ideas in the table you made in your science notebook.

8. In your science notebook, make a list of the following statements. Make a mark next to statements that you think constitute scientific evidence.
   a. The Iceman carried arrows made with flint arrowheads.
   b. The Iceman used mushrooms as medicine.
   c. The Iceman spent some time at lower altitudes.
   d. The Iceman had bits of wheat from a lower altitude on his clothing.
   e. The Iceman wore clothing made from animal products.
   f. The Iceman knew how to sew.
   g. The Iceman was a hunter.
   h. The Iceman used grass for several purposes.
   i. The Iceman lived at a time when people knew how to work with metals.

9. Think about whether the statements in step 8 describe evidence or inference, as you read the need to know, *Evidence and Inference*. The information will help you learn the difference between evidence (observations you can make directly) and inference (logical assumptions based on evidence, but that you have not directly observed).

NEED TO KNOW

ENGLISH SPANISH

Evidence and Inference

When scientists find human remains and artifacts, they work carefully to gather as much information as they can from their findings. Often what they find is incomplete, but the remains are *evidence* that scientists can use to draw conclusions about the individual. Scientists try to be aware of their own beliefs, moods, and prior experiences when they look at evidence. That way, they will not let these factors affect their conclusions. Conclusions that follow logically from some form of direct evidence are known as *inferences*. (Conclusions that do not follow logically from evidence are just guesses. Guessing is not an acceptable way to draw scientific conclusions.)

For example, if you came home and found some dirty dishes in the sink, you might infer that your older brother was in a rush to eat before leaving the house. An illogical assumption would be that a robber had stolen some things and then eaten something before leaving. There is no additional evidence that a robbery had taken place. Sometimes more than one inference could be drawn from the evidence. For example, another inference could be that your brother had been too lazy to wash the dishes before he left.

In science, the strongest inferences are the ones that are made with the most evidence and that provide the simplest explanation. If you saw that in addition to the dishes, there were answering machine messages that hadn't been listened to, a lamp was left on, and there was a note reading "Back at 6 after job interview—Dave," you might conclude that the strongest inference is that your brother was in too much of a rush to wash his dishes. With all of that evidence, the idea that Dave was just lazy is a weakly supported inference.

© Dreamstime/Tadija Savic

10. Decide with your team whether each of the statements in step 8 describes *evidence* or *inference*. Record your ideas next to the list in your science notebook, including why you think each statement is evidence or is inference.

11. Look back at the ideas you recorded about each artifact in step 7. Were your ideas about how the Iceman used the items based on evidence or inference? Write "evidence" or "inference" next to each statement, using a different-colored pen or pencil.

12. Discuss with your team the kinds of cultural artifacts that are worn and carried by people today. In your science notebook, make a table with 2 columns. List the Iceman's artifacts on one side and the modern-day equivalents of those artifacts on the other side.

13. Calculate how many human generations have passed between the Iceman's time and ours, working cooperatively with your team. Record your finding in your science notebook.

Recall that the Iceman lived about 5,300 years ago. The length of a single human generation is approximately 28 years.

Analysis

Answer the following questions in your science notebook. Be prepared to share your ideas in a class discussion.

1. Review the questions you wrote in step 5. Did your team's analysis lead to answering any of these questions?
   - If your answer is yes, describe how evidence or inference helped to answer the question.
   - If none of your questions were answered, propose a reason for why they weren't. For example, was it because the question was not testable, or because additional evidence would be needed to test it?
2. Review the table of evidence and ideas that you constructed in step 7, and then answer these questions.
   a. If you could have 3 more pieces of evidence to help you complete your understanding of the Iceman, what would they be?
   b. What information would these pieces of evidence give you that would help you understand how the Iceman lived or died?
3. Review the description of the Iceman's body from the reading in step 2, and then answer these questions.
   a. Do you think there have been greater changes in humans physically or culturally in the last 5,300 years? Give 1 reason to support your answer.
   b. Propose a reason for why the Iceman's physical features are similar to those of humans today.
4. Review the distinctive human physical features that you investigated in the Explore activity, *Primates Exploring Primates*.
   a. How would the Iceman and his people have produced the kinds of artifacts that were found with him? In particular, how would they have used distinctive features of their hands and brains to make artifacts?
   b. How do people today use their distinctive physical features to make objects similar to the artifacts found with the Iceman?

Explaining Humankind

Have you noticed that puppies can be separated from their mother within two months of birth, and a newborn foal will be up and walking around within minutes of its birth? A human child, however, usually stays with its mother for years and does not begin to walk until it is close to one year old. Have you ever wondered why this is so?

The collection of physical characteristics that sets humans apart from other organisms results in some behavioral differences as well. You have explored various aspects of the human brain and have compared it with the brains of other organisms. You also have explored evidence of an ancient human's culture and compared it with your own culture. But what does that really mean? How do the features of the human brain, and cultural characteristics, contribute to behaviors that make us different from other organisms? In this activity, *Explaining Humankind*, you will explore possible answers to those questions. You are also likely to come up with more intriguing questions of your own.

You have already made observations of humans, other primates, and a collection of brains, and you have reflected on the similarities and differences you found. After exploring humans' long childhood in this Explain activity, you will have an even better idea of the range and subtlety of characteristics that make us unique. You will begin to develop a special project to show that you understand what it means to be human.

Materials   (per person or team of 2)

Part A
resources on gestation and the development of animals after birth

Part B
You may need an assortment of materials to help you create your project:

- poster board
- old photographs
- magazines
- tape recorder
- video camera

- musical instruments
- cardboard boxes
- felt-tipped markers
- glue

online resource (optional)
different-colored pens or pencils (optional)

PROCESS AND PROCEDURES

Part A   A Long Childhood

1. Take notes as you have a class discussion of the following question:

   "How are humans similar to and different from other organisms, with respect to the following characteristics? Consider the length of gestation, the care of young, and the milestones of childhood."

2. In your science notebook, create a table similar to that shown in figure 1.17. The table will help you organize and record information about the gestation and development of humans and other animals.

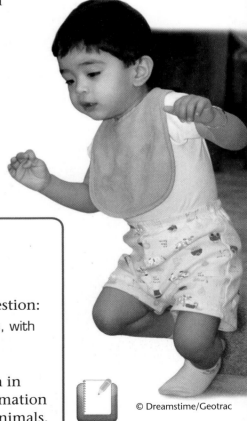

© Dreamstime/Geotrac

Figure 1.17
Sample table of information on animals. A table similar to this one will help you organize your information in a way that makes it easy to use.

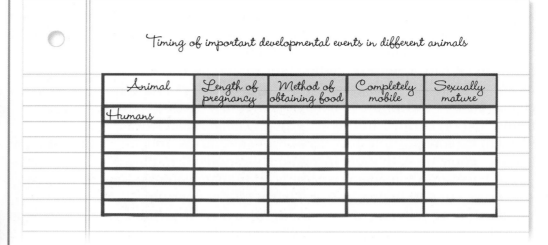

Timing of important developmental events in different animals

Animal	Length of pregnancy	Method of obtaining food	Completely mobile	Sexually mature
Humans				

Topic: animal adaptations
Code: human4E58

3. Select an animal to research. Answer the question in step 1 for that animal and record your answers in the table.

   Use the resources that your teacher provides or resources from the library or the Web.

4. Contribute your answers to a class data table. Record the class's data in the table in your science notebook.

5. Discuss with your classmates the patterns that emerge as you compare the data for humans with those of the other animals. Use the data to identify the animals that have long "childhoods."

6. Write "long" next to those animals that have a long childhood and circle the pieces of data that support that idea.

7. Briefly discuss the following questions with a partner. Then record your answers to these questions in your science notebook as you read the essay, *The Importance of Being Children*.
   a. How does a long childhood help humans develop complex culture?
   b. How does our language ability help us develop complex culture?
   c. How does our ability to learn help us develop complex culture?
   d. Compare and contrast learned behavior and innate behavior.
   e. Give 2 examples of other animals that exhibit a certain capacity for learning, language, and culture.
   f. Is it possible to infer whether the Iceman would have had a long childhood? Use evidence to support your answer.

Part B   Portraying Humankind

1. Think about designing a project to illustrate your understanding of what it means to be human, from a scientific perspective.

   Think of an activity that you enjoy doing and consider what human characteristics make it possible for you to do this activity. Perhaps you can incorporate a demonstration or description of this activity into your project and presentation.

"When will I be a grown-up?"

This is a question that four-year-olds all over the world ask in hundreds of different languages. The words may be different, but the question is the same—"When will I know all that I need to know to be me?"

Think about the following examples:

- A human newborn usually doesn't start to walk until he or she is at least 10 months old.
- On average, children and young adults in the United States are required to go to school until age 17.
- In the United States, people are not allowed to vote until they are at least 18 years old.

Compared with other animals, humans take a long time to become adults. Why do humans have such a long childhood?

A Long Childhood Allows Humans Time to Learn

One answer to the question about why humans have a long childhood is that humans need to learn a tremendous amount of information and concepts. It is amazing to stop and think about how much you really know. Humans and many other animals have incompletely formed brains at birth. However, a human's brain continues to develop for a much longer time than other animals' brains. As a result, our life experiences influence us to a greater degree. The ability of the brain to be shaped and changed by experience is particularly true of human infants and young children. It is during these critical years that an incredible amount of information is learned. The long time it takes for our brains to develop, reflected in our long childhood, helps explain why humans have such a great capacity for learning.

Humans' ability to learn helps us develop the skills and knowledge needed to survive and contribute to our culture. Culture is the sum of all the knowledge that is passed from generation to generation. The skills and knowledge that are passed down often strongly depend on the places and times at which people are born. Think about the Iceman and the kinds of information and skills he needed to learn in his culture. For example, he needed to learn and practice hunting. He probably needed to learn to identify mushrooms to make sure he used the correct kind. The markings on his skin indicate that he also probably learned certain ceremonies and rituals. To obtain items he needed, he also probably had to understand a system of trade or exchange. What kinds of knowledge and skills are important for people to learn in your culture?

Humans are also very good at using the knowledge we learn to solve problems in new ways. Obtaining, organizing, and sharing knowledge through education allows human cultures to change rapidly. This type of change is called cultural adaptation. More than any other animal, humans make and use tools to solve problems. Compare the tools and technology used by the Iceman with the tools and technology available to you. This technological progress is an example of the power and speed of cultural adaptation. Cultural adaptation is distinct from biological evolution.

A Long Childhood Allows Humans Time to Acquire Language

Our long childhood and our great ability to learn also give us time to acquire language. Language is one of the most important things that humans learn. Most languages have numerous complicated rules of grammar and tens of thousands of vocabulary words. Once we learn language, we can communicate an infinite number of thoughts and ideas. Others who speak the same language can understand our thoughts and ideas.

Even though the process of learning a language appears to be tremendously complex, it occurs quite naturally. Children who grow up hearing one

language at home and a different language among their peers can become fluent in both languages. Often, they appear to do this with little effort. Language, like many cultural behaviors, is learned, or *acquired*, as part of normal development. However, after age 10 or so, the capacity for learning a language decreases. This limitation explains why it is more difficult to learn a new foreign language in high school or college.

Language helps us record and communicate our culture efficiently. Imagine what our world would be like if we eliminated just one of our uses of language, the preservation of information in libraries. Passing on all this information by word of mouth would be difficult. Another benefit of language is that it allows people to get to know each other quickly. This helps us live closely with many other humans who are not our relatives. Language helps us maintain our complex social organizations. The interplay between language and culture helps to further distinguish humans from all other animals.

The long childhood of humans helps us develop our language and learning skills. Both of these help us live in complex, technologically advanced societies. But what about other animals? How do they learn and communicate? Do some other animals have complex societies?

How Do Animals Communicate?

Animals can communicate with each other through sounds, smells, displays, and movements (see figure 1.18). Some communication is purely visual, such as the colorful breeding plumage of many birds. Bees have a complex display known as the bee dance. Through this dance, illustrated in figure 1.19, a bee can communicate the location of food to other bees in the hive. Other social animals, like apes and monkeys, make different noises in different situations. For example, baboons can make and understand up to 22 different calls. They can also identify individuals by specific calls. But do we

consider these activities language? Though animals have the capacity for language-like behavior, they lack precise words for things and do not have formal grammar. Thus, these communications are not considered language.

You explored another form of communication in the *Engage* section at the beginning of this course. Termites communicate primarily through the release of chemicals, called pheromones, that other members of their society can sense. Your experiments showed how tracking pheromones can be used to communicate which path a termite should follow. You may wish to use other resources to look up how your favorite animal communicates.

Do Animals Learn?

Many researchers study how animals learn. One broad category of behavior is called learned behavior. *Learned behaviors* are the responses an organism develops as a result of specific interactions with the environment. The other type of behavior is innate behaviors. Organisms are born with the

Figure 1.18 Communication between wolves. Animals communicate in a variety of ways with different levels of complexity. Wolves communicate with each other through vocalizations such as howling, barking, and growling, as well as through behaviors such as licking and submissive postures.

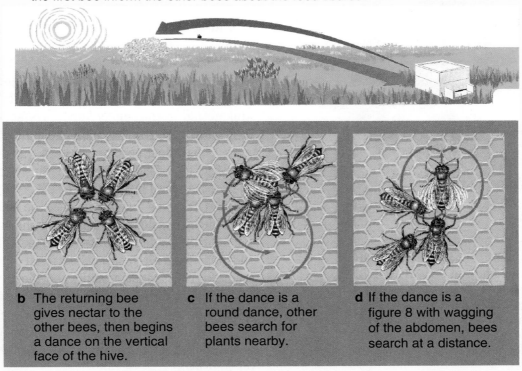

a A foraging honeybee returns to the hive after finding a nectar source. Other bees soon leave the hive and fly to the same source. How does the first bee inform the other bees about the food source?

b The returning bee gives nectar to the other bees, then begins a dance on the vertical face of the hive.

c If the dance is a round dance, other bees search for plants nearby.

d If the dance is a figure 8 with wagging of the abdomen, bees search at a distance.

Figure 1.19   The bee dance. Honeybees communicate the location of food through a set of signals known as the bee dance.

ability to perform **innate behaviors.** An example of an innate behavior is a baby's ability to nurse. Babies are born knowing how to nurse and do not generally need to be taught this behavior. Scientists have discovered that all behaviors fall somewhere along a continuum between those that are primarily innate and those that are primarily learned.

In primate societies, flexible learned behaviors are important characteristics. One famous example of learned behavior occurs in some macaque monkeys, as shown in figure 1.20. In the early 1950s, on an island off Japan, scientists had begun feeding macaque monkeys potatoes to get

closer to the monkeys and to make observations. In 1953, a scientist saw a young female macaque monkey wash a sweet potato in a stream before eating it. Within a few months, the monkey's playmates and mother were also seen washing their potatoes. Within five years, more than three-fourths of the individuals in the population were washing their potatoes before eating them. Within 10 years, almost all of the monkeys in the population were washing their potatoes. They are still doing it today. This behavior demonstrates a creative response to a new situation and the transmission of that behavior between generations.

Figure 1.20   Behavioral flexibility.
When a feeding station was established, one macaque learned to wash sweet potatoes in the water before eating them. This behavior was adopted by most of the macaques in the community and even was passed on to the next generation of macaques.

Social Animals

The societies of humans and other primates are familiar to most people. However, biologists are also interested in the social organization of other animals. Termites are, once again, a very interesting example. Termites live in large families, called a colony because it is so big. In a termite family, the king and queen are actually the only father and mother in the colony. Termite offspring who stay within their home colony adopt one of two main "jobs." Most become workers who dig tunnels, find food, feed and care for the young, and fix the nest. A small number of the offspring become soldiers. In some termite species, the soldiers have huge, muscle-filled heads and sharp jaws for fighting. Soldier termites are special because they also have *altruistic* behavior. In other words, soldier termites instinctually sacrifice their own lives to save their fellow nest mates from danger. Termites are just one of many fascinating examples of complex animal societies. You may wish to research the social organization of other animals on your own.

2. Write some brief notes in your science notebook about the format of your project and the information you want to include. This will remind you of your ideas when you share them with your partner in step 3.

Select a medium that you are comfortable with to create your project. Some possibilities are a poster, a diorama, a poem, a story, a report, a musical piece, a play, a TV show, or a video. As you think about and plan your project, use the criteria in the *Portraying Humankind Rubric* provided by your teacher to guide your work.

3. Share your ideas with your partner. Answer any questions he or she may have about your project.

4. Obtain and read a copy of the *Portraying Humankind Rubric* that your teacher will use to evaluate your project.

5. With your partner, take turns explaining the following ideas. Reviewing this information will help you prepare to design your project.
   a. How humans are structured to be bipedal (walk on 2 feet)
   b. How the human hand is similar to and different from the hands of other primates
   c. How different parts of the cerebrum are associated with different behaviors
   d. How different parts of the human brain are similar to and different from the brains of other animals
   e. Why the human brain is responsible for complex human behavior
   f. How artifacts can be used as evidence to learn about culture
   g. How the long childhood of humans affects our learning, language, and culture

   > If you would like more information to help you explain these ideas and design your project, the sidebar, *On Being Human*, and the video segment, "More about the Brain," provide useful information.

6. In your science notebook, write a short description of your project. List 4 or 5 concepts from the essays and the previous activities that you plan to incorporate into your project.

Analysis

1. Analyze your project using the TSAR strategy, as described here.
   a. Read the description you wrote. *Think* about whether there are any parts that are unclear and whether it meets all the criteria on the rubric.
   b. *Share* your ideas with your partner by reading your description to your partner word for word from your science notebook. Listen carefully as your partner reads his or her description to you and ask your partner about things he or she wrote that you do not understand.
   c. *Advise* your partner on anything you think might improve his or her project. Also advise your partner on how well his or her project meets the criteria listed in the rubric. Listen carefully to the advice from your partner on your project and ask questions if there are aspects of the advice that you do not understand.
   d. *Revise* or add to your description, using a different-colored pen or pencil, if you think your partner's advice is helpful. Record why you did or did not make revisions.

   > You will present your project to the class as the Evaluate activity for this chapter. Refer to *How to Use the Think-Share-Advise-Revise (TSAR) Strategy*, in appendix B3, for more information on how to use this strategy.

On Being Human

Have you ever seen a cow laugh or a cat tap its foot in time to music? Have you ever heard a human purr exactly like a cat? Humans are animals, yet humans do things that you would never expect to see in other animals. And other animals do things that you would never expect to see a human do. What is it that makes humans unique?

Humans do many unusual things. For example, imagine a surgeon reaching carefully past an assistant to insert a small bit of vein that will bypass a blockage in the patient's artery. The assistant firmly places the correct tool in the surgeon's palm and watches as the delicate procedure is completed.

Across town, in a concert hall, a guitarist waits for the applause to subside before beginning the next song. The fingers of the left hand push against the strings, while the fingers of the right hand rapidly pluck them to produce a distinct pattern of notes. The audience recognizes the song

and applauds. These examples show some of the characteristics that distinguish humans from other animals—even from other closely related animals, the other primates. Humans, like many other primates, can grasp things with their hands and fingers. Almost all primates can grasp with their feet, a trait humans do not share. Although some humans can pick up objects with their toes, they cannot grasp objects with the foot itself. However, the fine dexterity, or skill, required to repair an artery or to play a complicated pattern of notes on the guitar is mainly a human trait. (The drawings in figure 1.21 allow you to compare a series of primate hands.)

This dexterity is possible because humans have fully opposable thumbs that can move to touch the pad of any of the other fingers with precision. Not only is our grasp precise, it is strong. It is strong enough to grasp a baseball bat and hold on to it as we swing it with force or to grasp a hammer and use it to pound a nail into a solid piece of wood.

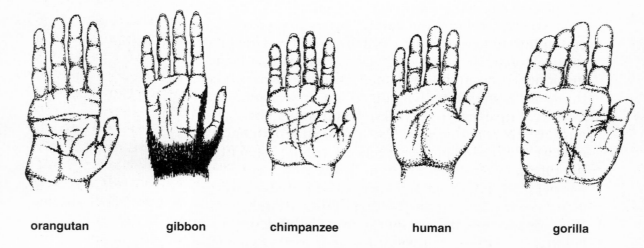

orangutan   gibbon   chimpanzee   human   gorilla

Figure 1.21 **Ape and human hands.** Use these drawings to supplement your observations of primate hands. Which hands look capable of a power grip? Do you notice anything different about muscle development in the hands? Which hands do you think could use the precision grip? (See the sidebar, *Do You Have a Grip on That?*, in the Explore activity, *Primates Exploring Primates*.)

Other primates share some degree of these various grips. A baboon that had been stung by a scorpion was able to grip the stinger and remove it. This action, however, does not require the grip to be strong. The structure of the human hand allows room for additional muscle attachment, which results in a more flexible, more precise grip and greater manual dexterity than that of the baboon.

Degree of dexterity is not the only characteristic that distinguishes humans from other primates and all other animals. Humans stand on two feet and walk fully upright with the body balanced directly over the feet. This bipedal method of locomotion is very different from that of other animals such as horses, spiders, or animals that fly. Although other primates can walk upright for short distances, humans are the only primates that are *consistently* bipedal. Most primates are quadrupedal and use four feet when they walk. African apes, such as gorillas and chimpanzees, travel on the ground by a very special means—they knuckle-walk. What advantage does bipedalism have over knuckle-walking? Traveling on the ground on two feet requires less energy if you need to travel long distances.

For any animal with a skeleton, the skeleton has features particularly suited to the animal's way of moving. Bird bones, for example, are mostly hollow and consequently are light—a property important for flying. Humans have thicker leg bones that support their weight. Human thighbones insert into the pelvis in a way that places most of the body's weight directly over the knees and feet. In contrast, a gorilla's knees and feet are positioned away from the middle of the body

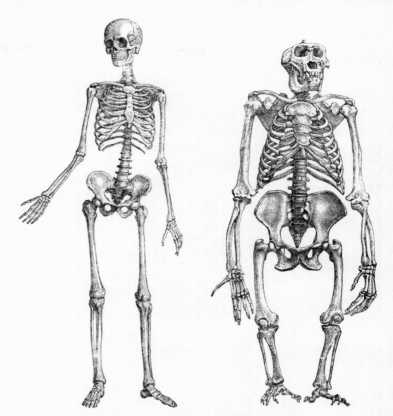

Figure 1.22   Gorilla and human skeletons. Notice that the knees of the gorilla are positioned slightly to the sides of the body, while the human's knees and feet are positioned directly under the pelvis.

(see figure 1.22). The bones of the human spine also form an S-shaped curve that helps disperse the impact from the ground when walking on two feet. However, the large number of people with back problems shows that this is far from a perfect solution. The gorilla usually uses all four limbs and walks on its feet and on the knuckles of its hands. Like all nonhuman primates, it can travel for brief periods of time on two feet, but it doesn't have the correct positioning of leg bones and the S-shaped spine needed for consistent bipedalism (see figure 1.23).

Humans have other adaptations suited to bipedal walking. Look at your foot. The average human foot has a broad heel, an arch at midfoot, shorter toes than those of other primates, and a thick big toe that

Figure 1.23   Methods of movement.
The gorilla is quadrupedal and walks on its hind feet and knuckles. Humans are completely bipedal, except as infants.

cannot grasp (see figure 1.24). When we walk, we hit the ground on the broad heel of the foot. The arch acts like a spring to roll our weight forward. We then begin the next step by pushing off with the thick big toe. As we move, our weight is constantly redistributed throughout the foot. At the same time, forces from the ground are transferred upward through our knees, then hips, and into our S-shaped spinal columns. If we had perfectly straight backs, these forces would not disperse and we would probably get sore necks or have headaches. A gorilla's foot certainly is more similar to a human foot than that of a cow or a lizard, but like all nonhuman primates, it has longer toes and a grasping big toe that looks and functions like a thumb.

Think back to the example of a surgeon (a tool user) repairing a damaged blood vessel. Even if a chimpanzee or gorilla could hold the surgical tools, would you want it to perform surgery on you? The human surgeon has a characteristic that makes such activities possible: humans have large and complex brains. All primates have relatively large brains compared with other mammals. But the modern human has the largest brain of all primates. The human brain is not the largest on Earth—the elephant's brain and the whale's brain are larger, but so are their bodies. For the size of our bodies, humans have exceptionally large brains. The brains of all animals control similar functions such as breathing, movement, and other body activities. But the part of the brain that controls abstract thinking and reasoning is very large and well developed in modern humans. In this function, the human brain appears to surpass all other animal brains—even those of relatively intelligent animals such as

Figure 1.24 **A gorilla foot and a human foot.** Notice how the gorilla foot is similar to the gorilla hand (figure 1.21). But the human foot, adapted for upright bipedal movement, is significantly different from the human hand.

chimpanzees or dolphins. As a human, you have special abilities to find solutions to puzzles, to use complex language that is based on symbols, to use memories of the past to plan the future, and to reflect on all of these many abilities. You also have the unique ability to infer what another animal does or does not know. Scientists call this the theory of mind. This important characteristic is not well developed in other primates, as far as scientists can tell.

Although other animals may have some small degree of these characteristics, these abilities are much better developed in humans. As a collection, these characteristics distinguish humans from other organisms. Every organism has a combination of characteristics that makes it distinctive. Organisms also share many characteristics with other living things, an idea you will explore later in this chapter. Characteristics are more specialized in some organisms compared with others. For example, human vision is better than that of a dog, but not nearly as acute as the vision of an eagle, which must spot

prey on the ground from high in the air. The dog, however, has an acute sense of smell to help it hunt, which is much better developed than in humans or eagles. Humans are not nearly as fast as a cheetah, but humans are much faster than an armadillo or a slug. Each organism shares many basic life properties but each can be recognized by a collection of special traits.

Among the huge and diverse groups that make up animals, humans belong to the group known as mammals. Why aren't we reptiles, birds, or fish? We are mammals because we have mammal traits such as having hair or fur, giving birth to live young, and producing milk to nurse our offspring. Within the group known as mammals, humans belong to the group known as primates. We have primate traits such as eyes that face forward and nails, rather than claws, on our fingers and toes. And now, having read this sidebar, you have accomplished something that, as far as we know, no organism other than a human can do: you can read.

Further Challenges

1. Together with other interested classmates, find out about the existence of culture and society in other animals.
2. Do further library research on the learning abilities of other primates or dolphins.
3. Learn more about your own learning style. Your teacher may have resources to get you started.

   Your learning style is the way you prefer to learn. There are questionnaires you can take to find out more about how your brain works best for learning new information. If you are interested in taking a learning style questionnaire, talk to your school counselor.

ELABORATE

How Similar Are We?

"He can climb like a monkey."
"She soaks up sunshine like a flower."
"You're acting like an animal!"

Have you ever been compared to another organism? Why do humans do this? Perhaps it is because we recognize that we share fundamental characteristics with other living things.

You have now thought more carefully about how humans are unique. In this Elaborate activity, *How Similar Are We?*, you will consider the question of what similarities humans share with other organisms, and you will develop your ideas around what it means to be alive.

Materials (per class)

unifying principle cards (1 card per team)
online resource
different-colored pens or pencils

© Dreamstime/Socrates

PROCESS AND PROCEDURES

1. Brainstorm with your team a list of characteristics that humans share with other organisms, recording all ideas in your science notebook.

   Use the photographs provided by your teacher as well as photographs like figure 1.24 in the sidebar, *On Being Human*, to stimulate your thinking. Challenge one another to find fundamental similarities between humans and these organisms. For example, what do you have in common with a plant? Plants may not move like humans do, but like humans, they cannot survive for too long without water.

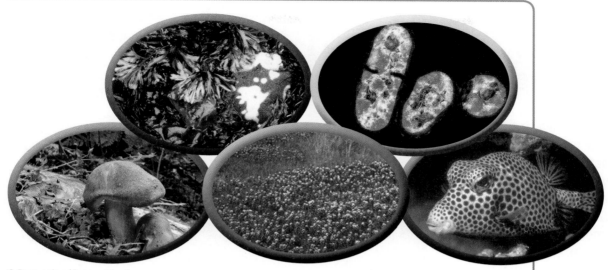

© Dreamstime/George Wood

2. Identify any characteristics on the list from step 1 that you think humans share with *all* other organisms (figure 1.25). Mark these with the word "all" in a different-colored pen or pencil.
3. Choose a team member to report the characteristics that you identified as being shared among all organisms.
4. During the class discussion, record the class's list in your science notebook under the title "class list of characteristics shared by all organisms."
5. Obtain a unifying principle card for your team from your teacher. Then read the essay, *Describing Life: An Impossible Challenge?*, to learn what these unifying principles mean. Write a definition of each of the 6 unifying principles in your science notebook, using your own words.

   This portion of the activity will help you explore whether scientists recognize the similarities that the class identified. You will also learn whether there are additional similarities that the class didn't mention yet.

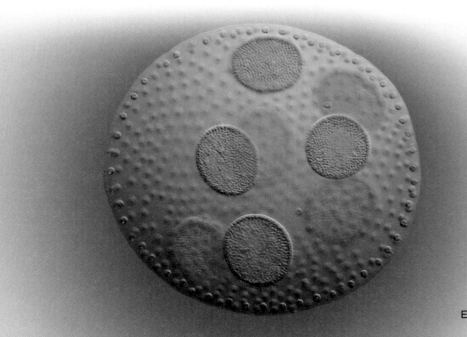

Figure 1.25 **What do humans share with this organism, called a volvox?** Magnification = 10×.

Describing Life: An Impossible Challenge?

ENGLISH SPANISH

A spaceship is orbiting Mars to make observations. It ejects a special robotic rover to land on the planet's surface (figure 1.26). Its mission: to determine whether life exists on the planet. At first, the rover sits motionless on the bleak landscape. Then, slowly, it activates its electronic senses. It rotates its cameras to scan the horizon. It uses special equipment to detect the gases in the air. The atmosphere is thin, but it does contain some water vapor. This is a good sign . . .

Recognizing life on an alien planet such as Mars is indeed a challenge. To begin with, we need a good idea of how to recognize life on Earth. But even this task is not simple. Living systems share many characteristics. But do any of these characteristics distinguish living things from nonliving things?

You probably already have some ideas about what makes living things unique. If you were to ask your classmates to identify a tree, a dog, and a rock as living or nonliving, all their answers

Figure 1.26 **Technology to explore Mars.** In May 2008, the Phoenix spacecraft landed at the north pole of Mars and sent data back to scientists on Earth.

would be the same. However, if you asked your classmates how they know what is living and what is not, their responses probably would vary. And suppose you asked them about a less familiar object, such as the scaly, grayish-green lichen on a boulder (like the one depicted in figure 1.27)? This time, some of your classmates might not be so sure if it is living or not.

All forms of life share many basic characteristics. This holds true even for very different life-forms such as humans, apple trees, spiders, and microscopic bacteria. Understanding these common characteristics is fundamental to understanding biology. In fact, these characteristics are so important that we have summarized them as six unifying principles of biology. The flow of topics in this course is organized around them. In this unit, you will study evolution, one of these principles. As you begin to achieve a deeper understanding of the remaining five principles, you will be developing a rich understanding of biology.

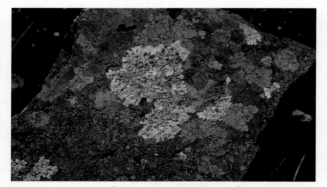

Figure 1.27 **Lichens are organisms that consist of a close association between a fungus and a photosynthetic organism such as an alga.**

Figure 1.28 An anole lizard can change color in response to its environment.

Evolution: Change in Living Systems

One significant characteristic of living systems is that they evolve, or change, over time. The fossils of organisms from a long time ago reveal many organisms that look different from organisms today. Changes in populations of living things have resulted in an amazing diversity of characteristics. Changes over time can also lead to the generation of new species. All species are linked because they share a common ancestor with all other living things. *Evolution* represents the first unifying principle considered in this course.

Homeostasis: Maintaining Dynamic Equilibrium in Living Systems

A second characteristic of life—and a second unifying principle of biology—involves a living system's ability to maintain an *internal balance*. This is called homeostasis. All organisms regulate their internal systems in response to changes in their surroundings. Have you ever noticed how your heart beats faster when you are startled? Quickly pumping blood through your body helps you respond quickly to a potentially dangerous situation. In fact, all organisms show interesting kinds of internal regulation. Bacteria can adjust their production of certain chemicals. Plants respond to changes in humidity by opening or

closing tiny holes in the underside of their leaves. And some animals can change colors to match their environment (see figure 1.28).

Energy, Matter, and Organization: Relationships in Living Systems

Another common characteristic of life is *organization*. All living systems are highly organized forms of *matter*. One of the most remarkable similarities among all living things is that they are mostly made up of only a few types of atoms. These are mainly carbon, nitrogen, oxygen, hydrogen, phosphorus, and sulfur. In organisms, atoms are often held together in large, complex molecules.

The molecules of living materials are organized into complex structures known as cells. Cells are the basic structural units of living matter, but they are too small to see with the unaided eye. As figure 1.29 illustrates, cells are baglike structures surrounded by a barrier called a membrane. Membranes allow cells to accumulate certain substances and exclude other substances. In this way, cells can maintain a different composition from their environment.

A related property of all living systems is that they require *energy* to build their structures and to carry out their activities. Organisms typically harness light energy from the Sun or chemical energy from other organisms. Think about what

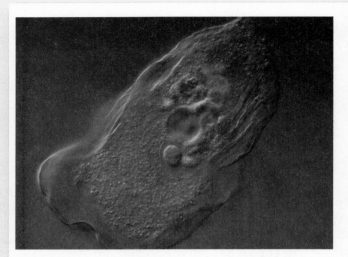

Figure 1.29   The cell is the basic unit of living matter. Cells typically range in size from 1 to 100 μm in diameter. Notice the organization of the interior of this *Thecamoeba* cell, which is 10 μm in diameter.

happens when an organism dies. A dead bird, for example, loses its ability to use matter and energy to keep its body repaired and functional. Over time, it will become indistinguishable from the matter around it. Together, the ideas of matter, energy, and organization represent the third unifying principle of biology.

Continuity: Reproduction and Inheritance in Living Systems

All living systems depend on plans that are encoded in genetic material, or DNA. The specific information in your DNA has shaped how your body has grown and developed. DNA is a long and complex molecule that stores information. One of the most significant characteristics that unifies living systems is the universal nature of this DNA. All organisms, from bacteria to plants to humans, use DNA to provide instructions for building and maintaining their cells and bodies. In addition, all organisms have the ability to transfer those instructions—through DNA—to the next

generation during reproduction. Together, DNA and reproduction make up a fourth important unifying principle of life: *continuity* (see figure 1.30).

Development: Growth and Differentiation in Living Systems

The *ability to develop* represents the fifth unifying characteristic of living systems. Growth is an important activity for young organisms, as the body assembles new tissue. As an organism grows, the way in which the organism is organized also changes. For example, many plants begin life as small seedlings that push up through the soil. They grow into mature plants that look very different from the seedlings. Differentiation—the way in which cells "specialize"—occurs in organisms with more than one cell. This allows the body to "divide the labor" that it must carry out. Differentiated cells, like skin cells and neurons, develop

© Dreamstime/Pixbilder

Figure 1.30   DNA allows genetic information to be continually passed from one generation to the next.

Figure 1.31 Organisms along and in this stream interact and depend on one another.

specific shapes and carry out specific functions. Development is the sum of all the growth and differentiation that occurs over the lifetime of an organism.

Ecology: Interaction and Interdependence in Living Systems

Finally, all living systems on Earth interact and depend on other organisms in the web of life (refer to figure 1.31). Imagine a wooded area on an early summer day. Plants provide shelter and food for a variety of birds. A rabbit has created a burrow nearby and is feeding on wild berries. Not far away, a fox just left her den in search of food for her young. This community of different, but connected, living systems illustrates the sixth unifying principle of biology: the *interactive and interdependent nature of life.*

We might say that in this short list of characteristics we have described life—as it exists on Earth. Can we say that any one of these principles *defines* life, in the sense that it alone is an indicator of life? Probably not. Just as a *combination* of characteristics identifies you as a human, a *combination* of these principles indicates the presence of life.

Now that you have a clearer picture of the characteristics of life on Earth, how do you think scientists should look for life on other planets? Should they look for signs of evolution, of growth and development, of reproduction? Although these are characteristics of life, they probably occur too slowly to be detected by a tiny robotic craft.

Scientists decided to collect Martian soil samples for more-immediate, more easily recognizable signs of life. They tested for signs that have to do with a living system's requirement to use

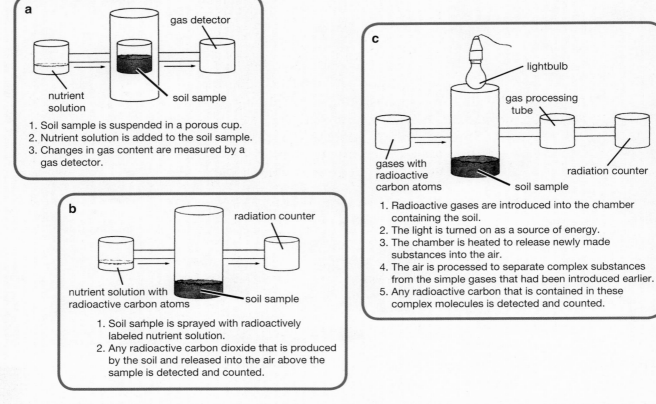

a

gas detector

nutrient solution

soil sample

1. Soil sample is suspended in a porous cup.
2. Nutrient solution is added to the soil sample.
3. Changes in gas content are measured by a gas detector.

b

radiation counter

nutrient solution with radioactive carbon atoms

soil sample

1. Soil sample is sprayed with radioactively labeled nutrient solution.
2. Any radioactive carbon dioxide that is produced by the soil and released into the air above the sample is detected and counted.

c

lightbulb

gas processing tube

gases with radioactive carbon atoms

radiation counter

soil sample

1. Radioactive gases are introduced into the chamber containing the soil.
2. The light is turned on as a source of energy.
3. The chamber is heated to release newly made substances into the air.
4. The air is processed to separate complex substances from the simple gases that had been introduced earlier.
5. Any radioactive carbon that is contained in these complex molecules is detected and counted.

Figure 1.32   Three experiments to test Martian soil. (*a*) A gas exchange experiment tested the Martian soil in 2004 for evidence of organisms. The experiment examined whether something in the soil took in gases and gave off other gases as wastes. A controlled experiment was run by testing soil from Earth. (*b*) A second experiment tested for the release of carbon dioxide as a waste gas. (*c*) A third experiment tested the Martian soil for evidence of organisms that might build large, complex substances out of simple gases in the Martian atmosphere. Tests with Earth's soil successfully detected the production of sugars by microorganisms. However, tests with Martian soil did not show similar activity.

matter and energy. In particular, they performed tests to see if anything in the Martian soil was using gases in the atmosphere, similar to how humans take up oxygen when we breathe.

Ultimately, although two of the three tests described in figure 1.32 yielded some interesting results, scientists could not duplicate the results with later samples. Scientists eventually agreed that the data they collected could be explained as resulting from purely chemical (not biological)

causes. Two rovers that landed on Mars in 2004 did not find life. But they did find evidence indicating that water, a necessity for life as we know it, existed on Mars in the past.

Describing life . . . a difficult, but not an *impossible*, challenge. Looking for life, using Earth's criteria, in a very different environment more than 40 million miles away . . . more difficult to be sure, but *impossible*?

What do you think?

6. Rotate your science notebook sideways and make a large table similar to that shown in figure 1.33. Make the rows for your team's unifying principle extra deep.

7. Complete the following tasks while watching the video segment, "A Diversity of Organisms."

Online Resource

a. Fill in your team's row of the table. Write notes about how each major type of organism (Archaea, Fungi, and so on) displays your team's unifying principle.

b. List 1 organism from each group that you notice displays your team's unifying principle in an interesting way. Be prepared to explain why you chose each organism.

> Focus your note taking on how each major type of organism displays your team's principle. For example, suppose you are tracking the principle of ecology (interaction and interdependence). You would record the fact that plants supply the oxygen to the air that both plants and animals require for life. You would *not* take notes about specific places where each type of plant is found.
>
> Use the video as a jumping-off point for thinking about this task. Use what you know about humans to fill in the "animal" portion of your table. Make notes of any relevant observations and logical thoughts you have, not just what the narrator says. For example, if you are looking for the unifying principle of development, you can describe how any multicellular organism from the video would logically have to develop from a single-celled embryo.

Unifying Principle	Type of Organism					
	archaea	bacteria	protist	animal	fungi	plants
Evolution						
Homeostais						
Matter, Energy, and Organization						
Continuity						
Development						
Ecology						

Figure 1.33 Summary Table. Use a table like this to record your observations and summarize the presentation.

Do not be concerned if you cannot complete your table from the information presented in the video segment. Some principles are easier to observe in such images than others are. Step 10 offers another opportunity to complete your table.

8. Discuss with your team what evidence best supports your unifying principle. If you did not find evidence for your unifying principle in the video, use the *Three Domains* essay to fill in gaps. You could also list evidence that you think a scientist might be able to find.

9. Agree on a team presenter for step 11. The presenter will need to explain what your unifying principle means, describe the evidence your team found, and explain why the evidence relates to your unifying principle.

10. As teams present their evidence, fill in the appropriate rows in the table you made in step 6. Think about whether their presentations make sense to you. Write down any ideas or questions in your science notebook.

11. Contribute ideas and questions to the class discussion of the following questions.
    a. Does the evidence support the idea that humans share fundamental characteristics with all other organisms?
    b. Do the unifying principles leave out some characteristics that the class identified in step 4 as being shared among all living things? Does this change your ideas about those characteristics?

Analysis

1. In your science notebook, record your answer to this question: "What characteristics unify all living things?" In other words, what makes something alive?

2. Earlier in this chapter, you recorded your initial ideas about similarities between humans and other organisms. In your science notebook, review and revise the answers that you wrote for the following questions. Use a different-colored pen or pencil to make any revisions you would like. Put a single line through your previous thinking to indicate you have revised it.
   a. Engage, *How Different Are We?*, *Analysis* question 3
   b. Explore, *A Cold, Hard Look at Culture*, *Analysis* question 3b

3. In your science notebook, propose a reason for why living things share fundamental characteristics.

Three Domains

Scientists recognize three major domains (or groups) of life: the Bacteria, the Archaea, and the Eukarya. The domain Eukarya contains humans and most of the organisms you may have observed outdoors or through the microscope: animals, plants, fungi, and protists. Each of these groups of eukaryotes is called a kingdom. Organisms in different domains and kingdoms may appear extremely different from one another, but they all share certain fundamental characteristics of life.

Domain Bacteria

The main criteria (or qualification) for membership in the domain Bacteria is that the cell lacks membrane-enclosed compartments and has a unique method of using its genes. Bacteria usually are single cells, but they may occur in groups of cells. Bacteria come in a variety of shapes, as depicted in figure 1.34. Some swim by means of long, whiplike tails. All bacteria reproduce by dividing into two. But some also exchange small amounts of DNA—a form of sexual reproduction. Bacteria live in almost every environment, from the soil to inside the human mouth.

Bacteria show a great diversity in the processes that they use to obtain energy. Many bacteria can use the Sun's energy directly to power the reactions required for making their own food through photosynthesis. Others use energy derived from the matter (food molecules) that they acquire from their environments. As a group, bacteria can digest almost anything—even oil. This ability is fortunate for us. Bacteria that can recycle matter through decomposition are increasingly being used to help with environmental cleanup efforts.

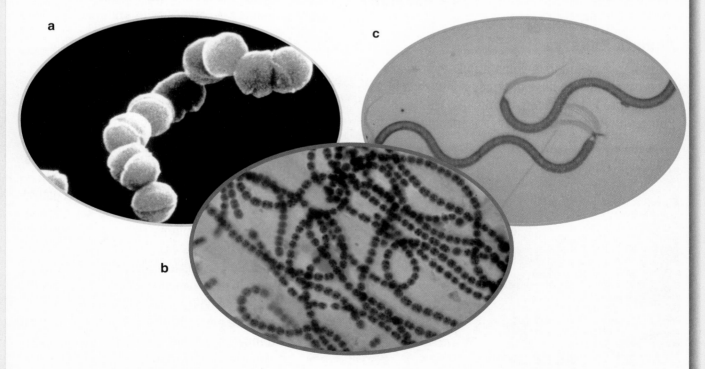

Figure 1.34 **Examples of bacteria.** (*a*) These *Streptococcus* bacteria (photographed at 40,000×) can cause strep throat. (*b*) *Nostoc* (photographed at 400×), a cyanobacterium, is common in freshwater lakes. (*c*) *Spirillum volutans* (photographed at 400×) is part of a group of bacteria named for its characteristic spiral shape.

Domain Archaea

DNA evidence suggests that archaea are more closely related to eukaryotes than they are to bacteria, despite the fact that both bacteria and archaea lack a nucleus. Archaea have unique ways of building their cell membranes and their flagella. Although they are found in every environment, archaea may be the only life-forms in some extreme environments (figure 1.35). Some live at high temperatures or in highly acidic conditions; others live in high-salt conditions. Some archaea live in environments where there is very little oxygen; these produce methane gas. Most recently, archaea have been discovered in very cold environments, such as the deep ocean. Most archaea cannot be cultured in the lab, so much more remains to be discovered about how these organisms obtain and use energy and the roles they may play in diverse ecosystems.

Domain Eukarya

Humans are found in domain Eukarya, as are most other multicellular organisms. Eukarya is divided into four kingdoms: Animalia, Plantae, Fungi, and Protista. All eukaryotic life shares the criterion of having membrane-bound compartments in their cells, such as nuclei. Together with Archaea and Bacteria, the four kingdoms of Eukarya make up six major groups of organisms.

Domain Eukarya, Kingdom Animalia

Animals are multicellular—they have a complex organization of many specialized cells. Animals also are characterized by their ability to bring food into their bodies and digest it. In addition, most animals reproduce sexually and have senses and nervous systems that enhance their ability to move.

Animals live in marine and freshwater environments, inhabit the soil, and live on land. In addition, animals come in a range of sizes, from microscopic worms that live in human blood to whales that can reach lengths of 27 m. Figure 1.36 shows a diversity of animals.

Domain Eukarya, Kingdom Plantae

Another eukaryotic kingdom, the kingdom Plantae, includes organisms that acquire their energy not from eating but from the Sun. Plants carry out photosynthesis, a process by which cells use energy from sunlight to produce their own food. Photosynthesis takes place in membrane-enclosed structures within plant cells called chloroplasts. Chloroplasts contain chlorophyll, the light-absorbing pigment that gives plants their characteristic green color.

Plants are multicellular, and their cell membranes are surrounded by a rigid cell wall that provides support. Most of them reproduce sexually. Plant forms are diverse and include mosses, liverworts, club mosses, ferns, conifers, and flowering plants, as shown in figure 1.37. Plants produce the bulk of the food for humans and much of the world's oxygen.

Figure 1.35   Minerva Terrace, Mammoth Hot Springs, Yellowstone National Park. Archaea live in many environments, including these hot springs.

Figure 1.36 **Examples of animals.** (*a*) These tube sponges are from the Red Sea in the Middle East. (*b*) This click beetle is from Arizona. (*c*) This male hooded oriole is from the southwestern region of the United States.

Domain Eukarya, Kingdom Fungi

Kingdom Fungi, also a eukaryotic kingdom, includes organisms that grow directly from reproductive cells called spores. Fungi, like plants, have cell walls, but they do not carry out photosynthesis. You probably are more familiar with the members of this kingdom than you realize. Fungi such as mushrooms become large, multicellular organisms, with tissues made of slender tubes of cells (hyphae). Other fungi, such as yeasts, live as single cells during their entire life cycle. Still others, such as molds and rusts, live as tiny multicellular structures on the surface of decaying things, such as bread that has been sitting around too long or lettuce that is "going bad."

Fungi do not digest food inside their bodies as humans do. Instead, they release molecules called enzymes into their surroundings. These enzymes

© Dreamstime/Rainer

Figure 1.37 **Examples of plants.** (*a*) This moss, *Lycopodium*, grows in moist areas. (*b*) The sword fern, *Polystichum munitum*, grows in Olympic National Park, Washington. (*c*) This apple tree, *Malus domestica*, is in full bloom.

break down (digest) biological material that other living systems have produced. The smaller food molecules then are absorbed into the cells. Thus fungi, along with many bacteria, play an important role as decomposers in many communities of organisms. The diversity of fungi includes yeasts, molds, morels, mushrooms, shelf fungi, puffballs, and plant diseases such as rusts and smuts (see figure 1.38). Some fungi also interact closely with green algae or cyanobacteria to form the organisms known as lichens.

Domain Eukarya, Kingdom Protista

Finally, the kingdom Protista is a grab bag of all the remaining eukaryotes that do not belong to the animal, plant, or fungi kingdoms. Protists live in water and in moist habitats, such as in the soil, on trees, and in the bodies of other organisms.

Protists show a remarkable range of diversity in their methods of obtaining food, their methods of reproduction, their life cycles, and their lifestyles. Most protists are tiny, single-celled organisms, though many grow as colonies—clusters of individual cells. However, some protists, such as brown algae living in the ocean, may form multicellular structures up to 100 m long. Algae form three groups of protists that produce their food through photosynthesis. Other protists, like the slime molds, obtain their food by decomposing the dead tissues of other organisms. Still other protists are parasites of animals, plants, or fungi. A single droplet of pond water viewed under the microscope reveals a world of protists in their myriad of shapes. Figure 1.39 depicts several protists.

Figure 1.38 Examples of fungi. (*a*) The mycelium of a wood-rotting fungus, *Stereum complicatum*. (*b*) A mushroom fungus, *Marasmius scorodonius*. (*c*) *Microstoma floccosa*, a small, cup-shaped fungus.

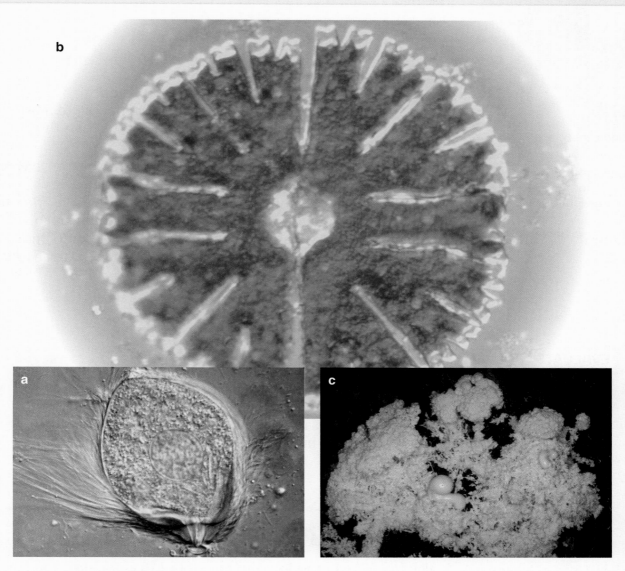

Figure 1.39 **Examples of protists.** (*a*) *Trichonympha* (photographed at 135×) is a protist that lives in the gut of termites. (*b*) *Micrasteria* (photographed at 100×) is a type of green algae. (*c*) *Fuligo septica* is a slime mold.

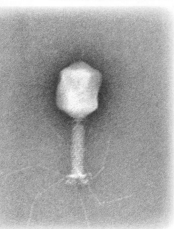

Figure 1.40 The bacteriophage (photographed at 240,000x) is a virus that attacks bacteria.

Further Challenges

1. Read these observations about a virus, called a bacteriophage (see figure 1.40), that infects bacteria.

   A bacteriophage
   - contains genetic material,
   - reproduces only when inside another organism,
   - has an outer case made of protein,
   - injects genetic material into a bacterial cell, and
   - uses the energy and the structure of the bacterial cell to make parts that assemble into copies of itself (and often kills the bacterial cell).

   You may have noticed that neither the video segment, "A Diversity of Organisms," nor the essay, *Three Domains,* contained any reference to viruses. Yet we often think about viruses in relation to life. For example, have you ever heard someone complain about being *attacked* by a virus? Use your knowledge of the unifying principles of life to construct a well-reasoned argument to answer the question, "Is the bacteriophage alive?"

EVALUATE

What Does It Mean to Be Human?

In this Evaluate activity, *What Does It Mean to Be Human?*, you will demonstrate what you have learned in chapter 1. You will use your project to show how this new knowledge helped you answer the question, "What does it mean to be human?" from a scientific perspective.

PROCESS AND PROCEDURES

1. Make the following addition to the project that you began in part B of the Explain activity, *Explaining Humankind*:

   Develop a summary of your understanding of how humans are similar to all other organisms.

   The unifying principles and your science notebook notes from the Elaborate activity, *How Similar Are We?*, will help you with this task.

2. Present your project to your classmates according to your teacher's directions.

3. Take notes while other students are presenting. Pay particular attention to the ideas that seem to be included in more than 1 presentation. Note aspects of presentations that you think are particularly strong. Ask questions at the end of each presentation to clarify any information that you don't understand.

4. Using the criteria in the *Portraying Humankind Rubric*, identify what you think are the 3 strongest projects in your class. List these in your science notebook and justify your choices.

Analysis

On your own, write the following questions in your science notebook and take notes to answer them. Use your notes to participate in a class discussion. When you are through, write the best answers to the questions in your science notebook.

1. Use the rubric's criteria to rate your own project and presentation. How would you explain your rating?

2. How would you revise your own project to better match the criteria in the rubric?

3. What common characteristics did the class generally identify as distinguishing humans?

4. Scientists have changed their views of the features that distinguish humans from other primates. How does this fact illustrate the process of science?

2

Evolution:
Change Across Time

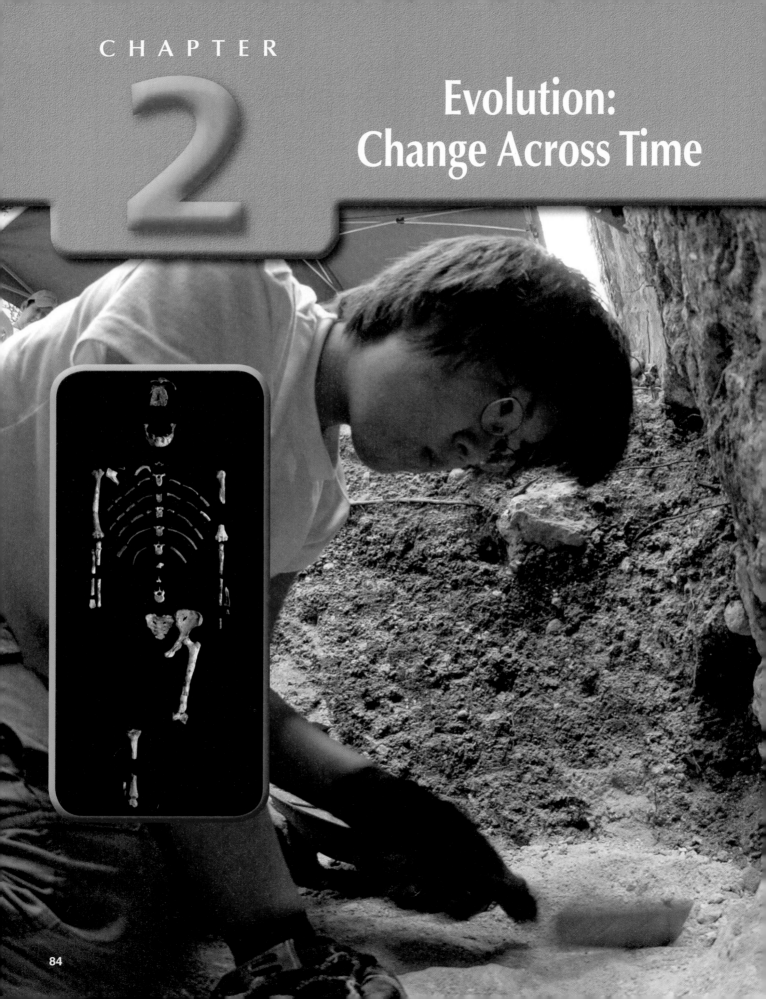

They were about to return to camp when Johanson noticed part of a fossilized arm bone lying on the ground partway up the slope of a gully.

Scenario: Digging Up the Past

Look at the fossilized bones in the photograph. What animal do you think of when you see these bones? It turns out that these bones are from a primate that lived about 3.2 million years ago. Fossil skeletons give scientists a tremendous opportunity to study the physical characteristics of organisms that lived long ago. As you look further and further into the past, most of the skeletons of ancient organisms look less and less like organisms that are alive today. Why? It is because populations of living organisms change across time, an idea you will explore in this chapter.

At the beginning of chapter 2, you will think about the fossil skeleton in the photograph. You will imagine how she may have looked and behaved at the time she lived and how the line of ancestors that led to her may have changed over time. Next, you will explore reproduction in populations and examine how individuals within a population differ. These observations will help you understand a model of how a population changes over time. Next, you will consider two different views on how the process of change in populations works. You will use your growing understanding to evaluate evidence that evolution has occurred. You will also make a timeline of Earth's history to help you appreciate the large time spans over which life has evolved. You will then examine what the word "theory" means. Finally, you will evaluate your understanding of evolution by analyzing an example of evolution in action.

GOALS FOR THE CHAPTER

Throughout chapter 2, you will work to gain an understanding of the following concepts:

✔ Many different sources of evidence support biological evolution.

✔ Natural selection is a major mechanism of evolution that can result in adaptations.

✔ Life has been shaped by evolution, extinction, and geologic events over vast periods of time.

✔ Scientific theories are supported by independent sources of evidence.

✔ Scientific studies often develop models of natural phenomena to assist in making explanations and predictions.

To help you develop these understandings, you will complete the following activities.

ENGAGE	Lucy
EXPLORE	Exploring Change
EXPLAIN	Explaining Adaptation
ELABORATE	Evidence for Evolution
ELABORATE	Modeling Earth's History
ELABORATE	Just a Theory?
EVALUATE	Evolution in Action

Linking Question:
What characteristics of populations could lead to changes over time?

ENGAGE

Lucy

Key Idea: Scientists use evidence and logical inference to understand how organisms have changed through time.

Chapter 2

EXPLORE

Exploring Change

Part A: Seeds of Change
Part B: Celebrate Diversity
Part C: Modeling Change
Key Idea: More offspring are born than can survive, and individuals in populations have some differences. This situation leads to a process of change over time.

MAJOR CONCEPTS

✔ Many different sources of evidence support biological evolution.

✔ Natural selection is a major mechanism of evolution that can result in adaptations.

✔ Life has been shaped by evolution, extinction, and geologic events over vast periods of time.

✔ Scientific theories are supported by independent sources of evidence.

✔ Scientific studies often develop models of natural phenomena to assist in making explanations and predictions.

Linking Question:
What process of evolution leads to adaptations?

EXPLAIN

Explaining Adaptation

Part A: Two Views of Adaptation
Part B: The Zebra's Stripes
Key Idea: Adaptations are a product of natural selection.

Linking Question:
What is the evidence that life has changed over time?

EVALUATE

Evolution in Action

Key Idea: Evolution by natural selection can result in changes in populations that affect humans.

Linking Question:
How do natural selection and evolution work in today's world?

Evolution: Change Across Time

ELABORATE

Just a Theory?

Key Idea: The theory of evolution is based upon multiple lines of evidence, which together form a powerful explanation for how organisms change across time.

Linking Question:
Given what has been discovered about evolution, why is it considered a theory?

ELABORATE

Modeling Earth's History

Key Idea: Events in Earth's history took place over vast periods of time.

Linking Question:
On what scale did the changes that support evolution take place?

ELABORATE

Evidence for Evolution

Key Idea: Multiple lines of evidence support the theory of evolution.

Lucy

Populations of living things on Earth change over time. Scientists use evidence and logical inference to reconstruct these past events. For example, since the mid-1800s, scientists have been piecing together the long line of species and populations from which modern humans emerged. This long line of ancestors is called a **lineage**. Some of the most important pieces of this complex puzzle are the fossilized skeletal remains of individual hominids that lived millions of years ago. **Hominids** are erect-walking primates that include modern humans and extinct, humanlike species. Dated at about 3.2 million years old, the skeleton shown in the opening photo is one of the oldest and most complete hominid fossils. Scientists named the skeleton Lucy, after a song that was popular when it was recovered.

But how do populations of living things change? Writing your ideas about this question will be your main task in this Engage activity, *Lucy*. Both evidence and inference will guide your thinking on the topic.

PROCESS AND PROCEDURES

1. Read the scenario, *Digging Up the Past,* to learn about the discovery of Lucy. As you read, write a statement in your science notebook about the aspects of inquiry in which the scientists were participating.

   Use the scientific inquiry diagram (figure En.4) and your notes from the *Engage* section Explain activity, *Thinking as a Scientist Thinks*, to review all the steps of scientific inquiry.

2. Describe in your science notebook how Lucy may have looked. Use words and sketches to convey your ideas.

   Use the photograph of the fossil skeleton in the opening photo to this chapter and your notes from chapter 1, *The Human Animal*, to help you develop your description. Pay particular attention to Lucy's hands, feet, posture, and way of moving.

3. Describe 3 things Lucy might have done during a typical day and how she would have gone about doing them.

4. Make a T-table in your science notebook with the 2 columns labeled "evidence" and "inference."

   The resource *How to Use and Create Organizing Tables*, in appendix B4, can help you with this task.

HOW TO

5. Fill in your T-table with examples as you read the following information about how scientists use evidence and inference to gain insight into the past.

   Though Lucy's complete skeleton was not recovered, scientists are still able to infer many things about her. For example, the structure of Lucy's pelvis (the bones that make up the hips) was carefully documented. Her pelvis was compared with those of modern chimpanzees, apes, and humans. Humans walk upright. Scientists call this bipedal. Apes and chimps are knuckle-walkers and are not

Digging Up the Past

No one knows how Lucy died. She apparently died quietly. If a lion or a leopard had killed her, her bones probably would have been splintered and crushed. Instead, she died by the edge of an ancient lake, where mud and sand covered her.

Lucy lived in what is today the Afar desert, a remote region of northeastern Ethiopia in East Africa (see the map in figure 2.1). The large lake that once existed there has long since dried up. The area is now hot and sandy. Even though she was fully grown and probably in her 20s when she died, Lucy stood only 1 m tall. Her head was a bit larger than a softball, and her brain could not have been much larger than that of a modern chimpanzee. The shapes of her knee joint and pelvis bones indicate that she walked upright on two legs. For more than 3 million years, Lucy remained buried in the ancient lake bed.

In 1973, Donald Johanson, a young anthropologist from the United States, arrived in Ethiopia to look for fossils. Working with two Frenchmen, Maurice Taieb and Yves Coppens, Johanson found a primitive primate knee joint that had washed out of a slope during a rain. It seldom rains in the Afar desert, but when it does, the rain is heavy, cutting gullies into the

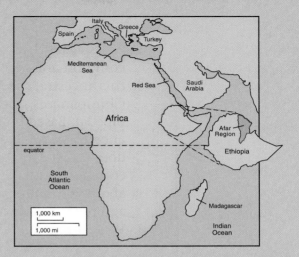

Figure 2.1   Map of the Afar region in Ethiopia.

gravel and bare rock. On very rare occasions, these rains uncover ancient fossils. As luck would have it, such a rain occurred not long before Johanson's arrival. This fossil knee joint was intriguing because it was about 3 million years old. Its structure indicated that this individual had walked erect.

Because of this find, Johanson decided to return to the same ancient lake bed the following year to continue the search. If any more humanlike fossils were embedded in the ground, they might be of a similar age. Johanson and his colleague, Tom Gray, had been searching all fall with no success when they parked their vehicle on the slope of a gully on the morning of November 30, 1974.

The temperature had reached 43°C (110°F), and they were about to return to camp when Johanson noticed part of a fossilized arm bone lying on the ground partway up the slope of a gully. As he searched further, he found pieces of a skull, thighbone, and pelvis, along with other skeletal parts. Remarkably, the skeletal parts all seemed to be from one individual, and a very humanlike individual at that. The two scientists barely could contain their excitement. They had just made an amazing find.

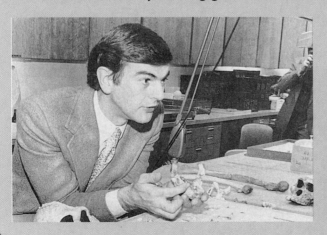

bipedal. Lucy's pelvis shared many features with the pelvis of modern humans. From the evidence of Lucy's fossilized pelvis and the pelvis of modern humans, scientists made the inference that Lucy walked upright. Evidence from Lucy's knee bone also supports this inference.

Scientists agree that hominids, apes, and chimpanzees came from one species that existed in the past. This extinct species is called the common ancestor of all three species. Recent estimates suggest that this ancestral species lived most recently about 7.3 million years ago. Chimpanzees, apes, and all other primates are not exclusively bipedal. Based on this evidence, scientists infer that the common ancestor of apes, chimpanzees, and hominids was not bipedal. What does this mean about Lucy? In the lineage from the most recent common ancestor of apes, chimps, and hominids (which existed about 7.2 million years ago) to Lucy (who lived 3.2 million years ago), there was a change from not being bipedal to being bipedal.

6. Write 1 or 2 short paragraphs that summarize how you think a scientist would explain how the lineage that led to Lucy changed over time. Explain how the lineage changed from an ancestral population that was not bipedal to a population that was bipedal.

> As you proceed through this course, you are learning to see the world the way that scientists do. It is important to remember that in science, explanations must be based on evidence from nature. Natural causes can be tested by other scientists. Scientists cannot make explanations based on forces that are outside of nature. Such explanations are not testable. It is OK not to know at this point how scientists describe the process of change over time. But it is important that you make your best attempt. You will revisit your answers later in the chapter.

Analysis

Use the information you recorded in your science notebook during this activity to answer the following questions as part of a class discussion.

1. Compare hominids from Lucy's lifetime with hominids living today (humans) by answering these 2 questions.
   a. Do you think there have been more changes in the physical characteristics of the body (such as hands, feet, head, and posture) or more changes in how hominids lived (types of shelter, ways of getting around, and ways of gathering food)?
   b. Do you think the processes that cause change in physical characteristics are the same or different from the processes that cause change in how hominids build shelters? Explain your answer.
2. Examine the answers you gave to *Process and Procedures* steps 2 and 3 and answer the following.
   a. Which aspects of your descriptions did you base on evidence?
   b. Which aspects of your descriptions were inferences related to evidence?
   c. Which aspects of your descriptions were guesses?

Exploring Change

Lucy was an individual who was a part of a larger population. Biologists define a **population** as a group of individuals of the same species that live in the same place at the same time. Lucy's population had characteristics that were different from the populations of hominids before her time. Similarly, modern human populations are different from ancient populations of our ancestors. But what process might explain how this change over time can happen? In other words, how might evolution work?

In the Explore activity, *Exploring Change*, you will make observations similar to those made by naturalists in the 1800s. You will learn to make predictions from your observations by using a simple model involving mathematical calculations. These observations will lead to a logical conclusion. The result of your conclusion will be a model for how evolution can work. You will then perform a simulation and use your model of evolution to explore the results.

Materials

Part A (per team of 2)
  1 section of a piece of fruit with seeds
  1 scientific calculator
  paper towels
  1 plastic spoon or knife

Part B (per team of 3)
  25–50 objects of 1 type (for example, dried bean seeds, peanuts in the shell, or leaves from different individuals of the same type of tree)
  1 metric ruler
  different-colored pens or pencils

Part C (per team of 4–5)
  3 forceps (optional)
  1 bag of beans of mixed colors, labeled "starting population"
  4 bags of 50 beans, each bag containing a different color of bean
  3 plastic cups or other containers
  1 empty bag or cup
  4 colored pencils similar to the color of the dried beans
  2 sheets of graph paper
  1 large sheet of fabric

PROCESS AND PROCEDURES

Part A   Seeds of Change

In part A, *Seeds of Change*, you will make simple observations of something you probably see every day—pieces of fruit. You will learn about how models help scientists understand the natural world. Then you will use your observations in a mathematical model that has some basic assumptions. You will examine the model to see if the assumptions seem realistic.

1. Obtain a whole fruit or a section of a fruit, a paper towel, and a plastic spoon or knife from your teacher.
2. Remove all the seeds from your fruit using the plastic spoon or knife. Place the seeds on the paper towel.

   You may want to read the sidebar, *Fruit or Vegetable?*, to learn more about the way biologists define the term "fruit."

3. Count the number of seeds in the fruit.
4. Write a definition for the term "model" in your science notebook, using your own words.
5. Read the need to know, *A Simple Mathematical Model.* As you read, write a scientific definition of a model in your science notebook. Describe how this definition is different from the definition you wrote in step 4.

SIDEBAR

Fruit or Vegetable?

What is a fruit? Answering this question may not be as easy as you think. This is a case in which the scientific definition of a term is different from the common definition of the term. Scientifically speaking, fruits are made by all species of flowering plants. They are the mature (or ripened) part of a fertilized flower that contains seeds. When most people think of fruits, though, they think of the scientific fruits that taste sweet. Fruits might be something you could eat as a dessert. Many scientific fruits are called vegetables in everyday language. What is a vegetable? The term "vegetable" has no scientific meaning or definition. It can refer to any plant part, including leaves, stems, roots, flowers, seeds, or even fruits.

Believe it or not, the U.S. Supreme Court has actually had to weigh in on this issue. In the late 1880s, there were laws that imposed a tariff on vegetables, but not on fruits. An importer of

© Dreamstime/ Lana Langlois

tomatoes wanted to avoid paying the tariff and argued that tomatoes are fruits. They are ripened parts of a fertilized flower that contain seeds. The importer argued that he shouldn't have to pay. Scientifically speaking, he was right. But the Supreme Court ruled in 1893 that the tomato is a vegetable. It used the common definition, noting that tomatoes are usually served with dinner, not as a dessert. This ruling doesn't change the fact that, scientifically speaking, tomatoes really are a fruit. Learning to use scientific words in their proper context is a skill you will practice in this course.

NEED TO KNOW

ENGLISH SPANISH

A Simple Mathematical Model

What do you think about when you hear the word model? Some of you may think of a handsome man on a runway, showing off a pair of fashionable jeans. Others of you may remember the model of the solar system that you built in elementary school. Still others may think of model cars or model airplanes.

The natural world that scientists study is very complex. Some natural events and systems are too large, too small, or too complex to study directly. To learn about these natural events and systems, scientists use models. Your elementary school solar system model is an example of a simple scientific model.

A scientific model is a simplified system that mimics a more complex system. Scientists use models in their work to help them explain and predict phenomena. A model of the atom helps your teacher explain the tiny particles of the atom in a way that you can visualize. All models represent something. This could be a process, a physical object or being, a mathematical relationship, an event, a system, or even an idea. Models are created with certain assumptions in mind, and all models have limitations.

For example, if you used Styrofoam balls in your solar system model, your model would have the assumption that the planets were made of the same materials. This assumption isn't true. But if you were only trying to develop a useful picture of how planets are arranged relative to the Sun, this assumption would not affect your final project. An important part of being a critical thinker is to understand and analyze the assumptions in the models that you study.

You will use a simple mathematical model to explore the following assumption: *All the seeds from a fruit survive, become adults, and make their own fruits.* The simple mathematical model you will use requires four other assumptions.

1. The fruit you have represents the last fruit of its kind on Earth.
2. All plants will die at the end of each year.
3. Each plant needs a square of land 1 m long by 1 m wide (1 m^2) to grow.
4. Each plant makes the same number of fruits per year. A green pepper plant will make eight green peppers. An apple tree will make 850 apples. An orange tree will make 300 oranges. A tomato plant will make 13 tomatoes.

The output from your model will be the number of plants in the next generation. You will track the number of plants for seven generations.

Row no. 1	Generation	0	1	2	3	4	5	6	7
2	Number of plants	*							
3	Number of fruits per plant (This number will be the same each time.)	*							
4	Total number of fruits in this generation (= row 3 × row 2)	1							
5	Number of seeds per fruit (This number will be the same each time.)								
6	Total number of seeds in this generation (= row 4 × row 5)								
7	If all survive, how many will make it to the next generation? (Use this value in row 2 for the next generation.)								

Figure 2.2 Seeds of Change Data Table. Copy this table into your science notebook, making it specific to the type of fruit you studied. The asterisks show the assumption that the fruit that you started with represents the last fruit of its kind on Earth.

6. Place a copy of the *Seeds of Change Data Table* in your science notebook, or draw your own table similar to the one in figure 2.2, making it specific to the fruit you are using.
7. Listen as your teacher explains how to perform the calculations for the first generation.

    You may want to take notes as your teacher is explaining the calculations.

8. Carry out the calculations for 7 generations.

    You will probably want to express some of your numbers with scientific notation. For practice using scientific notation, see *How to Use Very Large and Very Small Numbers* in appendix D1.

9. Look over your completed *Seeds of Change Data Table*. On your own, circle the data that you think are the most important.
    a. Write the phrase "What I see" near the data you circled and describe the pattern you notice.
    b. Write the phrase "What it means" under your "What I see" phrase. Then write 1 or 2 short phrases that summarize what you think caused the pattern you observed.

        Remember, these two phrases together are called *highlight comments* since they represent the essence, or the highlights, of the data in the table. For more information, see *How to Write Highlight Comments and Captions* in appendix B6.

HOW TO

HOW TO

10. Use the data in the *Seeds of Change Data Table* to help you answer the following questions in your science notebook.
    a. If we assume that each plant takes up 1 m² of space, how many generations will it take to fill up all the usable farmland on Earth with this plant? *Good, farmable land surface area* = 4.5×10^{13} m².
    b. If all the seeds survive, how many generations will it take to completely cover the total surface area of Earth with this plant? *Total surface area of Earth* = 5.11×10^{14} m².

11. Write in your science notebook whether you think the following assumption is true: "All the seeds from a fruit survive, become adults, and make their own fruits." Also describe whether you think this assumption would be true for organisms other than plants, such as bacteria and animals.

12. Read the following paragraph. Then answer the question posed at the end in your science notebook.

    Biologists monitor the number of individuals in populations for many different types of organisms. Forestry officials may monitor the number of Douglas fir trees in a forest. Fishery biologists keep track of the number of salmon in major rivers. Observations of a large number of organisms in a large number of different parts of the world suggest that most populations normally stay about the same size.

    You created a model about the growth of populations if every seed survives. You also read the observation that most populations are stable in size. How can you reconcile these two pieces of information?

Part B   Celebrate Diversity

In part A, you used a mathematical model to make an observation that the naturalist Charles Darwin made. The observation you made is an important observation about the behavior of populations in nature. What else can we learn about the individuals that make up populations? Well, take a look at the people around you. Do the individuals in other populations of organisms differ from one another as humans do? You will explore the answer to this question in part B, *Celebrate Diversity*.

© Dreamstime/Ukrphoto

1. Choose 1 object from your pile. Using a metric ruler, measure the length of the object to the nearest millimeter. Then record its length in your science notebook.
2. Find the longest object and the shortest object in the pile.
3. Guess how many millimeters larger the longest object will be. Then guess how much smaller the shortest object will be. Record your 2 guesses in your science notebook.

    You are making an estimate of what you expect to find when you measure the remaining objects. Having a rough idea of what you expect to find will help you know if you make a measurement that is way too long or too short to be accurate.

© Dreamstime/Gary Boisvert

4. In your science notebook, create a data table in which you will record the measurements of each of your objects. Make sure that you label your data table.

Figure 2.3 Count the millimeter markings on the ruler to determine the length of the object.

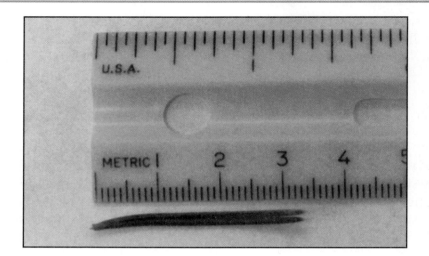

5. Choose 2 team members to measure the objects. The third member will record the data. Measure the length of the remaining objects to the nearest millimeter (see figure 2.3). Record the measurements in your data table.

> Round off your measurements to the nearest millimeter. If an object measures 11.5 mm, for example, round up to 12.0 mm. If it measures 11.2 mm, round down to 11.0 mm.

6. Work with your team to construct a frequency distribution table similar to the one in figure 2.4. Draw it in your science notebook by using the following steps.

> Creating a frequency distribution table is an important first step in summarizing your data.

a. Determine the range of lengths in the sample by finding the difference between the largest and smallest objects.

b. Divide the range into 5–8 intervals, selecting a convenient size.

> For example, if the range of the sample is 24 mm (the smallest, 6 mm; the largest, 30 mm), it could be divided into five intervals of 4 mm each, as follows: 6–10, 11–15, 16–20, 21–25, and 26–30.

c. Assemble your data in a table with the interval listed in the first column and the number of individuals in each interval listed in the second column.

Figure 2.4 Frequency distribution table. This table summarizes how many measurements are placed in each interval. The table lets you know how frequently measurements from each interval occurred in your sample.

Intervals (mm)	Number of individuals in the interval
6–10	2
11–15	6
16–20	10
21–25	4
26–30	3

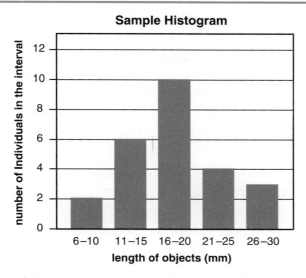

Sample Histogram

length of objects (mm)

number of individuals in the interval

Figure 2.5
A histogram.

7. Construct a histogram similar to the one in figure 2.5. Use the data from your frequency distribution table.

   A histogram is simply a bar graph with the intervals on the horizontal axis and the frequency on the vertical axis. To learn more about making histograms, see *How to Create Graphs* in appendix D3.

HOW TO

8. Calculate the mean, or average, of your data. Draw a dashed vertical line on your graph to indicate the mean.

   The mean is the sum of all measurements divided by the number of individuals you measured.

9. Gather with your team and discuss the following questions. In your science notebook, write down the best ideas you hear.
   a. Are all your samples the same for the feature you measured, or do the samples vary?
   b. What features of the graph you developed help you answer the question about whether the samples are the same or vary?
   c. What might cause some individuals to be different from others for the characteristic you measured? List at least 3 different possible causes.
   d. Of the causes you listed, which ones would be passed on to the next generation?
   e. Imagine that only the individuals in the intervals to the right of the mean on your graph survived and reproduced. What would a graph that summarized the variation in length for the offspring from these surviving individuals look like? Draw the answer you would expect on your original graph, using a different-colored pen or pencil.

Part C   Modeling Change

   In parts A and B, you learned some important characteristics of populations. The observations you made about these populations occur in some way in every population of every different kind of organism on Earth. But what happens to populations that have these characteristics as they move forward in time? One way to answer this question is to develop a model. In part C, *Modeling Change*, you will model what happens to a population of prey that is being hunted by predators. In your model, you will use fabric to represent the environment and beans to model a population of prey in that environment. Not all the individual prey are the same, however, because they are represented by different-colored beans. You and your classmates will be the predators. Your task is to explore how the prey population changes over time.

1. Spread out your fabric in 1 of the locations provided by your teacher. The fabric represents a habitat.
2. Decide on your roles for the activity.

   Three members of your team will be predators. The beans will be your prey. As predators, each of you will hunt the prey in your environment. The fourth member will be the game warden, who will be in charge of the hunting.

3. Place a copy of the *Modeling Change Data Table* in your science notebook, or draw your own table similar to the one in figure 2.6.
4. Examine the beans in the bag labeled "starting population." Record the number of individuals of each color in your table as the first-generation starting population.

   The beans (prey population) represent a variation in the color of individuals within a species. The individuals of this species can be one of four color variations. There should be 25 "individuals" of each color. Do you notice any other traits that vary beside color?

5. Set up the simulation as described in the protocol, *Simulation Roles and Rules.*

PROTOCOL

Population	Bean color number 1	Bean color number 2	Bean color number 3	Bean color number 4
First generation starting	25	25	25	25
First generation surviving				
Number of offspring to add before the next hunt (*beans left alive × 3*)				
Second generation starting (*beans left alive + offspring added*)				
Second generation surviving				
Number of offspring to add before the next hunt (*beans left alive × 3*)				
Third generation starting (*beans left alive + offspring added*)				

Figure 2.6 Modeling Change Data Table. Use this table to keep track of your simulation data. Write in the colors of your beans in the top row.

PROTOCOL

Simulation Roles and Rules

Game warden: You are in charge of telling the predators when they can hunt. Go through the following rules with the predators before the first round of hunting.

1. Direct the predators to face away from the environment.
2. When you say "hunt!," the team members acting as predators will turn around and have 1 second to visually identify a bean and grab it.
3. Predators must use a pinching motion with 1 hand (or use a pair of forceps) to pick up beans 1 at a time.
4. Predators can only pick up 1 bean at a time. They should locate the prey using their eyes before picking it up.
5. They must place their captured bean (prey) in their cup and turn their backs away from the environment.
6. You will repeat this cycle until there are only 25 beans left.

Once you have read the rules to the predators and they have turned away from the habitat, spread the beans from the bag labeled "starting population" throughout the selected habitat.

> Spread the beans as uniformly as possible so that no beans are sticking together or covering others.

Predators: Listen to the rules explained by the game warden. Ask questions about any steps you do not understand.

When the game warden has finished explaining the rules, obtain a cup in which to put your captured prey. Show that you are ready to begin the simulation by facing away from the selected environment.

6. Begin to hunt according to the rules, as directed by the game warden. For a team of 3 predators, each predator should pick up 25 prey to finish 1 round.
7. Finish round 1 of predation in your simulation as follows.
   a. Predators: Place the "eaten" prey from your cup into the empty bag. You might need to reuse these prey later to represent offspring.
   b. Game warden: Collect the remaining ("surviving") prey from the environment and sort them by type. Count the number of each color of prey that survived.

      To make them easier to count, arrange the beans in rows.

   c. Game warden and predators: In your data tables, record the number of each color of prey that survived as the first-generation surviving population.

8. Prepare for round 2 of predation in your simulation as follows.

   a. Simulate reproduction among the surviving prey by multiplying the number of surviving beans of each color by 3. Record this value in your data table.

   > Mathematically, this is represented as *number of offspring = beans left alive* × 3.

   > The fact that the offspring are the same color as their parents indicates that the color was passed from one generation to the next. It was inherited. This is an important assumption in your model. You might also recognize that this model assumes that each surviving bean leaves three offspring.

   b. Calculate the total number of each color that will begin the next generation. To obtain this number, add the number of offspring to the number of beans left alive. Record this value in your data table.

   > Mathematically, this is represented as *number starting the next generation = beans left alive + offspring added.*

   c. Count out the number of beans needed for the starting population of the next generation.

   > Obtain the beans from the bags containing the single colors of beans. If necessary, use the beans that have already been "eaten." You should end up with a total of 100 prey.

   d. Game warden: Ask the predators to turn away from the habitat. Spread the beans for the second generation throughout the habitat.

9. Repeat steps 6 through 8b for round 2 of predation. Use the second-generation starting population as your prey.

   > You will calculate the number of beans that would be present at the beginning of the third generation. You will not simulate a round of hunting on this generation.

10. As a team, use colored pencils and graph paper to prepare bar graphs that show the number of each color of bean in each of the 3 starting populations (see figure 2.7).

    > Use colored pencils that correspond to the colors of the beans. You should have three bar graphs when you are finished with this step. Name them "starting population 1," "starting population 2," and "starting population 3." If you need help making bar graphs, refer to *How to Create Graphs* in appendix D3. Include a description or sample of the habitat near the graph.

HOW TO

11. Study the bar graphs of each starting population (or generation). With your teammates, consider the following questions and record your team's responses in your science notebook. It may be helpful to refer to specific parts of the graphs in your answers.

    a. Which, if any, colors of beans had a better survival rate than other beans in the second- and third-generation starting populations?

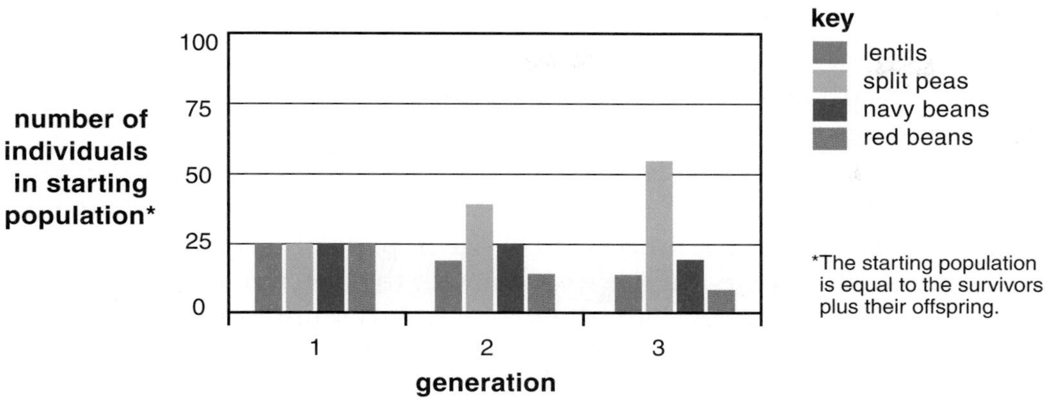
key
lentils
split peas
navy beans
red beans
100
75
50
25
0
number of individuals in starting population*
1
2
3
generation
*The starting population is equal to the survivors plus their offspring.

Figure 2.7 **Graph of sample data from three generations of the predator-prey simulation.**

b. What might be the reason that predators did not select these colors as often as they did other colors?

c. What effect did capturing a particular color have on the numbers of that color in the following generations?

12. Clean up by sorting the beans into their respective plastic bags as they were at the beginning of the experiment. Then return the bags to the materials area.

Analysis

Complete the following tasks as a team. Record your team's responses in your science notebook.

1. In part A, you observed that more offspring are born than can survive. How was this observation represented in your model of how the population of beans changed over time?
2. Your model made the assumption that bean color is passed from one generation to the next. Why was it important that you include this assumption in your model?
3. Based on your explorations, describe what might cause a population to change over time (figure 2.8).

Figure 2.8 **Ptarmigan.** How might this ptarmigan's coloring help it avoid predators?

○ **EXPLAIN**

Explaining Adaptation

In the Explore activity, *Exploring Change,* you investigated a way that populations can change over time. You know about many types of change. Think about what you were like a year ago. What has changed? Your height, the shoes you wear, your hairstyle? These were all changes that you made as an individual. Do you think that populations change like you do as an individual, or is the process of change in populations different?

For hundreds of years, people wrestled with the question of how organisms come to "fit in" with their habitat. For example, there is a flower in the tropics that has a tube that is a half meter (18 in) long, with nectar at the bottom (figure 2.9b). In that same area of the tropics, there is a moth with mouthparts that are over a half meter (18 in) long (figure 2.9a). Inherited features of organisms that help them survive in their environment, like the moth's long mouthparts, are known as **adaptations.** Adaptations help organisms "fit" their environment.

How do these adaptations arise? Do individual organisms help form their own adaptations, by actions they take in their lifetimes? Or is adaptation a biological process that only emerges in a population over the course of generations? About 150 years ago, the answer to this was not very clear. Since then, the weight of scientific evidence has clarified how adaptations arise. In *Explaining Adaptation,* the Explain activity, you will examine scientific data about the adaptations of finches and zebras, and you will learn that adaptations arise from a biological process that affects populations.

Materials

Part A
different-colored pens or pencils

Part B (per team of 4)
online resource (optional)
different-colored pens or pencils

© iStockphoto/Luministes

Figure 2.9 (*a*) The nectar-feeding organ of this moth is about half a meter (18–20 inches) long. (*b*) It is adapted to the long tube of the orchid.

PROCESS AND PROCEDURES

Part A   *Two Views of Adaptation*

1. Brainstorm a list of 3 unusual organisms that interest you. Write your list in your science notebook.
2. For each organism you listed, write down 1 characteristic that you think can be passed from one generation to the next. Explain how this characteristic might benefit the organism in its natural environment.
3. Contribute 1 idea from your brainstorming session to a class discussion about adaptations in organisms.

4. Read the scenario, *Finches in a Drought,* to learn about how the beak of 1 population of finch changed due to a severe drought on the island where it lives. As you read, add any unfamiliar terms to your personal glossary.

To learn more about the Galápagos Islands, where these finches live, read the sidebar, *The Finch Scientists of the Galápagos.* For more information about keeping a personal glossary, read appendix B8, *How to Develop a Personal Glossary.*

HOW TO

SCENARIO

Finches in a Drought

The Galápagos Islands are dry places, receiving on average 25 cm (10 in) of rainfall a year. But in 1977, the Galápagos island of Daphne Major received nearly zero rainfall—only 24 mm, less than 1 in. Using tweezers and nets, scientists on the island recorded how the number of seeds, insects, and cacti on the island declined sharply, as organisms struggled to grow and survive without enough water. Small, soft seeds were favored by several species of finches on the island. These were eaten first, leaving only the hardest, most difficult-to-open seeds (figure 2.10).

The medium ground finch was hard hit by the changes in its food supply. Its beak is not large enough to crack a whole caltrop seedpod. Instead, it has to go through a labor-intensive process of holding the seedpod to the ground

Figure 2.11 Beak depth is measured at the widest point of the beak. Finches are caught when they fly into fine nets. They are then carefully untangled and measured.

while peeling back layers of woody material, finally revealing a few seeds nestled inside. In 1977, many medium ground finches did not have beaks large enough to accomplish this. All over the island, medium ground finches began to die. The struggle to survive was so severe that none of the medium ground finches mated in 1977.

The drought ended in the spring of 1978. Only 20 percent of the original population of medium ground finches remained. Scientists measured the beak depth of all of the finches on the island, before and after the drought (figure 2.11). As a group, those that had survived were different from those that had perished (figure 2.12).

Did *individual* finches change due to the drought? Scientists measured each finch before and after the drought. These finches did lose a lot of weight. But their beaks, made of a hard

Figure 2.10 **Caltrop seed and medium ground finch.** Scientists found that the seeds of the caltrop plant can only be cracked by finches with beaks over 10.5 mm deep.

	No. of birds	Average beak depth (mm)
Original population	642	9.42
Drought survivors	85	9.96

Figure 2.12   Beak depth of medium ground finches before and after drought.
Source: Adapted from Boag, P. T., & Grant, P. R. (1981). Intense natural selection in a population of Darwin's finches (Geospizinae) in the Galápagos. *Science, 214*(4516), 82–85.

material like your fingernails, were each the same size before and after the drought.

The scientists knew from past studies that beak size is a heritable trait. **Heritable traits** are passed from one generation to the next. In other words, they are **inherited**. Because beak size is heritable, the scientists predicted that the offspring of the surviving finches would have beaks that resembled their parents' beaks.

In the spring of 1978, the surviving medium ground finches reproduced. There weren't many left, and there were many more males than females amongst the survivors. But the males sang their courtship songs, and the females chose their mates. The pairs made nests in the bushes and cactus plants, just as finches have been doing for millions of years. What do you think the offspring looked like? In particular, how deep do you think the offspring's beaks were?

To answer this question, study figure 2.13, which shows the beak depth of medium ground finch offspring born in 1976, before the drought, and in 1978, after the drought.

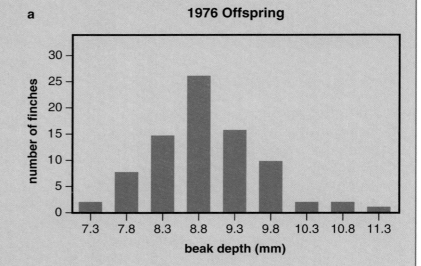

a   **1976 Offspring**

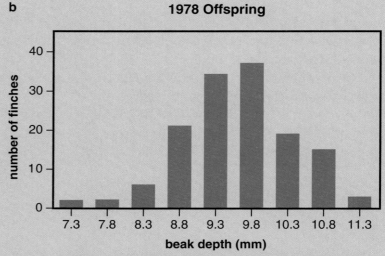

b   **1978 Offspring**

Figure 2.13   **Medium ground finch offspring beak depth in (*a*) 1976 and (*b*) 1978.** How were the postdrought offspring different from the predrought group?
Source: Adapted from Grant, B. R., & Grant, P. R. (2003). What Darwin's finches can teach us about the evolutionary origin and regulation of biodiversity. *BioScience, 53*(10): 969. Copyright, American Institute of Biological Sciences.

ENGLISH SPANISH

The Finch Scientists of the Galápagos

The Galápagos island of Daphne Major is not a typical tropical vacation destination, even though it is located close to the equator (figure 2.14). If you were visiting there, your packing list might look like this:

- 2 pairs of sunglasses
- 1 broad-brimmed hat
- 2 bottles of sunscreen
- 2 bottles of body lotion
- canvas pants
- long-sleeved shirts
- gardening gloves
- food and water for 2 weeks
- 1 stove
- 1 tent
- pencils
- 1 ruler
- 1 scale
- 2 types of nets
- science notebook
- 3 types of tweezers

You might have noticed that a swimsuit isn't on the list. This is because Daphne Major doesn't have a beach. Its coast is steep and rocky. Why would you need so much lotion to visit Daphne Major? In a normal year, the Galápagos Islands get only about 25 cm (10 in) of rain. That's less than an inch a month. You might wonder, can anything live in such a dry environment?

In fact, life thrives on Daphne Major. There are many species of plants, including shrubs and cacti, many species of insects, and several types of birds, tortoises, and iguanas. Ancestors of all these organisms originally arrived on the island after journeying over 950 km (600 mi) of ocean from South America or by moving from another of the islands in the group.

Figure 2.14 Daphne Major is one of the Galápagos Islands, located about 1,050 km (650 mi) west of South America. It was formed by an undersea volcano.

One group of bird species is known as Darwin's finches, because Charles Darwin collected the first specimens of these birds when he stopped on the Galápagos during his long voyage (see the sidebar, *The Voyage That Changed Biology,* for more about Darwin's historic trip). Although all the finches on the Galápagos are related to a single ancestor that migrated to the islands a little less than 3 million years ago, they display a wide variety of beak sizes and shapes (figure 2.15). Scientists who studied what these finches eat have found that their beaks are key to allowing each finch to specialize on a certain food during the leanest parts of the year—the dry season. Some specialize on very hard seeds, some on soft seeds, others eat cactus pads and fruits, and still others forage for insects.

You might have wondered why people visiting Daphne Major would need to bring all their food and water, and three pairs of tweezers. It's because this island is one of the uninhabited islands of the Galápagos. No bathrooms, no kitchens . . . no structures at all. If you go there, you must be prepared to survive its arid climate for weeks to months at a time.

Generally, people go to Daphne Major for only one reason: to collect data. Because

Large Ground
Finch

Medium
Ground Finch

Vegetarian
Tree Finch

Small Ground
Finch

Large Tree
Finch

EDGE CRUSHING
CRUSHING BILLS
MAINLY PLANT FOOD

BITING TIP
GRASPING BILLS

Sharp-beaked
Ground Finch

Small Tree
Finch

100%
ANIMAL FOOD

MAINLY
ANIMAL FOOD

PROBING BILLS

Cactus Ground
Finch

PROBING

Woodpecker
Finch
(tool user)

Warbler
Finch

Figure 2.15 Darwin's finches. The different sizes and shapes of the beaks show how the beak of each finch species has adapted to gathering a specific food source.

Darwin's finches, and other interesting organisms on Daphne Major, have been evolving undisturbed for several million years, the island of Daphne Major is an ideal place to conduct biological studies. That's where the tweezers come in. Tweezers are said to be the most essential equipment for work on Daphne Major, because they allow a biologist to quickly pick up, sort, and count seeds . . . one of the finches' favorite foods.

Drs. Rosemary and Peter Grant are a pair of biologists who realized that the Galápagos Islands are a living laboratory of evolution (figure 2.16). In the early 1970s, they began taking their students on yearly trips to the Galápagos, working mostly on Daphne Major. They returned every single year for over 30 years, often with their young daughters, Nicola and Thalia. Sometimes they camped on Daphne Major for months at a time. With the help of their students, the Grants caught, measured, and banded every finch on the island of Daphne Major. They found every nest made by finches, measured the eggs, and followed the chicks after they hatched. They even tried to find the remains of dead finches, collecting the regurgitated pellets of owls on the island and dissecting them to recover their bird bands and measure finch bones.

The Grants' scientific team observed finches during each season of the year to record what they were eating. They counted each type of food to find out how abundant it was in the environment. Over time, their incredibly thorough and detailed work paid off, giving them a glimpse of evolution in action.

Figure 2.16 Drs. Rosemary and Peter Grant realized that the Galápagos Islands are a living laboratory of evolution.

The Voyage That Changed Biology

It was just after Christmas in 1831. The 22-year-old Charles Darwin was nervous and excited as he climbed up the gangplank to the scientific research ship HMS *Beagle*. Darwin was hired to collect organisms as the ship sailed around the world. Just imagine how much more excited he might have been if he had known what his voyage would mean to modern science. Although young Darwin's journey would last only five years, what he learned would change his thinking about the living world. In turn, his ideas would change biology forever.

The mission of the *Beagle* was to make a detailed map of the coast of South America. While the ship's crew completed that work, Darwin spent his time onshore, collecting thousands of specimens. Back on the ship, he made detailed observations of the interesting and exotic organisms he encountered. Darwin observed organisms in such diverse environments as the jungles of Brazil, the harsh plains of Tierra del Fuego (near Antarctica), the grasslands of Argentina, and the Andes Mountains. Figure 2.17 shows all the amazing places Darwin visited.

During his travels, Darwin was puzzled by some of his observations. He found fossils of giant armadillos and wondered why the modern armadillos living in South America were much smaller. He noticed that the shells of giant tortoises varied a great deal between different Galápagos Islands. He wondered how those reptiles came to inhabit the islands in the first place. He also noticed that the mammals in South America were very different from the marsupial mammals he had read about living in Australia. He wondered if he could find a way to explain all of these patterns.

After he returned to England, Darwin spent nearly 20 years collecting more observations and testing his ideas. Then he published *On the Origin of Species*. You may be surprised to learn that Darwin did not use the word "evolution" in the first edition. Instead, he

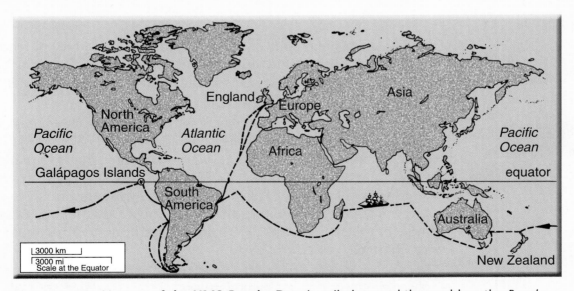

Figure 2.17 **Voyage of the HMS *Beagle*.** Darwin sailed around the world on the *Beagle*. The route included stops in South America and a stay in the Galápagos Islands. During the trip, Darwin collected evidence that he later used to support the theory of evolution.

used the phrase "descent with modification." A "modification" is a change in a feature of an organism. Darwin proposed natural selection to explain how populations become modified, or changed, over time. In this way, he could account for how the shells of different giant tortoise populations may change over time. "Descent" means that organisms are linked to the past through their ancestors. Recognizing this idea allowed Darwin to explain how ancient armadillos could be very large but still related to the smaller armadillos living today.

Overall, descent with modification helped Darwin explain the diversity of organisms that he had encountered on his travels. It also helped him explain why closely related species tend to be found on the same continent, like the marsupials of Australia.

Darwin and natural selection seem to go together like peanut butter and jelly. However, Alfred Russel Wallace had the very same idea, at about the same time. Wallace made observations of organisms in the area now known as Malaysia. In fact, if Wallace had not made his ideas known, Darwin might not have published *On the Origin of Species* before he died. In a letter to Darwin, Wallace included a rough draft of his theory of evolution. His paper provided fewer examples of evidence than Darwin had collected. But Wallace clearly used natural selection to explain the evidence.

Darwin was shocked to learn that another scientist might publish the idea of natural selection before he did. Darwin had to acknowledge the excellence and importance of Wallace's work, so he gave Wallace's paper to another noted scientist for public presentation. Knowing of Darwin's nearly 20 years of study, the scientist decided to present both Wallace's and Darwin's work simultaneously. Darwin then worked feverishly for almost a year, finally completing a manuscript of over 500 pages, titled *On the Origin of Species*, in 1859. Wallace published his paper first, but Darwin's book contained more evidence. Consequently, Darwin is known as the main author of the theory of evolution.

HOW TO

5. Paste or sketch the graphs in figure 2.13 into your science notebook.
6. Write at least 3 highlight comments on the graphs in your science notebook to describe what you see and what you think it means.

   Focus on the highest points you see in each graph. For more information about how to use this strategy for steps 6 and 7, refer to *How to Write Highlight Comments and Captions* in appendix B6.

7. For each graph, write a caption in your own words that summarizes the main point of the graph.
8. In your science notebook, record and answer this question: "How do you think a scientist would explain what caused the finches' beaks to change between 1976 and 1978?" Be as specific as you can about what changed, when, and why.

   Remember that scientists are limited to explanations based on observable evidence and natural causes.

9. Create a 2-column table in your science notebook with the title "two views of adaptation." The first column should be narrow and titled "ideas about how adaptations occur." The second column should be

much wider and titled "what I learned." In the first column, write out the terms "inheritance of acquired characteristics" and "natural selection," leaving plenty of space in between them.

10. Read the essay, *Two Views of Adaptation*. As you read, fill in your *Two Views of Adaptation* table, using your own words.

Two Views of Adaptation

How do changes across time occur to produce adaptations? In other words, what is the mechanism that causes populations to change over time? Two ideas have been important in the history of biology: acquired characteristics and natural selection.

Inheritance of Acquired Characteristics

The idea that organisms can change themselves was generally accepted by scientists in the 1800s. This is the idea that the changes that parents acquire during their lifetimes are inherited by their offspring. So individual parents can try to change, and the changes they make (or that they *acquire*) are passed on to the next generation (they are *inherited*). As a result, the population changes over time. This idea is called the inheritance of acquired characteristics. Another way of saying this is that individuals acquire adaptations because they want or need them.

This idea is still used by people today as a common-sense explanation for change. After all, humans change certain aspects about their bodies all the time. You can go to the gym and work very hard to make your muscles larger. It seems to make sense that other organisms make changes to themselves.

The inheritance of acquired characteristics was used to explain how specific adaptations came to be (figure 2.18). Think about trying to explain what caused the changes in the beak depth of the population of finches after the drought. An explanation based on the inheritance of acquired characteristics would go as follows:

Figure 2.18   Jean-Baptiste Lamarck, a prominent French scientist born in 1744, made many important contributions to science. He invented the dichotomous key, helped found the science of paleontology, and described many species of animals. Importantly, he popularized the idea that all living things were related and had changed over time. He thought that change occurred as acquired characteristics were inherited.

- During the drought, soft-shelled seeds were quickly eaten and then were gone. The only source of food left for the finches was the hardest, most difficult-to-open seeds.
- Some finches tried to change their beaks to make them deeper and stronger.
- The finches that could change their beaks were able to eat seeds and survive.
- The surviving finches reproduced.
- The next generation had deeper and stronger beaks.

Natural Selection: A Population View of Adaptation

In 1858, Charles Darwin and Alfred Russel Wallace (figure 2.19) made a joint presentation to the Linnean Society in London, England. They had each come up with the same explanation for how organisms change over time. Their explanation did not rely on an individual organism "willing" those changes to occur. The process they described is called natural selection. Natural selection is based on some critical observations and one logical conclusion that is the outcome of the observations:

- Observation 1: More offspring are born than can survive.
- Observation 2: Individual organisms within a population vary from one another in particular characteristics.
- Observation 3: Some variations among individuals can be passed from parents to offspring. Scientists call this heritable variation.
- Conclusion: Individuals that have inherited traits that better enable them to survive and reproduce will leave more offspring. The frequency of these traits will increase in future generations. In other words, the population will change over time. These beneficial traits are called adaptations (figure 2.20).

Let's use natural selection to explain the changes in the beak depth of the population of finches after the drought:

- More finch offspring are born than can survive. An important factor that limits the size of the finch population is the food supply—in this case, seeds.
- The finch population had individuals with different beak depths.
- Beak depth can be passed from parents to their offspring.
- During the drought, soft-shelled seeds were quickly eaten and then were gone. The only sources of food left for the finches were the hardest, most difficult-to-open seeds.
- More individuals with deep beaks survived.
- These individuals produced more surviving offspring than individuals with shallow beaks.
- The whole population changed because, on average, more individuals in the next generation had deeper beaks.

Figure 2.19   Charles Darwin and Alfred Russel Wallace. Born in 1809, Charles Darwin first studied medicine and theology to please his father. Alfred Russel Wallace was born in 1823 and trained as a surveyor. Both men developed their ideas during, and after, international voyages. Read the sidebar, *The Voyage That Changed Biology,* for more about Darwin's voyage.

Figure 2.20   **Examples of adaptations: (*a*) leaf insect, (*b*) flicker, (*c*) red Irish lord fish.** Can you identify the adaptations possessed by these organisms? How might each adaptation benefit the organism? How do adaptations develop?

It is important to recognize a few facts about natural selection. First, natural selection describes how populations change over time. Individuals do not evolve. Second, the process of natural selection is not random. The variation present in a population is somewhat due to chance. So are changes in the environment. But the characteristics that become more frequent in a population are the very ones that help individuals survive and reproduce. Thus, the process is not random.

11. Which of the following statements represents an explanation based on the inheritance of acquired characteristics, and which represents an explanation based on natural selection? Record your answers in your science notebook and prepare to explain them during a class discussion.
    a. The beak size of parent finches increased during their lifetimes because they needed to crack hard seeds. Those changes were passed down to their offspring.
    b. The beak size of parent finches did not change during the drought, but parent finches that had larger beaks survived the drought to have offspring. Those offspring had beaks like their parents.
12. With your partner, review your work from step 8 by reading the question and the answer you wrote in your science notebook. After you review your answer, complete the following tasks.
    a. Was the answer you wrote in step 8 based on the inheritance of acquired characteristics, natural selection, a mix of the 2, or some

other explanation? Write your response next to your answer to step 8, using a different-colored pen or pencil.

b. Write a new answer to step 8 that uses only natural selection as an explanation. Briefly explain how this answer is different from your previous answer. Use the following words in your answer:

- Variation
- Over-reproduction
- Natural selection

Your new explanation should be in your own words.

13. Participate in a class discussion of the ideas of inheriting acquired characteristics and natural selection.

14. Make a 2-column table in your science notebook. Title the left column "why scientists accept natural selection." Title the right column "why scientists reject the inheritance of acquired characteristics." As you read the essay, *Natural Selection: A Powerful Idea*, write 2 or 3 observations into each column of your table.

Natural Selection: A Powerful Idea

Scientists have collected large amounts of evidence that supports natural selection as an important way that populations can change over time. Scientists have documented the following three facts:

- If there are no limits to population growth, organisms would reproduce very rapidly.
- Even so, our observations tell us that most populations in the wild stay fairly constant in size.
- Resources available in any natural environment are limited.

In other words, there is ample evidence from the natural world that most populations produce many offspring and, at most times, more offspring are born than can survive.

What about variation? In every population of living organisms that has ever been examined, scientists find some form of variation. And scientists know how to test to see if specific variations can be inherited. Many traits that vary among individuals in a population can be inherited. In fact, in a growing number of cases, scientists can now point to specific changes in an organism's DNA that cause specific variations. On the other hand, variations that appear during an organism's lifetime are often not heritable and cannot affect the course of evolution.

Just like the finch study, scientists have collected evidence of natural selection in a wide range of organisms. Natural selection is indeed a powerful mechanism of evolution. But maybe you're not convinced. Have you heard the saying that the "proof is in the pudding"? You might think you have good ideas about how to make pudding, but the true test is in how it tastes. Similarly, a strong test of scientific ideas is when they are put to practical use. Let's explore the results from attempts of people to put both the inheritance of acquired characteristics and natural selection to practical tests.

From the 1930s to the 1960s, the Soviet agricultural minister Trofim Lysenko wanted to change crop plants to grow better in cold regions of the Soviet Union. Winter wheat could grow successfully in cold regions. But a different type of wheat called spring wheat matured more quickly

Figure 2.21 Six types of kale. These kale plants differ primarily in the part of the plant that stores the most starch.

and could result in larger yields. Lysenko used the idea of acquired characteristics to try to change spring wheat so it could thrive in cold regions. To do this, he told farmers to soak and bury spring wheat seeds in snow the winter before planting. This grand experiment failed miserably. Lysenko's ideas kept Soviet scientists from finding effective answers to agricultural problems for decades.

In contrast, the idea of natural selection has been very important for agriculture. One major issue in agriculture today is the damage caused by insects and other pests. Scientists in a field of science called resistance management use models of natural selection to help keep our crops safe from pests. Understanding natural selection also helps us understand a related process called artificial selection. In **artificial selection**, a human chooses the individuals that will reproduce, based on certain traits. In natural selection, some part of the environment favors certain variations. Artificial selection can cause rapid changes in a group of organisms. For example, figure 2.21 illustrates six different types of vegetables that humans eat. All six plants are from the same species. Humans selected different traits in the ancestors of these species to suit different human tastes. Artificial selection has been important in shaping every agricultural product on which your life depends.

The idea of natural selection is the foundation for the rapidly growing field of biotechnology. Biotechnology is a $30 billion a year industry. This industry uses ideas of natural selection and artificial selection to help develop new drugs, vaccines, and other important industrial products. Scientists use an understanding of natural selection to develop a new vaccine against the virus that causes the flu every year.

Aside from biotechnology, an understanding of natural selection has influenced medicine in other ways. An understanding of natural selection helped doctors develop new strategies for treating people infected with HIV. They use similar strategies to keep us safe from disease-causing bacteria and viruses that become resistant to specific drugs.

Finally, natural selection's explanation of change that occurs within populations, not individuals, explains some truly bizarre facts of life. For example, some female spiders attack and eat their mates (after mating). Natural selection provides a way to understand how the male spider becomes the nutrition that will help his offspring survive.

Part B   The Zebra's Stripes

You have now examined beak adaptation in finches and proposed reasons for how natural selection can explain how beak depth can change over time in a finch population. Now consider this idea: *Natural selection provides one adaptive explanation for every feature of an organism.*

Do you think this is true? Do all the features we see result from selection for adaptive characteristics? Are there some features for which it may be hard to tell why the feature is adaptive?

Figure 2.22 What benefit might stripes have for this zebra?

1. Assemble a team of 4 to work together on this activity according to your teacher's directions. Begin by observing the stripes of the Grant's zebra in figure 2.22.
2. Brainstorm with the other members of your team about the significance of a zebra's stripes. Where do zebras live? How might these stripes benefit zebras in their environment? List all of the team members' ideas in your science notebook.

3. Read and discuss the 2 explanations for the benefits of stripes for zebras in the handout, *Ideas about the Zebra's Stripes*.

4. Make 2 tables in your science notebook like the one in figure 2.23. In the first table and first column, list all the statements from the *Ideas about the Zebra's Stripes* handout that relate to the claim that stripes help camouflage the zebras. In the second column, write whether each statement is evidence, inference, or a guess. In the third column, place an *X* next to any statement that doesn't support the claim. Repeat this process for the second table, for the claim that stripes help zebras recognize one another and make a herd.

> A claim is an assertion or conclusion that addresses the original question or problem. In this case, the question is, "Why do zebras have stripes?" Remember, it is possible that some statements may not support the claim.

5. Discuss the strengths and weaknesses of each of the 2 explanations, using data from your tables. During the discussion, decide which claim best explains why zebras have stripes. Then discuss with your team the reasons why that explanation is best. Record your answer in your science notebook.

> Weigh the data that you have collected by asking yourself questions such as, "What pieces of information are most relevant to each explanation?" "What are the most serious flaws of each explanation?" and "Might there be more than one explanation to account for the stripes?"

6. Discuss and write down at least 1 way that scientists could make additional observations or tests that might support the explanation you chose in step 5.

7. Participate in a class discussion about the alternative explanations for why zebras have stripes.

Claim: Zebras have stripes for camouflage		
Statements made about claim	Evidence, inference, or guess	Does not support claim (X)

Figure 2.23 Sample table. Use tables like this one to organize ideas about why zebras have stripes.

Analysis

Answer the following questions in your science notebook. Be prepared to contribute your ideas to a class discussion.

1. Review the list of 3 organisms you wrote for step 1 of part A, *Two Views of Adaptation*. From your list, choose 1 adaptation for an organism and explain how it may have changed from an ancestor that had a different form of the trait. Include the terms "heritable," "variation," "population," "over-reproduction," and "natural selection."

2. During step 6 of the Engage activity, *Lucy*, you recorded your initial ideas about how Lucy's lineage may have changed over time from an ancestral population that was not bipedal to a population that did walk upright. Now that you are more familiar with the concepts of natural selection and adaptation, revise your answer to this question to incorporate these concepts.

   When you revise a previous answer, use a different-colored pen or pencil. Draw a single line through sentences you are revising to indicate that you have changed your thinking. Revisions are important to help you monitor your own understanding. Documenting how your ideas have changed makes learning easier.

3. What are the differences between a cultural adaptation and an adaptation generated by natural selection?

   Reviewing the definition of cultural adaptation in the introduction to the chapter 1 Explore activity, *A Cold, Hard Look at Culture*, and your answers to *Analysis* questions 3 and 4 in the same activity may help you with this task.

Further Challenges

1. To apply your learning about natural selection to a human example, carry out the optional activity, *Human Skin Color Adaptations*, found on the online resource.

2. To learn more about Peter and Rosemary Grant, read *The Beak of the Finch* by Jonathan Weiner, a Pulitzer Prize–winning account of their work with Darwin's finches.

Evidence for Evolution

In the Explore activity, *Exploring Change*, you saw how variation, over-reproduction, and selection can lead to change in a population. In the Explain activity, *Explaining Adaptation*, you practiced using the idea of natural selection to explain how these changes produce adaptations in finches and zebras. You may wonder, though, how we know that changes in living organisms have happened across time. When scientists are researching a topic, how do they convince themselves that their ideas are valid? As you have already learned, they use evidence.

In this Elaborate activity, *Evidence for Evolution*, you will study some of the evidence that different scientists have accumulated about evolutionary change. To do this, you will assume the role of a specialist and work to collect evidence about biological changes across time. Your team of specialists will use this collection of evidence to develop a presentation. As you learn from the presentation from another team of specialists in the class, you will begin to see how combinations of evidence from different branches of science can support the same explanation.

PROCESS AND PROCEDURES

In this activity, you will examine evidence that supports the idea that biological changes are the result of evolutionary processes. You will see some of the changes brought about by the processes you have studied during the previous activities. You will also learn about how scientists study these changes.

1. Work with your team of 4 to decide how to split into 2 pairs. One pair will take on the role of a paleobiologist, and the other pair will take on the role of a physical anthropologist:
   - Paleobiologist: A scientist who investigates biological change by studying fossils and the history of Earth. Skim the sidebar, *Interview with a Paleobiologist,* for more information. You will read it more carefully later in the activity.
   - Physical anthropologist: A scientist who investigates biological change by studying ancient hominids and living primates, including humans. Skim the sidebar, *Interview with a Physical Anthropologist,* for more information. You will read it more carefully later in the activity.

2. With your partner, read and study the information assigned to your role. Complete the procedures outlined for your role. As you work with your partner, make certain you both contribute ideas.

   The information and procedures for both the paleobiologists and the physical anthropologists can be found under the heading Procedures for the Specialists. After everyone has had time to study his or her special field of science, you will meet again with your team of four so that you can teach each other what you have learned.

ENGLISH SPANISH

Interview with a Paleobiologist

INTERVIEWER: Why did you go into the field of paleobiology?

MS. SCHUTZ: Because I love solving puzzles. Initially, I studied forensics. However, I realized that I wanted to ask questions that were more broad and included nonhumans. In essence, I try to understand how mammals lived by looking at their skeletons. I study both living and extinct mammals. I am interested in how the shapes of skeletons evolve and how this affects how mammals move.

INTERVIEWER: You're a graduate student. What does that mean, and how did you get to this place in your career?

MS. SCHUTZ: A graduate student is like an apprentice. Graduate school is a place where you learn your craft with the assistance of scientists who are already established, after you have completed college.

So, as you can imagine, it is very important to choose the right mentor to follow. You need mentors to be good at their craft, but you also need them to be effective teachers, so they can help you become a master yourself.

How did I get to where I am? Well, I am a curious person. I love finding out how things work. This ranges from how airplanes fly to how the bones of birds are structured so they hold up to all the abuse that comes with flying. Have you ever seen an albatross land, or a cormorant dive from a great height into the ocean? The forces involved are incredibly strong, strong enough to break human bones. It is all about form and function.

Growing up, I was very lucky to have a very adventurous grandfather who encouraged me to go after whatever made me curious. I spent the first nine years of my life growing up in Colombia, South America,

Heidi Schutz. Heidi Schutz is a graduate student in the Department of Ecology and Evolutionary Biology, University of Colorado at Boulder.

being exposed to a great deal of nature. Once I caught an absolutely stunning little frog that had colors so bright they looked like they came out of a crayon box. My grandfather took one look and slapped it out of my hand. Then he washed my hands and arms maniacally. I later realized that he had probably saved my life because I'd caught a poison dart frog.

My family was also not into "gender" roles or at least less so than the families of other girls my age. I played with any kind of toy I wanted—regardless of whether or not it was a "boy" or "girl" toy. My greatest possessions as a kid were my telescope, my radio-controlled car, and my three-foot-tall stuffed pony.

INTERVIEWER: What do you find most interesting or exciting about your work?

MS. SCHUTZ: Digging fossils can be exciting. Once I was working in a cave in Colorado that had very little room. The roof of that particular room collapsed and a poor camel was standing there at the time. Yes, camels once were prevalent in North America. We also had cheetahs . . . ever wonder why pronghorn are so fast? Because I'm not very tall, I was able to spend about nine hours a day in that hole to recover the camel fossil.

I like learning something new every day and the challenge of working on puzzles that are really hard. I also really enjoy interacting with other people who do what I do. A common misconception about scientists is that they sit around all by themselves in their offices or their labs being "brilliant." There is also the idea that scientists are so smart that they can barely function in the social world. That is just not true. To me, science is about

teamwork. The best scientific discoveries, in my mind, are made when people from different fields work together and combine their knowledge.

INTERVIEWER: What do you find most challenging or frustrating about your work?

MS. SCHUTZ: Sometimes . . . even now, I am treated differently because I am a woman or because I am Latina—or both. That really frustrates me. However, it also motivates me to change those attitudes in my profession. It motivates me to make it easier for people after me who want to get into this line of work. I am beginning a new job next year as a postdoctoral fellow, and it will involve mentoring minority and female graduate students as I conduct further research.

Interview with a Physical Anthropologist

INTERVIEWER: Why did you decide to become a scientist, and how did you choose this field for your specialty?

DR. COVERT: As a child, I was quite interested in nature. I enjoyed hiking, camping, and fishing with my family. When I entered college in 1972, I was excited about studying the natural world. I took classes in chemistry, physics, biology, and anthropology in pursuit of knowledge on this subject. As the semesters passed, I realized what I was most interested in was the evolutionary history of humans and our closest relatives, the nonhuman primates, so I decided to specialize in physical anthropology. I was fortunate to study this subject at the University of Massachusetts for my BA, Arizona State for my MA, and Duke University for my PhD. During the past 20 years, I have participated in paleoanthropological research in Egypt on four occasions, in Vietnam on five occasions, and in North America on 15 occasions. I have been a

Herbert H. Covert. Herbert Covert is a professor in the Department of Anthropology, University of Colorado at Boulder.

professor of anthropology at the University of Colorado at Boulder since 1986.

INTERVIEWER: What is the most interesting or unusual thing that has ever happened while you were doing research?

DR. COVERT: In 1981, I had the good fortune of discovering the facial skeleton of an early monkeylike primate called *Aegyptopithecus*, a creature that is thought to be a good model for the last common ancestor of humans, apes, and Old World monkeys. It was quite exciting to carefully excavate it from the ancient sands of the Sahara desert. With each sweep of the paintbrush I was using to uncover it, I was able to get a more complete view of the face of my great-great grandparent removed by 32 million years or so!

INTERVIEWER: What do you find to be the most fun or most challenging aspect of your work?

DR. COVERT: I find traveling and meeting people that share my interests in the natural history of life is the most rewarding aspect of my job. Knowing that scholars in Vietnam and Egypt have the same intellectual aspirations and interests as I have is a wonderful reminder that people from around the world share the same wonderful curiosity about the natural history of our planet.

3. Return to your team of 4 and prepare to share what you learned with your team and to learn from your other team members.

4. On a new page in your science notebook, create a data table or diagram like the one shown in figure 2.24 to help you track the evidence from your team. Label the table "evidence for evolution." Leave at least 2 more pages blank in your science notebook to add more evidence for evolution from your studies later in this chapter and the next.

5. Work with your partner to complete these tasks.
   a. Describe your specialist role to the other members of the team. Make sure your description includes the following:
      - Briefly describe the procedures you followed to gather your evidence.
      - Explain how the poster you made shows evidence to support the idea that organisms change across time.

Type of study	Evidence
Paleobiology	
Physical anthropology	
…	

Figure 2.24 Evidence for Evolution table. Draw a table like this in your science notebook to help you keep track of each specialist's evidence for change across time.

b. When the other team of 2 is describing its procedures and evidence, take notes in your *Evidence for Evolution* table. Be sure to ask the team to clarify any evidence you do not understand.

6. Discuss with your partner how having more than 1 type of evidence is stronger than any of the separate pieces. In your science notebook, record the main ideas from your discussion.

> You have learned about evidence that supports evolution that comes from the work of two different types of scientists. Think about why a combination of evidence from both scientists would be stronger than evidence from only one.

Procedures for the Specialists

Paleobiologists

Paleobiologists are scientists who specialize in the study of fossils and the history of life. Much as detectives reconstruct a crime from the evidence left behind, paleobiologists search for clues to biological change by studying fossils. A fossil is any preserved part or impression of an organism that lived in the past. Plants, insects, fish, plankton, and mammals are just a few examples of organisms that leave fossils. One method used in research is a process of dating rocks and fossils called stratigraphy. **Stratigraphy** is the study of how the layers on Earth are organized. "Strata" is another name for "layers." The singular form to refer to one layer is **stratum**. For this task, you will study and make a model of Earth's strata. In your role as a paleobiologist, you will examine both geologic and fossil evidence because understanding biological change requires an understanding of geologic change.

Materials (per 2 students)

1 glass beaker with strata (prepared by your teacher)
1 empty glass beaker
strata materials
1 set of colored envelopes
online resource
poster board or butcher paper
felt-tipped markers

SCILINKS®
NSTA
www.scilinks.org
Topic: paleontology
Code: human4E121

1. Read the sidebar, *Interview with a Paleobiologist*. Think about how you will explain the job of a paleobiologist to your teammates.
2. Complete the following activities with your paleobiologist partner.
   a. Observe the beaker of strata provided by your teacher. Work with 1 other team member to make a copy of each stratum and its marker in your own beaker.

   > Look closely at the layers. Make your beaker's layers match as closely as possible.

b. Answer the following questions about your beaker and its strata. Record the answers in your science notebook.

　1) Which layer of materials is the oldest (has been in the beaker the longest)?

　2) If these strata were layers in Earth, what inferences might you make about the relationship between the depth of the layer and the amount of time that has passed?

　　Consider how the strata might be similar to a stack of papers and books in your locker, as shown in figure 2.25.

Figure 2.25
Books and papers stacked in a locker.
How old are the books and papers below the pink memo? Above the memo?

c. Consider the locations of the 3 colored markers that you placed in the strata. If you found these colored markers in Earth's strata, which would you infer to be the oldest?

d. Obtain 3 colored envelopes from your teacher. Each envelope corresponds to 1 of the colored markers in your strata.

e. Imagine that each envelope represents a fossil discovery. Which fossil would be the oldest? Which would have formed most recently?

f. Open the envelopes and carefully observe the fossil pictures in each.

g. In your science notebook, compare each fossil with each of the others and with modern-day organisms. What similarities and differences do you observe?

　　Consider how the fossils look and their relative ages.

Topic: fossils
Code: human4E122a

3. Create a poster with your partner that you can use to explain to your teammates how fossils form and how they can be dated. Include an illustration of your strata model.

　The essay, *Fossils: Traces of Life Gone By*, and the sidebar, *Technologies for Dating Fossil Evidence*, are resources that will help you understand fossil formation and provide more information for your poster.

http://www
Online Resource

4. Watch the video segment, "Plate Tectonics," which is about continental drift, and think about the changes that the continents have undergone over time.

a. In your science notebook, explain how you think the movement and separation of continents affected organisms living on land in Earth's distant past. Explain what types of evidence you would expect to see to support the idea that continents have separated.

Topic: radioactive dating
Code: human4E122b

b. Add information to your poster about how the evidence for plate tectonics supports the theory of evolution.

5. Check that you have completed all the steps for the paleobiologists. Finish preparing your poster to use as a visual aid when you teach your teammates about paleontology. Return to step 3 in the general procedure.

Fossils: Traces of Life Gone By

Glancing around nervously, a whalelike creature waddles awkwardly on its very short legs down the sandy slope. Once it enters the water, however, it moves gracefully, swimming with its powerful tail.

The mammal described is an extinct *Rodhocetus*. Scientists infer that this animal was closely related to an ancestor in the lineage that led to modern whales. As a result, it shared many features with an ancestor of modern whales. *Rodhocetus* also has something very special in common with some dinosaurs, bacteria, ferns, horses, and even Lucy. The bodies of some members of these species became fossils after they died. In each case, a series of unusual events occurred that preserved their bodies in the form of fossils. Scientists search for these fossils and use them in their studies of biological change.

Fossils do not form easily. You may have seen scavengers eating dead animals or seen how microorganisms can decompose dead bodies. Sometimes, though, all or some of the body parts of a dead organism such as a plant or animal fossilize. Usually, the hard parts of organisms (such as bones, teeth, shells, or wood) fossilize, not the soft parts (such as flowers, organs, or fat). This is because hard parts decompose slowly, while soft parts decompose quickly. There are several ways that fossils are formed. These include petrification, preservation, and trace records.

Although fossilization is rare, it can happen in several ways. Some fossils form when minerals dissolved in groundwater seep into the tissues of a dead organism and turn it into stone. This is called petrification. Others form when organisms are buried in the mud at the bottom of lakes and rivers. Before the organisms decompose, minerals in the water replace atoms and molecules in body tissues and form a cast in the shape of the organisms. Occasionally, the impressions organisms make in mud or sand dry out, are covered, and turn to stone. These impressions are called imprints.

Preservation can occur in a variety of ways (figure 2.26). Some fossils form when organisms become trapped and preserved in amber or tar.

 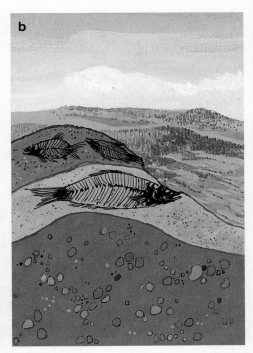

Figure 2.26 Fossil formation. (*a*) Dead organisms or their skeletons may remain intact in underwater sediments through long periods of time. Eventually, minerals circulating in underground water replace the bone of the skeletons, forming fossils. (*b*) Buried fossils may be brought to the surface by any of the forces that uplift segments of Earth's crust. Once near the surface, the fossil-containing rock layers are subject to erosion, which can expose the fossil from the rock.

Amber is a sticky substance produced by evergreen trees that hardens when it dries. Tar is a gooey, oily substance that sometimes forms in the ground when plant material decays. Finally, fossils sometimes form when organisms are covered by snow or ice and freeze before they start to decay.

In rare cases, scientists have found soft parts of fossilized organisms. Examples include entire woolly mammoths frozen in arctic ice and prehistoric insects fossilized in amber. In 2007, a high school student found a mummified dinosaur with intact skin and muscles in South Dakota.

We are most familiar with the fossilized remains of the parts of plants and animals. However, organisms with soft bodies can leave fossilized traces of their activity, such as burrows. Impressions such as footprints, feather prints, and leaf prints can also fossilize (figure 2.27). These types of fossils allow scientists to make inferences about an organism's life and behavior. For example, footprints of dinosaurs that walked in soft sand or mud sometimes survive as recognizable tracks in solid rock. These trace fossils suggest how the animal walked, including the length of its stride and where it placed its feet.

Figure 2.27   Fossil footprints.   Trace fossils include footprints, like these made by hominids around 3.6 million years ago.

The fossil record not only provides information about once-living organisms, it also shows how Earth itself changed across very long periods of time. For example, if we find fossils of marine animals on what now are mountaintops, we may infer that the rock in that area formed under a sea. This may be because mountain-building geologic forces lifted up an ancient seabed. In this way, the rocks in which fossils are found give clues to physical changes in climate and land conditions.

Sometimes fossils are destroyed by animals, weather, or other changes in Earth's surface. If a preserved fossil escapes destruction, it may become exposed on the surface of Earth by erosion. Often, this is how fossils are discovered. Even if a fossil survives and becomes exposed at Earth's surface, it cannot serve as evidence of biological change unless someone discovers it and realizes its importance.

Another way the geologic record can show changes in Earth is through the study of fossils that are similar but are found in different places on Earth. About 230 million years ago, all the land on the planet was grouped together in one gigantic continent called Pangaea. Since that time, the land has broken apart and moved into the current arrangement of continents. The scientific theory that is related to the movement of the continents is called the theory of plate tectonics.

The movement of the landmasses can be tied to changes in Earth's biological makeup. Sometimes the changes in land connections allowed organisms to migrate to a new area. Other changes in the land caused connections to be lost, so some populations of organisms were isolated. For example, scientists have found identical plant fossils along the coasts of western Africa and eastern South America. This is strong evidence that these continents were once connected and have moved apart due to plate tectonics. Have you ever wondered why kangaroos are only found in Australia? This continent has been isolated from other landmasses for about 80 million years. Over this time, mammals in Australia have evolved into a number of unique groups including the kangaroo, the echidna, and the extinct Tasmanian wolf (figure 2.28). A combination of what we know about fossils and about the physical structure of Earth serves as a geologic record of change.

By looking at fossil evidence and comparing fossils with the organisms living today, a fundamental feature of living organisms becomes

a

© Dreamstime/Christopher Meder

b

© Dreamstime/Robert Gubiani

c

Figure 2.28 Australian mammals. All of the mammals native to Australia are marsupials. After birth, their young develop fully within their mother's pouch. They include (*a*) kangaroo, (*b*) echidna, and (*c*) the extinct Tasmanian wolf.

Figure 2.29 **Extinct animals.** (*a*) xerces blue butterfly, (*b*) dodo bird, (*c*) Stellar's sea cow, (*d*) golden toad.

obvious. Throughout Earth's history, the different species of organisms living on Earth have changed. New species form, branching off from existing species. Other species die off. The most dramatic change possible for a species—its complete disappearance—is called extinction. Figure 2.29 shows several examples of species that have become extinct. The fossil record is full of many now-extinct species. Of all the species that ever existed on Earth, 99.9 percent are now extinct. Species continue to become extinct due to both natural and human-made changes in the environment. But new species continue to emerge as well, often occupying roles in the environment left vacant by extinct species. You will learn more about the formation of new species in chapter 3, *Products of Evolution: Unity and Diversity*. The fossil record provides a powerful line of evidence for evolutionary change.

Technologies for Dating Fossil Evidence

From sundials to atomic clocks, humans have invented many tools to measure time as it flows from seconds to minutes to hours. Certain natural processes also measure time. For example, a cut through the trunk of a fallen tree reveals growth rings. Counting those rings is a way to measure the number of years the tree was alive and growing. The rings, however, do not tell how long it has been since the tree fell. Scientists often want to know when a rock was formed or how long ago an organism lived. Clues often exist that paleobiologists can use to calculate how long ago a fossilized organism lived, with the help of technology.

The age of a fossil can be calculated in two ways. First, the *relative* age of the fossil can be determined by studying how the layers of rock containing the fossil were deposited. Another word for "layers" is "strata." So this method is called stratigraphy. Second, the age can be calculated directly, from the age of the rock containing the fossil or from the fossil itself.

In stratigraphy, each rock layer provides a record of past events and past environments (see figure 2.30). The relationship between layers of rock and the occurrence of certain fossils was noted over 200 years ago. Around 1800, William Smith, an English civil engineer, became interested in rock strata because of their relationship to the structural success of canals he was building. He noticed that certain layers contained fossils and that throughout England there was a match between the type of rock layer, its placement between other layers, and the fossils it contained.

About the same time, two geologists, Georges Cuvier and Alexandre Brongniart, were studying fossils in rock strata in France. When they compared the fossils they found with modern life-forms, they discovered that the modern forms were more similar to the fossils from the higher rock layers than those from the lower layers. In fact, no modern species were found in the oldest and deepest layers. The reason is related to the way fossils are formed. Sediment that settles on top of a dead organism is more recent than the sediment under the dead organism. Thus, scientists infer that any fossils that they find in a particular rock layer are older than any fossils found above that layer and younger than fossils found below that layer. Using this knowledge and other techniques, geologists can develop estimates of the time period for each layer of rock. They can then determine the approximate age of a fossil.

Figure 2.30 Stratigraphy is a relative dating method. The stratification of rock in this cliff was exposed when a highway was built. Fossils of older organisms are found in the deepest layers. Organisms that lived more recently are found in the youngest layers.

a Living organisms incorporate carbon-14.

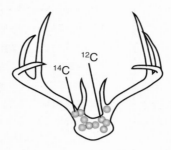

b The proportion of carbon-14 to carbon-12 in an organism's remains indicates how long it has been dead.

Figure 2.31 **Carbon-14 becomes part of plants and animals.** Small amounts of carbon-14 exist in the atmosphere as carbon dioxide, which plants incorporate into their tissues. This carbon-14 enters animals when they eat plants. Scientists can measure the amount of carbon-14 in fossils. Because they know that the half-life of carbon-14 is 5,730 years, they can calculate the age of the organism.

Direct dating methods can determine the age of fossils with great accuracy. Direct dating methods depend on naturally occurring radioactive elements. These elements are unstable forms of matter that break down, or decay, into other chemical elements at a steady rate. Different radioactive elements decay at different rates. For a particular element, however, decay occurs at a constant rate. Elements that undergo decay are called **radioactive isotopes.**

One method that is useful for dating organic material is carbon-14 (^{14}C) dating. Scientists can determine the age of material that is between 500 and 47,000 years old using this method. Normally, carbon atoms contain six protons and six neutrons. The unstable carbon-14, however, has six protons and eight neutrons. Carbon-14 atoms are naturally a part of some carbon dioxide molecules ($^{14}CO_2$) in the atmosphere. Plants take in this carbon dioxide and use the carbon-14 to make sugars during photosynthesis. Animals take in carbon-14 when they eat plants.

While plants and animals are living, they contain stable amounts of carbon-14 and carbon-12. The amount of carbon-12 in an organism does not change, even after death. After the organism dies, however, the level of carbon-14 in their tissues begins to go down as it loses its "extra" neutrons. Scientists can determine the proportion of carbon-14 to carbon-12 to estimate the age of a fossil. Older fossils have a lower amount of carbon-14 compared with living things, because some amount of the carbon-14 has been lost by radioactive decay. Fossils that are not as old have proportions of carbon-14 to carbon-12 that are more similar to living things today. This is because there has not been as much time for the decay to happen. Figure 2.31 helps illustrate this process.

Other types of radioactive dating can be used to measure material that is much older. These techniques are used to determine the age of the rocks in which the fossils are found. One example uses the radioactive element potassium-40. Potassium-40 decays at a much slower rate than carbon-14. Because of this slow rate of decay, geologists have used it to date rocks that are up to 4 billion years old. By choosing the appropriate radioactive element, scientists can date all kinds of rocks and fossils, whether they are a few hundred years old or a few billion years old.

Scientists often combine radioactive-isotope dating techniques with other methods for dating material, such as measuring magnetic properties. This improves the accuracy of their estimates of fossil ages because the combination of techniques lets them check for the consistency of the dates. These multiple lines of evidence, which support scientific reasoning, strengthen scientists' confidence in the accuracy of their fossil dates.

Physical Anthropologists

Physical anthropologists are scientists who compare ancient hominids with living humans and other primates to understand how humans have changed over time.

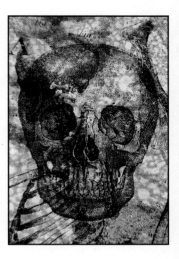

Materials (per 2 students)

2 small, clear, flexible metric rulers
2 protractors (jumbo sized, if available)
online resource
glue
poster board or butcher paper
scissors
felt-tipped markers
different-colored pens and pencils
1 set of selected human, chimpanzee, and mystery fossil bone pictures

Topic: anthropology
Code: human4E129

1. Read the sidebar, *Interview with a Physical Anthropologist.* Think about how you will explain the job of a physical anthropologist to your teammates.
2. Complete the following activities with the other physical anthropologist on your team.
    a. Obtain an envelope that contains pictures of selected human, chimpanzee, and mystery bones. Then work with a partner to do the following tasks.
        1) Carefully observe the human and chimpanzee bones for similarities and differences.
        2) Make a list in your science notebook of all the similarities and differences you can find.

        3) Compare each of the mystery fossil bones with the human and chimpanzee bones. In your science notebook, make a 3-column table to record your observations. In the first column, list each mystery bone. In the second column, record whether each mystery bone is either more like human bones, more like chimpanzee bones, or not like either human or chimpanzee bones. In the last column of your table, briefly describe the evidence that led to your decision in column 2.
        4) Based on your observations, write an explanation in your science notebook for how the mystery fossil bones might be related to humans and chimpanzees. Use the evidence you have from your observations to support your ideas.
    b. View the image sequence "Hominid Skulls" on the video and make observations. As you compare the skulls, focus on the following features, make measurements where appropriate, and record the information in your science notebook:

        • Size of lower jaw
        • Prominence of brow ridges
        • Slope of face
        • Width of face
        • Size of forehead
        • Size of brain case
        • Size of molars

Figure 2.32
Compare the features listed in step 4b on these (*a*) gorilla and (*b*) early hominid skulls.

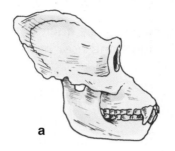
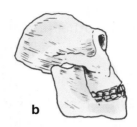

a   b

Fossil name	Trait						
	Jaw size	**Brow ridge**	**Slope of face**	**Face width**	**Forehead size**	**Brain case size**	**Molar size**

Figure 2.33
Record of fossil measurements.

Use the sketches of skulls in figure 2.32 to help you determine which measurements to make. Create a data table like the one in figure 2.33 to record your results. Review the sequence of skulls or individual frames as many times as necessary to make your comparisons.

c. Read the essay, *Primates Show Change Across Time,* and discuss the following questions in your group. Record your ideas in your science notebook.

    1) What evidence did you find in the essay and in your observations of the hominid skulls that indicates change occurred between early and modern hominids?

    2) What evidence indicates similarities between early and modern hominids?

d. Summarize the pattern of changes that you observe in the hominid skulls from *Australopithecus afarensis* to *Homo sapiens.*

3. Create a poster with your partner about the evidence you have studied.

a. Glue the human, chimpanzee, and mystery bones onto a poster board.

b. Add a summary, in your own words, for how humans have changed over time.

    You will use this information to teach your teammates about the evidence that physical anthropologists contribute to our understanding of how species change over time.

4. Check that you have completed all the steps for the physical anthropologists. Finish preparing your poster to use as a visual aid when you teach your teammates about physical anthropology. Return to step 3 in the general procedure.

A carpenter walks up to a cabinet she is building and places a metal handle in a spot she has marked. Holding the handle with her left hand, she turns a screwdriver with her right hand to attach the handle to the wood. Somewhere, 5,000 years ago, a hunter stepped quietly through a thin forest, keeping his sight fixed on a small deer a short distance away. As he walked, the hunter pulled an arrow from his quiver and set it to the bow, ready for a shot that may win his family several good meals and a hide for clothing.

Walking upright is an advantage for humans because it allows us to save great amounts of energy when we move long distances. It also allows us to use tools while we move about. While all primates are able to grasp objects with their opposable thumbs to some degree, humans have very nimble fingers and hands. The biological changes that made the refined use of our hands possible took place over a long period of time.

The fossil record of primates provides evidence for the idea that biological changes have occurred at various rates in primate history. Living primates include lemurs, chimpanzees, gorillas, orangutans, and humans. All the species of primates alive today descended from one ancestral species that lived millions of years ago. Primates that are most closely related to each other share additional, more recent common ancestors.

Early hominids like Lucy had brain cases more similar in size to those of apes than to those of humans. Still, hominid skulls show that their brains were larger for their body size than those of modern apes. Lucy belongs to a group of hominids called *Australopithecus*. Compared with modern primates, individuals in this group had front teeth that were more humanlike, being considerably smaller than those in modern apes. Lucy's pelvis and knee bone support the idea that she walked upright. Taken together, Lucy's skeletal remains suggest that her species had characteristics that fall in between more apelike ancestors and modern humans.

In 1995, a new species of hominid was uncovered in the Lake Turkana region of Kenya, in East Africa. It had many of the same features found in Lucy. In particular, its leg bones suggest that it stood upright and walked upright. It was named *Australopithecus anamensis*, and it was scientifically determined to be around 4.1 million years old. This date makes *A. anamensis* more than half a million years older than Lucy's species.

Scientists continue to discover fossils that provide evidence for the idea that hominids have changed over time. Three fossils were found in Africa between 2001 and 2004 that are several million years older than Lucy. One of these, *Sahelanthropus tchadensis*, dates to between 6 and 7 million years old. It was first thought to be a hominid. Later, it was classified as an ape, partly because of its small brain size. The two other fossils, *Orrorin tugenensis* (around 6 million years old) and *Ardipithecus ramidus* (around 4.4 million years old), were also discovered. They walked upright and had teeth that were more similar to modern humans' teeth than to apes'. These two new fossils are now considered to be the oldest known hominids.

These fossils have helped scientists understand how hominids evolved. Using these fossils, scientists now think that hominids split from the common ancestor shared with chimpanzees between 7 and 6 million years ago.

Other hominids that lived on Earth around 2 million years ago, such as *Homo habilis* and *Homo erectus*, show a more humanlike appearance than Lucy and other hominids. They have a more vertical face, smaller front teeth, a smaller lower jaw, and a significantly larger brain case. Though these past species were probably not the direct ancestors of humans, these specimens suggest that the hominid lineage that led to humans gradually changed in form over time. These fossils are consistent with the scientific explanation that humans evolved from earlier hominids.

Analysis

Complete the following tasks individually and record your response in your science notebook.

1. Review the *Evidence for Evolution* table you made to record information from paleontology and physical anthropology. With different-colored pens or pencils, circle groups of evidence that you consider to be different lines of evidence supporting evolution.

   A line of evidence is generally generated by scientists of one type, like paleobiologists. Scientists using different methods generate different, independent lines of evidence.

2. Add a new line of evidence to your *Evidence for Evolution* table called "natural selection in living populations." Fill in this evidence column with the most-relevant information you learned about finches in the Explain activity, *Explaining Adaptation.*

Further Challenges

Plate tectonics, the movement of continents, and the ice ages have had a tremendous effect on the distribution of living organisms throughout Earth's history. The movement of continents and the rising and falling of sea levels created and destroyed many land bridges. These land bridges connected one continent to another. Think about these concepts as you use the fossil data in figure 2.34 to complete the following tasks.

1. Propose a place of origin and a migration route for marsupial mammals.

   Mammals are animals characterized, in part, by hair, sweat glands, and the nursing of young with milk secreted by mammary glands. Marsupials are mammals that produce embryos that spend only a short time in the mother's uterus. At birth, the immature infants must crawl into the mother's pouch, where they continue to mature while nursing from the mother.

2. Consider what the fossil record indicates about ancient distributions of marsupial mammals (figure 2.34). Then propose an explanation for the present marsupial mammal distribution.

**Figure 2.34
Distribution of
marsupials.**

Continent	Oldest marsupial fossil (mya = million years ago)	Present marsupial distribution (number of families)
North America	110 mya	1
South America	75 mya	2
Antarctica	55 mya	0
Europe/Asia	52–58 mya	1
Africa	50 mya	0
Australia	30 mya	10

Modeling Earth's History

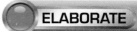
In the previous activities, you read about how biological changes can take place over vast periods of time. The Lucy fossil is extremely old—more than 3 million years old. In the Elaborate activity, *Evidence for Evolution*, you learned that the split between the chimpanzee and hominid lineages occurred between 7 and 6 million years ago. According to geologists, however, Earth formed 4.6 billion years ago. This is a time span that is difficult to comprehend because time for humans generally means tens and hundreds of years. The time span of Earth's history is called **geologic time**. One way to grasp the immensity of Earth's history is to make a model of a timeline. In this Elaborate activity, *Modeling Earth's History*, you will develop a model of a timeline of Earth's history to help you better understand when certain human events and major geologic and biological events occurred. You will also begin to see patterns in how events took place. This timeline should help you appreciate geologic time and the changes that have taken place since the formation of Earth.

Materials (per team of 4)

clothespins or paper clips (optional)
chart paper
event cards that your teacher provides

PROCESS AND PROCEDURES

1. Discuss the following question with your teammates: "How long ago do you think each of the following events took place, and in what sequence?"
   - First evidence of dinosaurs
   - Breakup of Pangaea
   - First evidence of hominids
   - First evidence of life (bacteria)
   - Formation of Rocky Mountains
   - Anatomically modern humans becoming common
   - Significant amounts of oxygen in atmosphere
   - First evidence of land plants
   - Lucy

   At one time, all the continents were joined in one gigantic continent called Pangaea. It is OK if you are not confident about the sequence of some of these events. Try to place the events you know something about first, and then make your best educated guess about the sequence of the remaining events.

2. Make a list on chart paper of the events in the order that your team thinks they happened. You may have some ideas about when certain events occurred. If so, next to those events write your best ideas about how many years ago you think the event took place.

List the most recent event at the top of the paper. Write large enough that the class will be able to read your list when you post it at the front of the class.

3. Post your team's list of events at the front of the class as your teacher directs.

4. Compare your team's estimated times and sequence with those of other teams. Then discuss the following questions with your teammates.

   a. Consider your estimates. Explain whether they were guesses or inferences based on evidence.

   b. Why did your team's estimates differ from those of other teams?

5. Examine the *Major Events in Earth's History* table that your teacher provides. Then answer the following question in your science notebook: "Which times or sequences of occurrence surprised you?"

   Scientists use several tools to understand geologic time. One of these tools is the use of evidence and inference. This table is based on inferences from evidence that scientists have gathered about the history of Earth and its living organisms, much as you did in the Elaborate activity, *Evidence for Evolution*. It also is based on scientific theories that geologists and paleobiologists have developed about the time spans and patterns of change in Earth's history. For these reasons, the dates in this table are generally considered to be accurate. For a review of evidence and inference, read the chapter 1 need to know, *Evidence and Inference*, in the Explore activity, *A Cold, Hard Look at Culture*.

6. Study the marked clothesline that your teacher has prepared. Discuss with your teammates how it might be used to represent when events occurred in Earth's history.

7. Study the event cards that your teacher provides. Be sure you understand what the event is and when it occurred. Fold each card in half, crosswise, to form a tent.

8. Calculate where on the timeline each event card should go and place your cards in the appropriate locations.

   The distance between the red marks on the clothesline represents 1 billion years. The distance between the short black marks represents 100 million years.

9. Locate the correct time on the timeline for each of your events. Fasten your event cards to the timeline as your teacher directs.

10. Create your own version of the timeline in your science notebook. Be sure to include information on the length of time between markings as well as the sequence of events.

Dinosaurs lived on Earth millions of years ago. Birds are thought to have evolved from dinosaurs.

Analysis

Discuss the following questions with your teammates, and then answer them in your science notebook. This will prepare you to participate in a class discussion.

1. Think about how much time is required for biological changes to occur.
    a. How many years passed between the appearance of the first hominids and modern humans?
    b. Imagine that the generation time of hominids was 20 years. (In fact, this is an estimate, as we do not know the actual generation time of hominids.) How many generations passed between the appearance of hominids and modern humans?
    c. What does this tell you about the rate of biological changes in organisms with long generation times?
2. What did the timeline help you understand about Earth's history?
3. Look at the events that represent changes in Earth's surface or atmosphere. Compare the location of these events on the timeline with the events showing the first evidence for certain plant or animal groups. How do you think these events might be related? Describe at least 2 patterns.
4. Describe in 1 or 2 sentences how the timeline you developed is a model. Add to your description by including the following:
    - Two strengths of your model
    - Two weaknesses of your model
    - One assumption in your model

    You may wish to review the need to know, *A Simple Mathematical Model*, in the Explore activity, *Exploring Change*, as you answer questions about your model.

Just a Theory?

You have now studied several lines of evidence for how biological changes have occurred over time. This evidence supports the theory of evolution. In this Elaborate activity, *Just a Theory?*, you will think about the meaning of the scientific terms hypothesis, theory, and law. You will then reflect on the meaning of the word theory. You will see why biologists say that evolution is a scientific theory, and how that differs from the way the word theory is commonly used. Then you will respond to a blog entry that suggests evolution is "just a theory."

Materials

different-colored pens or pencils

PROCESS AND PROCEDURES

1. Make a table with 2 columns in your science notebook. In the left column, write the words "hypothesis," "scientific theory," and "scientific law." In the right column, write a definition for each word.

   Use your own ideas to write the definitions. Leave enough space to revise your definitions after you learn more about these words. Remember, learning is easier when you compare your thinking before and after you read something new.

2. Below your table, write a sentence about how you think a hypothesis could be related to a scientific theory and to a scientific law. Again, leave room to revise.

3. Read the essay, *Just a Theory?* As you read, reflect on how the reading relates to what you wrote in your table.

Just a Theory?

ENGLISH SPANISH

What do we mean when we say that we have a theory about something? Usually, we mean that we have an idea about how to explain something (figure 2.35). We may suggest a theory about who killed the butler in the late-night thriller. Or we may have a theory about why Ms. Figueroa always looks so tired when she delivers the mail on Monday morning. Or we may have a theory about what the coach of the local baseball team said to his pitcher after the team lost last night's big game.

When we use the word theory in this way, we're talking about ideas we have that are tentative. That is, when we say that we have a theory about something, we may mean that we don't have much evidence. If we don't have much evidence, other people don't usually agree with or share our theories. Nevertheless, it is fun to suggest clever ideas.

In contrast, scientists use the word *theory* in a very different way than we just described. A **scientific theory** is a comprehensive explanation of a set of natural phenomena. Every scientific theory is supported by vast amounts of evidence from multiple sources. Evidence for a theory is collected by many different scientists, not just

one. Scientists rely on scientific theories because they explain so much.

A good example of a scientific theory is the atomic theory. It was proposed in 1803 by the

Figure 2.35 The word "theory" often means different things to different people.

British chemist John Dalton. One of Dalton's important ideas is this: *All matter (or things) in the universe is composed of tiny particles called* **atoms**. Physicists have collected an enormous amount of evidence for Dalton's idea. Some evidence came from technological breakthroughs. They allowed physicists to detect and subdivide atoms. Even though Dalton did not predict that atoms could be broken into smaller pieces, like electrons and protons, the general idea of his theory still stands. This example helps show that useful theories in science gain explanatory power as more evidence is discovered. New evidence leads to improvements on the details of the theory, and the theories we have today in science have stood the test of time. However, science is always open to revising theories, based on new evidence.

Another example is the germ theory. This theory describes how some diseases are caused by microorganisms, like bacteria. It used to be that people thought supernatural forces or invisible vapors caused diseases. But in 1876, Robert Koch found that bacteria caused the disease anthrax. Scientists then continued to look for other bacteria that caused diseases. Now we know that many diseases are caused by bacteria or other microorganisms. All this evidence strengthened the germ theory of diseases. Today, no scientists doubt that microorganisms can cause disease.

From both of these examples, we can see that scientific theories have many pieces of evidence that support one broad idea. In this way, a scientific theory is similar to a bicycle. A bicycle is made of many different parts, which all support one another. As people work with bicycles, the details of the parts change, producing a better bicycle. But the overall purpose of the bicycle (to provide fast, human-powered transportation) does not change. What is the purpose of a scientific theory? To explain how something in nature works. The role of theories in science has not changed.

Clearly, scientists use the word theory very differently from the way most nonscientists do. To understand how an explanation becomes known as a scientific theory, we need to know the term hypothesis. You may have already learned that a **hypothesis** is a trial idea about something. Hypotheses are not guesses; they are based on some observation and logic. However, they have not been thoroughly tested. Testing our hypotheses allows us to decide which trial ideas adequately explain what we study and which ideas do not.

You probably can see, then, that the everyday ideas we call "theories" are usually *hypotheses*. These trial ideas or explanations can be tested, but they aren't scientific theories. In scientific terms, the police officers who investigate a murder do so by testing a set of hypotheses.

In contrast, a scientific theory is built upon evidence from a large number of tested hypotheses. So a single hypothesis does not turn into a theory. As new hypotheses are tested, the theory helps explain the new information. Scientific theories can even help scientists think of new hypotheses to test (figure 2.36). This is because they often predict undiscovered phenomena. For example, when a new disease is discovered today, germ theory allows scientists to predict that they may find a bacteria or virus that causes it.

Why do scientists call Darwin's explanation the *theory* of evolution instead of the *hypothesis* of evolution? Why is evolution almost universally accepted by scientists around the world?

First, evolution is considered a theory because of the enormous amount of evidence that supports it. All of this evidence—not just some of it—supports evolution. The evidence comes from many different areas of science. Evolution also successfully predicts new phenomena. For example, evolutionary theory predicts that fossils should exist that have characteristics that are in between those of fish and reptiles. In 2006, scientists

Figure 2.36 When used by scientists, the word theory means an explanation that is supported by evidence and well accepted by other scientists.

reported that they had discovered such a fossil, which they named *Tiktaalik* (figure 2.37).

Did Darwin explain everything there is to know about evolution? Absolutely not. As one example, Darwin was not able to explain *how* characteristics are passed from one generation to the next. In fact, the ideas he had about inheritance were wrong. This is because he lived before the concept of genes was widely known. However, this does not make Darwin's theory incorrect. Scientists have added information about genetic inheritance to the theory of evolution. And because scientists have been able to add to Darwin's ideas, it shows that evolution is a sound scientific theory. When they found new information, their findings supported Darwin's theory, rather than contradicted it.

You are now probably wondering, if scientific theories are so important, how are they related to scientific laws? Social laws are very

important for human societies. If you break the law, you are likely to get in a lot of trouble. Fortunately for you, scientific laws are virtually impossible to break. They describe relationships between things in the natural world. Often, you can recognize a law because it has its own mathematical formula. Scientific laws always produce a predicted result given a specific set of circumstances. You may have tested some of them in school. For example, Newton's law of universal gravitation predicts how fast gravity will pull a falling object toward Earth.

Scientific laws and scientific theories are both important. But laws are more limited than theories in what they explain. In fact, many scientific laws are a part of a larger scientific theory. Gravitational theory includes Newton's law of universal gravitation. But it also includes an explanation for why gravity works the way it does.

Keep in mind that the ideas (hypotheses) you think of are important, too. While not being the same as scientific theories, your ideas can often be tested. If you find evidence for your hypothesis and other people see its importance, it has the potential to make a lasting impression on science.

Figure 2.37 *Tiktaalik* is an extinct animal that has many characteristics of a fish, such as scales, fins, and gills. But it is the oldest fossil known to have a movable neck and wrist bones. These characteristics are found in modern amphibians. For these reasons, scientists call *Tiktaalik* a transitional fossil.

Analysis

Complete the following tasks individually and record your responses in your science notebook.

1. In your science notebook, revise the table and sentence you wrote about hypothesis, scientific theory, and scientific law. Remember to use a different-colored pen or pencil.
2. Consider what you have studied about scientific theories and lines of evidence for evolution while you read the scenario, *Puzzled by Evolution*. Imagine that you found this blog entry while surfing the Web one afternoon. Then, in your science notebook, write an answer to the blogger's questions.

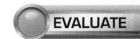

Topic: comparing brains
Code: human4E139

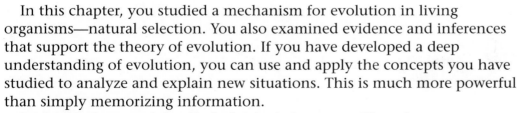

SCENARIO

Blogger: biostudentsRULE
Subject: Puzzled by evolution
Date: September 14

It seems that evolution has become a hot topic. I read about it in magazines and see shows about it on TV. But I don't understand why there's so much attention paid to the *theory* of evolution. If it's just a theory, it means that we aren't sure about it, right? What makes Darwin's idea any better than a theory that you or I come up with?

Evolution in Action

In this chapter, you studied a mechanism for evolution in living organisms—natural selection. You also examined evidence and inferences that support the theory of evolution. If you have developed a deep understanding of evolution, you can use and apply the concepts you have studied to analyze and explain new situations. This is much more powerful than simply memorizing information.

In this Evaluate activity, *Evolution in Action*, you will apply your knowledge to explain three possible endings to a story about a teenage girl who had surgery. Use the vocabulary and concepts that you have learned to write well-reasoned explanations for the three possible outcomes to the scenario. By successfully completing this activity, you can demonstrate to yourself and your teacher that you truly understand.

PROCESS AND PROCEDURES

1. Read the scenario, *A Turn for the Worse*.
2. Read the following 3 scenarios of possible outcomes for the opening scenario. Each scenario takes place in a different time period in the history of Western medicine.

Scenario 1

The year is 1925: The girl becomes delirious from fever. After a few days, she dies.

Scenario 2

The year is 1945: The girl receives an injection of the antibiotic penicillin, followed by repeated doses. Within 24 hours, her fever is reduced. In a week, she is released from the hospital, well on her way to recovery.

Scenario 3

The year is 1965: The girl receives an injection of the antibiotic penicillin, followed by repeated doses. At first, she seems to be getting better. But after two days, her fever rises rapidly again and she becomes delirious. After a few days, she dies.

3. Read the background information in the need to know, *Antibiotics*. As you read, write in your science notebook any facts that may help explain the 3 scenarios you read.

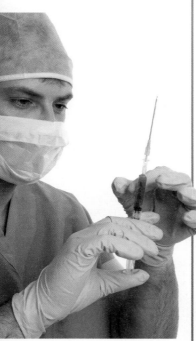

© Dreamstime/Showface

SCENARIO

 ENGLISH SPANISH

A Turn for the Worse

The attendants wheel the teenage girl into the operating room. Her mother waits anxiously in the sitting room at the end of the hall. The doctor worries that the girl's inflamed appendix might burst before she can perform the operation. In spite of the danger, she successfully removes the appendix from the girl's abdomen. After surgery, nurses take the patient to the recovery room. After about 30 minutes, she regains consciousness and speaks to her mother.

All seems to be going well in the first 24 hours after surgery. However, on the following day, the girl begins to run a fever, which quickly rises to 41°C (105°F). The doctor realizes that her patient is again at risk of dying.

The girl in this story has a bacterial infection. A strain of *Staphylococcus* bacteria entered her abdomen during surgery. It is now rapidly multiplying inside her body. Will she survive this infection? Use your knowledge of evolution and your scientific thinking skills to propose an explanation for what happens next. As you complete this activity, you will evaluate what you have learned about the way living organisms change across time.

Antibiotics

An antibiotic is a medicine that kills certain types of bacteria. Fortunately, antibiotics do not affect human cells. You may have heard of antibiotics such as penicillin and tetracycline. Researchers discovered a few antibiotics in the 1920s, but these drugs were not widely available until the 1940s. Penicillin was the first widely available antibiotic. It quickly became an important tool for fighting bacterial infections. Before antibiotics, bacterial infections killed many people.

Today, doctors choose from a wide range of antibiotics. They use these to treat a variety of bacterial infections such as strep throat, pneumonia, and even acne. The dependence of modern medicine on antibiotics has changed the way we think about health. This is a good example of how technology leads to cultural change. Many patients now demand antibiotics, even when an antibiotic will not cure their illnesses. For instance, antibiotics do not kill viruses. The common cold is most often caused by a virus. So taking antibiotics for a cold is not useful. Also, not every antibiotic is effective against all bacteria. Doctors must know which bacteria are causing the illness. This is why doctors usually take a sample, like a throat swab, before prescribing an antibiotic.

When antibiotics are not used correctly, they may not kill all of the problem bacteria. The bacteria that survive have inherited differences in their DNA that allow them to survive exposure to the antibiotic. These bacteria are said to be *resistant* to the antibiotic. The survivors may then reproduce and become more abundant. They pass the genetic differences on to their offspring.

The evolution of resistant bacteria is most likely to occur when individuals do not take all of their antibiotics. When all of an antibiotic is taken, all of the bacteria are usually killed. When a patient stops taking antibiotics early, though, the most-resistant bacteria remain. The person may feel better, but the resistant bacteria then start to reproduce. When many people misuse antibiotics over many years, the antibiotic may eventually become ineffective. This is because all of the problem bacteria have inherited the differences that allow them to be resistant.

In recent years, scientists have found bacteria that are resistant to several antibiotics at once. Just one example is the bacteria that cause tuberculosis. Tuberculosis is a lung infection that causes death if not treated. It has become more common around the world due to multidrug resistance. The problem is currently most severe in Russia,

China, and India. Fortunately, tuberculosis is not nearly as easy to catch as the common cold or the flu. However, tuberculosis can be spread through the air when people are in close quarters. Because of this, doctors suggest that patients with multidrug-resistant infections should not travel by airplane.

HOW TO

Figure 2.38
Increase in resistance of hospital strains of _Staphylococcus aureus._

4. Sketch the graph in figure 2.38 in your science notebook. Then apply the highlight comments and captions strategy to your sketch.

   Use this strategy to refer to parts of the graph that you think are important (what you see) and explain why you think it is important (what you think it means). Then write a caption for the graph that summarizes how the graph may help you explain the three scenarios you read. You can review _How to Write Highlight Comments and Captions_ in appendix B6.

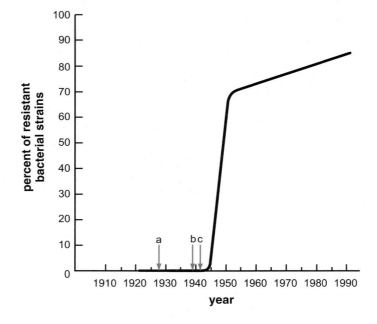

   a. 1928: In the laboratory, Sir Alexander Fleming observed that the mold _Penicillium_ kills the bacterium _Staphylococcus._

   b. 1939: Ernest Chain, Sir Howard Florey, and researchers at Oxford University isolated the antibiotic penicillin from the mold _Penicillium._

   c. 1941: Large-scale production of penicillin begins.

5. For each scenario, write 1 paragraph that explains why its outcome was possible at that time in history.

   Base your explanations on your experiences in this chapter. Give a basic overview of how these scenarios could have happened.

Analysis

1. In a short essay, explain how these 3 scenarios illustrate evolution in action in modern times. Write your essay to explain what changed over time and how it happened. A good explanation will
   - describe the evolutionary change that occurred,
   - identify the selective pressure in the bacteria's environment,
   - explain the role of variation in characteristics of the bacteria,
   - explain the role that new generations of bacteria played,
   - use the terms "adaptation" and "natural selection" in the context of the scenarios, and
   - use specific examples and evidence to support your claims.

2. The frequency at which a species reproduces (generation time) affects how quickly evolution occurs. Explain why the trait of penicillin resistance could become common in populations of *Staphylococcus* bacteria in less than 24 years, while changes in other populations may take millions of years.

   > You may want to consider the following: The generation time for humans is about 28 years. The generation time for bacteria is about 20 minutes.

3. Consider the observation that bacteria evolve resistance to antibiotics. Is this observation a new line of evidence for evolution or is it an example of one of the lines of evidence that you learned about in this chapter?

   > To prepare to answer this question, first review your answer to *Analysis* question 2 in the Elaborate activity, *Evidence for Evolution*. In your table, add any new lines of evidence you learned about from the Elaborate activity, *Modeling Earth's History*. Then think about whether the observation that bacteria evolve resistance is a line of evidence or an example; explain why.

Further Challenges

1. Describe in 2 or 3 sentences the interaction between culture and medicine.

   > You do not need to refer to the scenarios that you wrote about in the general procedure or in *Analysis* question 1.

2. Farmers sometimes add antibiotics to their livestock feed. This has been shown to enhance the growth of the livestock. What effect might this practice have on the evolution of bacteria, if used frequently by most farmers in a community?

3. You might want to read the *Discover Magazine* article "Bugs Declare War on Drugs" (October 2005) or the *Newsweek* article "Caution: Killing Germs May Be Hazardous to Your Health" (October 2007). Briefly summarize how human behavior can influence the evolution of certain disease-causing organisms (pathogens).

4. Write a summary of how medicine is practiced in another culture. The PBS series *Healing and the Mind* is a good resource to use.

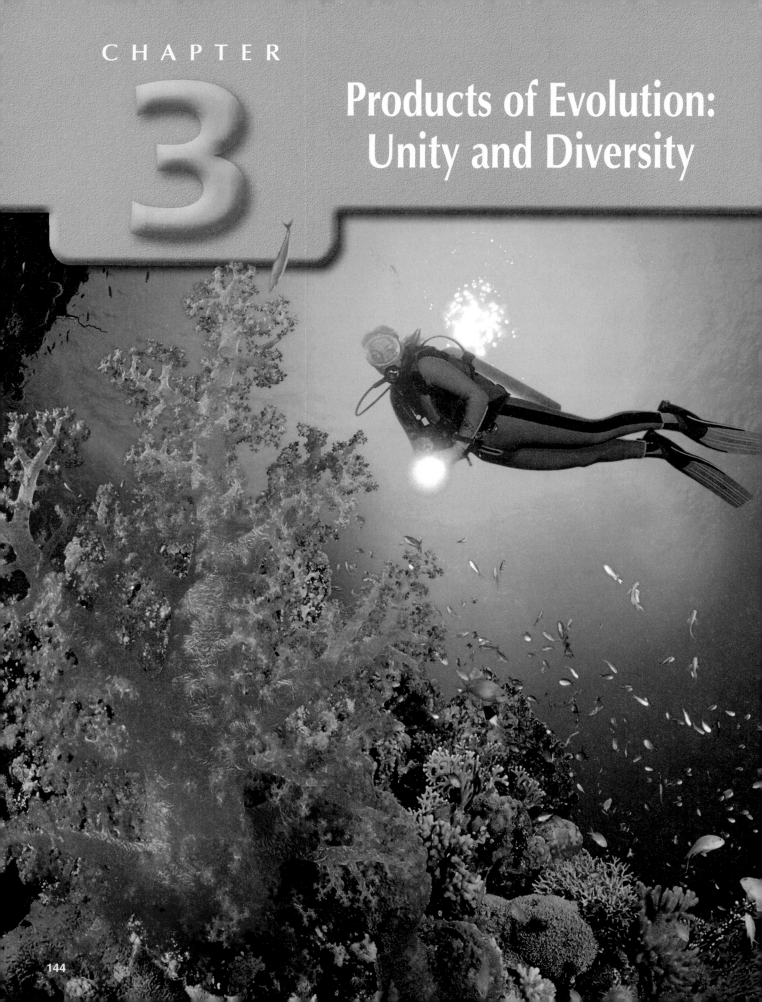

3

Products of Evolution: Unity and Diversity

... the Tree of Life, which fills with its dead and broken branches the crust of the earth, and covers the surface with its ever branching and beautiful ramifications.

Charles Darwin

ow many different types of life can you find in this coral reef? How many different types do you think you would find if you went snorkeling among the soft coral, fish, and other organisms of this coral reef?

One of the most remarkable aspects of life is its enormous diversity. Think of the differences between the microorganisms in the ocean and the blue whales that feed on them. In chapter 2, *Evolution: Change Across Time*, you learned how populations of organisms become different from one another over time through natural selection. In this chapter, you will consider how differences that accumulate in populations can lead to the formation of new species.

Your challenge in this chapter is to look at life's diversity as a scientist. Though living organisms are diverse, they also have many features in common. This is because all living things are linked to one another through ancestors in the past. Living things are descended from a common ancestor, but lineages change over time. This is why Charles Darwin described evolution as "descent with modification." Have you ever seen a diagram of your family's tree? In this chapter, you will learn how scientists use diagrams similar to a family tree to represent the relationships among organisms. You will examine how the unity that underlies all of life helps scientists organize and explain life's diversity. In addition, you should find, as many scientists do, that a close study of all the different kinds of life on Earth will increase your appreciation for life's diversity and complexity.

GOALS FOR THE CHAPTER

Throughout chapter 3, *Products of Evolution: Unity and Diversity*, you will work to gain an understanding of the following concepts:

✔ Common ancestry helps explain why organisms share so many features.

✔ Over vast periods of time, life on Earth is shaped by natural selection, speciation, and extinction.

✔ Biological classification is based on the natural nested groups in the tree of life.

✔ Many different sources of evidence support the theory of biological evolution.

✔ Scientific theories are supported by independent sources of evidence.

✔ Scientific explanations are tentative and change over time as more evidence is discovered.

To help you develop these understandings, you will complete the following activities.

ENGAGE	How Many Kinds of Zebras?
EXPLORE	Using Unity to Explore Diversity
EXPLAIN	Evolutionary Trees—the Pattern of Evolution
EXPLAIN	Descent with Modification
ELABORATE	Evidence for Common Ancestry
ELABORATE	Using Unity to Organize Diversity
EVALUATE	First Encounter with the Critter

Chapter 3

ENGAGE

How Many Kinds of Zebras?

Key Idea: Because of life's diversity, determining which groups of organisms represent distinct species can be complex.

Linking Question:
How can we use unifying features to explore diverse forms of life?

EXPLORE

Using Unity to Explore Diversity

Key Idea: We can use characteristics that are shared among groups of living organisms as evidence of evolutionary relationships.

Linking Question:
How do scientists represent the unity and diversity of life on Earth?

MAJOR CONCEPTS

✔ Common ancestry helps explain why organisms share so many features.

✔ Over vast periods of time, life on Earth is shaped by natural selection, speciation, and extinction.

✔ Biological classification is based on the natural nested groups in the tree of life.

✔ Many different sources of evidence support the theory of biological evolution.

✔ Scientific theories are supported by independent sources of evidence.

✔ Scientific explanations are tentative and change over time as more evidence is discovered.

EXPLAIN

Evolutionary Trees—the Pattern of Evolution

Key Idea: Evolutionary trees are claims about relationships and are based on data that scientists use to understand the patterns of evolution.

Linking Question:
How do new species develop from common ancestors, as depicted in evolutionary trees?

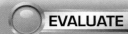

EVALUATE

First Encounter with the Critter

Key Idea: Evolution is the process that explains both the unity and the diversity of life.

Linking Question:
How can a specific organism be understood through the unifying principle of evolution?

Products of Evolution: Unity and Diversity

ELABORATE

Using Unity to Organize Diversity

Part A: Classification as a Tool
Part B: Classifying Organisms
Key Idea: Biologists use a classification system based on the natural nested groupings found in the tree of life.

Linking Question:
How can we use the tree of life to organize life's tremendous diversity?

ELABORATE

Evidence for Common Ancestry

Key Idea: Evidence for descent with modification comes from studies of comparative anatomy, development, and biological molecules such as DNA.

EXPLAIN

Descent with Modification

Key Idea: Natural selection can result in changes in characters that affect reproductive isolation among different populations. This causes speciation. The branching process of speciation results in life's diversity.

Linking Question:
What is the evidence that organisms share common ancestors in 1 great tree of life?

ENGAGE

How Many Kinds of Zebras?

In chapter 2, you studied adaptation and considered several explanations for why zebras have stripes. In *How Many Kinds of Zebras?*, you will study zebras again, but you will focus on the different kinds of zebras. If you were to travel across Africa, you would notice that in certain places, the zebras look different. Are these differences just variation within a species, or are there different species of zebras?

Take a look at the zebras in figure 3.1. Is each different type a different species? This question may seem easy to answer, but in fact, the identification of species can be difficult for scientists, especially if only a little is known about the organism. Sometimes scientists discover new information about an organism that leads them to change their minds about what they call a species. In this Engage activity, you will participate in a process to learn about the difficulties that scientists face as they sort through life's diversity. Can you tell a zebra by its stripes?

Figure 3.1 Zebras. All these zebras live in Africa but each group has a different common name. What similarities and differences do you observe among these four zebras?

Materials (per team of 4)

online resource (optional)

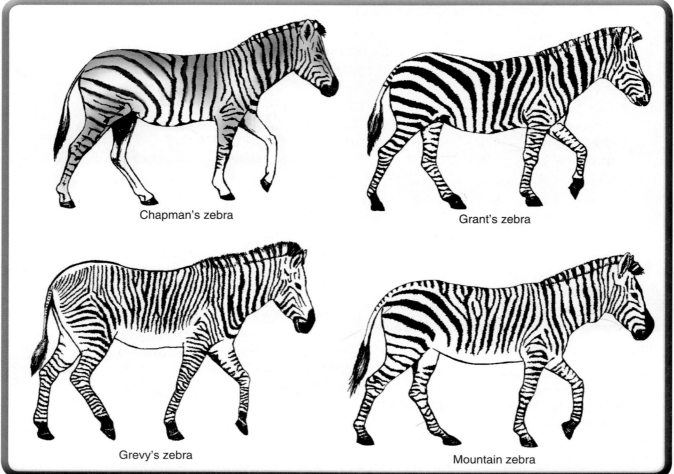

Chapman's zebra

Grant's zebra

Grevy's zebra

Mountain zebra

PROCESS AND PROCEDURES

1. Make a table in your science notebook similar to the one shown in figure 3.2.

Characteristic	Zebra			
	Chapman's	Grant's	Grevy's	Mountain
Overall size				
Shape of head				
Stripes on belly				
Width of black stripes				

Figure 3.2 Sample observation table. Record your observations in a table similar to this one.

2. Fill in your table using what you observe in figure 3.1. Discuss your observations with your team.

3. Write down an initial hypothesis about how many species of zebras you think there are. Make sure to record the reasoning you used to make your decision.

   The fundamental question here is whether each group of zebras represents a separate species or whether some are members of the same species. Provide reasons for your answer, using the information you listed in your table.

4. Label a new row in your table as "range overlap." Examine the map in figure 3.3. Estimate how much each zebra's range overlaps with the range of the other types of zebras. Fill in this new information in your table. If your ideas about the number of zebra species have changed, write a revised hypothesis under your original. Include the reasons you revised your hypothesis.

   "Range" describes where scientists have found an organism. For example, the area in which the mountain zebra is found is in southwestern Africa, so its range is southwestern Africa.

5. Read aloud the information on the *African Zebras* handout, taking turns with your teammates. Add to new rows in your table information you think is important. Write down a final hypothesis about how many zebra species there are.

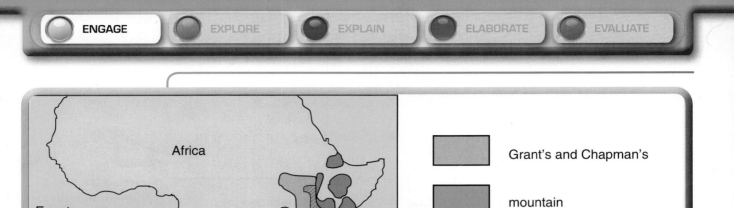

Figure 3.3 How do the ranges of the four zebras compare?

6. Discuss the number of zebra species with your teammates. Revise your hypothesis of the number of species if your teammates convince you of their reasoning. Record the reasons you revised your hypothesis.

Analysis

Answer the following questions in your science notebook.

1. Review your hypotheses about the number of zebra species. As you gathered more information, did your ideas change about how many species of zebras exist? Explain why or why not.
2. Write down an initial definition of "species." Use your own words and leave some space in your science notebook to revise your answer later.
3. Write down your ideas for why the 4 types of zebras have so many features in common, such as their striping, their diet, and their behavior.

4. Imagine 2 zebras that are different species. There was a time in the past when these 2 species did not exist. Instead, 1 zebralike species existed. Write a short story explaining how you think these 2 distinct species might have arisen from a common ancestor that was a single zebralike species.

It is OK if you aren't sure how a new species forms. What is important is that you write out any ideas you already have about this scenario. Feel free to use your imagination to compose a logical scenario.

Using Unity to Explore Diversity

In the Engage activity, *How Many Kinds of Zebras?*, you thought about the definition of the word species. You compared various characteristics found in different kinds of zebras to help you refine your thoughts. You also thought about why the different types of zebras have a lot in common.

Every species has peculiarities of structure, function, and behavior that make it distinctly different from all of the others. In chapter 2, you learned that natural selection is one very powerful way that populations of organisms change over time. Yet all living organisms share certain features. In this Explore activity, *Using Unity to Explore Diversity*, you will focus on these shared features in order to explore how different species are related. Your focus question is, "How can similarities, or unifying features, be used to explore diversity?" To do this, you will make observations of several different kinds of plants and an alga (figure 3.4).

Materials (per team of 4)

plant and alga cards (1 set of 5 cards)
large sheets of paper
felt-tipped markers
different-colored pens or pencils

Figure 3.4 U.S. researcher Karla MacEwan collecting plant samples in Costa Rica.

PROCESS AND PROCEDURES

1. Read the scenario, *Exploring Nature,* to help you get ready for your exploration.
2. Gather as a team of 4. Examine the plant and alga cards that your teacher provides your team. While you compare the pictures of each card, think about how these organisms may be related to one another.
3. Discuss the following question with your team and record your answer in your science notebook. One way to begin exploring relationships is to think about characteristics (or characters, for short) that organisms share with other organisms. How can the number of shared characteristics help scientists determine how closely related 2 organisms are?
4. Copy figure 3.6 onto a new page in your science notebook.
5. As a team, make observations of your plant and alga cards as you fill in your *Plant Exploration* table. If you think the specimen has the character listed in the table, place an *X* in the appropriate cell in the table. Otherwise, leave the cell blank. Discuss any patterns you notice.
6. Compare your team's table with the *Plant and Alga* table that your teacher will show you. Ask questions about any characters that you do not understand.

SCENARIO

Exploring Nature

You wake up excited. Today, you get the chance to roam through the Cascade Mountains with your new friend Chang, a foreign exchange student visiting the state of Washington from China. Though she doesn't yet speak a great deal of English, you two have become good friends. Though it often rains, today the Sun is shining brightly.

While exploring, you and Chang come upon some very interesting organisms. Along the trail is a big-leaf maple. But it is not alone—growing on the tree is a lot of moss and a licorice fern (figure 3.5a). Chang is surprised when you take out your pocketknife and slice off a small piece of the fern for each of you to taste. To her surprise, it tastes like licorice. You continue on your hike into a large grove of massive evergreen trees. Some of these Douglas fir trees (figure 3.5b) are up

to 90 m (295 ft) tall. After taking a break for water, you continue to follow the trail up the side of the mountain. You see fewer and fewer trees. Finally, you reach your destination, a high alpine lake. The meadow around the lake is filled with red columbine plants. You choose to eat your lunch on some rocks near the edge of the lake. As you look down, you notice large clumps of green algae in the water.

As you are walking down from the lake, you reflect on the various organisms you have seen. They look so different, but your biology teacher has said that algae and plants are related. You and Chang decide it would be interesting to try to collect evidence to study how these organisms are related. Since you don't speak the same language, you also want to find a way to represent these relationships with a diagram.

© iStockphoto/Shane Crockett

Figure 3.5 Some of the plants seen on the hike: (*a*) licorice fern and (*b*) Douglas fir.

Character	Alga	Moss	Fern	Conifer	Flowering plant
Parts of the organism are green.					
Has cells.					
All species have more than 1 cell.					
Grows > 10 cm tall.					
Makes seeds.					
Makes cones.					
Makes flowers.					

Figure 3.6 Plant Exploration table. Copy this table into your science notebook.

7. As a team, examine the row of data for "makes seeds." What does the pattern of data for this character say about the relationships among the 5 plants and alga? In your science notebook, draw a diagram that represents your team's ideas. Repeat this process with the character "grows > 10 cm tall."

8. Divide your team into groups of 2. With your partner, use all of the data in your *Plant Exploration* table to create a diagram in your science notebook that summarizes how the 5 plants and alga are related.

   You may want to try arranging the plant and alga cards on your table as you discuss how to draw your ideas. Continue examining your data row by row, as you did in step 6. Once you have made a diagram for each character, look to see how you might combine those diagrams for all five types of plants and algae.

   Another way to approach this task is to start by thinking about which two plants you think are most closely related, and why. Then ask, "How could we represent this in a diagram?" Then try adding the next-most-related plant to your diagram. Continue until all of the specimens are represented.

9. Trade the diagram that you and a partner created with the diagram of the other pair on your team. Do not tell the other pair how to read your diagram. Try to determine the pattern of relationships on your teammates' diagram.

10. Explain to your teammates how you came up with your diagram. Discuss the similarities and differences between your diagrams.

11. Ask your teammates for advice on ways to improve your diagram. If something doesn't make sense to you about your teammates' diagram, provide advice on ways to improve their diagram. Revise your original diagram in a different-colored pen or pencil.

12. Work with your partner to draw your final diagram on a large sheet of paper. Your diagram should summarize the relationships between the 5 plants and alga, based on data in your *Plant Exploration* table.

Analysis

Work with the members of your team to answer the following questions about how scientists study the relationships among living organisms. Record your answers in your science notebook.

1. During the activity, you wrote an answer to the question, "How can the number of shared characteristics help scientists determine how closely related 2 organisms are?" Using a different-colored pen or pencil, revise your answer to this question, based on your exploration and discussion with your team.

2. Select 1 of the diagrams from your class that you think most clearly represents the relationships among the specimens. Write down the features of the diagram that make it easy to interpret.

3. Imagine that you collect more data on your specimens using different characters. Do you think your ideas about the relationships among the plants and alga could change based on these additional data? Explain your answer.

Further Challenges

To expand your knowledge of the diversity of plants and algae, use the plant and alga challenge cards to add data to your *Plant Exploration* table. Then draw an expanded diagram of plant and alga relationships that includes all 10 plants and algae.

EXPLAIN

Evolutionary Trees—the Pattern of Evolution

Every living organism on Earth is related. Mountain lions and house cats are an example of species that share a common ancestor somewhat recently. Bacteria and corn plants, on the other hand, share a common ancestor that lived a very long time ago. In this Explain activity, *Evolutionary Trees—the Pattern of Evolution*, you will learn to interpret the diagrams that biologists use to summarize patterns of relationships among living things. As you do so, focus on the question, "How do scientists represent the unity and diversity of life on Earth?"

Materials (per team of 2)

various materials for constructing evolutionary trees
Who Is More Closely Related? animation on the online resource
different-colored pens or pencils

PROCESS AND PROCEDURES

1. Copy or paste into your science notebook the diagram from the *Scientific Relationships* handout that your teacher will show you. This diagram summarizes scientific claims about the relationships among the plants and alga you studied in the Explore activity, *Using Unity to Explore Diversity*.

   Does the shape of this diagram remind you of any particular living organism?

2. Compare and contrast the diagram you see on the *Scientific Relationships* handout to the diagram you and your partner developed in step 12 of the Explore activity, *Using Unity to Explore Diversity*.

   Make a T-table in your science notebook with the columns "similarities in the diagrams" and "differences between the diagrams." Think about whether or not the two diagrams show the same pattern of relationships.

3. Place the following characteristics onto the evolutionary tree shown in the *Scientific Relationships* handout.
   a. Has chloroplasts (green color).
   b. Has cells.
   c. All species have more than 1 cell.
   d. Grows > 10 cm tall.
   e. Makes seeds.
   f. Makes cones.
   g. Makes flowers.

      In the Explore activity, *Using Unity to Explore Diversity*, you used these characters to make a claim about evolutionary relationships. Now you are trying to understand when and in which groups these characters evolved. You will revisit your answers later in the activity.

4. Read the essay, *From Cell to Seed,* for a short description of the evolution of modern plants and algae. As you read, examine where you placed the characters on the evolutionary tree in step 3.

5. Copy or paste into your science notebook the diagrams from the *Comparing Evolutionary Trees* handout that your teacher will show you. Answer the questions associated with each image.
   a. According to the diagram in image 1, is the whale more closely related to the dog or the fish? Explain your answer.
   b. The evolutionary tree shown in image 2 has similarities and differences to the tree shown in image 1. According to this diagram, is the whale more closely related to the dog or the fish? Explain your answer.
   c. Explain whether the relationships shown on the two evolutionary trees in image 3 are the same or different.

Topic: plant evolution
Code: human4E155

From Cell to Seed

ENGLISH SPANISH

Have you thanked a green plant today? Plants play a critical role in our existence on Earth. They produce most of the oxygen that we breathe, the food that we eat, and many materials that we use—from rubber, to lumber, to medicines, to coffee. Perhaps we should ask, "Have you thanked a 3.5 billion-year-old single-celled organism today?" Such an organism likely was the ancestor of all modern plants. To understand how that could be, we need to trace the history of plant evolution. One of the ways we can begin to understand this history is to recognize that each of the major events in the evolution of different plant groups involved the evolution of a major adaptation. These events led to the emergence of the hundreds of thousands of different species of plants that currently inhabit every imaginable place on Earth, from the frozen arctic tundra to lush tropical rain forests.

The Ancient Seas

We begin our survey at a point about 3.5 billion (3,500 million) years ago (see the timeline in figure 3.7). Evidence indicates that plants, like all other modern species, evolved from single-celled organisms that first lived in ancient seas and resembled modern bacteria in many ways. The atmosphere above these seas is thought to have consisted of a mixture of gases, largely water vapor, carbon dioxide and carbon monoxide, nitrogen, hydrogen sulfide (the gas that makes rotten eggs smell), and hydrogen. Because this mixture of gases probably contained little or no oxygen, animals and plants, as we know them today, could not have survived.

The first single-celled organisms that lived in these seas most probably used complex molecules from their environment as their source of energy. At some point, however, the growing population of living cells probably started using these complex molecules faster than they were being formed.

era	millions of years ago	major evolutionary event
Cenozoic	7	Most recent common ancestor of gorillas, chimpanzees, and humans exists.
Cenozoic	60	Evolution of primates.
Mesozoic	66	Extinction of dinosaurs.
Mesozoic	130	Evolution of flowering plants.
Mesozoic	210	Evolution of mammals.
Paleozoic	360	Evolution of amphibians.
Paleozoic	430	Evolution of land plants.
Paleozoic	500	Evolution of vertebrates (jawless fishes).
Precambrian	1,200	Evolution of multicellular organisms.
Precambrian	2,400	Free oxygen builds up in the atmosphere.
Precambrian	3,500	First single-celled organisms evolve.
Precambrian	4,100	Oldest Earth rocks form.
Precambrian	4,600	Earth originates.

Figure 3.7 **Timeline of major evolutionary events.** Why do you think each of these events is significant?

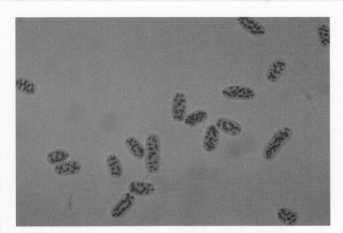

Figure 3.8 Phototrophic bacteria, *Chromatium okenii*, though only 15 μm long, can build complex molecules. The globules you see are sulfur particles.

Scientists think that the limitation of resources favored the survival of occasional cells that were able to make their own molecules. These cells are thought to have used sulfur compounds, carbon dioxide, and the energy in sunlight to build their own complex molecules. Bacteria that use these kinds of chemical reactions, such as those in figure 3.8, still exist today.

The Accumulation of Oxygen in the Atmosphere

Bacteria that could use light, water, and carbon dioxide instead of sulfur compounds to make their own food were favored by natural selection. This process, called **photosynthesis**, releases oxygen gas. This gas was a substance that probably was not present in the atmosphere of the primitive Earth. By about 2.1 billion years ago, so much oxygen had been released by these tiny photosynthesizers that the composition of Earth's atmosphere was fundamentally different.

Scientists think that photosynthetic organisms like these were the ancestors to modern plants. Today, photosynthesis is the major method of supplying energy either directly to living systems or indirectly to organisms that prey on others. Modern photosynthetic cells, such as the blue-green bacteria shown in figure 3.9 and including those cells found in plants, contain a green pigment called chlorophyll that absorbs energy from sunlight.

The Evolution of Eukaryotic Cells

The fossil record indicates that at just about this time, another key evolutionary event occurred. Somewhere between 2.1 and 1.6 billion years ago, more-complex cells show up in the fossil record. These cells had a structure called a nucleus. A nucleus is a compartment for the storage of genetic material. Organisms with cells that have a nucleus are called **eukaryotes**. Amazingly, there is evidence that some of these early eukaryotes incorporated photosynthetic bacteria within their cells. As a result, they were able to carry out photosynthesis. The descendants of these bacteria are known today as chloroplasts. Algae and all plants contain chloroplasts.

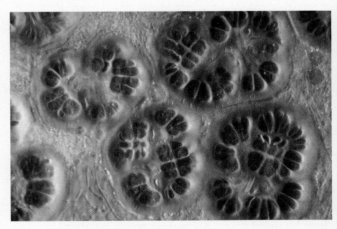

Figure 3.9 **Photosynthetic bacteria.** Bacteria such as these *Gomphosphaeria*, which are each 1 μm in diameter, contributed to the production of oxygen in Earth's early atmosphere.

The Evolution of Multicellular Organisms

About 1.2 billion years ago, eukaryotic organisms made up of more than one cell first evolved (they were multicellular). Within these multicellular organisms, some cells were able to perform special functions that were different from the functions of other cells. This enabled multicellular organisms to exploit more resources from their environment. These benefits of multicellularity may have enabled the movement of organisms from the ocean to land. A multicellular organism would have had a better chance of surviving on land than would a one-celled organism. The outer layer of cells may have protected the inner cells from drying out rapidly. The inner cells may have been efficient at photosynthesis. The first land dweller may have been a multicellular organism that looked somewhat like the alga *Chara* in figure 3.10. The common ancestor of *Chara* and land plants was only able to live and reproduce on land if ocean spray or tides kept it moist.

Two plant groups apparently evolved from such multicellular green algae. One group is represented today by mosses. These organisms possess few adaptations to life on land and require a moist environment in order to live and reproduce. The other group, which includes fossils of the oldest land plants, has many adaptations to life on land. This group includes modern ferns, conifers, and flowering plants.

Adaptations That Enhanced Survival on Land

One adaptation to life on land was the development of a waxy material that reduced water loss by providing a protective covering over the outer plant cells. The development of vascular tissue was another important adaptation (figure 3.11).

Figure 3.10 *Chara. Chara* is a multicellular alga. The orange and yellow globules are reproductive structures.

Part of this "plumbing system" carries water from the ground up through all the parts of the plant. A vascular system enables plants to grow to large sizes (far greater than 10 cm).

The oldest common ancestor of modern vascular plants probably existed about 420 million years ago. The earliest vascular plants required a moist environment to reproduce. As a consequence, these plants were more successful in environments that contained at least a moderate amount of moisture.

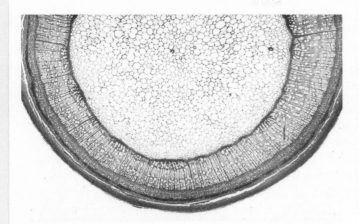

Figure 3.11 This magnified cross section of a young maple tree stem (photographed at 7×) shows the vascular tissues as rings around the outside.

Eventually, however, new species evolved that carried out sexual reproduction internally. This eliminated the need for a very moist environment. These changes probably occurred about 400 million years ago and enabled these new species to inhabit drier areas. In the most complex modern vascular plants, the reproductive structures are located in cones or flowers.

Another adaptation that evolved about 350 million years ago was the production of seeds. Seeds are products of sexual reproduction. They contain an inactive, tiny plant embryo packaged in material that provides food when the seed germinates and begins to grow. This system allows wide dispersal of new organisms because the seeds are spread by various means (wind, animals, or water) and begin to grow in new locations.

In cone-bearing plants such as pines and firs (refer to figure 3.12a), seeds are dispersed from open structures. But in flowering plants, seeds develop inside a specialized structure that becomes the fruit of the plant (see figure 3.12b). Fruits are made from structures in flowers. Not surprisingly, flowers evolved in flowering plants. The flowering plants, products of millions of years of evolution, are the most successful type of living plants. They are represented by more than 250,000 species and have adapted to every continent on Earth except Antarctica. Your life depends on them.

© Dreamstime/Inacio Pires

Figure 3.12 How are these seeds likely to be dispersed? (*a*) The female cone in this piñon pine will mature and have seeds on the inside of the scales. (*b*) A papaya has seeds inside the fruit.

d. Explain whether the relationships shown on the two evolutionary trees in image 4 are the same or different.

> When you first learned about graphs, it was important for you to practice interpreting what the information in a graph means. Similarly, you need to be able to interpret evolutionary trees to understand the unity and diversity of life. Recording your initial ideas makes your learning easier.

6. Use the TSAR strategy to compare your answers for step 5 with those of a partner.

> Remember that in the think-share-advise-revise (TSAR) strategy, you first *think* about the answer to the question. Your thinking should be recorded in your science notebook. You then *share* your answer with your partner and listen to your partner's answer. In the next step, you *advise* your partner on ways to improve his or her answer and listen closely to the advice from your partner. Finally, you *revise* your answer using a different-colored pen or pencil if you decide to change parts of your answer. For more information about using the TSAR strategy, see *How to Use the Think-Share-Advise-Revise (TSAR) Strategy* in appendix B3.

HOW TO

7. Read the essay, *Interpreting the Tree of Life,* to help you explain how to interpret an evolutionary tree and how biologists use evolutionary trees to explain evolution. As you read, write definitions for new terms in your personal glossary. Also label the following on the evolutionary tree from the *Scientific Relationships* handout: node, branch, taxa, and root.

Interpreting the Tree of Life

All the organisms on Earth are linked together through a long line of ancestors. A diagram that summarizes these relationships is called an **evolutionary tree**. The tree of life is an evolutionary tree that summarizes the patterns of relationships among every living organism. Scientists' understanding of the tree of life is growing rapidly as improvements in technology enable them to study the relationships among many different types of organisms. Claims about relationships are based on characters that are shared with some living things and not shared with other living things. More closely related organisms are expected to share a larger number of characteristics. Evolutionary

trees, then, are claims based on evidence about who is more closely related to whom. They also summarize claims about when different characters evolved.

Not all characters are significant when considering questions of relatedness. Some characters are acquired during an organism's lifetime, such as bigger muscles built up by weight lifting. Because these characteristics cannot be inherited, they cannot be used as clues to evolutionary relationships. The characteristics that represent biological relatedness are those that are heritable. These characteristics can be passed on from parents to offspring by way of DNA. Biologists use heritable characteristics to make claims about relationships.

Today, biologists most frequently use patterns in DNA itself as a source of evidence for evolutionary relationships. Just as with other characteristics, the greater the similarities in DNA sequences, the more closely related two organisms are thought to be. (Refer to figure 3.28, which compares DNA across primates.) As is true in any scientific investigation, claims about relationships are more likely to reflect true evolutionary history when they are supported by more than one line of evidence. Thus, most modern studies of relationships involve multiple lines of evidence.

To learn how to interpret evolutionary trees, first identify what each part of the tree represents. The evolutionary tree in figure 3.13 shows the relationships among four major groups of animals. Refer to figure 3.13 as you read the following descriptions:

- The green arrow points to the specific organisms that scientists studied. The organism may represent one species or a larger group of species. For example, the sea star represents a larger group of organisms known as echinoderms. Notice that in this diagram the top of the y-axis is labeled as present time. This means that all the groups in the study are alive today.
- Each of the blue arrows points to a different lineage of organisms. Each line, or lineage, is called a branch. Notice that all the branches on the tree are connected at some point.

- The purple arrow points to a lineage that went extinct. Though they are not shown, many extinct lineages would exist on this evolutionary tree.
- The red arrow points to the common ancestor of all the animals on the diagram.
- The numbered circles show the splitting of lineages.
  - Point 1 is the most recent common ancestor of all the animals.
  - Point 2 is the most recent common ancestor of insects, vertebrates, and echinoderms.
  - Point 3 is the most recent common ancestor of vertebrates and echinoderms.

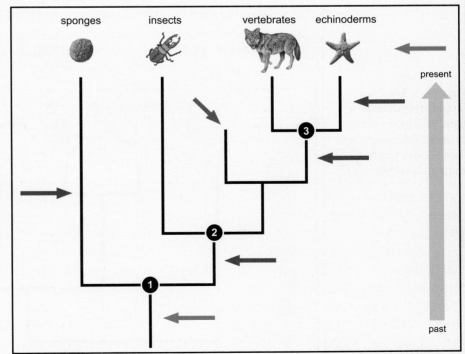

Figure 3.13 Relationships among some major groups of animals. Vertebrates are animals with a backbone. Echinoderms are a group of animals that include sea stars and sand dollars.

8. Work with a partner and view the *Who Is More Closely Related?* animation on the online resource. As you view the animation, write down the steps for using an evolutionary tree to determine who is more closely related to whom. Also write the answers to each question posed on the screen.

9. Revisit your answers to the questions posed in step 5. Revise your answers, using a different-colored pen or pencil.

10. Examine figure 3.14, which shows the relationships among groups of vertebrates. Using the materials your teacher provides, apply what you learned in the previous steps to make at least 1 more evolutionary tree that shows the same patterns of relationships in an alternative way. Make a 3-dimensional model and draw your model in your science notebook.

11. Exchange the evolutionary tree you developed in step 10 with a partner's. Examine his or her tree and determine if your partner's tree depicts the same patterns of relationships as those shown in figure 3.13. Give your partner feedback to improve his or her tree. Use your partner's feedback to improve your evolutionary tree.

    It will be helpful to review the steps for using an evolutionary tree to determine who is more closely related to whom. You recorded these steps in your science notebook during step 8.

12. With your partner, brainstorm a list that includes at least 3 practical benefits of knowing evolutionary relationships.

    You have seen that knowledge of evolutionary relationships helped you interpret patterns of plant evolution. In what other ways would

Figure 3.14   A larger evolutionary tree of some vertebrates. Can you show these same relationships in another way?

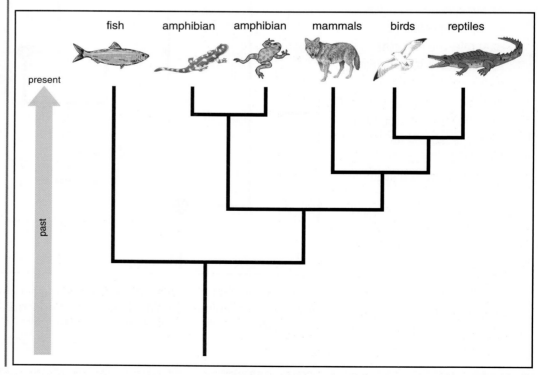

knowledge of relationships be helpful? Could this knowledge help you interpret fossils that you find? Help you identify an unknown organism, such as one that causes disease? Help solve a crime? Think broadly.

13. Make a list in your science notebook titled "uses for evolutionary trees." Add ideas from your brainstorming session that you think should go on the list. Then read the essay, *Using Evolutionary Trees*. As you read the essay, add more items to the list.

    To learn more about how evolutionary trees have helped us understand human evolution, read the sidebar, *Human Evolution*.

Using Evolutionary Trees

ENGLISH   SPANISH

Scientists use data to explore relationships among organisms. They often look for patterns in the relationships they uncover. Natural groups, also called **clades**, are one pattern that scientists try to identify. A clade includes an ancestor and all the groups that are descended from that ancestor. In this case, ancestors are lineages, not individuals. Look at the evolutionary tree in figure 3.15. Insects and crustaceans form a clade. The ancestral group and the two lineages that split from that group are shown in red.

Use the evolutionary tree in figure 3.15 to practice identifying clades. Do insects, crustaceans, and echinoderms form a clade? In fact, they do not form a clade because the vertebrates are not included. All the groups that came from an ancestor must be included. Vertebrates, insects, crustaceans, and echinoderms do form a clade. These groups of organisms belong to a clade that includes all the animals that have bilateral symmetry, at least in early developmental stages. This means that the animal has two halves that are nearly mirror images. There are four clades on the evolutionary tree in figure 3.15. Can you find them all?

The tree of life helps biologists classify all of life's organisms. But identifying the clades to which an organism belongs provides other

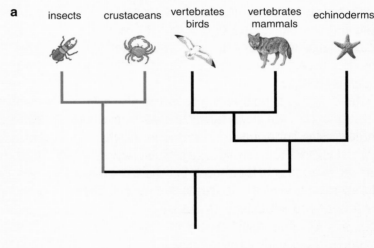

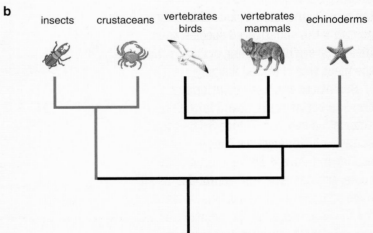

Figure 3.15 Identifying clades. (*a*) Insects and crustaceans form a clade. (*b*) Insects, crustaceans, and echinoderms do not form a clade. Overall, how many different clades can you identify on this evolutionary tree?

useful benefits to our society. It is very important for medical personnel to use "tree-thinking" skills to better understand disease-causing agents. For example, scientists have constructed evolutionary trees to examine the patterns of evolution of the HIV virus responsible for AIDS. Some argue that AIDS is one of the most serious infectious diseases to have ever affected humankind. From these studies, scientists identified that there are two main types of HIV. They determined this because the two types formed two different clades. One type evolved from a virus in chimps, and the other type evolved from a similar virus found in a type of monkey called the sooty mangabey monkey. Scientists also determined that HIV moved from chimps and these monkeys into humans multiple times.

Understanding evolutionary trees can also help scientists track the illegal selling of meat from endangered species. For example, many species of whales are endangered, and special laws prohibit hunting and the marketing of their meat. But there are other closely related whales that are more abundant. Their meat is legal to sell. Scientists can analyze the DNA of meat sold in suspect products. If the analysis shows that the meat came from a clade that only contains the endangered species, then investigators have strong evidence that the meat was obtained illegally.

Scientists can use evolutionary trees to better understand how characteristics evolved. Figure 3.16 is the same evolutionary tree that you saw earlier in figure 3.15. Vertebrates, insects, crustaceans, and echinoderms all have bilateral symmetry. Scientists infer that the common ancestor of all the animals shown on this diagram also had bilateral symmetry. This observation explains why bilateral symmetry is found in all the groups that evolved from this ancestor.

Birds and mammals are part of a clade called the vertebrates. Fish, amphibians, and reptiles are also vertebrates but are not shown on this tree. Scientists say that the presence of a backbone is a shared, derived characteristics of the vertebrates. Studying charactersistics of organisms using an evolutionary tree helps scientists infer when these features evolved. The tree in figure 3.16 shows that bilateral symmetry evolved early in this group of animals. The vertebral column evolved later, and only in some animals. Where do you think feathers evolved on this evolutionary tree?

The fact that clades of organisms share certain features has many practical benefits. Almost all new medical treatments are tried out first on laboratory animals such as rats and mice, instead of experimenting directly on humans. Because they share a common ancestor in the past, mice and rats share many biochemical and physiological features with humans. As a result, experiments on these animals give scientists an indication of how treatments may affect humans.

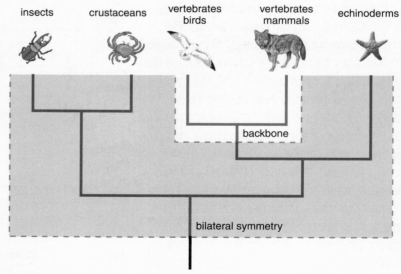

Figure 3.16   Character evolution. Evolutionary trees can be used to identify when and in what group certain characteristics evolved.

Human Evolution

An evolutionary perspective gives us the opportunity to reconsider and revise some previous ideas about how living things change. This perspective also sheds valuable light on what it means to be human. Figure 3.17 depicts evolution by using the metaphor of a ladder. In this model, more-complex groups replace simpler groups through time, with the evolution of humans at the end point of the line. People have this model of evolution in mind when they ask questions such as, "If humans evolved from chimpanzees, why are there still chimpanzees?" There are two errors in the figure 3.17 model. Examine the evolutionary tree for living primates in figure 3.18 as you use your tree-thinking skills to help you recognize the errors. First, humans did not evolve from chimpanzees.

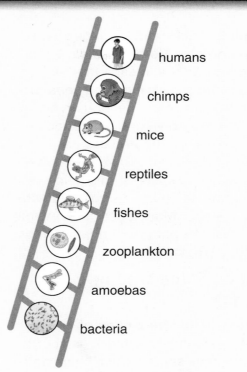

Figure 3.17   Ladder of evolution. Ancient philosopher Aristotle proposed that living things followed a progression, with more complex beings replacing simpler beings. What evidence do you have that this model is incorrect?

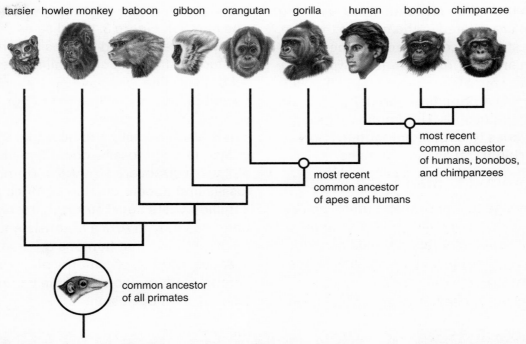

Figure 3.18   Primate evolutionary tree. This tree shows the relationships among the groups of living primates. The common ancestor of all primates lived about 60 million years ago.

Instead, chimpanzees and humans share a common ancestor. Both the lineage that led to humans and the lineage that led to chimpanzees have been evolving separately for about 6 million years. Second, evolution does not simply involve one group replacing another. Through the process of speciation, two species can evolve from what was previously one species. This helps us understand how the planet is covered with millions of species. Many speciation events result in a bushlike pattern of relationships, not a ladder of replacements.

Humanity's Place among the Animals

What does an understanding of evolutionary relationships teach us about humans? Humans share certain characteristics with certain other animals (for example, a backbone and mammary glands) that identify us as vertebrates and as mammals. Within the mammals, we humans and our close relatives are classified as primates. An important feature that distinguishes primates from their close relatives is having eyes that are located in the front of the face.

Scientists have concluded that the common ancestor of all primates was a mouselike animal that lived about 60 million years ago. The primates eventually split into three major lineages. The *hominoid* group includes apes (gibbons, orangutans, gorillas, and chimpanzees) and humans.

The Hominid Family Bush

The lineage that produced human beings is called the *hominid* family. Unlike apes, which walk on all fours, hominids are bipedal. Scientists have used fossilized bones and teeth to reconstruct our family tree, but it isn't easy. Since hominids have been evolving as a separate group for only 6 million years, the fossil record is not very long and the differences among fossils are not always obvious. This means that different scientists sometimes interpret the fossil record differently. Like the rest of science, our knowledge of human evolution is tentative and subject to change. As new fossils are found, our understanding of human evolution improves.

Despite uncertainties about the status and classification of some fossils, scientists have established many facts about hominids. For example, over the past 6 million years, the hominid lineage diversified. By looking at the fossil record, scientists have concluded that the hominid tree contains many species (perhaps 16 or more). The time frame for the existence of these species is shown in figure 3.19. You may notice that figure 3.19 does not show the relationships among the different hominid species. Reconstructing these relationships is an area of active research and debate. It is interesting to note that some of these different species of hominids overlapped in time and lived alongside one another. Figure 3.19 indicates that as many as five hominid species may have coexisted in Africa about 1.8 million years ago. All of these lineages have become extinct except one—the one that led to our own species, *Homo sapiens*.

It is also interesting to note that the oldest hominid fossils, about 6 million years old, were discovered in Africa. Hominid fossils first appear outside of Africa nearly 2 million years ago. The early presence of hominids only in Africa is consistent with the hypothesis that humans originated in Africa. Studies of patterns of diversity among modern peoples of the world also support this conclusion.

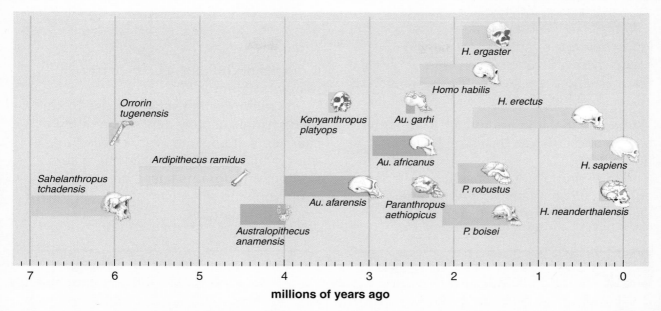

Figure 3.19 **Timeline of hominid evolution.** The fossil record of hominids shows that several species of hominids existed at the same time during the later stages of human evolution. Although scientists are not certain about the specific evolutionary pathway that led to modern humans, new discoveries will undoubtedly lead to new ideas.

Analysis

1. Describe how evolutionary trees are claims based on evidence that may be revised as scientists gather additional data.
2. How do evolutionary trees help us understand the unity and diversity of life on Earth? Include the terms "common ancestor" and "characteristics."
3. Revisit and revise your answer to *Analysis* question 3 from the Engage activity, *How Many Kinds of Zebras?* Make your revisions in a different-colored pen or pencil.

Further Challenges

1. To practice using data on characters to build evolutionary trees, read the example in the sidebar, *Constructing an Evolutionary Tree.*

Constructing an Evolutionary Tree

Imagine that you are trying to construct an evolutionary tree based on the data in figure 3.20.

In this example, A represents squirrels and their close relatives, B represents elephants and their close relatives, and C represents goldfish and their close relatives (figure 3.21).

The methods that scientists use to study relationships usually depend on many characters. It becomes very difficult to track by hand the patterns in characters. Computer programs based on models of evolution help scientists infer evolutionary trees from their data.

Specimens / Characters	Squirrel	Elephant	Goldfish
1. Has tusks.		X	
2. Climbs trees.	X		
3. Has mammary glands.	X	X	
4. Has a backbone.	X	X	X

Figure 3.20 **Character Data Table.**

Instructions	Example
1. Identify which 2 species or groups have the most characters in common. In this case, squirrels and elephants share 2 characters. Goldfish only share 1 character with each of the other 2 groups. Thus, we infer that squirrels and elephants probably share a more recent common ancestor than either share with goldfish. To construct the evolutionary tree, first write each species (or group) from left to right. Place groups that you think are closely related next to each other. This row represents the present time. Next to this line, write the word "present."	A B C present
2. Each species represents a lineage that extends into the past. To represent these separate lineages, draw a vertical line straight down from each species.	A B C present | | |

Figure 3.21 **Constructing an evolutionary tree.**

Instructions	Example
3. Because squirrels and elephants share 2 characters and both only share 1 with goldfish, you can infer that squirrels and elephants may be more closely related to each other than either is to the goldfish. Represent this by drawing a horizontal line to connect the lines from the two closely related species. This shows that the 2 lineages used to be part of the same lineage.	A B C present
4. Once a union between 2 lineages is made, make a new vertical line in the middle of the horizontal line. Continue to extend any lineages that are not connected to other lines.	A B C present
5. Represent the common ancestor of the next 2 lineages by drawing a horizontal line to connect the vertical lines. Repeat steps 4 and 5 until all the species are united.	A B C present
6. After all the species have been connected, draw in 1 last vertical line to represent the common ancestral lineage of all the species. Place the word "past" at the bottom of the diagram and put an arrow leading from the past to the present.	A B C present past
7. Place the characters from the study on their appropriate places on vertical lines. Notice that characters can change anywhere along branches, not just at nodes.	A B C present climbs trees — tusks mammary glands backbone past

 EXPLAIN

Descent with Modification

It is helpful to frequently reflect on what you have learned. In chapter 2, you learned that natural selection is a powerful mechanism that results in changes in populations over time. In the Engage activity, *How Many Kinds of Zebras?*, you examined some of the products of natural selection, namely four different groups of zebras. These groups of zebras have many similarities and also some differences. You worked with your classmates to decide which groups of zebras represent different species. You also started thinking about how these different kinds of zebras are related. In the Explore activity, *Using Unity to Explore Diversity*, you investigated how living things are related. In the previous Explain activity, *Evolutionary Trees*, you learned how evolutionary trees summarize the patterns of relationships among different organisms. All living things share a common ancestor with one another at some point in time.

Life on Earth is incredibly diverse—scientists estimate that there are 40–100 million species. But how do new species come about? In the Engage activity, you wrote down your ideas about how new zebra species may have formed. In this Explain activity, *Descent with Modification*, can you use your growing understanding of evolution to add to your explanation for the origin of species?

Materials (per team of 2)

Descent with Modification animation on the online resource
Speciation animation on the online resource
Reproductive Isolation animation on the online resource
different-colored pens or pencils

PROCESS AND PROCEDURES

1. Work with a partner to create an initial concept map of some important terms you have studied so far. Use the following terms in your map: "evolution," "natural selection," "species," "evolutionary tree," "populations," "individuals," and "geologic time."

   Concept maps are a way for you to explore and represent how different concepts are connected. You will draw arrows to link terms and then use verbs or short phrases to describe the connections among the different terms. Concept maps help you organize information, which helps you learn. For more information about developing a concept map, see *How to Construct a Concept Map* in appendix B7.

2. Continue to work with a partner and open the *Descent with Modification* animation on the online resource. Follow the instructions on the first 2 panels.

3. Write an explanation in your science notebook of how the image on the second panel is a summary of descent through time for the population of plants (figure 3.22).

   Remember the difference between a population and a species. A population is a group of organisms of the same species living in one area. A species usually is made of many populations.

4. Work with your partner to answer the following questions in your science notebook.

   a. Would you expect that many different physical traits would vary among individuals in 1 population of these plants? Why or why not?

   b. Think of just 1 trait, for example, petal length on a flower. If you compared the average length in 2 different populations, do you think the averages would be the same or different? Explain your answer.

Figure 3.22 Plant populations through time. This figure represents a population of plants going forward in time. Most populations would have many more individuals, but the number was kept small in this example for clarity. The green lines show the parent-offspring relationships over several generations. Over several generations, this population is mixed. Less mixing occurs among different populations, and little to no mixing occurs among species.

You might want to look over your notes from the chapter 2 Explore activity, *Exploring Change*, and Explain activity, *Explaining Adaptation*, to help you answer these questions and think about variation.

5. Click on the third panel of the animation and read the information on the screen to help you answer this question: "How are populations and species represented in evolutionary trees?"
6. As you read the essay, *A Closer Look at Species*, enter terms that are new to you into your personal glossary. Make sure to include drawings and other connections to help you remember these terms.

A Closer Look at Species

ENGLISH   SPANISH

The long line of species and populations from which modern humans emerged is called a lineage. Today, all living species represent different lineages that are united with other lineages at some point in the past. We call each distinct lineage a species. Perhaps the most common definition of a **species** is "a group of organisms that is capable of breeding or mating to produce fertile offspring." Species are the fundamental unit of biological classification. Scientists estimate that 40–100 million species exist on Earth today, yet only about 2 million have been formally named. There are plenty of new species left to be discovered.

As lineages of species go forward over long periods of time, interesting things can happen. Lineages of species can split and form new lineages. This results in the formation of new species. This process is called **speciation**. Some lineages leave no descendants. This is called **extinction**.

When lineages permanently split in the process of speciation, three things happen:

1. Some sort of barrier prevents the individuals in the two populations from breeding with one another. In some cases, populations may become separated by a physical barrier, such as a mountain range or a canyon.
2. Over long periods of time, the two separated groups of populations keep changing due to

natural selection and other mechanisms of evolution.

3. Eventually, changes develop in the two groups that prevent individuals from the different groups from breeding successfully with each other. These two groups are now **reproductively isolated**.

Once groups of populations have lost the ability to interbreed, they are forever on different evolutionary paths. After reproductive isolation evolves, many scientists consider the two lineages separate species.

In some ways, it seems that the definition of a species is straightforward. However, the diversity in different types of organisms poses some problems with a simple definition. Defining species based on their ability to interbreed is not always possible. For example, many organisms that reproduce sexually do not interbreed in natural conditions. Consider strawberry plants. Strawberries reproduce mainly by means of shoots or roots that grow into new plants, as shown in figure 3.23a. Also, many organisms, such as bacteria and other microbes, rarely or never reproduce sexually. Instead, they divide into two cells or a new cell buds off (depicted in figures 3.23b and 3.23c). In these cases, biologists must use other data to define the boundaries between species.

7. Revisit your answers from the Engage activity, *How Many Kinds of Zebras?*, and complete the following tasks.

   a. Revise your definition of a species given in Engage *Analysis* question 2, using a different-colored pen or pencil.

   b. With your partner, brainstorm at least 2 factors that may keep individual zebras from breeding and making fertile offspring in the groups that you identified as different species.

   > Think about all the factors that may affect whether two individuals breed and form fertile offspring. Could changes in behavior, timing of breeding, or physical factors be important? Can you come up with other ideas?

Though the term species is not easy to define, the process of speciation is incredibly important. As you observe all the organisms around you, it is astonishing to think that each of the millions of species, from bacteria to pine trees, came about through speciation.

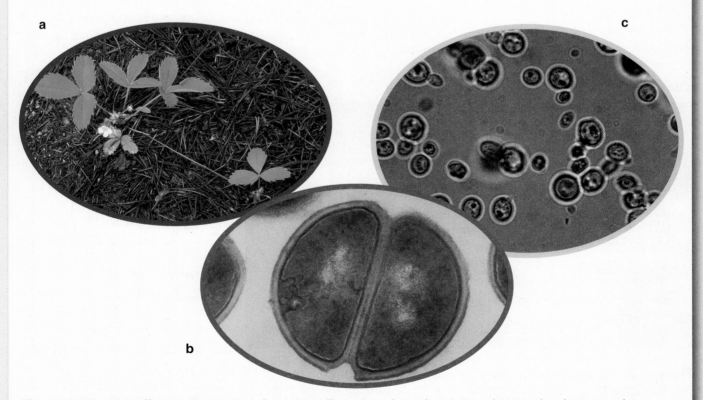

Figure 3.23 Not all organisms reproduce sexually or interbreed. (*a*) Strawberries develop new plants at the ends of runners. (*b*) Bacteria (*Staphylococcus*), photographed at 10,000×, divide into two new bacteria. (*c*) Yeast bud off new cells (photographed at 600×).

HOW TO

HOW TO

8. Work with a partner and view the *Speciation* animation on the online resource.

9. Place a copy in your science notebook of the *Squirrel Speciation* handout that your teacher will give you; it is shown in figure 3.24. Use highlight comments to help you interpret the series of lines on the right side of the image.

   It may be helpful to reread portions of the essay, *A Closer Look at Species*. Remember, you want to describe what you see and what you think it means. Appendix B6, *How to Write Highlight Comments and Captions* may be a helpful resource.

10. Work with a partner to complete tasks on the *Reproductive Isolation* animation on the online resource. As you interact with the animation, enter terms that are new to you into your personal glossary.

    The resource *How to Develop a Personal Glossary* is found in appendix B8.

11. With your partner, decide which reproductive isolating mechanism you think may have played a role in the isolation of 2 of the different zebra species. Write a short paragraph summarizing the reproductive isolating mechanism and how you think it affected the 2 zebra groups.

    To learn more about how scientists observe and study speciation, read the sidebar, *Speciation*.

Current Distribution of Populations

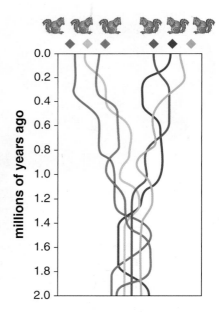

Figure 3.24   Squirrel speciation. The *y*-axis for the graphic on the right represents the relative degree of isolation among the different populations. Why do some of the lines start to diverge?

Speciation

Melon fly (*Bactrocera cucurbitae*). Researchers use these flies as a model system for studying reproductive isolation. These flies have a very fast generation time.

It is amazing to think about the millions of species on Earth and realize that they all came about through the process of speciation. But how do biologists study speciation? Biologists study the formation of new species by exploring the evolution of reproductive isolation. Remember, once two lineages can no longer interbreed, they are forever on different evolutionary paths. However, it may take hundreds of thousands of years, or even over a million years, for reproductive isolation to evolve between two new species. To overcome the challenge of time, scientists try to understand speciation by developing models. Scientists then study those models in laboratory experiments and experiments in more natural settings.

One exciting group of studies involves a type of fly called a melon fly (*Bactrocera cucurbitae*). Melon flies are found all over the world and cause damage to more than 81 plant species. Scientists like to study these flies because they can produce a new generation in as little as 11 days. This means scientists can form many generations each year. Like many insects, melon flies develop from eggs into larvae. Larvae then develop into adults that can mate, and females can form new eggs.

In one experiment in the lab, scientists noticed that the larvae vary in how long they take to develop into adults. The scientists artificially selected the slowest-growing larvae to survive and then allowed the individuals to reproduce. They did the same thing with the fastest-growing larvae. After only 40–50 generations (about five years), this process of artificial selection led to some populations of flies that completed the larval stage in six days (the S, or short, populations) and others that completed

the larval stage in 12 days (the L, or long, populations). The scientists were amazed to discover that the individuals from the S and L populations also differed in the time of day they liked to mate. When they put individuals from the different populations back together, individuals from the S populations mated only with other S individuals. The same was true of the individuals in the L populations. In other words, scientists were able to demonstrate the evolution of reproductive isolation in only 40–50 generations.

Other researchers study reproductive isolation in plants. Figure 3.25 shows two closely related species of plants called monkeyflowers. These species mostly live at different elevations, but they sometimes overlap. The two species do not mate with each other in nature. Researchers suspected that one of the main reasons the two species are isolated is because they have different pollinators. The pink species is pollinated mostly by bees, and the red one is pollinated mostly by hummingbirds. But why are hummingbirds attracted to one species and bees to the other? Researchers suspected that flower color played an important role. In other words, flower color might be causing the reproductive isolation. In a fascinating experiment, scientists were able to use genetic techniques to change flower color (figure 3.25). Then they planted the newly colored species in the wild. They found that the hummingbird-pollinated species that had been changed from a red to a pink color received 74 times more bee visits. The bee-pollinated species that had been changed from pink to red received 68 times more hummingbird visits. These results show that flower color can play a major role in reproductive isolation.

Overall, scientists continue to gather more and more evidence about speciation. Although most evolutionary change is too slow to see, there are examples in which it has been observed. Using models like the melon fly and the monkeyflower, scientists can demonstrate how the processes of evolution can lead to speciation.

Figure 3.25 **Reproductive isolation in monkeyflowers.** (*a*) Lewis's monkeyflower (named for Meriwether Lewis of the Lewis and Clark expedition) is pollinated by bees. (*c*) Red monkeyflower is pollinated by hummingbirds. Scientists were able to move a hereditary unit for color between the two species (*b* and *d*).

Analysis

1. Revisit your concept map from step 1 and complete the following tasks.
   a. Add the terms "speciation," "reproductive isolation," and "extinction" to your concept map, linking them to other concepts.
   b. Revise your concept map based on your new understandings. Use a different-colored pen or pencil for your revisions.
2. Propose a general explanation of how descent with modification and extinction are involved in shaping the diversity of life on Earth.

Evidence for Common Ancestry

In chapter 2, you gathered evidence that supports the idea that biological changes are the result of evolutionary processes. In this chapter, you have been learning about how species have all descended from ancestors in the past. In this Elaborate activity, *Evidence for Common Ancestry*, you will learn about additional evidence for evolution—evidence that indicates that organisms share common ancestors in one great tree of life.

PROCESS AND PROCEDURES

1. Work with your team of 4 and decide how to split into 2 pairs. One pair will take on the role of an evolutionary biologist, and the other pair will take on the role of a scientist who studies evolution and development:
   - Evolutionary biologist: A scientist who studies the relatedness of living organisms and how they change across time.
   - Evolutionary developmental biologist: A scientist who studies how the processes of growth and development occur and change over time.

2. With your partner, read and study the information assigned to your role. Complete the procedures outlined for your role. As you work with your partner, make certain you both contribute ideas.

   The information and procedures for both the evolutionary biologists and the evolutionary developmental biologists can be found under the heading Procedures for the Specialists. After everyone has had time to study his or her special field of science, you will meet again with your team of 4 so that you can teach each other what you have learned.

3. Return to your team of 4 and prepare to share what you learned with your team and to learn from your other team members.

   a. Open your science notebook to the *Evidence for Evolution* table you created in chapter 2. When your teammates describe their procedures and evidence, take notes in your *Evidence for Evolution* table. Be sure to ask them to clarify any evidence you do not understand.

   b. Work with your partner and describe your specialist role to the other members of the team. Make sure your description includes the following:
      - Briefly describe the procedures you followed to gather your evidence.
      - Explain how your poster shows evidence to support the idea that organisms change across time.

Procedures for the Specialists

Evolutionary Biologists

Evolutionary biologists are scientists who generally study the relationships among organisms and how lineages of organisms change across time. The field of evolutionary biology is broad and includes scientists who work mostly in the laboratory, those who work outside in the field, and some who work primarily on computers. Evolutionary biologists may study ecosystems, whole organisms, fossils, anatomy, molecules, and/or genetic information. In this activity, you will act as an evolutionary biologist who studies anatomy in different organisms. You'll use evidence and knowledge of the tree of life to figure out the origin and history of certain body parts.

Materials (per team of 2)

2 pairs of disposable gloves
2 laboratory aprons
1 dissecting tray and 1 teasing needle
1 chicken wing
1 envelope containing examples of vestigial structures
colored pencils
1 piece of poster board
felt-tipped markers

Topic: evolutionary
    biology
Code: human4E178a

Topic: homologous and
    vestigial structures
Code: human4E178b

1. Read the sidebar, *Interview with an Evolutionary Biologist*. Think about how you will explain the job of an evolutionary biologist to your teammates.

2. Complete the following activities with your evolutionary biologist partner.

   a. Work with your partner to carefully dissect a chicken wing. As you complete the dissection, compare the bones that you find with the chicken wing anatomy diagram provided by your teacher.

   b. *Wash your hands with soap.*

   c. Locate the bones listed in the bird wing anatomy diagram and color them in using the colored pencils. Color-code the diagram so that each of the underlined bones is a different color.

   d. Obtain 1 bat wing diagram and 1 human hand diagram and their keys.

   e. With your partner, color the bones of the bat wing and human hand with the same color-coding that you used on the chicken wing diagram.

   f. In your science notebook, explain the similarities that you found between a human hand, a bat wing, and a chicken wing.

   g. Mount your diagrams on a poster board to share with your classmates.

Interview with an Evolutionary Biologist

INTERVIEWER: Why did you go into the field of evolutionary biology?

DR. EDWARDS: I started first as an ornithologist [bird biologist] and then became interested in using genetic tools to study evolution. With my interest in birds from an early age, I knew that organisms and natural history and working in the outdoors were important to me. As an undergraduate, I realized that to study birds well one has to know about a wide range of topics, from genetics to population studies to behavior. Evolutionary biology is a field that is broad enough to encompass all these interests.

INTERVIEWER: You're a professor with your own research lab. What does that mean, and how did you get to this place in your career?

DR. EDWARDS: I am in charge of a group of researchers—some postdoctoral fellows who have their PhDs, some graduate students who are working on their PhDs, and some undergraduates, who may just be dreaming about a PhD. I have even had some high school students and teachers work with me. It's very easy to do research, if one has the curiosity and a little bit of training. I got that sort of training as an undergraduate, and that got me fired up to go on and do more research. As a researcher, your goal is to ask questions and find the answers through science. If you do this long enough, and well enough, you'll eventually get a PhD, and this will be your way of telling society that you've mastered a particular body of knowledge. Running a lab then just becomes an extension of your curiosity—except that now you've got extra hands to help you find the answers!

INTERVIEWER: What do you find most interesting or exciting about your work?

DR. EDWARDS: I will never forget my first glimpse of a bird of paradise on the island

Scott Edwards, PhD. Scott Edwards is Professor of Organismic and Evolutionary Biology and Curator of Ornithology at the Museum of Comparative Zoology at Harvard University in Cambridge, Massachusetts.

of New Guinea. The pictures in my field guide were too bizarre and flamboyant to actually convince me that these things really existed. I happened to meet a native who insisted on my visiting his village in the mountains to see the birds of paradise in his area. I didn't believe we'd see any, but still rode for a day and half in the back of an old pickup truck, and finally arrived at his village. A short walk up in the hills brought us to a fruiting tree, and after a few minutes a remarkable iridescent crow-sized bird with a pair of three-foot long, pure white tail feathers flew in to feed on the fruit. It was a ribbon-tailed astrapia, and it was real! It still boggles my mind that such species exist and that they can make their way through the forest with such long, cumbersome tail feathers (which probably hinder rather than help their flight).

I enjoy the mix of fieldwork and lab work that I do, and the challenges of bringing those two areas together. Both are a type of exploration. I would not be in this business if it weren't for the opportunity to travel to some really cool places and see some really cool animals and their habitats. It's an opportunity that I feel extremely fortunate to have had, and it's what often gets people asking how things came to be and how such different habitats and biological communities were produced. But the fieldwork is not everything. I can go only so long without taking a shower or having the control over my surroundings that a laboratory provides. In the lab, I'm able to weave together the wonderful patterns and behaviors observed in the field with the 21st-century tools of genetics. The genetic work is like trawling through yet another jungle—except here it is a morass of DNA letters. Unraveling the evolutionary meaning of those letters and linking them back to the lives of the birds and other animals we study is very exciting.

INTERVIEWER: What do you find most challenging or frustrating about your work?

DR. EDWARDS: The level of funding for evolutionary biology in the United States is frustratingly low. There is much more funding, for example, for biomedical science, perhaps because there is a perception that biomedicine is more directly related to human health and happiness. Yet even biomedical scientists are learning that evolutionary biology provides a very compelling context in which to understand the interaction of humans, their behavior, and their environments and, indeed, sometimes to predict the future of the human species. My hope is that society will recognize the important contributions that evolution can make to improving human well-being—and the well-being of the other 12 million species on the planet.

INTERVIEWER: Do you think it is important for all students to study evolution? If so, why?

DR. EDWARDS: Yes, I believe it is important for everyone to study evolution. Of course, it is a very sensitive issue, since everyone has their own personal perspective on the world, and has their own story as to how it came to be. These stories are an important part of the diversity of human cultures, and in fact are sacred in many societies, and so I don't believe the teaching of evolution should supplant these other points of view. But I do think that evolution holds a special place, not only in biology, but in science in general. The bottom line is, evolution is one key to answering many questions that we desperately need answers to—from cures for AIDS to the control of invasive species and the response of dwindling habitats to climate change—and for this reason evolution should not just be a luxury but a necessity in our schooling.

3. Read about homologous, analogous, and vestigial structures in the essay, *Modern Life: Evidence for Descent with Modification.*
   a. On the diagrams that you colored, are the parts of the animal limbs homologous, analogous, or vestigial? Why do you think so?

   How would an evolutionary tree showing common ancestry help you make a decision?

The fossil skeleton of Lucy has many of the same features as skeletons of modern humans. But modern human skeletons display some significant differences. Comparisons of fossils from long ago with modern organisms provide one line of evidence that living systems share common ancestors, and that they also change. It is important to remember that the process of change occurs not only in the past, such as when Lucy lived. It is going on in all of the living systems alive on Earth today.

The process and pattern of change are explained by the phrase "descent with modification." Major pieces of evidence for descent with modification come from studies of comparative anatomy. This branch of biology concentrates on the similarities and differences in anatomical features of different species. When you take a close look at living organisms, you will see that many species share structural similarities. A pattern of similar characteristics may suggest that organisms share common ancestors. For example, compare the structure of the animal forelimbs shown in figure 3.26. Although they have

different functions, these limbs show consistent similarities among the organisms. In addition, the limbs have the same relationship to the body (they all are forelimbs), and they develop in the same way in the young. Because of these consistent similarities, biologists infer that the forelimb structure is **homologous**. Homologous characteristics are similar among different organisms because they evolved from a common ancestor. The forelimb structure seen in modern species is also found in fossils. In contrast, structures that function or appear similar between species, but are not evolved from a common ancestor, are called **analogous** structures. An example of this is a bird's wing and an insect's wing, since flight evolved independently in these two groups.

In making anatomical comparisons, scientists also discover structures that are functional in some species, but seemingly useless in others. We refer to these apparently useless structures as **vestigial**. This term comes from the word "vestige," meaning "a remnant of." The goose bumps that you get when you are cold are an example of vestigial structures. Small erector muscles in the skin produce goose bumps. In other mammals and birds, the contraction of erector muscles causes the fur or feathers to fluff up. This mechanism helps the organism warm up. Modern humans do not have very much hair, but we have retained the erector muscles. Figure 3.27 shows more examples of vestigial structures.

Why do organisms have vestigial structures? Because they inherited the structure from a common ancestor. It is important to remember, however, that a claim about a structure being vestigial is a hypothesis. Future data showing that a vestigial

Figure 3.26 **Homologies are characteristics that suggest common ancestry.** Although adapted for different functions, the bones of these forelimbs (not drawn to scale) show comparable structures. What similarities can you find?

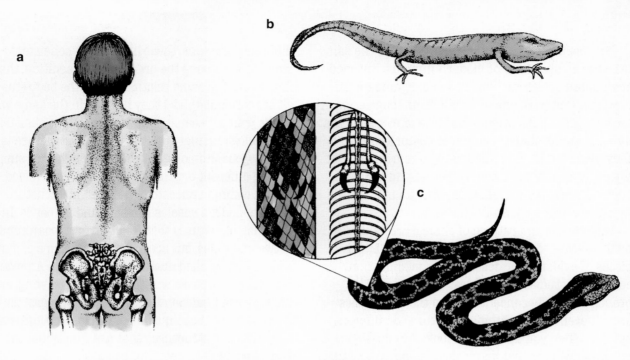

Figure 3.27   **Examples of vestigial structures. (*a*) Human tail structures.** Most mammals have a well-developed tail, but this is lacking in apes and humans. Still, the tail is represented by the last three to five bones in the backbone of humans. Even though an external tail usually is not present, the muscles that move the tail in other mammals also are present in humans. On rare occasions, a fleshy tail in a human extends a few inches. **(*b*) Blind salamander.** These salamanders from Arkansas and Missouri adapted to life in deep caves with no sunlight. They possess eyes but they do not function. The salamanders are blind, but they inherited the ability to make eyes from a sighted ancestor. **(c) Snakes with legs.** Notice the bony parts of the python's pelvic girdle, to which tiny limb bones attach. The legs serve no function.

structure has an important function may cause the hypothesis to be revised.

Homologies and vestigial structures are examples of similar features shared by organisms due to their common ancestry. Is there additional evidence to suggest that the tremendous diversity of life arose from a common ancestor? The answer is yes. This evidence is found by comparing modern species. You can study single-celled bacteria such as *Staphylococcus*, protists such as *Amoeba*, fungi such as mushrooms, or the more familiar plants and animals. In each case, you will find that each stores its genetic information in the same complex molecule, DNA

(deoxyribonucleic acid). DNA stores important information for making many of the characteristics of each species. Yet the method of storing that information, including the code that is used to interpret the information, is essentially the same in any living organism. For all of its incredible power, DNA is a code based on just four types of molecules, summarized as A, C, G, and T.

Scientists use DNA to make detailed claims about the relationships among organisms. Biologists have compared the DNA among modern species and even among modern and extinct species in rare cases. In fact, new laboratory techniques enable molecular biologists to transfer DNA from one species to another, where the DNA functions successfully. Even cells from a human can receive and decode the DNA from a bacterium. Figure 3.28 shows the similarity of DNA among some primates.

The probability that the primates listed in figure 3.28 developed an identical DNA code without being related to one another is extremely small. A much more likely explanation for this close similarity is that they inherited the genetic code from the same ancestors. The similarity in genetic code across living organisms strongly suggests a common origin for all modern life.

Animal	Percentage of DNA That Is the Same as Human DNA
Monkey	93%
Gibbon	95%
Chimpanzee	98+%

Figure 3.28 **Comparing DNA across primates.**

    b. Title your poster with the correct term (homologous, analogous, or vestigial structures). Write a definition for the term, in your own words, beneath the title.

4. Obtain an envelope containing examples of vestigial structures. Study the structures inside.

    a. On the *Human Vestigial Structures* handout, write a brief, logical explanation about why each structure is considered vestigial.

    b. On the *Whale and Snake Vestigial Structures* handout, write a brief, logical explanation for why these hind limb bones are considered vestigial.

        Make sure to include how the idea of common ancestry helps you explain vestigial structures.

5. Make a poster about vestigial structures, using the space on the back of your poster about homologous structures.

6. Check over your posters. You will use your posters to teach your original team about the evidence contributed by evolutionary biologists to the theory of evolution. Return to *Process and Procedures* step 3.

Evolutionary Developmental Biologists

Scientists in the field of evolutionary development ("evo-devo") biology study the stages of growth and development that living organisms pass through as they grow from fertilized egg to mature adult and beyond. These scientists use information from the tree of life to inform their studies of

development. Often, they use evolutionary trees in their studies; the trees are made with data from other sources, like DNA. The work of **evolutionary developmental biologists** helps refine hypotheses about the relationships among organisms and provides clues about how adaptations evolve.

Materials (per team of 2)

online resource (watch as a team)
1 embryo puzzle
1 piece of poster board

SC*LINKS*®
NSTA

www.scilinks.org

Topic: developmental biology
Code: human4E184

1. Read the sidebar, *Interview with an Evolutionary Developmental Biologist*. Think about how you will explain the job to your teammates.
2. Complete these activities with the other evolutionary developmental biologist on your team.
   a. Read and discuss the information in the need to know, *Embryos*. Have your teacher listen to your explanation of the information in the box and confirm your understanding before you proceed.
   b. Study the individual drawings of embryos that your teacher provides. Try to arrange all of the embryonic stages in a developmental order for each animal. When you have finished, your arrangement should show 3 stages of embryonic development for a fish, a frog, a chicken, a calf, and a human.

      These drawings depict various embryonic stages of five different vertebrates. These stages are relative. They do not represent the same point in time, but rather the same relative amount of development.

   c. Compare your work with your teacher's version of the embryo puzzle.

SIDEBAR

ENGLISH SPANISH

Interview with an Evolutionary Developmental Biologist

INTERVIEWER: What inspired you to go into the field of evolutionary a biology?
MR. PANG: I am fascinated by the diversity of animal life and curious as to how it came to

be. Yet with all the differences, almost all animals start off as a fertilized egg and go through a developmental program to become an adult. The field I study, evolutionary developmental biology, integrates cell biology, molecular biology, and the study of living organisms.

INTERVIEWER: What is evolutionary developmental biology, and what do you study?

MR. PANG: Evolutionary developmental biology, or "evo-devo," as it is commonly referred to, is the study of how things evolved by comparing differences or similarities in development.

My work focuses on two groups of animals that diverged from the rest of the animals early in the tree of life. One group includes jellyfish and sea anemones. The second group includes animals called comb jellies. The bodies of these animals are somewhat jellylike and are relatively simple compared to other animals'.

Though their bodies seem simple, the genes that guide their development are similar to those of all other animals. I can find similar genes in the starlet sea anemone that I study, *Nematostella vectensis*, as you would find in vertebrates. This is amazing because these animals shared a common ancestor over 500 million years ago! So I try to see how these different organisms use all these genes to make their bodies. My main area of focus is exploring how the developing embryo "decides" what part of the body goes up, and what goes down.

INTERVIEWER: What do you find most interesting or exciting about your work?

MR. PANG: The coolest part of my work is the animals that I work on, the warty comb jelly—*Mnemiopsis leidyi*—and the sea anemone. The warty comb jelly can be found off the Atlantic coast of the United States, but it can't be grown in the lab. So for the first year of my project, I was only working with its DNA. When I finally saw a living warty comb jelly, it made me wonder why more people don't study these exquisitely beautiful animals. The way they move by beating their plates of cilia, with light refracting off of them making them appear iridescent, is almost indescribable. Seeing them give off light, or bioluminesce, is also quite a fascinating experience.

I also genuinely enjoy my work. While most of the year is spent in the laboratory, working with embryonic tissue and DNA, during the summer I work in the field. I go to the Atlantic coast to collect my animals. I like the balance of doing molecular work but also being able to see the animals that I work on.

INTERVIEWER: What do you find most challenging or frustrating about your work?

MR. PANG: Working on an organism that few people study is both challenging and exciting. It is exciting because anything we find out sheds new light on the topic. Sometimes it would be helpful if more people studied these animals. We often apply ideas and techniques from more well-studied animals and see if they work in ours. While some methods carry over quite easily, others require a lot of troubleshooting.

Kevin Pang. Kevin Pang is a graduate student at the University of Hawaii.

NEED TO KNOW

ENGLISH SPANISH

Embryos

Developmental biology focuses on the early development of organisms before they are born or hatched. Scientists call developing organisms "embryos." Evolutionary developmental biologists compare the processes that affect development in the embryos of organisms as diverse as fishes, amphibians, reptiles, birds, and mammals. They find that the embryos of these vertebrate animals (animals that have backbones) resemble one another and use very similar processes.

Make certain that everyone understands these concepts before continuing to step 2b.

d. Discuss the following questions with your partner and record your answers in your science notebook.

  1) In general, which organisms have embryonic stages that are the most similar? The least similar? Explain your answers.

  2) What do you think these similarities and differences tell scientists about how these organisms are related?

  Consider whether you expect related organisms to look similar or not. Would you also expect related organisms to go through similar stages of development? Consider the later stages of development. Do the more closely related organisms look more or less similar?

  3) Frogs, chickens, cows, and humans all have four limbs. These structures develop in similar ways, and similar processes control this development. What does this evidence suggest about common ancestry among these organisms?

e. Work with the other evolutionary developmental biologist on your team to make a poster that you will use to teach your original team about embryology.

  Your poster should show the embryo stages that you studied. It also should include a summary of how comparing the development of embryos contributes to scientists' understanding of how different species share common ancestors.

3. Review the essay, *Modern Life: Evidence for Descent with Modification*. Use the information in the essay to help you accomplish the following tasks.

  a. In your science notebook, explain where DNA is located and what its purpose is.

Topic: embryo
development
Code: human4E186a

Topic: DNA
Code: human4E186b

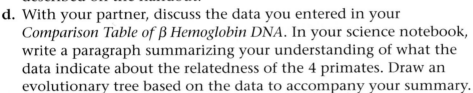
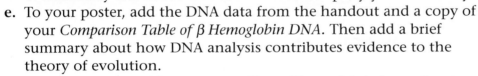

	Chimp	Gorilla	Orangutan
# DNA letters different from human			
# DNA letters similar to human			
% similarity with human			

Figure 3.29
Comparison Table of β Hemoglobin DNA (between humans and other primates).

b. Obtain the *DNA Comparison* handout from your teacher. This handout shows a comparison of the DNA that codes for the β hemoglobin protein, which is found in blood.

c. Copy figure 3.29 into your science notebook to prepare to use data from the *DNA Comparison* handout. Follow the procedures described on the handout.

d. With your partner, discuss the data you entered in your *Comparison Table of β Hemoglobin DNA*. In your science notebook, write a paragraph summarizing your understanding of what the data indicate about the relatedness of the 4 primates. Draw an evolutionary tree based on the data to accompany your summary.

e. To your poster, add the DNA data from the handout and a copy of your *Comparison Table of β Hemoglobin DNA*. Then add a brief summary about how DNA analysis contributes evidence to the theory of evolution.

4. Review your poster and your notes. You will use this information to teach your original team how evolutionary developmental biologists contribute to our understanding of evolution. Return to *Process and Procedures* step 3.

Analysis

Examine your *Evidence for Evolution* table. Discuss with your partner how having many different types of evidence makes the argument for biological evolution stronger than any of the separate pieces. In your science notebook, record the main ideas from your discussion.

Using Unity to Organize Diversity

ELABORATE

Do you remember the pictures of fungi and bacteria from chapter 1, *The Human Animal*? They seem so different from humans. However, in the chapter 1 Elaborate activity, *How Similar Are We?*, you discovered that all organisms display the unifying principles of life. In the chapter 3 Elaborate activity, *Evidence for Common Ancestry*, you learned how scientists use evidence to show that all living organisms are related. You can now appreciate that life displays unifying principles *because* living things share common ancestors. Because everything is related through common ancestry, scientists can infer a tree of life that includes every species.

Biologists use an understanding of the evolutionary relationships to organize the diversity of life on Earth. In this Elaborate activity, *Using Unity to Organize Diversity*, you will practice using the classification system that biologists use. You will further develop your growing understanding of biological diversity (figure 3.30), its origins, and the ways scientists study and make sense of it.

Materials

Part A
1 set of nonliving objects
1 index card

Part B
1 set of organism cards
1 large sheet of paper
1 set of colored felt-tipped markers
tape

Figure 3.30
Algae at Yellowstone National Park in Wyoming, Montana, and Idaho.

PROCESS AND PROCEDURES

Part A Classification as a Tool

1. Work with your team to examine the set of nonliving objects. What, if anything, do all of these objects share in common? What characteristics do some objects possess that others do not? Record your observations in your science notebook.

2. Sort the objects in your set into 4 different categories.

   When you sort your objects into categories, you are *classifying* them. The system that you use to sort your objects is called a *classification scheme*.

3. Write your team's classification scheme on an index card. Leave the card face down on the table with the sorted objects.

4. When directed by your teacher, go to another team's table and try to guess what its classification scheme is. Compare your classification scheme with that of the other team. Are the categories the same? Could you easily recognize its categories?

5. Answer the following questions in your science notebook.

   a. Your team and the other team probably used a different basis for your classification schemes. Nevertheless, each team used *some* basis. That is, each team used some general *criteria* to determine what groups it would include in its scheme and what objects would go into each group. Is it possible to classify without establishing such criteria? Support your answer with a different example of classification drawn from your life experience.

b. Consider the categories of objects that you created in your classification scheme. Could you further separate (or classify) the objects in any of these categories into smaller groups within the large category? Support your answer with specific references to the objects and the classification scheme that you developed.

Part B Classifying Organisms

1. Obtain a set of 4 organism cards. With your partner, take turns reading the information about the organisms.

2. Work with your partner to divide your organism cards into 2 groups. Write your groups into your science notebook, along with the criteria you used to form the groups.

> The groups you create do not have to contain equal numbers of organisms. Use biological characters for your criteria for classifying the organisms into groups. The characters can be physical features or behavioral features of the organisms.

3. Copy the diagram in figure 3.31 onto a large sheet of paper. Make the smallest boxes big enough to contain at least 3 of your organism cards.

4. Use the information in the need to know, *Levels of Classification,* to determine the phylum for the organisms on your cards. Write this phylum name at the top of your diagram.

5. Use the information in the need to know to identify a characteristic that all organisms in that phylum share. Write that next to the phylum name.

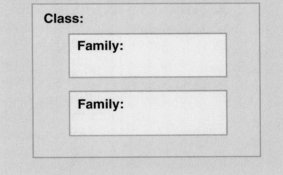

Figure 3.31   Sample diagram. You will use a diagram like this to practice biological classification.

NEED TO KNOW
ENGLISH SPANISH

Levels of Classification

Domain, kingdom, phylum, class, order, family, genus, species. What do these terms mean to you? They are all names of groups that biologists use when classifying organisms. Why do biologists have so many different names for groups of organisms? The names that biologists give to different levels of classification can be thought of as corresponding to larger or smaller groups in a nested group diagram. "Domain" is the name of the level of classification that includes the largest diversity of organisms. Members of the same domain form a natural group, but the common ancestor for all of them existed long, long ago. "Species" is the name for organisms that are very closely related.

In this activity, you are examining specific organisms to determine their classification at three different levels. One level that contains several species is called a family. The next level is called a class, and it may contain many families. The next level is called a phylum, and it may contain many classes. Are you starting to see how your sample diagram in figure 3.31 can represent groups that nest together?

Biologists use more than three levels in the organizational system for life. You can find out more about all the levels of classification in the essay, *Organizing Diversity*. To complete this activity, use the following information about a few specific phyla (plural of phylum), classes, and families of organisms.

The kingdom Animalia is organized into 38 living phyla. For example, the phylum Chordata includes organisms with backbones. The phylum Arthropoda includes organisms that have external skeletons and jointed legs. In addition to the 38 living phyla, there are many extinct phyla as well.

The phylum Chordata is organized into 15 living classes. These include the class Aves, which is made up of feathered organisms with other adaptations for flight, like lightweight bones. Another example is the class Amphibia (figure 3.32), which includes all organisms with backbones that have porous skin and lay eggs without shells.

The phylum Arthropoda is organized into 17 living classes. These include the class Insecta, which is made up of organisms with six jointed legs. Another class is Malacostraca, which includes organisms with 10 jointed legs. Most malacostracans spend some part of their lives in the ocean.

Most classes of animals are made up of many orders, and within these orders there are dozens to hundreds of families. In the class Aves, some of these families are the accipters (hawks), the phasianids (pheasants), the cathartids (vultures), the columbids (pigeons), and the tytonids (barn owls). In the class Mammalia, families include the ursids (bears), the delphinids (oceanic dolphins), and the dasypodids (armadillos). In the class Insecta, families include blattids (just one of six families of cockroaches), phasmatids (stick insects), hesperiids (skipper butterflies), and the papillonids (swallowtail butterflies).

Did your organisms fit any of the described phyla, classes, and families? See if you can accurately classify them.

© Dreamstime/David Cabral

© Dreamstime/Nouubon

© Dreamstime/Carol Buchanen

Figure 3.32 Which of these chordates is a member of the class Amphibia—the painted turtle, the cane toad, or the reef shark?

6. Determine the class for the organisms on your cards based on the information in the essay, *Organizing Diversity*. Write that name along the top of the middle box, along with a characteristic that all organisms in that class share.

   Take turns doing these steps with your partner. The essay, *Organizing Diversity*, provides additional information that may help you with this task.

7. Divide your organism cards into 2 groups, based on the family information in the need to know. Tape each of your organism cards into 1 of the 2 small boxes on your paper and write its family name along the top, along with a characteristic that organisms in that family share.

8. Form a team of 4 by merging with another pair of students who had organisms in your phylum. Briefly present your diagram and listen to the other pair's presentation.

   Be sure you explain the character or characters that led you to classify each organism into a particular family, class, and phylum.

9. Form a new team of 4 by merging with a pair of students who classified organisms in a different phylum. Briefly present your diagram to your new teammates and listen to their presentation.

10. Revise your diagram with your partner if your discussions with the other teams have given you a reason to do so. Then copy your entire diagram into your science notebook, with the title "biological classification diagram." Be sure to include the biological characteristics you used to classify each nested group.

Organizing Diversity

ENGLISH SPANISH

Whenever people collect information, they develop systems for organizing it. Think of the ways people organize the following: notes for research papers, computer files, recipes, or music collections. Imagine—if you had 2 million songs stored on your computer, how would you possibly organize them? Many people use a nested series of folders on their computers to organize songs, documents, and pictures. For example, you might store all songs in your "music" folder, and within this folder you might store separate folders for each singer or band. Then, within your favorite band's folder, you would likely have several folders, each containing a CD of songs. This organization system has two requirements:

1. A way of forming groups that can be divided into smaller groups; in other words, the groups can be nested

2. A naming system

Biologists have described over 2 million species. That is a tremendous amount of diversity. The process of organizing and describing this diversity is called **biological classification**. Biologists use an organizational system just like the one described for music. Classification plays an important role in biologists' attempts to understand life. First, it helps subdivide the numerous types of living (and extinct) organisms into groups that can be studied productively. Second, classification gives each organism a unique name, which helps biologists communicate.

Though many different types of groups could be used for classification, biologists use groups defined by evolutionary history. Evolution produces organisms that are nested into groups (clades) based on common ancestry. It is a natural form of organization. Biologists use this system of nested groups to organize all of life's species.

Modern biological classification schemes generally contain a number of categories. Each category represents a natural group of organisms with a particular degree, or level, of relatedness to each other. The following groups are frequently used in biological classification, going from the most specific to the most general groups. Organisms that have the greatest number of shared characteristics are grouped together in the lowest level, the category of species. Think of all the dogs you have seen. Great Danes, German shepherds, and toy poodles are all members of the species known scientifically as *Canis familiaris*. The second name, *familiaris*, describes the dog species. Can you see why scientists picked *familiaris* to describe dogs? The first name, *Canis*, is the name of a group of species that form a larger category, known as a genus. Other species in the genus *Canis* include the gray wolf (*Canis lupus*) and the coyote (*Canis latrans*).

Groups of similar genera (plural of genus) form a family. Related families are organized in a large group known as an order. Related orders are grouped together in a class. And a group of related classes form still larger categories known as phyla, sometimes called divisions in plants. See figure 3.33 for an example of the classes that might be contained in one phylum. But classification doesn't stop there. Related phyla are grouped into kingdoms, and related kingdoms are grouped into domains. The domain level of the biological classification system includes the greatest diversity of related organisms. The biological classification assigns each organism to these series of categories. The classification of both dogs and your species is shown in figure 3.34.

Evolutionary trees summarize the nested and hierarchical relationships among species. So evolutionary trees are also used for classification. Let's examine how biologists use evolutionary trees for classification. In the tree in figure 3.35, clades

Phylum:	Chordata	
Classes:	tunicates	cartilaginous fishes
	lancelets	acanthodians †
	hagfish	ray-finned bony fishes
	conodonts †	lobe-finned bony fishes
	lampreys	amphibians
	cephalaspids †	sauropsid reptiles
	pteraspids †	birds
	placoderms †	mammals

Figure 3.33   The phylum Chordata contains many classes, including all the classes of vertebrates. Some of the classes of Chordata are extinct (†).

have been assigned different levels of classification. For example, all the odd-toed hoofed mammals are in the order Perissodactyla. Within this order is the family Equidae, and within that family is the genus *Equus*, which contains horses and zebras.

It is important to remember that scientists *will never be able to completely prove* evolutionary relationships. Scientists are always seeking new information. As new information becomes available, understandings of relationships may change. What does this mean?

1. Evolutionary trees are claims based on data. Some parts of the tree of life are supported by large amounts of evidence. Other parts have less evidence.

2. As scientists collect more data and adjust their thinking about these relationships, the ways in which they organize classifications may change. Thus, the ways we classify organisms today are different than they were in the past.

© Dreamstime/Vchphoto

© Dreamstime/Franz Pfluegl

Figure 3.34 **The classification of two familiar species.**

Classification level	Dogs	Humans
Domain	Eukarya	Eukarya
Kingdom	Animalia	Animalia
Phylum	Chordata	Chordata
Class	Mammalia	Mammalia
Order	Carnivora	Primates
Family	Canidae	Hominidae
Genus	*Canis*	*Homo*
Species	*familiaris*	*sapiens*

The second aspect of an organizational system involves assigning names. How do biologists handle naming?

People in every culture throughout history have given names to the living organisms they encountered. But the names typically differed from one culture to the next, making communication difficult. As a result, people recognized hundreds of years ago that a standard naming system had many advantages. Scholars in the Middle Ages started to develop a standard naming system for organisms, beginning with the names used by the ancient Greeks. One major problem, though, was how to handle new organisms. Scholars started adding numerous adjectives to the names of species to help differentiate new species from previous species. This system quickly got complicated. Some species names included nine or more words.

A more effective naming system was proposed by Carolus Linnaeus in 1735. He suggested that the official name for each species should consist of just two words (**binomial nomenclature**). In this system, the name for a species is simply the name of an organism's genus and its specific species

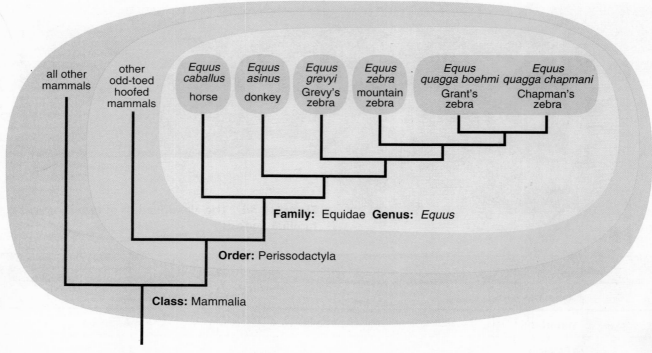

Figure 3.35   Relationship between classification levels and an evolutionary tree of some mammals, featuring zebras.

name. Scientific names are written in italics. Also, the name for a genus is capitalized. There are two rules for assigning names using binomial nomenclature.

1. The name of each genus needs to be unique.
2. Each species within a genus has a unique species name.

For instance, humans are in the genus *Homo* (Latin for "man") and have the species name *sapiens* (Latin for "wise" or "knowing"). So the scientific name for humans is *Homo sapiens*. Sometimes a genus is only represented by one living species. This is the case for *Homo*. However, there are several extinct *Homo* species known from fossils. These include *Homo habilis*, *Homo neanderthalensis*, and *Homo floresiensis*. Also, sometimes the genus name is abbreviated, for example, *H. sapiens*.

Although common names for a species may vary in different regions or different countries,

scientific names do not vary (figure 3.36). The standard use of scientific names is very important to accurate communication and efficient research. For instance, there are many common names for Chapman's zebra, including plains zebra, common zebra, and painted quagga. Different African languages include at least 16 more names, including *eutulege*, *lagwar*, *itiko*, *injiga*, *hares*, and *mangwa*. Clearly, if scientists referred to zebras by their common names, it could cause a lot of confusion. Using scientific names reduces the problem.

Does classification matter? Consider the case of Preble's meadow jumping mouse. There is disagreement over whether this mouse (*Zapus hudsonius preblei*) is different enough from other meadow jumping mice to be protected by the Endangered Species Act. Different sets of data indicate different conclusions. The disagreement over this tiny mouse made news headlines in the states of Wyoming and Colorado, because protecting its habitat is at odds with people who would like to develop the land for human use. Millions of dollars are involved. The mouse will continue to be protected until its classification is resolved.

Overall, the usefulness of the biological classification system is illustrated by its enormous lasting power. This system developed gradually over about 100 years from Linnaeus's system of naming species. It has accommodated a tremendous volume of new knowledge that has been added in the past 250 years. And, if biologists are correct in their estimates of the number of species that remain to be discovered and described, we can expect it to accommodate the data yet to be examined and added.

Figure 3.36 The common bird *Sturnus vulgaris* is called a "starling" in the United States and Britain, but it is called an *étourneau* in France.

Analysis

Prepare for a class discussion of the following questions by discussing them with your final team of four. Record the ideas in your science notebook.

> The essay, *Organizing Diversity*, provides additional information that may help you answer these questions. You may also want to review the sidebar, *Changing Views of the Tree of Life*, for useful information.

1. Review your original grouping of organism cards from part B, step 2. Did you change the groups after learning more about biological classification? Why or why not?
2. List 2 similarities and 2 differences between the classification schemes the class made for nonliving objects in part A and the one you made for organisms in part B.
3. Explain which happened more recently in evolution: a split between 2 zebra species or a split between the chordate and arthropod phyla. Explain why.
4. How do you think the organisms you classified are related by common ancestry? Draw an evolutionary tree that summarizes the classification of the organisms you worked with in part B, step 10.
5. Identify the 3 most important ideas about biological classification that you think you and your classmates should understand. Summarize these ideas in 3 concise statements and record them in your science notebook.

ENGLISH SPANISH

Changing Views of the Tree of Life

Which organisms shared a common ancestor more recently, the organisms in figure 3.37 or in figure 3.38? Figure 3.37 shows two animals that seem to bear little resemblance to each other. In contrast, figure 3.38 shows three single-celled organisms, each looking very similar.

Surprisingly, from an evolutionary point of view, the two animals in figure 3.37 shared a common ancestor much more recently than the three single-celled organisms. The animals are an African elephant and a close relative, a small mammal known as a hyrax. What you cannot see in figure 3.37 is all the ways in which these organisms are similar, from the basic structures of their cells to the structures of their feet and teeth. These two species inherited these similar structures from their common ancestor.

On the other hand, the organisms in figure 3.38 are very distant in their evolutionary connection, despite the fact that each is a single cell. This means that they share a common ancestor in the very distant past—in this case,

probably over a few billion years ago. If you look closely, you can find one of the characteristics that makes *Peranema* different from the other two. Notice that *Peranema* has an interior compartment that is missing in the other cell. That compartment is a nucleus, so *Peranema* is a eukaryotic organism. The second cell is a bacterium called *Escherichia coli*. Like other types of bacteria, its DNA is not separated from the rest of the cell contents by a surrounding membrane. It lacks a nucleus. The third cell is an archaea called *Sulfolobus acidcaldarius*. It, too, lacks a nucleus, but it has features that make it different from both *Peranema* and *E. coli*. Like some other archaea, it lives in an extreme environment, the hot springs of Yellowstone National Park in Wyoming, Montana, and Idaho.

The three single-celled organisms in figure 3.38 illustrate the three largest groups of life that biologists recognize. All the species on Earth are a member of one of these three groups: the Bacteria, the Archaea, and the Eukarya, as shown in figure 3.39. How do you fit into these three big groups, and how are they related to one another?

The organisms in domain Bacteria and domain Archaea look very similar—so

Figure 3.37 (*a*) African elephant (*Loxodonta africana*). The average male African elephant is 350 cm high and weighs 5,000 kg. (*b*) **Rock hyrax** (*Procavia capensis*). A rock hyrax may be 30 cm high and weigh 4 kg.

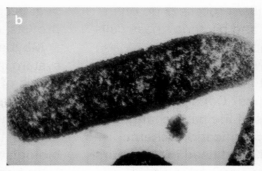
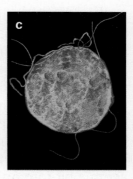

Figure 3.38 (*a*) This *Peranema* is about 40 μm. (*b*) This *Escherichia coli* is 3.5 μm long (photographed at 35,000×). (*c*) This *Sulfolobus acidcaldarius* is photographed at 85,000× magnification.

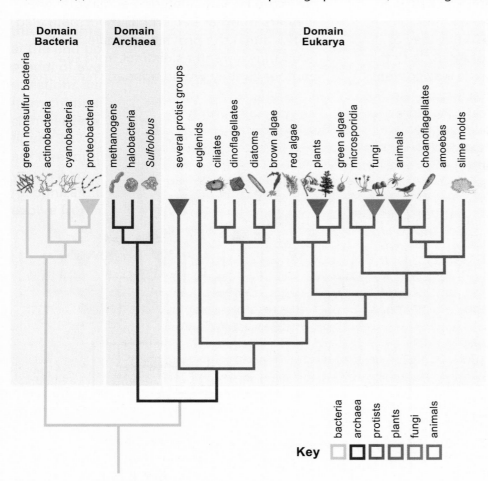

Figure 3.39 **The three-domain system.** The domain Bacteria includes the organisms that do not have membrane-bound organelles. Those in domain Archaea are also single celled, but are genetically distinct. Plants, animals, fungi, and protists are all in domain Eukarya. What differences do you think separate the organisms in each domain?

similar that the two groups were originally considered to be the same. But analysis of the DNA of archaea has shown that they form a clade that is distinct from the bacteria. Archaea differ from bacteria in the ways that they use their DNA, build their membranes, and construct their flagella (structures that they use for movement). Eukaryotes, including humans and *Peranema*, have cells with nuclei. Eukaryotic cells also may have additional membrane-enclosed compartments that perform a variety of functions, such as energy transformation and protein storage and packaging.

Although many similar processes go on in the cells of archaea and bacteria, these cells do not contain compartments.

How has our growing understanding of the relationships of life on Earth affected classification schemes? Consider how views of the major groups of life have changed. Does the modern classification scheme shown in figure 3.39 and used in this course seem a bit foreign to you? After all, as children you learned to focus on the two groups of organisms you can easily see: plants and animals.

Children are not alone in this way of thinking. From the days of Aristotle to the mid-1800s, almost everyone was content with this simple subdivision. They called the two major groups of plants and animals "kingdoms." By the middle of the 19th century, however, some scientists had started to question whether single-celled organisms and fungi really fit well with either the plant kingdom or the animal kingdom. Despite these questions, suggestions to increase the number of major groups were largely ignored. It was not until the 1960s that the prevailing attitude in the scientific community began to change. Scientists were discovering new forms of life and were using new microscopic and biochemical techniques to examine cell structure and function in even well-known organisms. This led to an increasing amount of evidence that supported proposals, beginning in 1968, to increase the number of major groups to

five: bacteria (also called kingdom Monera), protists, animals, plants, and fungi.

Maybe you learned about the five-kingdom system in the past. Take a look at figure 3.40. Which of the two groupings (three domain or five kingdom) best identifies natural clades within the giant tree of life?

Near 1980, new data convinced many biologists that archaea were very distinct from bacteria. The prokaryote "kingdom" did not form a natural group. The archaea are more closely related to eukaryotes than they are to other bacteria. Genetic data also showed that the protists, animals, plants, and fungi weren't as distinct from one another as they would appear. This spurred

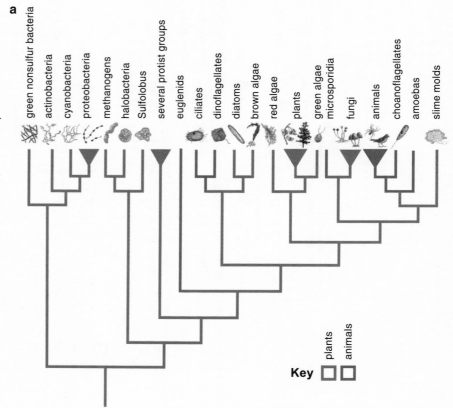

Figure 3.40   Scientific ideas change across time. (*a*) The first attempts to categorize life resulted in a two-kingdom division between plants and animals. (*b*) Scientists developed a four-kingdom scheme when they realized the great differences between eukaryotes and prokaryotes. (*c*) The five-kingdom system is currently the most familiar to students and teachers today, although it was recently replaced by the three-domain system. Are all the kingdoms natural groups or clades?

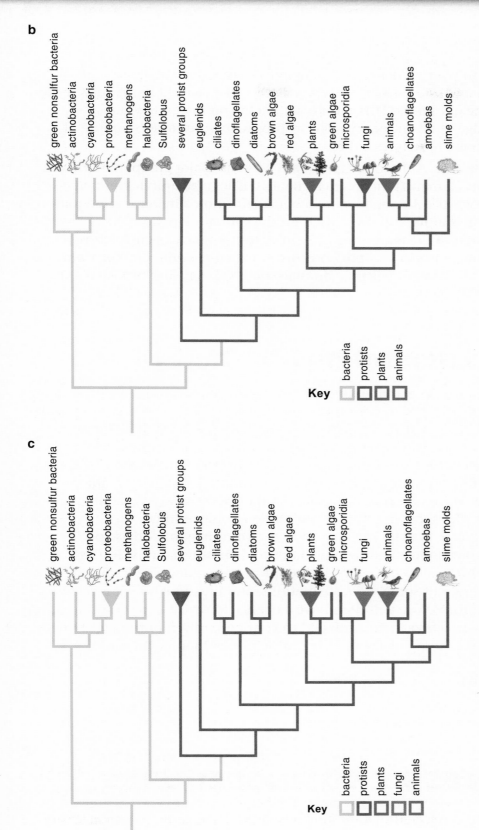

b

green nonsulfur bacteria
actinobacteria
cyanobacteria
proteobacteria
methanogens
halobacteria
Sulfolobus
several protist groups
euglenids
ciliates
dinoflagellates
diatoms
brown algae
red algae
plants
green algae
microsporidia
fungi
animals
choanoflagellates
amoebas
slime molds

Key bacteria protists plants animals

c

green nonsulfur bacteria
actinobacteria
cyanobacteria
proteobacteria
methanogens
halobacteria
Sulfolobus
several protist groups
euglenids
ciliates
dinoflagellates
diatoms
brown algae
red algae
plants
green algae
microsporidia
fungi
animals
choanoflagellates
amoebas
slime molds

Key bacteria protists plants fungi animals

the development of the three-domain system. Figure 3.40 illustrates the earlier classification schemes. These ideas will help you trace the changes that have occurred in scientists' thinking to bring us to the three-domain system that is the standard today.

Scientists are continually rethinking the classification system as they continue to learn more about the organisms that inhabit Earth. For example, birds are traditionally classified in the class Aves, as you learned in the need to know, *Levels of Classification*. Reptiles are traditionally classified as a separate class, Reptilia. However, evolutionary studies clearly show birds are a group *within* the reptiles. In fact, dinosaurs are more closely related to birds than they are to other reptiles. Because biologists strive to describe natural groups, or clades, of organisms, there are proposals to change the classification level of birds. This is a great example of the nature of science— claims of relationships change as more evidence is gathered.

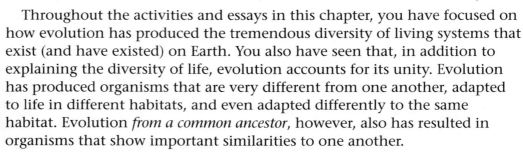

Further Challenges

Refer to your work from the chapter 1 Elaborate activity, *How Similar Are We?*, and the sidebar, *Changing Views of the Tree of Life,* to answer the following questions. This activity will help you integrate your knowledge of evolutionary relationships with your understanding of the unifying principles of life.

1. How does evolution help explain why the major groups of organisms share so many fundamental characteristics (the unifying principles)?
2. Why is the 3-domain system of classification a better representation of life's unity and diversity than the earlier 5-kingdom system?
3. Which of the 6 unifying principles seem to have been most useful to biologists in grouping organisms into the 4 different kingdoms within domain Eukarya (animals, plants, fungi, and protists)? Explain your answer.

First Encounter with the Critter

Throughout the activities and essays in this chapter, you have focused on how evolution has produced the tremendous diversity of living systems that exist (and have existed) on Earth. You also have seen that, in addition to explaining the diversity of life, evolution accounts for its unity. Evolution has produced organisms that are very different from one another, adapted to life in different habitats, and even adapted differently to the same habitat. Evolution *from a common ancestor*, however, also has resulted in organisms that show important similarities to one another.

This Evaluate activity invites you to use your imagination as you evaluate your understanding of evolution in an unusual way. In *First Encounter with the Critter*, you will "adopt" a critter, describe it, make hypotheses about some of its adaptations, and illustrate how it is related to other organisms. You will then have a chance to revisit your critter in units 2–6. During each visit, you will add to your description of the organism as your understanding of the unifying principles of biology increases.

Materials (per person)

1 habitat card
1 environmental change card

PROCESS AND PROCEDURES

1. Read the scenario, *Keep Your Eyes Open.* Then study the habitat card that describes where you are going. Draw a sketch of what you imagine the habitat looks like and label several important features. Write down a detailed description of the habitat you will be visiting.

SCENARIO

Keep Your Eyes Open

It was a thrill to hear that the research funds came through. Now you can embark on your long-awaited trip into the wilderness to observe and record data about several endangered species.

The conservation organization that is sponsoring your trip has assigned you to a team that will spend several weeks in one location. The organization has given you a list of organisms that you should observe. As a born naturalist, however, you are determined to keep your eyes open for whatever you find of interest.

Since this will be an ongoing project for the next few weeks, you will be recording facts about your "critter" in a folder separate from your science notebook.

2. Choose 1 of the multicellular organisms that lives in this habitat and adopt it. Then determine its scientific name. Write down its scientific name in large lettering. If it has a common name, write that down as well.

Your teacher may suggest some resources to help you consider the diversity of life in your habitat as you decide which critter to adopt. He or she will also help you research an organism's scientific name. You may be asked to adopt a critter from a particular group, in order to allow the class's projects to best represent the diversity of life.

3. Describe your organism by drawing 1 or more diagrams of it. Include labels with brief descriptions of its distinctive structures.

Remember that your critter is a member of a group of critters at the genus or family level. If you feel there is not enough information about your species of critter, use information about its genus or family to help you describe it.

It is also OK to use your imagination along with logic to describe your critter. For example, if your critter is the only member of its genus to live in an extremely cold environment, you should examine your critter carefully and think about the kinds of adaptations that it may have evolved to survive in this environment.

Remember, your description of the critter in this activity is the evidence that your teacher will use to evaluate what you have learned about evolution, biological diversity, and the unity of life.

4. Write a paragraph about the adaptations you labeled on your critter drawing. Select 1 adaptation as an example and describe your understanding of how scientists would explain how adaptations arise in a population.

   It is important to include all the necessary steps and requirements for the evolution of an adaptation.

5. Write a second paragraph describing a scientifically reasonable scenario by which your critter may have diverged from an ancestral species to form a new species.

6. Write a third paragraph that explains the characters that make your critter a member of its domain, kingdom, and phylum (or division). Then list at least 3 characteristics that your critter shares with *all* other forms of life.

   As you complete this task, you may want to review the notes and table you made about the unifying principles of life in the chapter 1 Elaborate activity, *How Similar Are We?*

© Dreamstime/Stormboy

7. Obtain an environmental change card from your teacher. Write down the environmental change in your science notebook. Then write a fourth paragraph predicting what might happen to your critter's species as a result of this change. If you predict that it will go extinct, explain how this may affect the evolution of other species. You may want to use the following terms in your explanation:
   • Natural selection
   • Extinction
   • Adaptation
   • Variation
   • Heritable

8. Obtain a *First Encounter with the Critter Rubric* from your teacher that explains the grading criteria for your critter. Read the rubric carefully. Use it as a checklist to be certain that you have described your critter effectively.

   You will know that you have generated a good description if it meets the following criteria:
   • It describes how your organism resembles all known forms of life.
   • It describes how your organism is adapted to the habitat in which you found it.
   • It identifies how your species is related to other organisms, and it describes the evidence on which you base your answer.

Analysis

Which of the following 2 statements is most consistent with scientists' understanding of the process of evolution, and why? What is wrong with the other statement? Record your responses in your science notebook.

© Dreamstime/Darksidephotos

- Statement 1: "The habitat that I worked in is very wet and salty. My critter has a common ancestor that evolved a rubberlike skin because it wanted to keep from shriveling up."
- Statement 2: "The habitat that I worked in is very wet and salty. My critter evolved a rubberlike skin because this trait provides protection from the harmful effects of all that salt."

Further Challenges

Put your critter into a broader perspective by constructing an evolutionary tree that includes examples of organisms from across the tree of life.

1. Create an evolutionary tree that illustrates the relationships between your critter and the following organisms that have appeared in unit 1.
   - **a.** *Sulfolobus acidcaldarius*
   - **b.** Fly agaric mushroom
   - **c.** Painted turtle
   - **d.** *Homo sapiens*
   - **e.** *Lycopodium* moss
   - **f.** Hooded oriole
   - **g.** Click beetle
   - **h.** *Escherichia coli*
   - **i.** Tube sponge
   - **j.** Reef shark
   - **k.** *Fuligo septica*
   - **l.** Cane toad
   - **m.** Volvox

   You may find example evolutionary trees to help you with this task. See, for example, figure 3.39 in the essay, *Changing Views of the Tree of Life*, and figure 3.35 in the essay, *Organizing Diversity*.

2. Add the following characters in the appropriate places on your evolutionary tree.
   - **a.** Multicellularity
   - **b.** Flowers
   - **c.** External digestion
   - **d.** Cells with membrane-enclosed compartments
   - **e.** Backbone
   - **f.** Amniotic egg
   - **g.** Four legs
   - **h.** External skeleton

Your body is constantly working to maintain a balanced, functioning state. Under normal conditions, this balancing act is an intricate, dynamic process that your body takes care of with little conscious effort. Think of a skier gliding over the water. Not only does she balance on the edge of her ski, but her body also maintains a balance in other, less obvious ways. Although cool water surrounds her, her body temperature remains within a relatively narrow range. As she exerts energy to maintain her balance over rough water or to hold her position in a curve, her heart and breathing rates also adjust to bring more oxygen to the cells of her body. In addition to temperature and oxygen levels,

her body continuously balances numerous other factors to keep them all within healthy limits. The skier's body is working to maintain a balanced internal environment. Her body is maintaining homeostasis.

In unit 2, *Homeostasis: Maintaining Dynamic Equilibrium in Living Systems*, you will examine some of the processes involved in maintaining balance in the human body. You will consider the components of the human body that allow the regulation of internal conditions. You also will apply what you have learned to study how the human body reacts when this balance is disrupted significantly.

UNIT 2

Homeostasis:
Maintaining Dynamic Equilibrium in Living Systems

By the end of unit 2, you should be able to understand that

✔ All organisms, organ systems, and cells are affected by interactions between their internal and external environments;

✔ Organisms' internal systems maintain a dynamic balance called *homeostasis;*

✔ Stressors may overwhelm the ability of organisms to maintain homeostasis; and

✔ Behaviors and physiological responses help maintain homeostasis.

You also will learn to

✔ write a hypothesis,

✔ design a controlled experiment,

✔ develop an explanation, and

✔ perform ethical analyses.

UNIT CONTENTS

4 The Internal Environment of Organisms

5 Maintaining Balance in Organisms

6 Human Homeostasis: Health and Disease

The Internal Environment of Organisms

*Kathryn C. Thornton, pictured here servicing the Hubble Space Telescope, logged over 975 hours in space, including more than 21 hours space walking.

My view of earth through the helmet visor was truly spectacular. At one point during a spacewalk as we were flying over the Gulf of Mexico, I could see both the east and west coasts of the United States, and at the same time I saw the aurora borealis over Canada. I wanted to breathe in the view so that it would become a part of me and I would never forget.

Kathryn C. Thornton*

What NASA spent millions of dollars to develop, your body does for free. Consider the importance of a space suit for astronauts who venture into space to retrieve a satellite. A space suit serves as an effective barrier between the extremely cold and airless external environment of space and the internal environment within the space suit. Without a barrier between the external and internal environments, people in space would die. Living organisms must maintain certain conditions within their bodies to stay alive.

Astronauts in space must consciously take care of the differences between their external and internal environments. The rest of us, however, usually pay little attention to these differences. As long as we eat and dress appropriately, complex systems inside our bodies constantly monitor and adjust to maintain the balance of conditions necessary to stay alive. A variety of processes maintain homeostasis. In this chapter, you will explore different systems in the human body—from the level of the cell to the body as a whole—to learn how the body maintains an internal balance.

The chapter organizer helps you remember what you have learned and where you are headed. It also helps you recognize the most important concepts to learn in a chapter. Look at the chapter organizer every day. Think about where you are in the chapter. Compare what you know now with what you knew a week ago. Let the chapter organizers help you map your learning and monitor your progress. That way, you can look back and see what you have accomplished.

GOALS FOR THE CHAPTER

Throughout chapter 4, *The Internal Environment of Organisms*, you will work to gain an understanding of the following concepts:

✔ The internal environment of living things interacts with the external environment.

✔ Living organisms have different levels of compartmentalization, which maintains boundaries between internal and external environments.

✔ Cells, tissues, organs, and organ systems have multiple ways to restore normal internal conditions.

✔ A reliable experiment must include controls.

✔ Scientists form explanations by combining evidence and reasoning to justify a claim.

To help you develop these understandings, you will complete the following activities.

ENGAGE	Can You Stand the Heat?
EXPLORE	Cells in Action
EXPLAIN	A Cell Model
EXPLAIN / ELABORATE	Regulating the Internal Environment
EVALUATE	Can You Stand the Heat—Again?

Can You Stand the Heat?

Key Idea: Organisms respond to the external environment.

Linking Question:
What parts of organisms respond to the external environment?

Chapter 4

MAJOR CONCEPTS

✔ The internal environment of living things interacts with the external environment.

✔ Living organisms have different levels of compartmentalization, which maintains boundaries between internal and external environments.

✔ Cells, tissues, organs, and organ systems have multiple ways to restore normal internal conditions.

✔ A reliable experiment must include controls.

✔ Scientists form explanations by combining evidence and reasoning to justify a claim.

 EXPLORE

Cells in Action

Part A: An Eggs-periment
Part B: Observing Cell Activity
Key Idea: Cells can respond to changes in the external environment.

Linking Question:
How do different substances move in and out of cells?

 EXPLAIN

A Cell Model

Key Idea: Substances move across cell membranes in different ways, including by osmosis, diffusion, facilitated diffusion, and active transport.

Can You Stand the Heat—Again?

Key Idea: Water balance in humans is an example of homeostasis and is maintained by the interaction of the body's systems and the individual's behavior.

The Internal Environment of Organisms

Linking Question:
How do the processes of osmosis, diffusion, and exchange apply to the whole human body?

 EXPLAIN 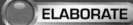 ELABORATE

Regulating the Internal Environment

Part A: Circulatory System
Part B: Making Exchanges

Key Idea: Cells of the circulatory and urinary systems exchange a number of substances between the internal and external environments.

Linking Question:
How are the processes that take place in cells important to larger systems of the body?

 ENGAGE

Can You Stand the Heat?

It's a scorching summer day. Getting out of the hot sun and into the shade seems like the natural thing to do. On a blustery winter day, seeking shelter in a warm house seems an obvious way to restore physical comfort. Even the family pets exhibit similar behaviors to minimize stressful external conditions. Seeking shelter from extreme heat or cold is an example of a behavioral response to help relieve stress placed on the body by the external environment. Are there other ways your body works to maintain its internal environment in the face of external stresses? As you complete this Engage activity, *Can You Stand the Heat?*, you will begin to answer this question. In the activities that follow, you will develop a more complete understanding of how the body maintains its internal environment.

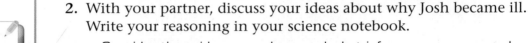

PROCESS AND PROCEDURES

1. Read the scenario, *Tougher Than the Sun?*, to yourself.
2. With your partner, discuss your ideas about why Josh became ill. Write your reasoning in your science notebook.

   Consider the evidence you have and what inferences you can make about how Josh's body responded to external stresses. You may wish to make a two-column table of evidence and inferences to keep track of your reasoning.

Analysis

1. As a class, develop answers to the following questions.
   a. What stresses from the external environment did Josh's body (his internal environment) have to balance?
   b. How did the choices that Josh made affect how his body was being stressed by the external environment?
   c. What symptoms did Maggie show that were evidence that her body (her internal environment) was under stress from the conditions outdoors (her external environment)?
2. Brainstorm a list of 4 terms or concepts that relate to ways that organisms maintain a stable internal environment, even when the external environment is changing. Work with your partner. In your science notebook, write the reasons why you chose these terms.

   To come up with terms, you might think about the following. How does the body respond to external stress? Which external stresses does the body need to manage? What are important materials that the body needs to keep in balance?
3. Contribute your list to a class concept map that shows what you currently understand about how organisms maintain internal balance, or homeostasis.

Tougher Than the Sun?

How much heat can you take? How does your body respond to the stress of a hot summer day, especially if you are involved in demanding physical activity? Perhaps you have experienced something like this and would not make the same mistake that Josh made . . .

Josh had just graduated from college in Minnesota and was visiting his parents in central Texas. He was planning to surprise his parents, who would be gone all day, by clearing a large area of brush in preparation for a barn they wanted to build.

As his parents drove off, Josh loaded the pickup truck with the gear he needed for the job. Their dog, Maggie, wanted to come along, so Josh let her hop in the truck. This June day was already hot. The temperature climbed past 35°C (95°F) by late morning.

Josh began the job enthusiastically. He started clearing brush, digging up sharp-spined cacti and raking debris. Even though he worked up a sweat, the small brush and cacti were no match for his muscles and tools. He thought that he could clear the entire area with one day of hard work, finishing before his parents returned.

After two hours had passed, Josh could see that the job might be bigger than he originally thought. This environment was about as hot as he

had ever worked in. His shirt was soaked with sweat, and he kept having to wipe drips away from his eyes. He was grateful for the liter bottle of ice-cold juice that he had brought. He drank often, although he kept reminding himself to conserve and make it last for the day. Maggie was obviously hot, too. She tried to find a spot of shade. She lay on the ground panting. Josh was sorry he hadn't thought to bring water along for the dog. He vowed that he and Maggie would get plenty to drink when they got back to the house. But first, he wanted to finish the job he started.

By midafternoon, Josh was out of juice. He noticed that his mouth was extremely dry. He wanted to stay and finish the work but decided that he should drive back to the house and get something more to drink. As Josh opened the kitchen door, Maggie eagerly ran to her dog dish and lapped up all the water in it. Josh opened the refrigerator to look for a refreshing beverage. The first thing he spotted were cans of a popular energy drink. He saw on the back of the can that it contained 300 mL of water, caffeine, sugar, vitamins, and minerals. He helped himself to one can and then another. Josh changed into a dry shirt and sat for a while in the air-conditioned house to cool down; then he drank one more can of energy drink. He refilled Maggie's dish with water, made a bathroom stop, and then headed back out to the truck. "Those energy drinks sure went through me fast," Josh thought as he drove back to the work site. Because he had less than an hour's work left, he didn't take anything along to drink.

Josh quickly worked up a sweat in the blazing afternoon sun. After half an hour, he experienced some dizziness and a faint touch of nausea. Nothing much, he decided. Besides, he would be quitting shortly. Soon, however, he noticed a pounding in his head and some changes in his vision. Instead of seeing in sharp color, Josh began to feel as though his world was slowly becoming black and white. His muscles ached, and he suddenly felt very tired. His dizziness increased so that he had a difficult time driving the pickup back to the house.

Josh's parents returned at the same time that he pulled into the yard. Josh collapsed on the couch, and his father brought him a big glass of water and a cool washcloth. Later, when Josh explained what had happened, his parents were pleased to hear about the work he had done, but they were not surprised by his condition . . .

Cells in Action

"A box without hinges, key, or lid, yet golden treasure inside is hid."*

Do you know the identity of the box in this riddle? Imagine the contents of boxes or containers that hold all sorts of treasures. While you might not think of an egg yolk as a "golden treasure," if you were a hungry hobbit, you might feel differently. Your body is another type of container that holds valuable contents. Think of the human body as a container with an inside environment that is different from the outside environment. This can help you understand what happened to Josh in the scenario, *Tougher Than the Sun?*

Because the human body is a large and complicated container, it can be difficult to study in detail. Let's begin to study it by examining cells, which are smaller containers within living systems. One way to study cells is to compare their contents to what is outside of them. In this Explore activity, *Cells in Action*, you will study several types of cells. You will place cells into different external environments and observe how they respond. Through scientific inquiry, you will begin to explore how cells maintain an internal environment that is different from the external environment.

*Tolkien, J. R. R. (1966). *The Hobbit.* Boston: Houghton Mifflin.

Materials

Part A (per team of 4)

4 pairs of safety goggles	4 pairs of gloves
4 lab aprons	3 500-mL beakers
1 balance	300-mL of corn syrup solution
300-mL of distilled water	300-mL of vinegar
specimen dishes	plastic wrap
coffee filters	1 slotted spoon
paper towels	different-colored pens or pencils

3 shell-less eggs in a beaker or bowl of vinegar

Part B (per team of 2)

2 pairs of safety goggles	microscope slide and coverslip
dropping pipet	forceps
compound microscope	dissecting needle with cork on the tip
scalpel	5% salt solution in dropping bottle
onion wedge	distilled water
online resource	paper towels

PROCESS AND PROCEDURES

Part A   An Eggs-periment

How big is a cell? Most cells are so small that you need a microscope to see them. But there are exceptions. A chicken egg is actually a single cell, although it is an unusually large one. It is protected by a hard shell that surrounds several soft membranes that you can see when you peel a hard-boiled egg. Placing an unfertilized chicken egg in an acetic acid (vinegar) solution for three days causes the calcium in the hard shell to dissolve. What remains is a fragile chicken egg surrounded by a soft membrane. This membrane separates the internal environment of the egg from its external environment. Even though the cells (the eggs) that you will be working with are not capable of growing into a chicken, you can study how the membrane acts as a barrier, creating a compartment (the eggs).

© Dreamstime/Edyta Pawlowska

1. Work with your partner to describe the internal environment of an egg. How is it different from the external environment? In your science notebook, record several differences.

    Title a new page of your science notebook "eggs-periment" and keep a running record of all work for this activity. You may already know that cells often contain a nucleus. Located inside the blastodisc on top of the yolk, the nucleus of a chicken egg is barely visible. (Do not confuse the egg yolk with the nucleus.) Compare figures 4.1 and 4.2, which illustrate a generalized animal cell and a chicken egg.

Figure 4.1
Generalized animal cell. All eukaryotic cells contain smaller functional parts called organelles. This is true for the cells of all protists, plants, fungi, and animals. The nucleus is one organelle. Do you recognize it in this animal cell? Can you name others?

Figure 4.2 This illustration shows the anatomy of a chicken egg.

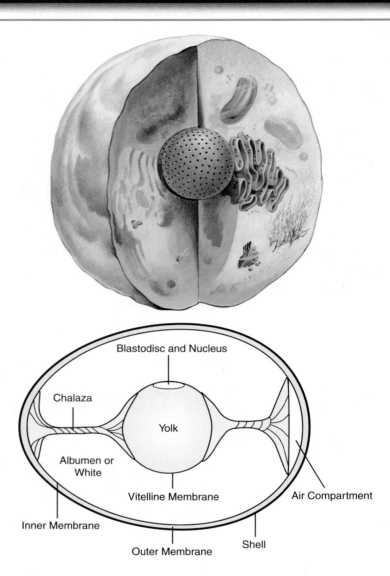

Blastodisc and Nucleus

Chalaza

Yolk

Albumen or White

Vitelline Membrane

Air Compartment

Inner Membrane

Outer Membrane

Shell

2. Observe the shell-less chicken egg that your teacher displays. With your partner, write 3 questions about what might happen if you were to place the shell-less chicken egg in a different external environment than it is in now.

Write questions that you might be able to test in your classroom. One way to change the egg's external environment is to place it in a beaker containing a solution. Distilled water and a corn syrup solution are two available resources you can use to test a question.

3. With your partner, choose a testable question from the ones you wrote in step 2. You will test this question in your eggs-periment. Discuss and write down ideas for how you might test this question within the guidelines of *The Eggs-periment Protocol*.

For help developing your testable question, see the need to know, *Testable Questions*, in the chapter 1 Explore activity, *Primates Exploring Primates*. Notice that *The Eggs-periment Protocol* does not include all the details you need to run an experiment. This is because you will

PROTOCOL

PROTOCOL

The Eggs-periment Protocol

1. Soak enough eggs in vinegar to provide 3 eggs per team. Soak the eggs for 3 days to remove the shells.
   a. Place the eggs in a beaker or specimen dish and add enough vinegar to cover them. Cover the container loosely with plastic wrap. The acid in the vinegar will dissolve the calcium carbonate in the shells. The reaction will release bubbles of carbon dioxide.
   b. After 24 hours, carefully remove the eggs using a slotted spoon. Wear gloves during this step. Pour off the used vinegar into a sink and replace with fresh. Repeat on the third day.
   c. ***Wash your hands thoroughly with soap and water after handling eggs.***

2. Very carefully remove any remaining shell from each egg.
   a. Wearing gloves, use the slotted spoon to remove each egg from the vinegar. ***Do not touch the eggs with your bare hands.***
   b. Carefully transfer an egg to your gloved hands. Gently hold the shell-less egg under warm running water while you carefully rub the softened shell with your gloved finger. This will remove any small patches of softened shell on your eggs.

   > Shell-less eggs are very delicate. Normally, both the shell and the membranes act as barriers between the egg's internal and external environments. All of the shell must be removed to be certain that you are only testing how the membranes create a compartment. Shell-less eggs should appear almost transparent, with no areas of opaque white remaining.

3. Measure the mass of each shell-less egg before the experiment begins.
   a. Before measuring and recording the mass of a shell-less egg, rinse it under running water. Then carefully blot the egg with a paper towel to dry it thoroughly.
   b. Use a coffee filter to hold each egg as you measure its mass.

4. Record other data about each shell-less egg (like its firmness, color, length, and texture).

5. Place each of your team's shell-less eggs into different external environments.

6. **Wash your hands thoroughly with soap and water after working with eggs.** Eggs may contain the bacteria *Salmonella*, which can cause gastrointestinal illness.

7. Wait at least 30 minutes.

8. Wearing gloves, remove each shell-less egg from its environment using a slotted spoon. Rinse off your shell-less egg if necessary, then measure its mass as you did in step 3.

9. Record other data about each shell-less egg as needed.

10. **Wash your hands thoroughly with soap and water after working with eggs.**

design the specifics of your experiment in order to best answer your testable question. By reading this protocol, you will become familiar with the materials you have to work with and can start to think of ideas for an experiment that might use these materials.

4. With your partner, design a controlled experiment to test your question. Your experimental design must:
   a. include all of the steps in *The Eggs-periment Protocol*,
   b. specify which kinds of data you will record about your shell-less eggs,
   c. specify the external environments that you will place your shell-less eggs into,
   d. describe which egg will be "the control" and why a control is needed, and
   e. specify how long your eggs will stay in their external environments.

   Read the need to know, *Background on Controlled Experiments*, to learn about how to include a control.

5. In your science notebook, write down the step-by-step experimental design that you and your partner have agreed upon. Review what you wrote to make sure it includes the specifics listed in step 4.

6. Create a table in your science notebook, similar to the one in figure 4.3, to record your predictions.

Figure 4.3 Sample Predictions table. In your science notebook, record your predictions and the types of observations you plan to make in a table like this one.

External conditions for the egg	Predicted change	Reason for prediction	Type of observation

Background on Controlled Experiments

The process of science includes asking questions, gathering information, and proposing explanations. In chapter 1, *The Human Animal*, you learned about asking testable questions. In this chapter, you will focus on designing controlled experiments to gather information about testable questions.

Often, scientists want to understand how some factor or event influences a living system. So they test that factor in an experiment that focuses on one measurable or observable aspect of their question. For the evidence to be meaningful, the scientists must control (keep constant) all factors—other than the one being tested—that could affect the results of the experiment. By controlling all other conditions, scientists can be more sure their experiment will answer the question they are asking. They will know that the effects they see result from the one factor they are testing.

For example, imagine you want to ask the question, "What effect does fertilizer have on houseplant growth?" You could design a controlled experiment to answer that question. First, you would identify all the factors that might affect the plant's growth. These factors are called **variables**. Possible variables for houseplants include the location of the plants, amount of water they get, type of plants selected, type and amount of soil they are in, and type and amount of light they receive.

To test the effectiveness of the fertilizer, you would need to choose at least two plants of the same type (like two bean plants) and control as many variables as possible. Place them in 250 g of potting soil from a new bag, in identical clay pots, on the same windowsill. Then water each at the same time with the same amount of water. But add fertilizer to one plant only. The plant without fertilizer would be called the **control**.

Scientists systematically test each variable and the interactions among the variables. They repeat their experiments multiple times. This approach increases the scientists' confidence in the results and helps them develop more complete explanations.

Topic: scientific investigation
Code: human4E217

7. Work with your partner to predict how you think the egg will react to your control condition. Fill in a row of your table with your control prediction and the reasons for your prediction.

8. Predict how you think an egg will react to the condition(s) that you will vary in your experiment. Fill in your table with at least 3 predictions and your reasoning for them.

> You will compare your results to these predictions after you complete the experiment. Your results will indicate whether the internal environments of the eggs have changed as a result of the external conditions you expose them to.

9. Discuss and decide whether each prediction you made involves *quantitative* or *qualitative* observation. Record your decision under the column "type of observation."

> Quantitative observations involve results that can be measured with standard scales (mass in grams or temperature in degrees Celsius, for example). Think of *quantity*—something that you measure—as part of quantitative.

> Qualitative observations involve verbal descriptions and results that can be measured with nonstandard scales (color or temperature described as "warm" or "cold," for example). Think of *quality*—the nature of something that you observe—as part of qualitative.

10. Review your experimental design with another team by using the TSAR strategy. Does your plan include steps to make observations that will allow you to test your predictions? If not, change your steps, using a different-colored pen or pencil, after consulting with your partner.

> For more information about using the TSAR strategy, see appendix B3, *How to Use the Think-Share-Advise-Revise (TSAR) Strategy*.

HOW TO

11. Review your *Predictions* table with your teacher and obtain approval of your experimental design. Then conduct your experiment.

> For more information about how to make a table to record your results, refer to appendix B4, *How to Use and Create Organizing Tables*.

HOW TO

SAFETY: Put on your safety goggles, gloves, and lab apron.

12. Enter your results in the class's data table when your experiment is complete. Participate in a class discussion of the data.

> Report your actual results; resist the temptation to change your results if they do not match your classmates' data.

13. Discuss the following questions with your partner and record your answers in your science notebook.
   a. What changes did you find, if any, in the internal environments of your eggs? Did your observations match your predictions? Support your answer by using specific evidence from your observations.
   b. Why is it useful to combine data from the entire class?
   c. You began this experiment to answer a question about what happens when a shell-less egg (or cell) is exposed to a different external environment. Write a sentence, or claim, that answers your question.

Your claim should make an assertion or conclusion that addresses the original question or problem. This may be in the form of a statement of trend, behavior, or generality. The claim should be based on the evidence you or the class found.

d. Now that you have made a claim, write a sentence explaining the reasons why you think your evidence helps answer your question.

Reasoning explains how your claim is connected to your evidence. For example, imagine you want to claim to your parents that your sister ate all the marshmallows. Your evidence is the empty marshmallow bag in the wastebasket in her room. You might back up your claim with the reason that you think she came home from school hungry and saw the marshmallows lying on the counter, so she ate them.

Part B Observing Cell Activity

In part A of this activity (*An Eggs-periment*), you explored the concept that cells function somewhat like containers, separating internal contents from an external environment. You put cells (eggs) in different solutions and observed the effect of those solutions on the cells. You discovered that the external environment affects cells. In this way, cells are different from most containers we use to hold things. Because the external environment affects cells, scientists use special terms to describe it with respect to the internal environment of cells. In part B, *Observing Cell Activity*, you will observe microscopic cells responding to changes in their environment.

1. With your class, read and discuss the need to know, *Background about Solutions*.
2. Turn to the *Predictions* table that you developed in your science notebook during part A. In the column "external conditions for the egg," label each entry with 1 of the following terms: "isotonic solution," "hypotonic solution," or "hypertonic solution."
3. Create a table with 3 columns in your science notebook. Label the columns "isotonic," "hypertonic," and "hypotonic." You will use this table to record your observations about cells in the video segment, "Blood Cells in Solution."

    This video segment illustrates the behavior of animal cells in different solutions.

4. View the video segment, "Blood Cells in Solution," with your class. Record your observations in your table.
5. To observe the responses of plant cells, prepare a wet mount slide of onion skin by following these steps (figure 4.5).
    a. Remove 1 layer from an onion wedge.
    b. Snap the layer backward.

    This should expose the edges of several smaller layers.

    c. Use forceps to separate a piece of the transparent, tissue-thin layer from the inside of the original layer.

SCiLINKS®
NSTA
www.scilinks.org
Topic: solutions
Code: human4E220

NEED TO KNOW

ENGLISH SPANISH

Background about Solutions

Solutions are uniform mixtures of two or more substances. They may be solids, liquids, gases, or a combination of these. The substances in a solution are classified as a **solute** or a **solvent** (see figure 4.4). The dissolved substance is called the *solute*. The substance that the solute is dissolved into is called the *solvent*. For example, when salt dissolves in water, salt is the solute and water is the solvent. In living systems, liquid water is frequently the solvent in a solution. Scientists often use special terms to describe how a solution compares to the internal environment of a cell placed in that solution.

An **isotonic** ("iso-" = "equal") solution provides an environment in which the concentration of solutes outside the cell equals the concentration of solutes inside.

A **hypertonic** ("hyper-" = "over") solution is one in which the concentration of solutes outside a cell is greater than the concentration inside.

A **hypotonic** ("hypo-" = "under") solution is one in which the concentration of solutes outside the cell is less than the concentration inside.

Can you think of other words that use the prefixes "iso-," "hyper-," and "hypo-" to describe something as the same, more than, or less than something else?

© Dreamstime/Eyewave

Figure 4.4 (*a*) *Solutions* are uniform mixtures of two or more substances. (*b*) The dissolved substance is called the *solute*. (*c*) The substance that the solute is dissolved into is called the *solvent*.

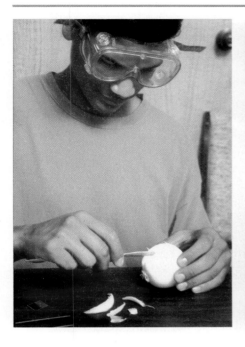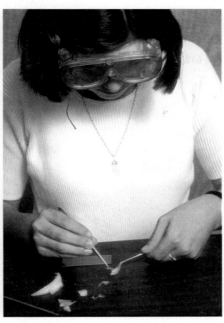

Figure 4.5
Preparing an onion skin specimen.

    d. Lay the piece flat on a clean microscope slide.

    e. As necessary, use the scalpel to trim the piece so that it will fit under a coverslip.

    f. Use a dissecting needle to smooth out any bubbles or wrinkles.

CAUTION: Scalpel blades and needles are sharp; handle with care. Replace cork on needle tip after use.

    g. Use the dropping pipet to add 1 or 2 drops of distilled water to the slide. Then place a coverslip over the piece of onion skin.

  6. Examine the onion skin under the low power of your microscope.

    Take turns observing the cells with your partner. For assistance with making a wet mount of onion skin and using the microscope, read appendix C1, *How to Use a Compound Microscope*.

  7. Switch to high power and focus sharply on a few cells. In your science notebook, make a detailed sketch of 1 cell.

  8. Test the effects of changing the external environment of the cells you are viewing. To do this, place a small piece of paper towel at one edge of the coverslip (see figure 4.6) to absorb some of the water. Then place several drops of 5% salt solution against the edge of the coverslip, opposite the paper towel.

  9. Observe what happens to the onion cells after adding salt solution. In your science notebook, record your observations and make a detailed sketch of 1 cell.

    You may need to repeat the step of removing some solution and adding more salt solution to your slide. Be sure to record how many drops of salt solution you added. Take turns observing the cells with your partner. Compare your onion cells with the generalized plant cell illustrated in figure 4.7.

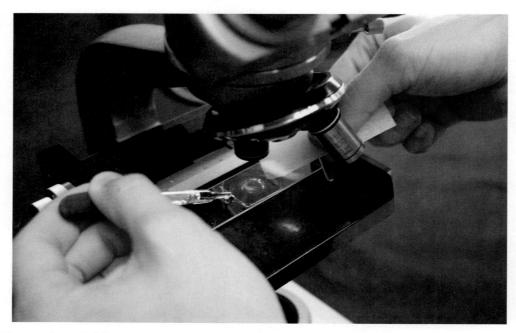

Figure 4.6   Adding solution to a wet mount slide.

10. Dilute the salt solution on the slide by adding distilled water. Hold a dry paper towel near the edge of the coverslip to remove the excess solution. Continue to add water until the cells return to their original condition. Make observations while you do this and record them in your science notebook.

Take turns observing these changes with your partner. Remember to record how much water you added.

Figure 4.7 Generalized plant cell. Plants are multicellular organisms. Their cells contain many of the same functional compartments, or organelles, that animal cells contain. One difference between plant and animal cells is the presence of an outer cell wall in addition to the cell membrane. The cell wall makes plant cells rigid and gives them a distinct shape.

11. Write highlight comments about what you see, and what you think it means, next to each sketch. Then write a caption for each of the cell sketches that you drew.

> For more information, see appendix B6, *How to Write Highlight Comments and Captions*.

Analysis

Discuss the following questions with your teammates. Then record your responses in your science notebook.

> The essay, *Compartments*, will be a helpful resource for this *Analysis* and for the next activity. You may also wish to review the information about scientific models in the need to know, *A Simple Mathematical Model* (chapter 2, *Evolution: Change across Time*, Explore activity, *Exploring Change*).

1. What evidence did you collect that indicates that a hypertonic external environment can affect a cell?

2. In this activity, how did the egg serve as a model of how cells function as containers in living organisms?

3. What do egg cells, plant cells, and the human body have in common?

4. Based on your observations of cells, what might have been happening in Josh's body in the scenario, *Tougher Than the Sun?*, when he did the following?
   a. First became hot and started to sweat
   b. Became thirsty
   c. Went to the house for refreshments
   d. Returned to work

Further Challenges

To learn more about how cell membranes function as a barrier and the way cells function as containers, look for internal structures in a fresh wet mount slide of an onion cell. A stain, such as Lugol's iodine solution, may make such structures more visible. Make sketches of what you observe and label all the compartments and boundaries.

WARNING: Lugol's iodine solution is a poison if ingested. It is a strong irritant and can stain clothing. Avoid skin and eye contact; do not ingest. If contact occurs, call the teacher immediately. Flush affected area with water for 15 minutes. If ingested, rinse mouth with water.

Compartments

How do you feel on a very cold day? If it is wet and windy outside, you might notice a cold sensation on your face. Your fingers and toes may become chilled or even a little numb. Yet if you pick up some snow and hold it in your bare hands, the snow melts. Your body is warmer than its snowy surroundings, even though your fingers and toes feel cold.

By contrast, what happens to your body on a very hot day? While you may feel hot and sweaty, your internal temperature does not vary much. In fact, if you compared your body's temperature under both the snowy and hot conditions, you would discover that your body maintains a fairly constant internal temperature.

How is it possible for your body to maintain an internal temperature that is very different from the external temperature? Part of the reason is that your body is a compartment, or container, with an internal environment that is kept separate from the external environment. You might think of all organisms as compartments with specialized contents that are held together and separated from their surroundings by external barriers. Think about how the wall of the thermos bottle in figure 4.8 helps to keep a hot beverage warm on a cold day.

Organisms and cells, like containers, have external boundaries. In humans, the skin separates the inside of the body from the outside environment. In single-celled organisms, the cell membrane (or cell wall) forms the boundary between the inside and outside environments. By forming a compartment, skin and cell membranes create conditions within the organism that may vary greatly from those on the outside.

Specific internal conditions must be met for life processes to take place in organisms. Temperature; water, mineral, nutrient, oxygen, and pH levels; and other balances must be maintained. For example, marine fishes are surrounded by water.

Figure 4.8 What do this sports fan and her thermos bottle have in common? How are they different?

Yet the water inside their bodies must be kept separate from the water that surrounds them. Why? Because seawater is much saltier than the fluids inside their bodies. The reverse is true of freshwater fishes. As you might expect, it is partly a fish's waterproof skin that allows the difference in salt levels to exist and allows the fish to live.

Complex organisms also may contain many smaller compartments, each with its own internal environment. Just as your skin separates the environment inside your body from the environment outside, the wall of your stomach separates the environment inside your stomach from the environment of the rest of your abdomen.

The same is true of plants. A form of compartmentalization can be seen in the network of veins that is embedded within a leaf (see figure 4.9a). These veins form separate compartments that connect to other tubular compartments in the stem. As figure 4.9b shows, microscopic examination reveals even smaller compartments.

Like humans and plants, most other complex organisms also have several levels of compartments. At the microscopic level, the basic unit

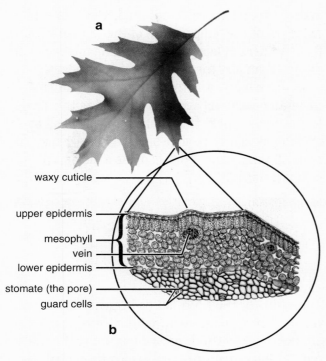

a

waxy cuticle

upper epidermis

mesophyll

vein

lower epidermis

stomate (the pore)

guard cells

b

Figure 4.9 (*a*) Notice the veins in this northern red oak (*Quercus borealis*) leaf. (*b*) A close-up view of a cutaway section of a leaf shows that the leaf is a large compartment made up of many smaller compartments, such as the epidermis and the veins.

of life is the cell. A cell is a compartment whose boundary is formed by a membrane. Some cells have an additional boundary called a **cell wall**. The cells of archaea and eubacteria consist of only one compartment, the cell itself. The cells of eukaryotic organisms contain smaller compartments called **organelles**. Many of these smaller compartments, as illustrated in figure 4.10, can only be seen with the aid of an electron microscope. One such subcellular compartment is the **nucleus**, which contains DNA. **DNA** is the genetic code for the organism.

What is the advantage of having so many compartments in living systems? Remember that all organisms require specific internal conditions for life processes to occur. The presence of many compartments within one cell or one organism

allows for the presence of many different internal environments. Each compartment can contain different substances that are required for specialized cellular functions. The environment within the nucleus, for example, provides the conditions required for DNA to perform its functions. In contrast, the environment within the **lysosome** (see figure 4.10) can kill invading bacteria and viruses. The environment in a human stomach is another example of a specialized environment. The pH of stomach fluid contents is much lower (more acidic) than the pH in the rest of the body. This pH difference is required for digestion to occur.

What would happen if conditions within compartments were to undergo a significant, lasting change? Changes beyond certain rather narrow limits can be dangerous to the organism. These changes disrupt the normal processes of life and can result in injuries, illnesses, and disease. Sometimes internal balance can be disrupted so severely that the organism dies.

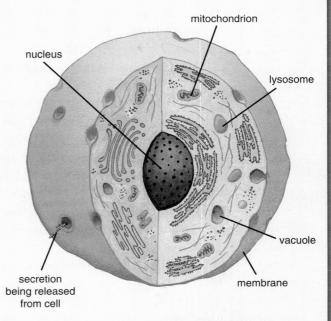

mitochondrion

nucleus

lysosome

vacuole

secretion being released from cell

membrane

Figure 4.10 The eukaryotic cell includes many internal compartments.

Think back for a moment to the sports fan and her thermos pictured in figure 4.8. The caption asks how the woman and her thermos are similar. Both the woman and her thermos are containers, or compartments, with outside boundaries. These boundaries allow the contents (in this case, their temperatures) to be different from their environments.

The caption also asked how the woman and her thermos are different. Consider what will happen to the temperature of the beverage in the thermos over time. In contrast, what prediction can you make about the temperature of the woman's body? Clearly, there is more to maintaining internal conditions than just the presence of a boundary.

In this chapter and the next, you will examine in detail how living systems respond to this challenge. And the next time you melt a snowball by gripping it tightly in your bare hand, perhaps you will think about your body as a biological compartment.

EXPLAIN

A Cell Model

You have been studying cell membranes, which act as boundaries separating the internal and external environments of cells. Boundaries exist in every organism, from the smallest cell to the largest plants and animals. In the last activity, you gathered evidence that materials can move in and out of cells. But though you experimented with different external environments for the cells, you could not directly manipulate the contents of the internal environments.

In this Explain activity, *A Cell Model*, you will construct your own cell models. You will use a synthetic material to simulate a cell membrane. These models will allow you to change both the internal and external environments. You will use several solutions to model these environments. In addition, you will have indicators to help you detect what substances can and cannot pass through the membrane. **Indicators** are chemicals that show the presence of certain chemicals. Using the models, you will continue your study of how cell boundaries affect the internal cellular environment. You will begin to answer the question, "How do materials move in and out of cells?" Your job is to develop an explanation, based on your observations of your model, of how boundaries help living systems maintain and regulate the conditions necessary for life.

Materials (per team of 2)

2 pairs of safety goggles
2 lab aprons
materials to carry out the experiment that you design
Osmosis in Cells and Organisms on the online resource

PROCESS AND PROCEDURES

1. In your science notebook, title a new page "a cell model." Below that, write the focus question for the activity.

   You will most often find the focus question for the activity in the introductory text for the activity or in *Process and Procedures*.

2. With your partner, read steps 1–5 of the *Process and Procedures* and review *Protocol for Making a Cell Model*. As you read, write down any ideas that may help you test the focus question in a controlled experiment.

3. Generate at least 2 specific testable questions about how materials move in and out of the cell (the focus question for the class).

   Consider the results that you found interesting from the eggs-periment in the Explore activity, *Cells in Action*. Choose questions that build on your experiences in that investigation. Your question must be testable using the materials available in your classroom.

4. With your partner, choose the testable question that you would like to investigate. Have your teacher approve your question.

PROTOCOL

PROTOCOL

Protocol for Making a Cell Model

For your cell models to work, the membrane must be the only barrier between the internal and the external environment (figure 4.11).

1. Rinse all lab equipment with water. Handle the internal and external solutions for your experiment carefully to reduce the chance of contamination.
2. Obtain a section of dialysis tubing. Securely tie 1 end of the tubing so that nothing can leak out of the knot.
3. Measure and record the amount of solution you will add to each cell model in your investigation.
4. Carefully pour the internal solution into your cell. Securely tie the open end of the tubing to prevent all leaking.
5. Rinse the outside of your cell models to be certain there is no internal solution present to contaminate the external environment.
6. Blot each cell model dry with a paper towel, and then record its initial mass.
7. After conducting your experiment, rinse, dry, and record the final mass of each cell model.

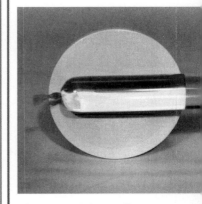

Figure 4.11 Cell model. Tie the ends of the dialysis tubing tightly so that nothing can leak in or out. Rinse off the outside of each cell model after it is constructed. This will minimize the risk of contamination.

5. With your partner, design an experiment to test the question you chose. Write each step in your science notebook. Make a sketch of each cell model you will set up. You should make at least 2 dialysis-tubing cell models to carry out your experiment. Your design must be safe, and it must use the following materials.
   a. Starch suspension or glucose solution
   b. Appropriate controls
   c. Appropriate indicators

   The need to know, *Cell Model Background Information*, may help you design your experiment.

6. Create a data table in your science notebook to summarize your experimental design and your predictions. Use the table in figure 4.12 as a model.

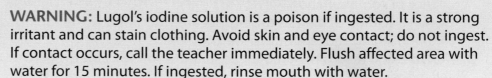

NEED TO KNOW

Cell Model Background Information

Dialysis tubing is a synthetic membrane made of a thin, cellophane-like material. Microscopic pores in dialysis tubing allow molecules smaller than a certain size to pass through the membrane.

Glucose is a simple sugar that dissolves readily in water.

Glucose test strips indicate the presence of glucose in solution by changing color. (Your teacher will give you information on how to interpret the color change.)

Lugol's iodine solution is an indicator that changes color from brown to blue black in the presence of starch. Use 1 drop of Lugol's iodine solution for every 1 mL of starch suspension.

WARNING: Lugol's iodine solution is a poison if ingested. It is a strong irritant and can stain clothing. Avoid skin and eye contact; do not ingest. If contact occurs, call the teacher immediately. Flush affected area with water for 15 minutes. If ingested, rinse mouth with water.

Starch is a complex molecule that forms a suspension in water. Starch turns blue black in the presence of Lugol's iodine solution.

The *size of a molecule* is an important characteristic that partially governs how the molecule behaves. Chemists have shown that all the molecules of a given substance are the same size. Molecules of different substances can vary significantly in size. In other words, all water molecules are the same size. But water molecules and glucose or starch molecules are not the same size.

Cell model	Contents of internal environment	Contents of external environment	Predicted change	Explanation for prediction
A				
B				

Figure 4.12
Sample table. A table like this one will help you record your plan and predictions.

7. Predict what will happen when you conduct the experiment. Record your predictions and your reasoning in the table you created in your science notebook.

8. Have your teacher approve your design before gathering the materials you need to carry out your experiment.

SAFETY: Put on your safety goggles and lab apron.

9. Set up your experiment. In your science notebook, sketch your "before" experimental setup and label each part. Leave room on the page to make a second, "after" sketch during the next class session.

10. Create another data table similar to the example in figure 4.12. Use this table to record your observations and results.

    For more information about designing tables, refer to appendix B4, *How to Use and Create Organizing Tables*. Make as many observations of your setup as possible and record all observations and results in your data table.

11. **Wash your hands thoroughly before leaving the laboratory.**

12. During the next class session, observe and sketch your setup again. Record your final observations and results in your data table.

13. **Wash your hands thoroughly and clean up your lab area as your teacher directs.**

14. Write highlight comments and captions next to your before-and-after experimental setup sketches. Be specific about what you saw change and what you think it means.

    For more information, see appendix B6, *How to Write Highlight Comments and Captions*.

15. Read appendix C4, *How to Develop an Explanation*. As you read, discuss each of the 5 parts with your partner.

16. Draw the *Explanation Template* in figure 4.13 into your science notebook. Complete it as follows.

    a. In the first row, write the specific question you were answering in this activity.

    b. In the first column, list the evidence you collected to help you answer the specific question. Add rows to the table as needed.

    c. Make a claim based on the evidence you have listed. Your claim should answer the specific question asked in the experiment.

    d. Explain your reasoning in the last column. Use "because" statements that connect your evidence and your claim.

Figure 4.13
Explanation Template.
Use this table as you
develop an explana-
tion of your experi-
mental results.

Question to answer:		
Evidence	**Claim(s)**	**Reason/Rationale**

Explanation:

_____ results in _____ because _____.
                                                   (evidence)   (my claim)
(reason/rationale)

Describe in these statements *why* you think the evidence supports
your claim.

    e. Finally, write a sentence that synthesizes all the information in
       your table. Use the sentence format in the Explanation section to
       construct your response.

17. Participate in a class discussion of the explanations that different
     teams developed for their experimental results.

18. Read the essays, *Membranes* and *Molecular Movement*. As you read, reflect
     on the explanation that you developed. Also enter the terms "selectively
     permeable," "diffusion," and "osmosis" in your personal glossary.

     For more information, see appendix B8, *How to Develop a Personal
     Glossary.*

Analysis

Complete these questions individually in your science notebook.

1. View the animation *Osmosis in Cells and Organisms* on the online resource.
    Sketch the diagrams into your science notebook and record the questions
    posed in the animation, along with your answers.

2. Describe how the shell-less egg and the dialysis-tubing cell model
    that you worked with in the last 2 activities are models of living cells
    in external environments. Show your understanding by making a
    table or diagram that shows what the different parts of each model
    represent about living cells or their environment.

     For more information on scientific models, see the need to know, *A
     Simple Mathematical Model* (chapter 2, *Evolution: Change Across Time,*
     Explore activity, *Exploring Change*).

3. Write your best answer to the question, "How do materials move in
    and out of cells?" Use evidence and reasoning from your cell models
    and the essays, *Membranes* and *Molecular Movement.*

4. Reflect on how you combined information from your cell model and
    the essays to answer question 3. Write down why using all available
    information to form explanations is important, in general, to science.

SCI LINKS®
NSTA

www.scilinks.org

Topic: function of the
    cell membrane
Code: human4E230

In some ways, a cell is like a carton of milk. The membrane around a cell is like the walls of the carton. The membrane forms a boundary that separates the *inside* of the cell from the *outside.* Like a carton of milk, a cell contains a fluid substance with a variety of molecules in it.

The cell membrane is more complicated, however, than the walls of a milk carton. The cell membrane lets *some* things pass through it. To act as an effective boundary, the membrane must prevent molecules from moving freely into or out of the cell. A membrane must be **impermeable** to most substances. In other words, the membrane must prevent most substances from being able to pass into or out of the compartment. Yet molecules that the cell needs for its activities (see figure 4.14) must somehow enter and exit the cell.

Because cell membranes are only **permeable** to certain molecules, they are said to be **selectively permeable**. A membrane's selective permeability (its ability to regulate the passage of molecules) depends on the structure of the membrane. As figure 4.15 shows, a typical cell membrane is made up primarily of fat, or lipid, molecules. The lipid molecules are not locked rigidly in place. They drift randomly in the plane of the membrane. An important property of lipid molecules is that they do not mix well with water. In the cell membrane, the lipid molecules are arranged into two layers (called the **lipid bilayer**). The parts of the lipid molecules that have the highest tendency to interact with water are oriented toward the outside and the inside of the cell. The parts of the lipid molecules with the lowest tendency to interact with water are oriented toward the interior of the membrane. The interior part of the membrane prevents molecules that are water soluble from passing easily through it. By contrast, fat-soluble molecules—like other fats—move through it with ease. Even though water molecules are not fat soluble, they can move through the membrane. This is because they are very small and their electrical charges are slight.

Type of molecule	Size	Building Blocks	Example functions in the body
Protein	Large	Amino acids	Enzymes break down food, build new molecules, and help "read" genetic information; Structural proteins make up many body parts; Proteins also carry materials, deliver signals, and receive signals
Carbohydrate	Large	Sugars	Storing energy
Fat (lipid)	Large	Fatty acids and glycerol	Storing energy; building cell membranes; sending signals
Nucleic acids	Large	Nucleic acids	Storing genetic information; carrying energy

Figure 4.14 Molecules of life. Proteins, carbohydrates, lipids, and nucleic acids are molecules that all living organisms use. Many of these molecules are large. Organisms also use a large number of smaller molecules and ions every day, including water, carbon dioxide, and oxygen (molecules), and sodium, potassium, and chloride (ions). Which of these substances do you think can pass through cell membranes?

Figure 4.15 shows that the membrane contains many protein molecules positioned among the lipid molecules. **Proteins** are large molecules made up of many smaller molecules (amino acids). These amino acids are linked together to form a long, folded chain. Some of these protein molecules, particularly those on the outer surface of the membrane, act as receptors. **Receptors** bind to specific molecules such as hormones. The hormones act as chemical messengers. By binding to their receptors on the external cell surface, hormones trigger a response inside the cell. In this way, a cell's internal components can respond to conditions outside the cell or body.

In addition to receptor proteins, cell membranes contain many other proteins. These proteins allow specific molecules to move into and out of the cell. In other words, some cell membrane proteins allow the membrane to be selectively permeable. For example, some proteins form channels through which glucose sugars and other carbohydrates move. Molecules like these are too big to pass directly through the lipid bilayer part of the membrane. The only way that they can enter the cell is through a specific protein channel.

Other proteins form channels through which **ions** (atoms or molecules that have an electrical charge) may pass. For example, dissolve table salt, NaCl, in water. It forms the ions Na^+ (sodium) and Cl^- (chloride). Ions like these are relatively small.

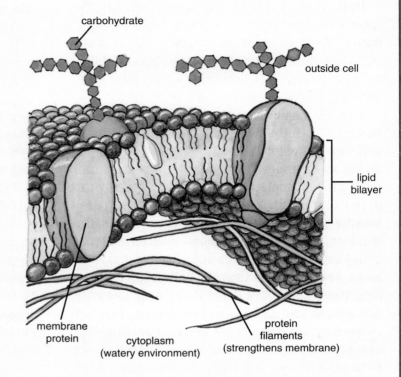

carbohydrate

outside cell

lipid bilayer

membrane protein

cytoplasm (watery environment)

protein filaments (strengthens membrane)

Figure 4.15   Diagram of a section of the lipid bilayer of a cell membrane. Lipids are oriented in such a way that the interior of the membrane repels water. Protein molecules may span the membrane or be exposed on the inner or outer surface. What structures facilitate selective permeability?

However, they cannot pass directly through the lipid bilayer. This is because the structure of the membrane is selectively permeable—it determines the specific molecules that are able to cross into and out of the cell. Thus, biological membranes are much more complex than the walls of a container of milk. They also perform a far more complex and important role in regulating internal conditions.

Someone in the next room opens the oven and takes out a loaf of freshly baked bread. Almost immediately, your mouth starts to water as you smell the bread. How does the odor get to your nose? Molecules from the bread were released by heat and travel through the air, most likely on currents made by the movement of people in the room. The protein receptors on cells in your nose detect these molecules.

This is an example of molecular movement. Molecules can be carried by the movement of the gas or liquid they are a part of. However, they can also disperse on their own, in random directions. If not disturbed by any other force, molecules tend to move from an area where they are more concentrated to an area where they are less concentrated. The dispersion continues until the concentration of molecules is the same everywhere (see figure 4.16). This type of molecular movement is called **diffusion**.

Imagine sampling the gelatin in figure 4.16b at different points along a line from the center of the spot of dye to the clear area. What do you think you would measure? You would find that the concentration of the dye decreases gradually. The gradual decrease is known as the **concentration gradient**. You can think of concentration like crowding. The more crowded the molecules, the more concentrated they are. Because molecules diffuse from areas of higher concentration to areas of lower concentration, they are said to move *down* the concentration gradient.

Diffusion occurs because the universe, and all the molecules in it, tends to drift into a less ordered state. Energy input is required to keep any system orderly. Think, for example, about your room. It takes your energy to maintain order—to keep your clothes off the floor, your video games in one place, and your papers on the desk. Without a continual input of energy, the organization of your room soon disintegrates and begins to look like figure 4.17. Organisms use energy continuously to maintain their own order and unique internal environment.

The diffusion of molecules from higher to lower concentrations occurs in liquids as well as in the air. For example, a solute, such as table salt, is

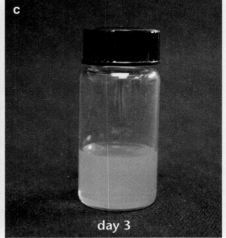

day 1   day 2   day 3

Figure 4.16 Diffusion is the movement of molecules from an area where they are more concentrated to an area where they are less concentrated. Eventually, this process results in an even distribution of molecules throughout. In (*a*), a spot of dye was placed on top of a jar of gelatin. The molecules diffuse through the gelatin (*b*) over a long time, eventually becoming well distributed (*c*).

Figure 4.17   Entropy, or the tendency toward disorder, in a system. What evidence of entropy do you see in this drawing? What is needed to put this room in order?

The pure water would move down the concentration gradient, to where there is a lower concentration of water. Water would rush into the cell. On the other hand, the other stuff in the cell, because the membrane is selectively permeable, cannot move out of the cell. In this way, osmosis can result in such a buildup of pressure inside the cell that the cell swells and bursts. Conversely, if the concentration of water is greater inside than outside a cell, water moves out to the external environment, and the cell shrinks. Figure 4.18 shows a range of cell responses in both animal and plant cells.

Osmosis plays a special role in plant cells because of their rigid cell walls. Plant cells have an internal water-filled compartment

dissolved in a solvent, such as water. The salt undergoes diffusion until it is uniformly distributed. Imagine a cell floating in saltwater. The movement of the salt molecules across the cell's membrane depends in part on the relative concentration of salt in the cell's internal and external environments. The movement also depends on special membrane proteins that act as carriers or channels.

One type of diffusion is called osmosis. **Osmosis** is the movement of water through a membrane from an area of greater concentration to an area of lesser concentration. Osmosis can result in the buildup of significant pressure inside a cell (or a compartment within a cell). For example, "pure" water has a high concentration of water (100 percent). Cells contain many other things besides water—proteins, salts, DNA, and more. Imagine that a cell contains 40 percent water and 60 percent "other stuff." If this cell were placed in a bowl of 100 percent water, what will happen?

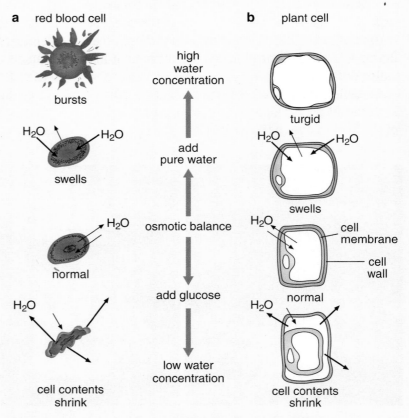

Figure 4.18   Osmosis. (*a*) An animal cell (red blood cell) in different solutions; (*b*) a plant cell in different solutions. What conditions make a cell shrink? What conditions make it burst?

known as a vacuole. The water in a vacuole exerts pressure on a cell's contents. It presses the cell membrane tightly against the cell wall. The pressure gives plant structures, such as leaves, their firmness. What do you think is happening in a vacuole when a leaf wilts?

Diffusion, including osmosis, accounts for much of the exchange of materials between the internal and external environments of individual cells. But not everything can diffuse across a cell membrane—cell membranes are *selectively* permeable. Large molecules or molecules with electrical charges cannot cross lipid membranes efficiently by diffusion alone. Cells have ways to control how fast these molecules move in and out. As figure 4.19 illustrates, membrane proteins can transport these molecules through membranes.

In **facilitated diffusion**, proteins form channels that allow substances to move *down* their concentration gradient, either into or out of the cell. Each type of protein transports only

specific substances. Cells use facilitated diffusion to move glucose and many essential ions. Along with osmosis and diffusion, facilitated diffusion is considered a form of **passive transport** because the cell does not need to use energy to move the material.

In **active transport**, cells use energy to move substances with the help of transport proteins. Through active transport, substances move across a membrane, against, or *up*, the concentration gradient. For example, molecules in the soil around a plant may contain low amounts of the elements necessary for the plant's growth, like nitrogen. Ordinary diffusion would not provide the plant with enough of these elements. By means of active transport, however, the plant uses energy to accumulate these elements in its root cells. This process is like collecting all of the clothes scattered about a room and placing them in a laundry basket. Once inside the roots, the elements are transported to all parts of the plant.

a passive transport

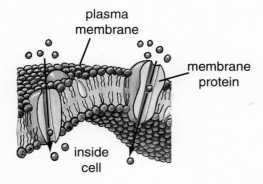

plasma membrane

membrane protein

inside cell

b active transport

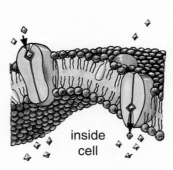

inside cell

Figure 4.19 **Facilitated diffusion and active transport.** (*a*) In facilitated diffusion, substances move across membrane proteins, down their concentration gradient. (*b*) Active transport uses energy and membrane proteins to move substances against their concentration gradient. Active transport also can move substances with their concentration gradient.

EXPLAIN

ELABORATE

Regulating the Internal Environment

Shrinking cells and exploding cells dramatically illustrate the internal response of cells to external conditions. In the previous activities, you studied the processes that allow substances to move between internal and external environments. In addition, you have seen that the membranes that form boundaries around the contents of cells influence the exchanges between compartments.

How are the same processes of exchange, diffusion, and osmosis important in large body systems (figure 4.20)? To begin to answer that question, consider two important compartments within the human body—the circulatory system and the urinary system (figure 4.21). In this Explain-Elaborate activity, *Regulating the Internal Environment*, you will see how these two systems help regulate the internal environment in humans.

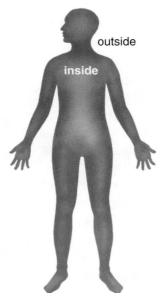

Figure 4.20 The body is a compartment. Conditions inside the body are different from those outside. All living things maintain an internal environment that is different from the external environment.

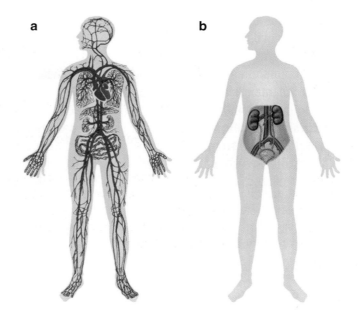

Figure 4.21 (*a*) **The circulatory system.** The heart and an extensive network of vessels make up the circulatory system. (*b*) **The urinary system.** The urinary system regulates water balance, the blood's ion levels, and blood volume, and it eliminates waste products from the body.

Materials

Part A
online resource
poster board, butcher paper, or drawing paper (1 sheet per student)
art supplies including colored markers

Part B
Molecular Movement in the Kidney on the online resource

PROCESS AND PROCEDURES

Part A Circulatory System

1. In your science notebook, write down the title "circulatory system" and the focus question, "What is the path of blood through the body?"
2. Watch the video segment, "The Circulatory System," with your class. As you watch, take notes on information that may help you answer the focus question. Ask questions if you need clarification about the path your blood takes and the functions of the structures in the circulatory system.
3. Imagine that you are a drop of blood. What path would you follow through a human's body as you travel from the left little toe, through the heart, and into the right big toe?
   a. On your poster board or paper, draw a large, simple outline of a human.
   b. Draw a heart (including all the chambers).
   c. Add enough vessels going from the heart, out to the toe, and back to the heart to trace the path of a drop of blood from the left little toe to the right big toe.
   d. Draw arrows inside or along the vessels to indicate which way the blood flows.
   e. Label your drawing and create a legend next to your illustration that describes the path.

      You may refer to figure 4.24, in the essay, *Making Exchanges throughout the Body*, to help you set up your drawing. Use your notes from the video segment, "The Circulatory System," to help you label your drawing. You will know that you have described your journey adequately if you have labeled

      • capillaries,
      • veins,
      • arteries,
      • all four chambers of the heart, and
      • the lungs.

Part B Making Exchanges

1. Create a table in your science notebook to describe how you, as a drop of blood, are involved in exchanging material with different tissues of the body. Refer to figure 4.22 for information and use figure 4.23 as a model.

   Leave room to add to your table as you learn more in the next chapter.

2. Complete the table with the help of your partner.

   The video segment, "The Circulatory System," and the essay, *Making Exchanges throughout the Body*, will help you with these tasks.

Online Resource

SCiLINKS®
NSTA

www.scilinks.org

Topic: circulatory/ cardiovascular system
Code: human4E237

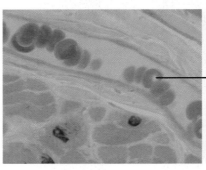 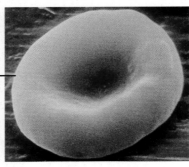

Figure 4.22   Red blood cells and oxygen transport. Red blood cells move single file through a capillary. Each red blood cell contains molecules that can bind to and transport oxygen. Although red blood cells transport some carbon dioxide, most of the carbon dioxide that enters the blood from the body cells is carried in the blood plasma, the liquid portion of the blood.

Direction of exchange	Tissues of the toe	Tissues of the kidneys	Tissues of the lungs	Tissues of the intestines	Tissues of the liver
Tissue to blood					
Blood to tissue					

Figure 4.23
Sample table. A table like this one will help you record some of the types of exchanges that take place in the body.

3. Read the essay, *Disposing of Wastes,* and view the animation, *Molecular Movement in the Kidney,* on the online resource. These will help you take a closer look at the urinary system. As you complete these tasks, add relevant information from the reading and animation to your table of the exchanges that take place in the body.

Making Exchanges throughout the Body

ENGLISH SPANISH

Imagine you are spending the day in a one-room apartment. You have easy, direct access to all that you need. Now imagine spending the day in a 20-story office building. Your office is on the 15th floor, the restrooms are on the 10th floor, and the cafeteria is on the third floor. The same daily tasks that you perform in the studio apartment suddenly become more complicated because you do not have direct access to all that you need. You require more-complex systems (for example, an elevator

and hallways) to help you move from place to place and complete your daily tasks.

In a similar way, single-celled organisms such as bacteria have their entire living compartment directly in contact with the environment that surrounds them. For multicellular organisms, however, life is more complicated.

Most of the cells in humans, other animals, and plants are buried deep inside their bodies. These cells are not in direct contact with the external environment. Still, all cells must obtain oxygen and food from the external environment. They also must remove wastes from their internal environments. You survive because your body is able to deliver needed materials to and take away wastes from each one of its trillions of cells.

Maintaining these internal conditions requires the organs of the body to interact. An **organ system** is a group of organs that work together to perform a common function. All organ systems are involved in exchanging materials between different parts of the body. Organ systems are also involved in regulating conditions within the body. They respond to signals from various parts of the body.

Three organ systems that primarily exchange materials include the gas exchange system, the circulatory system, and the urinary system. The **gas exchange system** is a delivery system that provides air to the lungs. It is also known as the respiratory system. In the lungs, oxygen moves from the air into the bloodstream. Carbon dioxide moves from the bloodstream to the lungs, and into the air. The **circulatory system** transports oxygen, nutrients, and other substances to cells throughout the body. It also carries waste products such as carbon dioxide from the cells to the lungs. The **urinary system** filters the blood to eliminate water, salts, and wastes that contain nitrogen. The activity of all of these systems depends on the exchange of materials across cell membranes. Most of these exchanges occur by diffusion, osmosis, facilitated diffusion, and active transport.

Let's look closely at one delivery system. The circulatory system is essential for maintaining appropriate internal conditions. It is successful because it forms an extensive network that distributes materials throughout the body. At the center of this network is the heart. The heart is a muscular organ that pumps blood through the entire circulatory system. Branching out from the heart is a series of blood vessels. These blood vessels are interconnected tubes that carry blood and help control its flow. The blood itself is a complex mixture. It is made up of water, dissolved gases, nutrients, cells, large molecules (like proteins), and a variety of other substances.

Blood flows in a giant circuit away from the heart, around the body, and back to the heart. Blood moves away from the heart through **arteries**. Blood returns to the heart through **veins**. Both types of vessels branch repeatedly to form billions of smaller vessels. Blood flows away from the heart into smaller and smaller blood vessels, until it reaches the smallest: **capillaries**. In fact, the human body has more than 10 billion capillaries. These narrow, thin-walled vessels are just wide enough to allow blood cells to flow through, single file. From the capillaries, blood flows into larger and larger vessels as it moves back toward the heart. Figure 4.24 illustrates the human circulatory system.

The network of capillaries in the body is extensive, allowing capillaries close contact with cells of the body. Very few living cells lie farther than 0.01 mm from a capillary. Why do cells need to be close to capillaries? The close proximity of capillaries, along with their thin walls, allows for the exchange of materials between the blood and the body's cells. As blood passes through a capillary, oxygen, glucose, and other substances in high concentration move out of the capillary toward nearby cells. Then those substances move across cell membranes and into the cells. At the same time, carbon dioxide and other waste products that are in high concentration inside the cells move across membranes into the blood carried by the capillary.

The circulatory system is just one example of a system of exchange in the human body. Right now, your circulatory system is making thousands of exchanges a second. At the same time, your urinary system and gas exchange system are making many thousands more exchanges. It makes working in a high-rise building seem simple, doesn't it?

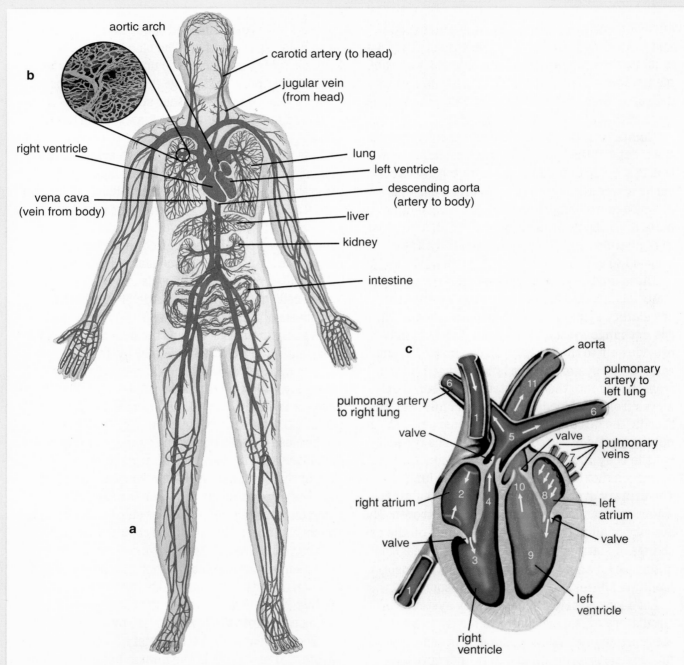

aortic arch

carotid artery (to head)

jugular vein (from head)

b

right ventricle

vena cava (vein from body)

lung

left ventricle

descending aorta (artery to body)

liver

kidney

intestine

a

c

aorta

pulmonary artery to left lung

pulmonary artery to right lung

valve

valve

pulmonary veins

right atrium

left atrium

valve

valve

left ventricle

right ventricle

Figure 4.24   Human circulatory system. (*a*) **Some of the components of the human circulatory system.** Blood vessels branch repeatedly to form smaller and smaller vessels, eventually ending in capillaries. (*b*) **Colored electron micrograph of a capillary bed (photographed at 100×).** Very fine capillaries (pink) branch off blood vessels (gray). (*c*) **Flow of blood through the heart.** The numbers in the illustration indicate the path of blood through the heart. Blood enters the right side of the heart, is pumped through the atria and ventricles, moves to the lungs, and then returns to the left atria and ventricles of the heart to be pumped through the rest of the body.

If you have ever taken out the trash, you have a good idea of how much waste people produce each day. Cells within our bodies produce waste as well because cells do not use all the matter that we ingest into our bodies. In addition, each cellular activity produces some waste materials. This waste becomes toxic if it builds up in our bodies.

Waste is disposed of in a variety of ways. As cells produce waste products, they often deposit them in the bloodstream. The bloodstream carries away the waste from cells. One waste product, carbon dioxide, is carried back to the lungs and eliminated by exhaling. Some excess salts are eliminated by sweating. Chemical waste produced by the cellular activities of the body is eliminated primarily by the urinary system.

Have you ever smelled the pungent odor of a glass cleaner? This odor comes from ammonia. Ammonia is a toxic waste product, produced by cells when proteins are broken down. If ammonia accumulates in the blood and tissues, it causes life-threatening illness. Humans, however, possess an organ system that efficiently removes ammonia and other toxins. As ammonia is formed, the liver is able to convert it to urea, a relatively nontoxic substance, and delivers the urea to the blood.

The urinary system is one of the body's regulatory systems. The regulatory organs of the urinary system are the two **kidneys**, which are illustrated in figure 4.25. The kidneys are small compared with other organs. Together they weigh only about 300 g, or 11 oz. However, the kidneys and their supply of arteries contain almost 20 percent of the heart's output of blood at any time. This amount can vary, depending on circumstances such as the body's hydration. As hydration varies, so does the rate of urine production.

The kidneys adjust the contents of the blood. First, the kidneys filter the blood to remove urea and other waste substances, producing urine. Then the kidneys restore the correct balance of water, salts, and other key compounds to the blood. In doing so, the kidneys play important roles in regulating blood pressure and hydration of the body. Each kidney is connected to the bladder by tubes called **ureters**. The **bladder** is a sac that holds the waste-containing urine until it is released from the body.

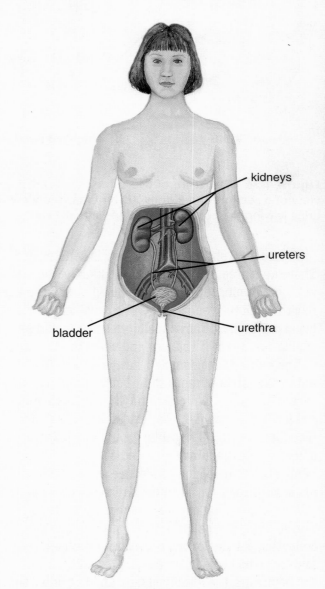

Figure 4.25 **The human urinary system.**

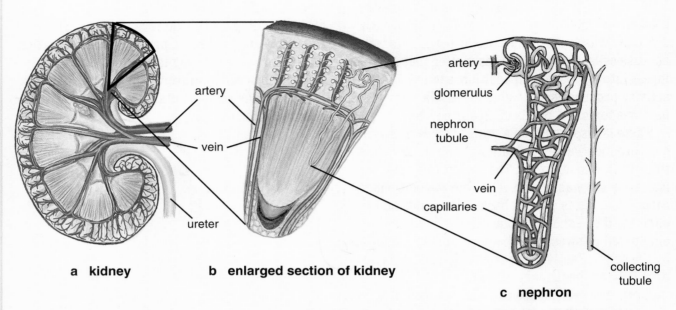

artery

vein

ureter

a **kidney**

artery

b **enlarged section of kidney**

artery

glomerulus

nephron tubule

vein

capillaries

collecting tubule

c **nephron**

Figure 4.26   **Structure of the kidney. (*a*) A cross section through the human kidney, (*b*) an enlarged view of a section of a kidney, (*c*) an enlarged view of one nephron with its surrounding capillaries.** The urine leaving the collecting tubule eventually enters the bladder, where it is stored temporarily.

Figure 4.26 shows how a kidney is constructed. There are three major tubes of the kidney: the artery, the vein, and the ureter. Blood enters the kidney through the renal artery. The renal vein carries blood out of the kidney. Smaller vessels, including capillaries, connect arteries and veins to each other.

The kidneys are complex, active organs. Each kidney consists of more than 1 million microscopic filtering units called nephrons. **Nephrons** are made of a capillary bed and a collecting tubule (see figure 4.26). A knotlike group of capillaries called the **glomerulus** is located at one end of the nephron. Because blood pressure at the glomerulus is very high, water and small solutes move into a neighboring capsule and collecting tube. The solutes, also called filtrate, move from the collecting tubules of the nephrons into the ureter, and then the bladder. By passing blood through the nephrons, the kidney cleans and regulates the composition of the blood.

The cleaning and regulation of blood composition occurs in phases along the nephron. These phases are called filtration, reabsorption, and secretion (figure 4.27). Together the two kidneys filter as much as 125 mL (about one-half cup) of blood *every minute*. If that entire amount were excreted, the effects of such fluid loss would be severe. To offset this fluid loss, you would have to drink 7.74 L (2 gal) of liquids *every hour*. That's 180 L (48 gal) *every day*. You would spend all your time drinking and urinating.

By the time the filtrate has moved through the nephrons, however, 99 percent of the fluid is reabsorbed into the blood. How does that happen? First, kidney cells use active transport to move sodium ions, sugar, vitamins, and other nutrients that were filtered out back into the blood. The movement of these molecules creates an osmotic pressure, so water also moves back into the bloodstream. If you are dehydrated, most of the water

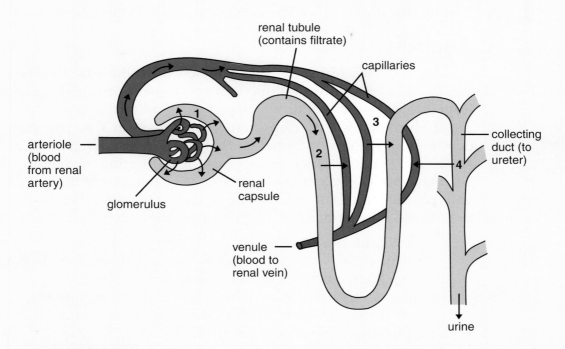

renal tubule
(contains filtrate)

capillaries

arteriole
(blood
from renal
artery)

glomerulus

renal
capsule

venule
(blood to
renal vein)

collecting
duct (to
ureter)

urine

Figure 4.27   Phases of kidney function. Blood moving through a nephron of the kidney is first filtered (*1*), then essential molecules and water are reabsorbed (*2*), then additional waste molecules are secreted (*3*), and finally even more water is absorbed (*4*).

is reabsorbed into the bloodstream. The urine excreted is dark. If, in contrast, you just drank several glasses of water, then much of the extra water passes quickly into the nephron tubule to be excreted as very lightly colored urine.

After some of the fluid is reabsorbed, the kidneys complete the process of secretion. Secretion provides a way for the body to maintain pH balance. pH balance is achieved through the controlled secretion of positive ions and the reabsorption of negative ions by the cells that line the interior of the nephron tubule. These processes allow precise adjustments in the composition of blood and the removal of waste products. Filtration,

reabsorption, and secretion are of vital importance. Untreated kidney failure rapidly leads to death because it quickly results in severe disruption to water and waste product balance.

In some cases, the kidneys' job of maintaining water balance is inhibited. Certain substances interfere with appropriate kidney responses. They cause the body to retain or dispose of too much water. A **diuretic** is a substance that increases how much urine is produced, often by increasing filtration and decreasing reabsorption. Caffeine and water are both mild diuretics. Large doses of diuretics may artificially change the water and chemical balance in the body by causing excessive urination.

4. To better understand regulation in this system, watch the video segment, "Regulation in the Urinary System." As you watch, enter into your table any additional materials that are exchanged between the blood and different parts of the urinary system. Record answers to the questions on the video in your science notebook.

Analysis

Topic: urinary system
Code: human4E244

Work with your team of four to complete the following tasks. Work together as a team to answer question 1. For questions 2 and 3, divide your team into two pairs. Decide which pair will develop a response to question 2 and which pair will develop a response to question 3. As you answer your questions, refer to the information that you developed in parts A and B of *Process and Procedures*. Include a supporting illustration in your response. You may wish to use an illustration similar to portions of figure 4.28. When both pairs are finished, present your responses to each other. Make sure you record both illustrations and answers in your science notebook.

1. What kinds of exchanges are made between the circulatory system and other parts of the body? Draw these exchanges on the diagram of the human body that you made in part A, step 3.
2. How does the circulatory system help regulate the internal environment of the body? How does the urinary system influence the work of the circulatory system?
3. How does the urinary system help regulate the internal environment of the body? How does the circulatory system influence the work of the urinary system?

Figure 4.28
Exchanges. Major body systems work together to maintain homeostasis.

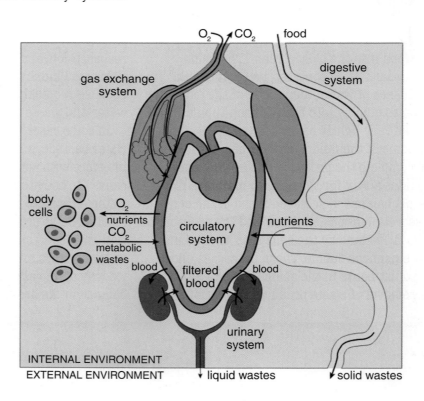

Can You Stand the Heat—Again?

In this Evaluate activity, *Can You Stand the Heat—Again?*, you will return to the opening scenario, *Tougher Than the Sun?*, to examine Josh's situation and homeostasis. Your job is to evaluate your understanding of how internal balance is maintained when the external environment places significant stress on it.

PROCESS AND PROCEDURES

1. Review the class's concept map that you and your classmates constructed at the start of this chapter. Think about all the new terms and concepts you have learned throughout the chapter.

2. On a full page in your science notebook, draw a new concept map that reflects your current understanding of homeostasis. Include all terms you think are important to your understanding of homeostasis, including the following:

   - Diffusion
   - Water
   - Gas exchange
   - Osmosis
   - Compartment
   - Concentration gradient
   - Waste removal
   - Cell membrane
   - Environment
   - Internal conditions
   - Homeostasis
   - Selectively permeable

   For more information, review appendix B7, *How to Construct a Concept Map*.

3. Read the following conclusion to Josh's scenario, *Tougher Than the Sun?*

4. Copy the tables in figures 4.29 and 4.30 into your science notebook. Add highlight comments regarding Josh's condition to each table about what you see and what you think it means.

   You may find it helpful to review appendix C3, *How to Interpret Patterns and Trends*, and appendix B6, *How to Write Highlight Comments and Captions*.

HOW TO

HOW TO

Body mass	Before working (a.m.)	After completing work (p.m.)
Josh's body mass (kg)	77.25	73.55*

*This measurement of Josh's mass was taken before he drank more water at the end of the scenario.

Figure 4.29
Change in Josh's body mass.

Fluids	While working	During afternoon break	After completing work
In	0.95 L juice and water	0.95 L energy drink	0.78 L water
Out	Constant perspiration	0.91 L urine	none

Figure 4.30
Tracking fluids.

SCENARIO

ENGLISH SPANISH

Tougher Than the Sun? (continued)

"You didn't take water out to the site with you?" his father exclaimed, when Josh reported that he had drunk a few energy drinks and was puzzled about why he got so dizzy. "You were seriously dehydrated. What did you learn about dehydration when you took biology in high school and college? You lose a ton of water sweating in heat like this, and the caffeine in those drinks doesn't help. It's a mild diuretic!"

"A diuretic! What is that? And how could I be seriously dehydrated?" Josh responded. "I drank both juice and the energy drinks, and I felt great at the time! Plus, I needed the energy boost." Josh felt considerably better now that he had drunk water and cooled down a bit. But he was irritated that his father had questioned his thinking. After dinner, Josh went to the computer to do a little research about dehydration. Is that what happened, and were the energy drinks really to blame?

Josh learned that the definition of "diuretic" is "a substance that raises one's amount of urination." He found out that while caffeine is a mild diuretic, water and cranberry juice are mild diuretics, too. On the other hand, Josh confirmed that people can sweat excessively—up to 8 L per day! He realized he probably lost more liquid to sweat than he thought, and he learned that his dizziness was indeed a sign of dehydration. He learned that dehydration is defined as a loss of 3–8 percent of body mass in the form of fluids. Josh was surprised to find out that moving from a cool to a warm climate can make someone more susceptible to becoming dehydrated. He also learned that dehydration increases the risk of heatstroke, the third-greatest killer of high school athletes in the United States.

Analysis

Answer the following questions to explain how Josh could have become dehydrated. Record your responses in your science notebook.

1. What percentage of body mass did Josh lose in the form of fluids? Do you think this represents serious dehydration? Explain your answer.

   Percentage body mass lost in fluids =
   [(*final mass – original mass*) / (*original mass*)] ×100.

   One liter of water weighs 1 kg.

2. How much fluid did Josh lose from sweating, versus from urination? Which factor was likely to be more important in causing his dehydration?

3. In what ways was Josh's body attempting to maintain an internal balance in spite of his external environment?

4. Imagine 1 of the cells that make up Josh's tongue (a taste bud). Draw sketches of what you think it might have looked like before Josh

© Dreamstime/Eric Gevaert

started to work and right before he stopped working for the day. Label key features of the cell. Then rewrite the scenario of Josh's day from the perspective of this cell.

Imagine, what did the cell experience as the day grew warmer? After Josh drank the energy drinks? When he resumed working? After he stopped working and returned home? Give your cell a personality as you write—be creative!

5. Use your knowledge of homeostasis to write a brief ⌣ and dry explanation about why a plant in the hot sunlight might wilt. Include the following terms in your answer, as well as any others that will show your level of understanding:

© Dreamstime/Evan66

- Osmosis
- Balance
- Compartment
- Cell
- Water
- Permeability
- Membrane

5

Maintaining Balance in Organisms

> The stability of the internal environment is the condition for the free and independent life.
>
> Claude Bernard

What do swelling and shrinking eggs and a thirsty college student have in common? They are all able to communicate information about external conditions to an internal environment. In eggs, this interaction is simply a matter of physics and chemistry. Communication in organisms is generally much more complicated. This is because complex living systems rely on a broad range of interactions to help them regulate internal conditions. These interactions are (1) chemical, such as diffusion in response to a concentration gradient; (2) behavioral, such as sitting in the shade on a hot day; and (3) physiological, such as the kidneys conserving water in response to dehydration.

Humans and other organisms do not have to consciously plan and carry out a response to every change in the environment. Most regulatory processes occur automatically. Well-coordinated and rapid changes in our organ systems mean that we usually can take the internal conditions of our bodies for granted. However, understanding and appreciating these conditions and the interactions that keep them within normal limits can contribute to a longer, healthier life. In this chapter, you will consider some of the ways that your body maintains its internal balance as you participate in everyday activities.

GOALS FOR THE CHAPTER

Throughout chapter 5, *Maintaining Balance in Organisms*, you will work to gain an understanding of the following concepts:

- ✔ Living systems detect and respond to changing conditions to maintain homeostasis.
- ✔ All organisms have mechanisms for regulating internal conditions such as temperature and pH.
- ✔ Regulatory mechanisms may be chemical, physiological, behavioral, or a combination of these.
- ✔ Maintaining homeostasis requires the interaction of many organ systems.
- ✔ If-then hypotheses assist in developing a controlled experiment.
- ✔ Technological tools are often used to gather data.

To help you develop these understandings, you will complete the following activities.

ENGAGE	The Body Responds
EXPLORE	
EXPLORE	What's Your Temperature Now?
EXPLAIN	Stepping Up the Pace
ELABORATE	On a Scale of 0 to 14
ELABORATE	How Do They Stay So Cool?
EVALUATE	Homeostasis in Your Critter

Throughout chapter 5, remember to refer to the chapter organizer to help you remember what you have learned and where you are headed.

The Body Responds

Key Idea: Changes in activity or the external environment result in bodily responses.

Linking Question:
In what ways does the body respond to temperature changes?

Chapter 5

 EXPLORE

What's Your Temperature Now?

Key Idea: The human body maintains an internal temperature despite external changes in temperature.

Linking Question:
How does the body respond to changes in activity?

MAJOR CONCEPTS

✔ Living systems detect and respond to changing conditions to maintain homeostasis.

✔ All organisms have mechanisms for regulating internal conditions such as temperature and pH.

✔ Regulatory mechanisms may be chemical, physiological, behavioral, or a combination of these.

✔ Maintaining homeostasis requires the interaction of many organ systems.

✔ If-then hypotheses assist in developing a controlled experiment.

✔ Technological tools are often used to gather data.

 EXPLAIN

Stepping Up the Pace

Key Idea: Several organ systems interact to maintain homeostasis when activity levels change.

Linking Question:
How does the body respond to substances of different pH?

Homeostasis in Your Critter

Key Idea: All organisms have ways to regulate temperature, pH, and water balance and to respond to stress.

Maintaining Balance in Organisms

Linking Question:
How do all of the responses I have learned about contribute to an organism's homeostasis?

ELABORATE

How Do They Stay So Cool?

Key Idea: In addition to physiological responses, organisms use behavioral responses to maintain homeostasis.

Linking Question:
How do organisms other than humans maintain a stable body temperature?

ELABORATE

On a Scale of 0 to 14

Key Idea: Cells regulate internal pH by using buffers.

ENGAGE

EXPLORE

The Body Responds

The bus is just starting to pull away as you turn the corner. You break into a sprint to try to catch it (figure 5.1). After 10 or 12 seconds, the driver finally sees you in the side mirror and stops to wait. Out of breath and red faced, you climb onto the bus and collapse in a seat while your friends cheer sarcastically. After a minute or so, your breathing returns to normal and you are talking with your friend about the game last Friday night.

This brief sequence of events probably seems trivial because your body responds to environmental factors all the time. However, the changes you felt while running for the bus and recovering from the run actually required your body to coordinate a tremendous number of responses. Think for a moment about how your rapid breathing slowed to normal. For that matter, consider why it sped up in the first place.

Before you plunge into the details about how such regulation of a response can occur, let's examine a range of possible responses. In this Engage-Explore activity, *The Body Responds*, you will view a set of simple human activities and try to match them with their internal responses. When you think about the surprisingly complicated biological responses, you may be grateful that you can usually take your internal conditions for granted.

Figure 5.1 Hurry, hurry, hurry! How can your body respond so quickly to changing conditions?

Materials

online resource

PROCESS AND PROCEDURES

1. Watch the video segment, "Just a Body Responding," and think about similar experiences that you have had.
2. Think of a short descriptive title for each of the scenes you see. Record your titles in your science notebook.

   These titles can be funny or serious, as you choose. Make sure that each title is descriptive enough to help you remember what happened in each scene.

3. Listen while your teacher reads 4 paragraphs about responses that occur within the human body. Decide which scene from the video segment would most likely cause the different body responses. Record the number of the paragraph that you think best matches each scene from the video next to the descriptive titles in your science notebook.

4. Discuss the following questions with your partner or team.
   a. Which video scene would you match to each description?
   b. Which observation was most important for making each of your matches?
   c. How did each internal response benefit the people involved?
5. Participate in a class discussion about the questions.

Analysis

Make a 2-column table in your science notebook. Identify 3 *behavioral responses* and 3 *physiological responses* to the 4 scenes you observed.

> *Behavioral responses* include any outwardly observable action of an organism, whether it is voluntary or involuntary. *Physiological responses* include internal biological and chemical functions, such as the actions of internal organs, which are mostly involuntary. Refer to appendix B4, *How to Use and Create Organizing Tables*, for more assistance with this task.

HOW TO

What's Your Temperature Now?

EXPLORE

Each character in the video segment, "Just a Body Responding," experienced a different set of external demands and internal responses. Did each character's body respond randomly? No, each body responded in a way that was appropriate for each situation. For example, the body of the person who ate a big meal responded by dilating the blood vessels in the stomach. This increased the stomach's circulation, a response that helps digestion. On the other hand, the blood vessels in the stomach of the frightened person constricted and reduced circulation. This response sent blood to other areas of the body, in this case, the muscles of the arms and legs. Understanding how the body responds to change requires an understanding of the automatic physiological processes that detect and respond to change.

In this Explore activity, *What's Your Temperature Now?*, you will explore the relationship between core (or internal) temperature and surface temperatures under different conditions. This exploration will help you understand how the body moderates specific external changes with specific internal responses.

Materials (per team of 4)

3 thermometers or 3 thermistors
crushed ice
water
plastic container
stopwatch or clock with a second hand
first aid tape
paper towels
graph paper
different-colored pens or pencils

PROCESS AND PROCEDURES

1. Write the following question and hypothesis at the top of a new page in your science notebook:
   - Question: Does the human body regulate internal temperature in response to changes in external temperature?
   - Hypothesis: If the human body can regulate its internal temperature, then cooling some of the surface of the body will result in a change in the core temperature of less than 2°C.

2. Write the following 2 assumptions into your science notebook. During this activity, your team will use these assumptions to help you carry out your experiment:
   - Core (internal) body temperature represents the temperature of the inside of the elbow joint (figure 5.2).
   - Surface body temperature equals the temperature of the index finger.

     In reality, the inside of the elbow is a few degrees cooler than the actual core temperature, and the body's surface temperature varies quite a bit. However, these two locations are convenient or easy places for measuring temperature, and they give a good indication of the difference between surface and core temperatures.

3. Discuss the following question as a team. Record in your science notebook all the useful ideas you hear.

   How can we measure and compare changes in internal body temperature, surface body temperature, and environmental temperature, all at the same time and using the materials available in the classroom?

4. Design an experiment to test the hypothesis in step 1, drawing upon your discussion from step 3. Work with your team on this task. You will know your experimental design is complete when you have included the following.
   - A method to measure the initial temperatures of the body core, body surface, and environment at the same time.
   - A setup that cools the body surface temperature safely. (You must not cool the body surface for more than 30 seconds at a time, because excessive cold can damage the skin.)
   - A setup that includes the following roles:
     - Test subject: Describes his or her feelings and sensations throughout the experiment. The team will monitor this person's body temperature during the experiment.
     - Timer: Keeps track of the time as the experiment proceeds. The timer also can operate the computer or probe ware if you are using it.
     - Observer: Records the time, observations of the test subject, and any comments the test subject makes. Observations

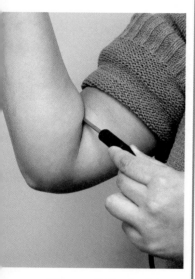

Figure 5.2 In this experiment, the temperature of the inside of the elbow joint represents the internal, or core, body temperature.

should include the color of the skin at each interval and the test subject's behavior.

- Recorder: Records temperatures in his or her science notebook. Recorders must enter temperature data in a data table at regular intervals.

- A data table for recording the color of the skin and the temperatures of the body core, the body surface, and the environment at regular intervals. Record data from the time that the body surface is cooled until it returns to its original temperature.

5. Below your experimental design, write 2 sentences describing the following.

   a. A prediction for how you think your test subject will respond to the environmental changes during the experiment

   b. Your reasoning for why your experimental design will provide a good test of the hypothesis you wrote in step 1

6. Decide as a group who will carry out the different roles and related jobs on your team (figure 5.3).

   Scientists often manage complex projects by dividing the duties among lab partners. Each scientist's individual role and responsibility, however, is crucial to the overall results. As you conduct this experiment, pay attention to your individual responsibilities as well as the work of the team.

7. Obtain your teacher's approval of your experimental design, and then conduct your experiment.

Figure 5.3 This team is sharing the responsibilities required to conduct its experiment.

SAFETY: Set up your experiment in a way that protects the computer from water. Do not put thermometers or thermistors in your mouth to collect data. Do not expose skin to ice water for longer than 30 seconds.

> When the experiment is completed, each team member should obtain a complete set of data from the recorder and the observer and then copy the results into a data table in his or her science notebook.

8. Calculate the changes (increase or decrease) in temperature (°C) for the test subject's body core and body surface and for the environment. Do this for each change by subtracting the starting temperature from the final temperature. Record these data in your table.

9. In your science notebook, construct a line graph of your team's data. The graph should show how the test subject's core and surface temperatures changed throughout the experiment.

> Plot the temperature along the *y*-axis and the time along the *x*-axis. Use dashed and solid lines or different-colored lines for the core and surface temperature data. If you need assistance with graphing techniques, refer to appendix D3, *How to Create Graphs*.

HOW TO

HOW TO

10. Write highlight comments and a caption for your graph.

> Refer to appendix B6, *How to Write Highlight Comments and Captions*, for more information.

11. Return to your team to answer the following questions, using evidence from your graph and observations. Record your answers in your science notebook.

   a. How do the data from the temperature readings compare with the observations made by the observer?

   b. Explain whether your experimental results support or refute the hypothesis given at the start of the experiment.

Analysis

Complete the following tasks on your own. First, read the questions to help guide your reading. Next, read the essay, *Homeostasis*, and enter new terminology in your personal glossary. Then record your answers to the following questions in your science notebook.

1. How might the changes that you observed in the core and surface temperatures benefit the test subject and help maintain homeostasis?

> It may help to think about an extreme example. Suppose the surface temperature became so cold that it damaged skin (frostbite). Would the maintenance of core temperature still be beneficial to the subject?

2. Review the 2 assumptions listed in step 2 of this activity. In what ways do you think these assumptions may have affected your findings?

3. Create and complete a table like the one in figure 5.4. Use it to identify stressors, behavioral responses, and physiological responses that help humans maintain homeostasis. In addition to temperature,

External stressor	Behavioral response	Physiological response
1. Low temperatures	1. 2.	1. 2.
2.	1. 2.	1. 2.
3.	1. 2.	1. 2.

Figure 5.4 Table for examples of stressors and some of the human body's typical responses.

name 2 other stressors that the human body might encounter and adjust to automatically. For each stressor, give 2 behavioral responses and 2 physiological responses that the body makes.

> A stressor is a factor that disturbs homeostasis. Think of factors that stress the body. Consider examples from the urinary and circulatory systems that you studied in chapter 4, *The Internal Environment of Organisms*.

4. Based on your current understanding, do you think responses that help maintain homeostasis are random or specific activities of the body? Explain your reasoning for your answer.

Homeostasis

ENGLISH SPANISH

Have you ever wondered why you don't faint every time you stand up? Does it surprise you that even if you skip lunch you still can walk and talk? Explanations of these occurrences are quite complex. For instance, all the cells in your brain are exceedingly sensitive to tiny changes in the levels of oxygen and sugar. Even small decreases in those critical substances can cause fainting. Your blood pressure automatically rises when you stand up in order to maintain adequate oxygen flow to your brain. Likewise, you can skip lunch because a declining level of sugar in your bloodstream triggers your liver to release sugar held in storage.

Your body must continuously make adjustments to create and maintain an environment for your brain and other organs to function. Many of these adjustments are made automatically. They assure that your body remains within fairly narrow ranges of values for a number of conditions. Overall, we call this condition of balance **homeostasis** (see figure 5.5).

Humans are not the only organisms that maintain homeostasis. In fact, homeostasis is a fundamental characteristic of *all* living systems. In animals, internal organs that are similar in function to those in humans help maintain homeostasis. In plants, specialized structures, such as the **stomata** illustrated in figure 5.6, help plants maintain an internal balance. In simpler organisms, such as the single-celled amoeba, processes such as diffusion and active transport are sufficient for homeostatic functions such as removing waste. However, the amoeba also behaves in complex ways that help maintain balance. For example, it seeks out lighted areas, where food may be

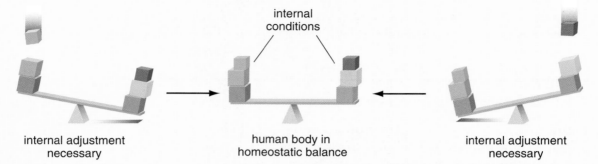

Figure 5.5 Homeostasis. The human body is maintained in a state in which the internal conditions are balanced. When the balance is disturbed, the body adjusts its internal conditions to restore balance.

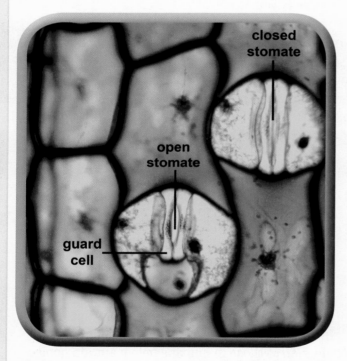

Figure 5.6 Guard cells control the rate of water loss in plants. Water loss is controlled by the condition of special cells, called guard cells. These cells regulate the size of microscopic pores in leaves. The pores are called stomata. When the plant has sufficient water, the guard cells swell and the stomata open. Water then evaporates and leaves through the pores. When the plant is low on water, the guard cells shrink. The stomata remain closed, which preserves water. Based on the appearance of stomata in this leaf, how would you describe this plant's water balance?

abundant. Maintaining balance means life. Losing homeostatic balance for an extended period of time means death.

To maintain homeostasis, two things are required. First, an organism must be able to *sense* when changes have taken place in the external and internal environments. Second, it must be able to *respond* with appropriate adjustments. For example, humans can monitor stimuli, or external signals such as cold, because we have **sensory neurons** in our skin. These specialized cells of the nervous system relay sensations to the spinal cord and the brain. By doing so, they allow us to feel the outside temperature. Once the message "cold" is received in the brain, our bodies can respond by changing blood flow. Our heart rates may increase. Certain blood vessels may constrict. This is an involuntary **physiological response**, or automatic response. We do not consciously control this process. In other words, we do not decide what the body should do. The body attempts to keep the brain, heart, and liver at a nearly constant temperature even if that means sacrificing fingers and toes.

Of course, the message "cold" can trigger other responses, including shivering, moving toward a source of heat, and putting on more clothing. Any response that involves movement requires that a signal from the sensory neurons be processed by the brain, and then returned as a signal that activates

motor neurons, which generate the movement. All three of the responses above are **behavioral responses** because they are outwardly observable. Some behaviors are consciously controlled, and some are not. Behaviors that are not consciously controlled are called **reflexes.** Do you think shivering is a reflex, or is it consciously controlled?

The human body's response to change is often quite specific. For example, the body responds to cold temperature by changing the pattern of circulation to keep the most important internal organs warm. This type of response is appropriate for the external condition. If the body becomes too hot, however, the circulatory system diverts blood flow away from the internal organs. This protects them from damage caused by excess heat.

These examples are rather dramatic. But the human body routinely senses and responds to thousands of small changes each day. It is through many small, specific, automatic changes that living organisms sense and react to an environment that is ever changing and sometimes hostile. But the mechanisms for maintaining balance are always on the job.

Stepping Up the Pace

 EXPLAIN

The average internal temperature of humans is 37°C (98.6°F). This temperature fluctuates over a small range, but in healthy people, it stays fairly constant and predictable. The automatic responses of the circulatory system help maintain this balance. The circulatory system responds specifically to certain changes in temperature, for example, by diverting warm blood away from the arms and legs when it is cold. Perhaps you observed some of these responses during the Explore activity, *What's Your Temperature Now?*

Did any of your observations suggest that organ systems other than the circulatory system might be involved in regulating temperature? The circulatory system is just one of several different systems that work together. Most of those other systems, however, are difficult to observe because their responses occur inside the body. The role of these other systems is important, because maintaining homeostasis involves the *interaction* of many systems. To understand homeostasis fully, you must gain an appreciation for how changes in one system affect the performance of another system.

One way to observe the interaction of systems is to consider systems for which internal changes have measurable external effects. As you have seen, you can detect change in the circulatory system by measuring temperature. Can you think of any other external methods of detecting change in circulation? External measures provide only an indirect view of the body's internal environment. Still, they are valuable in helping illustrate the complex interactions of internal organ systems. In this activity, *Stepping Up the Pace*, you will first learn new information about the roles of the nervous system and endocrine system in maintaining homeostasis. Then you will apply some of what you learned to an investigation of exercise. This

Explain activity will help you begin to explain how organ systems in the human body interact to maintain homeostasis.

Materials (per team of 5)

breathing rate sensor (optional; if using probe ware)
heart rate sensor (optional; if using probe ware)
thermistor or thermometer (optional)
alcohol wipes (optional; if using probe ware)
stepping platform
stopwatch or clock with a second hand
graph paper
different-colored pens or pencils

PROCESS AND PROCEDURES

1. Complete the rows marked "prereading" for each table in the handout, *Careful Coordination: Reflecting on My Understanding.*

   "Reflecting on my understanding" is a literacy strategy that will help you compare what you knew before and after reading. It can help you identify areas of new learning that you may wish to review and discuss in order to build understanding. To complete the prereading rows, reflect on associations you have between the idea of balance in the body and specific components of the body including the brain and hormones. You may also wish to review your science notebook entries from chapter 4 to review what you have learned about how different organ systems interact when exchanging materials.

2. Read the essay, *Careful Coordination.* As you read, fill in the postreading rows in the tables in your handout. Also add new terms to the personal glossary in your science notebook as you read.

3. Complete the following in your science notebook, drawing from your understanding of the essay, *Careful Coordination.*
   a. How does the endocrine system and the nervous system each contribute to maintaining homeostasis?
   b. Explain the role that sensory neurons play in the maintenance of homeostasis in the human body.
   c. Describe the general way that feedback systems work to adjust internal conditions in response to change.

4. In this activity, your team will design an experiment to investigate how pulse and breathing rates change during exercise. With your team, read aloud *Protocol for Conducting a Step Test* to learn 1 way to measure these rates while conducting a step test.

PROTOCOL

   Your team may not use this protocol exactly as written for your experiment. Instead, think about using this protocol as a jumping-off point to design an experiment that uses the materials available in your classroom and matches the exercise interests and abilities of your team.

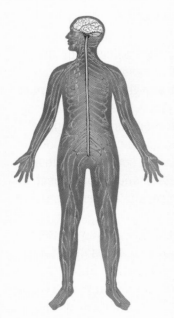

Figure 5.7 The nervous system is made up of the brain, the spinal cord, and the nerves that are found throughout the body.

Have you ever been so cold that you started shivering uncontrollably? Maybe your teeth even chattered. Perhaps you tried to stop the shivering, but your body continued to shake until you warmed up. The shivering that warms your body is an automatic response to the cold. For the most part, you cannot stop yourself from shivering. The **nervous system**, which is made up of the brain and an extensive network of nerves, regulates this and many other automatic responses.

The nervous system is also responsible for all of the body's voluntary responses. For example, you can choose to put on a sweater in response to being cold because of the work your brain does in sensing and helping you respond to your environment. The nervous system is made up of all the nervous tissue, the brain, and the spinal column (see figure 5.7). It plays a key role in coordinating internal balance.

The nervous system contains two types of cells: **neurons** and **glial cells**. Neurons produce, send, and receive signals. Glial cells protect, support, and insulate neurons. The rapid and accurate transmission of signals from neurons is responsible for every move that you make.

The command and control center for the nervous system is the brain. Recall from your earlier study of the brain that specific regions are responsible for receiving and transmitting different information. Which regions of the brain do you think might be involved in maintaining homeostasis? The brain stem directs the critical, automatic responses necessary to sustain life, such as breathing and heart rate. Many of these responses help maintain homeostasis. The cerebellum is responsible for balance and posture. The cerebrum is responsible for conscious thought, language, and voluntary movement. Can you think of some voluntary movements that might affect homeostasis? Located below the cerebrum is a specialized part of the brain called the **hypothalamus** (figure 5.8). The hypothalamus regulates many **physiological processes** important to homeostasis. These include water balance, body temperature, feeding, and sleep. It also helps to regulate several endocrine functions.

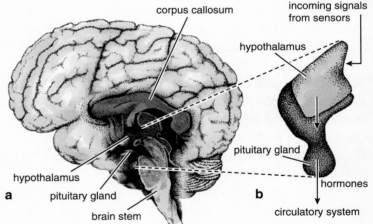

Figure 5.8 **The hypothalamus.** (*a*) The hypothalamus is a specialized part of the brain. It is part of both the endocrine system and the nervous system and is involved in detecting changes in internal conditions. (*b*) The hypothalamus responds to feedback by signaling other endocrine organs. In response to dehydration, the hypothalamus can release hormones that act on the pituitary gland. (The pituitary gland lies just underneath the hypothalamus in the brain.) The pituitary gland then releases hormones into the circulatory system.

SC LINKS®
NSTA
www.scilinks.org

Topic: endocrine system
Code: human4E262

The **endocrine system** is made up of many glands and some types of cells (see figure 5.9). Each of these produces and releases chemical messengers directly into the blood. These chemical messengers are called **hormones**. As a teenager, you probably have heard people refer to your "raging hormones." It is true that hormone levels change greatly as your body becomes sexually mature. But hormones play an important role in maintaining homeostasis for people of all ages. Many hormones function to regulate internal balances, such as water and blood sugar balance.

Hormones affect a variety of cells and organs throughout the body. Although the blood transports hormones past every cell of the body, only certain "target" cells and organs can respond. Whether a cell responds to a particular hormone depends on whether or not it has receptors for that hormone. **Receptors** are proteins that fit the shape of a specific hormone molecule. These receptors and their associated hormones work like a lock and key. When the receptor, or "lock," is exposed to the hormone, or "key," the hormone binds to the receptor. Once the key (hormone) is bound to the lock, the lock (receptor) can change. This change in the receptor causes the cell with the receptor to respond.

Hormones control a variety of processes. Let's examine what happens when someone becomes dehydrated. First, sensory neurons in the hypothalamus detect a shortage of water in the body. They are able to detect this because the concentration of sodium in the blood increases when there is less water. In response, neurons in the hypothalamus stimulate the release of a hormone. The hormone is called **vasopressin**, and it is released from the **pituitary** gland, which is part of the endocrine system. The release of vasopressin from the pituitary is a response to the signal of dehydration. Vasopressin, like other hormones, is then carried throughout the body in the blood. What organs or organ system would you expect to have target cells for vasopressin, a hormone that affects water balance?

Recall that the kidneys of the urinary system regulate the body's hydration in addition to filtering waste from the blood. Cells in the kidneys have receptors for vasopressin. When vasopressin encounters the receptors in the kidneys' cells, it stimulates a response. Vasopressin causes the membranes of the kidneys' tubules to become more permeable to water. This means that more

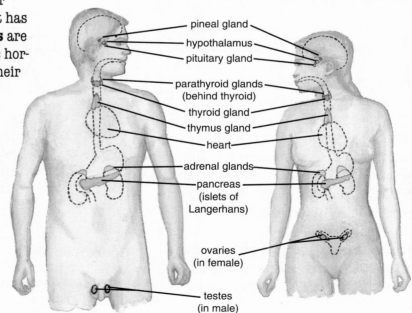

Figure 5.9   The endocrine system is a collection of glands, cells, and special neurons that produce and release hormones into the bloodstream.

water can be reabsorbed and less water is added to the urine. Vasopressin causes a response opposite to the response caused by diuretics, such as alcohol. It prevents the body's dehydration from becoming more severe (see figure 5.10).

At the same time that the endocrine system responds to dehydration, the nervous system also works to restore water balance. It does this by triggering thirst. How many systems have we described so far that are involved in maintaining the body's water balance? The endocrine, circulatory, and nervous systems each plays a role. Some of the body's responses are automatic, like the kidneys' response to vasopressin in the bloodstream. However, *you* decide whether or not to drink when you are thirsty. Your body maintains homeostasis by combining automatic responses and voluntary behaviors.

It is important for the body to keep its internal conditions stable. What keeps automatic responses from changing internal conditions too much? For example, how does the body know when to stop releasing vasopressin? The body uses **feedback systems** to maintain stability as internal conditions change (see figure 5.11).

Feedback can operate in one of two ways. **Negative feedback** systems work to shut off the response that the body had to being out of balance. The body uses negative feedback to regulate water balance after releasing vasopressin (see figure 5.10). Once water balance has been regained, the body signals the hypothalamus to reduce the release of vasopressin. In this way, the body continuously adjusts so that the right amount of water is reabsorbed in the kidney.

Figure 5.12 shows an example of **positive feedback**. Positive feedback adjusts internal conditions *toward* the initial condition. In the example shown, the initial condition is a small clot that begins to develop in response to a bleeding wound. Positive feedback causes more clotting fibers to build up at the injury site. It has the effect of

Figure 5.10 **Negative feedback regulation of water balance by vasopressin (also known as an antidiuretic hormone, or ADH).** When the sodium concentration in the blood rises, the hypothalamus and pituitary gland in the brain respond. This causes the release of vasopressin. Vasopressin stimulates the kidneys to reabsorb more water. As a result, the sodium concentration decreases, restoring water balance. What would happen if a person consumed a diuretic, such as alcohol? Diuretics block the production of vasopressin.

1. **Change in internal condition.** During exercise, water is lost through heavy breathing. This can lead to dehydration.

2. **Feedback from sensors.** Sensors in the hypothalamus and near the heart detect a loss of water. The concentration of certain components in the blood is an important signal.

3. **Regulation.** Hormones such as vasopressin are released into the circulatory system in response to the feedback signals. Vasopressin acts on the kidneys, causing them to retain water. You also feel thirsty.

Figure 5.11 Feedback and regulation work to reverse the effects of dehydration and restore balanced internal conditions.

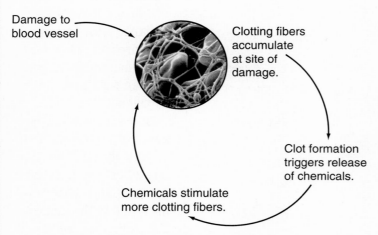

Damage to blood vessel

Clotting fibers accumulate at site of damage.

Clot formation triggers release of chemicals.

Chemicals stimulate more clotting fibers.

Figure 5.12 Positive feedback. In response to a given set of initial conditions, the body adjusts internal conditions. Positive feedback occurs when some critical process must be completed quickly. In this case, positive feedback assures that a clot will form rapidly to minimize blood loss.

increasing the size of the clot, which helps reduce blood loss. In this case, the initial condition is the presence of clotting fibers at the wound. The response is to send *even more* clotting fibers.

The nervous and endocrine systems are critical for homeostasis. The nervous system uses involuntary, short-term activities to keep the body stable. These include stimulating the hypothalamus and triggering sensations such as thirst, cold, and pain. The nervous system also helps the body respond voluntarily to these sensations. In contrast, the endocrine system usually causes changes over a longer period of time. For example, the secretion of vasopressin takes longer to occur than the sensation of thirst. The body combines fast and slow, automatic and voluntary responses. These responses are coordinated by the nervous and endocrine systems. However, all the body's systems work together to maintain balance. By delicately balancing positive and negative feedback mechanisms, the body maintains stability in the face of change.

PROTOCOL

Protocol for Conducting a Step Test

1. Count the test subject's resting pulse rate and breathing rate at the same time, for 30 seconds. Record the resting pulse rate and breathing rate per minute in a data table.

   a. To record the pulse rate, do 1 of the following:

   - Attach a heart rate sensor to the test subject's finger according to the sensor's directions. Time and record the pulse rate for 30 seconds. Then multiply this rate by 2 to obtain the *pulse rate* (heartbeats per minute).

   or

   - Locate the test subject's pulse by pressing on his or her wrist with your index and middle fingers, as shown in figure 5.13. Time and record the pulse rate for 30 seconds. Then multiply this rate by 2 to obtain the *pulse rate* (heartbeats per minute).

   b. To record the breathing rate, do 1 of the following:

   - Attach a breathing rate sensor to the test subject according to the sensor's directions. Time and record the breathing rate for 30 seconds. Then multiply this rate by 2 to obtain the *breathing rate* (breaths per minute).

   or

   - Instruct the test subject to count her or his number of breaths while a team member times and calls out 30 seconds. Count 1 complete breath—inhalation and exhalation—as 1 breath. Time and record the breathing rate for 30 seconds. Then multiply this rate by 2 to obtain the *breathing rate* (breaths per minute).

2. Record additional qualitative and quantitative data about the test subject at rest (such as core temperature, surface temperature, color of skin, and presence of sweat).

3. Record the test subject's pulse rate and breathing rate after the subject exercises. Follow this process:
   Timer: Tell the test subject when to start. Then quietly call out "step" every 5 seconds for 1 minute.
   Test subject: When the timer says "step," step up onto the platform with 1 foot, then with the other foot; next, step down with the first foot, then with the other foot.
   Timer: Say "stop" after 1 minute.

Figure 5.13
Checking pulse rate.

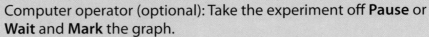
Computer operator (optional): Take the experiment off **Pause** or **Wait** and **Mark** the graph.

Timer: Immediately begin timing 30 seconds for the pulse counter and breathing rate counter.

Pulse counter: Count the test subject's pulse for 30 seconds immediately after exercise. Record the rate as heartbeats per minute. Record the beginning and ending **Mark** numbers (if using a computer) or enter data into a table (if not using a computer).

Computer operator (optional): **Mark** the graph at the end of 30 seconds.

Breathing counter: Count the test subject's breathing rate using the sensor or assist the test subject in counting his or her own breathing rate. Record the rate as breaths per minute. Record the beginning and ending **Mark** numbers (if using a computer) or enter data into a table (if not using a computer).

4. Record additional qualitative and quantitative data about the test subject after the first exercise trial (such as core temperature, surface temperature, color of skin, and presence of sweat).

5. Repeat steps 3 and 4 under increasing rates of exercise, taking data for 1 minute each time.

   a. 1 step every 3 seconds

   b. 1 step every 2 seconds

   c. 1 step every second

   d. 2 steps every second

5. Working individually, develop a testable question and a hypothesis about how exercise affects heart rate and breathing rate in humans.

Your body uses feedback systems to maintain appropriate heart (or pulse) rates and breathing rates for the body as you change from low to high levels of activity. What do you already know about how heart rate, breathing, and exercise are related in humans?

The hypothesis should provide a logical possible answer to a testable question. Refer to the need to know, *Testable Questions*, in chapter 1, *The Human Animal*, to review the criteria for testable questions.

6. Take turns reading aloud the questions and hypotheses each teammate wrote for step 5. Then, as a team, choose the question and hypothesis you will design your experiment to test. Write your team's testable question and hypothesis in your science notebook.

Practice the working-relationship skill of listening thoughtfully to your teammates' hypotheses.

7. Brainstorm ways that you might design an experiment to test your question. There are many things to consider, including

   • how the subject will be positioned when you are measuring breathing rate and pulse rate,

- how to measure breathing rate and pulse rate at the same time,
- what other quantitative and qualitative data are important to record,
- what kind of exercise the test subject will do,
- how many exercise trials the test subject will do,
- whether exercise trials will vary from each other,
- what part of the experiment serves as the control, and
- whether more than 1 test subject will be used.

8. Agree upon and write down your experimental design. In addition to writing out your step-by-step plan, identify the variables and control in your experiment. Write these in your science notebook.

Remember, your experiment must be safe, manageable in a classroom setting, appropriate for the length of the class period, use the materials available, and allow each team member to handle materials and record data.

9. Rewrite your hypothesis as an if-then statement and record it in your science notebook. Your if-then statement should be directly related to your experimental design.

In some experiments, you can make a specific prediction and then collect data to determine whether the prediction was accurate. For this experiment, it is useful to express the hypothesis as an if-then statement such as, "If milk gets hotter than 80°C, then it will boil." You tested a hypothesis written as an if-then statement in the Explore activity, *What's Your Temperature Now?*

10. In your science notebook, construct a data table for the experiment.

Include columns for each of the exercise rates and resting conditions that you decide to use. Make rows for pulse rate, breathing rate, and any other conditions. The exercise rate is the speed at which the test subject steps (or performs some other repetitive exercise). For help in making a data table, review appendix B4, *How to Use and Create Organizing Tables*.

HOW TO

11. Plan the roles for your team.

Decide who will be the test subject, who will be the timer, who will count and record the test subject's breathing rate, who will count and record the test subject's pulse rate, and who will record data or work the computer (if using probe ware). This activity will succeed only with the cooperation and support of all team members.

12. Have your teacher approve your design; then begin your test. Make sure each team member writes down the data in his or her science notebook before proceeding to the next step.

As you proceed with your test, you may need to modify the design of your experiment. If that happens, record the changes in your science notebook with a different-colored pen or pencil.

13. When you have completed your experiment, construct a graph that shows how pulse and breathing rates changed from the resting state through increasing rates of exercise.

Discuss with your team whether a bar graph or a line graph is most appropriate to display your data. Consider the range of pulse and breathing

Figure 5.14
Explanation Template. Use this table as you develop an explanation of your experimental results.

Question to answer:		
Evidence	**Claim(s)**	**Reason/Rationale**

Explanation:
_____ results in _____ because _____.
(evidence)   (my claim)   (reason/rationale)

rates you measured as you draw your *y*-axis. Consider how many types of rest and exercise conditions you tested as you draw your *x*-axis. Remember to label your axes and provide a short caption for your graph.

14. Develop an explanation that addresses your original question and uses your evidence, by using the *Explanation Template* in figure 5.14. Your claim should be related to the hypothesis you tested.

Analysis

Read the essay, *The Breath of Life*, to develop well-reasoned answers to the following questions. Consider using the data about breathing rate that you collected during your experiment to support your answers. Complete the questions individually and write your answers in your science notebook.

1. Explain how oxygen from the atmosphere can reach cells deep within the body. Develop your answer by using the concept of interacting systems and your understanding of how the body makes exchanges.

Figure 5.15
Flowchart of how exercise affects breathing rate.

2. Draw and complete the flowchart in figure 5.15 in your science notebook. Show how exercise affects blood acidity and, in turn, breathing rate.

Flowcharts are helpful for depicting chains of events. You can use them to illustrate how many different feedback systems work in the body. To complete this flowchart, fill in the blank circle and write a connecting phrase next to each arrow on the diagram.

increasing activity (exercise) → *leads to increased*

carbon dioxide levels in the blood →

_____ _____ →

the brain →

breathing rate

Take a nice, deep breath. Let it out slowly. What do you think happens in your body with each breath that you take?

Each time you breathe in, you draw air into your lungs. This action is important for your survival because air contains oxygen (O_2). Oxygen, as you may know, is a substance that every cell of your body needs. Each time you breathe out, you expel air out of your lungs. This action is also important because it helps rid your body of carbon dioxide. Carbon dioxide (CO_2) is a substance that is produced in cells as they transform the chemical energy in food into other forms of usable energy.

The process of breathing requires a finely regulated interaction of a number of organ systems. The organ system most directly involved in regulating your body's interaction with the atmosphere is the **gas exchange system**, also known as the respiratory system (figure 5.16). The central organs of the gas exchange system are the lungs. The lungs form two compartments that connect to the outside environment through your trachea (windpipe) and your nose and mouth. The air inside these lung compartments is not actually inside the internal environment of your body. Instead, the tissues of the lungs themselves separate this air from the rest of the cells of your body.

How does oxygen move from your lungs into the internal environment of your body? And how does

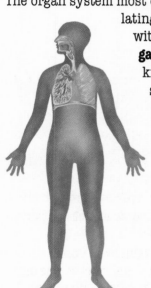

Figure 5.16   The gas exchange system.
The primary function of the gas exchange (or respiratory) system is to provide a large area within the body for the movement of gases between the air and the circulating blood.

carbon dioxide move from the internal environment back into your lungs and back into the external environment? The answers involve a combination of simple chemical processes and complex regulation to maintain homeostasis.

As you draw another deep breath, think about the path that the air must travel. The air passes through the nose, where it is warmed, moistened, and cleaned. Sometimes the air passes through the mouth instead. Then it enters the trachea and passes the vocal folds (vocal cords). The trachea divides into smaller tubes called bronchi. Bronchi divide into even smaller branches. The surfaces of these breathing tubes are lined with mucus-producing membranes and cilia. Cilia are tiny, hairlike structures that move in a wavelike manner. They sweep debris out of the passages. When the air finally reaches the ends of the passages in the lungs, it enters smaller compartments. These smaller compartments are made up of many tiny air sacs called alveoli. In the two human lungs, there are about 300 million alveoli. The pathway of air entering the lungs is shown in figure 5.17.

Once the oxygen is in the alveoli, it is in the smallest lung compartment. However, it has not yet passed into the body's internal environment. To enter the internal environment of the body, the oxygen must diffuse across the alveoli's thin walls. You would have to stack about 200 alveoli walls to equal the thickness of this page. These walls are called the alveolar membranes. The large number of alveoli increases the surface area of the lung tissue. In fact, the surface area of the alveoli is 40 times greater than the entire outer surface of the human body (see figure 5.18). The very high surface area increases the amount of oxygen that can move into the body's internal environment. It also increases the amount of carbon dioxide that can enter the lungs to be exhaled.

The movement of oxygen across the alveolar membranes involves the interaction of the gas

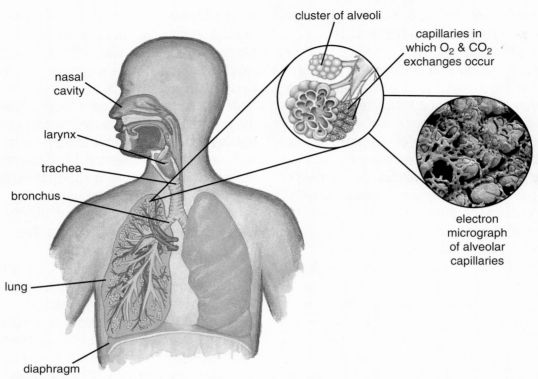

cluster of alveoli

capillaries in which O_2 & CO_2 exchanges occur

nasal cavity

larynx

trachea

bronchus

lung

diaphragm

electron micrograph of alveolar capillaries

Figure 5.17   The human gas exchange system. This lung has been cut away to expose the branching system of bronchial tubes. Part of the lung has been enlarged to show the air sacs and their relation to capillaries. Millions of air sacs in each lung give the tissue a spongelike appearance.

exchange system and the circulatory system. As shown in figure 5.19, a system of capillaries filled with blood surrounds each small group of alveoli. This blood comes into such close contact with the thin membranes of the alveoli that simple diffusion allows oxygen to enter the body. The diffusion of oxygen depends on its concentration in the air sacs and in the blood inside the capillaries that surround them. If the concentration of oxygen is lower in the blood than in the air sacs, the oxygen diffuses from the air sacs into the blood. In the blood, the oxygen binds to the protein hemoglobin. Hemoglobin is found in the red blood cells. Through the flow of blood, oxygen is then carried to all parts of the body. In this way, these two

systems work together to deliver oxygen to cells deep inside the body that have no direct contact with the outside environment.

At the same time that oxygen is diffusing into the blood, carbon dioxide is diffusing out of the blood and into the alveoli. Carbon dioxide is released from cells that are transforming stored energy into energy that they can use. Carbon dioxide is released from these cells and diffuses into the blood. The blood carries carbon dioxide away from cells all over the body and delivers it to the lungs. At the lungs, carbon dioxide diffuses across the alveolar membranes and goes into the air inside the lungs. The concentration of carbon dioxide in the blood and in the air inside the alveoli determines the direction of diffusion. Because the concentration of carbon dioxide is usually higher in the blood, carbon dioxide usually diffuses out of the blood and into the air inside the lungs. The enormous surface area in the lungs speeds up the release of carbon dioxide from the blood into the lungs. When you exhale, you release this carbon dioxide from your lungs into the external environment around you.

Like many other homeostatic processes, breathing involves precise feedback systems. These feedback systems involve the gas exchange system, circulatory system, and nervous system.

Consider, for example, what happens to your breathing rate during rapid exercise. As processes in the body speed up, the production of carbon dioxide also increases. Carbon dioxide causes the blood to become more acidic. Sensory nerve cells in the brain and in the arteries such as the aorta detect the increased acidity. These special cells send a signal to the respiratory centers in the brain. The respiratory centers respond by stimulating the diaphragm and rib muscles to contract more rapidly. Rapid contraction of these muscles increases the breathing rate. A faster breathing rate increases the rate at which oxygen is brought into the body. A faster breathing rate also

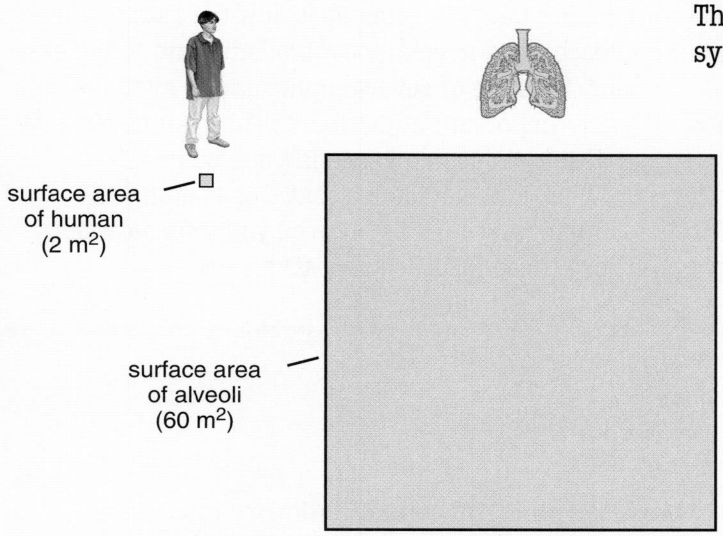

surface area of human (2 m²)

surface area of alveoli (60 m²)

Figure 5.18 If the surface of the human alveoli were spread flat, it would cover an area of 60 m² (646 ft²; about one-third the size of a tennis court). What is the advantage of such a large surface area?

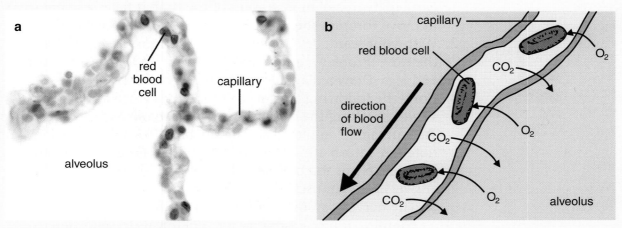

Figure 5.19 **The gas exchange and circulatory systems work together.** (*a*) This thin slice of an alveolus shows its close association with capillaries. (*b*) Carbon dioxide produced in body cells is transported by red blood cells from body cells to the lungs. Oxygen from the lung alveoli is transported by red blood cells to all body cells.

increases the rate at which carbon dioxide is released from the body. When you stop exercising, the rate of carbon dioxide production declines. The blood, then, becomes less acidic. The change is detected by the sensory receptors in the blood vessels. The information is relayed to the respiratory centers in the brain. Finally, signals are sent to the diaphragm and rib muscles to contract more slowly.

This regulatory system works automatically. You do not have to control your breathing rate consciously. The signals involved are very powerful. Although you have some control over your breathing rate, you cannot hold your breath indefinitely.

Once the carbon dioxide level in your blood reaches a critical level, the homeostatic signals override your efforts to hold your breath and you are forced to exhale and take another breath.

Take one last deep breath. Can you describe what is happening in your lungs as you inhale and exhale? Can you remember how the rate of your breathing is normally controlled? Now consider this. Because of several homeostatic systems, many important adjustments that you never have to think about take place in your body.

What is the evidence that this is going on? Think of all the little breaths you took between those three nice, deep breaths.

Further Challenges

In this activity, you investigated how the circulatory and respiratory systems work together with the nervous system to adjust to changes in the body's activity level. But how does the nervous system generate and transmit signals? Complete the following to deepen your knowledge.

1. Participate in a demonstration of the time it takes a nerve signal to move through the class, as directed by your teacher.
2. With your team, develop an explanation for the difference in the time it took for a signal to pass through the class via arms and legs. Draw a diagram to illustrate your reasoning.
3. Copy the following questions into your science notebook. While watching the video segment, "Nervous System and Nerve Transmission," and reading the sidebar, *Brains and a Lot of Nerve*, note any information that will help you answer these questions. Add new terms to your personal glossary. Then write final answers into your science notebook.
   a. The nervous system evolved in a way that uses a combination of electricity and chemicals to send signals, rather than sending chemical messages alone. What advantages might there be because the nervous system evolved in this way?

b. People suffering from Parkinson's disease have difficulty controlling their movements. The cause is a lack of a neurotransmitter called dopamine. Provide reasoning for why insufficient levels of a neurotransmitter would lead to a decrease in muscle control.

c. Draw a diagram of the reflex arc that would be triggered if a fly flew too close to your eye. Label the sensory neuron, the motor neuron, a synapse, a muscle, and neurotransmitters.

SIDEBAR

ENGLISH SPANISH

Brains and a Lot of Nerve

How many of the unique qualities of humans are possible only because of the way that the human brain works? What is it about the human brain that makes it able to think abstractly, remember complex information, and quickly process information from many sources at once?

Scientists who study the way the brain works use many methods to gather information about its functions. To aid their understanding, some scientists use computer programs that model the abilities and processes of the human brain. However, it has been difficult to get computers to do things that are easy for humans to do. For example, think of how quickly you can recognize a familiar face. While computer scientists have been able to program computers to scan and recognize faces, the computers quickly lose their accuracy when there are simple changes, like the addition of dark glasses. Recognizing a person's face is likely to be something your brain does at the same time that you smell the person's cologne, remember past experiences, and speak a greeting. Imagine how hard it would be to build a computer and develop a program that models all of the human brain's abilities.

One reason it is so difficult for scientists to build a computer model of the human brain is that the brain contains many nerve cells, or neurons. The number of interconnections that these neurons form in the brain is astounding. Your brain contains about 1 trillion neurons, and the many ways they can interconnect result in many trillions of potential associations. Until someone develops computer technology that can quickly form many more interconnections than are possible now, it will be difficult to model thinking that is similar to that of a human brain.

To understand how these interconnected neurons work, it is useful to look closely at the structure of a neuron. Figure 5.20 shows how unusual this cell is. At one end of a neuron are branched extensions, or **dendrites**, which act like antennae to receive incoming messages. At the other end of the neuron is an extension called an **axon**, which sends outgoing messages. Each neuron connects to hundreds or thousands of other neurons. This arrangement means that a single neuron can send or receive messages in many combinations with other neurons. For a message to travel to and from the brain, a sequence of interconnected neurons must receive and send the message. The neurons form an organized network of neuron connections that extends throughout the brain and body. The nervous system provides communication between the brain and different regions *inside* the body, as well as linking the *outside* environment with the *inner* enviroment of the body.

Imagine what happens when you see a friend walk toward you smiling. You see the approaching person and it catches your attention. The sight of the person walking toward you is information that you receive from the outside world. A **stimulus** is any incoming information that causes the body to respond. The sound of footsteps is another form of stimulus. Your nervous system, like those of all animals, collects information from stimuli and signals the brain. The brain then processes the information and responds by sending back a signal to the appropriate part of the body. For example, the stimulus of seeing your friend's face allows your brain to recognize the person. Your brain responds to the stimulus and signals your face to smile back.

How is a message sent from one neuron to another? The message is actually a combination of an electrical signal that passes through a neuron and a chemical signal that passes between neurons. Changes in the electrical charge of the neuron cause the signal. An electrical impulse moves along an axon to the end of the neuron. Can you think of a time when an electrical charge built up on your body? For example, when you run around on a carpet in your socks, you sometimes feel a shock when you touch the television or another person.

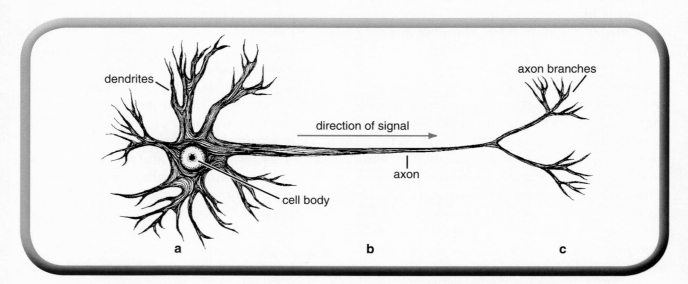

Figure 5.20 **A neuron is a nerve cell.** It has (*a*) extensions called dendrites, which receive nerve signals, (*b*) a long axon, which carries the nerve signals, and (*c*) axon branches, which transmit the nerve signals to the next neuron.

This example of an electrical charge has a much greater charge than the charge found in your neurons. But the transfer of the charge from your body to another person's has some similarities to passing the signal between neurons. However, when an electrical signal passes from one neuron to another, it is translated into a chemical signal along the way.

A small space, or gap, separates neurons. This gap is called a **synapse**. When a message in one neuron (an electrical signal) reaches a synapse, it cannot jump the gap and continue sending the message electrically. Instead, the electrical impulse triggers the release of chemicals into the synapse. These chemicals are called **neurotransmitters** ("neuro" = "nerve," "transmit" = "to send"). Neurotransmitters act as messengers that transmit the signal across the gap between neurons. When the neurotransmitters bind to specific proteins on the dendrites, or branching end, of the next neuron, the chemical signal is converted into an electrical signal. The electrical signal then travels along the length of the axon of the nerve cell. Once again, when the electrical signal reaches the next synapse, it will trigger the neuron to release neurotransmitters into the gap. This process is repeated to form paths of signals along the routes of various neuronal networks. These events happen very quickly, making it possible for you to have a thought and almost immediately signal your mouth to speak or your legs to run. The system of interconnected neurons and their ability to send and receive signals is generally found throughout different types of animals, not just humans.

Not all responses require processing through the thinking centers of the brain. If you touch a hot object, you will immediately withdraw your finger without having to think at all. Such a simple and quick response to a stimulus is called a reflex. The messages involved in this response travel from sensory detectors in your finger, through neurons in your arm, to the spinal cord. Then the messages go back to the muscles in your arm through other neurons, along a pathway called a **reflex arc** (see figure 5.21). At the same time, messages are sent from the spinal cord to the brain. When your brain receives these messages, you interpret them as "That thing is *hot*!" By this time, however, you have already removed your finger from the hot object because of your reflex response. The advantage of a reflex over a signal that the brain must process is speed. In such a situation, you would need to move fast to prevent damage to your body. Reflex responses can save your life.

Newborn human babies turn their heads toward a touch on their cheek. This reflex encourages newborns to nurse in the first few hours of life, but they lose this reflex as time goes by. Most human activity, however, is processed through the brain, not carried out as reflexes. The human brain, with its trillions of interconnections between neurons, is well equipped to handle the everyday business of directing the activities of human life. Even simpler animals such as earthworms respond with reflexes to stimuli from their outside world. The ability to respond to heat, light, and moisture helps the worm find food and keep from being dried out on a hot, sunny day.

The brain is responsible for so much complex human behavior. Responding quickly and appropriately to outside stimuli is just part of the human brain's job. It also must be able to store and retrieve information. For example, when you pick up a book and begin to read, you do not have to consciously think about how to read; you do it naturally. When you first were learning

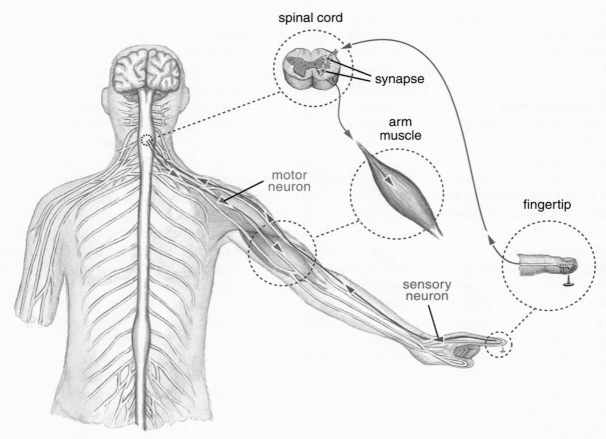

Figure 5.21   Reflex arc. A reflex is an automatic response to a stimulus that occurs before the message reaches the brain. This type of response reduces the reaction time to a potentially life-threatening situation.

how to read, however, you needed to think about the sounds that the letters represented, how letters went together to form a word, and how the words went together to form a meaningful sentence. These processes seem natural to you now because your brain has learned and stored the patterns for thousands of words and the patterns for a variety of sentence structures.

Now that you are at the end of this essay, what do you think your eyes and brain have been doing while you were reading?

 **ELABORATE**

On a Scale of 0 to 14

In the Explain activity, *Stepping Up the Pace*, you learned that several organ systems could interact to maintain homeostasis. In addition, you began to explore a chemical mechanism—the amount of acid in the blood—that links the circulatory system to the gas exchange system. The amount of acid in the blood is related to the amount of carbon dioxide in the cells of the body. By sensing and responding to these levels, the body can maintain a proper balance of oxygen and carbon dioxide in its internal environment. In this case, the acidity level is a regulatory signal. The body responds to this signal when maintaining the balance between two large organ systems. The acidity level, as measured on the pH scale, must remain balanced in humans and other organisms.

In this Elaborate activity, *On a Scale of 0 to 14*, you will elaborate on your understanding of physiological regulation. Consider the following: you put all sorts of foods and beverages into your body. Yet normally your body can keep its pH within a healthy range. How does your body balance the different pH levels that it encounters? More generally, how do living systems balance pH levels?

To study these questions, you will compare how a variety of materials respond to the addition of an acid and a base. Among these materials are **homogenates** (mixtures that are uniform throughout) made from living cells. Homogenates act as models of the internal environment of living systems. They will allow you to investigate how the level of acidity inside cells can be maintained within certain limits.

Materials

Part A (per team of 2)

2 pairs of safety goggles
2 lab aprons
2 pairs of gloves
household solutions that your teacher provides
pH probe or pH indicator strips
jar of tap water for storing pH probe (optional; if using probe ware)
bottle of distilled water

Part B (per team of 3)

3 pairs of safety goggles
3 lab aprons
3 pairs of gloves
50-mL beaker
50-mL graduated cylinder
petri dish half (optional; if using pH indicator strips)
forceps (optional; if using pH indicator strips)
pH probe or pH indicator strips
jar of tap water for storing pH probes (optional; if using probe ware)
distilled water
dropping bottle of 0.1 M HCl (acid)
dropping bottle of 0.1 M NaOH (base)
50-mL of liver or potato homogenate
graph paper
different-colored pens or pencils (optional)

PROCESS AND PROCEDURES

Part A   pH Is Everywhere

SAFETY: Put on your safety goggles, gloves, and lab apron.

1. If you were to compare 2 solutions, one with a pH of 6 and another with a pH of 2, how would they differ? Read the need to know, *Background Information about pH*, to find out.
2. Make a 3-column table on a new page in your science notebook. In the left-hand column, write the names of each household solution that your teacher provides (figure 5.22). Write "predicted pH" as the heading for the middle column and "measured pH" as the heading for the right-hand column.
3. Record in the predicted pH column what you think the pH of each solution is.
4. Working with your partner, determine the pH of the available solutions by using a pH probe or pH indicator strips. Record these pH readings in your data table.

   Rinse the pH probe with distilled water between uses.

5. Discuss the following questions with your class.
   a. Which pH measurements differ from your predictions?
   b. Which of the solutions that you tested could be harmful to the pH balance of your organ systems? Why?

Part B   Regulating pH

SAFETY: Put on your safety goggles, gloves, and lab apron.

NEED TO KNOW

ENGLISH SPANISH

Background Information about pH

We use pH to measure how acidic or basic a solution is. A pH of 7 represents a neutral solution that is neither acidic nor basic. The pH scale ranges from 0 (very acidic) to 14 (very basic). The scale is logarithmic. This means that each difference of one pH unit means a 10-fold difference in acidity. For example, a solution with a pH of 8 is 10 times more acidic than a solution with a pH of 9. In other words, a pH of 8 is 10 times less basic than a pH of 9. Strongly acidic and basic solutions can be quite harmful to the external environment of living systems. Strong acids and bases can burn skin badly. Even minor imbalances in internal pH, however, can disrupt the normal regulation of cells.

Figure 5.22
Household products.
Do you know which
products in your home
have a pH low enough
or high enough to
hurt you?

To investigate how living cells regulate pH, you and your teammates will compare how water and one type of cell homogenate respond to the addition of acids and bases. Water is not living. The homogenate, made from cells that were recently living, will model the internal environment of a living organism. Your job is to collect data that will allow you to compare the responses of a nonliving and a "living" substance to the addition of an acid and then a base.

1. With your team, read *Protocol for Systematically Increasing and Decreasing the pH of a Liquid*. Ask questions of your team and teacher as needed to ensure that you understand each step.

2. Determine which homogenate your team will be using.

   You will use either liver homogenate or potato homogenate. Your teacher made these homogenates by blending pieces of liver or potato at high speed to break open the cells and release their contents. Remember, these homogenates will act as models of the internal environments of living systems.

3. Draw the axes of a graph, as shown in figure 5.23. Work on your own and use a full page of your science notebook.

4. On the graph you set up, draw a line that represents your prediction for how you think the pH of the water will change as you add drops of acid. Then on the same graph, draw a line that represents your prediction for how the pH of the homogenate will change when you add acid.

   When you add the second line to your graph, draw it using a different pattern (for example, a dashed line) or a different-colored pen or pencil. Then enter the meaning of those colors or shapes into a key, placed just below or to the side of the graph.

PROTOCOL

Protocol for Systematically Increasing and Decreasing the pH of a Liquid

1. Pour 25 mL of distilled water into a 50-mL beaker.
2. Determine the initial pH of the solution as you did in part A, *pH Is Everywhere*, step 4.
3. Record the initial pH in a data table similar to figure 5.24 under the column labeled "0."
4. Add 0.1 M HCl (hydrochloric acid) to the beaker, 1 drop at a time, until you have added 5 drops. Gently swirl the mixture after each drop.

    You are making the water more acidic.

CAUTION: 0.1 M HCl is a *mild irritant* (an acid). Avoid skin and eye contact; do not ingest. If contact occurs, call the teacher immediately, and then flush the affected area with water for 15 minutes. If the acid comes in contact with your mouth, rinse your mouth with water.

5. Determine the pH of the solution. Record this reading in your data table.
6. Repeat steps 4 and 5. Record the pH after every additional 5 drops of acid until you have added a total of 30 drops of acid.
7. Discard the mixture in a sink and rinse the beaker and pH probe (if you are using one) thoroughly with distilled water.
8. Repeat steps 1 through 7, *but add 0.1 M NaOH (sodium hydroxide), drop by drop, instead of HCl.* Gently swirl.

    You are making the water more basic.

CAUTION: 0.1 M NaOH is a *mild irritant* (a base). Avoid skin and eye contact; do not ingest. If contact occurs, flush the affected area with water for 15 minutes; rinse mouth with water. Call the teacher.

9. Repeat steps 1 through 8. But instead of starting with distilled water in step 1, pour 25 mL of the homogenate into the beaker.

    You will be observing how the homogenate responds to the addition of an acid and then a base.

10. **Wash your hands thoroughly with soap and water after the experiment.**

5. Now draw 2 lines, using a different type of line or different colors, showing your predictions for how the pH will change when you add drops of a base to the water and to the homogenate.

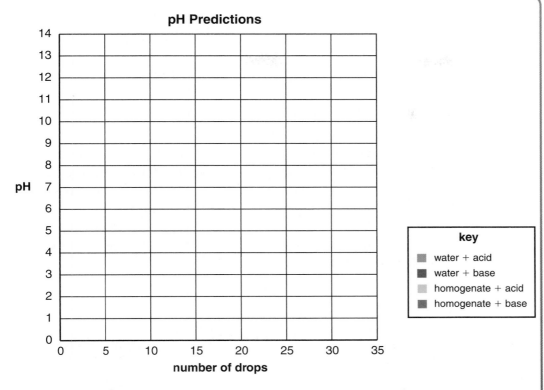

pH Predictions

key
- water + acid
- water + base
- homogenate + acid
- homogenate + base

Figure 5.23
Sample graph for recording pH predictions.

6. Below your prediction graph, write 1 or 2 sentences that describe the reasoning you used to make your predictions.

7. Divide the data collection jobs fairly among your team members. Your team will need someone who will perform the acid tests, someone who will perform the base tests, and someone who will record pH levels in a data table. Plan to change jobs after testing the water so that every team member takes a turn measuring the pH of a solution. The recorder should design a table similar to the *pH Changes* table in figure 5.24 to record the data that the team collects.

8. Carry out the acid and base tests, contributing your role to the team's effort.

9. **Wash your hands.** Then copy any data that you do not have into a table in your science notebook.

Figure 5.24   pH Changes table. You will need a table like this one to record your test results.

Solution tested	Tests with 0.1 M HCl							Tests with 0.1 M NaOH						
	# of drops added							# of drops added						
	0	5	10	15	20	25	30	0	5	10	15	20	25	30

10. On a new page in your science notebook, set up a large graph in the same way that you did to make predictions. Use the pH data that your team collected to make a line graph with 4 lines: 1 each for water plus acid, water plus base, homogenate plus acid, and homogenate plus base.

    Make a key for your different line types or colors, as you did for your prediction graph.

11. Discuss the following question with your team: What differences do you see in the results of adding acid or base to water, compared with adding them to a homogenate? Record a 1-sentence answer in your science notebook, based on the evidence from your graph.

12. Join a team that tested the other homogenate. Compare and contrast your results. Discuss ideas about why differences exist between the water and the homogenates.

pH of Common Foods

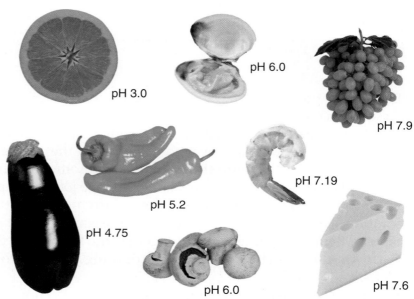

pH 3.0

pH 6.0

pH 7.9

pH 5.2

pH 7.19

pH 4.75

pH 6.0

pH 7.6

SCiLINKS.
NSTA

www.scilinks.org

Topic: buffers
Code: human4E282

HOW TO

13. Discuss the following questions with your team. Record the answers in your science notebook.

    You can use information in the need to know, *Background about Buffers*, for this task.

    a. Based on your results and using water as a comparison, can you make the claim that potato and liver cells are *buffered*? Write an explanation for your claim using the *Explanation Template* in figure 5.25.

       Review appendix C4, *How to Develop an Explanation*, for help with this task.

    b. Is it likely that all living systems contain buffers? Why or why not?

    c. At what pH do you think living liver and potato cells function best? On what evidence do you base this inference?

Question to answer:		
Evidence	**Claim(s)**	**Reason/Rationale**

Explanation:		

_____ results in _____ because _____.
     (evidence)   (my claim)   (reason/rationale)

Figure 5.25 Use this *Explanation Template* as you develop an explanation of your experimental results.

NEED TO KNOW

ENGLISH SPANISH

Background about Buffers

Proper pH balance is important because different chemical and metabolic processes in living organisms work best under specific pH conditions. In humans, for example, digestion in the stomach requires a low pH. But the functions of blood require a nearly neutral pH, not varying much from pH 7.2 to 7.4. In fact, each cell, tissue, and organ has a characteristic pH that is important for homeostasis.

Often, however, organisms are exposed to things that have a pH that is very different from their own. For example, much of the food that you eat has a pH that is different from that of your blood. How do living systems maintain a relatively stable pH in their internal environments when changes occur in their external environments?

A **buffer** maintains the pH of a solution within a narrow range of values even when external conditions threaten to change pH. In effect, this means that small additions of acid or base to a buffered solution do not cause a change in pH. Cells have physiological buffers that help maintain their characteristic pH; these buffers protect the internal environments. Different types of buffers are effective in maintaining pH within different ranges. One type of buffer might keep the internal pH in a slightly acidic range, and a different type might keep the internal pH of another cell in a neutral range.

Analysis

Answer the following questions in your science notebook. Be prepared to contribute your ideas to a class discussion.

1. Based on your data from the experiment in part B, *Regulating pH*, how might a buffer help maintain homeostasis? Explain your answer.
2. Many manufacturers claim that their health care and hair care products are pH balanced or buffered. How would you test their claims?

ELABORATE

How Do They Stay So Cool?

Animals regulate their internal conditions in a variety of ways. What methods of regulation have you experienced or observed so far in the world around you? Do you have a dog that pants on hot days? Have you seen a bird fluff up its feathers when the temperature drops? These are examples of temperature regulation through behavior.

During the heat of summer in the New Mexico desert, a collared lizard, like the one in figure 5.26, will wait beneath the cool shade of a rock. Other lizards dart about in the undergrowth. These reptiles survive in temperatures that most humans could not tolerate for even an hour. Temperatures at the surface of the soil can exceed 70°C, or 158°F. Yet the reptiles survive even though they have no sweat glands. What are the mechanisms that allow these reptiles to survive such high temperatures? In this Elaborate activity, *How Do They Stay So Cool?*, you will gather information about the mechanisms of temperature regulation in lizards and two other animals to compare and contrast with those of the human body.

Materials

online resource

Figure 5.26 The collared lizard. This species of lizard has adapted to the extreme temperatures of a desert environment.

PROCESS AND PROCEDURES

In this activity, you will examine the question, "How does the behavior of animals help them maintain homeostasis?" You will gather information to help you develop an explanation for this question.

1. Write down the focus question of the activity on a new page in your science notebook.
2. Draw a data table in your science notebook similar to the one in figure 5.27. You will record observations of desert lizards and other animals in this table.

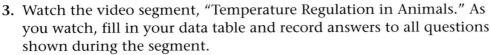

Type of animal	Behavioral responses to changes in temperature
Gila monster	
Horned lizard	
Give yourself room to observe 7 different types of animals.	

Figure 5.27 Use a table similar to this to record your observations.

3. Watch the video segment, "Temperature Regulation in Animals." As you watch, fill in your data table and record answers to all questions shown during the segment.
4. Add a row to your table and record the behaviors of a living animal that you can observe directly.

> Focus your observations on the behaviors that the living animal exhibits to regulate its temperature or to respond to changes in the external temperature. Consider observing an insect or amphibian in addition to the mammals and birds that may first spring to mind. Information in the essay, *Behavior and Homeostasis*, may help you describe an animal's behavioral responses to changes in external (environmental) temperature.

Analysis

Use observations from your science notebook and information in the essay, *Behavior and Homeostasis*, to answer the following questions. Write your responses in your science notebook.

1. What similarities and differences do you see between the behaviors that lizards and humans use to help regulate temperature?
2. What similarities and differences do you see between the way the animal you observed and humans regulate temperature?
3. Describe 2 homeostatic processes (aside from temperature regulation) that you or other animals regulate through behavior. For each process, identify the stimulus, feedback, and response. Record your responses in a table similar to figure 5.28.

Figure 5.28
Sample table for observations.

Condition that is maintained through homeostasis	Stimulus	Feedback	Behavioral response

Behavior and Homeostasis

ENGLISH   SPANISH

Remember Josh, the young man in the scenario, *Tougher Than the Sun?* (chapter 4)? What made Josh head to the refrigerator for a cool drink? Why does a lizard move toward a heated rock when its external environment cools off? What makes you reach for a sweatshirt when you enter an air-conditioned movie theater? All these behaviors seem to help maintain homeostasis. But what are the signals that prompt an organism to respond to changing conditions?

Homeostasis is maintained by processes inside the body. Sometimes these internal processes result in behaviors we can see. But what is happening on the inside? Your body's internal conditions are monitored by systems that are connected. All organisms receive stimuli that prompt their feedback systems. These stimuli arrive in many forms: light, temperature, sound, water, and chemicals. Living systems vary greatly in the type of response they have to different stimuli, and some of these responses are behaviors we can observe.

You have learned that carbon dioxide plays an important role in regulating breathing rate. In general, the acid-base balance of the blood determines your breathing rate. But when you exercise, what happens? Breathing fast is a typical behavioral response to increased exercise. This response restores carbon dioxide to acceptable levels.

Animals regulate their temperature in one of two ways. Animals that regulate their temperature by primarily using heat generated internally are known as **endotherms**. "Endo" means "inside," and "therm" refers to temperature. Animals that rely on the external environment to regulate their temperature are known as **ectotherms**. "Ecto" means "outside of." Mammals and birds are endothermic. Most fish, reptiles, and insects are ectothermic. For all animals, temperature regulation is a critical survival tool. Many cell processes function best in very narrow temperature ranges. This is why doctors are concerned when their patients run high fevers. A slight increase in temperature can help kill pathogens. However, a large or sustained increase will destroy vital cell functions. This situation can put the patient's life at risk.

Mammals and birds maintain relatively constant temperatures by balancing heat production with heat loss. For example, as you transform the chemical energy in food into other usable forms of energy, you generate heat. You can increase heat production by exercising, shivering (see figure 5.29), and increasing the rate at which you break down food. You can decrease heat loss by adding insulation. A bird, for example, fluffs up its feathers. You can put on a sweater. On the other hand, you lose heat through the evaporation of water by sweating and breathing fast. You also lose heat through the transfer of heat to the environment. These behaviors are all responses to changes in the external conditions. In each case, the organism uses feedback to regulate a response that started in the body. Each response also includes a behavior that we could see.

Figure 5.29 Violent shivering can increase the body's heat production by as much as 18 times normal.

Figure 5.30 **Polar bear.** Polar bears live only in the Northern Hemisphere, nearly always in association with sea ice. They maintain their internal temperatures in a very cold climate by hibernating in dens during the coldest months. What behaviors do you use to stay warm?

Animals have many adaptations for maintaining a nearly constant temperature (see figure 5.30). Endothermy has evolved separately in at least three groups: mammals, birds, and some fishes like tuna. Other mammals are notably adapted to extreme climates. For example, small desert mammals may live underground or be active at night to minimize the effect of the hot, dry days. Small mammals in very cold environments live in tunnels under the snow. The temperature in these tunnels does not drop below −5°C (23°F), even when outside air temperatures fall below −50°C (−58°F).

Ectotherms do not have internal processes that help regulate their internal temperatures. What do they do when their internal temperature rises or falls out of a safe range? They have internal receptors that trigger specific responses. The behavioral responses of desert lizards have been studied extensively. Biologists find that the lizards' responses are finely tuned. Some are able to maintain a body temperature between 36°C (97°F) and 39°C (102°F). How? Simply by moving in and out of the sunshine and by adjusting their orientation to the Sun (figure 5.31).

Reptiles, birds, fishes, and humans also have a variety of adaptations for regulating concentrations of salts like sodium and chloride. Marine reptiles like sea turtles have special salt glands above their eyes that excrete excess salt. Some birds, such as seagulls and albatrosses, have a similar adaptation, except that the salt solution drains out of their beaks (see figure 5.32). In humans and other mammals, excess sodium is removed by the kidneys and excreted in the urine. Spider crabs sense changes in the salt level of their habitats by the ocean. But they do not have a physiological mechanism for removing the salt. Instead, spider crabs move to areas of lower or higher salt concentrations. In this way, the spider crabs can maintain their internal balance.

Many animals have observable behaviors that are related to maintaining homeostasis. Humans have a unique capacity to think and make choices about their behaviors. Human behaviors increase the range of responses that we have. We can cool and heat our external environments. We have developed sports drinks to restore our electrolyte balance after we sweat. We have access to a wide

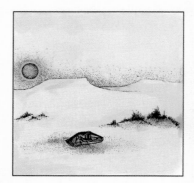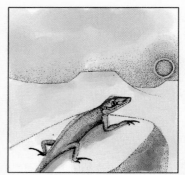

Figure 5.31 The lizard maintains a fairly constant body temperature by changing its body position relative to the position of the Sun.

range of foods, beverages, and drugs that can both restore or destroy a homeostatic balance.

Josh's body signaled him to restore the water balance in his body. But he decided how to try to restore that balance. By ignoring how thirsty he became, Josh made his internal condition worse instead of improving it. As you learned in chapter 1, humans are distinguished from other animals by a combination of characteristics. One of these, our powerful brains, gives us the capacity to choose to ignore certain signals or to do something about them.

Figure 5.32
Western gull (*Larus occidentalis*). Western gulls have a wingspan of 30–40 cm (12–16 in). Note the drop of salt-water at the tip of this bird's beak. Salt glands help seabirds eliminate excess sodium. How does your body control its salt concentration?

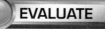 **EVALUATE** # Homeostasis in Your Critter

Throughout chapters 4 and 5, you have been exploring the concept of homeostasis. At this point, you should have a good understanding of the complex systems and processes that are involved. They help living systems maintain an internal condition of dynamic balance even while external conditions change dramatically.

In this Evaluate activity, *Homeostasis in Your Critter*, you will return to the description of the critter that you "adopted" in the Evaluate activity, *First Encounter with the Critter*, from chapter 3, *Products of Evolution: Unity and Diversity*. In doing so, you will evaluate what you have learned in this chapter. You will apply what you have learned about homeostasis to your critter. This will show your teacher what you have learned about how organisms maintain their internal environments when the external environments change.

Materials (per person)

descriptions and diagrams of your critter from chapter 3
materials for adding to your critter descriptions

PROCESS AND PROCEDURES

1. Work individually to write 2 paragraphs that answer the following questions.
   a. Summarize your understanding of homeostasis. Include a definition in your own words and describe several examples.
   b. Explain why it is important for organisms to maintain homeostasis. Give examples of scenarios when homeostasis is disrupted.
2. Read over the description and sketch of your critter that you completed in chapter 3. As you read, think about scenarios in which the homeostasis of your critter would be challenged.
3. List at least 5 specific environmental stressors that your organism would likely experience in its environment.
4. Develop a response to this question: In what ways does your critter maintain its internal environment, considering the external stressors that it experiences?

You will know that you have adequately addressed the question if your response includes an explanation, illustration, or demonstration of the following.
   a. How your critter responds to changes in external temperature
   b. How your critter regulates water balance
   c. How your critter responds to at least 2 other stressors caused by changes in the external environment
   d. How at least 2 key systems in your critter interact to adjust internal conditions

   > You can choose an appropriate medium for your response. A medium is the method or materials you use to convey your response. You could write a response, draw a picture or diagram, develop a collage, or use some other method that your teacher approves.

Analysis

Evaluate your work according to the handout, *Homeostasis in Your Critter Rubric,* that your teacher provides. Your teacher will use these guidelines to evaluate your work as well.

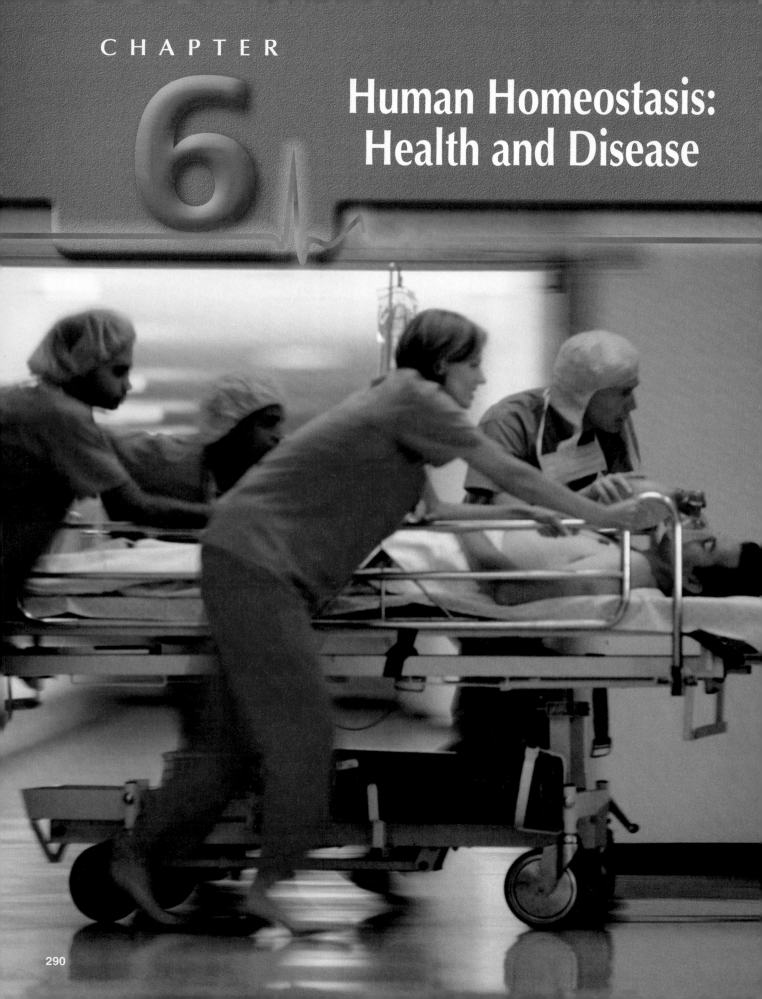

6

Human Homeostasis: Health and Disease

> The coordinated physiological processes which maintain most of the steady states in the organism are so complex and so peculiar to living beings ... that I have suggested a special designation for these states, homeostasis.
>
> Dr. Walter Cannon

The processes of homeostasis allow most people to enjoy relatively long and healthy lives. For these people, the common cold and other minor illnesses are only temporary disruptions. Their bodies are quite capable of recovering through normal regulatory processes. Occasionally, disruptions in our homeostasis can affect our health in more serious and sometimes even permanent ways. These cases often require medical care to help the body stay within the internal limits necessary for life.

In chapter 6, *Human Homeostasis: Health and Disease*, you will examine what happens when homeostasis is disrupted in various ways. You will explore the effects of severe dehydration, allergic reactions, trauma, and a variety of other emergency health care situations. You also will consider how medical technology can help compensate for disruptions in the body's homeostasis. Then you will examine how certain personal behaviors can increase or reduce your risk of disrupting your body's homeostasis. After you have completed these activities, you will evaluate your understanding of disruption by developing a mock proposal that requests funds for a worthy health care initiative of your choice.

GOALS FOR THE CHAPTER

Throughout chapter 6, you will work to gain an understanding of the following concepts:

✔ Homeostasis in the human body may be disrupted by external and internal factors.

✔ Homeostasis often can be restored, but extreme disruption of homeostasis can result in death.

✔ The immune system helps protect the body against infection and cancerous cells.

✔ Humans are subject to many health risks, which are affected by each person's behavior and by societal and cultural factors.

✔ Scientific explanations can change with the discovery of additional evidence.

✔ Ethical analysis can be used to make health care and other decisions.

To help you develop these understandings, you will complete the following activities.

ENGAGE	Pushing the Limits
EXPLORE / EXPLAIN	Hospital Triage
EXPLAIN	Self-Defense!
ELABORATE	Tony's Brain
ELABORATE	What's the Risk?
EVALUATE	Health Care Proposal

Throughout chapter 6, keep referring to the chapter organizer to help you remember what you have learned and where you are headed.

ENGAGE

Pushing the Limits

Key Idea: External factors can challenge homeostasis in the body.

Linking Question:
How can we treat severe disruptions of homeostasis?

Chapter 6

EXPLORE   EXPLAIN

Hospital Triage

Part A: Triage in the Emergency Room
Part B: Let's Get More Information

Key Idea: Some disruptions of homeostasis can be reversed with medical care, but some cannot.

Linking Question:
How does the body defend itself from infections that threaten homeostasis?

MAJOR CONCEPTS

✔ Homeostasis in the human body may be disrupted by external and internal factors.

✔ Homeostasis often can be restored, but extreme disruption of homeostasis can result in death.

✔ The immune system helps protect the body against infection and cancerous cells.

✔ Humans are subject to many health risks, which are affected by each person's behavior and by societal and cultural factors.

✔ Scientific explanations can change with the discovery of additional evidence.

✔ Ethical analysis can be used to make health care and other decisions.

EXPLAIN

Self-Defense!

Part A: Natural Defenses
Part B: Diagnosis: Two Puzzles

Key Idea: The human immune system provides protection against some disruptions to homeostasis. These disruptions are caused by infections and foreign toxins.

Linking Question:
Can disruptions to homeostasis in the brain affect behavior?

EVALUATE

Health Care Proposal

Key Idea: Health care programs help humans maintain homeostasis.

Human Homeostasis: Health and Disease

Linking Question:
How can society manage risks to homeostasis and make ethical health care decisions?

ELABORATE

What's the Risk?

Part A: Fluid Exchange
Part B: Risk Assessment
Part C: Ethical Analysis

Key Idea: Risky behaviors can threaten homeostasis. Ethical analysis helps humans make decisions about risk.

Linking Question:
How can individuals and societies make decisions to minimize disruptions of homeostasis?

ELABORATE

Tony's Brain

Key Idea: Mental illness is frequently linked to changes in the brain, which can be viewed as a disruption of homeostasis.

 ENGAGE

Pushing the Limits

Just how much stress can the human body endure and still function? As you work through this Engage activity, *Pushing the Limits*, you will examine the limits of the human body. In the activities that follow, you will deepen your understanding of the limits of homeostasis.

PROCESS AND PROCEDURES

1. Read the scenario, *A Sweltering Experience*. As you read, use your science notebook to record details about the physical condition of the 2 hikers at the time of their rescue.

2. Complete the following tasks with your partner. Write your responses in your science notebook.

   a. List at least 4 human body systems that need to respond to restore internal balance (homeostasis) in the hikers. Next to each system you list, write why you think that system would need to respond.

      Think about your work in chapter 4, *The Internal Environment of Organisms*, and chapter 5, *Maintaining Balance in Organisms*. To complete your list, use your understanding of the interacting body systems that work to maintain homeostasis.

   b. List 4 other scenarios you can imagine that could also severely disrupt homeostasis.

Analysis

Answer the following questions in your science notebook.

1. Recall that factors that disturb homeostasis and stress the body are called stressors. List 2 mild stressors and 2 severe stressors. Describe the effects that each stressor would have on the human body.

   You made notes about stressors in the chapter 5 Explore activity, *What's Your Temperature Now?* You may find the information in the sidebar, *Beyond the Limits*, to be helpful.

2. From your personal experience, describe 2 disruptions of homeostasis that could occur in *nonhuman* organisms.

3. From your personal experience, describe a mild or severe disruption of homeostasis that happened to you or to someone you know. Describe the effect on the person's body, his or her body's response, and the response of other people such as parents or doctors (if involved). Finally, describe how the experience affected your emotions and decision making (if at all).

A Sweltering Experience

The two hikers were not worried about a thing. The day was beautiful: warm and clear, with a pleasant breeze sweeping off the high desert. The canyon trail offered great views. Monique and her father, Nelson, tromped enthusiastically downward. They stopped to enjoy the brilliant wildflowers and watched their steps as they skirted around a narrow switchback. Monique cried out in delight as she spotted an eagle soaring nearby, riding the warm air currents rising from the canyon depths.

They never thought about the distance, trekking downhill over 14 km (9 mi) of trail before they began to grow tired. They stopped to rest. Nelson removed his jacket, tying it around his waist, while Monique applied more sunscreen to her face. They remarked, with some surprise, that it was much warmer in the canyon than they had expected.

It was then that Nelson pointed out that they had finished most of the water from the single canteen they had brought. Neither of them was tired. But given the heat, and the distance remaining to the bottom, they decided they had better turn around and start back up toward the rim where they had left their car in the parking lot.

Almost immediately, the effects of gravity became apparent. A trail that had been an easy stroll going down now became a daunting ramp rising steeply upward. Their progress was slow, and the canyon rim seemed impossibly high overhead. Monique started to feel concerned as, after an hour of climbing, they finally reached the switchback that had been just a few minutes away when they were going down.

They were very thirsty but had to ration the last few mouthfuls of water carefully. Frequently, they stopped to mop the sweat from their faces, drawing deep, ragged breaths of dry air that didn't seem to refresh them much at all. They had no strength for conversation, merely plodded along slowly, kicking up clouds of dust with each footstep on the dry, gritty trail.

Suddenly, Monique cried out in pain and slapped at her leg, swatting away a bee—but not before the insect had driven its stinger through her skin. Grimly, she continued on. But within minutes, her leg began to swell around the sting. Limping in pain, she moved even slower than before, and soon she had to stop and rest.

Nelson was growing frantic. They still had 5 or 6 km (3 or 4 mi) to go to reach the parking lot. They had seen no other hikers during the whole day. Their cell phones were useless in the desolate canyon. Nelson found a small patch of shade near the trail and told Monique to stay there while he went for help. Leaving her the canteen, with its remaining sip or two of water, he started climbing as fast as he could. He hoped to find a ranger or call for help if his cell phone found a signal at the top of the canyon.

Climbing with all his strength and speed, gasping for breath and sweating profusely, Nelson still took two hours to reach the rim. When he arrived at the car, he was badly dehydrated. His body could no longer cool itself adequately through perspiration. He was dizzy and nauseous, suffering from an excruciating headache, so confused that he couldn't think of what to do next.

It was only good fortune that a ranger who was a trained paramedic drove into the parking lot on a routine patrol. Immediately, he noticed that Nelson needed help. The hiker was breathing loudly and rapidly through his mouth, and the skin of his hands was hot and dry to the touch. Yet his face was not very flushed. Even as he radioed for a backcountry rescue team to go after Monique, the ranger knew that Nelson himself was dangerously ill.

The rescuers reached Monique three hours after she had been stung. Her condition was alarming. They quickly loaded her onto a stretcher and carried her to the nearest clearing wide enough for a helicopter to land. Meanwhile, the ranger reported Monique's condition to the emergency room personnel.

"Her vision is blurred, and her breathing labored. Her leg is red and swollen near the bee sting, and she has a rash over her leg, spreading to her stomach. Her lips are cracked—she had trouble drinking when we gave her water."

The helicopter flight will not take long, but Nelson's and Monique's fates both remain uncertain. It is up to you, the emergency room personnel, to save them.

SIDEBAR

Beyond the Limits

The human body has a remarkable ability to adjust to changes in the environment. The human body also has its limits. When people are in a harsh environment such as the desert, the body's challenge to maintaining internal balance is even greater than usual. In such situations, small errors in judgment, such as not drinking enough water, can have serious consequences. Homeostasis may also be disrupted if one or more of the body's regulatory systems break down.

The factors that disturb homeostasis and stress the body are called **stressors**. Sunlight can be a stressor and so can a physical injury. You already are familiar with some of the disruptions that can take place on a hot day when you are dehydrated. The body will be able to recover normal balance if the stress is mild or acts briefly. For example, a deep cut that bleeds heavily can temporarily disrupt the body's fluid balance. If the bleeding stops, the body may be able to return to a balanced state. With a more serious injury, a transfusion of blood may be necessary to restore balance. If the disruption is extreme, the body may be damaged permanently. In some cases, the body may not be able to reestablish balance. For example, a very bad cut to the leg may bleed faster than the body's ability to adjust to the condition. If medical help is not immediate, serious illness or even death can result (figure 6.1).

Even if a disruption in balance is less severe, the disruption still can be a serious threat if it lasts for a long time. Diseases such as diabetes (figure 6.2) or heart disease are examples of this type of disruption. In such long-term disruptions, organ systems or tissues often are damaged slowly over time. The body's attempt to regain

balanced conditions becomes harder and harder.

Other stressors that could overwhelm balance in the body include a lack of nourishment (starvation); a lack of oxygen (suffocation); the presence of toxins (air pollution or drug overdose); or a serious bacterial infection. These examples are familiar because they are human injuries or illnesses. However, every organism is at risk of homeostatic disruptions. Every species on Earth is adapted for survival in a specific habitat and under specific conditions.

If an organism's environment changes quickly, its ability to maintain internal balance may be pushed beyond its limits. Consider the very different situations faced by fishes living in freshwater and those living in saltwater (see figure 6.3). Both types of fishes must adjust their internal concentrations of water and solutes such as sodium chloride (salt) to maintain the proper balance. Processes have evolved that are

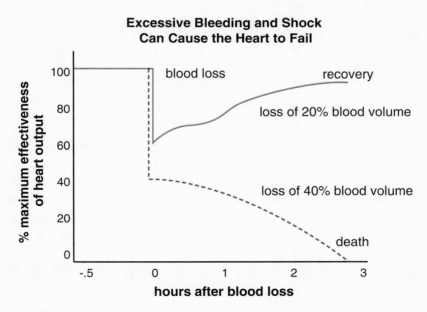

Figure 6.1   Blood loss. The body adjusts for blood loss in several ways, including clotting the blood and increasing the heart rate. These responses slowly restore the effectiveness of the heart's output. This is the case if the body loses 20 percent of its blood (red line). There is a limit to how much blood can be lost and still have homeostatic mechanisms restore function. Do you see evidence for this in the graph when the body loses 40 percent of its blood volume (blue line)?

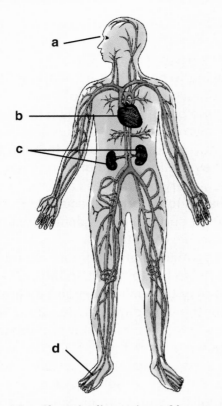

a freshwater fish

b marine fish

Figure 6.2 **Chronic disruption of homeostasis.** Diabetes mellitus is a chronic disease that can cause tissue damage throughout the body. The disorder is caused by inadequate amounts or functioning of the hormone insulin. Insulin regulates levels of glucose (sugar) in blood, liver, and muscle cells. If this disease is not well controlled, diabetes can result in poor circulation. It can damage tissues such as (*a*) the eye, (*b*) the heart, (*c*) the kidneys, and (*d*) peripheral tissue.

Figure 6.3 (*a*) Freshwater fishes must continually remove large amounts of water so that the solutes in their internal environments are not diluted. (*b*) Marine fishes must drink water to maintain the water balance in their bodies. They must remove solutes such as sodium chloride via their gills. The kidneys remove other kinds of salts from the fishes' bodies. What do you think would happen if each of these organisms were placed in the other's environmental setting?

effective at accomplishing this task for each type of fish. Kidneys help regulate the same conditions in humans. The internal processes of fishes, however, are sufficient only for the usual variations in water and salt balance. That is why we define homeostasis as maintaining conditions *within certain limits.* If either type of fish were suddenly put in the other's external conditions, the fish would be beyond its limits. The fish most likely would die. Extreme stressors on any organism can be fatal.

Hospital Triage

You and your partners are a team of physicians in the emergency room of Desert Metropolitan Hospital. It is about 8:30 p.m. on a Friday in July. You have been busy, as you usually are on summer weekends. Unfortunately, you are about to become even busier. You have just received a flurry of calls from local paramedics, and now you and your colleagues are preparing for an influx of patients suffering from a variety of illnesses and trauma injuries. The influx includes a helicopter carrying Monique and an ambulance carrying Nelson, the two canyon hikers discussed in the scenario, *A Sweltering Experience.*

Because there are many patients and only a handful of doctors, you cannot treat every patient at the same time. In the activity, *Hospital Triage*, your first task is to assess the severity of each patient's condition and establish a "priority for treatment," which is called **triage**. Triage is a process used in emergency rooms as well as in battlefields and disaster areas to assign the order for assisting patients and maximizing medical efficiency and success. You will need to use everything you currently know about the body's normal homeostatic mechanisms to complete the triage. Keep in mind that there is not a single "right" answer for your medical team. The most important measure of your success in this Explore-Explain activity will be your team's ability to *explain* the treatment choices that you will make.

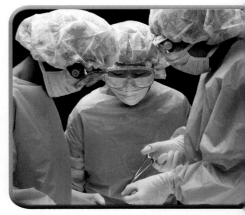

PROCESS AND PROCEDURES

Part A   Triage in the Emergency Room

When you visit your doctor's office, a medical professional first measures and records your vital signs including temperature, blood pressure, heart rate, and breathing rate. Have you ever considered what your vital signs tell the doctor? Vital signs are body characteristics that can be measured quickly. They provide important information about major body systems. This information is particularly important for quickly determining when patients are experiencing severe trauma.

1. With your team, read the need to know, *Glossary of Vital Signs,* in preparation for interpreting your patients' conditions. As you read, enter new terms into your personal glossary.

   Pay particular attention to the normal, serious, and critical ranges for each vital sign. You will refer to this information to determine the level of trauma that your patients are experiencing.

2. Read the handout, *Patients' Vital Signs: Preliminary Information,* as a team. Briefly discuss the condition and future outlook of each patient.

   Pay particular attention to the description of each patient's injury or illness.

SCI LINKS®
NSTA

www.scilinks.org

Topic: vital signs
Code: human4E299

NEED TO KNOW

ENGLISH   SPANISH

Glossary of Vital Signs

Vital signs are body characteristics that can be measured quickly. They provide important information about major body systems:

- **Pulse** is the rate of the heart's beating. It provides clues to how well the heart is functioning. It also indicates how well the blood is carrying oxygen and other important substances to the tissues, including brain tissues.

- **Blood pressure** is another indicator of circulation. It is measured at an artery and is usually represented as two numbers such as 125/85 (read as "125 over 85"). The first number (**systolic pressure**) is a measurement of the force of blood against the walls of the arteries, veins, and chambers of the heart as the heart contracts. The second number (**diastolic pressure**) is a measurement of the lowest pressure reached as the heart relaxes.

- **Body temperature** can indicate how the body is responding to a disruption in homeostasis. An elevated body temperature may indicate a fever generated by the body to fight an infection. A low core body temperature indicates hypothermia or shock.

- **Breathing rate** reflects how well oxygen is being delivered to the body. It also is associated with heart rate and circulation.

Taken together, vital signs give the physician a quick view of a patient's internal state, even if the patient is unconscious and cannot explain how he or she feels. These measurements vary over a relatively narrow range in healthy people, indicating that the body normally has precise control of internal conditions. When the vital signs are far outside the normal ranges, homeostasis usually is disrupted in the patient. Under these circumstances, the vital signs are direct indicators of problems with internal systems that are involved in maintaining homeostasis. Vital signs, however, usually do not indicate the precise cause of the disruption of homeostasis.

What determines the value of a "normal" vital sign? In figure 6.4, "normal" is defined by averaging the values found in healthy people. Occasionally, healthy individuals have normal readings that are outside of these average ranges. For example, highly trained athletes may have low resting heart rates. Normal ranges of vital signs also vary by sex and age. Many young people have systolic blood pressure lower than 100 millimeters of mercury (mm Hg). In general, blood pressure is

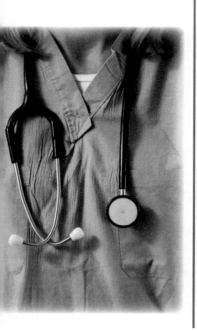

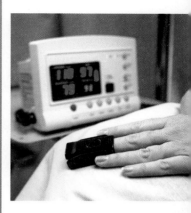

Vital sign	Normal range	Serious range	Critical range
Blood pressure	110/70–140/90 mm Hg (systolic/ diastolic)	90–100 mm Hg systolic	< 90 mm Hg systolic
Resting pulse rate	60–100 beats/min	< 60 or > 100 beats/min	< 50 or > 120 beats/min
Temperature	37°C (98.6°F)	39°C–40°C (102.2°F–104°F)	> 40°C (> 104°F)
Breathing rate	10–20 resp/min	< 10 or > 20 resp/min	< 10 or > 30 resp/min

Key: mm Hg = millimeters of mercury, a measure of pressure; < is less than; > is greater than; resp/min = respirations per minute.

Note: The figures quoted above are simplified from those used by medical personnel.

Figure 6.4   Table of normal, serious, and critical ranges of vital signs for adults at rest.

evaluated in relation to other vital signs and the patient's age and condition. For the purposes of this activity, assume that the normal state for each patient is within the normal ranges listed in the table.

3. Divide your triage team to work in pairs. Each pair should complete the following tasks for half of the patients, using the *Triage Data Sheet* handout:

Task 1: Record the vital signs of each patient and mark whether they are within or outside normal ranges.

Procedure: Use the information in the need to know, *Glossary of Vital Signs,* to decide whether or not each vital sign for each patient is within normal limits. Record the vital signs for each patient in the "vital signs" column on the data sheet. In the "range of vital signs" column, record a checkmark (√) to indicate vital signs that are within normal limits. Use an *X* to indicate those outside normal limits.

Task 2: Identify the body systems that are most likely disrupted by each patient's injury or illness.

Procedure: Work with your partner to develop a list of systems that are disrupted for each patient. Systems might include the gas exchange system, the circulatory system, the nervous system, the immune system, the muscular-skeletal system, and the urinary system. Record your lists in the "disrupted systems" column on your data sheet. Remember what you learned in chapters 4 and 5 about the interactions between internal body systems in maintaining homeostasis. Use your knowledge to make logical inferences from vital signs that are outside normal ranges.

4. How will your team decide whom to treat first? Read the need to know, *Patient Assessment Guidelines*. As you read, note whether any of your patients has an airway obstruction, critically impaired breathing or circulation, shock, or hyperthermia.

NEED TO KNOW

ENGLISH   SPANISH

Patient Assessment Guidelines

1. All emergency care begins with the ABCs. Make sure there is an open <u>a</u>irway, that the patient is <u>b</u>reathing, and that the patient has adequate <u>c</u>irculation.

   a. *Airway.* Remove obstructions from the mouth, if necessary. Move the tongue if it is obstructing the airway. Close openings such as the nose or wounds that prevent the lungs from filling with air.

   b. *Breathing.* Restore breathing by artificial resuscitation. (In artificial resuscitation, another person or device can temporarily provide air to a patient.) Or administer oxygen, if necessary.

   c. *Circulation.* Checking and restoring circulation take priority over airway and breathing. Restore heartbeat by cardiopulmonary resuscitation (CPR), if necessary. CPR is a technique in which another person temporarily provides air and heart contractions for a patient whose heart has stopped beating or is not pumping blood effectively. Stop blood loss from serious wounds.

2. Look at the patient and assess his or her injuries. Immobilize any injuries to the neck. The patient may become paralyzed if you initiate any movement. Always suspect neck injuries when there is extensive injury to the head or face.

3. Check the patient for **shock**. This condition is extremely serious and life threatening. It occurs when blood flow to the tissues drops to a dangerously low level. Often, shock is accompanied by very low blood pressure. When a person is in shock, the circulatory system no longer delivers adequate supplies of oxygen and nutrients to the tissues. Shock can result from failure of the heart to pump vigorously enough. It can also result from serious blood loss or from a reduction of effective blood volume due to pooling in the capillaries or to dehydration.

   Shock due to reduced blood volume can be treated by elevating the feet, by using pressure suits that force blood from the extremities (arms and legs) back into the body core, or by infusing

© iStockphoto/Lovleah

© iStockphoto/Jeanell Norvell

blood or saline solution into the circulatory system. Shock due to weakness of the heart or damage to the circulatory system may require medications or mechanical devices that assist circulation.

4. Check the patient's temperature. The hypothalamus normally controls internal body temperature. If this control is lost, the core body temperature can rise to dangerously high levels, a condition known as **hyperthermia**. Extreme hyperthermia can kill cells, particularly brain cells. In these cases, external measures must be taken, such as rubbing the patient with ice to bring the body temperature back within normal limits.

   Conversely, the body can cool to dangerous levels. This is a condition known as **hypothermia**. Hypothermia can occur when people are cold and wet for a long period of time. Rapid evaporation of water can cool a person quite quickly, even if the air temperature is not extremely cold. In such cases, the body must be warmed slowly to bring it back within normal limits.

5. Consolidate your assessment by designating the patient's condition as critical, serious, or stable. "Critical" indicates that the patient has a life-threatening condition. "Serious" indicates that the patient has a condition that causes a loss of normal function. "Stable" indicates that the patient's condition will not change quickly and that a delay in treatment would not cause further harm.

5. Complete the next 3 tasks as a group of 4. Draw upon the *Patient Assessment Guidelines* need to know, and the patients' vital signs to determine priority and treatments for each patient:

   Task 1: Compare all your patients and, as a team, decide treatment priorities for each patient.

   Procedure: Assign treatment priorities of critical (+++), serious (++), or stable (+) to each patient and record them in the "treatment priority" column of the *Triage Data Sheet*. Encourage all team members to contribute ideas about what treatment category each patient falls into.

   Task 2: Suggest initial triage treatments and explain your priority choice for each patient.

   Procedure: Write the kind of triage treatment each patient should ideally receive into the "initial triage suggestions" column of the *Triage Data Sheet*. Write a brief justification for the treatment priority that your team assigned each patient during step 5, task 1.

   Task 3: Decide the order that patients should be given their triage treatments.

   Procedure: For each patient, consider how many of the patient's vital signs are in the serious range and how fast you think the patient may be declining. Listen carefully to the reasoning of your teammates. In the first column of the data sheet (the "patient" column), next to each patient's name, write the number that corresponds to the order of treatment that your team agrees upon.

Part B   Let's Get More Information

While you were performing your triage evaluation, hospital staff continued to monitor the patients' vital signs (figure 6.5). This new information will help you reprioritize the order of care.

1. Read the *First Priority* handout. Then discuss with your teammates the importance of the new information about Monique, Nelson, and Albert.

2. With your team, reevaluate the order you should treat each remaining patient. Record your order of priority in the "part B modified priority" column of the *Triage Data Sheet*. The new order may be different from the order you wrote in the first column.

   Be prepared to share your ideas and your team's triage results in a class discussion.

3. Write your team's reasoning for the rankings you made in the "part B explanations" column of the *Triage Data Sheet*.

   Your reasoning may include nonmedical factors, such as behavior and luck, which your team may have taken into consideration.

4. Read the *Additional Information* handout to learn about the outcome of your secondary triage decisions.

5. As a team, discuss what the long-term outlook is for each patient now that each has moved out of the emergency room. Prepare to present your reasoning and other thoughts about the activity in a class discussion.

   For example, you might think that some patients will recover completely, others will recover slowly and may suffer long-lasting effects, and others may never recover and even die because of their injuries or illnesses.

© iStockphoto/Steve Dangers

Figure 6.5
Examples of technology in medicine:
(*a*) defibrillator paddles, (*b*) CT scans, (*c*) intensive care monitoring station.

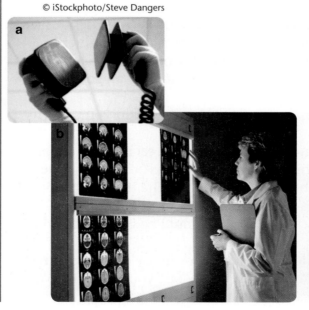
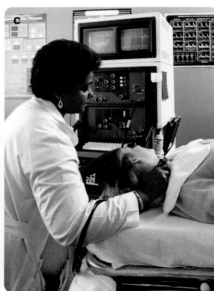

Analysis

Work individually to respond to the following. Write your answers in your science notebook.

> The sidebar, *Coping with Disruptions: The Role of Medicine in Homeostasis*, and the facts in the need to know sections, *Glossary of Vital Signs* and *Patient Assessment Guidelines*, provide important background information for writing well-reasoned answers.

1. Why are vital signs so valuable in quickly assessing a patient's condition?
2. Explain how a head injury, such as the one Albert suffered when his motorcycle crashed, could affect several body systems at once but leave others unaffected.
3. Monique and Nelson both had very high temperatures when they were brought into the emergency room. Why do you think Monique's heart rate was high and Nelson's heart rate was low?
4. Why was Monique likely to survive if she received treatment in time, but Nelson died in spite of the priority he was given?
5. What, if any, nonmedical considerations did you use to rank the patients? Explain your response.
6. In 1 or 2 paragraphs, compare and contrast an illness or injury that the body can recover from on its own with one that requires medical intervention. Explain how the responses of internal body systems that are necessary to maintaining homeostasis differ in the 2 situations.
7. Compare and contrast the process of triage with the process of scientific inquiry.

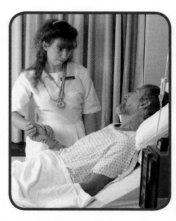

ENGLISH   SPANISH

Coping with Disruptions: The Role of Medicine in Homeostasis

What happens if internal conditions go beyond our body's ability to recover? Scientists and doctors have developed tools that provide both temporary and long-term help. Some of these tools help correct internal conditions. Other tools may temporarily take over one of the body's organs. Some cases require surgery. Surgeons can repair heart defects by replacing valves in the heart. In other cases, surgeons may insert a permanent device in the body. For example, a pacemaker is an electronic device that corrects an irregular heartbeat.

Other medical devices work outside the body. For example, if a person's lungs have collapsed, physicians can use a mechanical ventilator. The ventilator inflates the lungs so that oxygen enters the bloodstream. It also removes carbon dioxide from the patient's body. People with kidney failure can be helped by dialysis machines, which filter blood and assist with fluid regulation.

Health care professionals also use technology to gather information about a person's injury or illness. They can collect important information by checking the vital signs of the patient. This is the first step in a diagnosis. Medical workers can make accurate measurements by using tools that extend their senses. The tools include X-rays, electrocardiographs, stethoscopes, blood pressure cuffs, and thermometers. X-ray images provide experts with a way to assess internal structures. The bones of the arm are shown in an X-ray in figure 6.6. An electrocardiograph maps the rate and patterns of the beating heart. This instrument also prints out a record such as the ones shown in figure 6.7. The record is called an electrocardiogram. It helps a heart specialist determine the health of a patient's heart and circulatory system.

A health care professional can also learn a lot about a patient from the composition of the patient's blood. In one type of test, technicians count each type of blood cell. In a healthy person's blood, red blood cells generally are present in a much higher concentration than white blood cells. Generally, the ratio is about 700:1. An abundance of white blood cells usually indicates an infection. The components of blood plasma also may vary with certain types of imbalances. Plasma is the noncellular, liquid part of the blood. Plasma components include cholesterol, lipids, protein, glucose, and electrolytes. Electrolytes are solutes such as chloride, potassium, calcium, and sodium.

In cases where physicians find an internal imbalance, they sometimes prescribe a drug to treat it. They can use specific drugs to treat high blood pressure, heart disease, diabetes, and cancer. The widespread use of antibiotics has resulted in a dramatic decline in fatal bacterial infections.

Antibiotics and many other drugs are recent developments. They provide an example of how technology has changed our cultural view of medicine during the past 70 years. Unfortunately, overuse of antibiotics has resulted in the evolution of some bacterial strains that are resistant to certain antibiotics. Bacterial infections once again are becoming more difficult to treat. Figure 6.8 shows an experiment that tested the resistance of two types of bacteria to an antibiotic.

Figure 6.6 Imaging technology reveals internal structures. The diagnosis of disruptions such as broken bones or tumors is made more efficient through the analysis of X-rays and other images that allow physicians to view internal structures. Physicians used this X-ray of an arm to determine the extent of the injury.

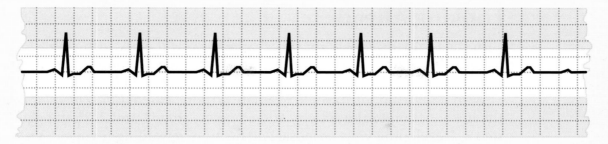

a normal heart rhythm

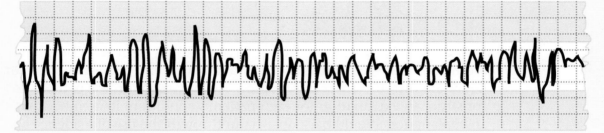

b disrupted heartbeat

Figure 6.7 **Electrocardiograms help physicians assess heart function.** Electrocardiograms reveal (*a*) normal and (*b*) disrupted heart function. This particular disruption in heart function is called a ventricular fibrillation. It occurs when the muscles of a ventricle contract rapidly and continuously in an uncoordinated manner. How would a disrupted circulatory system affect gas exchange?

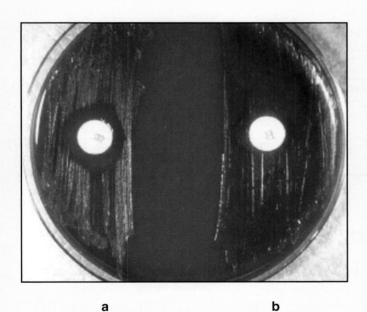

a   **b**

Medical technology has increased the life span of many people. Researchers are continuing to make advances. However, some of these advances raise ethical questions. Health care professionals and the public struggle with deciding when to use life-support systems. When a patient is terminally ill, the choices can be difficult. The costs for many advanced medical treatments are also extremely high. As our medical knowledge increases and as we develop more tools to assist medical professionals, society must learn how to balance the costs and benefits of the treatments.

Figure 6.8 **Bacterial resistance to antibiotics.** On this petri dish, two strains of bacteria were spread evenly across a nutrient material. Disks soaked in the antibiotic bacitracin were then added to the plates. The two bacterial strains were observed after further growth. The clear area in (*a*) indicates a lack of growth near the antibiotic disk. In (*b*), there is no clear area around the disk, which indicates that the bacteria grew there. What evidence do you see that indicates that bacteria can be resistant to the effects of antibiotics?

Looking Ahead

In the Evaluate activity for this chapter, you will work with your teammates to develop a health care proposal. Because you will need extra time to collect information for your proposal, you need to start now.

With your team, turn to the Evaluate activity, *Health Care Proposal*. Read the introduction to the activity and complete steps 1 and 2. Then begin step 3. Developing your proposal will be more rewarding if you are well prepared.

Further Challenges

After 3 of the patients left the emergency room for regular hospital rooms, lab tests were returned for Esther, Maria, and Ed. Use the data in figure 6.9 with the other information you have about these patients to construct an explanation for each patient's condition. Remember that an explanation should back up a claim through the use of evidence and reasoning. Also provide treatment recommendations for each patient based on the patient's lab results.

Figure 6.9
Summary of lab test results conducted on blood and fecal (solid waste) samples taken from three patients.

Lab test	Esther	Maria	Ed
Potassium	1.7 times above normal	70% of normal	Not checked
Chloride	1.3 times above normal	Not checked	Not checked
Sodium	Not checked	Normal	Not checked
Glucose	Normal	Normal	Normal
Total cholesterol	Normal	Normal	1.5 times above normal
Fecal test	Not checked	Positive for *Salmonella*	Not checked

Self-Defense!

You have seen how the body corrects minor disruptions in homeostasis and how medical technology can help when the disruptions are more serious. But would you believe that a battle is going on inside your body even when you are healthy? The battle is being fought by internal body systems that work together to protect your body against external conditions *before* they threaten to disrupt your body's normal balance.

As a living organism, your body constantly defends itself from foreign chemicals and invading microorganisms and viruses. Where do the invaders come from? Recall the bee sting that Monique, the hiker, suffered.

When a bee stings you, it injects venom into your body. Venom is made up of molecules that are foreign to your body, and your body reacts to them. Another source of invading particles is the air that you breathe. Air may contain particles of pollutants, spores of fungi and bacteria, and virus particles. You are likely to breathe in many microorganisms if someone with a cold sneezes near you (figure 6.10).

It might seem impossible for living organisms to protect themselves against the disrupting influence of so many threats. Yet all living systems have some means of protecting their internal environments against infection. Humans and other vertebrates have a particularly elaborate system of natural defense, which is known as the immune system. Although it is not perfect, the immune system generally wins its battles. This Explain activity, *Self-Defense!*, will help you explain how your body defends itself.

Materials

Part B (per team of 4)
  test subject card
  scenario card

Figure 6.10 A single "kachoo" can release 10,000 to 100,000 virus particles.

PROCESS AND PROCEDURES

Part A   Natural Defenses

1. Consider these 3 questions: How does your body know that a foreign cell is different? Why do antibiotics fail to help with the common cold? How does a vaccination against polio protect you for your whole life? Read the essays, *Avoiding Disruptions: The Immune System* and *Medicine and the Immune System,* as you investigate these questions. As you read, enter new terms into your personal glossary.

   The information in the need to know, *Glossary of Immune System Components,* should also help.

Avoiding Disruptions: The Immune System

Each organ system of the human body maintains some aspect of homeostasis. The immune system protects your body from disruptions in homeostasis caused by infections and toxins. Like a fortress, your body's immune system has many different defenses to keep out and kill invaders. The immune system uses two types of defenses. We will first explore the **nonspecific barriers**, and then examine the specific immune responses.

Nonspecific Immunity

The body's largest organ is the skin. The skin provides a nonspecific barrier or defense against invaders. A nonspecific barrier is one that does not have to recognize a particular invader. As the body's first line of defense, the skin helps guard the body's internal environment from attack. A second nonspecific barrier consists of millions of harmless bacteria that live on the skin (refer to figure 6.11). In most cases, these bacteria are beneficial to humans. They keep disease-causing microorganisms, or **pathogens**, from living on the skin. In return, these bacteria are able to live on the skin—a resource-rich environment.

Like the walls of a fortress, the skin helps guard your internal environment from outside attack. This wall, however, is not perfectly secure. There are natural "doors" to the internal environment, including the mouth, ears, eyes, nose, and genital, urinary, and anal openings. The doors allow for the invasion of pathogens. Additional nonspecific defenses have evolved to protect the natural openings. The defenses include saliva, tears, mucus, and sweat. Some of these bodily secretions have an enzyme that kills bacteria. Cuts in the skin provide easy avenues for infection, allowing pathogens to bypass all of the skin's nonspecific defenses.

Protection against pathogens is not unique to humans. All organisms have some resistance to

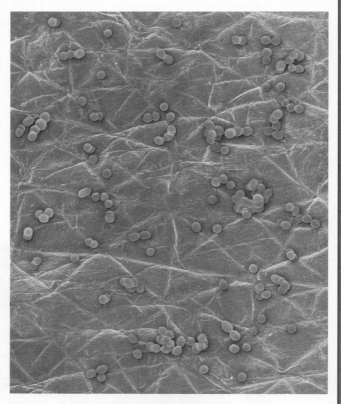

Figure 6.11 Scanning electron micrograph of bacteria on skin, magnified 24,000×.

invasion. For example, bacteria produce special enzymes that destroy foreign DNA. Plants have many defenses. They are at a high risk for pathogens because they do not move. One defense they have is to produce chemicals that kill plant tissue infected by fungus. The plant sacrifices the infected part. But the loss is less dangerous than an infection that spreads throughout the plant.

If pathogens reach the inside of a human body, they face an army of new defenses carried by the blood. A third line of nonspecific defense is made of cells that recognize and scavenge many types of invading organisms and toxins. Among the scavenger cells are macrophages. Figure 6.12 shows a macrophage in action.

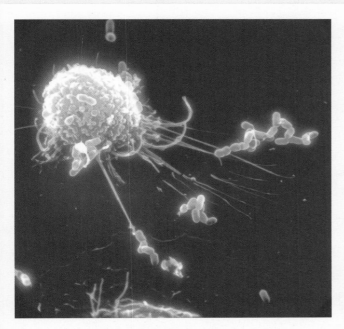

Figure 6.12 Macrophage engulfing bacteria.
A macrophage is a nonspecific scavenger cell that helps protect the body against pathogens. In this photograph, cellular extensions from a macrophage have captured several bacteria. Macrophages also play a role in the specific immune response.

Specific Immunity

Now let's look at the immune system's specific responses. The **specific immune response** is very different from the nonspecific defenses that act to repel all invaders. This part of the immune system recognizes and responds to particular pathogens. The drawback is that this response is somewhat slow. However, the specific immune response also uses a type of "memory." This way, the immune system can act much more quickly if a specific invader returns. This component of the immune system evolved relatively early in the vertebrate lineage, about 500–450 million years ago.

We discussed macrophages in the section on nonspecific immune response. But macrophages also act like "generals" in the specific immune response. They can coordinate an army of specific cells to attack only *certain* invaders. When they find a foreign object, macrophages alert **helper T cells**. In turn, helper T cells "recruit" more immune cells to defend the body. They do this by releasing specific molecules called lymphokines.

Once lymphokines are released, two lines of defense can begin. The first line of specific defense is called the **cell-mediated response**. In this response, lymphokines from helper T cells activate killer T cells. **Killer T cells** then recognize and kill body cells infected with pathogens. Figure 6.13 summarizes these interactions.

Cell-mediated responses help defend against viruses. Viruses enter normal cells of the body. They reproduce by using the cell's energy and materials. When viruses are inside cells, macrophages cannot find them. With this effective adaptation, viruses use the host cells as both a shield and a way to reproduce. So how does the body repel viruses? Killer T cells can distinguish virus-infected cells from uninfected cells. Infected cells put molecules from pathogens on the outside of their cell membranes. Killer T cells recognize these molecules and destroy the infected cells.

Many people think that they can take antibiotics to combat a viral infection. You may have taken an antibiotic, such as penicillin, when you were sick with a bacterial infection like strep throat. But antibiotics only kill bacteria, not viruses, because they disrupt elements in bacterial cell walls. Viruses are not constructed with the same elements, so antibiotics are ineffective against them.

The second line of specific immune defense is called the **antibody-mediated response**. Macrophages also trigger this response. They activate a group of cells called B cells. B cells make defense molecules known as antibodies. Antibodies are proteins that are carried by the bloodstream throughout the body. Antibodies bind, or attach, to specific molecules called antigens. Often, antigens are made by pathogens. A pathogen that has

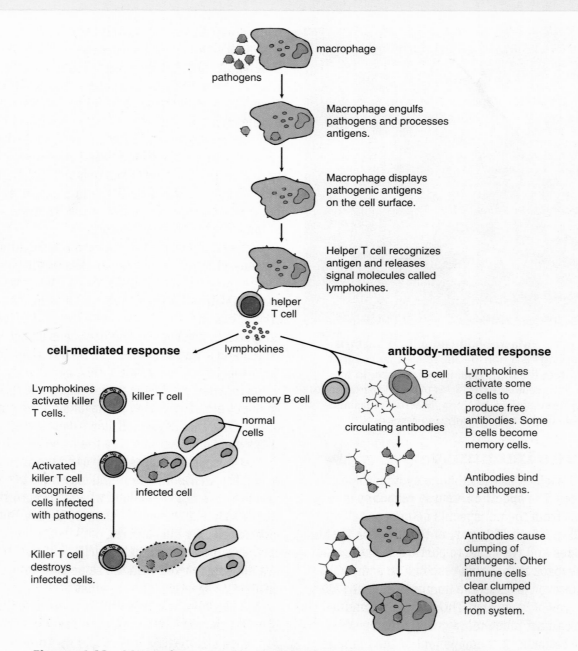

macrophage

pathogens

Macrophage engulfs pathogens and processes antigens.

Macrophage displays pathogenic antigens on the cell surface.

Helper T cell recognizes antigen and releases signal molecules called lymphokines.

helper T cell

cell-mediated response   lymphokines   **antibody-mediated response**

B cell

Lymphokines activate killer T cells.   killer T cell   memory B cell   Lymphokines activate some B cells to produce free antibodies. Some B cells become memory cells.

normal cells

circulating antibodies

Activated killer T cell recognizes cells infected with pathogens.   infected cell   Antibodies bind to pathogens.

Killer T cell destroys infected cells.   Antibodies cause clumping of pathogens. Other immune cells clear clumped pathogens from system.

Figure 6.13   Macrophages perform several functions as part of our immune system defenses. Macrophages scavenge pathogens nonspecifically. But they also play an important role in directing specific immune responses. During specific immune responses, macrophages interact with helper T cells. Helper T cells respond by producing signal molecules called lymphokines. Lymphokines can activate cell-mediated responses. These responses involve killer T cells in a process that destroys pathogen-infected cells. Lymphokines can also activate antibody-mediated responses. These responses involve B cells in a process that destroys circulating pathogens.

antigens on its surface becomes covered in the specific antibodies that match the antigen. This can cause the pathogens to clump together. It also helps macrophages recognize the pathogen. The pathogens are then quickly destroyed. Figure 6.13 illustrates this response.

The antibody-mediated response allows for a type of immune system memory. You can think of immune system memory as a type of memory that is stored outside your brain. This memory is possible because a few of the immune cells that fought a particular invader in the past remain in your body. Each time you are infected, your body stores a few of the B cells that respond. These memory B cells are already programmed to quickly make antibodies if the same pathogen tries to invade again. When that happens, your body produces a faster and more powerful attack against pathogens due to your immune system's *memory of infection.*

With this programmed response, your body may fight off the infection without ever having symptoms of illness. We call this "being immune to a disease." Most people become immune to measles, mumps, or chicken pox after they have been infected once.

Imperfect Immunity

With so many lines of defense, why does anyone ever get sick? The answer is that the immune system has limits. There are limits to how many pathogens or cancer cells the immune system can control. Sometimes the invader escapes detection. The body may not be able to maintain stability if infections destroy too much tissue.

People also become sick when stressors weaken their immune systems. Stressors include inadequate sleep, smoking, drug use, and anxiety. People with weakened immune systems make fewer immune cells. They also have a slower specific response to infection. Acquired immunodeficiency

syndrome, or AIDS, is a disease that causes extreme damage to the immune system. AIDS is caused by the human immunodeficiency virus, or HIV. HIV directly attacks the immune system's helper T cells. Without helper T cells, most of the immune system's specific responses do not function. As a result, the affected person cannot fight off minor infections, such as the common cold. He or she is also vulnerable to fatal illnesses such as pneumonia and cancer. The rapid course of untreated AIDS highlights how well the body usually is able to defend itself. Scientists use information about the evolution of HIV to seek cures for AIDS.

Sometimes the immune system works against the body. Not all antigens are harmful to the body. Nonthreatening antigens include insect venom, pollen, animal dander, and food. The immune system overreacts to some of these substances in people who suffer from **allergies**. Swelling, sneezing, and itchiness often result. Many of these symptoms are caused by the release of chemicals called histamines. As a result, medicines that counteract these symptoms are often called antihistamines. At other times, allergic reactions can be life threatening and require rapid medical assistance.

The specific immune defense works because immune cells know which cells are yours (self) and which are foreign (nonself). However, sometimes the immune system mistakes normal cells for foreign matter. In fact, many diseases are caused in this way. These diseases are called **autoimmune diseases**. An autoimmune disease causes the body to damage itself. Autoimmune diseases include rheumatoid arthritis and multiple sclerosis (MS). Rheumatoid arthritis is caused when immune cells attack the joints. Multiple sclerosis is caused when immune cells attack parts of the nervous system. Scientists seek to understand how the body normally distinguishes between self and nonself. This knowledge will help them find cures for autoimmune diseases.

Medicine and the Immune System

Given the strength and specificity of the immune system, it makes sense that doctors and scientists like to find ways to harness its power to treat disease. One of the most powerful immune-related technologies are **vaccines**. Scientists develop vaccines to train the body's immune memory. Vaccines "trick" the body into reacting against a pathogen that has the same antigens but is not a threat to health. The vaccinated person becomes immune without ever being exposed to the real pathogen. Edward Jenner developed the first vaccine in 1796 (see figure 6.14).

In the past, vaccines were often made by killing the pathogen, then injecting it into the body. This is how the original vaccine for polio was made. Some vaccines only introduce some of the pathogen's molecules, particularly the antigens. Some vaccines are made when scientists place viruses in a different environment. When the viruses evolve in the new environment, they are less harmful to humans. Today, most vaccines are made using biotechnology. In the laboratory, the genetic information to make viral antigens is moved to other cells. The new cells then produce viral antigens, which are injected into the patient's body. All types of vaccines trigger a minor immune response and produce memory B cells.

As figure 6.15 shows, vaccines can have a dramatic, positive impact on the spread of disease. There are vaccines for tetanus, rabies, chicken pox, some types of flu, and many others. Recently, a vaccine against human papillomavirus (HPV) was developed. The vaccine protects girls and women from cervical cancer. It is challenging to develop vaccines for some pathogens. Some diseases, such as the common cold, are caused by a broad group of pathogens. Vaccines developed against one common cold virus do not provide protection against all of the other varieties. Certain other diseases are difficult to prevent with vaccines because they evolve so rapidly. HIV evolves so rapidly that different strains can appear in one individual. Once again, understanding the evolution of HIV helps scientists learn how to treat people with AIDS.

Doctors must be careful to respect the immune system's ability to distinguish self from nonself when prescribing treatments. Some patients have allergies to certain medicines such as penicillin. You may also know that doctors must match the **blood type** of donated blood to the patient before performing a blood transfusion. What makes blood from different people different? The surface of red blood cells contains proteins that immune system cells recognize. These protein molecules are the basis for distinguishing blood as a certain *type* (figure 6.16). Blood type varies among individuals, and blood type proteins are identified

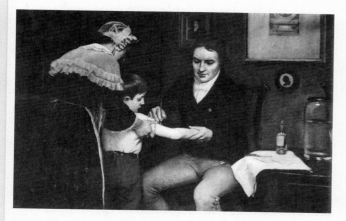

Figure 6.14 Edward Jenner discovered the first vaccine in 1796. At that time, smallpox was a deadly viral disease that had killed thousands of people throughout the world. Jenner gave patients doses of a virus that caused a much milder disease in humans, the cowpox virus. His patients developed antibodies that were effective against the smallpox virus. Then, when the patients were exposed to the smallpox virus, their immune systems could recognize the disease in time to mount an effective response and destroy the invading virus.

by the immune system as belonging to either self or nonself. The transfusion of one blood type into a person with another blood type causes the patient's immune system to attack the blood. The resulting blood clotting may make the patient so dangerously ill that death may occur.

As you have read, immune defenses destroy foreign material and infected cells. However, did you know that they also identify and destroy cancer cells? Cancer cells arise when normal cells become faulty. They begin to divide continuously. If many faulty cells accumulate, a tumor forms. Cancer cells may also move to other areas of the body. Cancer eventually causes death by robbing healthy parts of the body of resources. To prevent that, an active, healthy immune system is an essential protection.

Cancer is uncommon in young people because their immune systems usually attack and destroy abnormal cells before a cancer develops.

Occasionally, when a person is treated for cancer, the treatment destroys the immune system cells as well as the cancer cells. Doctors may replace immune system cells by performing a bone marrow transplant. Both red and white blood cells are formed within our bones, so bone marrow is the best source of newly dividing immune system cells. Bone marrow can be taken from a patient before treatment, or a bone marrow donor may be found. Because the patient's body continues to recognize self from nonself material, the donor is frequently a close relative, which helps "match" the tissue to the patient.

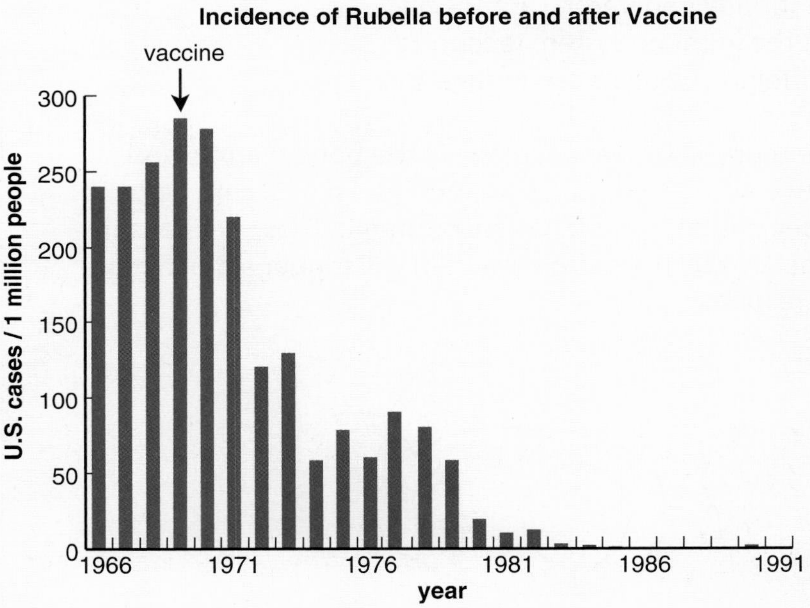

Figure 6.15 **Vaccines and disease.** The widespread use of a vaccine has virtually eliminated rubella, or German measles, in the United States.

Blood type	Molecule on red blood cell	Antibody in plasma
O	None	Anti-A, anti-B
A	A	Anti-B
B	B	Anti-A
AB	A and B	None

Figure 6.16 **ABO blood types.** Blood types are inherited. A patient with type A blood will have antibodies against type B molecules. That is, the antibodies will recognize type B blood as foreign, and the patient's immune system will attack the type B blood. People with blood type O can donate to people with other blood types without danger. This is because there are no blood type molecules on type O cells to which antibodies can bind. The blood recipient's immune system will not attack type O blood. People with type O blood, however, can only accept blood transfusions from type O blood. Can you explain why?

NEED TO KNOW

ENGLISH SPANISH

Glossary of Immune System Components

Antibodies are protein molecules that B cells produce when they have been activated in response to foreign antigens, such as those present on pathogens. Antibodies may be located on the surface of certain immune system cells. Or they may circulate freely in the bloodstream.

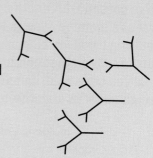

Antigens (<u>anti</u>body <u>gen</u>erators) are specific molecules that the immune system recognizes as nonself, or foreign. Antigens can induce an immune response.

B cells are immune cells that are made in the bone marrow and circulate in the blood. They produce antibodies. Some B cells help the body "remember" the antigens it has encountered. These cells ensure that future infections by the same pathogen will trigger a much more rapid immune response.

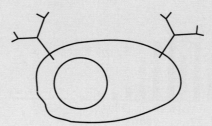

White blood cells include several types of immune system cells, including the B cells and T cells.

Macrophages are scavenger cells of the immune system that are present throughout the body. They engulf the foreign material, including pathogens, that they encounter. Then they degrade it and present its antigens on their surfaces. Macrophages can interact with and activate other immune cells, including B cells and helper T cells.

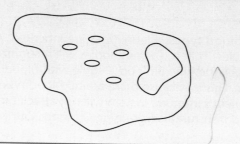

Pathogens are organisms such as a bacterium, fungus, or virus that have the potential to cause a disease.

T cells are immune cells that are formed in the bone marrow but mature in the thymus. They circulate in the blood. There are at least two types. Helper T cells respond to macrophages or B cells that are fighting an antigen. They help send messages to trigger a rapid and strong immune response. Killer T cells carry out cell-to-cell combat. They destroy cells that are infected with a virus as well as cells that have become cancerous.

2. Answer the following questions using the information you read about how the immune system helps maintain homeostasis. Record your answers in your science notebook.
   a. Why is it important for the body to distinguish material that is part of itself from foreign material? Explain what happens when the body fails to make that distinction.
   b. Provide 2 examples of the immune system's nonspecific defense mechanisms. Explain how nonspecific immunity differs from specific immunity.
   c. Explain why viruses are unaffected by antibiotics.
   d. Describe how vaccination is a technological innovation that takes advantage of a basic property of the immune system.
3. Write a brief story that summarizes how either the cell-mediated response or the antibody-mediated response defends the body from a pathogen. Make sure that all the necessary "characters" from the immune response are included. Be creative, but accurate.

Part B   Diagnosis: Two Puzzles

Now you will use your knowledge about pathogens and the immune system to solve a puzzle. Use all available resources, including what you have learned in earlier activities. First, you will see how each test subject reacts to the *same, known* pathogen. Then you will use this information and similar strategies to try to determine the identity of an *unknown* pathogen.

1. Gather as a team and read the test subject card that your teacher provides. Your subject has just been exposed to the influenza (flu) virus.
2. As a team, generate a prognosis for your test subject. In your science notebook, write down the evidence and inferences that support your reasoning about whether and how long the subject will be ill.

© Dreamstime/Sebastian Kaulitzki

A "prognosis" is a prediction based on evidence and inference about whether a person will become ill, and if so, how soon he or she will recover.

3. Discuss what effect penicillin would have if it were administered on the first day that symptoms occur. Write your team's prediction in your science notebook.
4. As your teacher directs, share your team's prognosis for your test subject with your classmates.
5. Obtain a scenario card that describes what happened after your test subject was exposed to an unidentified pathogen. Read it with your team.

   This is a new version of the activity. Your test subject remains the same, but instead of knowing the *identity* of the pathogen and determining the prognosis, now you will know the *prognosis* of your test subject. Your job is to identify the pathogen that infected your test subject.

6. Draw a table like the one in figure 6.17 into your science notebook.

Figure 6.17 Pathogen Identification table. Use a table like this to organize your thinking.

Test subject:		
Can eliminate:	**Reason(s):**	**Pathogen(s) still possible:**

7. Use information from your test subject and scenario cards to *eliminate* at least 1 of the 3 pathogens listed below that could have infected your subject (figure 6.18). Discuss and listen to your team's ideas. Record your reasoning for your actions in your table.
   - *Streptococcus* bacterium, which can cause "strep throat"
   - Rhinovirus, which can cause the common cold
   - Rubella virus, which causes German measles

Figure 6.18 (*a*) One symptom of rubella is a skin rash. (*b*) One symptom of a *Streptococcus* infection is a red, very sore throat.

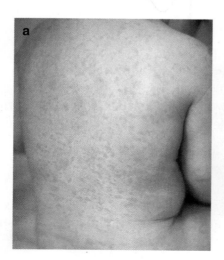
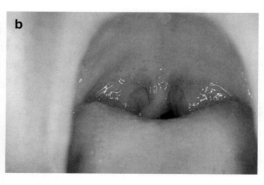

It is unlikely that there is enough available information for you to be sure of your test subject's pathogen. However, you can use the information you have to narrow the possibilities. Support your decision with reasons based on evidence. In your team, practice using the skill of consensus building.

8. With your team, read the entire *Complete Scenario Information* handout. With this new information, determine with greater certainty the pathogen that infected your subject. Justify your answer with reasons and evidence.

   The additional information should allow you to use a process of elimination to determine the unknown pathogen. You may wish to add rows to your table to organize your reasoning.

9. Participate in a class discussion of the results of this exercise. Use the table you generated as a record of your thinking.

Topic: stress (management, body's response)
Code: human4E319

Analysis

Answer the following questions in your science notebook.

1. In this activity, you first used information from a single scenario card to try to identify a pathogen. You then used information from several different scenarios to refine your ideas. Explain how a combination of information was more helpful in identifying the pathogen than a single source of information was.

2. Explain the effect that stressors such as fatigue, anxiety, and smoking have on a person's ability to defend himself or herself against infection. Use evidence from the activity to support your reasoning.

3. Suppose a rubella outbreak is occurring in your community. Each of the following people is healthy and 25 years old. How will each respond to being exposed to the rubella pathogen?
   a. Subject 1 had rubella as a child.
   b. Subject 2 was vaccinated against rubella as a child.
   c. Subject 3 never encountered the rubella pathogen or vaccine as a child.

Tony's Brain

ELABORATE

   In chapter 5, you learned about how signals from the brain regulate many homeostatic processes, such as your heart rate, breathing rate, and blood pressure. In the Explore-Explain activity, *Hospital Triage*, you learned that a head injury or brain damage caused by overheating can affect the homeostasis of many different organ systems. You also use your brain for every voluntary action you take to respond to challenges to homeostasis, for example, taking a drink of water when you are thirsty. But here is a question that will really intrigue you: What regulates the homeostasis of your brain? What happens if the brain itself is off balance in some way? Is mental illness a disruption of homeostasis?

In this Elaborate activity, *Tony's Brain*, you will explore homeostasis within the brain by trying to discover the causes for a problem involving a teenager named Tony. To complete this task, you will need to make observations and gather evidence. You will use the observations that you make and the evidence that you gather to make inferences about Tony's problem. That is, you will use evidence to develop an explanation of what caused the particular problem. You also will explore how explanations can change when more observations and evidence become available.

Materials

online resource

PROCESS AND PROCEDURES

1. Discuss these questions with your team. Record a consensus definition of "mental illness" in your science notebook.
   a. How is human behavior related to the function of the brain?
   b. How is mental illness similar to and different from physical illness?
   c. Define mental illness.
2. Meet with another team to compare your definitions of mental illness. Explain why your team defined mental illness as it did.
3. Read the scenario, *Tony's Unusual Behavior*.
4. Brainstorm reasons that might account for Tony's behavior and contribute them to a class list. Write this list in your science notebook.

   Generate as many explanations as possible. At this point, do not discuss which explanations are better than others.

SCENARIO

Tony's Unusual Behavior

Tony is one of your best friends. For years, you have known him as a happy, generous, and sometimes shy person. For most of his life, Tony has enjoyed relatively good health. He is active in your school's drama club and plays on the baseball team.

Recently, Tony celebrated his 15th birthday. Soon afterward, you noticed that he began to exhibit strange behaviors. His sister told you that he has nightmares, repeated insomnia, and an overall nervousness. At times, you see that Tony is ecstatically happy. At other times, he seems depressed and sad. You are very worried about your friend.

During the course of several months, Tony continues to show increasing signs of unusual behavior. His mood swings become more dramatic and more frequent. During his winter vacation, Tony didn't even get out of bed.

5. Discuss the following question with your team: Why would it be unscientific to strongly support 1 of these explanations over all the others?

> Each member of the team should take a turn giving his or her reasons.

6. Read the information on the *Personal Interview with Tony* handout to help you understand more about Tony's condition. Then, with your teammates, eliminate or add reasons from the class list for Tony's behavior so that your team's list contains only those that are reasonable in light of this new information.

> Where possible, support an explanation by including evidence that you found in the handout.

7. Watch the video segment, "Behavioral Disorders and the Brain." Then, with your team, review the information in the *Some Disorders of the Brain* handout. Revise your list again, if this new information helps you eliminate or add any evidence or reasons to it.

8. Read the additional information on the handout, *Results of the Doctors' Investigations of Tony's Behavior*. Revise your list again, removing or adding any evidence or reasoning.

9. With your team, draw a conclusion about which disorders from the table in *Some Disorders of the Brain* that Tony most likely suffers from. List 3 pieces of evidence that support your conclusion.

Analysis

With your team, consider the following questions, and then record your responses in your science notebook.

1. Tony's feelings and behaviors were apparently affected by his mental illness because they changed so dramatically. At the same time, there is medical evidence of physical changes in his brain. Explain whether you would now change your original definition for mental illness.

2. In this activity, you conducted an analysis by drawing inferences from evidence. How does new information affect the conclusions you might draw? When can you be certain that you have arrived at the correct explanation for a problem like Tony's?

3. Read the following paragraphs. Then explain how the changes in the brain of a person with Alzheimer's disease relate to the changes in the way the person behaves or remembers.

> As humans age, the brain undergoes changes that, in some individuals, can affect a person's memory. Some people might also respond more slowly to certain things. These difficulties can be caused by a slight decrease in the number of neurons or in their connections in some areas of the brain. The changes are normal.

> In the brains of people who have Alzheimer's disease, however, extensive changes take place. Changes that happen in the production of two proteins lead to the buildup of plaque and "tangles" that affect the

neurons' ability to function. These neurons cannot communicate normally with other neurons. As a result of this buildup, the neurons eventually die from impaired function. We see evidence of the neurons' death as shrinkage of the cerebral hemispheres.

4. Explain how Tony's brain was affected by a disruption of homeostasis.

ELABORATE

What's the Risk?

Have you ever cut your finger while you were slicing vegetables or fallen and broken a bone? Your homeostasis can be disrupted at any time by accident or illness because you are exposed to many risks in your daily life (see figure 6.19). You probably accept, consciously or subconsciously, some of these risks as unavoidable, while you try to minimize other risks. In this Elaborate activity, *What's the Risk?*, you will explore controllable and uncontrollable risks and explain what some of these risks mean in your life.

Materials

Part A (per student)
  prepared test tube or cup
  additional materials your teacher supplies

© Dreamstime/Zsolt Biczo

© Dreamstime/Greg Epperson

Figure 6.19 Humans are exposed to many risks. Some risks are affected by behavior. Others are unavoidable despite an individual's behavior. Think about the risks involved in each of the images depicted and how those risks compare with one another.

PROCESS AND PROCEDURES

Part A   Fluid Exchange

1. Choose 1 test tube or cup from those at the station your teacher has prepared.
2. Follow your teacher's instructions.
3. When you have completed the tests, return the test tube or cup to the station. **Wash your hands thoroughly.**
4. Add your data to the class's data table and use the information to try to trace the original 3 infections.
5. Discuss the following questions with your classmates.
   a. What observations about the fluid exchange surprised you?
   b. Many illnesses, including the common cold, hepatitis, and AIDS, are spread by fluid transfer (figure 6.20). What types of behaviors spread those illnesses, and what body fluids are involved?
   c. How can people completely eliminate their chances of contracting a sexually transmitted disease?

Part B   Risk Assessment

1. Develop a list of at least 20 risks faced by humans that could disrupt homeostasis. Do this step individually.

   Use your personal experience and the essay, *Avoiding Disruptions: Behavior, Choices, and Risk,* to make your list. Include risks that could cause disruption in both the short term and the long term.

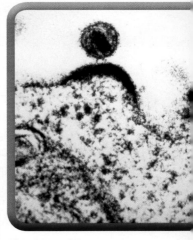

Figure 6.20
Electron micrograph of the human immunodeficiency virus (HIV).

Topic: AIDS
Code: human4E323

Avoiding Disruptions: Behavior, Choices, and Risk

What human behaviors reduce the risk of disrupting homeostasis? Simple reflexes are protective behaviors. They include closing your eyes in response to a sudden, threatening movement or retracting the fingers quickly from a hot surface. In addition, humans have a tremendous capacity for complex thought. Therefore, humans may choose behaviors that prevent the disruption of bodily functions. For example, you can avoid being around someone who has the flu. You can choose to always buckle your seat belt while in a car. You can adopt the habits of getting adequate sleep and eating nutritious food. None of those behaviors will eliminate the risk of injury or illness. But they all represent choices that reduce the risk of either mild or major disruptions.

Some risks are within our control, while others are not. It is important to distinguish controllable from uncontrollable factors. For instance, inheriting a genetic disease is not under your control. Would exposure to toxic substances in polluted outdoor air be under your control? What about factors at your workplace that could be unsafe?

The risk of developing cancer is complex. It often involves both controllable and uncontrollable factors. One of the most controllable factors related to lung cancer is cigarette smoking. Cigarette smoke damages the lungs' protective mechanisms. A smoker is more vulnerable than a nonsmoker to infection or to damage from other pollutants. Smoking does not guarantee that lung cancer will develop, but it greatly increases the risk. Smoking also increases the risk of heart disease because it damages blood vessels. A further consequence of smoking is that it damages the elasticity of lung tissue with each inhalation of smoke. This damage is progressive and results in the slow, and often painful, fatal disease known as emphysema. Figure 6.21 compares healthy lungs with diseased lungs.

Many smokers find it extremely difficult to quit smoking. The nicotine in tobacco is one of the most addictive chemicals known. What is more interesting is why people who understand the effects of smoking choose to start smoking. An individual must weigh the risks against the benefits to make an informed decision about smoking. The same is true for other controllable but risky behaviors. These include riding a bicycle without a helmet, drinking from the same cup as someone who has a cold, or driving without a seat belt. In many situations, people accept the long-term risks in exchange for short-term benefits. Do you think someone might think differently about these decisions weeks or years down the road?

Even if the immune system is strong, it may not successfully combat an infection if the number of pathogens is very large or if the pathogens damage too much tissue. Once again, there are ways to reduce the risks and give the immune system a good chance to work adequately. Figure 6.22 lists behaviors that have positive and negative effects on the immune system. Avoiding exposure to polluted water, contaminated food, and animals or people with contagious diseases will reduce your risk to infection. Keep in mind that exposure may

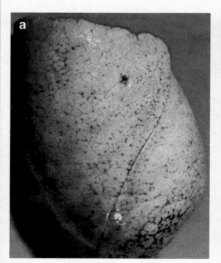
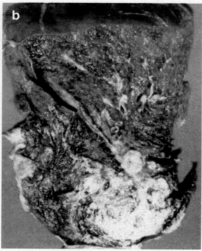
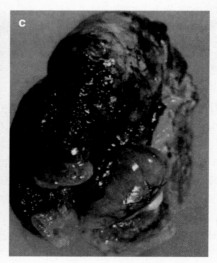

Figure 6.21　Smoking increases the risk for developing lung disease. A healthy lung (*a*) is light in color and has a consistent alveolar structure. Lungs damaged by cancer (*b*) or by emphysema (*c*) are dark and unable to function as efficiently as healthy lungs.

Enhances defense	Impairs defense
Adequate rest	Fatigue and lack of sleep
Moderate exercise	Extreme exercise (marathons, cross-country ski racing)
Good nutrition	Poor nutrition
Positive mental attitude	Anxiety or depression
	Smoking
	Excessive alcohol use
	Excessive antibiotics use
	Certain infections (such as mononucleosis or HIV)

Figure 6.22   Behaviors that influence immune function.

not mean simply being near the source of infection. Sitting in the same room with contaminated food will not make you ill, but eating it may do so. Can you catch a cold by shaking hands with a person who has a cold? Yes, if the person has just covered his or her mouth while sneezing, and then you touch your mouth or nose. Can you catch HIV by shaking hands with a person infected with HIV? No, you must share body fluids with a person infected with HIV. This could occur with direct blood contact or by having sexual intercourse. Overall, the immune system, like the body itself, needs to function in a balanced manner, as indicated in figure 6.23.

You may be able to reduce some risks by making healthy choices. You depend on other people, however, to cooperate in order to reduce other risks. For example, you may make the

Level of immune function	Response of immune system to stressor	
	Internal	External
Overactive	Autoimmune diseases	Allergies
Normal	Removal of abnormal cells	Removal of toxins and successful fighting of infection
Underactive	Cancerous cell growth	Susceptibility to infections

Figure 6.23   Relationship between immune function and various stressors. Like other homeostatic systems, the immune system can become improperly regulated. The result is disruptions caused by over- or underactivity.

choice never to drive a car recklessly or while under the influence of alcohol. Yet an accident caused by someone who does could injure you (figure 6.24). In this case, the source of danger (drunk or reckless driving) is controllable, but not by you.

The society you live in, including your group of friends, also plays a role in determining your health risks. For example, if your friends smoke, you will be affected by secondhand smoke. A society with laws restricting air pollution reduces everyone's risk of getting lung cancer. Is this a factor within your control? If you vote to support pollution restrictions, then as an individual, you contribute to the reduction of risk. But your contribution alone will not have much effect. It takes many personal decisions to make laws that affect everyone in your city, state, or nation.

Figure 6.24 Uncontrollable risks. Even though the driver of this car was driving carefully and wearing a seat belt, she was severely injured by a reckless driver.

© iStockphoto/Dlanier

2. With your team, read the headings on the *Risk Assessment Data* handout. Decide who will be responsible for analyzing each of the following risk categories.
   a. Alcohol
   b. Cancer
   c. Sex and sexually transmitted diseases
   d. Smokeless tobacco and smoking

3. Divide the remaining categories evenly. In your science notebook, record the categories for which you are responsible.

4. Study the information in your risk categories.

   a. Highlight the statements in each category that provide information about whether that risk is a serious threat for teenagers only (T) or for the general population (G).

      Label each of these statements with a "T" or a "G" to distinguish them.

   b. Use an asterisk (*) to mark the most shocking or surprising statistic in each of your categories.

   c. For each of your categories that is affected by behavior, record in your science notebook 1 or 2 behaviors that might reduce the risk.

5. Briefly discuss the results of your analysis by sharing some of the more relevant or surprising statistics with your teammates.

6. As a team, complete the following tasks in your science notebook.

   a. Make a list of 3 risks in our society that could be reduced if people changed their behavior.

      Select risks that would have a significant impact on the *entire population* if they were reduced.

   b. Make a list of 3 risks in our society that are unlikely to be reduced, either because the risk is not controllable or because people would be unwilling or unable to change their behavior.

   c. Next to each item on your 2 lists, write a brief explanation for your choice.

7. Complete the *Taking Risks: A Self-Evaluation* handout to determine your own personal risk level.

   Tape this handout into your science notebook. This is your personal information, so you will not be asked to share it with your classmates or your teacher. After using it for the *Analysis*, remove it and your answers to step 8 from your science notebook.

8. On a separate page in your science notebook, write a reflective paragraph about your overall level of risk. Develop an explanation of why your overall risk is at the level it is. In a second paragraph, analyze behaviors that you could change to reduce your own risk level.

© Dreamstime/Ilja Masik

Part C   Ethical Analysis

1. Draw a vertical line to divide a page of your science notebook in half. Title the left half "ethical analysis." Title the right half "scientific inquiry."

2. Read the essay, *Ethical Analysis*. As you read, write the steps of ethical analysis on the left side, in your own words. For each step of ethical analysis, write down a related process of scientific inquiry in the right-hand column.

   > For example, you might list the first step as "Identify the question precisely." You may find that the *Scientific Inquiry Diagram* that your teacher displays will help you complete the right-hand column.

3. Based on the essay, make an entry for the term "ethical dilemma" in your personal glossary.

4. With your team, discuss the following questions.
   a. How does the process of ethical analysis compare with the process of scientific inquiry?
   b. How are these 2 processes similar?
   c. How are these 2 processes different?

Analysis

Answer the following questions individually. Be prepared to discuss questions about risks and your society with the class.

1. Identify several behaviors that are socially acceptable even though they may have a negative impact on others. Explain why you think these behaviors are tolerated by our society.

   > Use the information from your notes from this activity, from the essays for this activity, and from the *Risk Assessment Data* handout.

2. Explain how a behavior you read about or identified in question 1 poses an ethical dilemma. State whether society has made any policies that affect those behaviors and what those policies are.

3. Review your copy of the survey, *Taking Risks: A Self-Evaluation*. Compare the high-risk behaviors that you have engaged in with those of other students your age, and with those of society as a whole that you learned about on the *Risk Assessment Data* handout.
   a. Which, if any, of the risks that students your age commonly take match the risks that your team felt could be reduced if people changed their behavior?
   b. If any of these risks are the same, why do you think students your age take these risks?

      > Use the list your team made in part B, step 6.

Science can tell you about how things work. Science can help predict whether something could happen in a given situation. Science, however, cannot tell you what you *should* do in a given situation. Questions that involve issues of "should" are ethical questions. When a situation doesn't have a clear answer about what should be done, it is known as an **ethical dilemma**. In such situations, people hold different opinions about which choice is acceptable. For example, your mother may require you to wear a seat belt in the car, but your friends may make fun of you for doing so when you ride with them. Should society require you to wear a seat belt? This is an ethical dilemma. In an ethical dilemma, your choices depend not only on facts about the world, which science may help explain, but also on values. Values are those ideas that are important to you, your family,

or your society. The complex interactions between religion, philosophy, and culture shape our values (figure 6.25).

The analysis of ethical issues has some similarities to scientific inquiry. Scientists must gather data to support or disprove their hypotheses. In the same way, ethicists must work hard to develop strong arguments that support their positions. Evidence is as crucial to the ethical process as it is to science. It is hard to persuade someone to share your opinion if you can't support it with evidence. **Ethical analysis** is a process of reasoning for making ethical decisions. Judges, lawyers, human researchers, and doctors all use ethical analysis in their work. Ethical analysis goes beyond scientific inquiry. Science does not provide answers to what people should do, but ethical analysis provides a way to seek those answers.

Figure 6.25 Complicated issues have no simple solutions. The facts of such issues must be analyzed in light of the interests of everyone affected.

What are some steps in the process of ethical analysis?

1. *Identify the question about the issue of interest.* Make the question clear and precise. A clear question helps you construct strong arguments. For example, you might ask, "Is it ethical to have a law that requires car occupants to wear seat belts?"

2. *Gather information about the issue.* You are likely to find differing expert opinions. Experts such as philosophers, historians, and theologians may have written about the topic. You may find information from economists or scientists as well. Take information from well-known sources. Consider that every source may have some bias.

3. *Evaluate the information to understand how it applies to the issue.* You must consider how the issue affects the *interests* of specific individuals. Also consider how the issue affects particular groups and society as a whole. Next, consider how people are affected by possible *consequences* of any actions. Finally, consider any *rights*, or freedoms, that might be denied. For example, let's look again at the law requiring all people to wear seat belts. People are interested in the law because it reduces their chance of injury in a car accident.

Some argue, however, that it infringes on the rights and freedom of individuals to make their own choices.

4. *Use your data to form well-reasoned arguments.* Your arguments should support one or more solutions to the ethical issue. For example, suppose society must pay for the health care of car accident victims. Accidents also cost car owners more in insurance premiums. You might argue that the rights of individuals not to wear seat belts are less important than the increased costs of health care and insurance to society.

5. *Analyze your case to determine its validity.* You and the people to whom you present your arguments and conclusions must critically analyze your case. For example, an economist could show data challenging your health cost argument. This would seem to weaken your case. In such a case, you could analyze the economist's new cost data. Then you could determine whether the new data are more or less reliable than the data used to support your side.

6. *Make a recommendation about what should be done about the issue.* Use well-supported arguments to help decide how you or society as a whole plan to take action to address the issue.

Health Care Proposal

In this Evaluate activity, *Health Care Proposal,* your team will develop a health care proposal and apply for funds from the J. Nelson Jones Foundation. You will need to have a clear idea of what you want to do with the money and how your idea addresses society's needs. In addition, your job is to explain how your proposed program will affect the people involved. Specifically, you will need to describe the benefits to specific groups of individuals and specific body systems at risk for disrupted homeostasis and explain how your program will improve the groups' health. Remember, this assignment is an *evaluate* activity. Your proposal will be the evidence of what you have learned about homeostasis. To develop your proposal fully, gather information from different sources, such as this program, your science notebook, the Web, and the library.

Read the scenario, *Entrepreneur to Fund Worthy Health Care Programs,* to find out what types of proposals the foundation wants to fund. After you develop your proposal, your teacher will evaluate it based on the criteria established by the private foundation. These are listed on a scoring rubric that your teacher will provide.

An exceptional proposal may be funded in its entirety, or as many as three proposals may be partially funded. However, if two or more proposals are submitted that deal with the same topic, only the strongest will be chosen.

Materials

resource materials that your teacher provides

SCENARIO

ENGLISH SPANISH

Entrepreneur to Fund Worthy Health Care Programs

PHOENIX, ARIZONA Samantha S. Jones, whose son, Nelson, died recently while hiking, announced Thursday that she will contribute a portion of her software company's profits to establish a health care endowment fund, the J. Nelson Jones Foundation. An annual award of $1 million, which may be split among as many as three different groups, will be given to worthy health care programs. The money will be distributed by a panel of health care experts who will evaluate proposals and choose the best. Groups interested in obtaining funds must demonstrate that their program is biologically sound, cost effective, beneficial to a significant number of people, and sensitive to ethical concerns in society and within the health care industry. When asked why she decided to fund this type of program, Jones replied, "I'd like to create a world with better health care, better education, and a better understanding of the limits of the human body so that this kind of tragedy can be prevented."

© Dreamstime/Sophie Asselin

Samantha S. Jones creates health care endowment.

PROCESS AND PROCEDURES

1. Review *Health Care Options* at the end of this activity. Choose 1 option that interests your team.

   Your teacher will keep track of which teams select which options.

2. As a team, develop a short description of your program. Then decide which team members will gather information for each of the following sections of the proposal.
   a. Homeostasis
   b. Risk assessment
   c. Ethical issues

   > Refer to the need to know, *J. Nelson Jones Foundation Guidelines for Proposal Development*, to review the questions and issues that you must address in each of these sections. Regardless of which option your team chooses, you may use information from other options to support your position.

NEED TO KNOW

ENGLISH SPANISH

J. Nelson Jones Foundation Guidelines for Proposal Development

You must include each of the following sections in your proposal. Address each question or issue presented.

J. Nelson Jones Foundation

Short Description of the Proposed Program

- Give a brief overview of the program that you are proposing.

- Is the treatment or program that you propose the only one available? (In other words, do the participants in your proposed program have any other choices?)

Homeostasis

- Which organ or regulatory system does your proposal most directly affect or influence? The biology of this system will be the focus of your proposal. What is the normal function of this organ system in maintaining homeostasis? Include a description of the anatomy involved, the physiology, and the role of the immune system. (Many options involve several organ systems, but you need to describe only one system.)

- What is the nature of the homeostatic disruption that your proposal seeks to correct? How will the correction be accomplished?

Risk Assessment

- How common is the illness or injury that your proposal seeks to treat? For example, how many people will take advantage of your services?
- If your proposal targets a particular population, explain how this population will be informed about the program.
- How does behavior affect a person's likelihood of experiencing the risks that your proposal addresses?
- Describe the controllability or uncontrollability of the risks involved. How can a person change his or her behavior to minimize the risks?
- Explain how your program will intervene to reduce the risk of this health condition.

Ethical Issues

- Identify an ethical dilemma that could be associated with your proposal. For example, you may have to choose which patients are eligible for your program. Describe the concerns surrounding this dilemma.
- Use the six steps of ethical analysis to analyze the dilemma. Explain your decision about what should be done.

3. Individually, gather all the information that you will need to develop your part of the proposal. Analyze the information to identify the evidence that will support your arguments.

   Your teacher will suggest where you can find additional material. You will have about 1 week to complete this step.

4. If you researched homeostasis or risk assessment, present the information that you have analyzed to your team. Explain how this information will strengthen the proposal.

   Practice the skill of advocating a position.

5. Work with your team. Discuss the information and decide what specific data to include in your proposal and what to discard.

   Focus on the most important and persuasive data because proposal space is limited.

6. As a team, use the steps presented in the essay, *Ethical Analysis,* in the Elaborate activity, *What's the Risk?,* to conduct an ethical analysis of an issue that is involved in your chosen health care area.

   The team member who was responsible for gathering information on ethical issues should provide the team with several ethical issues to consider. Your team must choose one issue on which to focus the ethical analysis.

7. Write your proposal according to the foundation's guidelines. You should write a section that is different from the section you researched.

> Divide this task evenly among your teammates. Your work will be evaluated according to the criteria listed in the *Health Care Proposal Rubric* handout that your teacher distributed. Review those criteria carefully before you start writing. You may find you need to conduct additional research or collaborate with your team as you write.

8. Submit your proposal to your teacher.

Analysis

In your science notebook, write 1 paragraph in which you reflect on your experience of developing the proposal. Consider these questions as you write the paragraph:

- What section was hardest to write? Why do you think that was so?
- Why is ethical analysis a useful tool in science and in society?
- How can you positively or negatively influence the internal systems that are involved in maintaining homeostasis in your body?

Health Care Options

Option 1   Alcohol and Drug Treatment Program

Topic: alcohol and drug treatment
Code: human4E334

- In the United States, nine months of treatment for a drug-addicted mother costs approximately one-sixth what it costs to provide medical care for a drug-exposed baby for 20 days.
- Most people suffering from alcohol or drug abuse who cannot afford private treatment in hospitals receive their care as outpatients at clinics. Many receive no treatment at all. Because the addiction is so strong, many of these people eventually turn to crime to obtain the money that they need to pay for more alcohol or drugs.
- One federally funded treatment facility in a city of 300,000 serves 700 heroin addicts of all age groups per month. A staff of 18 full-time counselors and 17 part-time employees implement a program designed to eliminate chemical dependency. This program provides heroin addicts with daily doses of methadone, a chemical narcotic that minimizes the craving for heroin and helps the addicts "stay clean." There is no limit to how long an addict can participate in this program. Approximately 25–40 percent of those on methadone stay on it for a year or more. Many find it extremely difficult to quit the drug habit completely. About 30 percent, however, are able to find work and at least partially support themselves. Methadone treatment dramatically reduces crime committed by addicts. (Statistics show that crime dropped from 237 crime days per person per year before treatment to 69 crime days per person per year

after four months of treatment.) Methadone treatment also reduces HIV infection rates (from 39 percent among addicts not in treatment to 18 percent among addicts in treatment for three years).

Option 2   Heart Disease Prevention and Treatment

Topic: heart disease
Code: human4E335a

- The dietary habits of Americans are substantially different from those of residents in other countries. This difference has contributed to the prevalence of heart disease in the United States. For example, the typical diet in Japan contains far less cholesterol and saturated fat than the typical American diet. Consequently, a 50-year-old Japanese man has an average blood cholesterol level of 180 milligrams per deciliter (mg/dL). Compare that with an average of 245 mg/dL for a 50-year-old American man.
- Fifty-five percent of Americans in the United States are overweight or obese.
- After an individual has a heart attack, there is at least a 50 percent chance that the individual will die in less than five years unless the individual takes preventive measures.
- Heart disease (atherosclerosis) and heart attacks are two of the top five most costly diseases to treat, accounting for more than $64 billion in hospital charges.

Option 3   Education Programs Focusing on the Prevention of AIDS and Other Sexually Transmitted Diseases (STDs)

Topic: sexually transmitted diseases
Code: human4E335b

- Twenty-three percent of all 14-year-olds and 30 percent of all 15-year-olds have engaged in sexual intercourse.
- Sixty-two percent of sexually active 9th- through 12th-grade students reported using a condom the last time they had sex. Over half of all 9th- through 12th-grade students report that they are currently abstinent.
- Approximately 1 in 4 teenagers who are sexually active get an STD every year. However, 68 percent of sexually active teens do not consider themselves to be at risk.
- Antiretroviral drugs (sometimes called the "AIDS cocktail") given to HIV-positive individuals soon after infection help suppress the development of full-blown AIDS and the disabling effects of the illness.
- As of 2006, people without health insurance who are HIV positive cannot receive payment for HIV therapy through Medicaid until they are sick enough to qualify as disabled. Medicaid covers medical services for approximately 55 percent of all adults living with AIDS and up to 90 percent of all children living with AIDS.
- For individuals who qualify, Medicaid covers the costs for approved prescription drugs. These include drugs that help prevent opportunistic infections and those that treat AIDS, such as protease inhibitors.

- In 2004, hospital stays billed to federal and state Medicaid programs to treat HIV and AIDS were estimated to cost $1.4 billion.
- For every dollar spent notifying sex partners of HIV-positive patients, at least $11 is saved in annual medical care costs for each case of HIV that is prevented.

Option 4   Hospital Equipment and Procedures

Topic: hospital equipment and procedures
Code: human4E336

- Dialysis, a procedure that substitutes for the normal functioning of the kidneys, costs $5,800. A kidney transplant, which may eliminate the need for dialysis, costs approximately $33,400.
- An electrocardiograph (ECG), an instrument used to monitor and diagnose heart problems, costs approximately $12,000.
- Pacemaker surgery, a procedure performed on patients who suffer from certain forms of heart disease, costs approximately $15,200.
- Angioplasty, a surgical procedure to open arteries in the heart that are blocked by cholesterol and plaque buildup, costs approximately $12,000.
- An appendectomy, the removal of a diseased appendix, typically requires a three-day hospital stay and costs approximately $5,800.
- Alcohol and drug rehabilitation and detoxification costs approximately $3,000.
- A mastectomy, the removal of a cancerous breast, costs approximately $4,500.
- Arthroscopy, a surgical procedure to repair an injured joint, costs approximately $6,700.
- Magnetic resonance imaging, or MRI, is a technique in which strong magnetic fields generate a picture of the inside of the body (similar to an X-ray). Physicians use it to help them locate tumors in cancer patients or injuries and obstructions in people with difficult-to-diagnose illnesses (about $1,000 per use).
- A tonsillectomy, the removal of tonsils and adenoids, costs approximately $6,000.
- Radiation therapy often is used to reduce the size and spread of malignant tumors. This therapy can be used in place of or in addition

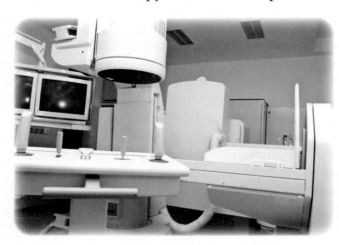

to surgery. It is frequently necessary if the patient is to have a chance of survival. Average cost for therapeutic radiology (to treat lung cancer, for example) is $9,000.

- Costs of procedures for patients without medical insurance are generally three to four times higher than the "negotiated prices" quoted here.

Option 5   Prenatal Care

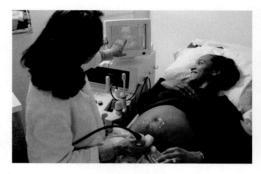

- Prenatal care for a pregnant woman for nine months (not including delivery) averages $750.
- For a very-low-birthweight baby, each day in the intensive care unit costs from $1,000 to $2,500. Low birthweight is often due to prematurity, which may be a consequence of poor prenatal care. The lifetime medical costs for one premature baby average $500,000.
- The cost of a normal delivery is approximately $2,500.
- The cost for a complicated birth ranges from $20,000 to $400,000.
- Some public health care clinics have been established with good success for improving prenatal care. A public health care clinic can provide prenatal care for women, including education about nutrition, exercise, and the avoidance of harmful behaviors. Such a clinic also could provide regular visits by nurses and handle uncomplicated deliveries. These programs are successful at producing full-term, normal-birthweight babies (greater than about 2.5 kg, or 5.5 lb). In fact, with a low-birthrate incidence of only 7 percent, they produce a higher percentage of normal-birthweight babies than privately funded health care facilities that do not offer a prenatal care program.

Topic: prenatal care
Code: human4E337a

Topic: cigarettes
Code: human4E337b

Option 6   Quit Smoking Program

- Cigarettes kill more Americans than do AIDS, alcohol, car accidents, murders, suicides, drugs, and fires combined (about 400,000 people per year).
- Seven percent of all 10th graders and 12 percent of all 12th graders reported smoking cigarettes daily in the year 2007.
- The Centers for Disease Control and Prevention estimate that, nationwide, medical care costs attributable to smoking (or smoking-related disease) are more that $50 billion annually. They also estimate the value of lost earnings and loss of productivity to be at least another $47 billion a year.
- Every dollar that is spent on smoking-cessation programs that are successful saves $21 in health care costs during a working lifetime (defined as ages 20–64).

©Dreamstime/Alexander Babich

Option 7   Vaccine Programs

- Nearly everyone in the United States got measles before measles immunization became available in 1963. At that time, there were approximately 3 million to 4 million cases of measles each year. Between 1953 and 1962, an average of 450 people per year died from measles.
- In industrialized countries, up to 20 percent of people with measles are hospitalized. Seven to 9 percent suffer from complications such as pneumonia, diarrhea, or ear infections. It is estimated that as many as 1 of every 1,000 people with measles will die.
- Measles is one of the most infectious diseases in the world and is frequently imported into the United States. More than 90 percent of people who are not immune will get measles if they are exposed to the virus.
- The measles-mumps-rubella vaccine led to a tremendous decline in the occurrences of the diseases (see figure 6.26). According to the 2007 Centers for Disease Control National Immunization Survey, approximately 77 percent of all children aged 19–35 months had received four doses of the combined series vaccine. The target vaccination rate set by Healthy People 2010 is 90 percent.
- Hepatitis B is an infection of the liver. It is caused by a virus found in the blood, semen, menstrual blood, and other body fluids of a person with hepatitis B. Five to 10 percent of adults who catch hepatitis B become carriers for the rest of their lives and can pass the virus on to others. About half of all adults who become infected with hepatitis B report never having felt sick at all. Symptoms, if present, are flulike.
- Hepatitis B infects more than 200,000 people each year and kills more than 5,000. The virus can be spread during sex, by sharing needles, or by being stuck with a dirty needle or tools used for tattooing or piercing. It can also be spread by getting blood or other infected fluids in the mouth and eyes or onto broken skin. The virus also can be passed from mother to baby during birth.
- Carriers of hepatitis B are at risk of liver problems, such as cancer or cirrhosis. Hepatitis B is 100 times easier to catch than the virus that causes AIDS. There is no cure for hepatitis B, but vaccination can prevent it.

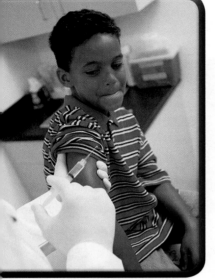

Topic: vaccinations
Code: human4E338

Figure 6.26
U.S. incidence of infectious diseases prior to the start of vaccination programs and in 2001.

Disease	U.S. cases (year)	U.S. cases (2001)	% change
Measles	319,124 (1950)	116	−99.96
Mumps	104,953 (1970)	266	−99.75
Poliomyelitis	33,300 (1950)	0	−100.00

Option 8 *Programs for Women, Infants, and Children*

- Inadequate nutrition during childhood affects brain development and reduces a child's ability to learn.
- Many U.S. counties have programs that try to prevent malnutrition in pregnant or nursing women and children under age 5. These programs provide food vouchers that families can redeem for wholesome foods such as formula, baby food, milk, cheese, eggs, cereal, dry beans, peanut butter, and tuna fish.
- In 2005, an average of 27 million people received food stamps in the United States each month. The program costs around $29 billion a year.
- Currently, the United States has medical costs of approximately $60 billion per year associated with osteoporosis. Teenage girls and adult women only consume two-thirds of the calcium that is recommended.
- Fifty percent of nutrition and health program participants adopt one or more habits that improve the development of healthy eating behaviors by their children.

Topic: women, infants, and children
Code: human4E339

© Dreamstime/Karen Struthers

Energy. We all need it in varying amounts, 24 hours a day, 365 days a year. What exactly is energy, and where does it come from? How is energy related to the matter we take in each day as food? How do matter and energy help organisms like us perform? Think of a runner nearing the finish line. What is the source of energy the runner needs for that final burst of speed?

In unit 3, *Energy, Matter, and Organization: Relationships in Living Systems*, you will explore matter, energy, and the relationship between them. You will investigate how concepts about matter and energy can help explain how a runner can sprint to the finish line at the end of a long race. Then you will see how cellular processes in the body transform energy from the food consumed by this runner. You will learn how the molecules in food affect the amount of energy you can derive from food. Before beginning chapter 9, *The Cycling of Matter and the Flow of Energy in Ecosystems*, you will construct experimental worm habitats and observe how the worms interact with their environments. Through the worm habitat activity and others in chapter 9, you will see how matter and energy link all of the organisms in a community.

Energy, Matter, & Organization: Relationships in Living Systems

By the end of unit 3, you should be able to understand that

- ✔ human performance and physical fitness depend on diet and exercise;
- ✔ the conservation and transformation of energy and matter are found in all living systems;
- ✔ organisms release energy by breaking the chemical bonds of food molecules, forming different molecules that have lower amounts of energy;
- ✔ photosynthesis transforms light energy into chemical energy, with dramatic effects on all living systems;
- ✔ energy flows through ecosystems, and matter cycles in them; and
- ✔ well-designed investigations collect data, compare results to controls, draw conclusions, and report findings.

UNIT CONTENTS

Physical Fitness and Performance

Durability is part of what makes a great athlete.

Bill Russell

What do the people in these photographs have in common? Each is engaged in an activity that requires a certain level of physical fitness. The person cross-country skiing may not necessarily have the same degree of athletic fitness as a tennis player, but to live an active, healthy life, they still must meet a certain standard of fitness.

In chapter 7, *Physical Fitness and Performance*, you will learn how matter and energy are related to human physical performance. You will explore your understanding of the term "physical fitness" and why being fit should be an important priority for all of us. You will investigate the biological explanations for how exercise and good eating habits promote fitness. By the end of this chapter, you should begin to see how the foods you eat provide the matter and energy necessary to build your body and keep it functioning.

Chapter organizers help you remember what you have learned and where you are headed. They also help you recognize the most important concepts to learn in a chapter. Look at the chapter organizer every day. Think about where you are in its organization. Compare what you know now with what you knew a week ago. Let the chapter organizer help you map your learning and monitor your progress. That way, you can look back and see what you have accomplished.

GOALS FOR THE CHAPTER

Throughout chapter 7, you will work to gain an understanding of the following concepts:

✔ Athletic fitness can be distinguished from fitness for life.

✔ Human physical performance requires matter and energy that are derived from food.

✔ An animal's ability to move is related to the organization of its muscles and skeleton.

✔ An individual's fitness can be influenced by a variety of factors, including exercise and diet.

✔ Positive and negative controls can improve experimental designs.

✔ We can gain insight from comparing predicted results with actual results.

To help you develop these understandings, you will complete the following activities.

ENGAGE	Thinking about Fitness
EXPLORE	What Determines Fitness?
EXPLAIN	What Is in the Food You Eat?
EXPLAIN	You Are What You Eat
ELABORATE	Structures and Functions
EVALUATE	Marathon

ENGAGE

Thinking about Fitness

Key Idea: Individuals differ in their physical fitness levels for peak performance and for life.

Linking Question:
What factors affect my fitness levels?

Chapter 7

MAJOR CONCEPTS

EXPLORE

What Determines Fitness?

Part A: Looking at Physical Activity
Part B: Looking at Diet
Key Idea: Diet and exercise affect physical fitness.

Linking Question:
How do the components of my food affect my fitness?

- ✔ Athletic fitness can be distinguished from fitness for life.
- ✔ Human physical performance requires matter and energy that is derived from food.
- ✔ An animal's ability to move is related to the organization of its muscles and skeleton.
- ✔ An individual's fitness can be influenced by a variety of factors, including exercise and diet.
- ✔ Positive and negative controls can improve experimental designs.
- ✔ We can gain insight from comparing predicted results with actual results.

EXPLAIN

What Is in the Food You Eat?

Key Idea: Specific types of molecules necessary for life are contained in food.

Linking Question:
How does my body process and use food?

Marathon

Key Idea: Energy availability, conditioning, and genetic factors contribute to physical performance.

Physical Fitness and Performance

Linking Question: How do diet, exercise, and fitness level combine to affect the performance of athletes?

 ELABORATE

Structures and Functions

Key Idea: Matter and energy are used to build and move muscles.

Linking Question: Once food has been used by my body, how is it used to make me move?

EXPLAIN

You Are What You Eat

Part A: Starch—Break It Down!
Part B: Food for the Body's Building Blocks

Key Idea: Digestion relies on enzymes and provides molecules for biosynthesis.

 ENGAGE

Thinking about Fitness

What is required of the body during extreme levels of human performance? What is required to sustain even basic levels of nonathletic activities such as climbing stairs or playing catch with a friend? Let's begin our exploration of the biology behind human performance with a look at what it means to be *physically fit*. "Fitness" often means different things to different people. Physicians may view fitness as freedom from disease. Coaches may emphasize physical performance.

On the other hand, you may have heard the phrase "survival of the fittest." The word fitness has a different meaning for evolutionary biologists than it does for doctors and coaches. When evolutionary biologists say an organism is "fit," they mean that it is relatively successful at reproducing.

In chapter 7, you will be investigating physical fitness, not evolutionary fitness. In this Engage activity, *Thinking about Fitness*, you will think about some possible meanings of the term "physical fitness." How might this concept apply to you?

PROCESS AND PROCEDURES

1. Carefully consider your answers to the following questions. Record your responses in your science notebook.
   a. What is your personal definition of physical fitness?
   b. What factors do you think most affect your level of physical fitness, as you defined it?
2. As you read the scenario, *The Sky Awaits*, think about how the characters in the story might define physical fitness. Do you think their definitions would be different from yours?
3. Copy the fitness scale diagrams shown in figure 7.1 into your science notebook.
4. With the members of your team, discuss and complete the following questions about the fitness scale diagrams in figure 7.1. Write your answers in your science notebook.
   a. What does scale A represent? What physical and behavioral characteristics would you expect to find in an individual who scores very high on such a scale?

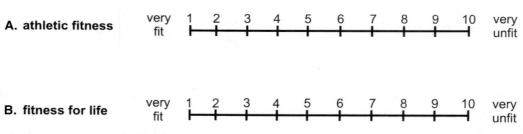

Figure 7.1   Types of fitness. An individual's level of athletic fitness (scale A) does not necessarily correspond to his or her level of fitness for life (scale B). What is your level of fitness on each of these scales?

The Sky Awaits

It is 4 a.m. The Sun has not come up yet on this day in early August, but there is work to be done. Captain Yates rolls out of bed, takes a shower, dons a flight suit and boots, and heads for the kitchen of the small apartment. Breakfast consists of a slice of grilled ham, two eggs over easy, wheat toast with strawberry jam, a glass of orange juice, and a cup of coffee.

Yates steers the bright-red sports car onto the highway and heads out to the air base. As the car approaches the main gate of the base, the sky begins to brighten in the east. It looks as though it will be a good day to fly. As an instructor pilot in the U.S. Air Force, Yates flies a T-38 Talon—a supersonic jet trainer capable of speeds up to 1,450 km/h (900 mph).

After parking the car, Yates checks the schedule and learns that the first student pilot today is Second Lieutenant Sullivan. Yates then checks the weather forecast: no ceiling, unlimited visibility, and calm winds until about 1100 hours, when clouds will begin to build. After the preflight briefing, the two pilots get into their G suits and parachutes. At the airplane, they go through the preflight checklist, run up the engines, and check the equipment that will deliver 100 percent oxygen for them to breathe. They taxi onto the runway. Almost immediately, it is their turn to take off. Yates stands on the brakes and sets the throttles at full afterburner. The takeoff roll is smooth. Sullivan retracts the wheels as the jet soars into the brilliant sky.

This flight is an acrobatics mission in a practice area some 120 km (75 mi) west of the air base. At an altitude of 7,925 m (26,000 ft), the outside air temperature is −26.2°C (−15.2°F). Yates executes a roll to look in every direction, and then Sullivan takes over for the next phase of the mission.

The first maneuver is a G-awareness turn. This prepares Yates and Sullivan for the rigors of the training mission. In the first half of the turn, a 70°–80° bank, the pilots strain against the pull of up to four times the force of gravity, or four Gs. Because of the acceleration forces that result from making sharp turns at high speeds, Yates and Sullivan weigh almost four times their normal weight. Their G suits automatically inflate around the lower portion of their bodies so blood will not pool in their hips, legs, and feet. If their blood did pool, they might black out from a decreased flow of blood and oxygen to their brains. Sullivan tightens the turn to a 90° bank. This produces almost six Gs before the plane rolls back to a straight and level flight.

The warm-up is the beginning of a strenuous and physically exhausting routine that lasts almost 30 minutes. The routine consists of loops, rolls, stalls, and other similar high-G maneuvers. During this routine, the pilots' bodies strain against blacking out from the added force. Their heart rates soar, their muscles tense as hard as rock, and their breathing is labored.

When their maneuvers are complete, Yates and Sullivan begin to relax. The return flight is much less demanding. The approach to the base and the landing are uneventful. As they walk off the flight line and enter the squadron building, both pilots realize that they are now very hungry and a bit tired. It is no wonder. The physical demands of the morning's flight were similar to those required of highly trained, competitive athletes. The training and level of fitness necessary for this work are a way of life for Captain Jennifer Yates and Second Lieutenant John Sullivan.

b. What does scale B represent? What characteristics would you expect to find in an individual who scores very high on this scale?

c. Where on each scale would you place Captain Yates? Place her name at an appropriate level on the 2 diagrams you copied into your science notebook. Below the diagrams, write a sentence explaining why you placed Yates at those positions.

d. It is possible for a person to lack special athletic skills and still be very fit for life. Write "healthy" where you would place such an individual on each scale. Below the diagrams, write a sentence describing the benefits you think might be associated with a high level of fitness for life.

e. Where would you place yourself on the fitness-for-life scale? Write "me" at the level you think you fall on each scale. Below the diagrams, write a sentence listing several ways that you could modify your lifestyle to improve your position on the scales.

What Determines Fitness?

At times in our evolutionary past, *Homo sapiens* depended on strength and endurance to survive. Gathering food and staying safe determined one's physical fitness. Advances in technology, however, have helped shape a lifestyle in which most people in technological societies can obtain food and shelter without performing any *strenuous* work. Nevertheless, medical evidence suggests that a basic level of physical fitness is essential to withstand the stresses of life, maintain a sense of well-being, and extend the life span.

A number of factors determine fitness. In this Explore activity, *What Determines Fitness?*, you will explore two factors, exercise and diet, that affect your level of fitness. Remember, your goal in this chapter is to understand the *biological basis* for how exercise and diet influence human fitness.

PROCESS AND PROCEDURES

Part A Looking at Physical Activity

1. On your own, complete the *Physical Activity Analysis* handout that your teacher provides.

   Place this analysis in your science notebook. You will refer to it during subsequent activities.

2. Answer the following questions individually. Record your answers in your science notebook.
   a. How do you think your personal physical activity level (from figure 4 on the handout) compares with that of a typical student in your class (see figure 7.2)?
   b. How do you think your personal activity level might compare with that of Captain Yates from the scenario, *The Sky Awaits*?

3. On the sheet that your teacher circulates, place a checkmark (√) next to your activity level, which you determined in step 1.

   Your teacher will use this information to create an activity level profile for the class.

4. Enter the activity level profile for the class into figure 5 on the *Physical Activity Analysis* handout.

Part B Looking at Diet

1. On your own, complete the *Dietary Analysis* handout that your teacher provides.

   Place this analysis in your science notebook; you may need to refer to it in subsequent activities.

© iStockphoto/technotr

© Dreamstime/Miodrag Gajie

Figure 7.2 Comparing activities. Which group of people is using more energy?

2. Answer the following questions individually. Record your answers in your science notebook.
   a. How do you think your diet compares with that of a typical student in your class?
   b. How do you think your diet might compare with that of Captain Yates?
3. Work with your team to complete the following steps. The data you provide will help your teacher generate a dietary profile of a typical student in your class.
   a. Choose 1 of the food groups listed on the *Dietary Analysis* handout. Ask 4 students outside your team how many servings from that group they ate yesterday. Record their responses.

   Each member of your team should choose a different food group.

   b. Calculate the average number of daily servings (from the food group you chose) that you and the 4 students you polled ate yesterday. Record this information in the margin of your *Dietary Analysis* handout.

   Average number of servings = (total number of servings eaten in 1 day by you and 4 other students)/5. This calculation will give you a rough approximation of how much a typical student in your class eats from that food group.

   c. Contribute your data to the dietary profile of a typical student that your teacher will compile.
4. Enter the information for this typical student into the column titled "class profile" on the *Dietary Analysis* handout.
5. Participate in a class discussion of the following questions about this activity.
   a. Are you surprised at the activity profile or the dietary profile of your class? Are you surprised at how your own profiles compare with the class profiles? Explain your answers.
   b. Identify ways in which the class profiles may not accurately represent typical activity levels and dietary patterns in society.
   c. Why do you think many people fail to sustain an adequate level of physical activity or fail to eat an appropriate number of servings from each food group?
6. Write the following questions in your science notebook, leaving plenty of space to answer them. Working individually, answer the questions as you read the essay, *Human Performance: A Function of Fitness*.
   a. What resources does your body require during extreme levels of physical performance?
   b. What resources does your body require to sustain basic levels of nonathletic activity?

Human Performance: A Function of Fitness

ENGLISH   SPANISH

For Captain Yates and Second Lieutenant Sullivan, the characters in the scenario, *The Sky Awaits*, being physically fit means being able to successfully perform a demanding physical task. To be physically fit, however, do you really need to have the strength required to put a supersonic jet into a 90° bank at six Gs? Do you need to have the speed and endurance necessary to place in the top 10 percent of a marathon? Is the level of fitness required to be an athlete the same as the level of fitness required for good health?

If exceptional athletic performance were the standard, then very few of us could consider ourselves fit. But Yates and Sullivan, prepared as they are for their type of work, would not necessarily be prepared for all types of athletic activity. The two individuals must be able to withstand sudden, strong forces without blacking out or losing concentration. Even with their level of physical fitness, they might not be great sprinters or weight lifters. Likewise, the special qualities required of a sprinter may not be suited for the tasks required of high-performance pilots.

Is it possible for a person who lacks athletic skills to be physically fit for life itself? To function normally, our bodies must be capable of performing certain basic physical activities. We walk, talk, gesture, and sometimes run. Even when we sit still, our bodies maintain a basic level of internal function. Fit-for-life individuals usually are in good health. These individuals find that they can perform the routine activities of life easily, as illustrated in figure 7.3.

What, then, is a useful definition of *physical fitness*? Definitions vary according to the activities that a person is engaging in. Some authorities define "fitness for life" as "the ability to perform routine physical activities, such as walking, talking, lifting, and carrying, with enough energy in reserve to meet an unexpected challenge." An

©Dreamstime/Pierdelune

Figure 7.3   Human performance. Consider the different levels of performance in this variety of complex human activities. Some activities are a part of daily life; others are highly specialized. Each has its own special requirements, although general fitness for life helps in all cases.

athletically fit individual can run up three flights of stairs carrying a heavy book bag to class, and still answer the question, "Why are you late?" A less fit person may have to stop to catch his or her breath at the top of the second flight. This person may have to breathe heavily for a while before answering any questions.

Whether flying jets, swimming, running to catch a plane, or just walking to school, the body requires two basic resources: matter and energy. In fact, all biological activity requires regular amounts of matter and energy.

Consider three scenarios: first, a ballet dancer executing a complex spin; next, a cheetah racing to attack a gazelle; finally, a lily bud opening its petals. What do they have in common? Each of those activities requires matter, which is organized into specific structures. For the human and the cheetah, the muscles of the body act against the skeleton to produce coordinated movement. For the lily, the petals are precisely constructed, producing a symmetric flower. In each case, a highly coordinated interaction of structural systems must take place.

Biological activity also requires energy. What is energy? "Energy" is defined as "the ability to do work." Movement, for example, contracting muscles or opening flower petals, requires work. It takes work to organize matter, such as building the proteins needed for muscles or flower petals. So these processes, and all other processes in living systems, require some sort of energy. Even though many cellular processes cannot be seen with the naked eye, they require energy as well (figure 7.4).

If all human performance requires matter and energy, what is the difference between a person capable of winning a grueling bike race and another who can only watch the race on TV (figure 7.5)? They differ in their ability to apply matter and energy to a specific task. The racer's matter is

Figure 7.4 What structural systems must interact for this activity to take place?

organized more effectively for biking than that of a less fit person. Although the two individuals may weigh the same, the racer's muscles are larger and stronger. As a result, he or she is better able to apply force to the pedals. Likewise, the racer's body supplies matter and energy more effectively than that of a less fit person. Although the two individuals both have circulatory and gas exchange systems, the racer's heart pumps blood more efficiently. The racer's body has a more extensive

Figure 7.5 Typical "couch potato." The typical diet and exercise profile for a couch potato might be weight: 70 kg (154 lb; much fat, little muscle); exercise level: low; diet: high in fats and sugars.

capillary system. This system delivers oxygen and nutrients to muscles. It also removes carbon dioxide and other waste products. Therefore, the racer's legs can pedal and the brain can function all the way to the finish line.

Analysis

1. Refine and rewrite your personal definition of fitness from step 1a of the Engage activity, *Thinking about Fitness*. Incorporate any new ideas you have learned.
2. Work with your partner to complete the following task. Then follow your teacher's instructions for posting your advertisement.

Imagine that you are the owner of a new health club in your neighborhood. Create a 1-page newspaper advertisement for your club that would draw a reader's attention to the most-compelling reasons you know for maintaining or improving a person's fitness for life.

What Is in the Food You Eat?

Do you ever read food labels or the Nutrition Facts labels on the boxes of the cereal that you eat for breakfast? These labels list the names of all the ingredients, some of which are probably familiar while others may be unfamiliar. Many of these ingredients include the nutrients that supply the matter that is essential for your body to function naturally. Consider the previous Explore activity, *What Determines Fitness?* Perhaps it is now clear that the energy source required for human physical fitness is food. The nutrients in food supply both the matter and the energy that your body requires for performance. How do food scientists know what nutrients are present in particular types of food? This is the question you will answer in the first part of this Explain activity, *What Is in the Food You Eat?*, as you determine the presence or absence of specific nutrients in a set of foods. You will combine your test results with the dietary analysis that you completed in the Explore activity, *What Determines Fitness?*, to discover what you *really* ate last week.

But are all of these nutrients equivalent? To answer this question, you will read an essay summarizing some important properties of the molecules found in food and in the bodies of living organisms.

Materials (per team of 5)

For the nutrient tests

5 pairs of safety goggles
5 lab aprons
5 pairs of plastic gloves
500-mL beaker
5 10-mL graduated cylinders
12 18 × 150-mm test tubes
test-tube clamp
3 test-tube racks
dropping pipet
hot plate

Benedict's solution in dropping bottle
biuret solution in dropping bottle
indophenol solution in dropping bottle
isopropyl alcohol (99%) in screw-cap jar
Lugol's iodine solution in dropping bottle
2 glass-marking pencils
4 food samples
water
brown paper bag

For the positive controls

4 100-mL beakers
6 18 × 150-mm test tubes
5 10-mL graduated cylinders
50-mL of 1% ascorbic acid (vitamin C)
small amount of lipids (margarine or oil)
50-mL of 6% suspension of gelatin
50-mL of 10% solution of glucose
50-mL of 6% suspension of starch
2 glass-marking pencils

For the negative controls

6 100-mL beakers
tap water

PROCESS AND PROCEDURES

To begin developing your own explanation for what is in the food you eat, you will set up a series of nutrient tests. Your team will test foods for five different nutrients: starch, sugar (glucose or fructose), vitamin C, fats and oils, and protein. You will use different indicators in the course of your tests, and you will use positive and negative controls to check your results. Other teams in the class will test different foods, and the class will compile its data to arrive at a fuller explanation of the question, "Which nutrients are in different foods?"

1. Working with your team of 4, obtain food samples to test according to your teacher's directions.

2. Create a table for recording data. You should include columns for the foods that the class will test (all 12), your predictions about the nutrients each food contains, and the actual test results. Use a full page of your science notebook.

   > Each team will test 4 foods. But your table should have space to record your predictions and the class results of 5 tests for each of 12 foods. Refer to appendix B4, *How to Use and Create Organizing Tables*, for more assistance with this task.

   HOW TO

3. Enter your predictions about which of the nutrients you will find in each of the 12 foods available to test. Record your predictions in your table, then discuss them with your other team members.

   > Indicators are available to test for the following nutrients: starch, sugar (glucose or fructose), vitamin C, fats and oils, and protein. *Indicators* are chemical or physical methods used to test for the presence of certain substances.

4. Read *Protocol for Nutrient Tests*. Each member of your team will test 1 food for each of the 5 nutrients. Decide which team member will conduct which test. **You will not start doing your nutrient tests until step 6.**

   PROTOCOL

   > Be sure to use the correct indicator for each test. Carefully follow the safety guidelines and directions for its use.

5. Read the information in the need to know, *Using Positive and Negative Controls*, to help you understand of the use of positive and negative controls in investigations.

6. As a team, make a complete set of positive and negative controls for each of your 5 nutrient tests.

SAFETY: Put on your safety goggles, lab apron, and gloves. Tie back long hair.

> Be sure to label each test tube clearly with the nutrient that the indicator tests for. Use a plus sign (+) if it is the positive control and a minus sign (−) if it is the negative control.

PROTOCOL

Protocol for Nutrient Tests

Nutrient	Test
Fats and oils	Rub a drop of ground-up food on a piece of brown paper. Hold the paper up to a light after the water in the sample has evaporated. Fats and oils make a translucent greasy spot on paper. No translucent spot appears in the absence of fats and oils.

Note: When food contains only a small amount of fats or oils, they may not be detected by this method. If you do not detect fats or oils, do the following:

1. Place the assigned food in 10 mL of isopropyl alcohol (99%). Alcohol is a fat-and-oil solvent.

WARNING: Isopropyl alcohol is *flammable* and is a *poison*. Do not expose the liquid or its vapors to heat, sparks, open flame, or other ignition sources. Do not ingest; avoid skin and eye contact. If contact occurs, flush affected area with water for 15 minutes; rinse mouth with water. If a spill occurs, flood spill area with water; *then* call the teacher.

2. Allow the food to dissolve in the alcohol for about 5 minutes.
3. Place 10–20 drops of the mixture on brown paper. The spot should dry in about 10 minutes.
4. Check the paper for a translucent spot.

Nutrient	Test
Protein	Place 5 mL of ground-up food in a test tube. Add 10 drops of biuret solution. Biuret solution is an indicator (see figure 7.6). The biuret test gives a pink to purple reaction in the presence of protein. No color change occurs in the absence of protein.

SCI**LINKS**®
NSTA

www.scilinks.org

Topic: proteins/enzymes
Code: human4E356

Figure 7.6 Indicators are substances that show the presence or absence of another substance by changing their characteristics, especially color.

WARNING: Biuret solution is a *strong irritant* and may damage clothing. Avoid skin and eye contact; do not ingest. If contact occurs, call the teacher immediately. Flush the affected area with water for 15 minutes. If contact occurs with the mouth, rinse the mouth with water.

Nutrient	Test
Starch	Add 5 drops of Lugol's iodine solution to a 5-mL sample of ground-up food. Lugol's iodine solution turns bluish black in the presence of starch. No color change occurs in the absence of starch.

WARNING: Lugol's iodine solution is a *poison* if ingested, is a *strong irritant*, and can stain clothing. Avoid skin and eye contact; do not ingest. If contact occurs, call the teacher immediately. Flush the affected area with water for 15 minutes. If contact occurs with the mouth, rinse the mouth with water.

Nutrient	Test
Sugar	Add 3 mL of Benedict's solution to a 5-mL sample of ground-up food. Place the test tube in a beaker of boiling water. Heat for 5 minutes. If the test tube contains glucose, fructose, or both sugars, the Benedict's solution will react and turn orange or brick red. If the test tube contains either sucrose or no sugar, no reaction will take place. The solution will remain pale blue.

CAUTION: Benedict's solution is an *irritant*. Avoid skin and eye contact; do not ingest. If contact occurs, call the teacher immediately. Flush the affected area with water for 15 minutes. If contact occurs with the mouth, rinse the mouth with water.

WARNING: Use test-tube clamps to hold hot test tubes. Always hold a hot test tube in such a way that the mouth of the test tube is pointed away from your face and anyone else's. Contact with boiling water will cause second-degree burns. Do not touch the beaker or allow boiling water to contact your skin. Avoid vigorous boiling. If a burn occurs, *immediately* place the burned area under cold running water, even if it will further wet the clothing; *then* call the teacher.

Nutrient	Test
Vitamin C	Add 8 drops of indophenol solution to a 5-mL sample of ground-up food. Blue indophenol becomes colorless in the presence of vitamin C. Disregard the intermediate pink color that may occur as you stir. In the absence of vitamin C, indophenol remains blue.

CAUTION: Indophenol solution is an *irritant*. Avoid skin and eye contact; do not ingest. If contact occurs, call the teacher immediately. Flush affected area with water for 15 minutes. If contact occurs with the mouth, rinse the mouth with water.

v

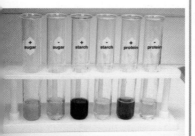

Figure 7.7 Make and label a set of positive and negative controls for each nutrient that your team will test.

NEED TO KNOW
ENGLISH SPANISH

Using Positive and Negative Controls

When scientists use indicators, they run positive and negative controls side by side with the unknowns. **Positive controls** show the expected results if a given substance is *present*. **Negative controls** show the expected results if a given substance is *absent*. For example, a known sample of glucose tested with a glucose indicator gives a positive result. This would be a positive control. If you see the same result after testing a sample of food, you could conclude that glucose is part of that food. In contrast, water tested with a glucose indicator would give a negative test result (see figure 7.7). This would be a negative control. Recall that all controls, except for the variable under study, should be handled in exactly the same manner as the experimental materials. Not every experiment has both positive and negative controls.

7. Complete your tests. Follow the instructions in *Protocol for Nutrient Tests*. Record your observations about the final color of each test. Then record a plus sign (+) in the results column of your table if the food tests positive for a certain nutrient. Use a minus sign (–) in the same column if the nutrient test is negative. For later reference, indicate how sure you were about your interpretation of each test result.

   Remember, compare the appropriate negative and positive controls each time you test your food for a nutrient.

   Pay particular attention to the warning and caution statements for each of the indicators.

8. Clean up your lab materials. **Then wash your hands thoroughly with soap and water.**

   Follow your teacher's instructions for disposing of all waste materials.

9. Share your results with the other members of your team. Then enter their test results in your data table.

   Be sure that you understand the results of each test.

10. For the food item that you tested, develop an explanation of the question, "Which nutrients are in different foods?" Use the *Explanation Template* shown in figure 7.8 as a guide for making a statement containing your evidence, claim, and reasoning.

11. In the class's data table, list the foods that your team tested. Enter your team's test results.

Question to answer:		
Evidence	**Claim(s)**	**Reason/Rationale**
Explanation:		

_____ results in _____ because _____ .

      evidence)   (my claim)   (reason/rationale)

Figure 7.8 Explanation Template. Copy this table into your science notebook. Use the table to organize your data and your analysis of the experiment.

12. Complete your data table by entering the class data for the foods your team did not test.

> Some foods may have been tested by more than one team. Enter all results in your table. As a class, discuss any discrepancies in the results.

13. Discuss the following questions with your teammates. Record your answers in your science notebook.
    a. How did the predictions that you made in step 3 compare with the test results? Which results were the most surprising? Why?
    b. How might the natural colors of the foods affect the results?
    c. Why was it important to test each indicator by using water as the negative control?
    d. Why was it important to test each indicator with a positive control?

14. In your science notebook, create a table like the one in figure 7.9. As you read the essay, *Food: Our Body's Source of Energy and Structural Materials*, fill in information for each of the 4 major macromolecules. Also enter any new terms into your personal glossary.

Macromolecule	Building blocks	Functions	Examples
Proteins			
Lipids (fats)			
Carbohydrates			
Nucleic acids			

Figure 7.9 Major Molecules in Living Organisms table. Create a similar table in your science notebook.

Food: Our Body's Source of Energy and Structural Materials

ENGLISH SPANISH

They sat in the cold mess-hall, most of them with their hats on, eating slowly, picking out putrid little fish from under the leaves of boiled black cabbage and spitting the bones out on the table.... The only good thing about skilly was that it was hot, but Shukhov's portion had grown quite cold. However, he ate it with his usual slow concentration.... Sleep apart, the only time a prisoner lives for himself is ten minutes in the morning at breakfast, five minutes over dinner and five at supper.

The skilly was the same every day. Its composition depended on the kind of vegetable provided that winter. Nothing but salted carrots last year, which meant that from September to June the skilly was plain carrot. This year it was black cabbage. The most nourishing time of the year was June: then all vegetables came to an end and were replaced by groats[1]. The worst time was July: then they shredded nettles[2] into the pot.

The little fish were more bone than flesh; the flesh had been boiled off the bone and had disintegrated, leaving a few remnants on head and tail. Without neglecting a single fish-scale or particle of flesh on the brittle skeleton, Shukhov went on chomping his teeth and sucking the bones. He ate everything—the gills, the tail, the eyes when they were still in their sockets ...

A spoonful of granulated sugar lay in a small mound on top of [his bread ration] ... he sucked the sugar from the bread with his lips ... and took a look at his ration, weighing it in his hand and hastily calculating whether it reached the regulation fifty-five grammes. He had drawn many a thousand of these rations

in prisons and camps, and though he never had an opportunity to weigh them on scales ... he, like every other prisoner, had discovered long ago that honest weight was never to be found in the breadcutting. There was short weight in every ration. The only point was how short. So every day you took a look to soothe your soul—today, maybe, they won't have snitched any.

Source: From *One Day in the Life of Ivan Denisovich*, by Alexander Solzhenitsyn, translated by Ralph Parker; Penguin USA and Victor Gollancz, Ltd.

Note: Shukov is a character in this novel, which takes place in a labor camp in the Soviet Union during the 1950s.

In its most basic sense, **food** is any substance that your body can use as a raw material to sustain its growth, repair it, and provide energy. In extreme situations such as Shukhov's, food is whatever will keep you alive.

The food we eat is made up of hundreds to thousands of different types of molecules. However, humans can obtain the energy they need for life from only three major classes of energy-yielding nutrients: **proteins**, **lipids**, and **carbohydrates**. These three classes of molecules are examples of **organic molecules**. **Molecules** are a combination of atoms that have combined chemically. Organic molecules are based on the important element **carbon**. They also usually involve the elements oxygen and hydrogen. Carbon-based organic molecules can take on many different shapes—straight chains, rings, or large, complexly folded three-dimensional structures. All these different shapes allow the many functions carried out by living things. Carbon is the central element in the molecules of life.

---

[1]Groats are hulled and crushed oats or wheat.
[2]Nettles are a coarse herb with stinging hairs.

Let's examine each of these classes of molecules in more detail.

Proteins

In the opening story, Shukhov ravenously ate his "putrid little fish." The fish probably provided him with a critical source of protein. What makes protein in the diet so important? Your body uses the building blocks of protein to make new proteins that have many functions. Some are involved in helping chemical reactions occur, for example, an enzyme in saliva called amylase. Some build structures in a cell or form things such as hair or fingernails. Keratin is a protein that makes up your hair and the feathers of birds. Some proteins are messengers or receivers of messages, for example, the protein insulin. Some proteins such as hemoglobin transport other molecules. Other proteins such as antibodies help defend against diseases.

The building blocks of proteins are **amino acids**. Look at the structure of an amino acid in figure 7.10. What elements are in all amino acids? Amino acids can join together to form chains. In cells, this chain starts to fold and twist in

interesting ways. The result is a complex three-dimensional shape that determines the function of the protein (figure 7.11).

Humans obtain needed protein from a variety of sources. This variety is necessary to provide all of the essential amino acids required for good health. The human body can synthesize most of the 20 amino acids needed in proteins. However, the body cannot make eight of the amino acids. These eight must be obtained from food. High-protein food from animal sources (meat, milk, eggs) has the proper balance of amino acids for the human diet, as does the plant source soybeans. Other plant-derived foods, such as grains, nuts, and seeds, are good sources of protein as well. But most plant-derived

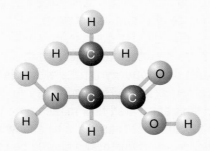

alanine

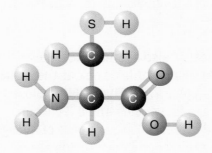

cysteine

Figure 7.10   Amino acids. All amino acids have the same structure, but each type varies in one region. All the organisms on Earth mostly use only 20 different amino acids.

Figure 7.11 Protein folding. In this diagram, different amino acids are represented by different-colored circles. The string of amino acids in (*a*) may coil. For simplicity, this string may be drawn as a flat ribbon, so the coil would look as shown in (*b*). Using a convention similar to the ribbon, but with a tube around the coil, the shape of a folded protein would look like (*c*).

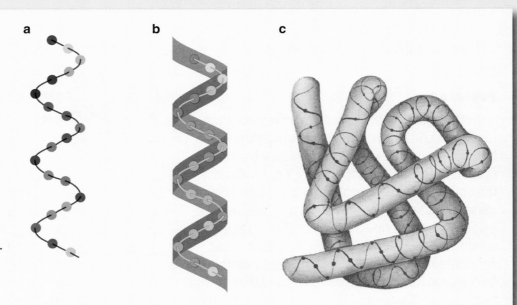

a   **b**   **c**

foods lack one or more of the essential amino acids. It is possible, however, to obtain completely balanced amino acids by combining these plant-derived foods in the diet. The combination of legumes (beans, peas, and peanuts) with grains or nuts can provide balanced-protein diets. This is why peanut butter sandwiches are good for us. The amino acids in the peanuts complement the amino acids in the bread grains to provide a useful balance for our bodies.

Lipids

The fish probably also served as Shukhov's only significant source of fat. Look at the structure of a fat in figure 7.12. The building blocks of simple fats are fatty acids and a 3-carbon molecule called glycerol. Fats are part of a larger group of molecules called lipids. Lipids are a diverse group. What this group of molecules has in common is that these molecules do not dissolve easily in water. Lipids are important nutritionally for making hormones and cell membranes and for storing energy.

Unfortunately, most Americans consume too many fats, and many of these fats are the wrong type. Of particular concern are saturated and trans fats. Saturated fats are present in animal products such as meat, cheese, and butter. Trans fats are synthesized by adding hydrogen atoms to vegetable oil, which enhances its ability to preserve food. Trans fats are commonly found in fried foods, as well as in processed foods such as crackers and shortenings.

Because of the links between fat intake, obesity, and cardiovascular disease, doctors recommend that fats should make up less than 35 percent of a person's daily energy intake, which is measured in **kilocalories** (kcal). However, they further recommend that saturated fats make up no more than 10 percent, and that trans fats be as low as possible. Therefore, most fat intake should be of "healthy" fats: monounsaturated, polyunsaturated, and omega-3 fatty acids. For example, fish oil contains omega-3 fatty acids, which is beneficial for the heart and required for normal development of the nervous and reproductive systems.

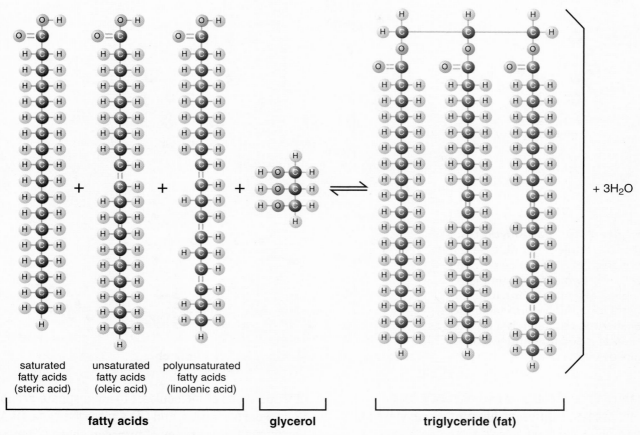

Figure 7.12 **Structure of a fat.** Fats are made from fatty acids and a molecule called glycerol. The fatty acids in a fat can be the same or different.

saturated fatty acids (steric acid)

unsaturated fatty acids (oleic acid)

polyunsaturated fatty acids (linolenic acid)

fatty acids

glycerol

triglyceride (fat)

+ 3H₂O

Carbohydrates

A third group of important organic molecules is carbohydrates. Shukhov obtained some carbohydrates from the carrots, cabbage, and groats in his diet. The name "carbohydrate" tells you something about the elements in these molecules. "Carbo-" refers to carbon, and "hydrate" refers to water, which contains oxygen and hydrogen. The building blocks of carbohydrates are single sugar units (also called monosaccharides—"mono-" means "one," and "saccharide" means "sugar unit"). Look at the structure of the simple sugar glucose in

figure 7.13a. Glucose is the sugar in your blood. It is the preferred energy source for most cells.

Simple sugars are used as sources of energy for almost all organisms. But they can serve other functions also. Many simple sugars like glucose can bond together to build complex carbohydrates. Complex carbohydrates contain many sugar units, so they are also called **polysaccharides** ("poly-" means "many"). One example of a complex carbohydrate is starch. Plants use starch as an energy-storage molecule. It is a major part of many plant seeds. Your muscles and liver make a similar complex carbohydrate called glycogen, also called animal starch.

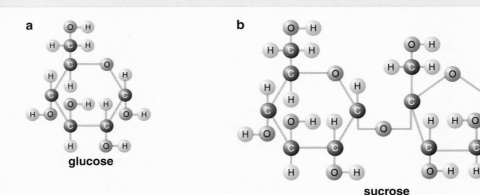

Figure 7.13   Carbohydrates.
(*a*) The simple sugar glucose is the preferred energy source of many cells. (*b*) Two different simple sugars, glucose and fructose, can bond together to form table sugar, or sucrose. (*c*) Starch is a polysaccharide made up of hundreds of glucose sugars.

A third type of complex carbohydrate called cellulose has a different function. Have you ever seen cellulose? Take a look at a piece of wood. A large part of wood is the structural molecule cellulose. In fact, dietary fiber is mostly cellulose. Most organisms, including humans, cannot breakdown cellulose. However, cellulose absorbs water and toxins and helps ensure regular elimination of waste.

Nucleic Acids

Carbohydrates, lipids, and proteins are the sources of energy for fueling your life. A fourth important group of molecules that your body needs is called nucleic acids. These molecules play vital roles in cells, but they are not used as sources of energy. Two types of nucleic acids are DNA (deoxyribonucleic acid) and RNA (ribonucleic acid). Both DNA and RNA are made up of building blocks called **nucleotides**. Each nucleotide, in turn, is made up

of three types of molecules: (1) a phosphate group, (2) a 5-carbon sugar, and (3) a nitrogen base. DNA has four different types of nitrogen bases (adenine [A], cytosine [C], guanine [G], and thymine [T]).

Nucleotides can join together to form chains (figure 7.14). (Does this sound familiar?) Two strands of DNA join together in a specific way and form a coil, making a double helix. What does DNA do? DNA stores information for forming proteins. The information in DNA can also be copied and passed from one generation to the next.

Additional Molecules and Elements

Most of the substances we call food consist largely of water. A tomato, for example, is about 95 percent water. Water is an important nutrient that we often take for granted. Water isn't considered food, however, because humans do not derive energy from it. Our bodies need enormous amounts of water in comparison to other nutrients. An average American diet includes about 2 L, or 2,000 g, of water each day. In contrast, most of us eat only about 50 g of protein in a day and only milligrams of many vitamins and essential elements.

What else does the body need? The body needs small amounts of vitamins and essential elements (also known as minerals) for proper functioning, even though they are not a source of energy. Partnered with enzymes, **vitamins** regulate cellular activities. Vitamins, therefore, are necessary for normal growth and maintenance of life. Thiamine and riboflavin, for example, are B-complex vitamins. B-complex vitamins help release energy from food. Thiamine deficiencies can lead to muscle atrophy, paralysis, mental confusion, and even heart failure. The sources, functions, and deficiency symptoms of vitamins are found in appendix E. Elements are the basic components of matter. Essential elements such as sodium and calcium are important to maintaining homeostasis. Appendix E describes the sources, functions, and deficiency (and excess) symptoms of some important **essential elements**.

Nutrition

Having examined some important molecules gives you a good perspective to study nutrition. What constitutes good nutrition? The phrase "good nutrition" means ensuring that your body receives what it requires to remain healthy and functional. It also means avoiding those things that may cause it harm. Exactly what constitutes *good* may vary somewhat with the circumstances.

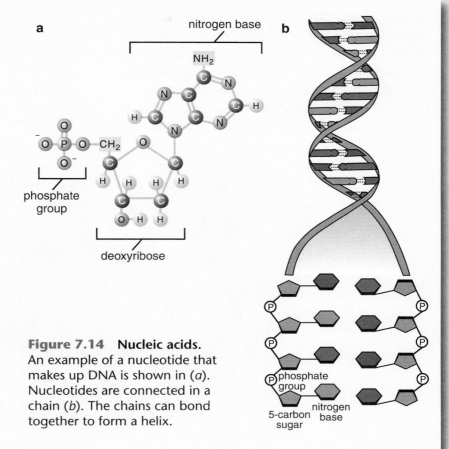

Figure 7.14 Nucleic acids. An example of a nucleotide that makes up DNA is shown in (*a*). Nucleotides are connected in a chain (*b*). The chains can bond together to form a helix.

For example, although not consistent with the general guidelines for a healthy diet, Captain Yates's breakfast was appropriate for her unusual type of physical activity. With its relatively high-fat foods, her breakfast contained stored energy and low bulk. A dense breakfast such as pancakes and cereal would have put strain on her digestive system.

Determining what constitutes a level of good general nutrition is the job of biochemists, nutritionists, and other health professionals. Their understanding of how the body uses energy and matter is critical to their work. As their understanding improves through research, the nutritional guidelines that professionals suggest often change. Figure 7.15 outlines some nutritional guidelines for

general fitness. (Note that the "Calories" listed on food labels are actually kilocalories; 1,000 calories equals 1 kcal. Nutritionists often represent 1 kcal by *Calorie*, with a capital *C*. A Calorie is a measure of the energy contained in food.) To learn more about the food pyramid, read the sidebar, *Pioneers: The Changing Face of the Food Guide Pyramid*.

There are many ways to achieve the balance of nutrients outlined in figure 7.15. An individual's *diet*—the types of food that he or she eats on a regular basis—is a reflection of many influences. Your cultural background, your personal preferences, and the varieties of foods available all influence what you eat.

Figure 7.15   USDA food guide pyramid for a 2,000 Calorie diet. Foods provide fuel for energy and matter for body structures. People in different cultures select and prepare foods in a variety of ways. However, 2,000 Calories is an appropriate amount of energy for many people. What foods would you choose to meet the USDA recommended guidelines?

Pioneers: The Changing Face of the Food Guide Pyramid

Chapter 7 has introduced you to the ways your body uses the foods you eat. How do you choose those foods? Have you ever seen a food guide pyramid? The standard food guide pyramid was originally designed to help people meet nutritional and dietary needs. Do you think this guide is appropriate for all people? Alternative food guides suggest ways that people with different dietary preferences may also get the nutrition necessary for a healthy lifestyle.

What are some ways you might use a food guide pyramid in your life? A good place to begin is knowing the difference between a serving and a helping. A *serving* is the amount of a food item that has been analyzed for nutritional value. A *helping* is the amount you choose to eat. Some food guides may tell you exactly how much of a food you should eat. Many newer versions merely suggest foods to choose from on a daily or weekly basis.

Does the guide consider foods that you enjoy with your family or friends? The standard food guide does not reflect cultural differences among families (figure 7.16). Also, a great variety of food is available across the United States. Compare the standard guide

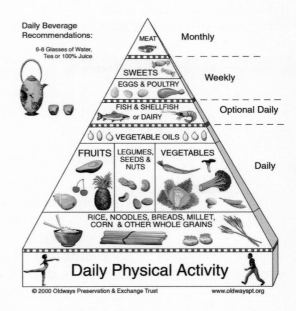

Figure 7.16 Alternative food guide pyramids. Food guides for different cultural groups include (*a*) Mediterranean Diet Pyramid for Children, (*b*) Asian Diet Pyramid for Children, (*c*) Latin American Diet Pyramid for Children, (*d*) Vegetarian Diet Pyramid for Children.

c

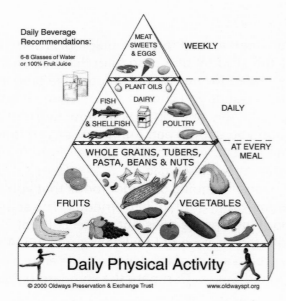

d

and the Latin American native foods guide. The vegetarian food guide is for people who do not eat meat.

Does the guide recommend foods that every person can eat and digest? Humans differ in their ability to digest milk. This adaptation, known as lactose tolerance, arose

multiple times in human evolution among cattle-herding populations in Europe and some parts of Africa. However, over half of the human population cannot digest milk. Many African Americans, Hispanics, Asian Americans, and Native Americans are included in this group.

Analysis

In your science notebook, record your responses to the following questions.

1. Examine the *Dietary Analysis* handout that you completed in the Explore activity, *What Determines Fitness?* Notice that the foods you tested in the laboratory included 1 from each of the 6 food groups in this analysis. You can use your test results to help you determine the nutrients that were likely present in the foods you listed on your dietary analysis. Identify which foods you listed on your *Dietary Analysis* handout that your body could use as a source of the following.
   a. Protein
   b. Sugar
   c. Starch
   d. Vitamin C
   e. Fats and oils

2. Compare each of the class's test results with the predictions you made in step 3 of this activity. Write down any discrepancies you find. Describe how the discrepancies highlight the following.
   a. Problems with the specificity or accuracy of the tests
   b. Ways in which your thinking about nutrients in food has changed
3. Which, if any, of the foods that you ate contained all of the nutrients for which you tested? What does this mean for eating a balanced diet?

You Are What You Eat

In the previous activity, you investigated what is in the food that you eat. But once this food is inside you, how does it become useful to your body? What does your body do to this matter so that you can use the energy it contains for performance? How does your body prepare this matter so that you will have the building blocks necessary for growth and repair? In this Explain activity, *You Are What You Eat*, you will look at digestion to understand the role it plays in preparing to release the energy stored in food molecules and in providing a source of building blocks for the body to use.

Materials

Part A (per team of 4)
   4 pairs of safety goggles
   4 laboratory aprons
   2–3 unsalted soda crackers
   other materials to be decided by each team

Part B
   online resource

PROCESS AND PROCEDURES

Part A Starch—Break It Down!
Your team will explore the effects of an enzyme called amylase. To investigate how enzymes work, your class will answer the focus question, "How do different variables affect enzyme reactions?" You will use the actions of amylase and how it operates in different environments to develop a model for how all enzymes work. Is enzyme function important? Your life depends on the proper functioning of enzymes.

1. Each team member should put half a cracker in his or her mouth. Chew the cracker but don't swallow it.

2. Let the cracker and saliva mix in your mouth for at least 2 minutes. Report to your team when or if you start to taste something different than when you first tasted the cracker.

3. Answer this question in your science notebook: What do you think is happening to cause the different taste to appear in some people's mouths? Be specific.

4. Read the background information in the need to know, *Experimenting with Starch and Enzymes*. This information will help you design an appropriate experiment.

NEED TO KNOW

ENGLISH SPANISH

Experimenting with Starch and Enzymes

Starch is made up of hundreds or thousands of individual glucose molecules that are linked together. Because starch has so many individual sugar units, it is considered a polysaccharide. Another term for carbohydrates that contain many linked sugar units is complex carbohydrates. Starch is a complex carbohydrate that is used as an energy-storage molecule in plants. Many plants have large reserves of starch in their seeds and in their roots. Can you think of the reason plants would have a great deal of starch in their seeds?

Animals, fungi, and plants can all break down starch and use its stored energy. How do these organisms carry out this microscopic reaction? In many organisms, glucose units are cut off two at a time, leaving a 2-sugar unit (a disaccharide; remember that "di-" means "two") called maltose (see figure 7.17). Humans have an enzyme called amylase that helps break down the starch to simple sugars. Amylase is found in your saliva, and your pancreas also secretes it. Amylase is also found in a wide range of bacteria, plants, fungi, and animals.

You will investigate the role of amylase in breaking down starch. Read about some of the materials available for experiments.

Benedict's solution is an indicator that changes color in the presence of simple sugars like glucose and maltose. The indicator does not change color in the presence of polysaccharides or table sugar (sucrose). To use this indicator, add 3 mL of Benedict's solution to 5 mL of sample solution. Place the test tube in a beaker of boiling water. Heat for 5 minutes.

Buffers can be added to a solution to control the pH.

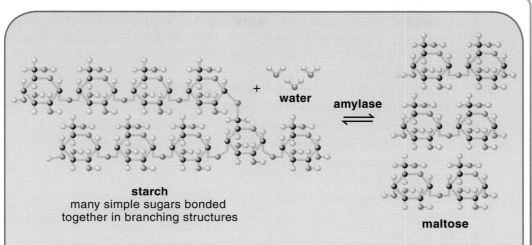

starch
many simple sugars bonded
together in branching structures

maltose

Figure 7.17   Breakdown of starch by amylase. Notice that starch is broken down into the 2-sugar-unit carbohydrate called maltose. This reaction is catalyzed by the enzyme amylase. In this diagram, white spheres represent hydrogen atoms, black spheres represent carbon atoms, and red spheres represent oxygen atoms.

Enzymes are almost always proteins that work as catalysts. Catalysts speed up the rate of a chemical reaction and are not used up in the reaction. The molecules on which an enzyme acts are known as substrates. The molecules formed by an enzyme-catalyzed reaction are called products. A solution containing an enzyme must be added to a solution containing the appropriate substrates before the reaction can begin. Several factors affect the activity or effectiveness of an enzyme, including the following:

- Temperature
- pH
- Concentration of enzyme
- Concentration of substrate
- Amount of time the enzyme is in contact with the substrate

Glucose test strips can be used by people with diabetes to check the concentration of glucose in their urine. These strips indicate the presence of glucose in a solution by changing color. Conveniently, these strips also indicate the presence of other simple sugars (sugars with only one or two sugar units), such as maltose.

HCl reaction stopping solution (0.1 M HCl, or hydrochloric acid) prevents the amylase enzyme from working.

Lugol's iodine solution is an indicator that changes color in the presence of starch. In a spot plate or test tube, use 1 drop of Lugol's iodine solution for 2 mL of the sample solution you are testing.

5. Your teacher will perform a demonstration. You will observe how amylase works and how you can study how amylase works. Pay close attention and answer the following questions in your science notebook.
    a. What solutions are being used?
    b. What is the function of each of the solutions?
    c. What is the role of amylase in breaking down starch?

6. Choose a variable that might affect the rate of the amylase-starch reaction. Develop a hypothesis about its effect on the reaction. Variables that you might consider include
    • the concentration of amylase,
    • the concentration of starch,
    • the temperature, and
    • the pH.

7. In your science notebook, write a hypothesis for your experiment. Explain how you think your variable will affect the amylase-starch reaction and why.

    You may want to write your hypothesis as an if-then statement combined with an explanation.

8. With your team, develop an outline of a controlled experiment to investigate the effect of the variable you selected. Make sure you include the question or questions you are trying to answer in the experiment.

    Think about what will constitute a control or controls in this experiment. Think critically about what data you will collect. Will the data you collect be sufficient to answer your question? Also, make sure to use the background information in the need to know, *Experimenting with Starch and Enzymes*. See appendix C2, *How to Design an Investigation*, for information on investigation design.

9. Have your teacher check your outline to review your experimental setup. Your teacher should also approve your hypothesis.

10. Carry out your experiment and record all results in your science notebook.

CAUTION: Put on your safety goggles and laboratory apron.

11. ***Wash your hands thoroughly when you are finished.***

12. Copy the *Explanation Template* in figure 7.18 into your science notebook. Fill it in to help you organize your data and your analysis of this experiment.

    For more information on this template, see appendix C4, *How to Develop an Explanation*.

Question to answer:		
Evidence	**Claim(s)**	**Reason/Rationale**
Explanation:		

_____ results in _____ because _____.
      (evidence)   (my claim)   (reason/rationale)

Figure 7.18 Explanation template. Copy this table into your science notebook. Use the table to organize your data and your analysis of the experiment.

13. Present your results. Take notes during the discussion of each team's results.

   Take notes on the effects of variables on enzyme reactions. Your classmates' results will be important for your final analysis.

14. Based on your class's data, add a final summary to your *Explanation Template*. Include an analysis of the effect of different variables on enzyme reactions.

15. Copy figure 7.19 into your science notebook. As you read about enzymes and energy in the essay, *Activate Me,* fill in the empty cells. Filling in an analogy table will help you make sense of the example described in the reading.

Feature of figure 7.20	is like ...	feature of a catalyzed reaction ...	because ...
A ball on top of a hill	is like	the substrates in a catalyzed reaction	because it has potential energy to roll downhill.
The small hill the ball has to climb before rolling downhill	is like	the energy barrier that keeps substrates stable	because the ball will not roll down the hill unless enough energy is put into moving the ball up the hill.
The energy the person at the top of the hill puts into moving the ball up the small hill	is like		
The ball at the bottom of the hill	is like		
The difference in height between the starting and ending position of the ball	is like		

Figure 7.19   Activation Energy analogy table. The two first rows have been completed for you. Copy the table and fill in the remaining rows as you read the essay, *Activate Me*.

Activate Me

You have witnessed the breakdown of starch to simpler sugars. Typically, energy is released in reactions that break large molecules into smaller ones. But think about a bag of flour, which is mostly starch. You can stare at it all day, but the starch won't be broken down to sugars. Why not? It turns out that there was not enough energy to start the reaction. The energy required to start a reaction is called the **activation energy**. It is easy to get confused here. Let's compare activation energy with something that is easier to understand.

Imagine that you are near the top of a hill that is shaped like the one in figure 7.20. Your friend is at the bottom of the hill. You think that it would be hilarious to roll a ball down the hill to surprise your friend. Lucky for you, and for the sake of this analogy, the hill is smooth. To start the ball rolling down the hill, you first have to expend some

energy pushing the ball up the hill. The energy it takes to push the ball uphill is the *activation energy*. After the initial input of energy, the ball rolls downhill, much to the surprise of your slightly annoyed friend.

How is this like the bag of flour? The "hill" in this case is very high indeed. So what happens if you mix the flour with some water and add an enzyme? The flour starch starts with a high amount of potential energy. Look again at figure 7.20. Point A represents the energy level of starch. You then add an enzyme. This lowers the activation energy needed to start the reaction. With the enzyme's help, the starch breakdown is like only having to push the ball straight across to the point where it starts to roll on its own. This allows more starch molecules to overcome the activation energy. From there, the breakdown

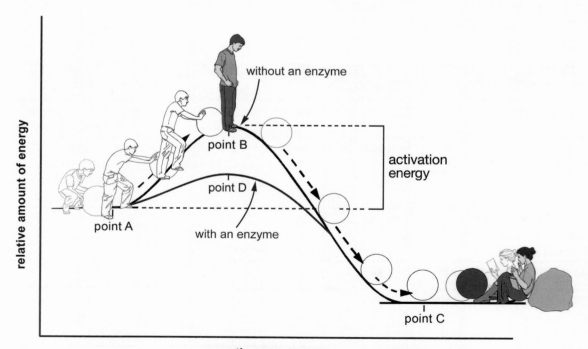

Figure 7.20 Activation energy. It takes an initial input of energy to move the ball from point A to point B. This amount of energy is the activation energy. Enzymes lower the activation energy.

of starch into maltose is able to proceed, just as the ball is able to roll downhill to point C.

So enzymes have two characteristics that help cells control chemical reactions. First, enzymes reduce the energy needed to start chemical reactions. Second, they control very specific reactions. Each enzyme reduces the energy of activation for a particular chemical reaction. These reactions involve just one specific molecule or a small set of molecules. What molecules interact with amylase?

How can an enzyme lower the energy required for activation? How can enzymes be so specific in the reactions they catalyze (figure 7.21)? Enzymes are large structures, and they are almost always proteins. They are usually much larger than the molecules that they cause to react. The reacting molecules, or substrates, fit into grooves or notches on the enzyme's surface. The grooves or notches are called active sites. Only the specific molecules (substrates) involved in the reaction will fit in the enzyme's active site. That explains how enzymes can be specific. Once the substrate enters the active site, the enzyme temporarily changes shape. By changing shape, the enzyme holds the substrate in its active site in such a way that the reaction is more likely to happen (figure 7.22). This explains how enzymes lower the energy of activation.

Over the billions of years of life on Earth, organisms have evolved millions of different types of enzymes to catalyze the reactions necessary for life. The collection of enzymes in an organism allows all of the needed reactions to take place rapidly and precisely at the relatively low temperatures at which most life exists. Enzymes are truly amazing molecules.

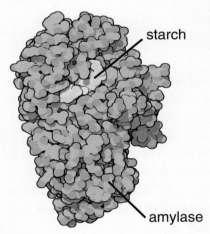

Figure 7.22 Model of the structure of amylase. Amylase is a protein that has a complex, three-dimensional structure. Computer models and other types of studies suggest that amylase has the shape shown in the figure. The arrow is pointing to a small polysaccharide that represents starch fitting into the active site of amylase.

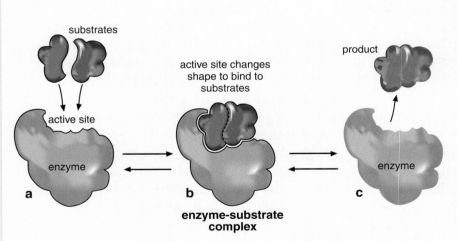

Figure 7.21 Model of enzyme action. (*a*) The substrate molecules randomly collide with the active site of the enzyme. (*b*) As the substrates bind to the enzyme, the enzyme changes shape temporarily, helping the reaction take place between the substrates. (*c*) The product is released, and the enzyme returns to its original shape. So the enzyme is unchanged by the reaction. How does this process relate to energy?

Part B   Food for the Body's Building Blocks

Food provides energy. But it also is the source of matter that animals use to build new structures necessary for body maintenance and growth. In this activity, you will begin to explore how the body digests, breaks down, and builds new molecules.

1. Take notes as you watch the video segment, "Introduction to Biosynthesis."
2. Participate in a class discussion about this question: What happens when a foreign protein is ingested by an animal?
3. Read the essay, *What Happens to the Food You Eat?* As you read, create a flowchart or diagram in your science notebook that summarizes how proteins, carbohydrates, and fats in a cheeseburger are digested and where they are absorbed. Make sure to describe the role of the enzymes and the specific organs involved in each pathway.
4. Read the essay, *Anorexia Nervosa: Dying to Be Thin.* As you read, write an explanation in your science notebook of how a person suffering from anorexia nervosa obtains the building blocks needed for biosynthesis.

What Happens to the Food You Eat?

Have you ever watched a pizza commercial on television and heard your stomach growl as the actor pulls up a warm slice with stringy cheese trailing behind? When you feel hungry, whether in response to your body's actual need for nutrients or just over thoughts of a tasty slice of pizza, hormonal signals begin to prepare the digestive system for action. How does this work when your body truly needs nutrients? A decrease in nutrient levels in your blood sends a signal to the hunger center in your brain's hypothalamus. The hypothalamus responds by triggering the release of digestive juices into the stomach. A feeling of hunger then motivates you to find food. The initial responses to hunger stimulate the secretion of hormones such as gastrin. Those hormones, in turn, stimulate further secretion of digestive juices in the stomach. Thus, a feedback system alerts your body that it needs (or wants) food.

Once you have eaten food, your body must break the food into smaller pieces that can be absorbed and used by cells. This is the process of **digestion**. There are two types of digestion. **Physical digestion** is the breakup of large pieces of food into smaller ones. In humans, it involves chewing. Chewing performs an important digestive function. As you chew, the surface area of your food increases greatly. Increased surface area means that the chemical reactions involved in digestion can take place more quickly. In addition, chewing moistens the food with saliva. Salivary glands located under your tongue secrete saliva.

The mechanical breakdown of food is not enough. No matter how finely you chew bits of steak, the proteins remain intact. If your body is to use the proteins, it must break them down into subunits: amino acids. Similarly, chewed bread still has its carbohydrates intact, mainly in the form of long starch molecules. Your body must break down starch to sugars to use it. **Chemical digestion** involves breaking bonds within the large molecules that make up food to form smaller molecules. In general, digestive enzymes break down complex molecules to their simple components. You have begun to explore the role of enzymes in this process.

Humans rely on digestion outside of their cells, also called extracellular digestion. Does that sound odd? Think of it in this way. Your digestive tract is really just a tube within your body. It is open to the outside environment, even though you control what enters and leaves. As food moves through this long tube, cells lining the tube secrete enzymes and fluids into it. So, the digestion happens outside the cells, and technically within the outside environment.

Most animals secrete digestive enzymes into a digestive cavity, where the chemical digestion of food yields simpler molecules that can be absorbed by cells. Specialized cells, tissues, and organs contribute to the digestion of complex molecules. Figure 7.23 shows the components of the human digestive system. Figure 7.24 lists some examples of digestive enzymes, the reactions they carry out, and the pH conditions under which they function.

After you swallow, it takes fewer than 10 seconds for the chewed and moistened food to pass through the esophagus into the stomach. Smooth muscles encircle the digestive tract. These muscles contract in a coordinated fashion, called *peristalsis*, to move food through the digestive tract.

In the stomach, food churns and mixes with digestive fluids for three or four hours. The

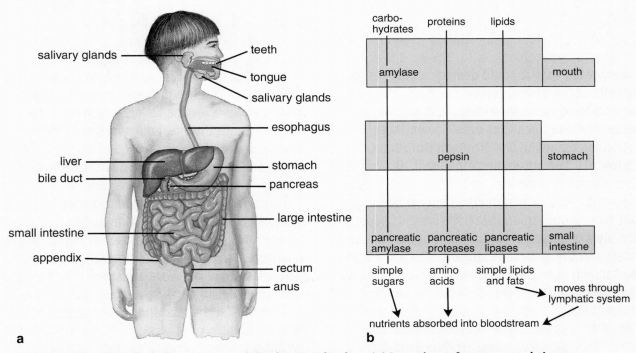

Figure 7.23 **The digestive system of the human body.** *(a)* **Location of organs and tissues involved in digestion.** *(b)* **Examples of enzyme action in breaking down food.** Notice the compartments in which the enzymes for specific substrates act.

Type of enzyme	General reaction	Optimal pH
Amylase	Starch → double sugars (maltose)	pH 6.9–7.0
Proteases	Protein → amino acids	pH 2.0 (pepsin); pH 7.0–8.0 (most others)
Lipases	Fats → fatty acids + glycerol	pH 8.0

Figure 7.24 Roles of some digestive enzymes.

stomach stretches during this process and makes you feel full. The sensation reduces your motivation to continue eating. (Unless the food tastes so good that you ignore these signals and continue eating anyway.) This is another example of negative feedback, which you studied in chapter 5, *Maintaining Balance in Organisms*. The digestion that occurs in the stomach is primarily physical, breaking food into very small bits. With the exception of some proteins, most food molecules are not broken into their building blocks in the stomach. The stomach is a very acidic environment. Glands in the stomach secrete hydrochloric acid. The acid is so concentrated that it could destroy living tissue. The cells of the stomach lining are not harmed, however, because some secrete a thick coat of mucus. The enzymes that break down large protein molecules in the stomach function best at a low pH. The active protein-digesting enzyme in the stomach is pepsin, which is secreted in an inactive form. Can you imagine why this enzyme must be secreted in an inactive form? If pepsin were always active, it would start to degrade the proteins in the cells that made it. The low pH in the stomach changes pepsin into its active form. Pepsin breaks down large proteins to smaller polypeptides.

From the stomach, partially digested food passes into the small intestine. The final digestion of the complex food molecules, breaking down to their simple components, happens here.

The cells that line the small intestine release some digestive enzymes. The pancreas and liver also deliver digestive enzymes to the small intestine. The pancreas is an organ in the abdomen that produces 1.4 L (3 pt) of fluid per day. The fluid contains enzymes that contribute to the final digestion of the remaining macromolecules in the small intestine. The liver produces 0.8–1.0 L of bile per day. Bile is stored in the gallbladder. It is released into the small intestine after a meal. Bile contains bile salts, which act in a manner similar to detergents. Bile breaks fat into tiny droplets. This increases the surface area of the fats so that enzymes can work on them easily.

The end products of digestion are amino acids, simple sugars, fatty acids, and glycerol. Cells that line the small intestine absorb these small molecules through their cell membranes. If the molecules are moving from an area of low concentration to an area of high concentration, they must be moved inside by active transport.

The surface area of the small intestine is greatly increased by folding as well as by millions of small "bumps" called villi that look like very small fingers (see figure 7.25). Each bump contains capillaries. Capillaries are blood vessels that are very thin and allow molecules to move in and out. Simple sugars, amino acids, fatty acids, and some glycerol, minerals, and vitamins pass through the cells of the villi and enter the bloodstream through capillaries. Fatty acids and glycerol first move into the lymph system, and eventually join the bloodstream.

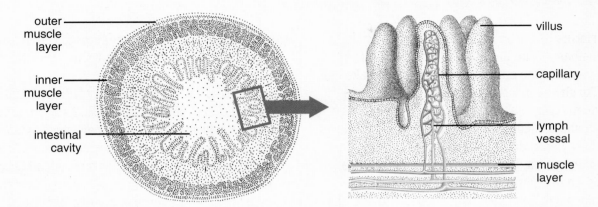

outer muscle layer

inner muscle layer

intestinal cavity

villus

capillary

lymph vessal

muscle layer

Figure 7.25 Cross section of the small intestine. Notice the large amount of folds in the small intestine. The folds are called intestinal villi. The products of digestion enter the blood through the villi. What other parts of the body do you know of that have a large surface area such as the small intestine?

The blood ultimately moves the products of digestion to all the cells in the body. Once inside the cells, the molecules are either broken down or used to synthesize substances the organism needs for growth and repair. This process is called **biosynthesis**. Reactions that break down large molecules tend to release energy, whereas those that build up larger molecules require energy.

Liver cells monitor nutrient levels in the blood and adjust them as necessary. Simpler substances present in excess amounts are removed and stored. For example, glucose molecules can be linked together and stored as glycogen molecules. Do you think this process requires energy? Simpler substances that are lacking can also be increased. The liver accomplishes this by breaking down storage molecules such as glycogen into simple sugars. Say, for example, you exercise heavily. Glucose levels drop in your bloodstream. Sensors trigger the liver to break down glycogen. The glycogen is quickly broken down into glucose to replenish the exhausted supply. Liver cells also remove and correct potentially toxic substances (such as alcohol and other drugs) from the blood.

Normally, digestion and absorption are completed in four to seven hours. Substances left in the small intestine then pass into the large intestine, where more water is absorbed. There is almost no absorption of food molecules in the large intestine, though some fatty acids may be absorbed. Undigested foods, indigestible substances, mucus, dead cells from the intestinal lining, and bacteria are concentrated by water removal to form waste matter, or feces. The feces then exit the body.

Though the processes that have been described are relatively simple, many of the interactions that occur in digestion are complex. For example, consider that a large number of microbes exist in the small and large intestines. There are about 10 times more bacterial cells in or on humans than there are human cells. These microbes play important roles in helping you absorb certain nutrients. Antibiotics can disrupt the complex interactions of microbes in the digestive tract, explaining why an "upset stomach" is a common side effect of many antibiotics.

Anorexia Nervosa: Dying to Be Thin

Christine has been getting increasingly moody and she hasn't had her period (menstruated) in three months. The circles under her eyes make her look like she hasn't been sleeping well. The cold she caught two weeks ago has lingered on and on. Though she denies feeling tired, she seems to have less energy each day. Yesterday, her father noticed her swaying a bit—dizzy, perhaps?—when she jumped up to answer the phone. Dinner was an unhappy meal. Her parents pushed her to eat, and Christine insisted she was not hungry. Then she went out to run her customary 3 km (1.9 mi).

Although Christine doesn't know it, she has anorexia nervosa. Anorexia nervosa is an eating disorder that affects an estimated 1 million people, mostly teenage girls, in the United States. Christine probably wouldn't admit that she is undernourished. In fact, she will insist against all evidence to the contrary that she is fat and needs to lose weight. She denies her hunger and exercises relentlessly until she is convinced that she has burned off any "excess" calories she might have consumed. Her friends admire her self-discipline, but they also worry about her.

Left untreated, Christine likely will continue starving herself, possibly to death. As her nutritional base deteriorates, she will experience profound physical changes. Her reproductive hormone levels will continue to drop. Her heart muscle will become weak and thin, as her body breaks down its structural proteins as a source of energy. Her digestive system will begin to function less and less efficiently. Electrical activity in her brain may become abnormal. Electrolyte imbalances in her body will put her at risk for sudden heart failure.

Treatment of anorexia nervosa is complex. The underlying causes involve self-image and mental attitudes. Successful treatment must take into account the whole person: the physical self, the cultural self, and the psychological self. Not surprisingly, treatment is most successful when the entire family is involved and participates honestly in the process.

Structures and Functions

Recall from the previous Explain activity, *You Are What You Eat*, that the food you eat is broken down by the digestive system. The raw materials that result from digestion, macromolecules such as amino acids, sugars, and fatty acids, serve as building blocks in the synthesis of various body structures. Muscle tissue is a good example. For instance, amino acids are the building blocks your body requires for the proteins that make up muscle tissue. They are used to repair as well as synthesize muscle proteins. Once these building blocks are made into muscle protein, they become part of a larger structure: a muscle. The function of muscles is to provide mobility. But not all proteins (for example, enzymes like amylase) provide mobility. What is special about how muscle proteins are arranged into structures that allow physical activity?

In this Elaborate activity, *Structures and Functions*, you will think about how building blocks obtained from the matter of digested food can become organized into larger structures that have very specific functions. You will also relate the relationship between structure and function to human fitness and performance.

Materials (per team of 2)

online resource
1 brass brad
25-cm piece of string
rubber bands
roll of tape
scissors
sheet of thin cardboard
different-colored pens or pencils

PROCESS AND PROCEDURES

1. View the video segment, "Muscle Movement at the Molecular Level." Work with your partner to answer the following questions. Write your answers in your science notebook.
   a. What type of movement does the structure of muscles permit?
   b. What are the advantages and the disadvantages of this structural arrangement of muscle fibers?
2. With your partner, write down how you think your biceps and triceps muscles act to bend your forearm up. Then write down how these muscles act to straighten your arm from a bent position.

   To investigate how these muscles work, bend and straighten your arm while using your other hand to feel what happens to your biceps and triceps. Consult figure 7.27 in the essay, *Making and Moving Muscles*, if you are not sure where the biceps and triceps are located. This step helps you explore the function of muscle fibers at a higher level of organization, where matter is organized in a way that moves larger structures of the body.

3. Work with your partner to construct a working model of a human thigh and lower leg. Be sure to show the attachment sites of the muscles on the front and back of the thigh.

   You should be able to demonstrate with your model how the muscles of your thigh work together to move your lower leg. Use your own thigh and figure 7.26 to determine how many muscles you need to model and where their attachment sites may be. Decide with your partner whether it is necessary to model the gluteus maximus muscle in addition to the hamstrings and quadriceps. Use materials provided by your teacher. For example, you might use the cardboard for bone, the string or rubber bands for muscle, the tape for tendons, and the brad for the knee. You may use a different combination of parts to form your model.

4. Place your model on the table with the leg straight. With your partner, pull on the muscles of your model to develop answers to the following questions. Support your answers with observations taken from your model.
   a. What movement of the lower leg does a hamstring contraction (shortening) cause?
   b. What movement of the lower leg does a quadriceps contraction cause?
   c. Does a muscle cause a pulling motion or a pushing motion, or can it produce both motions?
5. Copy the following questions into your science notebook, leaving plenty of space to write answers. Then answer these questions while reading the essay, *Making and Moving Muscles*.
   a. Explain the statement, "Muscles work in pairs." Why is it important for muscles to be present in pairs in the human body?
   b. What is the role of the joint in producing movement?
   c. Recall from the video segment that the molecular filaments in muscles can shorten muscles but cannot lengthen them. How do you think it is possible for us to push on anything?

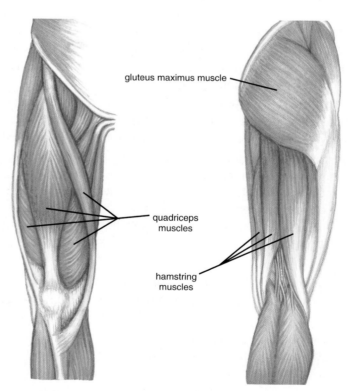

gluteus maximus muscle

quadriceps muscles

hamstring muscles

Figure 7.26 Muscles of the human leg. The quadriceps and hamstring muscles each extend across the knee to connect to the bones of the lower leg.

You may wish to test your answer by pushing on a wall. Feel both your biceps and triceps muscles. How are they acting to stabilize your arm? Why is this important to your ability to exert force against the wall?

6. Discuss the following questions with a partner and record your ideas in your science notebook.
   a. Why can you run at full speed for only a few seconds?
   b. Why do your muscles get sore after a really tough workout?

Making and Moving Muscles

ENGLISH SPANISH

Mary, James, Lolita, Madonna, Rodriguez . . .

Writing your name seems simple enough, doesn't it? To do even this simple task, however, requires a highly coordinated series of muscle movements in your arm, hand, and fingers. Energy is necessary for all of these movements. Indeed, energy is required even to transmit nerve impulses.

All physical activities require some type of structure that can transform the energy of food into useful biological work. The muscles and skeleton of your arm, hand, and fingers, as well as the neurons that transmit nerve impulses, are biological structures. The functions of these structures are quite specific. A neuron alone cannot move your fingers, nor can a muscle carry nerve impulses. These examples illustrate that there is a close relationship between a physical structure and its function.

Consider, for example, the organization and function of skeletal muscle. Skeletal muscle produces the movements of your limbs. To generate most types of movement, muscles must work in opposing groups against the skeleton. Figure 7.27 illustrates the organization of muscles in your arm. Notice that the biceps and triceps attach to the bones of the upper and lower arm by tendons. Tendons are flexible cords of connective tissue. The biceps's tendon attaches to the bone of the lower arm on the *inside* of the elbow joint. When you

contract the biceps, your arm bends. By contrast, the triceps's tendon attaches to the bone of the lower arm on the *outer side* of the elbow. When you contract the triceps, your arm straightens.

Muscles in a vertebrate limb work on the bone just as a force works on a lever. A relatively small amount of shortening of a muscle produces a large movement. Even though this is the case in a wide variety of organisms, the details can vary greatly. These differences mean that different organisms are capable of different types of movements.

This variation is especially evident in organisms that have the same overall body plan but have adapted to different situations. Compare, for example, the forelimb of the cheetah to that of the mole in figure 7.28. Both are vertebrates. Their limbs work according to the same principles (and even use the same muscles) as the human arm. The primary functions of these limbs differ greatly, however. The cheetah's limbs are adapted for running after fleet-footed prey. The mole's limbs are adapted for burrowing in the ground. What structural details underlie these adaptations?

The mole's digging forelimbs must generate power rather than speed. As the illustration in figure 7.28a shows, the bones of such limbs are short and thick. In addition, look at the projection at the elbow to which the muscles attach. It is quite long in proportion to the lower

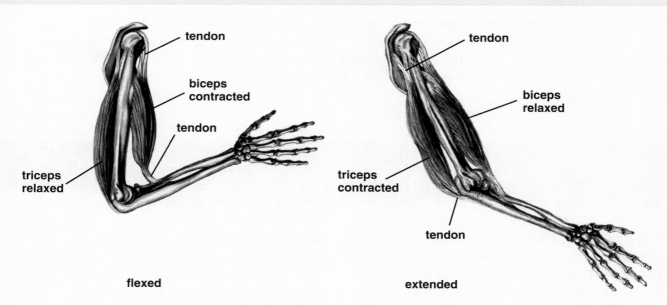

Figure 7.27   The human arm functions like a lever. The biceps and triceps muscles act on a fulcrum point, the elbow. Although these muscles are attached to the bones in the upper and lower arms, muscle contraction causes only the lower bone to move.

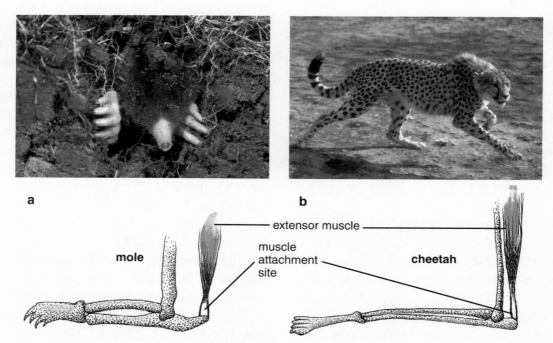

Figure 7.28   Structure and function in moles and cheetahs. The type of movement possible in an organism depends on the precise arrangements of the skeleton and the muscles. (*a*) Short, heavy bones, like those of the mole, are typical of animal skeletons that require power. (*b*) Thin, light bones, like those of the cheetah, favor speed. Think about the effect of applying forces to the two muscle attachment sites.

limb bone. Because of this structural arrangement, the muscles generate great power in the lower limb when they contract. Now look at the limb of a running animal such as the cheetah (figure 7.28b). The extension at the elbow to which the muscles attach is very short in proportion to the long lower limb bone. As a result, the same amount of contraction by the muscles moves a cheetah's foot much farther than a mole's foot. Therefore, a cheetah can run at great speeds.

The importance of structure to the function of muscles is certainly apparent in the size and shape of the limbs. However, it also is apparent at the microscopic level. Examine the internal organization of skeletal muscle in figure 7.29. As you can see, a muscle consists of many bundles of muscle fibers (figure 7.29a). The thin and thick lines visible in figure 7.29c are filaments. Filaments are specialized structures within muscle fibers. They consist of two types of long, thin protein molecules. When you contract a muscle, energy enables the filaments within each fiber to slide past each other. Think about how your interlocked fingers can slide past each other when you move your hands together. The sliding of the individual filaments shortens the larger muscle fiber. Together, the shortening of many muscle fibers shortens the whole muscle. When you

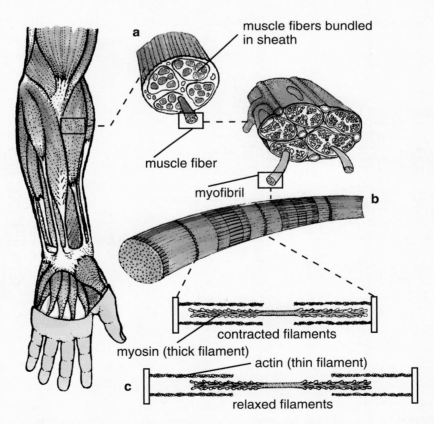

Figure 7.29 (*a*) A muscle is composed of many muscle fibers bundled in a sheath. (*b*) Each muscle fiber is made up of many parallel myofibrils. (*c*) Each myofibril is made up of protein molecules organized into thick filaments made of myosin molecules and thin filaments made of actin and some other protein molecules.

relax your muscle, these filaments return to their original positions. The muscle then regains its initial appearance and shape.

Studying muscle fibers at a subcellular level explains why it is important that muscles work together. While the movement of the molecular filaments past each other can shorten the muscle, it cannot lengthen the muscle again. That is, when a muscle relaxes, it cannot return to its normal length by itself. Because a muscle cannot lengthen, a muscle cannot push on anything. It can only pull. For every set of muscles that pulls a limb bone in one direction, another set pulls it back the other way. Were that not the case, many movements would not be possible.

The advantages of different structures also are evident in organisms that have body plans different from ours. In vertebrates, groups of muscles work in opposing pairs against an internal support system, the bony skeleton. Invertebrates have different types of support systems. For example, many soft-bodied invertebrates have a support system composed of a surprising substance: water. A water-based support system, or hydrostatic skeleton, is not as odd as it might sound. Water, like other liquids, is not compressible. This characteristic means that although a flexible container filled with water may change shape in response to pressure, its volume remains constant.

Look at figure 7.30. The contraction of the circular muscles around the segments of a worm's body squeezes on the watery fluid in those segments. This causes them to become longer and thinner. Contraction of the opposing longitudinal

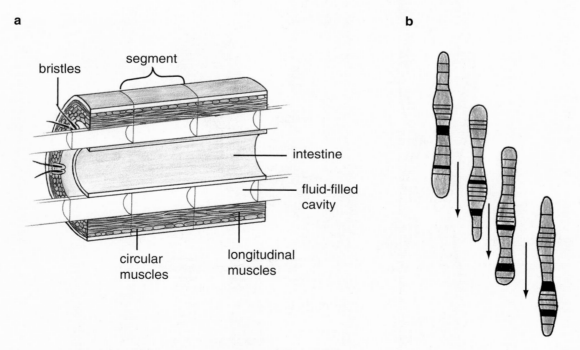

a

b

bristles

segment

intestine

fluid-filled cavity

circular muscles

longitudinal muscles

Figure 7.30   The earthworm has a hydrostatic skeleton. Each segment of the skeleton contains a fluid-filled cavity. (*a*) When the circular muscles around the segments of the worm's body contract, the fluid in those segments is squeezed. As a result, the segments become longer and thinner. (*b*) When the longitudinal muscles contract, the segments become shorter and thicker. The earthworm moves by anchoring one part of its body with its bristles while it extends another part.

muscles, on the other hand, causes the segments to become shorter and thicker. When the worm crawls along, it alternately extends and contracts different parts of its body in this way. The worm uses stiff bristles on each segment to anchor some sections while extending others. Many soft-bodied animals such as slugs and jellyfishes have variations on this system. They all have an internal hydrostatic skeleton surrounded by opposing groups of muscles.

Another common type of invertebrate support system is the exoskeleton. An **exoskeleton** is a hard skeleton on the outside of the body. (An **endoskeleton** is a hard internal skeleton such as that in vertebrates.) The grasshopper shown in figure 7.31a is a good example of an animal that has an exoskeleton. Figure 7.31b shows diagrams of a grasshopper's leg. Note the opposing set of muscles. When a grasshopper draws up its leg, the flexor muscle contracts while the extensor muscle remains relaxed. What happens when a grasshopper needs to hop? The upper extensor contracts while the flexor muscle remains relaxed. Although these muscles attach to the inside of an external skeleton, the mechanical aspects of the system are similar to those of the human arm. In addition to being quite strong for its mass, an exoskeleton also provides a layer of armor that protects the soft parts of the animal's body. What is the downside to an exoskeleton? The sidebar, *The Ant That Terrorized Milwaukee*, considers what happens if an animal with an exoskeleton becomes too big.

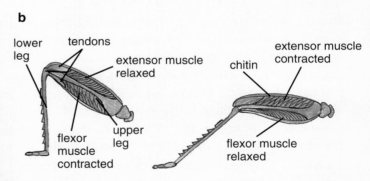

Figure 7.31 **Exoskeletons have muscles attached to the inside of the skeleton.** These muscles, however, still work in opposing pairs.

The Ant That Terrorized Milwaukee

The huge, black thorax towered over Damien, blocking the light. The enormous insect was rearing up on its back two pairs of legs. Its front legs pawed at the air like a huge stallion, or more accurately, like a menacing and hideous monster. Its antennae quivered and twisted in the air, searching for anything that might challenge it. The air was heavy with the animal's stench.

Now that he was this close, Damien could understand why his pitiful attempts to bring down the beast had failed so miserably. The animal's body was encased in a shiny, hard, black substance. The armor seemed impenetrable to any weapon Damien could get his hands on. Through his fear, he vaguely remembered something important he knew about insects . . . yes, that was it! A hard outer skeleton—what did Mrs. Baxter call it? But no, too late . . . As the moving mouthparts drew nearer, Damien's last thought was, "But she *insisted* they couldn't get this big . . ."

You may have heard the following statements: "An ant can carry 10 times its own weight. So an ant the size of a person could lift a car." "A grasshopper the size of a horse could jump the length of a football field." An overused plot in horror films has insects or other tiny creatures become gigantic. You have seen that multicellular organisms exhibit a wide range of body plans that work by the same basic principles. Is there any limit to how big, how fast, or how strong an organism might be?

For physical reasons, giant creatures usually are not possible. This is because basic structural and mechanical considerations limit the sizes for which particular body plans are suitable. For example, growth is one limitation to animals with exoskeletons.

The exoskeleton encases the whole body in armor. Thus, it must be shed completely every time there is significant growth. The animal is relatively helpless and vulnerable while the new exoskeleton hardens.

A second limitation to insect size is thought to be due to the way they deliver oxygen to their tissues: through simple tubes. The shorter the length of the tube, the more efficient it is at delivering oxygen. Giant insects like the dragonfly *Meganeura monyi* (figure 7.32) were able to evolve because during their time, 250 million years ago, up to 35 percent of Earth's atmosphere was

Copyright © Surface Vision.

Figure 7.32   Giant prehistoric insect *Meganeura monyi*. The giant insect *Meganeura monyi* grew up to a meter in length.

composed of oxygen, compared with about 20 percent today. There was enough oxygen in the atmosphere to allow the evolution of longer tubes, and consequently larger insects.

Another major limitation of the size of insect bodies is due to the material that makes up exoskeletons. The material is a complex carbohydrate called *chitin*. Hollow tubes of chitin are very strong for their mass. In larger sizes, however, the mass of the chitin that would be needed would increase to impossible levels for sufficient body support and bracing against muscle contractions. An ant the size of a person probably couldn't even pick itself up, let alone wreak havoc on Milwaukee.

7. Read the essay, *Energy's Role in Making Structures Functional*. After you finish reading, revisit your answers to the questions in step 6. Make revisions to your answers using a different-colored pen or pencil. Also explain why you made the changes you did.

Energy's Role in Making Structures Functional

ENGLISH SPANISH

The structure of muscle fibers explains how a muscle contracts. But where do muscles get the energy needed for contraction? They get this energy ultimately from the breakdown of food. But where and how does this happen?

Scattered among muscle fibers are structures called mitochondria. **Mitochondria** are oblong-shaped compartments, or organelles. They are located within cells, as shown in figure 7.33. Chemical reactions that involve oxygen, water, and the breakdown products of food take place within the mitochondria and result in the release of energy. The process is called **cellular respiration**. Because the reactions that take place in the mitochondria require oxygen, they are specifically called aerobic respiration. "**Aerobic**" means "occurring in the presence of oxygen." Aerobic energy production fuels most of our physical activity most of the time. The result of aerobic respiration is many molecules that are lower in energy, which a cell can use immediately to do the work required.

The most important of these molecules is called **ATP**, which stands for **adenosine triphosphate**.

But what happens when you need a sudden burst of energy, for example, to catch a bus pulling away from its stop? In this scenario, your muscle cells may not have enough oxygen for aerobic energy production. Then your muscle cells shift to another process called **fermentation**. This process does not require oxygen. In other words, it is **anaerobic**. Fermentation is not as efficient as cellular respiration. Fewer ATP molecules are made. Still, it can allow your muscles to continue working for a minute or two. A by-product of fermentation in most animals is called *lactic acid*. At one time, scientists thought that lactic acid caused soreness in muscles days after strenuous activity. These scientists now recognize, however, that lactic acid is rapidly removed from the muscles and broken down by the liver.

So why do your muscles get sore after hard exercise? Physiologists who studied muscle tissue samples from marathon runners found microscopic evidence of damaged muscle fibers. They believe the damage is a primary reason for delayed muscle soreness.

Contracting muscles demand more oxygen to rapidly break down glucose. For this reason, vigorous exercise requires a great increase in circulation. The blood flow to exercising muscles may reach 15 times that of their resting level. The

increased blood flow delivers enough oxygen for aerobic exercise and also removes waste products. Regardless, vigorous exercise eventually results in muscle fatigue. Normally, muscle cells store sugar in the polysaccharide glycogen. A fatigued muscle has a low supply of glycogen. The only solution for extreme fatigue is rest. With sufficient time and proper food, glycogen is replenished and normal functioning can resume.

generalized animal cell

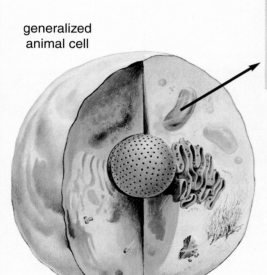

mitochondria: small organelles that are the site of energy-releasing reactions in all cells; enclosed by double membrane with inner membrane much folded

generalized plant cell

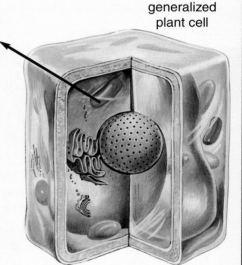

Figure 7.33 Multicellular organisms, such as plants, animals, and other eukaryotes, have mitochondria in their cells. These organelles are the sites of an aerobic breakdown process called cellular respiration. The process transforms the energy stored in matter to a more usable form in the chemical bonds of ATP.

SCiLINKS®
NSTA
www.scilinks.org
Topic: muscles
Code: human4E390

Analysis

Prepare to share your answers in a class discussion.

1. Explain what forms of matter and energy are needed for a muscle to contract.
2. What happens *biologically* when muscle fatigue occurs?

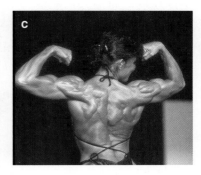

Figure 7.34 Examples of skeletons include (*a*) hydrostatic skeleton, (*b*) exoskeleton, (*c*) endoskeleton.

3. Describe the strengths and weaknesses of your leg model in modeling how a human leg works.

> Remember, we build models to mimic a structure or an event. Good models mimic the actual structure or event so closely that changes in the model predict what would happen in the real world. You may wish to review the information about scientific models in the need to know, *A Simple Mathematical Model*, in chapter 2, *Evolution: Change Across Time*.

4. Vertebrate muscles contract against the resistance of an internal skeleton (endoskeleton) made of bone. Create a table in your science notebook. Compare 2 advantages and 2 disadvantages of a hydrostatic skeleton, an exoskeleton, and an endoskeleton (see figure 7.34).

5. How does increased physical activity promote physical fitness? Be specific. Include the effect of increased activity on the structure and function of an individual leg muscle and on the muscle of the heart.

> Recall that your heart is a muscle. During vigorous activity, your heart pumps faster and harder. It delivers blood more rapidly to both the lungs and the exercising muscles.

Marathon

EVALUATE

Remember the last summer Olympic Games? Many athletes broke world records. If you watched the games on television, you may have thought that those athletes made it look easy. Nevertheless, you were watching some of the highest levels of human performance ever recorded. A tremendous number of biological and behavioral factors had to be just right for such exceptional performances.

One of the most physically challenging of all events is the marathon. This race covers a distance of 42.2 km (26 mi, 385 yd). Athletes usually train for many years to build up to the endurance level that is required to compete in this event. In this Evaluate activity, *Marathon*, you will follow the progress of four people who entered a marathon. You will propose explanations for the role that matter and energy played in their performances. Your analysis will provide evidence of your understanding of the relationships between matter, energy, and human physical fitness and performance.

Materials

online resource

PROCESS AND PROCEDURES

1. With your class, watch the video segment, "A Good Day for Running."
2. With your team of 4, take turns reading aloud the scenario, *The Race*. This story describes a marathon and the training and performance of 4 people who participated in it.

SCENARIO

ENGLISH   SPANISH

The Race

The Scenario

It is a mid-August day in a high-altitude town in Colorado. Runners are gathering for an annual marathon that has been held at this site for many years. The race is interesting because several shorter races and a full marathon are held simultaneously. All the runners start together. Each runner, either before or during the race, decides the exact distance he or she will run. The runners do so simply by stopping at certain measured increments. They may run 5 km, 10 km, 21 km, or the full marathon distance of 42.2 km. About 100 runners are lined up and ready to start.

Four of the Runners

Mel

Mel, a grandfather in his late 40s, is a college professor who began running in his early 30s. Mel decided to begin running to control his weight and discovered that he really enjoyed this activity. As his running program progressed, he went from recreational running to competitive running because of the many positive changes he saw in his body and his lifestyle.

Amy

Amy was a member of her cross-country team in college. Now, at age 33, she is a lawyer and maintains a high level of competitive fitness. Amy continues her running program as part of her lifestyle. She trains regularly and enters several races each year.

Neal

Neal is an exercise physiologist. He is currently employed as a scientist in a government laboratory. At the lab, Neal manages a wellness program for employees. He puts together exercise prescriptions for people who want to attain various levels of fitness. Neal was a track star and a classmate of Amy's in college. He also decided to make competitive running a major part of his life. He and Amy have run together many times.

John

John is in his early 40s. He is an engineer who always has enjoyed watching runners and has always thought about competing. One evening after a very greasy supper, John announced to his wife that he was going to train for and complete a marathon within a year. His wife just laughed. In contrast to the other three runners listed, John is a smoker, is slightly overweight, and has not previously trained to run except for occasional short-distance jogging. He drinks alcohol "slightly more than moderately" (in his words).

How the Runners Trained

Mel

This was Mel's first full marathon, but he had participated in many shorter-distance races and fun runs. The farthest he had run competitively was a half-marathon. He trained on a favorite practice course of about 8 km (5 mi). He ran this course about four days a week. About one month before the marathon, he increased his commitment to 13 km (8 mi), four days a week. Mel lived and trained at high altitude in Colorado. Leading up to the race, Mel ate regular meals with his family. These balanced meals included carbohydrates, proteins, low amounts of fats, and plenty of vegetables. He had a light meal of French toast and juice the morning of the race.

Amy and Neal

Amy and Neal had nearly identical approaches to training. They worked out at a moderate pace, consistently drinking plenty of fluids and eating a balanced diet. They participated in a regular training program in which they ran a variety of distances at different speeds. About six weeks before the marathon, they finally settled on a steady workout regimen of running 16 km (10 mi) four days a week. They included rest periods in their weekly schedules to allow recovery from mild stiffness, soreness, and tired muscles. For several days before the race, they ate large amounts of whole-grain bread, cereals, and pasta. On the morning of the race, their breakfast consisted of oatmeal with a little milk and several glasses of juice.

John

John described his first month of training as "terrible." He vowed to quit smoking over the year of training leading up to the marathon, but he only cut back to a few cigarettes a day. He struggled with shortness of breath during the early weeks, even though he lived and trained at a lower altitude than the race. He ran mostly at lunch and occasionally again after work. He limited his running to about 5 km (3 mi) per workout, five days a week. During the first month, his knees hurt so badly he seriously considered quitting. However, due to his increased activity, he lost 7 kg (15 lbs) over the first two months and his knees stopped hurting. John was proud of his new energy level, which markedly increased his alertness at work. He also found that he required less sleep and that he slept well. Like Mel, John ate balanced meals with his family during training. He justified eating dessert most nights since he was training so hard. In the six weeks before the race, John increased his training distance to 10 km (6 mi), four days a week. He did not have time to work out more than this. On the day of the race, he thought, "I feel ready!" About two hours before the race, he ate ham and eggs, grits, three pieces of toast, several glasses of juice, and one cup of coffee.

The Race

The race began at 8 a.m. sharp. The crisp air of the high-altitude summer morning was invigorating and added to the sense of excitement that all of the runners felt. Some of the participants had arrived nearly an hour before start time. They were slowly stretching both upper and lower body muscles, concentrating on their leg muscles to prevent pulling and cramping. Others were slowly jogging and drinking fluids. Friends and spectators were gathering for the start. Runners prominently displayed their numbers. The weather promised to stay cool and dry.

The runners lined up after some brief instructions and last-minute information about the condition of the course from the starter. How many would go the whole distance? The starter's pistol cracked, and the mass of runners moved forward.

During the first 3 km (2 mi), the line of runners gradually spread out. Five runners ran in a small pack a good distance out in front of the others and established a quick pace. Amy and Neal, running together for the moment, were in the front third of the main pack and running at a respectable but comfortable pace. John was pushing his pace, running slightly behind Amy and Neal. Mel was at the beginning of the final third of the pack. A few runners straggled well behind.

Because the first quarter of the race was a gentle downhill stretch, most of the runners felt good. Each established his or her desired pace and settled in for the long haul. At the 5-km mark, about 10 runners decided to call it a race. It had been fun for them. At the 10-km point, Amy, Neal, John, and Mel were in the same respective positions, all running steadily without tiredness, soreness, or fatigue. All felt that their training was serving them well. They watched as several more runners, including a couple of the front-runners, decided to stop.

The runners now were spread out over a 1.5-km (1-mi) length. As the 21-km (13-mi) marker came into view on an uphill segment, some runners were obviously struggling to continue. Having established a plodding gait, these runners were ready to call 21 km their distance. Several of the front-runners stopped here as well. Amy and Neal were now about one-fourth back in the remaining pack and still were running together. John had dropped back to among the last 10 runners. Mel was in the middle, now 400 m (437 yd) ahead of John. John was feeling a slight pulling sensation in his right calf muscle. He had altered his stride slightly to see whether it would work itself out.

The next 10-km segment was quiet and uneventful. All four of the racers settled into an automatic pace. Amy and Neal were running in relative comfort, pushing themselves slightly and maintaining their positions. Mel maintained his middle-of-the-pack position, but was beginning to experience some leg muscle fatigue. In fact, the race was becoming a serious effort. But he was still all right and willing to go the entire route. John noticed the beginning of a blister on his right foot as his shoe rubbed the same spot over and over. Both of his calf muscles were very tight and beginning to hurt, especially now that he was running on hard pavement. Like Mel, he was experiencing leg muscle fatigue, and he considered stopping where he was. Still, he ran on. Several other runners were dropping out, some limping, and a few holding pulled leg muscles. Some were holding their cramping abdominal muscles. Many would later describe feeling like they "hit the wall." They were suffering from severe fatigue, resulting from the nearly complete depletion of the energy reserves in their muscles.

The last 12 km (7 mi) produced the greatest change in the positions and welfare of the remaining runners. About 30 of the original 100 were left. Neal was running in sixth place. Amy was about 500 m (547 yd) back, but she still was running smoothly and steadily. Mel's stride was short, and he felt as though a brick was at the bottom of his chest. The race had become very hard work. His leg muscles were beginning to cramp. The only way he could relieve these effects was to reduce his pace and run with an exaggerated heel-toe gait. With 8 km to go, John hit the wall. His legs became so tired, heavy, and cramped that he could do little more than make slow and laborious forward progress. His pace was only slightly faster than a walk. His chest muscles ached severely, and he began to feel somewhat nauseated. He was in last place, hurting all over, but he still was determined to finish.

Neal moved up to fourth place. As he entered the last 2 km (1 mi), however, he experienced a "wall" effect. He pushed himself harder, seeing not only the end of the race, but the possibility of improving his position as well. He crossed the finish line in third place at 3 hours, 5 minutes, 5 seconds, edging out the next male competitor by 50 m (55 yd). His body went limp, and he had difficulty standing upright. He felt dizzy and slightly nauseous. Amy finished at 3 hours, 29 minutes, and was the fifth female competitor to cross the line. She experienced similar final effects as Neal. At 3 hours, 55 minutes, 10 seconds, Mel finished. His wall experience in the last 5 km had been quite dramatic. He had little drive left for a final sprint to the finish, but felt proud of his accomplishment. He grabbed a water bottle and slowly walked to the first place he could find to sit down—he was dizzy, too.

At 4 hours, 43 minutes, 20 seconds, John completed his first marathon in last place. His finishing pace was a slightly elongated walk. He held his middle. His legs would no longer support him. He went first to his knees, then over on his back in total collapse. His chest heaved with exaggerated breathing for several minutes before he was able to sit upright. As the other runners from the race were congratulating one another, John's thought was, "Maybe one marathon is enough."

3. Divide the 4 runners you read about among your team. Each team member will study a different runner in depth.
4. Study the criteria in the *Marathon Rubric* that your teacher distributes to your team. Ask any questions you have about the rubric before proceeding with the activity.
5. As a team, review and discuss the physiologic data related to physical performance in figure 7.35a–g, *Physiologic Data Related to Physical Performance*.

   Think about how each set of information might help you analyze your runner's training and performance. It might also help you suggest general strategies for a marathon runner. Propose your ideas to your teammates and listen to their ideas.

6. Complete the *Marathon Calculations* handout to calculate the following amounts of energy used in kilocalories by your runner.
   a. How many kilocalories did your runner burn, per week, during his or her most intense training?

   b. How many kilocalories did your runner burn, total, during the marathon?

   Use information from figure 7.35c, *Exercise and Energy Expenditure* table, and information from the scenario, *The Race*, to complete these tasks. Your teacher may assist by showing sample calculations that you can model. You may find it helpful to refer to the information in appendix D2, *How to Convert Measurements*.

7. Copy figure 7.35a, *Energy Expended in Training and Racing* table, into your science notebook. Fill in the last 2 columns ("kcal used/week, race training" and "kcal used for marathon") with your answers for steps 5a and 5b. Enter your teammates' calculations when they are complete.

8. Analyze your runner's training and performance on race day. In your science notebook, write brief answers to each of the following points.

   Use your understanding of biology, the data in figure 7.35, and the table that you just completed to complete this task. Although each of you should analyze only your own runner, remain in your team as you do so. As you work, share ideas and begin comparing the runners as you examine their training and performance.

   a. Examine your runner's training schedule. In what ways did this schedule prepare him or her to finish the race? How did your runner's energy expenditure per week of race training compare with the amount of energy he or she expended during the marathon?

   b. Examine the diet of your runner in the weeks preceding the race. Did your runner appear to be increasing or decreasing his or her intake of any particular class of nutrients during training?

   c. Summarize the strategy that you think your runner was using during training.

   d. Examine your runner's behavior on the race day before the race began. What strategies do you think he or she was using to prepare for the race?

   e. Examine your runner's performance during the marathon. For example, look at his or her pace, fluid intake, and apparent stamina and success. What strategies did your runner seem to be using?

   f. Propose reasons why your runner felt as he or she did at the beginning, middle, and end of the race.

   g. Propose ways your runner could have improved his or her performance on race day.

9. Meet with members of other teams who studied the same runner and compare your findings. Modify your conclusions based on the group input.

Figure 7.35a–g

Physiologic data related to physical performance. This collection of data provides various types of evidence related to diet and physical performance. Use the data to help you analyze your runner's preparation and performance and to help you suggest strategies for improving them.

Runner	Mass (weight)	Kcal used/week, normal workout (assume 5 min/km pace)	Kcal used/week, race training (assume 4.3 min/km pace)	Kcal used for marathon (see finish time)
Neal	68 kg (150 lbs)	N.a.		
Amy	50 kg (110 lbs)	N.a.		
Mel	82 kg (181 lbs)	2,624		
John	75 kg (165 lbs)		2,709	

Note: "N.a." means "not applicable."
Source: Wilmore, J. H., & Costill, D. L. (1994). *Physiology of sport and exercise* [1st ed.]. Champaign, IL: Human Kinetics.

Figure 7.35a **Energy Expended in Training and Racing table.**

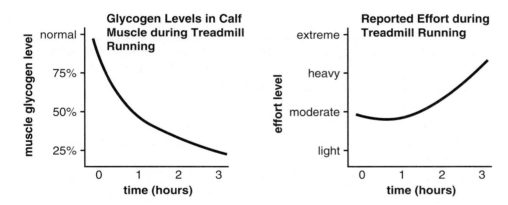

Figure 7.35b **Muscle Glycogen Level graphs.** These graphs show the levels in relation to perceived effort during three hours of treadmill training.
Source: Physiology of Sport and Exercise, [1st ed.], by Jack H. Wilmore and David L. Costill. © 1994 by Human Kinetics.

Exercise	Kcals used/kg per minute	Exercise	Kcals used/kg per minute
Bicycling Slow: 8 km/h (5 mph) Moderate: 16 km/h (10 mph) Fast: 21 km/h (13 mph)	 0.06 0.11 0.16	Skiing Downhill Cross-country (noncompetitive)	 0.13 0.17
Golf	0.06	Soccer	0.14
Hiking	0.09	Stationary Running (70–80 counts/min)	0.17
Running 6.2 min/km (10 min/mile) 5.6 min/km (9 min/mile) 5.0 min/km (8 min/mile) 4.3 min/km (7 min/mile) 3.7 min/km (6 min/mile)	 0.17 0.19 0.20 0.21 0.22	Swimming (crawl) 20 mi/min 50 mi/min	 0.07 0.16
Racquetball	0.14	Walking 19 min/km (30 min/mile) 12 min/km (12 min/mile)	 0.05 0.14

Figure 7.35c Exercise and Energy Expenditure table.

Diet	Amount of glycogen in muscles (g/kg)	Average endurance running at speeds characteristic of a marathon (min to exhaustion)
High-carbohydrate diet	40	240
Mixed carbohydrate and fat diet	20	120
High-fat diet	6	85

Source: Guyton, A. C. (1991). *Textbook of medical physiology* [8th ed.]. Philadelphia: W. B. Saunders Co.

Figure 7.35d Effect of Diet on Muscle Glycogen and Muscle Endurance table.

Food	Percentage of fat	Percentage of protein	Percentage of carbohydrate	Kcal (food value) per 100 g
Apples	0.4	0.3	14.9	64
Bacon, fat	76.0	6.2	0.7	712
broiled	55.0	25.0	1.0	599
Beef, medium lean	22.0	17.5	1.0	268
Bread, white	3.6	9.0	49.8	268
Butter	81.0	0.6	0.4	733
Cabbage	0.2	1.4	5.3	29
Carrots	0.3	1.2	9.3	45
Cheese, cheddar	32.3	23.9	1.7	393
Chicken	2.7	21.6	1.0	111
Corn (maize)	4.3	10.0	73.4	372
Haddock (fish)	0.3	17.2	0.5	72
Lamb, leg	17.5	18.0	1.0	230
Milk, whole	3.9	3.5	4.9	69
Oatmeal, dry (uncooked)	7.4	14.2	68.2	396
Oranges	0.2	0.9	11.2	50
Peanuts	44.2	26.9	23.6	600
Peas, fresh	0.4	6.7	17.7	101
Pork, ham	31.0	15.2	1.0	340
Potatoes	0.1	2.0	19.1	85
Spinach	N.a.	2.3	3.2	25
Strawberries	N.a.	0.8	8.1	41
Tomatoes	0.3	1.0	4.0	23

Note: "N.a." means "not applicable."

Figure 7.35e Energy and Nutrients table.

1. Mild to moderate increase in number of muscle fibers.
2. Increased capacity to transport oxygen from the blood to the mitochondria.*
3. Increased number of mitochondria.
4. Increased growth of capillaries serving the muscle.

* Mitochondria are the cell parts that are primarily responsible for the oxygen-requiring release of energy from glucose.
Source: Guyton, A. C. (1991). *Textbook of medical physiology* [8th ed.]. Philadelphia: W. B. Saunders Co.

Figure 7.35f   Effect of exercise on muscle structure.

	Stroke volume* (mL)	Heart rate (beats/min)
Marathoner		
Resting	105	50
Maximum	162	185
Nonathlete		
Resting	75	75
Maximum	110	195

* Volume of blood moved in 1 heartbeat.
Source: Guyton, A. C. (1991). *Textbook of medical physiology* [8th ed.]. Philadelphia: W. B. Saunders Co.

Figure 7.35g   Comparison of Cardiac Outputs of Marathoner and Nonathlete table.

Analysis

Review the following questions. Then read the essay, *Factors Influencing Performance*, while noting possible information you would like to use in your answers. Record your final answers in your science notebook.

Remember, your answers should involve evidence of everything you learned in chapter 7 about the biological basis of human performance and fitness. Draw from the data in figure 7.35 to give specific evidence to support your analysis.

1. Develop an explanation of why the 4 runners finished in the order that they did. Use evidence and reasoning from your team's calculations of the energy expended as well as what you have learned about factors that influence human physical performance.
2. Compare the training schedules and diets of the 4 runners before the race. Complete the following tasks.
   a. List at least 2 training and 2 dietary strategies that you would recommend to a friend just starting to train for a marathon.
   b. Explain the physiologic change or changes that you would expect to occur as a result of each strategy.
   c. Describe why such changes would be important to finishing the marathon. Support your answer with specific data from figure 7.35.
3. Explain how humans obtain energy from the energy-yielding nutrients they ingest.
4. Explain how the process of energy release from matter is more efficient in highly trained athletes than in most other people.
5. Write a 2- or 3-paragraph explanation for how the processes of digestion, aerobic respiration, and biosynthesis contribute to the repair of a torn muscle in a marathon racer.

Factors Influencing Performance

ENGLISH   SPANISH

Genetic and Gender Differences

Are great athletes or great dancers *born* or *made*? Their abilities are a product of both the factors they have inherited and their training. On the one hand, as humans, we are born with a certain basic set of physical capabilities. As individuals, we may have special abilities in a particular area. On the other hand, many things that we do and don't do affect how well we can use our inborn capabilities.

First, we are humans. We are not cheetahs, ants, or any other type of creature. As humans, we are capable of performing certain functions because our bodies can acquire and use energy in particular ways. As individuals, we inherit traits that may enhance or limit our capacity to perform particular activities.

For example, the genes we inherit largely determine our height, if we grow up with proper nutrition. A person's height affects whether or not he or she can become a professional basketball player. Inheritance also appears to be important for skills required for gymnastics. Most successful gymnasts have small, compact bodies. Our gender and genetic makeup also influence other physical factors. These include skeletal and muscle mass, lung capacity, and the rate at which our bodies use energy. All of these factors may influence the types of physical activity that we can perform best.

Gender clearly has an effect on the body's physical development. Some differences are caused by steroid hormones. One of these, testosterone, increases in young men during puberty. Rising testosterone levels cause an increase in muscle mass. Increased muscle mass, in turn, results in increased muscle strength. Therefore, males tend to be stronger than females of the same age and height. Anabolic steroids are used by some athletes because they mimic some of the effects of testosterone.

Steroids may improve athletic performance. They also have a number of serious side effects. These include high blood pressure, alterations in heart muscle, and reduced fertility. For these reasons and others, the National Collegiate Athletic Association (NCAA), the International Olympic Committee (IOC), and many other athletic organizations have banned steroid use.

Metabolism is the rate at which your body converts the chemical energy in food into other forms of usable energy. The rate differs among individuals. In general, females tend to have a lower metabolic rate than males. The combination of your average metabolic rate, diet, and level of exercise determines your body mass (commonly called your weight). If your food intake is balanced with your body's nutritional demands, metabolic rate, and activity level, then your body mass will remain about the same. If you take in excess food, then your body will store it as fat. A slight excess in food intake is necessary for proper development

during adolescence and the teen years. This is because the bodies of these young people are growing. Their bodies are producing more body tissues such as muscles, fat, and blood.

Remember the increase in muscle mass during puberty in boys? Girls experience an increase in body fat during adolescence in response to the release of estrogen. Estrogen and other hormones, along with the increase in body fat, are necessary for ovulation. All of this growth, as boys and girls become men and women, requires additional energy.

In moderate, controlled dieting, food intake is slightly less than your body's needs. Your body will then use stored fat for the matter and energy it needs. Long-term fasting or starving depletes the body's stored fat supplies. In such a case, the body breaks down its own structural components, such as muscle, to keep itself alive. This is why conditions such as anorexia nervosa may cause muscles, including the heart, to become thin and weak.

Conditioning

Human performance is also based in large part on general physical fitness. Consider what

happens with a group of hikers. Those who have a regular exercise program soon take the lead, while others lag behind. The slower ones may breathe heavily and later suffer from aching muscles. One basis for these differences is the way the body changes during a regular exercise program. A regular exercise program is called *conditioning*.

Conditioning can improve both fitness for life and athletic fitness in several ways. The major effect of regular exercise is to bring about changes in the structure and function of the body. Muscles enlarge and become stronger. The number and size of mitochondria in the muscle cells increase. The muscles' capacity for glycogen storage and blood supply increases. The net effect is a greater ability to convert the chemical energy in food into useful energy.

What is a reasonable amount of exercise for staying fit? As little as 20–30 minutes of moderate exercise three times a week can help your circulatory and respiratory systems work more effectively. Conditioning lowers your resting heart rate and increases heart output. Conditioning builds muscle mass and tone (firmness). It strengthens the skeleton by maintaining, or increasing, bone mass. It improves the communication between nerves and muscles. Better strength, coordination, and endurance are the rewards. Aerobic activities such as jogging, brisk walking, bicycling, or swimming can accomplish these goals.

Behavior

The lifestyle that an individual adopts also influences fitness. In addition to exercise, you decide what and how much you eat and drink. For example, individuals who wish to stay at a constant weight must keep the number of Calories they consume equal to the number they expend over the long term. On the other hand, people who are interested in losing weight must take in fewer Calories than they expend. Athletes who are training for a marathon may want to increase the amount of carbohydrates that they consume. Carbohydrate loading increases the amount of glycogen available to muscles. Figure 7.36 describes diets in each of these categories so that you may compare the relative amounts of servings in each food group.

A good mental attitude can help a person maintain good fitness for life. In contrast, mental and emotional disorders can endanger fitness.

Food groups (daily servings)						
	Milk	**Meat**	**Fruit**	**Vegetable**	**Grain**	**Fats, oils, and sweets**
Maintenance diet	3*	2–3	2–4	3–5	6–11	**
Weight-loss diet	3*	2	2	3–5	6	**
Carbohydrate-loading diet	3*	3 or more	7 or more	5 or more	11 or more	**

*Teenagers and young adults; 2 for older adults.
**You can select foods from the fats, oils, and sweets category only if you can afford the kcals after eating the recommended servings from the essential food groups.
Note: The diets listed in this table are approximations based on information from the U.S. Department of Agriculture's Daily Food Guide. *These do not constitute dietary recommendations.* Individuals should check with their physician before going on any diet.

Figure 7.36 Diet comparison. Depending on an individual's goals for fitness, he or she may choose a different diet.

For example, depression can lead a person to be inactive. However, symptoms of depression can also be relieved in part by regular exercise.

Toxins

The consumption of **toxins** also influences performance. Toxins are substances that ultimately cause diminished performance or impairment of health. Even some medications (ibuprofen, for example) may be toxic at high doses.

Illegal or so-called street drugs diminish performance in the same ways that legal toxins such as alcohol and tobacco do. While illegal drugs may produce temporary feelings of pleasure, they also cause negative, long-term consequences. Our bodies respond to some drugs by building up a tolerance to them. Increasingly larger amounts are required to produce the same effect. Our bodies may become dependent on addictive drugs. An addicted person cannot function normally without the drug. Withdrawal from the drug can be an extremely painful and difficult experience.

Alcohol is a drug that is legal for individuals over a specific age. However, consuming it can have negative consequences. Alcohol can produce a temporary sense of well-being. Under the influence of alcohol, we may think we are feeling and performing better. Actually, alcohol depresses the central nervous system. This causes a loss of coordination and impaired performance. It also impairs judgment. Alcohol causes cells to use oxygen less efficiently. Consuming large amounts of alcohol over long periods of time damages brain and liver tissue.

Like alcohol, the purchase of tobacco is legal, but restricted. Tobacco contains many substances that can adversely influence performance. Burning tobacco produces carbon monoxide. Carbon monoxide interferes with blood cells, causing them to carry less oxygen. A smoker who smokes two cigarette packs per day generates enough carbon monoxide to reduce his or her blood oxygen level significantly. The reduction is similar to that of a nonsmoker who is experiencing the thin air of high mountain altitudes (3,048 m, or 10,000 ft) for the first time. Both tobacco smoke and unburned tobacco such as chew or dip release high levels of nicotine into the bloodstream. Nicotine affects performance directly. It constricts blood vessels, thus impairing oxygen delivery. In addition, nicotine is one of the most addictive drugs known.

Other important aspects of lifestyle that affect fitness include the amount of sleep a person gets and how a person handles stress. By the choices that we make, humans can control many of the factors influencing fitness.

Technology

Technology can help us both measure and improve our individual fitness. Athletes use weight machines and computerized aerobic exercise machines to build and measure fitness. Specialized clothing and equipment enhance performance by increasing comfort level and efficiency. Computers can model the stresses that various activities

produce and help researchers design athletic shoes for specific sports. Sports equipment companies continually use technological advances to produce better equipment. For example, lighter-weight tennis rackets and more flexible vaulting poles can give athletes a competitive edge.

Athletes also use devices that simulate competitive conditions to improve their skills. At the Olympic Training Center in Colorado Springs, Colorado, swimmers test their fitness in a device called a flume, shown in figure 7.37. A flume is a simulator containing water that runs at gauged speeds. The swimmer can swim in place against moving water to increase speed and endurance. Ski team members can practice all year long on roller skis that duplicate the feel of cross-country skis. Therefore, snow is not a training requirement.

The use of such technologies may raise ethical questions. For example, do these technologies give an unfair advantage to competitors who can afford them? Do wealthy nations produce superior athletes? Is the use of such technology fair? To address these and other issues, regulatory agencies exist for each major sport and for large events such as the Olympics. Many of the agencies have an international scope.

We have seen that several factors affect human physical performance. They include genetic, behavioral, and technological factors. They all are related to how effectively we use our bodies' energy supplies.

Figure 7.37 Swimmers training for the Olympic Games can test their speed and endurance by swimming in a flume. This equipment controls the speed and direction of water flow through the swimming tank.

© Dreamstime/Tomasz Trojanowski

8

The Cellular Basis of Activity

© Dreamstime/Qwasyx

*Life's splendor forever lies in wait about each one of us in all its
fullness, but veiled from view, deep down, invisible, far off.*

Franz Kafka

asoline, nuclear power, and
electricity. All are obvious forms
of energy. But do you also think of
energy when you see sunlight or green plants?
In fact, energy is found wherever matter is
organized, from the molecules of rocks, to
cells, to entire living organisms. Most people
are not aware of the complex role that energy
plays in living systems. Without energy, life
would not be possible.

In chapter 8, *The Cellular Basis of Activity*,
you will begin to investigate the important
relationship between matter and energy. You
will consider examples of where and how energy
is stored and released. In chapter 7, *Physical
Fitness and Performance*, you studied the concept
that food contains energy that humans and
other organisms require for daily activities
and demanding physical performances. Eating
and digestion, however, do not explain exactly
how food molecules become useful as energy.
How is energy in food converted to fuel the
chemical reactions that keep cells, tissues, and
organisms alive? What is the original source of
the energy in food? Once you understand the
basic connections between energy and matter,
you will explore some of the specific cellular
reactions that require energy. You will study
the reactions that result in new molecules and
maintain the organization that is characteristic
of living systems.

GOALS FOR THE CHAPTER

Throughout chapter 8, you will work
to gain an understanding of the following
concepts:

✔ Matter and energy are related.

✔ Energy exists in different forms, such
as heat, light, and chemical.

✔ Photosynthesis converts light energy
into chemical energy, and it converts
carbon dioxide and water into energy-
storage molecules.

✔ Cellular respiration breaks down food
molecules and releases energy.

✔ All organisms fuel biosynthesis with
energy released by cellular respiration.

To help you develop these understandings,
you will complete the following activities.

ENGAGE	Releasing Energy
EXPLORE / EXPLAIN	Energy in Matter
EXPLAIN	Keep a Body Running!
EXPLAIN / ELABORATE	Using Light Energy to Build Matter
ELABORATE	Building Living Systems
EVALUATE	Tracing Matter and Energy

Throughout chapter 8, remember to
refer to the chapter organizer to help you
remember what you have learned and where
you are headed.

ENGAGE

Releasing Energy

Key Idea: Food contains enormous amounts of energy.

Linking Question:
What is the relationship between matter (such as food) and energy?

Chapter 8

EXPLORE **EXPLAIN**

Energy in Matter

Part A: Matter and Energy Interactions
Part B: Molecular Models

Key Idea: Changes in matter result in changes in energy, yet both energy and matter are conserved.

MAJOR CONCEPTS

✔ Matter and energy are related.

✔ Energy exists in different forms, such as heat, light, and chemical.

✔ Photosynthesis converts light energy into chemical energy, and it converts carbon dioxide and water into energy-storage molecules.

✔ Cellular respiration breaks down food molecules and releases energy.

✔ All organisms fuel biosynthesis with energy released by cellular respiration.

Linking Question:
How much energy is stored in different foods? How do organisms transform this energy to build and fuel their bodies?

EXPLAIN

Keep a Body Running!

Part A: Make a Snack
Part B: Explaining Our Bodies' Energy

Key Idea: Different foods contain different amounts of energy. Organisms use cellular respiration to generate small molecules that carry usable energy from food.

Linking Question:
Where does the energy stored in food come from, originally?

EVALUATE

Tracing Matter and Energy

Key Idea: The atoms that make up matter move through living systems.

The Cellular Basis of Activity

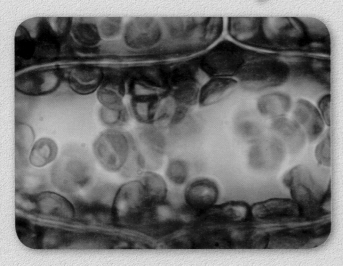

Linking Question:
How can I represent what I have learned about matter and energy?

 ELABORATE

Building Living Systems
Part A: Metabolism
Part B: Energy and Matter for Your Critter
Key Idea: Metabolism regulates energy release by breaking down and synthesizing molecules.

Linking Question:
How do organisms release the energy stored in food?

 EXPLAIN   **ELABORATE**

Using Light Energy to Build Matter
Part A: Measuring Photosynthesis
Part B: A Cell's View of Photosynthesis
Key Idea: Photosynthesis transforms light energy into chemical energy in the form of sugar.

ENGAGE

Releasing Energy

A runner in a marathon is pushing hard several miles before the finish line. But then she suddenly slows to a walk, clutches her side, and sways dizzily, about to fall. This athlete is said to have "hit the wall." She did not actually slam into a brick barrier, but she may feel as if she has done so. In this case, hitting the wall means that the runner has exhausted the energy supplies necessary to keep running.

After eating food and resting, those energy supplies will be replenished. Yet how does this additional food become the energy needed for physical activity? In this Engage activity, *Releasing Energy*, you will begin to examine the relationship between matter and energy. In the scenario, *A Matter of Explosions*, the matter you will examine is the molecules from a plant people use for grain (see figure 8.1). Where is the energy?

PROCESS AND PROCEDURES

1. Read or listen to the scenario, *A Matter of Explosions,* as your teacher instructs.
2. Consider the following questions. In your science notebook, write your ideas about how to answer them.
   a. Where did the energy for the grain explosion come from?
   b. How can energy be stored in grain?
   c. What started the explosion that released the energy?
   d. Why don't you explode when you eat grain products such as cereal or bread?
   e. What would you do to decrease the danger of explosion and better protect a grain-storage facility and its employees?
3. Contribute your thoughts about the questions to a class discussion.

SCENARIO

A Matter of Explosions

Brad celebrated his 20th birthday by starting a new job at the town's grain-storage facility. He was eager to make a good impression. Washington County Grain Cooperative was the largest employer in town. The company offered good wages, great benefits, and opportunities for advancement. The facility consisted of three huge grain elevators (see figure 8.2) that stored wheat. Each storage elevator was shaped like a giant cylinder that rose 30 m (about 100 ft) aboveground and descended 6 m (20 ft) underground. A series of tunnels connected the underground portions of the cylinders.

Figure 8.1 Grain-handling facilities are required by the Occupational Safety and Health Administration (OSHA) to meet certain standards that reduce the risk of safety and health hazards.

Figure 8.2 Grain-storage elevators hold massive amounts of grain.

The tunnels contained machinery that dropped the grain onto concave conveyer belts and moved the grain from one storage tower to another. In the storage cylinders, giant elevating platforms lifted the grain to the top of the tower.

Brad was in a small underground storage room next to one of the towers. He was waiting for his supervisor to arrive and give him instructions. The floor was covered with several inches of dust from the grain, and he was making a mess as he paced impatiently. Noticing a metal snow shovel by the door, Brad decided to get busy and clean up the place a bit. He was scraping the shovel along the cement floor when his boss and another worker appeared at the door. In an instant, they jumped at him, one grabbing his arms while the other grabbed the shovel. Brad was dumbfounded.

"Sorry to startle you," the boss said. "I know you haven't completed your orientation yet, but you've got to learn some critical rules. First and most important, don't do anything that could cause sparks!"

"But there's no gasoline around, just wheat. What difference would a few sparks make?" Brad responded, feeling embarrassed.

"Here, read this," the boss stated grimly as he removed a worn letter that had been posted on a bulletin board. This is what Brad read:

10 August

Dear Sarah,

I am amazed to be alive and able to write this letter to you—or actually to dictate it; my hands are burned too badly to write it myself.

As you heard on the news, the worst happened: an explosion in elevator number 2. We all had been warned, but I never imagined anything like this could actually happen. The whole terrible thing took only seconds. First, there was an odd "whoosh" noise, and my right side was seared with heat. Before I could think about what was happening, there was a deafening noise. I still have ringing in my ears.

I was lucky not to be at the center of the explosion. Four guys in there didn't make it. It's hard to believe that the whole thing probably started with a tiny spark from the conveyer belt gears while we were shifting grain—we'll never know for sure. The explosion was like dynamite. It blew the top right off the number 2 elevator, and then the fire took over.

I know your facility is similar to ours. Whatever you do, don't let this happen there.

Yours truly,

Mike

Brad looked silently at the others in the room. He had no idea that the flourlike dust from simple wheat could produce such an explosion and fire. He certainly couldn't explain *why* such a thing could happen or *how*.

EXPLORE

EXPLAIN

Energy in Matter

Explosions are dramatic examples of the release of a tremendous amount of energy. But what is the source of all that energy? In the case of the grain elevator explosion, the energy was stored within the molecules that made up the grain dust and gases in the air. These are two forms of matter that few people think of as energy sources. Grain and air, however, are not exceptional forms of matter; all matter contains energy. Not all matter contains the same *amount* of energy, however. The particular organization of atoms—the building blocks of matter—in a substance determines its precise amount of energy (see figure 8.3). In this Explore-Explain activity, *Energy in Matter*, you will investigate some of the links among matter, energy, and organization and attempt to describe the close relationship among them.

Materials

Part A (per team of 2)

2 pairs of safety goggles
2 lab aprons
Pyrex test tube
250-mL flask
2 microscope slides
graduated cylinder
dropping pipet
test-tube rack
spatula or spoon
thermometer or thermistor
hand lens or microscope (optional)
2-cm piece of magnesium ribbon
baking soda
vinegar
hydrochloric acid solution
saturated urea solution

Part B

online resource
materials for molecular model

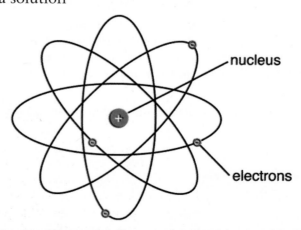

Figure 8.3 This is a graphic model of an atom. What do you already know about atoms?

PROCESS AND PROCEDURES

Part A Matter and Energy Interactions

1. Discuss with your partner how you would define "matter." In your science notebook, write your definition and 3 examples of matter.
2. Discuss with your partner how you would define "energy." In your science notebook, write your definition and 3 examples of energy.
3. Explain how matter and energy are related. Record your explanation in your science notebook. Include 1 or 2 examples to illustrate your ideas.

SAFETY: Put on your safety goggles and lab apron.

4. Carry out the following steps with your partner. In your science notebook, record your observations at each step of the task.
   a. Use a graduated cylinder to measure 5 mL of 0.7 M hydrochloric acid. Pour this into a test tube that is firmly seated in a test-tube rack. Do not remove the test tube from the rack.

WARNING: 0.7 M HCl is a *strong irritant*. Avoid skin and eye contact; do not ingest. If contact occurs, flush affected area with water for 15 minutes; rinse mouth with water. Call the teacher.

   b. Feel the outside of the test tube to note the relative temperature, as shown in figure 8.4.
   c. Carefully place 2 cm of magnesium ribbon into the acid in the test tube. Observe what happens as the solid reacts with the acid.
   d. Feel the test tube.
   e. Discuss the energy changes that you observed. Compare these changes with the events in the scenario, *A Matter of Explosions*.
   f. Discuss the changes in matter that you observed. Compare these changes with the events in the scenario.

Figure 8.4
This team is noting the relative temperature as magnesium reacts with hydrochloric acid.

Perhaps you or your partner know some terms that describe the types of chemical reactions that release and absorb energy from their surroundings (see figure 8.5).

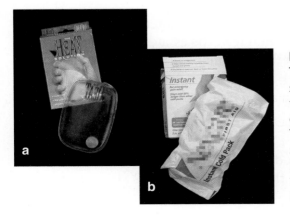

Figure 8.5 (*a*) **Exothermic reactions.** These reactions release energy to their surroundings. What form of energy does the hand warmer's chemical reaction give off? (*b*) **Endothermic reactions.** These reactions absorb energy from the surroundings. The reaction that takes place inside this cold pack is an endothermic reaction. What form of energy is absorbed?

5. Carry out the following steps with your partner. In your science notebook, record your observations at each step of the task.
   a. Put approximately 40 mL of room-temperature vinegar in a 250-mL flask.
   b. Use the thermometer or thermistor to measure the starting temperature.
   c. Carefully put about 2 spatulas of baking soda into the vinegar in the flask. Swirl it gently to dissolve the powder.
   d. Record the final temperature.
   e. Discuss the energy changes that you observed.
6. Carry out the following steps with your partner. In your science notebook, record your observations at each step.
   a. Use a dropping pipet to place 1 drop of saturated urea solution on a microscope slide.

WARNING: Urea solution is an *irritant*. Avoid skin and eye contact; do not ingest. If contact occurs, flush affected area with water for 15 minutes; rinse mouth with water if it is affected. Call the teacher.

   b. Use the edge of the second slide to spread the drop in a thin layer across the surface of the first slide.
   c. Watch the layer closely for changes. This may take several minutes to develop. Use a hand lens or microscope, if available.

   Include drawings to record the changes that you see.

   d. Read the following information. Then, in your science notebook, answer the questions.

   In the urea solution that you used, water was the solvent and urea was the solute. The solute molecules in a solution move about freely, according to the forces of diffusion. These molecules are not highly ordered, and energy is dispersed throughout the urea solution. This system can be described as having a great deal of entropy. Explain what appears to happen to the organization of urea molecules as the water in the urea solution evaporates. What do you think happened to the level of entropy? Do you think this requires or releases energy?

7. Clean up your area. ***Wash your hands thoroughly with soap and water.***
8. Record the following questions in your science notebook, leaving enough space to write answers. Then read the essay, *Matter and Energy Are Related,* to find information that will help you answer the questions.

   Be prepared to participate in a class discussion about the relationship between energy and the organization of matter.

   Answer these questions thoroughly, because you will refer to your notes throughout this chapter.

   a. Was the reaction you carried out in step 4 exothermic or endothermic? What about the reaction in step 5? State your evidence in each case.

b. Describe the original source of the energy absorbed in the endothermic reaction. In what form was the energy after the reaction?

c. Describe where the energy produced by the exothermic reaction originated and where it was transferred.

d. What do you think happened to the organization of the molecules of baking soda when they reacted with vinegar? How did that differ from what happened to urea?

e. Did any of the atoms of the chemicals involved in these reactions disappear as a result of the reaction? Explain your reasoning.

www.scilinks.org

Topic: matter and energy
Code: human4E415

Matter and Energy Are Related

ENGLISH SPANISH

If someone asked you to describe how skin, plant roots, water vapor, and a plastic cell phone are different, could you do it? Humans are usually good at identifying differences between things in our physical world. This is because we observe many characteristic features through our senses. If we can see, touch, smell, or hear differences, then we use those characteristics to help recognize our surroundings. However, identifying similarities can be more challenging. What do skin, plant roots, water vapor, and a plastic cell phone have in common? One similarity is that all are examples of matter, meaning that they are all made of atoms.

Atoms are the basic building blocks of all matter. You cannot see individual atoms with your eye or even with powerful microscopes. Atoms make up everything from the smallest virus to the stars in the largest galaxy (see figure 8.6). Different kinds of atoms are

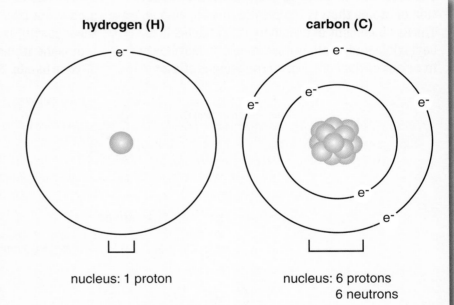
hydrogen (H)   carbon (C)

e⁻

nucleus: 1 proton   nucleus: 6 protons
                                       6 neutrons

Figure 8.6 Atoms. All matter is composed of elements, the simplest forms of matter. An atom is the smallest particle of an element that still has the properties of that element. Differences among elements result from the number and type of subatomic particles present in their atoms. For instance, six electrons, six protons, and six neutrons are characteristic of the element carbon (symbol, C). Electrons are extremely lightweight, negatively charged subatomic particles (symbol, e⁻). They orbit rapidly around the nucleus of an atom. The nucleus is located at the center of an atom. It is composed of two particles: protons, which are positively charged, and neutrons, which have no charge at all and thus are neutral. Protons and neutrons are heavier than electrons. The number of protons in an atom determines which element it is. Scientists have identified more than 100 different elements.

distinguished by the number of protons in their nucleus. These different kinds are called elements. While there are hundreds of different elements on Earth (see the Periodic Table of Elements on the inside back cover), only six different kinds of elements make up 99 percent of the human body. These are carbon, hydrogen, oxygen, nitrogen, calcium, and phosphorus.

Individual atoms are extremely small. But the matter that atoms make up is visible. The way that atoms assemble together determines the characteristics of the matter that we see. For example, skin is made up of a different combination of atoms than is the plastic in a cell phone. The arrangement of atoms in skin enables it to be flexible and to allow substances to move either in or out of the body; the arrangement of atoms

in the plastic of a cell phone makes it rigid and waterproof. As figure 8.7 shows, the source of this important atomic organization is chemical bonds. **Chemical bonds** hold atoms together in predictable ways to form molecules. Energy is stored within the structure of a molecule's bonds and atoms.

Because we cannot see atoms with the naked eye, we often overlook the importance of atomic interactions. However, these interactions are critical to understanding the relationship between matter and energy. It is difficult to describe exactly how energy exists in the structure of chemically bonded atoms. But let's try to imagine it by thinking about the following example. For this example, magnets represent atoms. Imagine holding a magnet in each of your hands. You slowly move them closer and

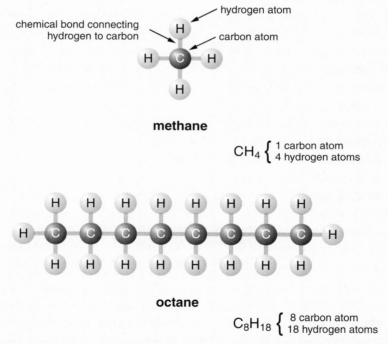

Figure 8.7   Molecules. Molecules are made of two or more atoms joined by chemical bonds. Each kind of molecule has atoms organized in a unique way. This accounts for the unique properties of materials. For instance, in one arrangement, carbon and hydrogen form a smelly gas called methane. In another arrangement, carbon and hydrogen form octane, a flammable liquid used in gasoline. Note that in both molecules, hydrogen always has one chemical bond and carbon always has four chemical bonds. The number of electrons orbiting around a particular atom determines its number of bonds.

closer together. You have to use energy to do this, right? When they are close enough, suddenly the magnets snap together. Notice a few things. First, energy was involved in rearranging the magnets. Second, energy is related to the stability of the magnets. When the magnets are stacked, they are more stable. Next, additional energy would be required to pull them apart. Finally, the total number of magnets remained the same.

What does this have to do with forming bonds among atoms? Energy must always be added to break a bond. Often (but not always), a chemical bond that has formed is fairly stable. When a chemical bond forms, energy is released. However, even though bonds form and break, the atoms remain. In other words, matter is conserved.

Now consider the magnet analogy again. Imagine that you move several magnets close to each other. The forces of attraction will cause them to form a solid, cylindrical stack. The energy stored in this stack of small magnets is much greater than the energy stored in any of the small magnets individually. Where did this energy come from? Remember, it took energy to move the magnets closer together. The force of attraction between many magnets is somewhat similar to the energy in many chemical bonds between atoms.

Magnetic energy is one familiar type of energy. What other forms of energy can you name? Energy comes in a variety of forms. These include heat, light, electrical, solar, nuclear, mechanical, and chemical energy. Thermal energy is a commonly recognized form. Energy can be transferred between any of these forms. Each transfer always releases some heat.

Most people are familiar with thermal energy through their experiences with friction. A rug burn is the result of the friction between a carpet and someone's moving skin. Bald tires are the result of friction between a road surface and rotating rubber treads. Heat also occurs at the molecular level. When molecules move, they encounter other molecules and generate friction. This produces heat. The greater the motion, the greater the heat that is released. For example, when you turn on an electric stove, electric current moves through the metal coils. The coils heat up because the current causes the metal's atoms to move rapidly.

Most substances absorb thermal energy. This happens when matter from one substance absorbs the thermal energy caused by the molecular motion of matter in a nearby substance. For example, you know that a hot pan placed in cold water becomes cool. The hot metal transfers its heat energy to the surrounding water molecules. Molecules in the pan slow down, and the temperature of the pan decreases. The water molecules respond to the transfer of thermal energy by moving faster, causing the water to become warmer.

Not all thermal energy is the result of friction between molecules. Chemical reactions can also release heat energy. Such reactions are called **exothermic reactions** ("exo-" = "out," "thermic" = "heat"). In an exothermic reaction, heat is *released* when the atoms in molecules are reorganized. Let's examine what happens specifically. The molecules present at the beginning of a reaction are called **reactants**. The reactants have a certain amount of stored energy. Some energy needs to be put into the system to break the bonds of the reactant molecules. This amount of energy is called the activation energy. But when new bonds form, energy is released. When more energy is released by bonds forming than by bonds breaking, the reaction produces heat.

For example, the explosive combustion of grain dust is an exothermic chemical reaction (see figure 8.8). What was required? The molecules that make up the grain dust, oxygen (present as a gas in the air), and a spark. The spark provided the activation energy to break the bonds in the grain dust and the oxygen. The atoms in the grain molecules and the oxygen are quickly reorganized into new molecules. Such a reorganization of matter can cause the

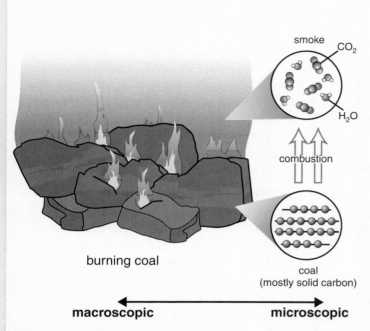

smoke   CO₂

H₂O

combustion

burning coal

coal
(mostly solid carbon)

macroscopic ←→ microscopic

Figure 8.8   Combustion of coal. Microscopic particles of coal interact with molecules in the air to make combustion products (such as carbon dioxide, or CO_2) and heat energy. What are similarities and differences between this reaction and the combustion of grain dust?

uncontrolled release of a tremendous amount of energy. Even though it would appear that the atoms that make up the grain molecules disappear in this reaction, they are simply transformed into other molecules of matter. In chemical reactions, matter is not created or destroyed; it only changes form.

Some chemical reactions absorb, or take in, heat energy from their surroundings. They are called **endothermic reactions** ("endo-" = "in," "thermic" = "heat"). In these reactions, energy is again needed to break the bonds of the reactants. Energy is also released when new bonds form, but less energy is released than was required to start the reaction. Such reactions require an overall *input* of energy to break and re-form chemical bonds. For example, the oxygen atom and the hydrogen atoms in a water molecule are quite stable when bonded to one another. It is

necessary to add energy, in the form of a spark or ultraviolet light, to break the bonds between the atoms. This can cause a molecule of oxygen (O_2) and two molecules of hydrogen (H_2) to be formed.

Other endothermic processes that you are familiar with do not involve chemical reactions. For example, when ice melts, it absorbs heat energy from another source. Think about a container of iced tea. When ice absorbs heat from the tea and the glass, the frozen water molecules in the ice begin to move more rapidly and become less organized. Absorbing the thermal energy alters the molecular organization of the ice, but not the strong chemical bonds. The ice melts as a result.

Many factors determine whether a particular molecular reorganization will be endothermic or exothermic. As figure 8.9 illustrates, the melting of ice is an *endothermic process*. But it is not an *endothermic chemical reaction*. This is because no breakage or formation of chemical bonds takes place. What happens is only a change in state: the water molecules organized as a *solid* become water molecules that are more organized as a *liquid*.

You can use magnets to model how matter and energy interact in chemical reactions. Rearranging the magnets transfers the magnetic force from one magnet to the group of magnets. In a similar manner, rearranging chemical bonds through chemical reactions transfers the energy stored in the matter. So when water molecules are formed or break down, energy transfers from one form to another as a result of rearranging the chemical bonds.

Understanding this link between energy and matter is important in biology. All living systems require energy and matter for survival. In the case of humans, thousands of different chemical reactions constantly occur in our cells. Each depends primarily on chemical energy. Within living organisms, these reactions have evolved to take place in a controlled manner—without sparks and explosions.

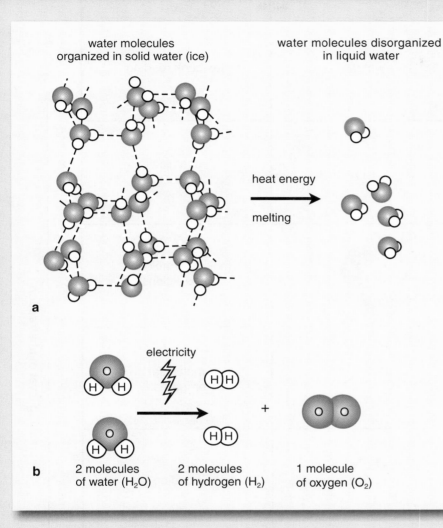

water molecules organized in solid water (ice)

water molecules disorganized in liquid water

heat energy

melting

Figure 8.9 **Endothermic processes and chemical reactions take in heat.** (*a*) An input of heat energy is necessary to melt ice. Note that there is no change in the chemical bonds of the water molecules that make up the ice. During the endothermic process of melting, the water molecules that are held rigidly in place in solid ice simply change state and become water molecules more organized to be in a liquid state. These molecules are free to move around. (*b*) In an endothermic chemical reaction, an input of energy causes the chemical bonds to break and re-form. Adding electricity to water molecules breaks and re-forms chemical bonds. This leads to the formation of two new molecules, hydrogen and oxygen.

electricity

2 molecules of water (H_2O)

2 molecules of hydrogen (H_2)

1 molecule of oxygen (O_2)

Part B Molecular Models

Complete part B, *Molecular Models,* individually.

1. Figure 8.10 shows several ways that molecules can be represented. Which representation would you use to demonstrate molecular structure (atoms bonded together) to a sixth-grade student who did not understand that matter is organized? In your science notebook, draw and explain your reasoning for your choice.

2. Consider the following question as you watch the video segment, "Molecular Models." In your science notebook, write down a possible answer.

   How do the atoms of simple molecules serve as building blocks for much larger and more complex molecules?

http://www
Online
Resource

Format of representation	Example of representation	When most used
words	water	textbook reading
chemical formula	H_2O	chemical reactions
electron cloud model	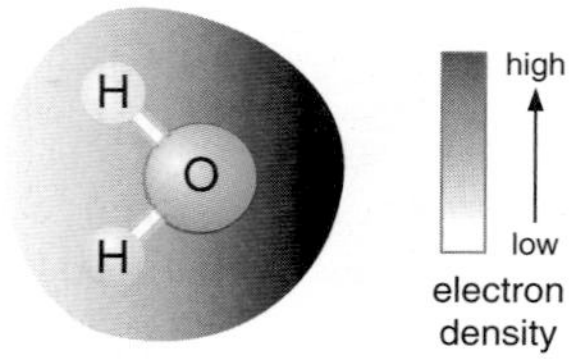	molecule-molecule interactions
structural formula	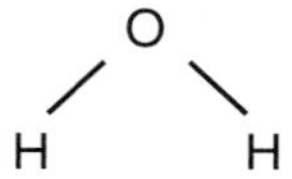	molecular properties
electron dot diagram	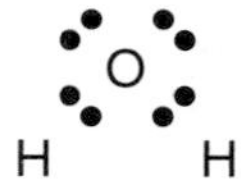	bonding
ball-and-stick (3-dimensional) model	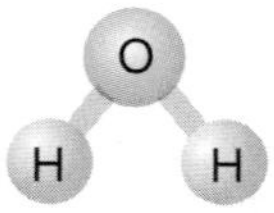	molecule geometry
particle model		molecule collisions

concrete → increasing level of abstraction → symbolic

Figure 8.10 Representations of a water molecule. There are many ways to represent a water molecule. Which way makes most sense to you?

3. Use the materials that your teacher provides to construct a model of a urea molecule. Base your model on information from the video, the essay, *Matter and Energy Are Related,* and the following information on bonding:

* Urea is represented by the chemical formula $CO(NH_2)_2$. The formula can be read to mean that urea has 1 atom of carbon, 1 of oxygen, 2 of nitrogen, and 4 of hydrogen. Two hydrogen atoms are always bonded to 1 nitrogen atom in a urea molecule.
* A carbon atom usually has 4 bonds with other atoms.
* An oxygen atom usually has 2 bonds.
* A nitrogen atom usually has 3 bonds.
* A hydrogen atom usually has 1 bond.

For more information about urea, see figure 8.11.

Analysis

Read the essay, *Energy Is Converted and Conserved,* and review figure 8.12 for information that will help you complete the following tasks. Record your answers in your science notebook. Be prepared to share your responses in a class discussion.

1. If an exothermic reaction releases heat, why is it inaccurate to say that an endothermic reaction releases cold?
2. What is the difference between kinetic energy and potential energy?
3. Explain why the energy that is stored in the chemical bonds of a molecule is not destroyed when that molecule is broken down to smaller molecules.
4. Define ATP's role as a link between matter and energy in living systems.
5. Revise your definitions of matter and energy and their relationship, which you developed in steps 1–3 of part A, *Matter and Energy Interactions.* It may be helpful to use diagrams or other visual aids with captions to explain your definitions.

Topic: atoms/molecules
Code: human4E421

© Dreamstime/Jeffrey Koh

Figure 8.11   Why are bird droppings white? In mammals, ammonia is produced when amino acids are broken down. This ammonia can be toxic. Mammals convert the ammonia into urea in the liver. The urea is excreted in urine produced by the kidneys. Birds, insects, lizards, and snakes convert the waste products from amino acid breakdown into uric acid, rather than urea. Uric acid does not dissolve easily in water, so it is excreted as a white paste with very little liquid.

Figure 8.12   Examples of energy conversion technology that generate electricity include (*a*) wind farms, (*b*) water dams, and (*c*) solar farms.

Energy Is Converted and Conserved

When electricity flows through the metal coils on a stove burner, it makes the coils red hot. But it does more than make the teapot ready for tea. It illustrates an essential property of energy. *Energy can be converted from one form into another.* In this case, electrical energy is converted into thermal energy. This property of energy has enabled scientists and engineers to develop techniques and tools for making energy accessible to humans. For example, power-generating dams harness the mechanical energy of water by passing water over turbines. The turbines rotate and convert the water's movement into electrical energy.

Without energy conversion, gasoline would not be much more than a smelly, toxic liquid. In fact, gasoline is an important energy source used in most societies. Gasoline stores a large amount of chemical energy in its molecular structure. Gasoline can be a dangerous substance because it is highly flammable. It is exactly that property, however, that makes it valuable as a fuel for industry and transportation. As figure 8.13 suggests, we have learned how to control the explosive

Figure 8.13   Energy conversion. Molecules of the chemical gasoline store energy. Combustion can reverse this energy and convert it into mechanical energy in an automobile. What other energy conversions can you think of?

property of gasoline. A gasoline engine converts the gasoline's stored chemical energy into a form of mechanical energy—a form that can be used to power machinery.

How is an exploding grain elevator an example of energy conversion? Such explosions illustrate that energy exists in two forms: an inactive form and an active form. The inactive form is called **potential energy**. Potential energy can be stored in the structure of matter and is available for use. When the potential energy in grain dust is released, it becomes active.

Active energy is called **kinetic energy**. A boulder sitting at the top of a hill contains a great deal of potential energy simply because of its position, as figure 8.14 shows. When the boulder is pushed off the cliff, however, its potential energy is transformed into kinetic energy, or the energy of movement. The potential energy poses no threat to you. You can sit on the boulder as it rests at the top of the hill. However, you would not want to come into contact with the boulder's kinetic energy as it rolls down the hill. Likewise, you are not afraid to pump gas, which has a tremendous amount of potential chemical energy, into a car's gas tank. But you don't want to light a match at the same time. If you do, you will see all of that potential energy converted into a dangerous amount of heat, a form of kinetic energy, very quickly.

Once potential energy has been converted into kinetic energy, one of two things can happen. The kinetic energy may be captured and made useful, or it may escape to the universe as heat. For example, what if the boulder at the top of the hill were attached to a rope that in turn, were attached to a wheel on a well? As the boulder rolls down the hill, it would turn the wheel and raise water from the well, spilling most of it as the bucket smashes against the wheel axle. In this example, some of the kinetic energy of the boulder would be stored as

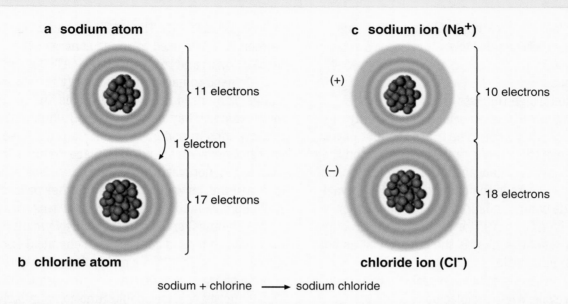

a **sodium atom**

11 electrons

1 electron

17 electrons

b **chlorine atom**

c **sodium ion (Na⁺)**

(+)

10 electrons

(−)

18 electrons

chloride ion (Cl⁻)

sodium + chlorine ⟶ sodium chloride

Figure 8.16   An example of ionic bonding. (*a*) Sodium (Na) and (*b*) chlorine (Cl) can react to form (*c*) table salt, or sodium chloride (NaCl). Sodium loses one electron, and chlorine gains one electron. The transfer of the electron makes each ion more stable. The two ions are attracted to each other's charge, forming a bond.

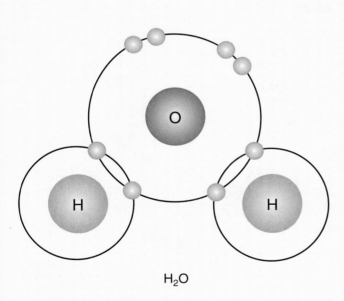

H_2O

Figure 8.17   Covalent bonds in molecules. A water molecule consists of one oxygen atom (which has six electrons in its outer orbit) sharing two of its electrons with two hydrogen atoms (which have only one electron each). The shared electrons represent a force of attraction known as a covalent bond.

hydrogen and oxygen in a water molecule. The carbohydrate molecules glycogen (in muscles and the liver) and starch (in plants) are complex molecules. They are also rich sources of potential energy. Each is a large molecule with many covalent bonds. A great deal of energy is needed to make or break covalent bonds. In most cases, enzymes catalyze these reactions in organisms.

Energy for Cellular Activity

Enzymes reduce the energy needed to start chemical reactions. Do you remember how? However, nearly all biological reactions require the input of some energy before they can proceed. Could a cell use a molecule such as glucose directly? Breaking down glucose releases a great deal of potential energy—so much that a cell would lose control. To make the energy stored in molecules such as glucose useful, the energy must be converted into a form that cells can use *directly*. This form is a special type of molecule called a̲denosine t̲riphosphate, or ATP. ATP connects many energy-conversion reactions and is called the "energy currency" of living cells (figure 8.18a). When ATP breaks down, it releases a smaller, but more easily used, amount of energy compared with glucose.

Imagine foreign tourists who arrive in the United States with no American dollars, only money from their home. The tourists must pay a fee to change their money into dollars, which they can use to pay for their activities. Similarly, cells transform or change the chemical energy in various organic compounds into the chemical energy of ATP. Then ATP "pays" for activities that require energy in cells. The "fee" is the energy lost as heat during the conversion.

ATP is constantly made and broken down in cells, forming a cycle. When a molecule of ATP (adenosine *triphosphate*) gives up one phosphate group, it becomes ADP (adenosine *diphosphate*) and releases a usable amount of energy (see figure 8.18b). The energy is available for cellular work. When ADP combines with a phosphate group, it forms ATP. This step requires energy. Thus, ATP acts as an energy carrier. It can be used to release energy (ATP breaks down) and to store energy (ATP forms).

Cells need to use chemical energy for many things. They need it for biosynthesis and to remove wastes. They need it to take in nutrients and to move ions in and out of cells. Cells also need energy to move from place to place, to move their internal structures such as chromosomes or vesicles around, as well as for many other processes. ATP supplies much of the energy for this work.

The chemical energy in the energy-yielding nutrients in food is converted to chemical energy in the form of ATP. Other molecules exist that have similar energy-transferring properties as ATP. These energy carriers could function similarly to ATP, but all known living cells use ATP as an energy carrier. This includes the cells of fungi, plants, humans, bacteria, and even archaea. The first organisms on Earth most likely used ATP as an energy source.

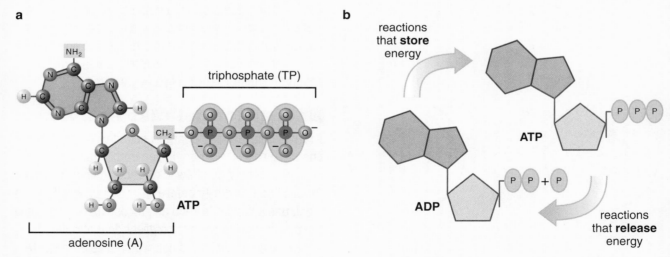

Figure 8.18 **ATP cycle.** Adenosine triphosphate (ATP) stores potential energy in its chemical bonds. Notice that ATP has three phosphate groups. A phosphate group has a phosphorus atom and four oxygen atoms. It is represented by the letter *P* in a circle. When the bond between the second and third phosphate groups breaks, ATP becomes adenosine diphosphate (ADP). ADP has two phosphate groups. The energy released from breaking bonds in ATP and forming new bonds in ADP becomes available for cells to use.

Further Challenges

1. Read the sidebar, *Historical Connections between Matter and Energy*. Write a short letter to Joseph Priestley that corrects his explanation that phlogiston killed the mouse in his experiment.

   Be sure to include descriptions of both the energy and the matter involved in his experiment.

2. In your science notebook, draw a diagram to show that starch is a large molecule made up of many glucose molecules. Then explain how the arrangement of matter determines its energy content.

3. A saturated solution is a solution in which the concentration of solute is so high that no more solute can dissolve. With that knowledge, explain what happened during the crystallization of urea in step 6, part A.

   Suppose you left a dilute solution of urea (one in which the concentration of solute is very low) uncovered for a long time. Do you think the urea would eventually form crystals as well?

SIDEBAR

ENGLISH   SPANISH

Historical Connections between Matter and Energy

Two thousand years ago, the Greeks had a thriving society that focused on the pursuit of knowledge and fitness (figure 8.19). These people understood that there is a connection between the fitness of the mind and the fitness of the body. They started the Olympic Games to let men show their athletic skill in different events. The Greeks also had a contest for women called the *Heraea* that was held every four years. One of the principal events of the games was the marathon. This race commemorates the feat of a Greek messenger, who ran from the city of Marathon to the city of Athens.

The distance between these cities is 42.2 km (26 mi, 385 yd), so that is the distance of the marathon.

While some Greeks were showing what their bodies could do, some were extending the limits of their minds by developing explanations for the natural world. A key assumption of their explanations was that the world was composed of four primary elements: fire, water, earth, and air. They described the composition of everything in the world by some combination of the four elements. These ideas were held to be true until the beginning of the 18th century.

Figure 8.19 Discus thrower (*Diskobolos*). This marble statue is a copy of one made by the Greek sculptor Myron around 450 BCE. It is an indication of the importance of fitness and sports in ancient Greek culture.

By the mid-1700s, scientists were using new explanations to describe the natural world. One of the ideas they focused on was the composition of fire. What was it made of? Unlike the Greeks, who assumed that fire was a primary element, 18th-century scientists experimented with fire and relied on observations to guide their explanations. They noted that when something like coal was burned, it gave off an oily substance. They named this substance *phlogiston*, meaning "fatty earth." The better something burned, the more phlogiston they assumed it contained. Coal apparently contained much phlogiston.

At that time, English clergyman and chemist Joseph Priestley used the idea of phlogiston to explain the results of one of his experiments. He stated that a mouse in a glass container with a burning candle dies quickly because phlogiston is poisonous. The more the candle burns, the more phlogiston is produced.

A few years later, in 1772, a Frenchman named Antoine-Laurent Lavosier generated an alternative explanation for the death of the mouse in Priestley's experiment. Lavosier reasoned that the mouse died not because phlogiston was *added* to the air, but because the fire *removed* something from the air. He performed experiments to test his idea. From his evidence, he concluded that burning flames require an element in the air. Lavosier called this potential element *oxygen*. When all of the oxygen was consumed, the mouse would die. Thus, not only does a flame require oxygen to burn, but mice require oxygen to live.

Lavosier's ideas form the foundation for today's understanding of fire. We now know that when matter is burned, chemical bonds are rearranged, new molecules are formed, and energy is released. Later scientists examined how energy is released within cells. They realized that energy is released systematically and slowly. For most organisms, oxygen is required for the systematic release of energy from food.

Keep a Body Running!

The connections among food, energy, and exercise were so interesting to one of your classmates that he decided to investigate the career opportunities for nutritionists and dietitians. He began by subscribing to several health and nutrition magazines. In last month's issue of *Athlete's World*, he ran across this interesting ad:

Tudor Valley Marathon Snack Contest

Enter the Tudor Valley Marathon Snack Contest to develop the best possible marathon snack. At the next Tudor Valley Marathon, we want to offer a new healthful snack. The snack must meet the following criteria:

- Provide approximately 200 kcal (kilocalories, commonly abbreviated as "Calories" on food labels) per 30 g.
- Be considered tasty by 8 out of 10 runners.
- Keep well for long periods of time and be able to be consumed "on the run."
- Include a snack brochure that explains how cells in the body convert this snack into fuel that can power muscles.

This Explain activity, *Keep a Body Running!*, provides the tools for you and your teammates to compete in the Tudor Valley Marathon Snack Contest. To successfully compete, you will focus on two questions: "How can you measure the potential energy stored in food?" and "How does the body harness the potential energy in food?"

Materials

Part A (per team of 3)

3 pairs of safety goggles
3 lab aprons
100-mL graduated cylinder
250-mL Erlenmeyer flask
thermistor or thermometer
balance
forceps
small container of tap water
jar of tap water for storing pH probes (optional; if using probe ware)
food samples
tin can with holes cut out for air and viewing
cork with wire sample holder (paper clip)
cork or other apparatus for suspending the thermistor or thermometer
matches or long-necked lighter
20 × 30-cm piece of extra heavy aluminum foil, plus extra foil
2 pot holders
materials to design a snack brochure

Part B

Cellular Respiration on the online resource (optional)
materials to design your snack brochure

PROCESS AND PROCEDURES

Part A Make a Snack

1. With your partner, read the following information about your task. Then discuss and begin developing your plan for creating a snack recipe that has the best chance of winning the Tudor Valley Marathon Snack Contest. Record your ideas in your science notebook.

   Your challenge is to select three different foods from the available choices. You will measure the potential energy in each using *The Calorimetry Protocol*. You will then use at least two of these foods in your snack recipe. You might look back at chapter 7 to remind yourself of the role of different components of food to diet and performance.

2. To measure the potential energy in 3 foods, you will carry out an experiment. Read the following information about the equipment you will use in this experiment. As you read, write a definition for the following terms in your personal glossary: "calorie," "kilocalorie," and "Calorie."

   A **calorimeter** is a device that scientists use to measure the heat generated by a chemical reaction. In this experiment, the calorimeter is measuring the amount of heat energy that is released

Topic: calories
Code: human4E430

in the combustion of the molecules in food. Scientists use calorimeters to estimate the amount of potential energy available in food samples. A **calorie** (with a lowercase *c*) is the amount of energy required to raise the temperature of 1 g of water by 1°C (degree Celsius). Thus, 1,000 calories equals 1 kilocalorie. The dietary Calorie (with a capital *C*; see figure 8.20) is equivalent to 1 kcal. The International System of Units uses the unit joule (J) for energy, but nutritional researchers still use kilocalories. One calorie equals 4.18 J.

Using a simple calorimeter (figure 8.21) and a thermistor or thermometer, you can measure the change in temperature of a known volume of water. The water absorbs most of the heat given off by burning a known mass of food. Based on the change in temperature, you can calculate the amount of energy that was contained in the food.

3. Read *The Calorimetry Protocol* with your partner, then finish writing your plan for developing your snack. A good plan will include the following.
   a. A statement of the reasoning behind why you selected the 3 foods you have chosen to test
   b. A plan for the work that includes the use of *The Calorimetry Protocol*
   c. Predictions for the results

   > Divide the responsibilities of *The Calorimetry Protocol* evenly between you and your team. Be sure to follow the correct safety procedures.

Nutrition Facts		
Serving Size 2.0 oz (56g/about ¼ cup dry rice & 1 Tbsp seasoning mix) (1 cup prepared) Servings Per Container about 3 (dry)		
Amount Per Serving	As Packaged	As Prepared
Calories	190	220
Calories from Fat	0	30
		% Daily Value**
Total Fat 0g*	0%	6%
Saturated Fat 0g	0%	11%
Cholesterol 0mg	0%	3%
Sodium 780mg	33%	34%
Total Carbohydrate 44g	15%	15%
Dietary Fiber 1g	5%	5%
Sugars 0g		
Protein 5g		

Figure 8.20 On food labels, kilocalories are written as "Calories," with a capital *C*.

PROTOCOL

The Calorimetry Protocol

1. Select samples of the foods that your team chose to test.
2. Put on goggles and a laboratory apron. Assemble a calorimeter like the one shown in figure 8.21. You will need a 250-mL Erlenmeyer flask, a tin can, a cork with sample holder, a piece of extra heavy aluminum foil, and the food samples. Practice assembling and disassembling the equipment (figure 8.22).
3. With the calorimeter disassembled, measure 100 mL of tap water. Pour it into the flask.
4. If you are using thermistors, start the computer application or set up the handheld device to measure temperatures between 15°C and 45°C.
5. Suspend your thermistor or thermometer in the water as follows. Use a loosely fitting cork or other apparatus to support the thermistor or thermometer in the flask. Make sure that the sensing element or bulb is submerged in the water without touching the glass.

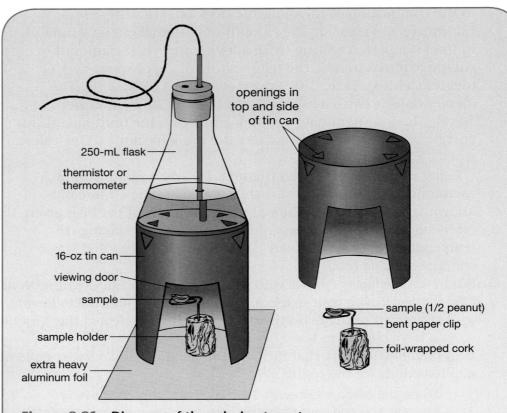

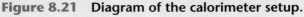

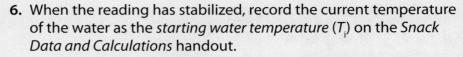

Figure 8.21 Diagram of the calorimeter setup.

6. When the reading has stabilized, record the current temperature of the water as the *starting water temperature* (T_i) on the *Snack Data and Calculations* handout.

   It is critical that you begin each new food trial with fresh, cool water.

7. Place a food sample in the wire holder (paper clip) anchored in the cork. Then place the cork on the piece of aluminum foil.

   For runny foods, you may need to use extra heavy aluminum foil to construct a holder shaped like a boat or platform.

8. Use the balance to determine the combined mass of the food sample, wire holder, cork, and piece of extra heavy aluminum foil. Measure to the nearest 0.1 g. Record this as the *starting mass* on the *Snack Data and Calculations* handout.

9. Carefully set fire to the food sample with matches or a long-necked lighter. This may require several matches. Discard burned matches in the container of water.

WARNING: Matches are flammable solids. In case of burns, place burned area under cold running water. Call your teacher immediately.

10. Place the tin can over the burning sample, with the viewing hole facing you, as soon as possible. Place the flask of water on top of the tin can.

Figure 8.22
Performing a calorimetry experiment. Your calorimeter setup should look similar to the one shown in the figure.

11. Continue monitoring the water temperature, even after the sample has burned completely. Record the *maximum water temperature reached* (T_{max}) on the *Snack Data and Calculations* handout.

   The temperature will continue to rise after the sample has burned completely, as the water absorbs heat from the tin can.

12. Allow the calorimeter to cool for at least 2 minutes before disassembling.

CAUTION: The flask and tin can will be hot. Use pot holders to handle these items and place them only on the aluminum foil. The sample holder also will be hot. Use forceps to remove the burned sample. In case of burns, place burned area under cold running water. Call your teacher immediately.

13. Use the balance to determine the combined mass of the burned food sample, wire holder, cork, and piece of aluminum foil. Measure to the nearest 0.1 g. Record this mass as the final mass on the *Snack Data and Calculations* handout.

14. Repeat the protocol 3 times for each type of food you are testing. You will obtain a more accurate measurement by averaging your 3 trials.

4. Have your teacher approve your strategy.
5. Conduct your tests. After you have collected all your data, clean your lab area according to your teacher's directions.

   Remember to follow the required safety cautions. Remember to repeat the procedure three times for each of your foods. Change the water in the flask each time.

CAUTION: Put on your safety goggles and lab apron. Tie back long hair, and roll up long, loose sleeves.

6. ***Wash your hands thoroughly with soap and water before leaving the laboratory.***
7. Analyze your data using the following steps. Enter the data on your *Snack Data and Calculations* handout. You do not need to calculate averages for the gray cells in the table.
   a. Compute the *mass of food that burned* in each trial. To do this, simply subtract the *final mass* of your sample from the *initial mass*: *mass of food that burned = initial mass – final mass.*
   b. Determine the *change in temperature* (ΔT) for each of your trials: $\Delta T = T_{max} - T_i$.
   c. Calculate the number of *calories produced* in each of your trials. To do this, multiply the increase in water temperature by 100 (the number of grams of water that was used): *calories produced* $= \Delta T$ (°C) $\times$ 100 (g of water).

d. Convert the number of *calories produced* to *kilocalories (kcal) produced* by dividing by 1,000:
kcal produced = calories produced/1,000.

> Note that kilocalories are the same as the dietary Calories (with a capital *C*) that you see on food labels.

e. Calculate the *kilocalories produced per gram* of food. To do this, divide the number of kilocalories produced by the mass of food that burned:
kcal produced per gram = kcal produced/mass of food that burned.

f. Compute the average number of kilocalories per gram for each of your different foods. To do this, add up the 3 values for kilocalories per gram from each trial and divide by 3:
average kcal produced per gram = (kcal produced per gram trial 1 + kcal produced per gram trial 2 + kcal produced per gram trial 3)/3.

8. Discuss the calorimetry results with your team.

9. In your science notebook, write down ideas you have for improving your snack recipe from step 1. Also write down why you think the changes would improve the snack.

10. Compare the kilocalories per gram that you measured with the Calories per gram given on labels for the same foods. Explain any discrepancies that you find.

> Some of the foods that you tested may be listed in figure 7.35e in chapter 7. Note that these values are given in kcal/100 g.

11. Begin developing a brochure about your snack by drawing a diagram illustrating how the approximately 200 kcal in your snack are distributed among the different ingredients. Label the different foods you used as being primarily composed of proteins, carbohydrates, or fats.

Part B   Explaining Our Body's Energy

You know from *Marathon*, the Evaluate activity in chapter 7, that long-distance running requires the transformation of an enormous amount of energy. By carrying out the calorimetry tests in part A, *Make a Snack*, you learned how much potential energy different foods store. You saw evidence of this energy in the flames released from the food. How does your body transfer the stored energy in food into chemical energy to use for running, thinking, and everything else you do? How does your body release this energy without starting an actual fire in your body?

1. Read the essay, *Cellular Respiration: Controlling the Release of Energy.* As you read, enter the terms "cellular respiration" and "ATP" into your personal glossary and answer the following questions.
   a. Explain how the overall process of cellular respiration releases energy in a controlled way.
   b. Examine the caption for figure 8.24. Why do plants, animals, and fungi each require cellular respiration to live?
   c. Compare the 3 stages of cellular respiration in terms of how much ATP is produced in each stage.

d. When energy breakdown occurs anaerobically, the first stage of glycolysis is completed, but molecules do not enter the Krebs cycle or the electron transport chain. Explain why it is more efficient for organisms to use aerobic cellular respiration to release energy from food.

Cellular Respiration: Controlling the Release of Energy

ENGLISH SPANISH

In the example of the grain-storage explosion, energy was released from matter suddenly and dramatically. When you eat bread or cookies, however, you do not explode. Clearly, your body must release the energy stored in grain in a more controlled way. When you eat bread made from grain, the cells in your body release the energy one small step at a time. Enzymes help lower the energy of activation of a series of specific chemical reactions. Cellular respiration is the name of this series of reactions. There are two kinds of cellular respiration: aerobic, which requires oxygen, and anaerobic, which doesn't require oxygen. We will focus on aerobic cellular respiration, which we will simply refer to as cellular respiration.

During cellular respiration, the potential energy in food molecules is transformed into molecules of ATP and heat (see figure 8.23). The ATP molecules store energy in smaller amounts, appropriate for fueling chemical reactions in the body. Carbohydrates such as starch, glycogen, or glucose may be used in this process. Each type of carbohydrate

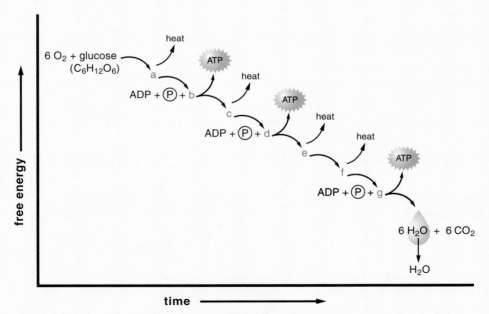

Figure 8.23 Energy transfer in cellular respiration. A series of reactions transfers the energy of glucose to ATP. The labels *a* through *g* represent intermediate compounds in the decomposition of glucose to carbon dioxide and water. Notice what happens to the relative amount of free energy.

contains atoms of carbon, hydrogen, and oxygen. The carbohydrates differ only in how those atoms are organized and how many of each atom are present. Molecules from fats and proteins can also be used in the process. Just like the grain explosion, aerobic cellular respiration requires oxygen. You need oxygen because it allows your cells to carry out cellular respiration. To explore this process, we will focus on the breakdown of the sugar glucose.

Three main stages divide the steps of cellular respiration, as illustrated in figure 8.24. The stages are known as **glycolysis**, the **Krebs cycle**, and the **electron transport system**. Glycolysis occurs in the cytoplasm of the cell. The Krebs cycle and the electron transport system occur in the mitochondria of the cell. The first stage, glycolysis ("glyco-" = "sugar," "lysis" = "to split"), occurs in nearly every living cell. Glycolysis is a series of reactions that splits a glucose molecule into two smaller molecules. This produces a small amount of ATP. These two molecules still contain much stored energy, however. In the Krebs cycle, a series of reactions breaks down the two small

Figure 8.24 **Stages of cellular respiration in plants, animals, and fungi.** Glycolysis, which occurs in the cytoplasm of the cell, breaks down glucose to smaller molecules. These molecules are transported into the mitochondria. They are further broken down to carbon dioxide in the Krebs cycle. In the electron transport system, the electron shuttle molecules made during glycolysis and the Krebs cycle are used to form many molecules of ATP.

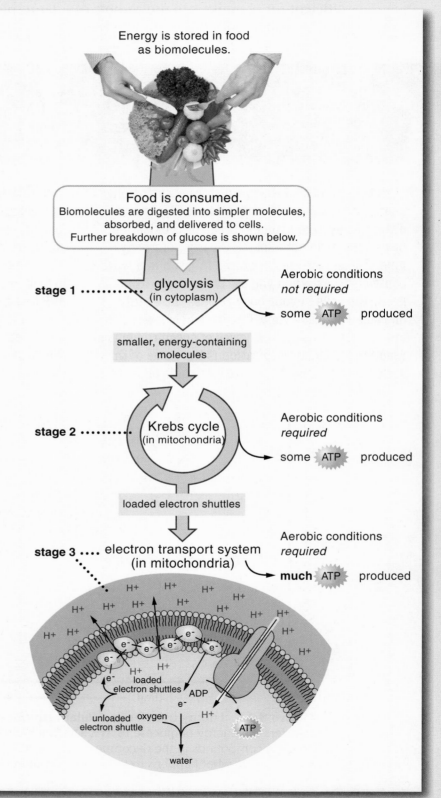

Energy is stored in food as biomolecules.

Food is consumed.
Biomolecules are digested into simpler molecules, absorbed, and delivered to cells. Further breakdown of glucose is shown below.

stage 1 ·········· glycolysis (in cytoplasm)

Aerobic conditions *not required*

some ATP produced

smaller, energy-containing molecules

stage 2 ········· Krebs cycle (in mitochondria)

Aerobic conditions *required*

some ATP produced

loaded electron shuttles

stage 3 ···· electron transport system (in mitochondria)

Aerobic conditions *required*

much ATP produced

loaded electron shuttles

ADP

unloaded electron shuttle

oxygen

water

ATP

molecules to carbon dioxide. This produces several more ATP molecules. When you breathe out, most of the carbon dioxide comes from the chemical reactions that occur in the Krebs cycle. In fact, when you lose weight, most of your "lost" weight leaves your body as you exhale carbon dioxide.

After the Krebs cycle, some of the glucose molecule's energy has been captured in the form of ATP. Energy was also transferred to other molecules known as loaded electron shuttles. These molecules received high-energy electrons during the Krebs cycle. The shuttle molecules move to the last stage of cellular respiration, the electron transport system. In this stage, the energy from the electrons on the electron shuttles is ultimately transformed into ATP. In fact, most of the ATP made from glucose is generated during this last stage of cellular respiration. At the end of the electron transport system, the electrons from the electron shuttles combine with oxygen (O_2) and hydrogen ions (H^+) to form water (H_2O). Finally, a significant amount of energy from glucose is released as heat.

Overall, the reactions of aerobic cellular respiration can be summarized as follows:

$$C_6H_{12}O_6 + 6O_2 \xrightarrow{\text{enzymes}} 6CO_2 + 6H_2O + ATP$$
glucose   oxygen   carbon dioxide   water   energy

There are four end products of cellular respiration. First, ATP molecules are made in each stage. Second, carbon dioxide is a by-product of the Krebs cycle. Third, heat is produced. Finally, water is formed at the end of the electron transport system. Cells can use ATP directly to fuel cellular work, such as muscle contractions.

2. Continue developing your brochure for your snack by drafting a paragraph that explains how the mitochondria in muscle cells convert glucose into energy that the body can use to move muscles.

   Consider this a draft paragraph that will help you organize your thinking and help you commit information to memory. Draw on the information and diagrams in the essays, *Energy's Role in Making Structures Functional*, in chapter 7, and *Cellular Respiration: Controlling the Release of Energy*. You will have a chance to revise and add to this paragraph in the *Analysis* of this activity.

3. To deepen your understanding about the 3 stages of cellular respiration, your teacher may have you watch the animation, *Cellular Respiration,* on the online resource. Copy into your science notebook each of the 3 review diagrams in the animation.

4. To solidify your learning about the 3 stages of cellular respiration, make a table with 4 columns in your science notebook. Label the columns as follows: "stage of cellular respiration," "energy going into the stage," "what is happening to the energy," and "energy going out of the stage." Fill in the energy transformations as you read the essay, *A Closer Look at Cellular Respiration*.

A Closer Look at Cellular Respiration

ENGLISH SPANISH

Let's take a deeper look at the process of cellular respiration. A unifying principle of biology is that all living systems require energy. What is the energy needed for? It is needed to move things, such as when muscles contract. It is used when active transport carries molecules across membranes. Organisms also need energy for synthesis, that is, to build things. Tissue repair and growth require all of these processes. Where does the energy come from? The potential energy in food molecules supplies the energy needs of organisms. However, the structure of these molecules does not store energy in a form that can be used *directly* for cellular work. Food energy must be converted into a more usable form.

Through natural selection, such processes evolved in the first organisms. The simplest processes for converting food to usable energy are remarkably similar in all living organisms. Organisms that are as different as bacterial cells and humans have nearly identical processes for producing ATP. How do organisms convert food energy into energy that cells use easily? Let's follow the path of a glucose molecule to see how and where a cell harvests its potential energy. Remember, specific enzymes control every chemical reaction in cellular respiration.

The process begins in the cytoplasm. Glucose in the cytoplasm can go through glycolysis. This process does not require oxygen (see figure 8.25). A glucose molecule has six carbon atoms. It is quite stable. That is, the bonds holding its atoms together are not easily broken. Because of this stability, the cell uses a small amount of energy to begin the glucose-splitting reactions (figure 8.25a). It takes energy from two ATP molecules. The reaction splits each ATP molecule into one stable ADP (<u>a</u>denosine <u>di</u>phosphate) molecule and one phosphate (P) molecule.

Glycolysis breaks glucose down to two molecules that have three carbon atoms each (figure 8.25b). Enzymes rearrange the atoms in these molecules to form two molecules of pyruvate (figure 8.25c). Glycolysis produces a small amount of ATP. Most of the energy of the original glucose molecule, however, remains in the two pyruvate molecules. Glycolysis may be followed by a pathway that does not require oxygen (figure 8.26). This is the only way that some bacteria and archaea access the energy they need. But many organisms proceed to the next two stages of aerobic cellular respiration.

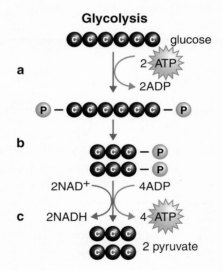

Figure 8.25   A molecular view of glycolysis. In glycolysis, glucose is broken down to two molecules of pyruvate. This takes place in many enzyme-catalyzed steps, illustrated by each red arrow. (*a*) The energy from some ATP is needed to begin the glycolysis reactions. Two ATP molecules each transfer a phosphate to glucose. (*b*) The glucose molecule is then broken down into two molecules that contain three carbons each. (*c*) In later steps, carbon atoms are rearranged to form pyruvate and ATP, and loaded electron shuttles (in this case, NADH) are produced.

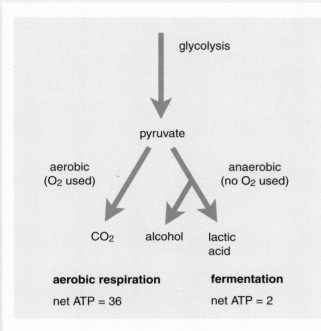

glycolysis

pyruvate

aerobic
(O₂ used)

anaerobic
(no O₂ used)

CO₂   alcohol   lactic
                              acid

aerobic respiration   **fermentation**

net ATP = 36   net ATP = 2

Figure 8.26   Aerobic and anaerobic energy release. When oxygen is present, pyruvate enters the Krebs cycle. The carbon in pyruvate is converted into carbon dioxide. Electron shuttle molecules transport electrons to the electron transport system. This system produces much ATP. In the absence of oxygen, pyruvate can be converted into alcohol or lactic acid through fermentation. What are the advantages of each process?

In addition to the ATP, glycolysis produces two molecules of NADH (nicotinamide adenine dinucleotide with a hydrogen atom). NADH is an example of a loaded electron shuttle. Some of the energy from the glucose molecule transfers to these electron shuttles. Cells sometimes use energy directly from loaded electron shuttles to do work.

The pyruvate molecules now enter the second stage of cellular respiration, the Krebs cycle. The Krebs cycle is a stage of aerobic respiration that involves many enzymes and molecular

rearrangements. These reactions release most of the remaining energy in pyruvate. The reactions occur in the cell compartments called *mitochondria* (see figure 8.27). Because the Krebs cycle only operates when oxygen is available, it is a part of *aerobic respiration.*

In preparation for the Krebs cycle, enzymes convert pyruvate into a 2-carbon molecule. This process releases a molecule of carbon dioxide. Next, the 2-carbon molecule combines with a 4-carbon molecule and is carried through a cycle of reactions

Figure 8.27   A mitochondrion. The reactions of aerobic respiration take place in this cellular organelle. Each mitochondrion has two membranes, an inner and an outer. The highly folded inner membrane forms the inner compartment. The space between the two membranes forms the outer compartment. The enzymes involved in the oxygen-requiring steps of cellular respiration are located inside the mitochondrion.

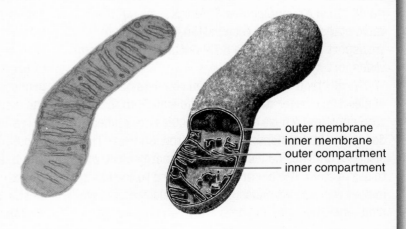

outer membrane
inner membrane
outer compartment
inner compartment

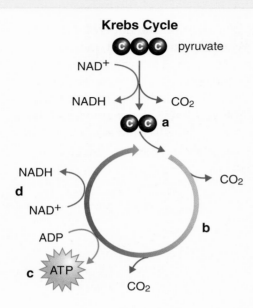

Krebs Cycle

Figure 8.28 **The Krebs cycle.** In preparation for the Krebs cycle, each pyruvate molecule produced by glycolysis is converted into a 2-carbon molecule. Many enzyme-catalyzed reactions occur that release two molecules of carbon dioxide and ATP. In addition, loaded electron shuttles (NADH) are produced at three different points in the cycle.

(figure 8.28). At the end of the cycle, carbon dioxide, a small amount of ATP, and several more loaded electron shuttles are formed. What do you think is released from the body as a result of these reactions? As with all transformations of energy, heat is produced. In humans, the circulatory system transports the carbon dioxide that was produced to the lungs. You exhale the gas as a waste product.

By the end of the first two stages of cellular respiration, the energy from glucose has been converted into energy in a few ATP molecules, loaded electron shuttles, and heat. Next, the energy in the loaded electron shuttles is converted into many more ATP molecules. This takes place in the third stage of cellular respiration, the electron transport system. Figure 8.29 outlines the electron transport system.

The electron transport system consists of a series of electron carrier molecules (different from the electron shuttles). These carrier molecules are embedded in the inner membrane of a mitochondrion. The electron shuttles deliver their high-energy electrons to the system. The electrons are passed to the chain of electron carrier molecules. As the electrons move from one carrier to the next, they release energy.

Some of the energy pumps protons (H^+) across the inner membrane of the mitochondrion. The protons accumulate in the outer compartment of the mitochondrion. This results in a higher concentration of protons in the outer compartment than on the inside (a concentration gradient).

A concentration gradient is a source of potential energy. The protons diffuse down the concentration gradient into the inner compartment. To diffuse into the inner compartment, the protons can only pass through an enzyme complex located in the membrane. The enzyme complex works much like a waterwheel. Waterwheels are sometimes used to transfer the energy of a flowing stream to a wheel used to grind wheat. In the electron transport system, the energy from the flow of protons through the enzyme complex is used to produce ATP. In this way, the energy carried into the electron transport system by electron shuttles is transferred to ATP. ATP is the ultimate product of cellular respiration. Carbon dioxide, water, and heat are by-products that we release when we exhale (figures 8.30 and 8.31). ATP can serve as the energetic *push* that starts many chemical reactions in the cell.

Electron Transport System

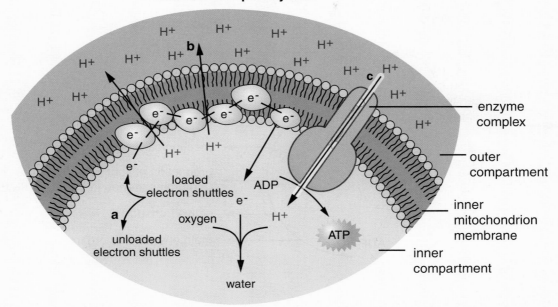

Figure 8.29 **Electron transport.** The final step in aerobic respiration is the transfer of electrons. (*a*) Electrons transfer from loaded electron shuttles to a chain of electron carrier molecules embedded in the inner membrane of the mitochondrion. The electrons pass from one electron carrier to the next. (*b*) As this happens, energy is released and hydrogen ions are pumped into the outer compartment. The resulting proton concentration gradient drives the production of ATP. (*c*) Protons flow back into the inner compartment of the mitochondrion, through an ATP-producing enzyme complex. At the end of the electron transport chain, the electrons join with oxygen and protons to form water.

But where do the electrons from the electron transport system go? At the end of the electron transport system, the electrons are accepted by oxygen molecules. The oxygen then reacts with hydrogen to form water. Imagine what would happen if there were no oxygen present for use in the electron transport system. What would build up, and what would happen to the body? You breathe because you need oxygen to keep the electron transport system and all its transformations of energy going. Humans, as well as other animals, plants, fungi, protists, and many prokaryotes, require oxygen for their survival. Transformations of energy are necessary for life.

Figure 8.30 How is perspiration related to electron transport?

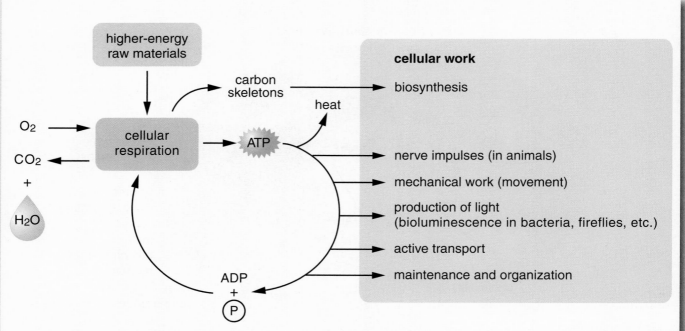

Figure 8.31 Products of cellular respiration. Cellular respiration breaks down sugars and other compounds. The products include carbon skeletons, which are used in biosynthesis, and ATP, which provides energy for work in cells. Heat and water are also produced. What kind of energy transformations occur in cellular respiration?

Analysis

Using the data from your calorimetry tests and the information from the essays and animation, as well as your learning from chapter 7, complete the following task.

1. Complete your brochure for your Tudor Valley Marathon Snack. In addition to being an attractive marketing tool for your snack, your package brochure should answer the following questions.
   a. What combination of foods did you decide to use in your snack and how much potential energy does each contain?
   b. How did your calorimetry data and your understanding of nutrition influence your decision to make your snack with these particular foods?
   c. What are the qualities that make the matter in your foods particularly good as a snack for marathon runners?

d. How is the potential energy in the food transformed into energy that can be used by a runner's body, at the cellular level?

> Your brochure should build on the diagram you drew for part A, step 11, and the paragraph you developed for part B, *Explaining Our Body's Energy*, step 2. Include information about nutrients, digestion, breakdown, synthesis, absorption, major types of molecules, building blocks the runner will need, and cellular respiration.

Further Challenges

Living organisms have evolved complex processes for extracting energy from matter and using it to fuel cellular reactions. As a result, when a cheetah accelerates toward a gazelle, it can produce enough ATP in its muscles to fuel the rapid contractions necessary for an explosive sprint. The same is true for an escaping gazelle. If the cheetah has too little energy, it would not catch its prey. Think back to the work that you did learning about homeostasis. Is it necessary for organisms to maintain a balance of energy to stay alive? Regulating the appropriate energy levels is another aspect of maintaining homeostasis. How do organisms balance their energy needs with their energy supplies? Read the sidebar, *Regulation and Energy Production*. Draw a diagram of a feedback loop that demonstrates how energy is regulated.

SIDEBAR

Regulation and Energy Production

Cellular respiration is carefully regulated to maintain an organism's homeostatic balance. Organisms must sense and respond to the available energy supply (see figure 8.32). Even when you are sitting on the couch, you need a supply of ATP. For example, your individual cells must maintain an osmotic balance with their surroundings. They do this by continually transporting sodium (Na^+) and potassium (K^-) ions across their cell membranes. The process requires energy from ATP.

Recall that ATP provides energy to another molecule by releasing one of its phosphate groups. ATP (adenosine triphosphate) then becomes ADP (adenosine diphosphate). What happens when an organism needs more energy than usual? Cells use up ATP rapidly, and ADP levels rise. The mitochondria detect increased ADP levels. They respond by increasing the rate of cellular respiration, which increases the production of ATP.

The level of ADP is not the only signal that influences energy production in cells. The level of oxygen is another critical signal. Remember, the Krebs cycle and the electron transport system cannot proceed

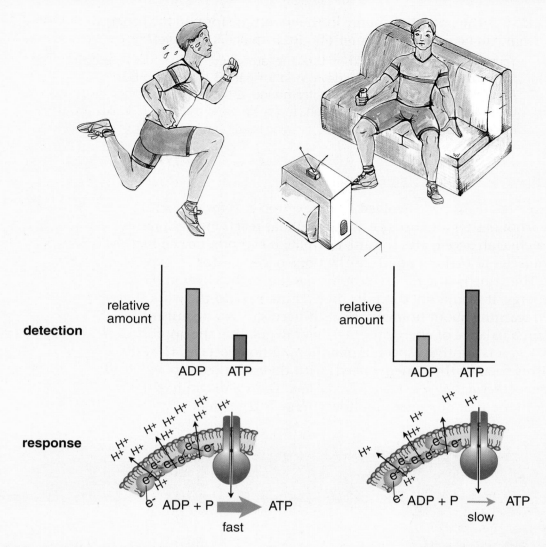

detection

relative amount

ADP   ATP

relative amount

ADP   ATP

response

ADP + P ⟶ ATP
fast

ADP + P ⟶ ATP
slow

Figure 8.32 **Regulation of energy.** Cells can detect and adjust the supply of available energy. When energy needs are low, there are low levels of ADP. ATP is made at a slow rate. When energy needs are high, there are high levels of ADP. ATP is made at a fast rate. The electron transport phase of cellular respiration speeds up. How does this system help maintain homeostasis? Is this an example of positive or negative feedback?

without oxygen. Glycolysis, on the other hand, is an anaerobic process—it does not require oxygen. The presence or absence of oxygen in the cell dictates the fate of the pyruvate formed in glycolysis. If oxygen is in short supply, energy production goes down. Respiratory centers in the brain respond by increasing the breathing rate.

Aerobic respiration did not evolve until about 2.5 billion years ago. The level of oxygen in the atmosphere was too low to sustain it until then. What changed?

Organisms that photosynthesize evolved. These organisms harness energy from the Sun to produce food. Photosynthesis releases oxygen as a by-product. That changed Earth's atmosphere forever.

The process of aerobic cellular respiration made the evolution of more-complex organisms possible. How? The amount of ATP produced during aerobic cellular respiration is about 18 times greater than that made using the anaerobic process of fermentation. The difference between the two processes in the efficiency of the energy released from glucose is significant. Remember that entropy means that energy tends to become dispersed across all parts of a system *in the absence of energy*. With an input of energy, however, order and organization in living systems can be increased. Thus, the process of aerobic respiration provided the energy for the evolution of more-complex organisms.

Aerobic respiration also explains why conditioning gives humans an advantage in performance. During conditioning that involves aerobic exercise, muscle tissues produce more mitochondria. This provides the potential for more-rapid energy transformations. In addition, circulation to the muscles improves, which provides a greater supply of oxygen. As a result of these two changes, aerobic respiration can convert a greater proportion of the energy in glucose into usable cellular energy. That makes an exercising muscle work more efficiently.

Using Light Energy to Build Matter

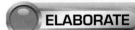

In the last activity, you studied cellular respiration. Cellular respiration is a method for obtaining energy from matter in a form that is useful for cell activity. The process depends on glucose molecules, which can be generated by breaking down glycogen, starch, and other carbohydrates. In humans, the glucose, and indeed all of the carbon in humans' organic molecules, originally came from molecules produced by other organisms. Many of these molecules come from the plants we eat. The rest come from animals or other organisms that depend on plants.

Humans, and all organisms that depend on previously assembled molecules for their carbon and energy, are called **heterotrophs** ("hetero-" = "other," "troph" = "to feed," figure 8.33). The dependence on other sources raises interesting questions about the *original* source of energy and matter. For example, how did energy first come to be stored in these molecules that are essential for life? The laws of nature tell us that energy cannot be created or destroyed, it can only be transferred. Since energy cannot be created, what is the original source of the energy that became stored in the macromolecules that build the bodies of heterotrophs?

The answer is that the energy came from green plants, which are quite different from heterotrophs. They are called **autotrophs** ("auto-" = "self," "troph" = "to feed"). This means they do not have to rely on other organisms for the complex molecules necessary for life. Autotrophs can make all of their own organic molecules. To grow, plants need only light, water, air, and a few essential elements that are available from the soil. In other words, plants can make their own food. They can make the carbon-containing molecules, such as simple sugars and starch, that are used to support their cellular activities. The process of making these carbon-containing molecules is called photosynthesis ("photo-" = "light," "synthesis" = "to make").

© Dreamstime/Istera

Figure 8.33 This bee obtains matter from the nectar it drinks. Which is the heterotroph, the bee or the plant with the nectar-bearing flower?

There are two focus questions for this Explain-Elaborate activity: "What factors affect how quickly a plant can carry out photosynthesis?" and "How do plant cells carry out photosynthesis?" A number of variables can influence the rate of photosynthesis. In *Using Light Energy to Build Matter*, you will identify a range of variables and test one. The process will help you put together the entire cycle of energy and matter in living systems. You will do this by examining the processes that capture energy and trap it in matter.

Materials

Part A (per team of 4)

250-mL beaker
2 250-mL flasks
250-mL graduated cylinder
thermistor or thermometer
1 pH probe (optional; if using probe ware) or pH strips sensitive to pH 1–2 and narrow-range pH strips (pH 4–11)
1 dissolved-oxygen probe (optional; if using probe software)
bromothymol blue
distilled water
4–6 sprigs of young, healthy *Anacharis* (*Egeria densa* or *Elodea spp.*)
jar of tap water for storing pH probes (optional; if using probe ware)
drinking straw with hole punched in it
fluorescent lamp
red, blue, and green cellophane (optional)
aluminum foil
tape
ruler

Figure 8.34
To generate a list of factors that may affect the rate of photosynthesis, consider what the environmental conditions are like when plants outside are thriving.

PROCESS AND PROCEDURES

Part A   Measuring Photosynthesis

1. Write the first focus question of the activity into your science notebook: "What factors affect how quickly a plant can carry out photosynthesis?" As you consider this question, read the essay, *Photosynthesis Brings Energy and Matter into Living Systems,* and write down the "big ideas" that you learn about.

2. With your teammates, develop a list of at least 3 variables that could affect the rate of photosynthesis.

    Draw on the essay, *Photosynthesis Brings Energy and Matter into Living Systems*, and figure 8.34 to help you generate your list. The sidebar, *Whose Discovery Is This?*, contains additional ideas.

3. Compare your list of variables with another team's list. Add any new ideas to your list.

Photosynthesis Brings Energy and Matter into Living Systems

ENGLISH SPANISH

There is a saying that you must have money to make money. A similar loop exists in biological processes: you need energy to get energy. Food supplies the energy and matter requirements of many organisms. But the food itself is usually derived from other organisms. How, then, do energy and matter get into organisms in the first place? The main way is through photosynthesis. *Photosynthesis* is the series of reactions by which some organisms use light energy from the Sun to synthesize large, energy-rich molecules from smaller ones. Plants, algae, and some eubacteria carry out photosynthesis.

You might think of a plant as a solar-powered factory. The factory converts the radiant energy of sunlight (solar energy) into stored chemical energy. The energy is stored in molecules of sugar and starch. The strength of solar energy varies. The warming rays of infrared light are lower in energy than the damaging rays of ultraviolet light (figure 8.35). Photosynthesis uses only certain wavelengths, or colors, of visible light. The green color of most plants emphasizes this fact. Plant pigments reflect green light, and they absorb other colors. Photosynthesis also depends on the intensity of the light. The ideal intensity of light varies for different plants. Of course, many factors, such as the availability of water and nutrients in the soil, also affect photosynthesis.

The reactions of photosynthesis take place in **chloroplasts**, small compartments inside certain plant cells. Figure 8.36 shows a plant cell and a chloroplast. Photosynthesis occurs in two phases. Two major events occur in the first phase, and one major event occurs in the second. Figure 8.37 summarizes the two phases of photosynthesis.

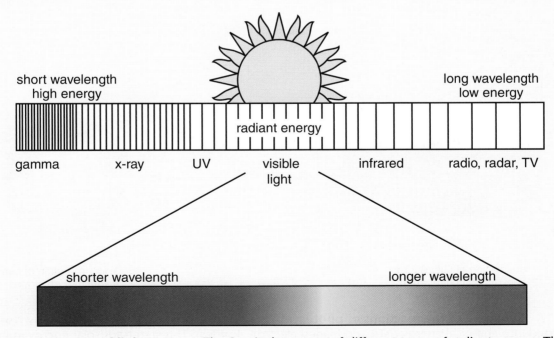

Figure 8.35 **Spectrum of light energy.** The Sun is the source of different types of radiant energy. The types include damaging ultraviolet (UV) light, light that can be detected by the human eye (visible light), and warming infrared light. Photosynthesis uses only a small portion of this spectrum of light energy.

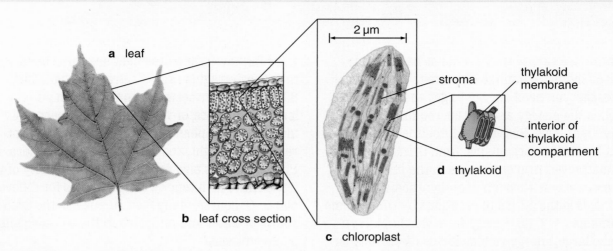

Figure 8.36 **The site of photosynthesis.** Where does photosynthesis take place? (*a*) This image shows a typical leaf. (*b*) The green disks in the cells in this diagram of a leaf cross section are chloroplasts. (*c*) This electron micrograph of a chloroplast shows the layers and stacks of the thylakoids. (*d*) The thylakoid membranes contain chlorophyll and other pigments. The symbol μm stands for micrometers (also called microns). One micron equals one-millionth of a meter.

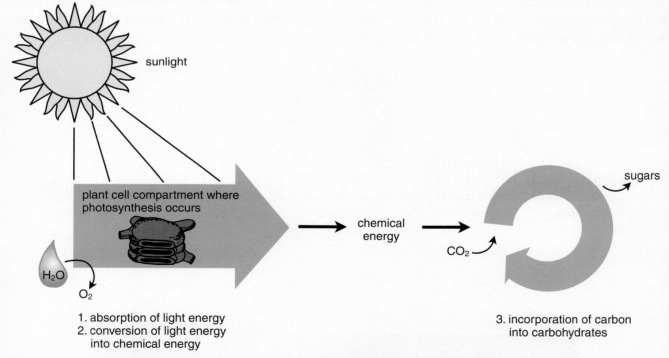

Figure 8.37 **Summary of the reactions of photosynthesis.** During photosynthesis, light energy is absorbed and converted into chemical energy (ATP and loaded electron shuttles). This step traps solar energy in matter. The chemical energy in these short-term storage molecules then powers the incorporation of carbon from carbon dioxide into carbohydrates. Carbohydrates are long-term energy-storage molecules. How can other organisms benefit from these long-term storage molecules?

In the first phase of photosynthesis, the "photo" part, light energy is absorbed by a molecule called chlorophyll. Next, enzymes and another type of electron transport system help convert the light energy into chemical energy. The chemical energy is stored in ATP and in another type of loaded electron shuttle, NADPH. Oxygen is released as a by-product of this phase. In the second phase, energy from ATP and loaded electron shuttles is stored in carbohydrates. Carbon dioxide from the air is the source of carbon to build the carbohydrates. Photosynthetic organisms use some of these carbohydrates for long-term energy storage. This is similar to the way humans use glycogen. Plants also use these carbohydrates to generate energy through cellular respiration and to form other molecules through biosynthesis. Of course, we use plant carbohydrates indirectly—every time we eat.

SIDEBAR

ENGLISH SPANISH

Whose Discovery Is This?

Two students working at the same library table looked up long enough to catch the librarian's stiff glare. They were talking too loud, again. Changing to a whisper, Inez asked, "What's your report on?"

Fernando whispered back, "The guy who discovered photosynthesis. Well, actually the guy who first figured out that plants use light and carbon dioxide from the air to make their own food. What's yours about?"

"Same thing," Inez replied.

"So you're looking up stuff on the Dutch physician Jan Ingenhousz?" Fernando asked.

"Ink and who?" Inez said. "No, a Swiss botanist and naturalist by the name of Jean Senebier. He was the first person to figure out photosynthesis."

By this time, the librarian, Mrs. Drexler, had heard enough of their talking and got up from her chair. "What's going on here?" she asked.

"We're trying to figure out who discovered photosynthesis," Fernando explained.

Mrs. Drexler relaxed, smiled, and said, "I was on the Web yesterday and found that scientists have now described 80 different chemical reactions that make up photosynthesis. I suggest that you focus your research on the history of photosynthesis. It might be more interesting than trying to find one person responsible for discovering it."

Three days later, Inez and Fernando presented their science teacher, Mr. O'Brien, with the results of their research. "We ran

© Dreamstime/Andres Rodriquez

across dozens of men and women who contributed to understanding photosynthesis," Inez said. "Some things are still being discovered about it."

"Yeah," Fernando said. "The list got so long we decided to pick out just a few people who played major roles in developing the whole idea of photosynthesis. Here's our list":

- During the 17th century, a physician named Jean Baptista van Helmont did an experiment to test the question of whether soil contributes to the mass of a willow tree.
- In 1772, Joseph Priestley, an English chemist and clergyman, did some experiments showing that plants release a type of gas that allows burning to occur. This was before oxygen itself had been discovered.
- Jan Ingenhousz discovered that sunlight is necessary for photosynthesis. He also showed that only the green parts of plants can

release oxygen. In doing this work, he performed more than 500 experiments in 1779 alone.
- In 1796, Jean Senebier discovered that carbon dioxide is required for plants to grow.
- In the early 1800s, Nicolas de Saussure, a Swiss chemist and plant physiologist, showed that plant growth results from the intake of both carbon dioxide and water.
- In 1845, Julius Robert von Mayer, a German physician and physicist, proposed that plants absorb light energy and convert it into chemical energy. The chemical energy is then stored in compounds.
- In the course of a long career from 1936 until 1991, Robert Hill demonstrated that oxygen is released from water molecules, not carbon dioxide.
- In the 1940s and 50s, Melvin Calvin, with several colleagues, used radioactive carbon dioxide to trace a series of biochemical reactions that resulted in the formation of sugar. His work was honored with the 1961 Nobel Prize in Chemistry, and this series of reactions was named the Calvin cycle.

Fernando and Inez anxiously watched Mr. O'Brien read their report. They hoped he would be pleased that they had found information about so many scientists. When he finished reading, Mr. O'Brien asked, "What have you learned from your research?"

Fernando replied, "No one person discovered photosynthesis." Inez chimed in, saying, "The understanding of photosynthesis developed over a long period of time, like most scientific ideas."

Mr. O'Brien smiled; Fernando and Inez were thinking like scientists.

4. With your team, read the following paragraph about the model system you will investigate.

> There are several ways to measure the rate of photosynthesis. You will use one model system of photosynthesis in this activity. Aquatic plants such as *Anacharis*, shown in figure 8.38, exchange gases with the environment just as land plants do. Gases such as carbon dioxide (CO_2) and oxygen (O_2) dissolve in water. When carbon dioxide dissolves in water, it combines with water (H_2O) to become carbonic acid (H_2CO_3). You can indirectly measure CO_2 concentration in an aquatic environment by measuring the pH. (pH is a measure of how acidic or basic a solution is.) When carbonic acid is added to water, the pH decreases. You can measure oxygen dissolved in water by using a dissolved-oxygen probe.

5. Read *The Photosynthesis Protocol* as a team to learn how to measure the gases exchanged by *Anacharis*. Write in your science notebook any questions that your team has about the protocol.

6. Participate in a class discussion about *The Photosynthesis Protocol* and how it could be modified to test the effect of different variables on the rate of photosynthesis.

7. Use *The Photosynthesis Protocol* and the materials available to you to outline an experiment that tests the influence of 1 of these variables (pH, oxygen, and temperature) on the rate of photosynthesis. In your outline, include the following:
   a. A testable question and a hypothesis
   b. The factor you will vary
   c. How you will use and modify *The Photosynthesis Protocol* to test your question
   d. A control

> For more information, refer to appendix C2, *How to Design an Investigation*.

PROTOCOL

PROTOCOL

The Photosynthesis Protocol

1. If probe ware is available, set it up according to your teacher's instructions.
   a. Calibrate the pH probe to a pH 4–11 range.
   b. Calibrate the dissolved-oxygen probe.
   c. Set up the thermistor.
   d. Choose appropriate settings to monitor the 3 probes (pH, oxygen, and temperature), save your data, and graph your results.

   Consult your teacher for help selecting the settings.

Figure 8.38
Anacharis. *Anacharis*, a common name for *Egeria densa* and several species of elodea, is found in ponds, lakes, and streams throughout North America. It is sold in pet stores as an aquarium plant. What gas do you think is present in the gas bubbles?

2. If you will not be using probe ware, follow your teacher's instructions for locating and using the following materials:
   - pH test strips
   - thermometer

3. Put 125 mL of distilled water in a 250-mL flask.

4. Put a straw in the flask and blow gently through the straw into the water for 3 minutes.

   Blow into the end of the straw with the additional small hole in it. This helps prevent you from sucking any liquid into your mouth. Discard the straw after use. What are you adding to the water?

CAUTION: Avoid getting bromothymol blue in mouth or eyes, or on skin.

5. Add 2.5 mL of bromothymol blue to the water in the flask that you have been blowing into. Swirl the flask to mix. Note the color.

6. In the second 250-mL flask, add 2.5 mL of bromothymol blue and 125 mL of distilled water.

7. Use a pH probe or pH strips to test the pH of the water in both flasks.

8. Place 4–6 sprigs of *Anacharis*, cut end up, into a 250-mL beaker.

9. Fill the beaker three-quarters full with the mixture from the second flask (the flask you *did not* blow into).

10. Place the thermistor or thermometer in the beaker. If using, place the pH probe and the oxygen probe in the beaker.

11. Position the beaker within 50 cm of a light source, as shown in figure 8.39.

    If you use colored cellophane to modify the light source, position the light only 10 cm away from the *Anacharis* to adjust for the drop in light intensity that the cellophane causes. Do *not* attach the cellophane directly to the light source. The heat from the light source may cause the cellophane to melt.

12. Take pH, oxygen, and temperature readings for at least 30 minutes. Record values every 5 minutes.

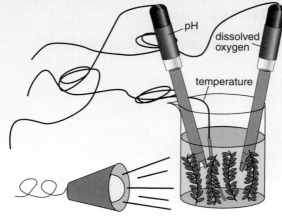

Figure 8.39 Follow this setup for measuring the rates of photosynthesis with probes.

8. Predict how the following will change during your investigation. Record your predictions in your science notebook.
   a. pH level
   b. Dissolved-oxygen level
   c. Temperature
9. Create a data table to record your data, including qualitative observations such as bubbling and color changes. Remember to make a column to record the time at which each set of observations is taken.

   > Review your design and procedure to help you decide what your data table needs to include. For more information, refer to appendix B4, *How to Use and Create Organizing Tables*.

HOW TO

10. After gaining your teacher's approval of your experimental plan and data table, arrange your setup to test your question and carry out your experiment.

    > Remember to record all data and observations in your data table.

11. Remove the probes and rinse them with distilled water. Follow your teacher's instructions about where to return the *Anacharis* plants. **Then wash your hands thoroughly with soap and water.**
12. Turn to a new page in your science notebook. Using your control data, generate 3 separate line graphs down the left side of the page showing pH, oxygen, and temperature (on the *y*-axis) against time (on the *x*-axis).
13. Using data from your experimental setup (where you varied a factor), generate another 3 separate line graphs on the right side of the page showing pH, oxygen, and temperature (on the *y*-axis) against time (on the *x*-axis). Make sure the two graphs showing the same information, like pH, are next to one another.
14. Title each of your 6 graphs to indicate the design of your investigation. Then add highlight comments to each set of graphs. In addition to placing comments on each graph, write 1 or 2 highlight comments that *compare* what you see between your control and experimental graphs.

    > An example title is "pH of water when *Anacharis* is placed 10 cm from light." For more information about highlight comments, refer to appendix B6, *How to Write Highlight Comments and Captions*.

HOW TO

15. Compare your results with your predictions from step 8. Discuss your results with your team and be prepared to share your results with the class.
16. Participate in a class discussion about the results of the different teams and the effect of light on gas exchange in *Anacharis*.
    a. Present your team's results, including your graphs, to the class.
    b. How did pH, oxygen, and temperature change in the different investigations?
    c. How did the color of bromothymol blue change over the course of the lab? What does this chemical indicate?

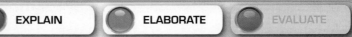

17. Your teacher has a test tube containing *Anacharis* and bromothymol blue solution that has been in the dark for at least 24 hours. The solution in it was blue initially. Predict the pH and color of the solution now.

18. Study the test tube that your teacher will show you. Answer the following questions in your science notebook.
    a. What color is the solution? What pH is the solution?
    b. Which teams observed similar changes in their solutions? Propose reasons why they observed similar changes.

Part B   A Cell's View of Photosynthesis

In part A, *Measuring Photosynthesis*, your class measured how quickly photosynthesis occurs under different conditions. You saw that plants carry out photosynthesis when the right wavelengths of light are present. But what is actually going on in those green cells of photosynthesizers? How is it possible for a cell to convert light energy to chemical energy?

1. Write the following questions into your science notebook, leaving plenty of space to write notes and answers. Answer them as you read the essay, *Photosynthesis: A Closer Look*.
    a. Where in a plant cell does photosynthesis occur?
    b. List 3 or more ways that plants use the 3-carbon sugars produced during photosynthesis.
    c. Describe why you think the 3-carbon sugars produced during photosynthesis are important for organisms that eat plants.
    d. Plants gain mass as they grow. What is the ultimate source of the carbon that plants use to build their bodies? Why is it incorrect to say that plants get their food from the soil?

2. Create a concept map of the process of photosynthesis by using the following words and any other words you would like to add. Remember to use verbs to connect the concepts to show relationships. Arrange the concept map so that the most universal concept is in the middle.
    a. Light energy
    b. Photosynthesis
    c. Chemical energy
    d. Chloroplast
    e. Water
    f. Carbon dioxide
    g. Oxygen

    For more information about concept maps, refer to appendix B7, *How to Construct a Concept Map*.

HOW TO

Plants, algae, and some eubacteria achieve something that humans and other animals can only ever dream about: synthesizing food from sunlight and air. Wouldn't it be wonderful to have an organ sticking out of your head that carried out photosynthesis? You would never suffer hunger pains sitting in class, just before lunch. Lunch would be "served" anytime you were exposed to enough sunlight. Let's look in detail at what goes on inside the cells of photosynthesizers such as *Anacharis*.

Bringing Solar Energy into Living Systems

The reactions of photosynthesis take place in chloroplasts, small compartments inside certain plant cells. Figure 8.36 shows a plant leaf and its chloroplasts. A system of membrane-bound compartments called the **thylakoids** is found inside the chloroplast. The thylakoids provide a lot of membrane surface area, similar to the folded membranes of a mitochondrion. Surrounding the thylakoids is a colorless fluid known as the **stroma**.

Embedded in the thylakoid membranes are pigment molecules such as **chlorophyll**. Chlorophylls and other pigments give plants their color. These pigments absorb light energy in the visible wavelengths. The absorbed energy causes a flow of electrons (e^-), as shown in figure 8.40. Electrons are removed from water molecules and passed to chlorophyll molecules, then passed to

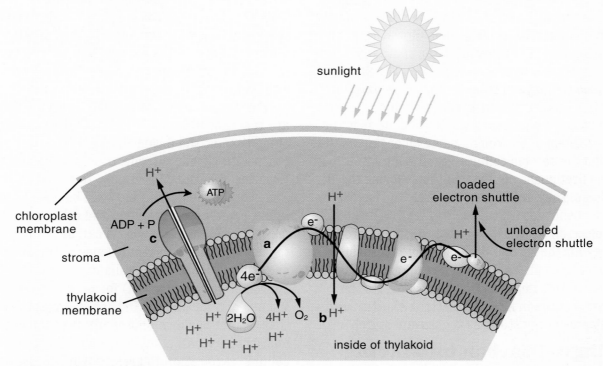

Figure 8.40 **ATP production in the chloroplast during photosynthesis.** (*a*) Absorption of light energy sets up a flow of electrons from water through pigments like chlorophyll and other molecules in the thylakoid membranes. (*b*) Protons accumulate on the inside of the thylakoids. The resulting proton gradient functions much like that in a mitochondrion. The gradient supplies potential energy. (*c*) This energy enables a membrane-spanning enzyme to synthesize ATP from ADP and phosphate.

an electron transport system in the same membrane. Some of the energy from the electrons is used to pump hydrogen ions (H^+) across the thylakoid membranes. The protons accumulate inside the thylakoids and form a concentration gradient. Just as in aerobic cellular respiration, the protons then diffuse down the concentration gradient through an enzyme complex in the membranes. The enzymes synthesize ATP as the protons pass through the complex. In addition to producing ATP, the flow of electrons produces loaded electron shuttles, similar to those formed during cellular respiration.

You might have noticed that chlorophyll loses electrons during photosynthesis. How are they replaced? In fact, new electrons are "stolen" from water. Photosynthesis cannot take place without water. Enzymes in the membrane remove electrons from water molecules. However, when the electrons are removed, water splits into oxygen (O) and hydrogen ions (H^+). The plant releases the oxygen from the water as oxygen gas (O_2). Oxygen is a by-product of photosynthesis. But it is no ordinary waste product. It is the same oxygen upon which nearly all organisms depend for aerobic cellular respiration.

The first phase of photosynthesis forms three products. They are oxygen gas, ATP, and loaded electron shuttles (in the form of NADPH). The ATP and electron shuttles are now available to provide energy for the second phase in photosynthesis. In the second phase, the reactions form carbohydrates. This important process converts the energy trapped in ATP and electron shuttles into long-term energy storage (sugars and starch).

Bringing Carbon into Living Systems

The final reactions of photosynthesis use ATP and loaded electron shuttles from the first phase of photosynthesis. The final phase rearranges atoms from carbon dioxide to form carbohydrates. Think about this fact for a minute. Carbon dioxide, an invisible gas in the air around you, is made into carbohydrates. These carbohydrates can be used to form the other molecules of life that become plant leaves, stems, and roots. Photosynthesis makes the invisible visible.

The process of converting carbon dioxide into carbohydrate molecules is called **carbon fixation**. The reactions incorporate, or *fix*, carbon into carbohydrates. Figure 8.41 is a simplified diagram of those carbohydrate-producing reactions. These reactions take place in the stroma of the chloroplast. First, carbon dioxide from the air enters the plant through the stomata (look back at figure 5.6). The carbon dioxide is added to an existing 5-carbon sugar, which creates a 6-carbon sugar. The 6-carbon sugar quickly splits into two 3-carbon sugars. These 3-carbon sugars have several possible fates.

In a cycle of reactions, these 3-carbon sugars are rearranged into a variety of other sugars. Some become the 5-carbon sugar that first combines with carbon dioxide. Others are exported from the chloroplast and used to form sucrose and starch. The carbon also can be used to form lipids, proteins, chlorophyll, and other molecules the plant cell needs. Sucrose can be transported to provide fuel to distant tissues of the plant such as the roots. Plant cells use sucrose as a source of matter (carbon) for producing new tissues and for energy. In that way, plant cells that cannot perform photosynthesis can obtain energy to live. All plant cells use the process of cellular respiration to break down sucrose and produce ATP. For that reason, plants are said to be producers. They produce their own "food" as well as food for other organisms.

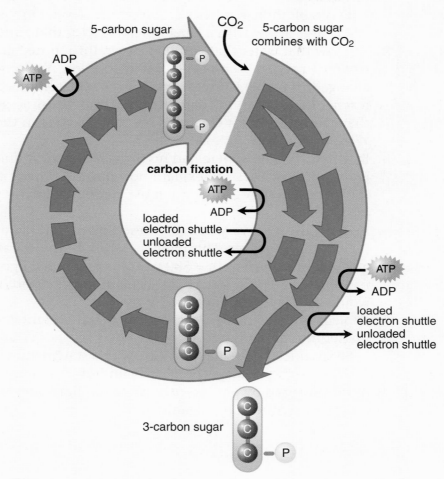

Figure 8.41 Carbon fixation. Carbon fixation takes place in the stroma of chloroplasts. The process uses carbon from carbon dioxide to build carbohydrates. The carbon fixation reactions organize matter and increase the total amount of carbon in the plant. ATP and NADPH provide energy for these reactions. The 3-carbon sugars that are produced can be exported from the chloroplast. Or they can proceed through many steps that regenerate the 5-carbon sugar that combines with carbon dioxide.

Analysis

Topic: photosynthesis
Code: human4E458

Complete the following tasks and questions individually.

1. In part A of the activity, your class varied several factors that influenced the rate of photosynthesis. Draw a basic diagram of the 2 phases of photosynthesis at the cellular level. On your diagram, add a large arrow with a label for each factor that varied in the lab.

2. You saw that water that you had blown into turned green or yellow when you added bromothymol blue solution. You observed the same change (from blue to green or yellow) in the test tube that your teacher had kept in the dark. Do you think the process in your body that caused the color change is the same process in the *Anacharis*? Why or why not?

3. Earth's early atmosphere had no oxygen. Use your understanding of plant photosynthesis to explain how photosynthetic organisms made the evolution of organisms that use aerobic cellular respiration possible.

4. Imagine the discovery of a new desert plant that has a unique pigment in its leaves. This pigment strongly absorbs all sunlight from green light (wavelength = 500 nanometers) to red light (700 nanometers). If you observed this plant in the desert, what color would the leaves appear to be? Why?

5. Explain this statement: Photosynthesis brings light energy and matter into living systems.

   Be specific about what portions of this statement occur during each phase of photosynthesis. Explain how the energy and the matter are used by photosynthesizers and how they are brought into nonphotosynthesizing organisms.

Further Challenges

Explore the diversity of photosynthesizing organisms by reading the sidebar, *Photosynthesis Isn't Just for Plants*. Then use the Web to research the scientist Lynn Margulis and her theory of endosymbiosis. Your research will help you deepen your understanding of the evolution of plants.

ENGLISH SPANISH

Photosynthesis Isn't Just for Plants

Like plants, most algae contain chlorophyll and other pigments and carry out photosynthesis. They may be single-celled or multicellular, or they may form colonies. Algae can be found just about anywhere you find tiny droplets of water: in the air, on tree trunks and branches, in the bottoms of streams, on soil particles, and on rocks at the seashore. Algae are found in diverse environments that include freshwater habitats, the ocean, desert sands, and hot springs. In aquatic environments, algae are the dominant photosynthetic organism. There are many different groups of algae. Although all algae are photosynthetic, not all of them appear green. Examples of algae include green algae, red algae, brown algae, diatoms, and dinoflagellates (figure 8.42).

Green algae are the most widely studied and the most similar to plants. You can find them in your aquarium at home or on the shady side of trees. Many green algae are single-celled and microscopic, but they may be so abundant that they color the

water of ponds and lakes green or form huge floating mats. Some marine species of green algae form large, multicellular seaweeds, such as sea lettuce (*Ulva*) (see figure 8.43).

The major seaweeds of the world are multicellular red and brown algae. The brown algae inhabit rocky shores in cooler regions. Kelps, for example, form extensive offshore beds (figure 8.44). Brown algae appear greenish-brown because they

© iStockphoto

Figure 8.43 **Sea lettuce.** Sea lettuce (*Ulva lactuca*) is a type of multicellular algae found on rocky shores.

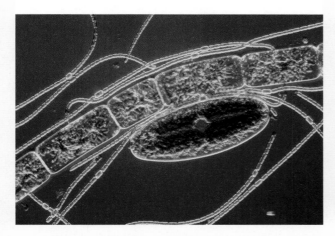

Figure 8.42 **Mixed algae.** How many types of algae can you see?

© iStockphoto/jfybel

Figure 8.44 **Kelp.** Kelp forests provide shelter and protection for many marine organisms.

contain gold and brown pigments as well as chlorophyll. Most seaweeds in warm oceans are red algae. They generally grow attached to rocks or other algae. Because red algae absorb blue light, which penetrates farther into the ocean water than other wavelengths of light, they can grow at greater depths than any other algae.

Diatoms are abundant in both freshwaters and marine waters. They are the primary photosynthetic organism in oceans. Diatoms have glasslike cell walls made of silica. They are some of the most intricately patterned creatures on Earth. Electron microscope studies have shown that the patterns on their cell walls are created by pores that connect the inside of the cell with the outside environment. As shown in figure 8.45, the silica cell walls of diatoms remain intact for many years after the organism has died. Great masses of shells that have slowly accumulated over many years are now mined as diatomaceous earth. That material is used in many ways, for example, as a filter (for swimming pools), as an abrasive in silver polish, and as a brightener for the paint used to mark highways.

Dinoflagellates are found primarily in marine waters. About half of the dinoflagellates are photosynthetic. In mid- to late summer, a surplus of nutrients can cause blooms of photosynthetic dinoflagellates. When dinoflagellates occur in large numbers, the water may appear golden or red, producing a *red tide*. When this happens, marine species may suffer because some species of dinoflagellates produce a neurotoxin, a poison that damages the nervous system. Humans are sometimes affected by red tides after eating fish or shellfish containing neurotoxins.

Some eubacteria are photosynthetic. However, most photosynthetic eubacteria do not produce oxygen as a by-product of photosynthesis. Some examples are purple bacteria, green sulfur bacteria, green nonsulfur bacteria, and heliobacteria. Cyanobacteria are the only group of eubacteria that produce oxygen through photosynthesis.

Purple bacteria are widespread, especially in anaerobic (without oxygen) environments such as sewage treatment ponds (figure 8.46). Green sulfur bacteria are found in the anaerobic zone at the bottoms of

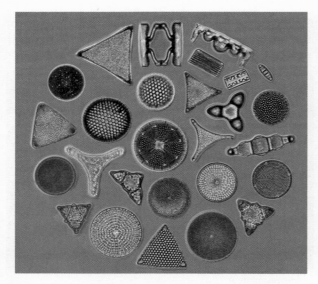

Figure 8.45 Diatoms. Each species of diatom has a characteristic shape. Notice the striking geometric patterns.

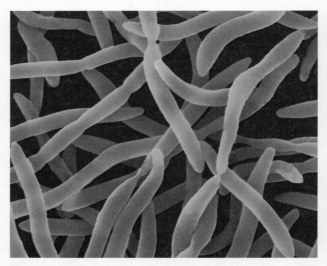

Figure 8.46 Purple bacteria. Most species of purple bacteria are anaerobic. Unlike cyanobacteria, purple bacteria do not produce oxygen as a by-product of photosynthesis.

lakes. Green nonsulfur bacteria are often found in microbial mats with cyanobacteria. Heliobacteria live in soil environments. Cyanobacteria are hardy and are found in almost every environment where light is available. They live in freshwater, marine, and terrestrial environments. They also live in extreme environments such as hot springs and rocks found in Antarctica, as well as scorching deserts.

Building Living Systems

The cells of your body must receive a constant supply of usable energy and matter if you are to grow into an adult. Even after growth has stopped, your body must be able to make new cells to replace damaged or infected ones. The process occurs wherever healing is necessary, such as the site of a skin cut. Cells use small, simple molecules (such as amino acids and simple sugars) to build more-complex biological molecules (such as proteins and glycogen). These molecules are important for the daily activities of all organisms. This building process is called biosynthesis.

At the same time that biosynthesis is taking place, many breakdown activities also are occurring. All organisms break down food and large molecules into the building blocks that their cells need. As you learned in chapter 7, one place this occurs is within the digestive system of our bodies. From the digestive system, the molecules of matter are absorbed into the bloodstream and distributed to different cells (see figure 8.47).

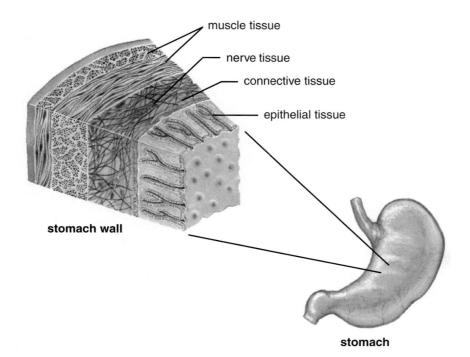

muscle tissue

nerve tissue

connective tissue

epithelial tissue

stomach wall

stomach

Figure 8.47 The stomach is an organ of the digestive system. An *organ* is a group of tissues that are organized together to perform a particular function. The stomach performs both mechanical and chemical breakdown processes during digestion. Where does absorption take place?

As you learned in the last activity, plants, algae, and some bacteria use photosynthesis to produce and store food molecules for later use in biosynthesis. For all other organisms, food molecules can come from a variety sources: bacteria, plants, animals, or fungi. The energy-yielding food molecules can consist of proteins, carbohydrates, or fats. Not surprisingly, the molecules that make up these other organisms are not always the same molecules that your body needs. In this Elaborate activity, *Building Living Systems*, you will deepen your understanding of how organisms take matter from an outside source, convert it into usable energy and matter, and rearrange the molecular structure of that matter to provide building materials for new molecules, cells, and tissues.

Materials

Part B (per person)

descriptions and diagrams of your critter from chapter 5

PROCESS AND PROCEDURES

Part A   Metabolism

1. Consider this question: How do organisms take in matter and energy and use it to build their bodies? Read the following scenario, *Hamburger or Beefburger?*, then answer the question in your science notebook. Incorporate your current understanding of energy, matter, and cellular respiration into your answer.

SCENARIO

ENGLISH　SPANISH

Hamburger or Beefburger?

Your high school women's basketball team won a hard-fought game against a rival team and qualified for the state basketball tournament. To celebrate, you and two friends go to your favorite local restaurant and order the usual burger (figure 8.48), fries, and soft drink. You notice that a new menu is on display. The restaurant is promoting the fact that it has switched to using all locally grown, grass-fed Angus beef. You see that the word "hamburger" was replaced by the word "beefburger." After a

Figure 8.48   Cheeseburger.
Could this food be more accurately named?

brief discussion with your friends, you see the logic of the change. Your burger *is* a beefburger. It is made from the molecules that came from a cow, not a pig. Then your friends start joking around, suggesting other names. "If you're going to get technical, why not call it a 'grassburger'? Or a 'sun-and-air-burger'? After all, aren't these names even more accurate at identifying the origin of the energy and matter in the burger?" The discussion takes off from there. As you finish your meals, you discuss how drastically matter is reorganized from grass, to cow, to burger, to your body.

2. With your partner, list 3 biological processes involving biosynthesis, breakdown, or both that you think your body could carry out using the matter and energy from the beefburger.

3. To deepen your understanding of biosynthesis and breakdown, copy the flowchart in figure 8.49 into your science notebook. Then complete the following tasks while reading the essay, *Metabolism Includes Synthesis and Breakdown*.

   a. Write a definition of metabolism in the center of the flowchart, in your own words.

   b. Incorporate each of the following terms into an oval of the flowchart.
   - Glycolysis
   - Krebs cycle
   - Photosynthesis
   - Glycogenesis
   - Digestion
   - Glycogen
   - Sugars
   - Fats
   - Fatty acids
   - Glycerol
   - Proteins
   - Amino acids

Figure 8.49
Metabolism
flowchart. Use this
flowchart to organize
your thinking about
terms and concepts
related to metabolism.

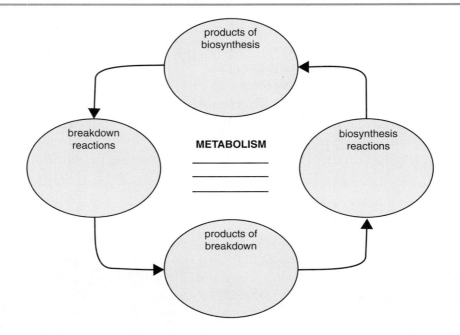

c. Place an asterisk (*) next to any of the *processes* that are not found in *all* organisms. At the bottom of the chart, make a note of what the * means.

d. Add arrows to the flowchart at any place where ATP molecules are generated, where ATP molecules are broken down to provide energy, where light energy is absorbed, and where heat energy is generated.

4. Exchange your flowchart with your partner. Use the TSAR strategy to review his or her work, offer advice, and incorporate your partner's advice into improving your flowchart.

> For more information, see appendix B3, *How to Use the Think-Share-Advise-Revise (TSAR) Strategy.*

HOW TO

Metabolism Includes Synthesis and Breakdown

ENGLISH SPANISH

Have you ever thought about how cities grow? Think about the latest highway expansion project. Lanes are closed; the old surface is torn up and hauled away to be recycled. Only after much time and inconvenience is new asphalt laid to create a wider, more efficient roadway. Similarly, to build a large office building in a densely packed city requires a lot of preparation. Older, smaller buildings first must be torn down and the debris cleared away. In both cases, the raw materials from the outdated structures are broken down and often recycled. Only then can new materials be used to make newer, larger, or more useful structures.

Living systems function in much the same way, except living systems continuously break down and build up molecules (see figure 8.50). Energy links the reactions that are responsible for both processes. For example, when you eat potatoes, your body breaks down potato starch. It breaks down the starch to the small glucose molecules that make up the starch. The glucose then can be broken down further during cellular respiration. This makes energy available in the form of ATP. On the other hand, the glucose can be transported to your liver or muscles and combined with other glucose molecules, in a reaction called **glycogenesis**, to form glycogen. **Glycogen** is a large energy-storage molecule. Your body uses some of the energy that is released during cellular respiration to build, or synthesize, the glycogen.

All the chemical activities and changes that take place in an organism are known as its **metabolism**. Generally, *breakdown reactions* (such as cellular respiration) release energy. *Synthesis reactions* (such as photosynthesis, protein synthesis, and glycogenesis) absorb energy. The ATP produced by the breakdown reactions becomes the source of energy for many cellular activities, such as muscle contraction. ATP provides a critical link between reactions that produce energy and those that require it. Without such links, the energy released from breakdown reactions would be wasted. Without ATP, no energy would be

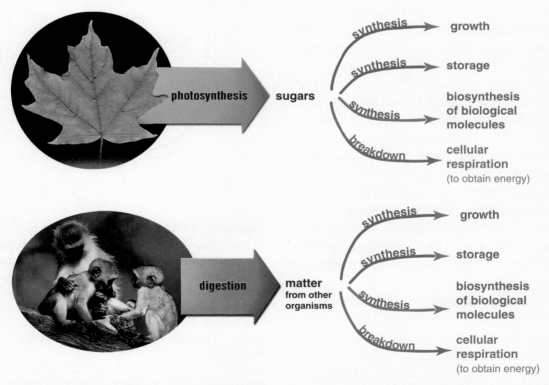

Figure 8.50   Synthesis and breakdown. Both plants and the organisms that consume plants use the sugars made during photosynthesis for biological synthesis and breakdown. These processes are necessary for life. Is photosynthesis a synthesis or a breakdown process? What about digestion?

available for synthesis reactions. Those reactions are necessary for growth, repair, and routine life processes.

The breakdown processes in cells produce a variety of smaller molecules. These molecules can be converted and used in cellular respiration. Although carbohydrates are frequently used as the basis for cellular respiration, other food molecules can be used as well. For example, *fats* can be broken down into *glycerol* and *fatty acids*. Glycerol can be converted into a 3-carbon molecule that can be used in glycolysis. Fatty acids can be converted into 2-carbon molecules that can enter the Krebs cycle. Similarly, *proteins* can be broken down to *amino acids*. After the nitrogen-containing group has been removed from the amino acid, the remaining amino acids can be further broken down to a carbon skeleton. The smaller molecules also can enter glycolysis and the Krebs cycle, as shown in figure 8.51.

Molecules such as glycerol and amino acids are used in synthesis reactions as well (see figure 8.51). Organisms require many types of large molecules for their structures and activities. For example, each chemical reaction that takes place in an organism requires a specific enzyme. The organism synthesizes the enzymes from amino acids. Cell membranes require specific lipids, which must be synthesized as well. Whether a protein, carbohydrate, or fat, each molecule must be synthesized from the matter that the organism takes in.

The tissues of most organisms are made of only a few elements. Vastly different organisms are made of the same four types of molecules of life. The particular molecular arrangements in a given organism, however, are different from all others. That is why the proteins that you consume in your diet, which were made by a different species, cannot be used directly by your body. Instead, the proteins that you consume are

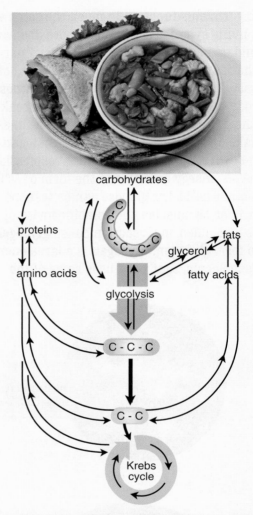

Figure 8.51   Metabolic pathways. Macromolecules in food, such as carbohydrates, fats, and proteins, are broken down to smaller molecules. The smaller molecules can be converted into the intermediates that are formed in glycolysis and the Krebs cycle. The intermediates then can be used in cellular respiration to produce ATP. The same intermediates also are a source of carbon skeletons for the synthesis of macromolecules.

broken down to their component amino acids. Then your cells assemble the amino acids into the specific proteins that your body requires.

Synthesizing new proteins is the body's most efficient use of amino acids. During starvation or anorexia nervosa, however, the body's cells turn to proteins for energy. The human body does this in an effort to maintain homeostasis. Unfortunately, when this happens, the muscles of the body are consumed as fuel. Although the breakdown of proteins is a last resort, it indicates how flexible cells can be in their metabolism.

Part B Energy and Matter for Your Critter

How does your critter use matter and energy to build its body and carry out activities? Respond with an explanation, diagram, model, or demonstration of your choice. You will know that you have adequately addressed the preceding question if your response meets the following criteria:

- It indicates the critter's source of energy and matter and how these are obtained from its surroundings.
- It demonstrates how energy is stored and made available for the critter's activities.
- It distinguishes the macromolecules that your critter can synthesize from those that it must obtain from its external environment (through diet or other means).
- It uses specific examples from your work in chapter 7 and this chapter as evidence of what you have learned.
- It meets all of the criteria in the *Energy and Matter for Your Critter Rubric*.

Tracing Matter and Energy

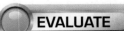

Biologists can investigate the steps in metabolic processes (synthesis and breakdown) by feeding extremely small (or trace) amounts of radioactively labeled matter to laboratory organisms. The labeled matter undergoes changes in molecular structure during chemical reactions within the organism that consumed it. But the label remains detectable. The labeled matter continues to be traceable through transfers between the organisms. As these changes and transfers occur, the scientists can collect samples. In this way, they can trace the course of events by following the radioactivity (figure 8.52).

In this Evaluate activity, *Tracing Matter and Energy*, you will trace the path of an imaginary, radioactively labeled *carbon atom* through the various molecules in which it is organized (figure 8.53). The atom begins its journey as part of a carbon dioxide molecule. It ends up as part of a muscle protein in a human arm. Your task is to use the knowledge that you gained in this chapter to draw a diagram of what happens to the atom during its journey. Then you will explain the source of energy for these events.

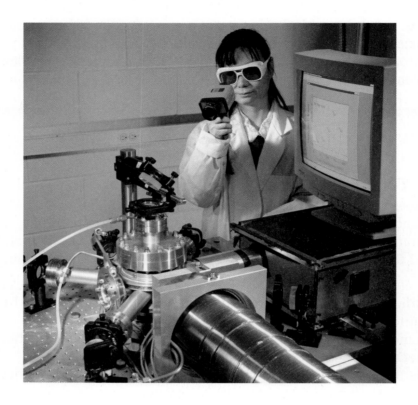

Figure 8.52 This scientist is working with radioactivity.

Figure 8.53 You will trace the path of an imaginary, radioactively labeled carbon atom. The atom begins its journey as part of an atmospheric carbon dioxide molecule (shown here). It ends up as part of a muscle protein in a human arm.

Materials (per person)

materials needed to complete your project, such as poster board and markers

PROCESS AND PROCEDURES

1. Construct a diagram or other visual aid to show a plausible set of events that could explain how a labeled carbon atom in a molecule of atmospheric carbon dioxide ends up in a human muscle protein.

   There is more than one possible scenario. But you must show a sequence that actually occurs in nature. You must be able to justify and explain the sequence that you choose.

2. Label your diagram so that it explains the sequence of events that you have illustrated. Clearly state the following.
   a. The type of metabolic process in each step (breakdown or biosynthesis)
   b. The energy source for each step
   c. The matter source for each step
   d. The names of the metabolic processes that occur in the sequence

Analysis

1. Participate in a class discussion of the questions that your teacher raises.
2. After participating in the discussion, add any appropriate changes to the steps in your diagram.

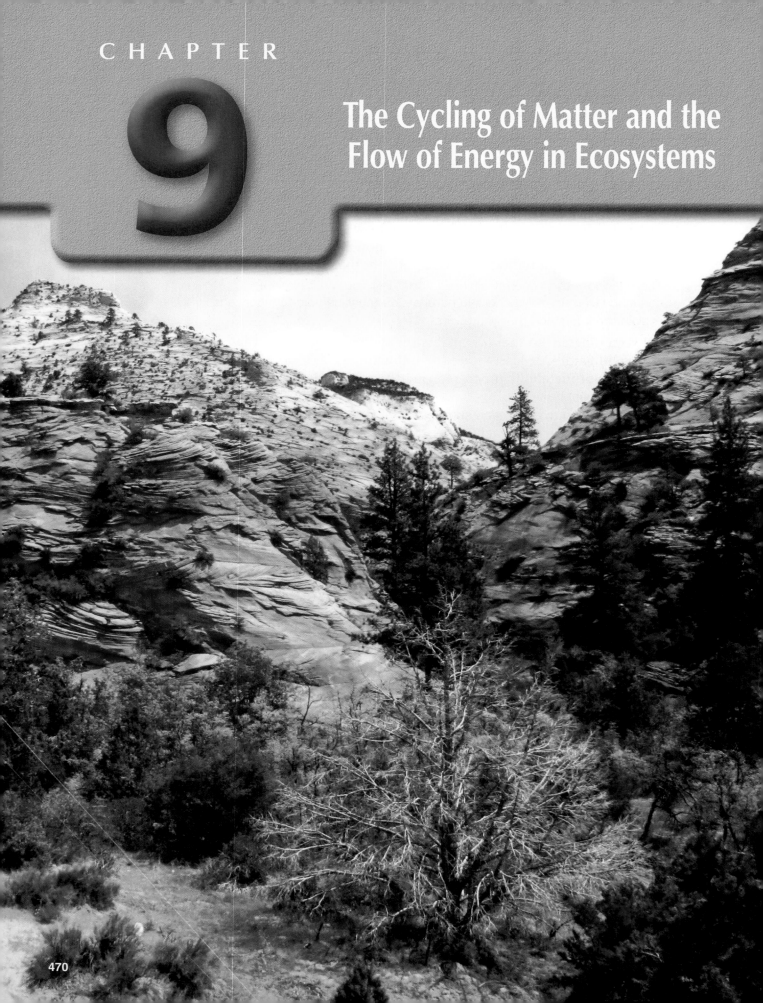

Climb the mountains and get their good tidings. Nature's peace will flow into you as sunshine flows into trees. The winds will blow their own freshness into you, and the storms their energy, while cares will drop off like autumn leaves.

John Muir

Think about your school community. Picture the organization and interaction of people, books, paper, furniture, and food. People move through the hallways in repeated patterns throughout the day. Books and papers are moved from lockers, to class, and back to lockers. Desks are rearranged to accommodate various activities and events. Food is moved from the kitchen, to lunch trays, to hungry students.

These things move through the organized community of your school. In much the same way, energy and matter move through organized communities of living organisms. In biology, we speak of a **community** as the group of living organisms that inhabit a specific area and interact with one another. An **ecosystem** is a community of organisms and the nonliving part of the environment. Consider a bird living in the sandstone rocks in this photograph. Now think about the insects it feeds on. Think about the trees and the many other organisms that inhabit this area. Together these organisms make up a community. Matter and energy move through these organisms and the environment in different ways. In chapter 9, *The Cycling of Matter and the Flow of Energy in Ecosystems,* you will use your experiences from a variety of activities and related essays to develop an understanding of how matter and energy move through ecosystems.

GOALS FOR THE CHAPTER

Throughout chapter 9, you will work to gain an understanding of the following concepts:

✔ The atoms that make up matter cycle repeatedly in ecosystems.

✔ As energy flows through biological communities, it eventually becomes unavailable for use by biological systems.

✔ We can investigate ecosystems by using models and controlled experiments.

To help you develop these understandings, you will complete the following activities.

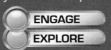 **ENGAGE** **EXPLORE**   A Matter of Trash

 **EXPLORE**   Matter Goes Round and Round

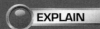 **EXPLAIN**   Spinning the Web of Life

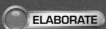 **ELABORATE**   Generating Some Heat

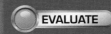 **EVALUATE**   Energy, Matter, and Disaster

Throughout chapter 9, remember to refer to the chapter organizers to help you remember what you have learned and where you are headed.

ENGAGE   EXPLORE

A Matter of Trash

Key Idea: Waste material contains matter and energy, and waste is generated by every community.

Linking Question:
Is it possible to observe or measure the cycling of matter in an ecosystem?

Chapter 9

MAJOR CONCEPTS

✔ The atoms that make up matter cycle repeatedly in ecosystems.

✔ As energy flows through biological communities, it eventually becomes unavailable for use by biological systems.

✔ We can investigate ecosystems by using models and controlled experiments.

 EXPLORE

Matter Goes Round and Round

Part A: Reflections on the Earthworm Habitats

Part B: Snails and Anacharis: What Can I Learn from Them?

Key Idea: The atoms that make up matter cycle repeatedly between the abiotic and the biotic components of an ecosystem.

Linking Question:
How do matter and energy move through an ecosystem that contains many different organisms?

 EXPLAIN

Spinning the Web of Life

Key Idea: Matter cycles, and energy flows, between organisms interacting in an ecosystem.

Energy, Matter, and Disaster

Key Idea: Disruptions to the movement of energy and matter can affect every organism in a community.

The Cycling of Matter and the Flow of Energy in Ecosystems

Linking Question:
What happens when the flow of energy and the cycling of matter are disrupted?

 ELABORATE

Generating Some Heat

Key Idea: Decomposers play an important role in the cycling of matter in an ecosystem.

Linking Question:
When an organism dies, what happens to its matter and energy?

ENGAGE

EXPLORE

A Matter of Trash

What are your chores around your home? Do you wash dishes, mow the lawn, feed pets, babysit for a younger brother or sister, or take out the trash? Think about the last time you took out the trash (figure 9.1). Did you look at what you were about to throw away? Where did the trash go after you put it out on the curb or tossed it into a trash container? What happened to the matter in the material you just discarded? Was much energy stored in that matter? Where did that energy go? Throughout this Engage-Explore activity, *A Matter of Trash*, think about the various forms of matter that you consider waste and what happens to this matter after you throw it out.

Figure 9.1 Trash. Where will the matter and energy in this trash end up?

PROCESS AND PROCEDURES

1. Examine the discarded items in the trash demonstration that your teacher presents. Create a table or other visual diagram that includes the following information.
   a. A list of the trash in the demonstration
   b. A list of the trash's origin (for example, newspaper originates from trees, wood, and pulp)
   c. An indication of which trash items match your household trash (write "yes" or "no")
   d. A list of at least 2 possible fates for each trash item (for example, it ends up in a landfill or a recycling plant (figure 9.2), becomes food for another animal, or is reused)

Figure 9.2 When plastics and paper are recycled, what becomes of the matter they are made from? What is the source of heat in a compost heap?

© Dreamstime/Joan Ramon Mendo Escoda

2. In your science notebook, write your best answer to the following question: Do you think that molecules in this trash contain potential energy? Describe evidence you could collect to back up your claim.
3. In your science notebook, write a short description of what you think might happen to the matter and the energy in 3 of the pieces of trash you listed, after each is thrown out.

Analysis

Working individually, answer these questions in your science notebook. Be prepared to share your responses in a class discussion. You can read the sidebar, *Garbage Among Us—from Then Until Now!*, to learn additional information about how matter moves through different communities.

1. In what ways might elements in the waste matter of one organism be useful to another organism? Give examples to support your answer.

   It might help to think of examples of matter that you interact with on a daily basis. Could an atom of carbon in you become an atom of carbon in a different organism? What might happen to the atoms of an apple core if you discard it in the woods?

2. How does your answer to question 1 support the idea that organisms in communities depend on one another for matter and energy?
3. Think about how matter may be recycled by organisms in the following 3 communities. How do these communities differ in the types of matter they interact with? Does matter take different lengths of time to be recycled in these different communities?
   a. A community of soil bacteria and fungi on a forest floor
   b. An isolated village of humans in the Amazon rain forest
   c. A neighborhood of humans in New York City
4. Write about ideas you have in reaction to this question: Do modern human societies have problems related to the kinds of matter they use or to how long it takes matter to be recycled within their communities?

Further Challenges

On a separate piece of paper, write 10–15 things you have thrown away in the past week. Exchange lists with your partner. Write 4 or 5 things that you might infer about your partner from his or her trash. Use information from the sidebar, *Garbage Among Us—from Then Until Now!*, to help you with your answer. Support your inferences.

Garbage Among Us—from Then Until Now!

Matter—lots of it. Wood. Paper. Glass. Metals. Plastics. Rubber. Cloth. Food. Yard waste. All of these types of matter end up in our landfills. In fact, did you know the following?

- In the United States, each person throws away an average of 1,645 lbs of garbage each year. This is more than any other nation in the world.

- In 2006, Americans recycled about 30 percent of the waste they generated (251 million tons). This is up from only 6 percent in the 1960s. However, the total amount of waste generated by each person has also doubled over this time.

- A convoy of garbage trucks long enough to encircle Earth six times would be required to carry all the municipal waste generated in the United States in one year.

- More than half of the states in the United States are having problems finding places to dump trash. Sometimes trash travels great distances before it is dumped (figure 9.3).

- Lettuce buried in a landfill may take more than seven years to decompose completely.

- A hot dog can last more than 10 years in a landfill.

- A steak buried in a landfill can retain its fat 15 years after burial.

- In spite of recycling efforts, waste paper is still a major component of landfills nationwide. It makes up about 15 percent of the waste in landfills.

You throw away things every day. But did you ever wonder what people could tell about you if they sorted through your trash? Garbage and waste can tell us quite a bit about how organisms acquire and use the matter and energy in their community. Let's consider a few different communities and reflect on the cycling of matter through them. How is this process similar and different in these communities? How does matter move from one organism to another? How much and what type of waste does each community produce? What happens to the waste in each community?

Figure 9.3 These barges are loaded with waste material that will travel to a final dumping ground.

Bats in Mammoth Cave National Park, Kentucky

Two bats flit about in the sky at twilight, barely visible in the last light of evening. They dart about, catching insects. One bat descends briefly, flying just above the surface of a pond to take a drink. Another nips a moth in midair. Soon, the bats dart into the entrance of a cave that is partially hidden by evergreens (see figure 9.4).

Several fleas, ticks, and mites have latched onto the bats' coats during the evening. As the bats sit on a cave ledge, resting and cleaning themselves, some of the insects fall to the cave floor. They become food for the organisms that dwell there. During the night, many bats excrete their wastes—a substance called "guano." Guano is not solid like human feces, but rather thick and mudlike. It covers the floor of the cave like carpeting. Bacteria, fungi, and other single-celled organisms grow on the guano and use it for food—their source of energy. In turn, many of these small organisms are destined to become the food for insects, and some of these insects may become the food for bats.

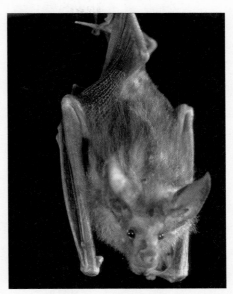

Figure 9.4 Brown bats live in caves throughout Mammoth Cave National Park, Kentucky.

The Earliest Ancestral Puebloans

The year is CE 950. As a hint of daylight appears in the east, a young Ancestral Puebloan woman awakens and checks on her two young children still asleep beside her in their cliff dwelling (figure 9.5). They live along a basin in the high-plateau region of the American Southwest. As the woman rises and starts a fire, her mate begins to stir. She retrieves some kernels of corn and begins to grind them into a coarse meal. It is late spring, and the couple hopes to finish planting the corn today. They want to work in the morning before the day becomes hot. To plant, they use a stick to make holes in the ground, drop kernels of corn into each hole, and then cover them with soil.

Figure 9.5 Cliff dwellings. The Ancestral Puebloans lived in cliff dwellings. These structures can be found throughout the Four Corners region of the American Southwest.

© Dreamstime/Zack Frank

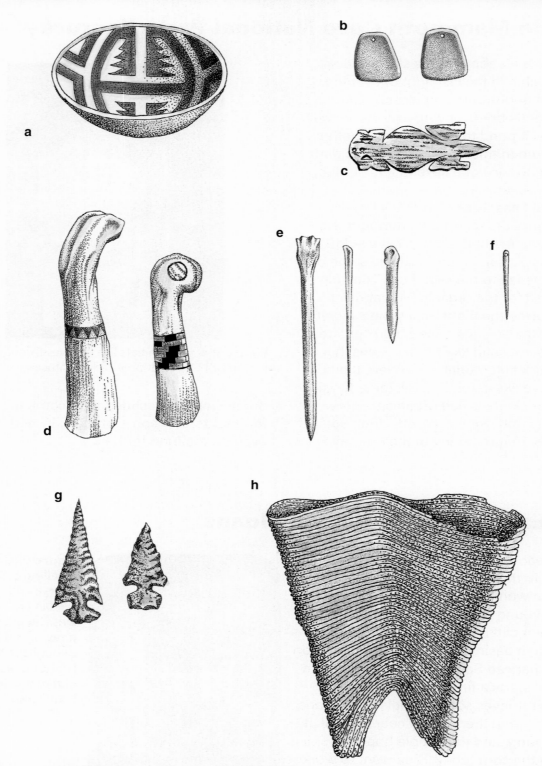

Figure 9.6 Artifacts from Pueblo Bonito. Archaeologists found these artifacts and more at the Pueblo Bonito site in the Chaco River Valley: (*a*) black-on-white bowl, 7 cm high; (*b*) turquoise pendants, 2.5 cm high; (*c*) shell ornament, 5 cm long; (*d*) bone scrapers, 16.5 and 12.7 cm long; (*e*) bone awls, 11.4–19.7 cm long; (*f*) bone needle, 7 cm long; (*g*) projectile points, 5 and 3.75 cm long; (*h*) basket, 39.4 cm high. They are dated at about CE 950–1000.

Later, the woman and her children join other women and children to gather yucca from the plateau. The Ancestral Puebloan families will not only eat the fruit and seeds of the yucca, but they will use the roots for soap and shampoo. They will use the strong, sturdy fibers from the leaves for making intricate baskets, sandals, aprons, mats, and cradle boards (figure 9.6). Small pieces of the yucca and other plant material are discarded in a pile along with corn husks and cobs, worn-out mats, and broken tools made out of bone.

Some mornings, the woman's mate joins other men in the community to hunt for rabbit and deer. In addition to preparing and eating the meat, the Ancestral Puebloans make clothing for the winter months from the rabbit pelts, and they make tools and utensils such as needles from the bones. Unused bones are discarded in the small but growing pile of waste. At the bottom of this pile, the organic material has decayed enough so that it is almost indistinguishable from the soil beneath it.

Family in Maineville, Ohio

A single mother looks in on her eight-year-old daughter, Sonya, who has the flu. Sonya has a big box of tissues beside her bed and a pile of used ones in the wastebasket nearby. She also has finished one carton of juice and has begun another. One of the family's three cats is resting at the foot of the bed. (Someone needs to clean the litter box today.)

This family lives in a three-bedroom, two-bathroom house at the end of a quiet street in a small community north of a major city. Sonya has a 15-year-old brother, Matt, who is keeping his distance because he doesn't want to get sick. He has a huge history report due Monday. He works away at the computer most of the afternoon and prints the entire report four times before he is satisfied. He places the rejected copies in the recycle bin in the kitchen.

The mother is an architect and has been working at home all day on a balsa-wood model of a hospital addition. (Scrap wood seems to be everywhere.) In the evening on the way home from the grocery store (with 10 bags of groceries), the mother stops at a fast-food restaurant and picks up some chicken dinners, which everyone enjoys—even Sonya, who is beginning to feel better. As Matt tosses the last dinner carton into the garbage, he notices that it's full again. Whose week is it to take out the garbage, anyway?

Matter Goes Round and Round

Have you ever watched ants in an ant farm? They always appear to be busy modifying their environment in some way. In this Explore activity, *Matter Goes Round and Round*, you will complete the observations of the earthworm habitats that you set up some weeks ago. Think about what your observations tell you about how these organisms interact with their environment. You also will reflect on your experiment's design. You will use this understanding to design another experiment to explore how other organisms interact with one another and with their environment.

Materials (per team of 4)

Part A

6 slides	2 paper towels
stereomicroscope	2 spoons
hand lens	small tray
earthworm habitats	metric ruler
control habitats	balance (optional)

Part B

250-mL flask	petri dish halves (optional; if pH paper is used)
4 25 × 200-mm test tubes	2.5-mL of bromothymol blue (optional)
test-tube rack	distilled water
thermistor or thermometer	1- to 1.5-cm freshwater snails
2 pH probes or pH strips sensitive to pH 1–12 and pH strips sensitive to narrower ranges	15-cm sprigs of *Anacharis* (elodea)
jar of tap water for storing pH probes (optional; if using probe ware)	light source
	aluminum foil
	graph paper
1-mL pipet (optional)	different-colored pens or pencils

PROCESS AND PROCEDURES

Part A   Reflections on the Earthworm Habitats

1. With your teammates, look at the earthworm habitats that you set up several weeks ago (figure 9.7). In your science notebook, record new observations and review the observations you made previously.

    Remember that the purpose of these habitats is to provide evidence of interactions between living systems and the physical environment, as well as evidence about the nature of these interactions.

Figure 9.7   In what ways do you think earthworms interact with their environment?

2. Discuss the following with your teammates. Record your ideas in your science notebook.

   a. What evidence did you collect that supports the idea that earthworms interact with and change their environment?

   b. Describe this interaction. What do you think happened in the earthworm habitats?

   c. What was the specific purpose of the control containers in helping you identify and describe the interaction of earthworms and their environment?

   > Compare the containers that had earthworms with each other. (One contained soil and organic matter, and one contained only soil.) Why was it important to observe both types of containers? What did your comparisons tell you about the interactions of earthworms with their environment?

3. Draw a diagram in your science notebook that shows different components of an earthworm habitat. Add a plant and some microorganisms to the diagram. Then, as you read the essay, *Worms, Insects, Bacteria, and Fungi—Who Needs Them?*, draw arrows to indicate how you think the atoms in a piece of banana might move through the different components of the habitat.

   > Check that your teammates understand the concepts in the essay and how the concepts relate to your findings.

Worms, Insects, Bacteria, and Fungi—Who Needs Them?

ENGLISH SPANISH

Did you know that approximately 100 million bacteria can live in a single gram of fertile soil (figure 9.8)? Did you also know that some 250,000 earthworms can live in a 1.25-acre field of rich topsoil?

This is one reason why earthworms are considered a farmer's best friend. Earthworms are organisms that decompose decaying organic matter. They can work through 10 tons of topsoil a year, aerating it and increasing its fertility.

The quality of the topsoil is important because topsoil serves as one important link between the living, or **biotic**, world, and the nonliving, or **abiotic**, world. Abiotic matter enters the living world when

Figure 9.8 A gram of soil contains a surprising number and diversity of bacteria.

molecules and elements such as carbon dioxide, nitrogen, and phosphorus are absorbed by plants. These molecules and elements are returned to the nonliving world when they are excreted by plants, animals, fungi, or microorganisms as waste, and when organisms die. The waste ends up in the topsoil or in the atmosphere. In the soil, the molecules are broken down to simple molecules or atoms by the soil's inhabitants. At this point, the cycle can begin again as plants reuse these molecules.

Earthworms play a vital role in keeping the nutrient levels in the soil high because they consume partially decomposed organic matter such as dead leaves and roots. They then excrete nutrient-rich waste. This mixes with the soil. Other organisms that perform a similar function in the soil are insects, bacteria, and fungi. In fact, bacteria perform most of

the decomposition in soils. Together these organisms help return vital elements, such as phosphorus, calcium, and nitrogen, to the environment, where other organisms can use them. Thus, each atom can cycle through a community of organisms multiple times.

Recyclable elements are important to the health of all communities, and they emphasize the role of organisms that decompose organic matter. This role is particularly apparent in the tropics. There, the layer of topsoil is thin, the temperature is high, days are long throughout the year, and rain is frequent. Under such conditions, organic matter is produced rapidly, and it also decomposes rapidly. Those nutrients that are not returned quickly to the living part of the ecosystem flow away in groundwater and are lost to the local community of organisms. Figure 9.9 illustrates this situation in a tropical rain forest. The

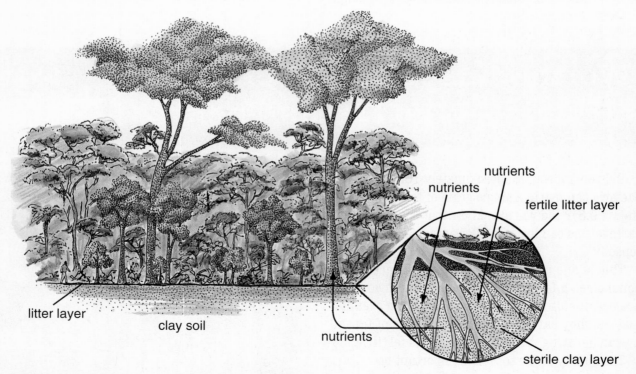

Figure 9.9   Tropical rain forest. In a tropical rain forest, most of the nutrients are held in the tissues of living organisms. As a result, the thin, nutrient-poor topsoils of tropical rain forests experience rapid recycling of any matter, including fallen fruits and leaves, that reaches the forest floor. What might happen to the nutrient levels of rain forest ecosystems if the number of living organisms were greatly reduced?

community appears extremely lush because most of the nutrients are held almost continuously in living material. The matter recycles rapidly between organisms, the atmosphere, and the soil. The critical location for this rapid recycling is the relatively thin layer of dead plant material that forms the topsoil on the forest floor. In the constant heat and moisture of the tropics, the insects and microorganisms in this layer quickly break down much of the fallen leaves and other dead organic matter. The nutrients they release into the groundwater then move downward toward the sterile clay, beneath where the rich network of tree roots quickly reabsorbs them. The nutrients move up through the trees' roots, trunks, and branches to their leaves. It is here that the nutrients from the soil are incorporated into living matter through a variety of biosynthesis reactions. Simultaneously, carbon dioxide from the air is incorporated into living matter through photosynthesis.

In environments with cooler conditions, decomposition is much slower and virtually stops in the winter. In these environments, dead organic material can remain in the topsoil much longer without having nutrients transported away to other communities by rain or flooding. Though slower, these processes of recycling eventually return the nutrients in fallen leaves and other dead organic matter to the plants.

4. Discuss the following question with your partner: Does the diagram you drew in step 3 point to evidence that some matter could *cycle* (move through a series of events that returns to the starting point) through an ecosystem containing soil, organic matter, earthworms, microorganisms, and plants? Write down your ideas in your science notebook.

Part B Snails and Anacharis: What Can I Learn from Them?

In this part of the activity, you will have the opportunity to devise an experiment aimed at collecting evidence for the cyclical movement of carbon in a model aquatic ecosystem. Your model ecosystem will contain snails and a plant, *Anacharis*. But first, you will need to find out about the cycles of several different atoms and molecules in ecosystems.

1. Read the following information and answer the questions in your science notebook, using information from the essay, *Endless Cycles of Matter*.

    At this moment, your body may be breaking down amino acids to fuel the body for daily activities, such as doing your homework. One by-product of this process is that molecules of ammonia (which are toxic) form. Your body is using biosynthesis reactions to convert the ammonia to urea molecules in your liver.

    Focus on the atoms of nitrogen in the urea (figure 9.10). How did this nitrogen enter your body? Once the urea molecule is excreted in your urine, where are the nitrogen atoms likely to go?

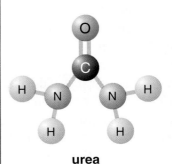

urea

Figure 9.10 A ball-and-stick model of a urea molecule.

Endless Cycles of Matter

ENGLISH SPANISH

Imagine a riverbed ecosystem. In such an ecosystem, matter is always on the move from one place to another. Water runs through it. Nutrients move from the soil into plants rooted along the river. Beavers gnaw through branches and twigs and use them to build their dams (figure 9.11). Matter is also moving between organisms. A great blue heron nabs an unsuspecting fish from the river. When the types and amounts of matter in such an ecosystem remain essentially the same across time, the ecosystem remains in balance. When the types or amounts of matter in an ecosystem change, the ecosystem is forced to change as well.

Let's look more closely at the biotic and abiotic components of the riverbed ecosystem. Within this ecosystem, matter cycles continuously between the biotic and the abiotic components. Beavers are part of the biotic matter along this riverbed. In the spring, two to four young beavers are born to each female beaver. As the young beavers grow and become more self-sufficient, the local beaver community can withstand the temporary increase in its population. A few of last year's young may remain, replacing the beavers that die or disperse. But many of last year's young will move out of the community to establish other dams. The total population of beavers in this area will remain relatively stable. If the number of beavers in this area increased significantly, it would stress the available resources. These resources include the food supply and the sites for building dams. Eventually, the resources might become so depleted that the environment would be unable to support any beavers. They then would die off or move elsewhere. Such a scenario would cause the community to change.

Not only does matter move through an ecosystem, but some of it makes a complete cycle within it. For example, when beavers die along the river, their bodies gradually decay. The nutrients derived from their bodies eventually mix with the soil. Plants then acquire some

© Dreamstime/Richard Gunion

Figure 9.11 A beaver busy at work. What effect might this beaver have on the movement of matter in its ecosystem?

of these nutrients from the soil. In turn, various animals (including beavers) feed on these plants. In this way, nutrients that once were part of an animal can cycle through various types of matter and be taken up by another animal.

Water is an example of abiotic matter that moves through and cycles within an ecosystem. Water is constantly moving through the river shown in figure 9.12. The water flowing through the river at a certain spot today is different from the water that flowed through this same spot yesterday. Water also is part of a cycle. Some is added to the river by rain or snow and from tributaries and groundwater reserves in the plateau. Some water leaves the river through evaporation. Much water also leaves as plants photosynthesize, through a process called transpiration.

If the net inflow of water is the same as the net outflow, the river remains essentially the same. A major increase in the water flow could cause the banks to flood, destroying many plants along the riverbed. A prolonged increase in the amount of water, however, may change the kinds of plants and animals that can live in the community. Similarly, a short-term decrease in the water

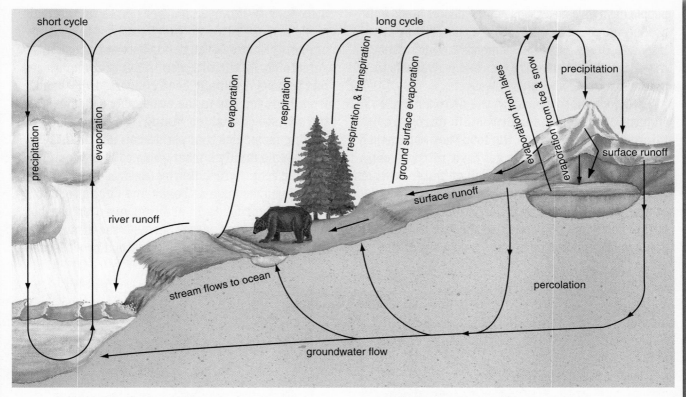

short cycle

long cycle

precipitation

evaporation

evaporation

respiration

respiration & transpiration

ground surface evaporation

evaporation from lakes

evaporation from ice & snow

precipitation

surface runoff

surface runoff

river runoff

stream flows to ocean

percolation

groundwater flow

Figure 9.12   The water cycle. The water cycle collects and redistributes Earth's water supply.

flow may cause certain plants and animals to die as competition for water increased. Again, if such a change were sustained, the makeup of the community would change as well.

These same principles of the movement and the cycling of matter apply to the many other, less obvious components that make up the riverbed ecosystem. Consider, for example, a single atom of carbon. If you could follow a single atom of carbon in the riverbed ecosystem through time, you would see it cycle through many different molecules. At one point, it may form part of a protein molecule in a floating leaf of duckweed. At another time, it may become one of the atoms within a DNA molecule in the genetic material of a fish or a frog that ate the duckweed. At still another point, the carbon atom may remain for a long period within dead plant or

animal material in the mud of the river until it is finally used by a bacterium or a fungus and rejoins the biotic community. Figure 9.13 illustrates some of these interactions and relationships in the carbon cycle. Again, when the total number of carbon atoms in an ecosystem remains approximately the same along with the proportion of carbon atoms to other atoms, the ecosystem remains essentially stable. When the number or proportion of carbon atoms changes significantly, the community changes.

Other cycles of matter in ecosystems depend on the existing environmental conditions. Essential elements, such as calcium, potassium, nitrogen, and phosphorus, are available to the biological community only after they dissolve in the groundwater and are taken up by the roots of plants. Through experience,

people have discovered that many desert lands will produce large crops, at least for a time, if they are irrigated. Often, essential elements are abundant in these soils, but they are not readily available to plants due to the shortage of water.

Let's look more closely at the nitrogen cycle (figure 9.14). All consumers obtain nitrogen-containing compounds from the food they eat (mostly from proteins). Producers get their nitrogen-containing compounds from the soil or water in which they grow. The lack of nitrogen limits the growth of many plants in many different ecosystems. This seems odd when you consider the fact that nitrogen gas (N_2) makes up about 78 percent of the

atmosphere. However, neither plants nor animals alone can use nitrogen gas directly. It takes a lot of energy to break the bonds between these nitrogen atoms. All the nitrogen in living communities had to have originally been converted, or "fixed," from nitrogen gas in the atmosphere. Bacteria in the soil are crucial for "fixing" the nitrogen-containing molecules that plants can use. Plants in the legume family harbor some of these bacteria in their roots, which is why farmers frequently plant legumes such as beans and alfalfa to help fertilize their fields. In addition, nitrogen can be fixed as lightning passes through the atmosphere, and through some human industrial processes.

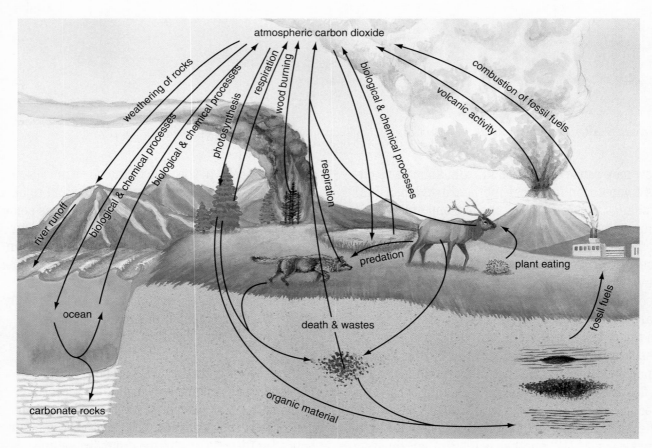

Figure 9.13 The carbon cycle. In a stable ecosystem, the total number of carbon atoms will remain approximately the same.

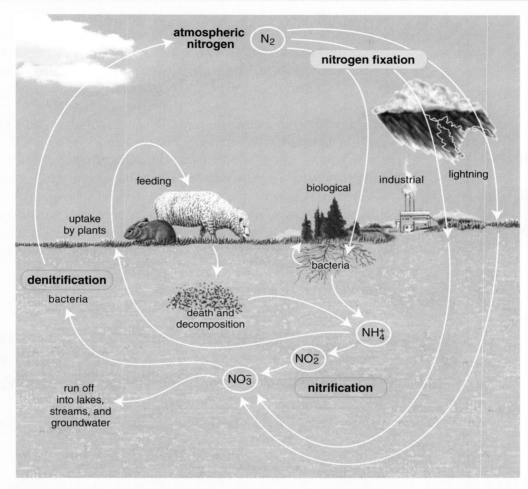

Figure 9.14 The nitrogen cycle. Think about the nitrogen in your body. At some point in the past, it was part of the atmosphere. How did it enter your body?

Consider another issue that is related to the cycling of matter. Various organisms in a community often cannot efficiently metabolize foreign compounds such as pesticides. As a result, foreign compounds may accumulate at toxic levels in the tissues of some organisms. They also may build up in the environment and persist there for long periods of time before they are returned to the cycle.

Taken as a whole, when a community is stable within an ecosystem such as the riverbed, the community exhibits a type of large-scale dynamic balance that resembles the homeostasis of individual organisms. The same is true in other communities such as those found in a desert, a temperate pond, a pine forest, or the arctic tundra. On a larger scale, the same also is true for the entire biosphere. The biosphere includes all the organisms as well as the soil, water, and air that surround and support them. As the environment changes, communities may change as well. Homeostasis continues around a balance point, but that point of balance can change through time.

2. With your team, carry out the following tasks to develop your experiment.

a. Briefly summarize what you have learned about how carbon cycles in an ecosystem, via the processes of photosynthesis and cellular respiration.

b. In your science notebook, draw a diagram of a closed system containing snails and *Anacharis* (figure 9.15). Use arrows to show the movement of carbon in this system. Use the information in the need to know, *Observing the Carbon Cycle in a Closed System,* to help you with this task.

c. Discuss with your team the materials available for you to use in your experiment, as well as the *Protocol for Monitoring pH in a Closed System.* Make additions to the diagram you drew in step 2b to capture ideas of how you might use your materials in an experimental setup.

d. With your team, generate and choose a testable question and a hypothesis about the cyclical movement of carbon in an aquatic ecosystem. Record your team's question and hypothesis in your science notebook.

You must be able to test the question using the materials available.

PROTOCOL

Figure 9.15 Snails and *Anacharis*. How do these organisms interact to cycle matter in their environment?

NEED TO KNOW

ENGLISH   SPANISH

Observing the Carbon Cycle in a Closed System

Plants and animals interact in a variety of ways. To limit the interactions that are possible in an experiment, you can conduct a study in a closed system. A **closed system** exchanges energy with its environment, but matter cannot move in or out of it. For example, by setting up a closed system with an aquatic plant and an aquatic animal, you can study a portion of the carbon cycle. The **carbon cycle** is one of the chemical cycles in which matter moves from the environment to organisms and back to the environment in different chemical forms.

Recall from chapter 8, *The Cellular Basis of Activity,* that carbon dioxide dissolves in water and forms a weak acid, which lowers the water's pH. A decrease in pH indicates an increase in the concentration of carbon dioxide in your experimental system. Conversely, an increase in pH indicates a decrease in the concentration of carbon dioxide.

e. Design an experiment to test your question. Outline your experiment in your science notebook. Your design should include the following features.

- Use of snails and sprigs of *Anacharis*
- Use of appropriate controls
- Use of the *Protocol for Monitoring pH in a Closed System*
- Collection of data every 5 minutes, for at least 2 hours
- Inclusion of a plan for recording and graphing data

As you consider different designs, you may want to review the design of the earthworm habitats. Apply your understanding of that design to the one you develop here. Also, consider the experiment that you designed to investigate factors that influenced the rate of photosynthesis in the chapter 8 Explain-Elaborate activity, *Using Light Energy to Build Matter*. You may use a similar experimental procedure.

f. Have your teacher approve your design.

PROTOCOL

Protocol for Monitoring pH in a Closed System

1. Put 125 mL of distilled water in a 250-mL flask.

   You may wish to add 2.5 mL of bromothymol blue to the water as an additional pH indicator.

CAUTION: Avoid getting bromothymol blue in mouth or eyes, or on skin.

2. Use a pH probe or pH test strips to test the initial pH of the water. Record this starting pH.
3. Add water and organisms to your control and experimental test tubes. Handle organisms safely, according to your teacher's directions.
4. Perform the following steps to set up your test tubes to collect pH data.
   a. If you are using pH probes, calibrate them to a pH 4–11 range. Choose appropriate settings to collect data using 2 probes. Save your data and graph your results.
   b. If you are using pH probes, carefully position them in each test tube so that they do not interfere with your closed system.
   c. Adjust the pH probe (if used) and thermistor or thermometer (if used). Secure them in place by crimping a small piece of aluminum foil around the top of the test tubes.

   The aluminum foil also can serve to stop the exchange of matter between your closed system and its environment.

      d. If you will be using pH paper, set up your test tube with enough room to slide a pipet into the test tube and withdraw a water sample.

5. Set your test-tube rack next to a light source, as agreed upon by the class or directed by your teacher.
6. Use a pH probe or pH test strips to test the initial pH of the water. Record this starting pH.
7. Take pH and temperature readings for at least 2 hours. In your science notebook, record the pH readings every 5 minutes.
8. In your science notebook, monitor and record any changes you see in the test tubes. Note the times when they occur.
9. ***Wash your hands thoroughly with soap and water each time you leave the laboratory.***
10. Clean up your lab area as your teacher directs. Be careful to follow all directions for cleaning and storing the pH probes.

3. Conduct your experiment.
4. Generate a line graph showing how pH changed over the time you tested in your control and experimental test tubes. Color-code your graph. Add a legend and a caption so that anyone reading the graph can interpret your results.
5. Prepare a lab report of your findings. Include the following sections.
    a. A statement of the testable question and hypothesis
    b The procedure for conducting the experiment, including the purpose of each test tube you set up
    c. A descriptive summary of your results, which refers to your graphed data
    d. A concluding paragraph or 2.

    In your concluding paragraph, include a summary of the evidence from each test tube and what you learned from each test tube. Also include a paragraph with your best explanation that answers your question. Remember, explanations should include a claim, supporting evidence, and reasoning. Finally, include 1 or 2 sentences about questions you still have about the carbon cycle that you would like to answer.

> See appendix C4, *How to Develop an Explanation*, for information that may help you write your concluding paragraph.

6. Work with your team to prepare a short presentation about your experimental design, results, and explanations. Make sure everyone has a role in the presentation.
7. With your team, present your experiment to the class.

Analysis

1. Participate in a class discussion of the various experiments conducted and the results that emerged.

2. With your teammates, create a visual diagram, such as a concept map, that represents your current understanding of the cycling of matter through an ecosystem. Include specifics about how carbon, nitrogen, and water each cycle.

> You might begin with the diagram you drew in step 3 of part A, *Reflections on the Earthworm Habitats*, and add to it a representation of the aquatic ecosystem that you studied in part B, *Snails and* Anacharis: *What Can I Learn from Them?*

Spinning the Web of Life

The next time you eat a hamburger, think about what it takes to make a pound of beef. You can see what goes into a hamburger by reading the scenario, *Recipe for 1 Pound of Beef.*

You have already explored how matter cycles through various ecosystems, and you should be aware that energy is stored in matter. When you eat various forms of matter, some of that energy is transformed. The transformed energy becomes available to you. It allows you to carry out the daily activities of life and the distinctive activities that make you who you are. Not all foods contain the same amount of energy. Not all organisms require the same amount of energy to live. So why does it take so much

SCENARIO
ENGLISH SPANISH

Recipe for 1 Pound of Beef

Begin with 1 calf. Add the following ingredients over a period of about 2 years:

- 36 m² of grazing land
- 22.7 g of phosphorus
- 6.7 m² of farmland
- 45.4 g of potassium
- 5.9 kg of forage
- antibiotics
- 1.4 kg of grain
- hormones
- 181 g of soybeans

© Dreamstime/Yulia Saponova

- pesticides
- 0.5 L (liters) of petroleum products
- herbicides
- 85 g of nitrogen
- 4,900 L of water, added regularly
- 43 million W (watts) of solar energy

Figure 9.16   Think of the many steps involved in putting bread or tortillas on your plate.

matter and energy to make 1 lb (0.45 kg) of beef? In terms of energy and matter, is there a difference between eating plants and eating animals?

Let's examine the larger picture of matter and energy in your world during this Explain activity, *Spinning the Web of Life*. By relating your food intake for one day to the plants and animals it came from (figures 9.16 and 9.17), you will explore how the energy that is stored in matter flows through your community and fuels the activities of its organisms.

Materials (per person)

large sheet of paper
set of different-colored pens or pencils, 5 colors

Figure 9.17
Consider the sources of matter and energy that go into raising the eggs and chicken that may be part of your diet.

© Dreamstime/Lucian Coman

PROCESS AND PROCEDURES

1. Following the steps outlined here, generate a food web. A **food web** is a visual diagram of the interactions of organisms in an ecosystem.

   a. In your science notebook, create your ideal menu for 1 day. Include snacks as well as meals.

      Choose your favorite foods and snacks.

   b. Make a 3-column chart in your science notebook. List the foods from your ideal menu in the first column and the ingredients in each menu item in the second column.

      Remember, many foods are combinations of different plants, animals, fungi, protests, or eubacteria. Record the ingredients of each food separately. For example, if you have a piece of cake for dessert, you should list oil, flour, sugar, butter, eggs, and milk.

   c. In the third column of your chart, list the sources for the ingredients of each menu item.

      For example, write "wheat" next to "flour," "sugarcane" or "sugar beet" next to "sugar," and "chicken" next to "egg."

   d. Create a second 3-column chart in your science notebook, on a new page. In the *second column,* list all of the different animals that appeared in your first chart.

   e. For every animal that you have listed, do the following.

      1) In the third column, list several foods that it eats.

         For example, next to "cow," you would list the grass and corn that cattle eat.

      2) In the first column, next to each animal that you listed in the second column, record 2 animals that might eat that animal.

         For example, next to "cow," you might list "wolf," "coyote," "mountain lion," or "human." Next to "fish," you might list "raccoon," "otter," or "seagull," depending on the type of fish it is.

   f. Create a food web from the information that you generated in your science notebook, as follows.

      1) Obtain a large sheet of paper from your teacher. Fold it like an accordion to create 5 equal-sized sections (figure 9.18). Gather 5 different-colored pens or pencils. Use a different color for each section.

      2) Turn your paper so the sections go from top to bottom. In the bottom section, list all the names of the plants.

      3) Write the names of all the herbivores (plant eaters) in the next section, above the plants (figure 9.19).

Figure 9.18 Obtain a large sheet of paper. Fold it to create five equal-sized sections. You will start your food web diagram in the bottom section by listing all the names of the plants.

© iStockphoto/qldian

© Dreamstime/Gwen Cameron

Figure 9.19 Classify the organisms in your charts by their diets. For example: (*a*) Herbivores primarily eat plants. (*b*) Carnivores primarily eat animals. (*c*) Omnivores eat both plants and animals. (*d*) Decomposers primarily feed off dead organisms and the wastes or cast-off fragments of living organisms.

    4)   Write all the names of the omnivores (animals that eat plants and animals) in the next section, above the herbivores.

    5)   Write all the names of the carnivores (animals that eat only meat) in the section above the omnivore row.

    6)   Write your name in the row that is appropriate for your diet.

  g. After you have all the names of the plants and animals organized, draw arrows from the organisms that *provide* energy to the organisms that *receive* energy.

> Pay particular attention to the direction that you draw your arrows. They should show the direction of energy flow, *not* who will be eaten. Say, for example, that your plant row includes grass and your herbivore row includes cattle. You would draw an arrow from grass to cattle with the point of the arrow aimed at the cattle because grass provides energy to cattle.

2. Deepen your understanding of food webs by reading the essay, *Let's Ask Drs. Ricardo and Rita.* As you read, enter the following terms into your personal glossary.

- herbivore
- carnivore
- omnivore
- producer
- primary consumer
- secondary consumer
- decomposer
- biomass

Drs. Ricardo and Rita, longtime colleagues at the same university, answer questions and concerns about relationships in communities.

Dear Dr. Ricardo,

I am a biology student who has just completed drawing a food web for class. As I was making it, I learned that a food web is the sum of all feeding interactions. I've included a sample (figure 9.20). Does it look right to you? My teacher keeps talking about communities, but I'm not sure what they are. How do communities relate to this food web?

Sincerely,

Juanita Perez

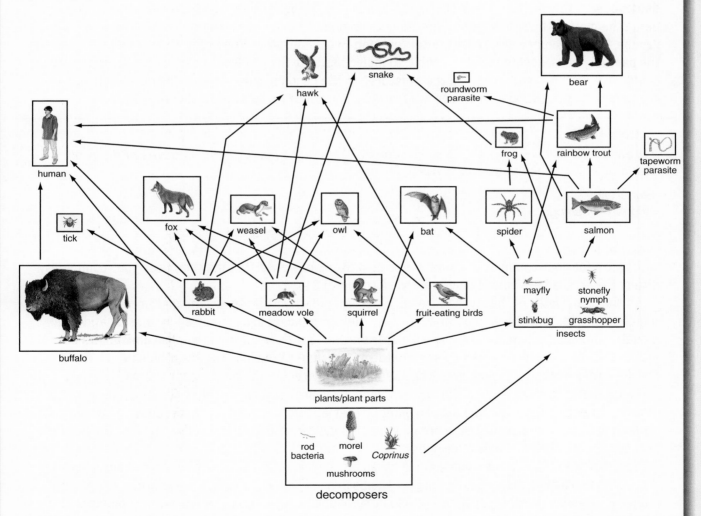

Figure 9.20 Juanita's food web. Food webs in a community can be very complex. Can you find any more relationships?

Dear Juanita,

Your food web is very detailed. Nice job! Because you included a large variety of organisms in your food web, you have also drawn a nice visual picture of a community. A *community* is a collection of organisms that live and interact with one another in a given area. You also described what biologists call biomass. **Biomass** refers to the mass of all living organisms in a given environment. As you probably know, some herbivores may not eat an entire plant. For example, a rabbit may eat only part of a violet. A carnivore, such as a mountain lion, may not eat the bones of the rabbit. What these creatures eat is considered the **consumable biomass**.

What happens to the remaining parts of the violet and the bones of the rabbit? These types of biomass, the leftovers, often represent a substantial portion of the total amount of energy and biological material in a community. This resource does not go to waste, however. Remember the **decomposers** in your food web? These organisms (for example, fungi and bacteria) specialize in using the matter that other organisms do not consume. Though generally not as visible as the other groups, these decomposers serve a vital function in communities. They reduce dead biomass, such as the partially consumed violet and rabbit, to molecules that the producers can reuse. So, you see, you could have drawn arrows from all the creatures to the decomposers. Since some small animals eat decomposers, you can also draw arrows from the decomposers to some of the insects.

Dear Dr. Rita,

I drew a food web in my class. But I still don't understand what it means in terms of the real world. Can you make this more realistic for me?

Sincerely,
Alfonso Washington

Dear Alfonso,

Thanks for your comment. I would love to help. Think of a river that may run near your community. Study the detailed drawing of such a riverbed (figure 9.21).

In the open water of the river, algae and microscopic water plants are the main **producers**. They make their own food through photosynthesis. These producers are consumed by insects and small aquatic animals such as the tiger salamander and various fishes. They are called **consumers** because they feed on other organisms. Higher-level consumers, such as the great blue heron, live by eating either first-level consumers (organisms that have eaten the producers) or smaller predators. Note that at every step in the process, some biological matter passes to the decomposers. The decaying matter they consume may be plant or animal parts, organic waste products, or whole dead organisms. The decomposers then break down this matter to simple molecules. In turn, the producers use some of these simple molecules.

The food web of the river ecosystem is based on solar energy that the producers convert into food. Not all ecosystems, however, support themselves in this manner. The seashore is a good example of a rich, natural ecosystem that is not self-supporting. Virtually all of the organisms that inhabit the zone between high and low tides are consumers. They ultimately depend on plant material and other living or dead organic matter that is brought in by each high tide. Many of the seashore creatures feed on this matter directly. For example, mussels and clams filter seawater for microscopic organisms and other tiny bits of food. Many other species are predators, such as the sea star, which preys on clams and mussels. The organisms in this community also depend on solar energy. But most of that energy is converted into food by producers that live in offshore ocean communities.

cottonwoods
sycamores

willows
service-
berries
dogwoods

monkshood
elephantellas
violets
sedges

great blue herons
dippers
raccoons

tiger salamanders
beavers
algae
watercress

Figure 9.21   Cross section through the edge of a riverbed in the southwestern United States. The interactions among organisms in an ecosystem involve the cycling of matter and the flow of energy. What is the ultimate source of energy?

Dear Dr. Rita,

I am worried that the food web I drew is all wrong. When I drew arrows between organisms, I pointed the arrow toward the organism that does the eating. But my friend drew the arrow pointing to the thing being eaten. Who is right? What do these arrows really mean?

Sincerely,
Dwayne Robertson

Dear Dwayne,
    Often, students who draw food webs for the first time want to draw the arrows pointing toward the organisms being eaten. But in this case, your food web is correct. Remember that the arrows represent energy flow, not the act of eating. For example, energy from grass is passed to a rabbit. The energy from the rabbit is passed to a mountain lion. Think of the arrows as meaning "the energy is passed to." A food web helps us understand the flow of energy through a community. Ultimately, the Sun is the source of energy for nearly all Earth communities.

3. Expand your food web in the following manner.
   a. Think of other organisms that might compete with you for your food. In your science notebook, make a list of organisms that eat some of the same foods that you eat.
   b. Add the organisms that you listed in step 3a to the appropriate level of your food web. Add the appropriate arrows.
   c. Add decomposers to the top section of your food web. Use arrows to indicate the relationship between these and the other organisms present.

   > If you had mushrooms in your list of foods, they belong in this section.

4. In the next 3 steps, you will consider the flow of energy through ecosystems. Use figure 9.22 and your understanding of the concepts from this chapter and chapter 8 to answer the questions in steps 4a–d.

   > In the previous steps, you considered the cycling of matter in ecosystems. But energy flows through ecosystems. It is not cycled. This fact has important implications for ecosystems. The diagram in figure 9.22 shows the amount of energy available at different trophic levels in an ecosystem. Notice the pyramid shape, with the largest amount of energy available at the level of producers, less energy available to the primary consumers, and even less energy available to the secondary consumers.

Figure 9.22   Energy pyramid. This idealized energy pyramid illustrates that only a portion of the energy available at one trophic level is available at the next-higher trophic level.

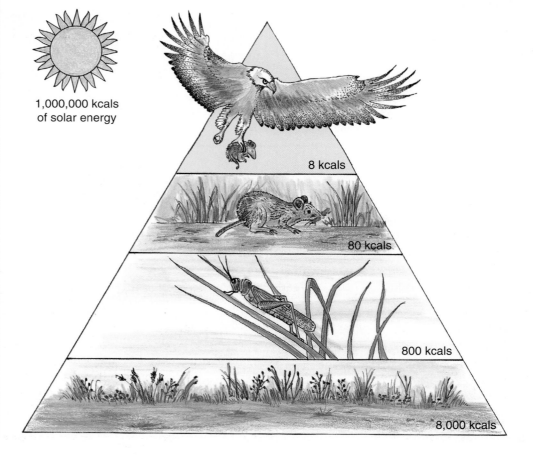

1,000,000 kcals of solar energy

8 kcals

80 kcals

800 kcals

8,000 kcals

a. An examination of the diagram shows that energy seems to be missing in transitions among trophic levels in ecosystems. The primary consumers have less energy available than the producers. But you know that energy is neither created nor destroyed, only changed in form. So the energy isn't really lost in the perspective of the universe. In what form or forms do you think the "lost" energy might be?

b. A famous ecologist named Paul Colinvaux wrote a book titled *Why Big Fierce Animals Are Rare*. If you asked a typical seventh grader why big animals are rare, what do you think the answer would be? How might you use figure 9.22 to help the student answer the question?

c. Explain to the same seventh grader why light from the Sun must be continuously supplied to most ecosystems.

d. How is figure 9.22 a scientific model for energy flow through an ecosystem? Explain why it is or is not a good model.

Do all organisms fit nicely into one trophic level?

5. To learn more about energy flow, read the essay, *Energy Flow in Ecosystems*. Study figure 9.23 carefully, as it may help you complete the task in step 6.

Topic: Energy pyramid
Code: human4E499

Energy Flow in Ecosystems

ENGLISH SPANISH

Each time that an organism uses energy, some energy is released to the external environment as heat. This means that only a portion of the solar energy that producers take up is stored in biomass that herbivores can eat. In turn, only a portion of the plant material that herbivores eat is converted into body parts that could become food for predators. Each transfer of energy from one organism to another results in a decrease in the amount of energy that is available (see figure 9.23).

Because energy is lost with each transfer to a different organism, sometimes ecosystems are illustrated using a pyramid-shaped diagram. The producers are located at the bottom level of the pyramid and contain the most total energy. Consumers that eat those producers, also known as primary consumers or herbivores, contain a smaller amount of energy. Secondary consumers or predators are on the next-smallest level of the pyramid. In any ecosystem, the number of levels in the pyramid is the same as the number of links in the longest possible food chain, with the top-level predators at the top. Each of these levels in the pyramid is called a **trophic level**, "troph" meaning "food" (figure 9.22).

What about omnivores? What about decomposers? What trophic levels do they occupy? They can occupy more than one. A decomposer can exist in the first trophic level when it breaks down the remaining biomass of a plant that was partially eaten by an herbivore. The same decomposer also might exist in the third trophic level when it breaks down the bones of a carnivore. Omnivores also occupy different trophic levels. When you eat a salad and a steak for a meal, you are occupying two trophic levels.

Ecologists can estimate the amount of energy that is stored in the biomass at each trophic level

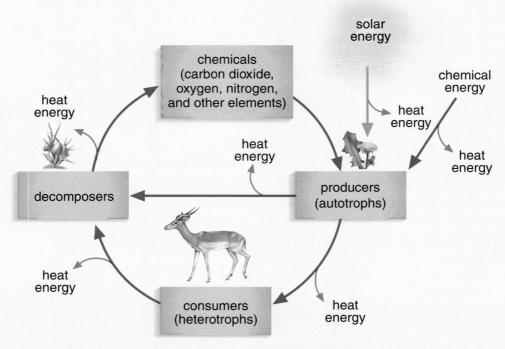

Figure 9.23 **Energy flow in a community.** As energy is transferred from one organism to another, some energy is always lost as heat.

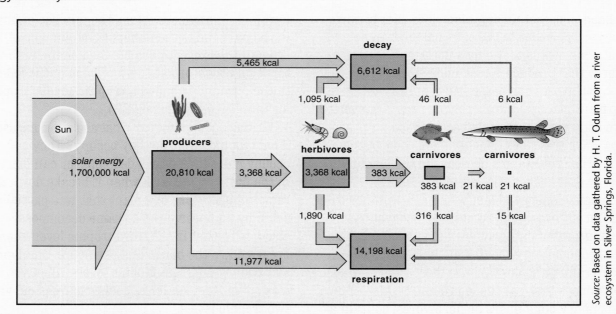

Source: Based on data gathered by H. T. Odum from a river ecosystem in Silver Springs, Florida.

Figure 9.24 **Energy flow diagram for Silver Springs, Florida.** How does the amount of energy (in kilocalories, or kcal) differ from one trophic level to the next? Can you calculate what percentage of energy is transferred from producers to herbivores?

of a community. They do this by taking a sample of organisms and calculating the total biomass represented by the producers, herbivores, and higher-level consumers. They then estimate the amount of potential energy (measured in kilocalories) in this organic matter.

With these data, you can illustrate the amount of energy entering and leaving an ecosystem at each trophic level. Study figure 9.24 to see how energy is distributed from one trophic level to another. Notice that producers are the foundation. Each trophic level above the producers receives less energy. In some ecosystems, each trophic level receives about one-tenth of the energy of the level below it. Where does the energy go? Some is used to fuel activities needed to keep organisms alive, while some dissipates into the environment as heat.

The flow and accompanying loss of energy from one trophic level to the next is the basis for the suggestion that people should eat at a lower trophic level when possible. For example, a person eating as an herbivore can create 1 kg of human biomass by eating 10 kg of plants. It takes about 100 kg of plants, however, to create 1 kg of human biomass if the person eats as a primary carnivore. You are eating as a primary carnivore if you eat the cow that ate the plants, instead of eating the plants directly (see figure 9.25).

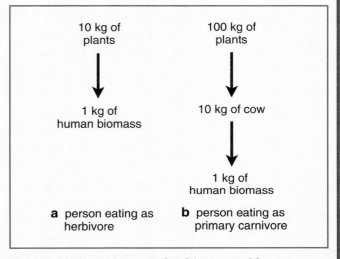

Figure 9.25 Human as herbivore and human as primary carnivore. The energy relationships between trophic levels are the basis for the suggestion that people should eat low on the food chain.

6. Work with a partner to generate a diagram that summarizes, in a way that makes sense to you, the data about the flow of energy in the Hubbard Brook ecosystem. Use information and data from the need to know, *Energy Flow in the Hubbard Brook Forest,* to complete the task. Your final diagram should include the following.
   a. Producers, primary consumers, and secondary consumers that are clearly labeled
   b. Boxes or levels that are scaled to represent relative amounts of energy
   c. Data about the energy that is available at each level
   d. An indication of what supplies the system with energy and where "lost" energy goes

   You might pattern your diagram after an energy pyramid like the one in figure 9.22 or the energy flow diagram like figure 9.24.

NEED TO KNOW

ENGLISH SPANISH

Energy Flow in the Hubbard Brook Forest

The Hubbard Brook Experimental Forest in New Hampshire has been the subject of ecological studies since the 1950s (figure 9.26). This forest has been designated as a Long Term Ecological Research (LTER) site. In 1978, a researcher named James Gosz and many fellow scientists attempted to quantify energy flow throughout the site's different trophic levels. The data that they collected follow (figure 9.27). Note that all the data are in kilocalories per square meter per year (kcal/m²/yr).

Figure 9.26 **A hardwood forest like those studied at Hubbard Brook, White Mountain National Forest, New Hampshire.** Scientists have carefully tried to account for the flow of energy and cycling of matter in this forest.

Measurement	Energy available to different trophic levels (kcal/m²/yr)
Solar energy available	480,000
Solar energy reflected	72,000
Solar energy converted to heat	136,800
Solar energy used to drive evaporation of water from surfaces or through plants	201,600
Solar energy converted by plants into chemical energy	9,600
Energy in the form of producer biomass available to primary consumers	4,800
Amount eaten by primary consumers	3,500
Energy in the form of primary consumer biomass available to secondary consumers	200

Source: Gosz, J. R., Holmes, R. T., Likens, G. E., and Bormann, F. H. (1978). The flow of energy in a forest ecosystem. *Scientific American, 238*(3), 92-102.

Figure 9.27 **Data from Hubbard Brook Experimental Forest.** Use these data to trace the flow of energy in this ecosystem.

Analysis

Participate in a class discussion of the following. Record your ideas in your science notebook.

1. Where is the most energy available in your food web? Explain your answer.
2. Why does it take more biomass to produce beef, compared with chicken or eggs?

   > It takes 16 lb of grain and soybeans to produce just 1 lb of beef. It takes 6 lb of grain and soybeans to produce a pound of pork, 4 lb for a pound of turkey, and 3 lb for a pound of eggs or a pound of chicken.

3. Compare the food web of a vegetarian in your class with the food web of someone who is not a vegetarian.
   a. What differences are evident?
   b. What do you think is significant about those differences?
   c. How does this relate to the recipe for 1 lb of beef?
4. Humans can eat organisms from multiple trophic levels. Why do you think top-level consumers (such as sharks) are rarely a part of a human diet?

Generating Some Heat

Let's read about a surprising source of heat in the scenario, *Saturday Chores*.

SCENARIO

ENGLISH   SPANISH

Saturday Chores

It's Saturday. You have a soccer game at noon. You promised your friends that you would be there a half hour early to practice. But you know you have to finish your Saturday chores before you leave. This is your week to cut the grass, so you get up early to begin the task. Because the morning is cool, you find yourself making quick progress. But time is passing, and practice is about to begin. In an effort to shave time off the job, you pile all of the clippings on some newly turned soil in a corner of the yard.

You think, "I'll bag the clippings later." Saturday and Sunday come and go.

School begins again on Monday. The clippings still are sitting there on the soil in the yard. Another Saturday rolls around, and you have another game. It's your sister's turn to cut the grass. Good! No grass today! Your game is early in the morning. On the way out of the house, your dad reminds you that last week's clippings are still sitting in the yard and that it's your responsibility to bag them before you head out. You run to the yard with some lawn bags and begin scooping up grass clippings. Again, the morning is very cool. As you dig into the pile, you notice something interesting. Steam is rising from the clippings (figure 9.28). In fact, the center of the clippings pile is hot, especially down near the soil. You wonder why the inside of the pile is so warm on such a cool morning.

Figure 9.28 Fresh-cut grass that is piled shortly after mowing gets hot after a few days.

From your experiences in this chapter, what do you think generated the heat in the pile of grass clippings? In this Elaborate activity, *Generating Some Heat*, you may find an answer to this question as you elaborate on your knowledge of the cycling of matter and the flow of energy in ecosystems. You will look, primarily, at the role of decomposers. You and your teammates are about to participate in a compost design competition. Your goal is to design a compost system that generates the most heat (figure 9.29). As you complete the challenge, consider the question, "How is the flow of energy in an ecosystem affected by decomposers?"

Figure 9.29
Organic materials can be composted. This causes the matter to be cycled more quickly than if it were left to decompose on its own. Where does the energy from the composted matter go?

Materials (per team of 4)

4 pairs of plastic gloves
1 measuring cup that holds approximately 250 mL
1 thermistor or nonmercury thermometer
1 compost column (made from 2-L bottles)
1 bag of potting soil
1 bag of shredded leaf or bark mulch
1 bag of grass clippings
1 box of compost starter inoculum (a mix of nutrients and
   microorganisms that is effective at decomposition)
other organic materials as needed
water
clear packing tape or masking tape
duct tape
insulation material (such as old towels)
1 trowel or spatula for mixing compost
1 plastic trash bag
1 pair of old nylons (optional)
rubber bands (optional)
graph paper
different-colored pens and pencils

PROCESS AND PROCEDURES

1. As a class, make the following decisions about your compost designs.
   a. How much compost starter inoculum all teams will use
   b. How much water all teams will use
   c. How much total organic matter (the mass) all teams will use

   Why is it important that all teams keep certain features constant?

2. Discuss the following questions with your team to help you decide on a recipe. Record your recipe in your science notebook. Be sure to give reasons for your decisions. Have your teacher approve your recipe.

   a. What organic matter should you use?
   b. Should you use 1 source of organic matter or a combination of sources?
   c. Should you pack your compost column loosely or tightly?

   As you develop your recipe, practice the working-relationship skill of reaching consensus. Think about processes in organisms that give off heat. Think about what you learned in chapter 8 about what organisms need to carry out cellular processes. Can you use what you have learned to predict which kinds of organic matter would decay the most quickly?

3. Create your composting system with your team (figure 9.30).

SAFETY: Put on your plastic gloves.

   a. Use the recipe that your team agreed on. Using the measuring cup, measure your soil and your organic matter 1 at a time from the materials you have available. Pour them into the plastic bag.
   b. Mix the ingredients in the plastic bag thoroughly with gloved hands.
   c. Add the amount of compost starter inoculum that your class decided to include.
   d. Add the amount of water that your class decided to include.
   e. Use the trowel to mix the compost ingredients thoroughly.
   f. Remove the upper portion of the compost column and place your mixed compost into the lower portion. Place the top back on the compost column and tape the lid into place.
   g. Insulate your compost column, as instructed by your teacher. Make sure the airholes on the bottom are not covered.

**Figure 9.30
Assembling a compost column.** It is important to mix the materials your team uses.

4. Make a data table in your science notebook to record temperature data twice a day over 3–4 days. Record the initial temperature of the compost column in your table. Continue to record temperatures over the next few days. The winning team will be the one that has the greatest change in temperature in its compost column.

5. Graph the temperature changes that you observed in your composting system. Add highlight comments and a caption to your graph.

> For help with this task, refer to appendix D3, *How to Create Graphs,* and appendix B6, *How to Write Highlight Comments and Captions.*

Analysis

Complete the following tasks as a team.

1. Present your team's compost recipe and graph to the class. Use your highlight comments to help guide what is most important to present.

2. Based on all of the teams' reports, determine which compost recipes generated the most change in temperature.

> You and your classmates will judge the effectiveness of each composting recipe by examining each team's data.

   a. Why do you think the most effective recipes worked so well?
   b. What role did the microorganisms play?

3. The heat that you noticed is a form of energy. What form did this energy take before it was released as heat? What cellular processes may have generated this heat? What happens to this energy after it is released as heat?

4. What does your answer to question 3 reveal about the flow of energy in a community?

Energy, Matter, and Disaster

EVALUATE

By now you should be aware of how closely connected the flow of energy is to the cycling of matter in ecosystems. In this Evaluate activity, *Energy, Matter, and Disaster,* you and your teacher will evaluate what you have learned about these concepts. You will work individually to think about the impact that a natural disaster would have on various communities on Earth. Then you will respond to some questions about survival in different communities.

PROCESS AND PROCEDURES

1. Read about the following catastrophe.

> Earth is entering a phase of instability that no one had predicted. Throughout both hemispheres, hundreds of volcanoes are erupting with great force (figure 9.31). Earth's atmosphere is thick with minute

volcanic debris and dust. As much as 75 percent of the sunlight is now blocked from reaching Earth's surface. This period of eruptions is expected to continue indefinitely. It is likely that soon virtually all sunlight will be blocked from reaching Earth's surface.

Figure 9.31 The community around this volcano was drastically changed after the eruption.

2. Review the *Energy, Matter, and Disaster Rubric* handout. Be sure to ask your teacher any questions you have about it.

3. Read the following questions and record your answers in your science notebook. Be sure to answer each part of each question.

   a. What might be the effect if 80–85 percent of the sunlight were blocked from Earth? What might be the short- and long-term effects on the following organisms: an earthworm, a shark, a maple tree, a saguaro cactus, and a teenager?

   b. Imagine that all sunlight is blocked from reaching Earth's surface.

   1) What might be the short- and long-term effects on the following organisms: the producers, the consumers, and the decomposers?

   2) Describe how the cycling of matter through an ecosystem would be affected.

Analysis

Work with a partner to discuss the following questions about survival in different communities. Then record your responses in your science notebook.

1. From the thousands that sprout, why will only 1 or 2 healthy trees grow into the available space between other existing trees?

    You learned in unit 1, *Evolution: Change in Living Systems*, that more organisms are born than survive. How is this pattern related to the availability of matter and energy on Earth's surface?

2. Are the fish that live 2 km (1.2 mi) deep in the ocean likely to be herbivores or predators? Explain.

3. DDT (a pesticide) was widely used for many years in the United States. This chemical does not break down in the bodies of organisms that ingest it. Therefore, it accumulates over an organism's lifetime. When DDT was being used, the populations of birds of prey, such as bald eagles, peregrine falcons, and ospreys, declined more than the populations of small songbirds. Why do you think that was so?

4. Human societies that live by hunting and gathering usually have much smaller populations than groups in a similar setting that live primarily by growing crops. Why do you think that is so?

5. Suppose you found yourself snowed in for the winter in a remote mountain cabin with no way of contacting the outside world. You must survive for several months with only what is on hand to eat. Aside from a small supply of canned peaches, your only resources are 2 100-lb sacks of wheat and a flock of 8 hens. Discuss the relative merits of the following strategies.

    a. Feed the grain to the hens and eat their eggs until the wheat is gone. Then eat the hens.

    b. Kill the hens at once and freeze their carcasses in the snow. Live on a diet of wheat porridge and chicken.

    c. Eat a mixture of wheat porridge, eggs, and 1 hen a week. Feed the hens well to keep the eggs coming until all of the hens are killed.

6. Every breeding pair of bullfrogs produces hundreds of eggs each spring. During the time they are growing up in the pond, the small tadpoles feed entirely on microscopic water plants. Predators living in the pond eat a large fraction of the tadpoles before they transform into frogs (figure 9.32). As adults, however, bullfrogs themselves are predators. Discuss why this strategy is more advantageous than one in which the tadpoles would be predators and the adults would be herbivores.

Figure 9.32
Bullfrog. Although adult bullfrogs are predators, the tadpoles are prey. Many tadpoles are eaten before they reach adulthood.

Further Challenges

1. There are several hypotheses about how dinosaurs became extinct. One of these hypotheses involves a climatic catastrophe that has some similarities to the one presented in step 1. See what you can find out about this hypothesis. Report your findings to the class.
2. Write and perform a skit that depicts organisms defending their role in a community. In it, describe the advantages, the disadvantages, and the importance to the community of a producer, a predator, and a decomposer.

Conducting Your Own Inquiry

510

> Plunge into the sublime seas, dive deep and swim far, so you shall come back with self-respect, with new power, with an advanced experience that shall explain and overlook the old.
>
> Ralph Waldo Emerson

Science can be a career, as it is for the people pictured here. Science is a way of studying and knowing the world around you, whether you make it a career or use it to make informed decisions. In this *Explain* section, *Conducting Your Own Inquiry,* you will exercise your inquiry skills. The activities throughout this course involve scientific inquiry. By now, you should have enough experience with those skills to realize that thinking scientifically is a valuable way of developing explanations for many kinds of questions. In this section, you will be asked to think like a scientist and apply your critical-thinking skills to evaluate new information.

In the activities in this section, you will look first at examples of science in the popular press and critique how the science is discussed. You will consider questions such as, "Is the science presented accurately?" "Is the science presented completely?" "Do the scientists or the writers present unbiased perspectives?" Next, you will investigate a scientific question of your own. You will decide what you want to study, where you will find background information, and how you will conduct your experiment. The choices for your inquiry are yours to make.

GOALS FOR THE SECTION

Throughout the *Explain* section, you will work toward the following understandings:

✔ How to evaluate new scientific information using your inquiry skills

✔ How to conceive, design, and conduct a scientific investigation of your own choosing

To help you develop these understandings, you will complete the following activities.

ENGAGE
EXPLORE — Science All around You

EXPLAIN
ELABORATE — Being an Experimental Scientist
EVALUATE

ENGAGE

EXPLORE

Science All around You

One reason to study biology is to learn to use the methods of science to study the organisms, interactions, and processes around you. Another reason is to understand the events that influence your life. The scenario, *Researchers Find Evidence That Prenatal Exposure to Ecstasy Can Cause Long-Term Memory Loss and Other Impairments in Offspring,* is an example of how science and technology are often reported in a newspaper. The article in this Engage-Explore activity, *Science All around You,* describes experiments related to research that led to a new understanding about the drug ecstasy.

Materials (per person)

newspaper or newsmagazine
scissors
tape, stapler, or glue

PROCESS AND PROCEDURES

1. To practice understanding science in the news, read the scenario, *Researchers Find Evidence That Prenatal Exposure to Ecstasy Can Cause Long-Term Memory Loss and Other Impairments in Offspring.* Then answer the following questions in your science notebook.
   a. What can you tell from the scenario about how the scientists collected their data and developed their explanation?
   b. Can you tell what questions the scientists asked?
2. To explore a science news article that interests you, first scan some newspapers or newsmagazines for articles about science.
3. Cut out the article that most interests you, and attach it to a page in your science notebook. Near the article, write the news source it came from and the date it was published.
4. To analyze this news article, answer the following questions. Write your responses in your science notebook.

   Base your answers on the information in the article itself and on what you infer.

   a. What testable question did the scientists ask?
   b. What background information informed the scientists?
   c. How did the scientists collect observations or data?
   d. What tools did the scientists use?
   e. What results did the scientists get?
   f. What conclusions did the scientists draw?
   g. What new questions are the scientists likely to investigate?

Analysis

1. Discuss your article and analysis with a partner.
2. Record in your science notebook at least 2 scientific questions that you would like to research.

> These questions may be related to the article you analyzed or to another area of science. Think about activities you have completed in this class. Did any leave you with questions you might like to research more fully?

SCENARIO

ENGLISH   SPANISH

Researchers Find Evidence That Prenatal Exposure to Ecstasy Can Cause Long-Term Memory Loss and Other Impairments in Offspring

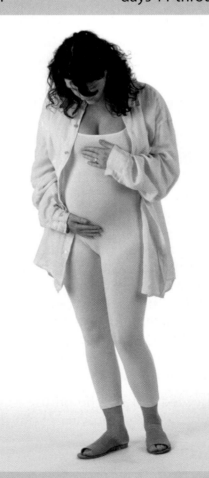

Researchers today reported the first evidence that a mother's use of MDMA (ecstasy) during pregnancy may result in specific types of long-term learning and memory impairments in her offspring.

The research, published in the May 1, 2001, issue of the Journal of Neuroscience, was conducted by scientists from Children's Hospital Research Foundation and the University of Cincinnati College of Medicine. The researchers administered MDMA to two groups of newborn rats. One group received ecstasy twice a day for 10 days after birth (analogous to early third-trimester brain development in humans); the other group received ecstasy twice a day during days 11 through 20 (analogous to late human third-trimester brain development). To determine the effects of ecstasy on cognitive abilities, a series of maze and swimming tests were conducted on the rats when they reached an average age of 60 days. While no cognitive changes were noted in the rats given ecstasy at an earlier age, memory and learning deficiencies were noted in the group exposed to ecstasy during days 11–20. The ecstasy-induced disruption in both sequential and spatial reference memory-based learning was long term and was still apparent after this group reached adulthood.

"This study adds to the evidence that ecstasy is a dangerous drug. Unfortunately, its popularity remains high, in part because some individuals still perceive that taking ecstasy is safe. As its use continues, increases in the number of users who are pregnant will inevitably occur. This study indicates that users may be damaging not only their own cognitive abilities but those of their children as well," says Dr. Alan I. Leshner, former director of the National Institute on Drug Abuse.

The timing of ecstasy exposure during brain development may be critical as evidenced by cognitive changes in the 11–20-day-old group. "The differences between the responses in newborn rats after MDMA administration most likely occur because of the stage of maturation of the central nervous system at the time of exposure to MDMA," explains Dr. Charles Vorhees, lead investigator.

He further explains that in adult animals, ecstasy exerts its effects by significantly decreasing serotonin levels and the number of re-uptake sites in the brain. However, in this study, only small changes in serotonin levels were noted in the brains of the newborn rats receiving ecstasy suggesting that developmental exposure to ecstasy may induce cognitive deficits in the fetus through different mechanisms than those of adults.

"These findings raise new concerns about ecstasy when exposure occurs during brain development in the human fetus," Dr. Vorhees concludes.

Source: Feuer, J. (2001, May 1). *Researchers find evidence that prenatal use of ecstasy can cause long-term memory loss and other impairments in offspring.* Retrieved March 31, 2009, from http://www.cincinnatichildrens.org/about/news/release/2001/5-ecstacy.htm

EXPLAIN

ELABORATE

EVALUATE

Being an Experimental Scientist

In the *Engage* section at the beginning of this course, you investigated ways that scientists think when they do their work. You conducted experiments to test a hypothesis, based on a realistic scenario. For this Explain-Elaborate-Evaluate activity, you will *be* a scientist as you carry out a full inquiry of your own design. Specifically, your inquiry will take the form of a controlled experiment. Remember that each of the *thinking* steps, such as asking a testable question, deciding how to investigate it, and analyzing the meaning of the data you collect, is just as important as the hands-on step of *doing* an experiment. Your performance in *Being an Experimental Scientist* will demonstrate both your understanding of the particular area of biology that you will investigate and your ability to explain and use scientific processes.

Materials (per person)

Materials needed will depend on the experiment you design. You will need your teacher's approval of your materials list before you assemble them.

PROCESS AND PROCEDURES

Part A   Preparation

1. To help you prepare to design your own experiment, answer the following questions about scientific inquiry. Write your answers in your science notebook.

   a. Which of the processes of science shown in figure Ex.1 were evident in the article that you analyzed in the Engage-Explore activity, *Science All around You*? Give specific examples and explain how they were evident.

   b. Identify 3–4 specific times or activities in this course when you have used processes shown in figure Ex.1.

   > Looking through your science notebook may help you answer this question.

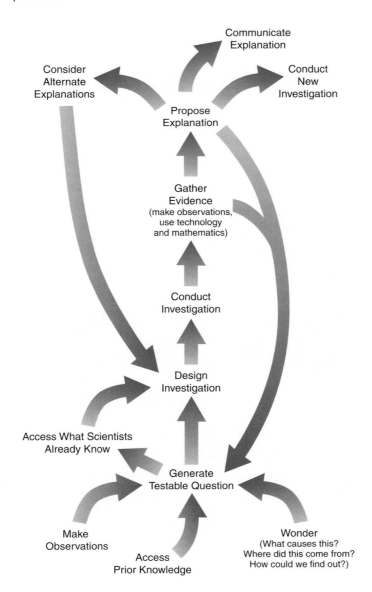

Figure Ex.1   The *Scientific Inquiry Diagram* illustrates a number of processes of science and how they are related to one another.

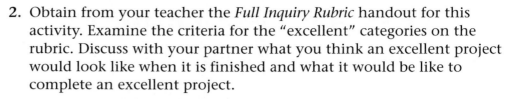
2. Obtain from your teacher the *Full Inquiry Rubric* handout for this activity. Examine the criteria for the "excellent" categories on the rubric. Discuss with your partner what you think an excellent project would look like when it is finished and what it would be like to complete an excellent project.

Part B   Conducting a Full Inquiry

Now carry out your own full inquiry by following these steps.

Asking the Question

1. Choose an area of biology that interests you. Identify a testable question within this area.

> If you are having difficulty thinking of a question, look back at your response to *Analysis* question 2 from the Engage-Explore activity, *Science All around You.* Review the experiments you have conducted so far in this class. Perhaps there is a question related to one of those experiments that interests you. Or do some library research about a topic that interests you. The new information will provide useful background and may give you an idea for a testable question.

    a. In your science notebook, record the question in 1 or 2 sentences.
    b. Describe what is already known about the topic or question.
    c. Describe why your question is interesting or important.
    d. Write down the hypothesis you plan to test.

> Remember, your hypothesis should be a tentative answer to your question. It may help to also write down the reasons behind your hypothesis. If you wish, you can state your hypothesis as an if-then statement. If you use this format, write your tentative answer after the "if" statement and your prediction for what you will see happen after the "then" statement.

    e. Record which of the 6 unifying principles of biology is most related to your hypothesis. (See the need to know, *Unifying Principles of Biology*.)

NEED TO KNOW

ENGLISH SPANISH

Unifying Principles of Biology

Which of these principles is related to your inquiry?
Evolution: Change in Living Systems
Homeostasis: Maintaining Dynamic Equilibrium in Living Systems
Energy, Matter, and Organization: Relationships in Living Systems
Continuity: Reproduction and Inheritance in Living Systems
Development: Growth and Differentiation in Living Systems
Ecology: Interaction and Interdependence in Living Systems

2. Show your question and hypothesis to your teacher for approval before you proceed.

Gathering Information

1. Use the library, local scientists, the Web, or other available resources to gather more information related to your question.

Scientists use multiple sources of information to develop explanations. They read reports that others have written. They also use data that they gather directly through observation or experiments. You should use a similar process in investigating your question.

2. Design an experiment to test your hypothesis by doing the following.

   a. In your science notebook, describe your experimental design and include these sections.
      1) Rationale (explain how this experiment will test your hypothesis)
      2) Hypothesis (explain what you think the answer to your question may be and why you think so)
      3) Procedure (include the materials you will need, the process you will follow, and a description of your controls and the role that they will play)
      4) Data analysis (explain how you will analyze the data)

      Your teacher may have specific suggestions about the length of time that you will have to conduct your experiment or the materials available that you may choose to use.

   b. In your science notebook, write a safety plan for your experiment. In your procedures, record the precautions that you will follow when and if you
      • use chemicals,
      • handle equipment, and
      • handle biological hazards such as bacteria or yeasts.

      Ask your teacher to explain any hazards he or she thinks are involved in your experiment. Your teacher should also help you identify the precautions necessary to prevent harm from an accident (see figure Ex.2).

      Review appendix A, *Laboratory Safety*. Be sure that you understand all the safety considerations involved in your experimental design. Make sure that you have read and understood the hazards and precautions described on the labels and Material Safety Data Sheets for any chemicals you plan to use in your experiment. Report all accidents, no matter how small, to your teacher.

Figure Ex.2
Scientists protect themselves by following safety procedures while working in the laboratory. What safety precautions has this scientist taken?

3. Discuss your library research, experimental design, and safety plan with your teacher before you continue. If your plans are reasonable and safe, your teacher will approve further work.

4. When you have your teacher's approval, carry out the experiment you have designed to test your hypothesis.

> Remember, carefully record in your science notebook each step of your work and your data. Use the proper controls to make it a valid test.

Analyzing Your Data

1. Organize your data in a way that makes it easier to see patterns or understand what the data show you (see figure Ex.3).

> This step will help you when you present your work in the *Drawing Conclusions* section. Consider using graphs, tables, flowcharts, drawings, or other ways to make your data easier to understand.

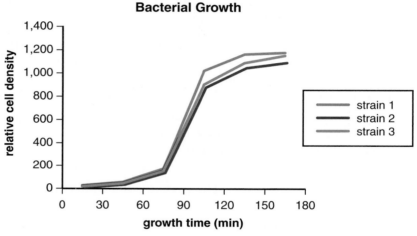

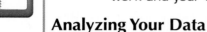

Figure Ex.3   Bacterial growth graph. Graphs can be a useful way to display data. This graph shows the growth profile of three different bacterial strains. Can any of your data be presented conveniently by using a graph?

2. Formulate an explanation of your data that includes a claim and the evidence and reasoning you can use to support that claim.

> For help with this step, see appendix C4, *How to Develop an Explanation*.

3. Describe any limitations of your experimental design and any unexpected results that you may have found.

Drawing Conclusions

1. In your science notebook, explain what your explanation indicates about the testable question you asked and your hypothesis.

2. Describe how your work connects to broader questions in biology and to the unifying principle most related to your inquiry.

Communicating Your Results

1. Assemble a presentation of your full inquiry that makes it possible for someone else to understand what you did, why you did it, and what you found out.

   A poster, a written or verbal report, or a video are examples of how you can communicate your results.

2. Be sure to identify any connections between your full inquiry and the following aspects of science.
   a. The unifying principles of biology
   b. Technology
   c. Culture
   d. History
   e. Ethics

   All inquiries will have connections to at least one of the unifying principles of biology. However, your inquiry may not have connections to all the other aspects of science. If you cannot identify a technological, cultural, historical, or ethical connection relevant to your inquiry, explain this in your presentation.

3. Listen carefully as other students present their results. Look for evidence or examples that show that they used a scientific approach in their inquiry. Contribute your observations to a class discussion of the projects.

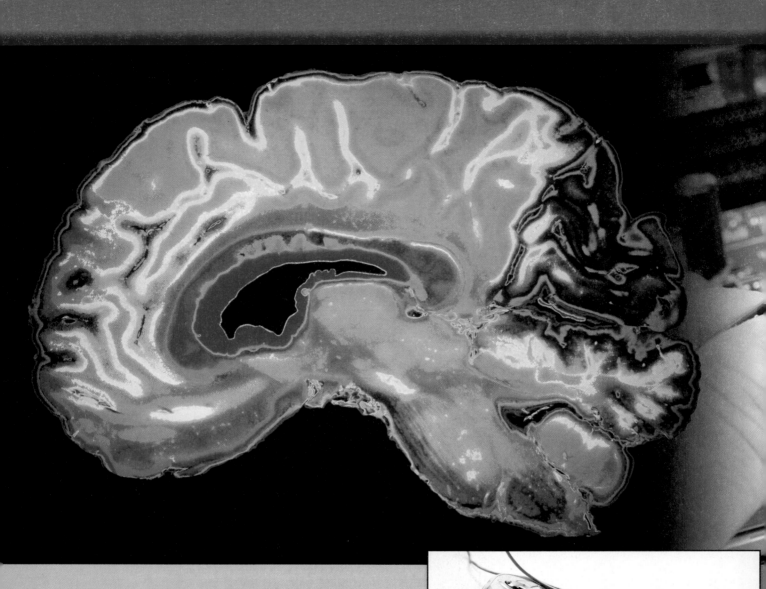

What do the things in these pictures have in common? Consider how each can store or transfer information, or do both. The storage and transfer of information allows continuity of that information: it is available and then passed on. Though each picture shows something that stores or transfers information, how the transfer is accomplished varies a great deal.

In unit 4, *Continuity: Reproduction and Inheritance in Living Systems,* you will explore the idea of continuity. You will examine the processes that contribute to the continuation of life on Earth, including the continuity of a species. These processes include reproduction as well as the storage and transfer of genetic information in living organisms.

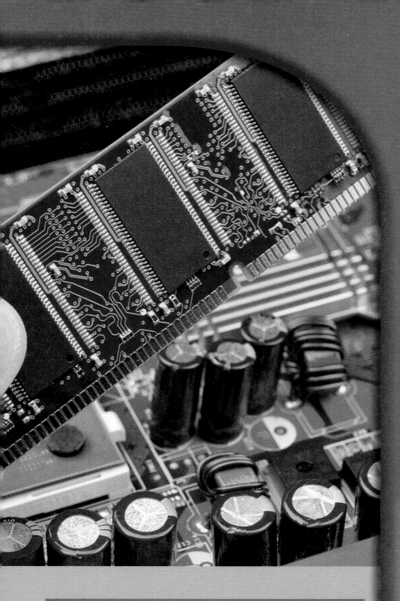

U N I T

4

Continuity:
Reproduction and Inheritance in Living Systems

By the end of unit 4, you should be able to

✓ compare and contrast the strategies that different organisms use for reproduction,

✓ explain that the continuity of a species depends on the transfer of genetic information,

✓ describe the structure of genetic material,

✓ explain how genetic information is expressed,

✓ illustrate how sexual reproduction and mutation increase genetic variation and why this is important for the evolution of a species, and

✓ appreciate the current and potential impact that technology has on our lives.

UNIT CONTENTS

10 Reproduction in Humans and Other Organisms

11 Gene Action

12 Continuity of Information through Inheritance

10

Reproduction in Humans and Other Organisms

If a single cell, under appropriate conditions, becomes a [human] in the space of a few years, there can surely be no difficulty in understanding how, under appropriate conditions, a cell may, in the course of untold millions of years, give origin to the human race.

Herbert Spencer

The opening photograph captures the moment of fertilization as a human sperm makes its way into an ovum. While technology has made fertilization possible in different settings, such as a laboratory, all human development begins with the union of genetic information from two individuals. Not all organisms begin this way, however. Among the diversity of organisms, there are several ways to make more offspring. Many individual organisms are capable of reproducing by themselves, without a mate. In this chapter, you will explore concepts about reproduction in general and about human reproduction specifically. As you do so, you will consider how reproduction contributes to both the continuation of life on Earth and the continuity of species.

GOALS FOR THE CHAPTER

In chapter 10, *Reproduction in Humans and Other Organisms,* you will work to gain an understanding of the following concepts:

✔ Organisms use a diverse set of reproductive strategies.

✔ Continuity of a species requires reproduction.

✔ The structure of the human reproductive system allows it to carry out the functions of producing gametes and fertilization.

✔ Birth control allows humans to regulate the reproductive cycle.

✔ Both human and nonhuman animals show mating behaviors.

✔ Reproduction is necessary for the continuity of life.

To help you develop these understandings, you will complete the following activities.

ENGAGE	A Zillion Ways to Make More
EXPLORE	Making Sense of Reproductive Strategies
EXPLAIN	Making Sense of Human Reproduction
ELABORATE	Regulation of Human Reproduction
ELABORATE	Analyzing Reproductive Behaviors
EVALUATE	A Reproductive Strategy for Your Critter

Remember to refer to the chapter organizer frequently as you complete the activities in chapter 10. It will help you gain perspective on the flow of concepts across the chapter and the connections between activities.

ENGAGE

A Zillion Ways to Make More

Key Idea: Different organisms display a variety of reproductive behaviors.

Linking Question:
In what ways do reproductive behaviors vary across species?

Chapter 10

EXPLORE

Making Sense of Reproductive Strategies

Key Idea: Different aspects of an organism's reproductive strategy are shaped by evolution.

Linking Question:
How do humans reproduce?

MAJOR CONCEPTS

✔ Organisms use a diverse set of reproductive strategies.

✔ Continuity of a species requires reproduction.

✔ The structure of the human reproductive system allows it to carry out the functions of producing gametes and fertilization.

✔ Birth control allows humans to regulate the reproductive cycle.

✔ Both human and nonhuman animals show mating behaviors.

✔ Reproduction is necessary for the continuity of life.

EXPLAIN

Making Sense of Human Reproduction

Part A: Parts of the Reproductive System
Part B: Hormones and Gamete Production in Humans
Part C: Fertilization

Key Idea: Human reproduction involves specialized structures, gamete production, and a joining of gametes.

Linking Question:
How can human reproduction be disrupted?

EVALUATE

A Reproductive Strategy for Your Critter

Key Idea: An organism's reproductive strategy consists of different factors, each with advantages and disadvantages.

Reproduction in Humans and Other Organisms

Linking Question:
How do all the parts of reproduction that I have learned about contribute to a specific organism's reproductive strategy?

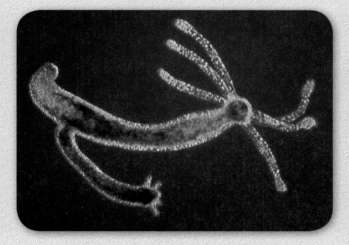

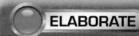

ELABORATE

Analyzing Reproductive Behaviors

Key Idea: Organisms, including humans, use reproductive behaviors to attract mates.

Linking Question:
How do sexually reproducing organisms attract a mate for reproduction?

ELABORATE

Regulation of Human Reproduction

Key Idea: Human reproduction can be interrupted physically, hormonally, and behaviorally.

ENGAGE

A Zillion Ways to Make More

You may have some ideas about how humans reproduce. But have you considered how squid or seaweeds reproduce? Humans are just one of millions of organisms on Earth that reproduce. Let's see what you really know about reproduction. This Engage activity, *A Zillion Ways to Make More*, will introduce you to several of the reproductive characteristics that exist.

Materials

online resource

PROCESS AND PROCEDURES

1. Think about the question, "How does a small cluster of trees become a forest?" To help you consider the question, read the scenario, *The Aspen Story*.
2. Come up with ideas about how reproductive processes are involved in the growth of a large cluster of trees from a single individual. List your ideas in your science notebook.

3. In your science notebook, write your ideas about the following questions.
   a. Is each tree in a cluster of aspens a new individual, even if the trees are all connected underground?
   b. Is it still reproduction if the trees remain connected?

SCENARIO

ENGLISH SPANISH

The Aspen Story

The pleasant fragrance of evergreen trees surrounded the small group of students and their teacher. They had stopped by a stream for a rest before continuing their field trip.

"How tall is that tree?" Kim asked, pointing at a ponderosa pine (see figure 10.1).

"Oh, I'd say around 30 meters (100 feet) tall," estimated the teacher. "Is that the largest tree you see here?"

"Yeah, but it's not all that big," observed another student, Paul. "Last summer I went to Yosemite National Park in California, and

they've got huge trees there, called sequoias. They're much taller than this."

"How do you know?" the teacher asked Paul.

"Well, there were pine trees like this nearby, and the sequoias just towered over them. And the trunks were much thicker, like five or 10 of these other pines put together. And the big sequoias are old. I read that some are close to 2,000 years old," Paul replied.

"Wow! Think of how many cones and new trees they must have made during that

Figure 10.1 **Ponderosa pine tree.** Ponderosa pine trees can grow to be more than 60 meters (200 feet) tall.

"I know! I read about that in a magazine," Meagan said. "All these aspen trees are really like branches coming off one giant tree trunk underground. Some parts die, but others grow up from the underground part that connects them all. So this whole group of aspens could be just one big tree."

"Then how do you explain that lone one over there?" Kim asked, pointing to a tree on a slope far beyond the stream.

"Aspens can also grow new individuals from seeds in the same way that oaks and pines reproduce," explained the teacher. "That one probably is a separate tree, not part of the cluster here."

"So if that lone tree grows some more tree-looking sprouts from its roots, has it reproduced?" Paul asked.

"What do you think?" his teacher asked in return.

Figure 10.2 **Aspen trees.** Aspen trees often grow in clusters that are connected underground. They may also grow as individual trees from seeds.

length of time," said Maria. "It's amazing the whole forest wasn't just sequoias!"

"Look at this cluster of trees with the heart-shaped leaves," the teacher said. "Does anyone know what they are?"

"Aspens," several students said simultaneously (see figure 10.2).

"Well, here's a puzzle: If I tell you this aspen is even bigger than the sequoia, how could that be true?"

4. Brainstorm about other ways organisms reproduce. To give you some ideas, watch the video segment, "What's Going on Here?" Make notes about what you see happening in each of the images and write questions about reproduction that come to mind.

Online Resource

Analysis

Now that you have started to think about how organisms reproduce, begin a concept map on a new page in your science notebook. Your map needs to show what the term "reproduction" means to you at this point in your study of biology. Include in your concept map some terms about reproduction that you may have already learned.

    a. Population
    b. Inheritance
    c. Hormone
    d. Embryo

Add other terms that represent your current understanding of reproduction. Leave room to add more concepts and to change your map later in the chapter. Be sure to include descriptions on the links between concepts that explain how the ideas are related.

> This concept map is a way for you to record your *early* ideas on the subject. You will refer back to it and reflect on how your view changes as you work through this chapter and unit. If you need help creating your concept map, refer to appendix B7, *How to Construct a Concept Map*.

HOW TO

EXPLORE

Making Sense of Reproductive Strategies

Reproduction, the making of offspring, is an essential process for the continuation of a species. In the Engage activity, *A Zillion Ways to Make More*, you began thinking about the behaviors and processes used by different organisms to help them reproduce. These behaviors and processes, in combination with other characteristics, make up an organism's **reproductive strategy**. To begin developing your understanding of reproduction, you will look at similarities and differences in the reproductive strategies of a number of species during this Explore activity, *Making Sense of Reproductive Strategies*.

Materials   (per team of 2)

2 reproduction cards
1 felt-tipped marker
1 large sheet of paper or poster board

PROCESS AND PROCEDURES

1. Choose 2 reproduction cards with your partner. Read the material on each one to begin your study of the variety of reproductive strategies that exist across different species.

Try to choose cards with organisms that are very different from each other. One big difference you may find is between organisms that reproduce sexually or asexually. For more information, read the need to know, *Sexual and Asexual Reproduction*.

NEED TO KNOW

ENGLISH SPANISH

Sexual and Asexual Reproduction

You, like all mammals, had two biological parents. Each parent contributed to your genetic plan, so your genetic information comes from a combination of two sources. This combining of genetic material is possible through **sexual reproduction**. Sexual reproduction requires the union of specialized reproductive cells called **gametes**. Gametes have only half the genetic information that other cells have. The female parent produces the gametes known as eggs, or **ova** (singular: ovum). The male parent produces the gametes known as **sperm**. When an ovum and a sperm come together during sexual reproduction, their nuclei fuse. The product of their fusion is a **zygote**. This zygote has the potential to develop into a new organism. It carries a unique combination of genetic information contributed by the ovum and the sperm. Humans, plants that grow from seeds, cockroaches, and elephants are a few examples of products of sexual reproduction. They all come from the union of gametes produced by two parents.

Not all organisms result from two parents. Bacteria, for example, simply split into two equal-sized offspring. This process is called binary fission. A hydra is a tiny animal that lives in water. Hydras can reproduce asexually by forming clusters of cells called buds on the side of their bodies, as illustrated in figure 10.3b. The bud enlarges until it grows into a new hydra that breaks off from the parent. Unless a mutation alters a

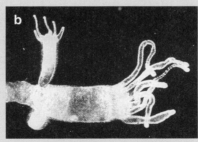
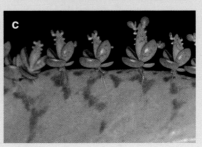

Figure 10.3 Three examples of asexual reproduction. (*a*) Amoebas (100×) reproduce by simple cell division (binary fission). (*b*) Hydras (100×) can reproduce by forming a bud that grows into a new individual. (*c*) The *Bryophyllum* leaf (1×) sprouts small plantlets that may grow into a new *Bryophyllum*.

particular trait, the offspring will have the same genetic pattern as its parent. Offspring produced from a single parent are called **clones**.

Any method of reproduction where the offspring are genetically identical to the parent is called **asexual reproduction**. The offspring have a genetic pattern identical to that parent. Figure 10.3 shows examples of organisms that reproduce through asexual reproduction. At the cellular level, the process of asexual reproduction is similar to the way cells in the bodies of multicellular organisms divide. When your cells divide, two new cells are made that have identical genetic information. The process by which these new cells are made is called **mitosis**.

Some species, such as aspen trees, can reproduce either sexually or asexually. For example, grass grows from seeds (sexual reproduction). It also grows by sending out underground runners (asexual reproduction). Yeast cells can either produce sexual gametes or asexual buds. In harsh conditions, hydras may also reproduce sexually by forming ova and sperm. Being able to reproduce both sexually and asexually is just one of many reproductive characteristics that exist among organisms.

www.scilinks.org

Topic: sexual and asexual reproduction
Code: human4E530

HOW TO

2. With your partner, look for similarities and differences in the 2 reproductive strategies described on your cards. Record this information in your science notebook.

> A T-table or Venn diagram is a useful way to summarize the similarities and differences between the strategies. If you need help creating a table, see appendix B4, *How to Use and Create Organizing Tables*. For help creating a Venn diagram, see appendix B5, *How to Use and Create Venn Diagrams*.

3. Prepare a short (3- to 5-minute) presentation that compares and contrasts the reproductive strategies of the 2 organisms that you and your partner studied. Create a visual diagram to use with your presentation. In your presentation, answer the following questions.

   a. What are some characteristics of each organism's reproductive strategy? Include the characteristics here that your organism displays. See figure 10.4 for an example of 2 characteristics of elephants.

   - Sexual or asexual reproduction
   - Mating behaviors
   - Number of offspring produced during each reproductive cycle
   - Frequency of the reproductive cycle
   - Specialized structures that are involved in reproduction
   - Life span of individuals
   - Age of sexual maturity
   - Length of gestation
   - Length of the period of offspring dependency

b. How are the reproductive strategies of your 2 organisms similar? How are they different?

> A large version of your T-table or Venn diagram is a good way to display the similarities and differences to the class.

c. What are the advantages and disadvantages of the reproductive strategies of your 2 organisms?

> For example, consider the amount of time and energy each strategy requires and the survival rate for the offspring.

Figure 10.4   A female elephant with her young. Elephants have the longest pregnancy of any mammal in the world—close to 22 months. The young nurse for three or four years.

d. How does each overall strategy ensure the continuation of the species?

> Think about how each characteristic that is part of the strategy contributes to the next generation.

4. Make your presentation to the rest of your classmates. See figure 10.5 for hints on making a good presentation. As you listen to the other presentations, take notes in your science notebook. Record the similarities, differences, and patterns between the reproductive strategies of different organisms.

5. Participate in a class discussion about patterns in reproduction that are emerging from the presentations. You might discuss how reproductive strategies relate to habitat, lifestyle, or the physical features of the organism.

6. Do you think humans use a reproductive strategy? Look back at the characteristics listed in step 3a. Write your ideas about each characteristic as they relate to humans.

7. In your science notebook, make a list of 3 concepts related to reproduction and the continuity of life that you think are important to the study of biology.

> Consider general ideas about reproduction rather than reproductive structures. For example, you might list the idea that reproduction can be a sexual or an asexual process.

8. Add your 3 concepts from step 7 to the concept map about reproduction that you started in the Engage activity, *A Zillion Ways to Make More*. Use verbs or short phrases to show how the concepts are related.

9. Compare your concept map with your partner's. Discuss any differences or similarities that you see. Make additions or revisions to your concept map to reflect your current understanding of reproduction.

10. Participate in a class discussion and construction of a reproduction concept map.

> Contribute ideas and explanations from your own concept map.

Figure 10.5   A student making a presentation. Make your presentation interesting and informative. Before you present, practice pronouncing the names of your organisms and the terms used to describe their reproductive strategies. If either of your organisms is unusual, be prepared to describe it for your classmates.

Analysis

Complete the following items individually.

1. Natural selection favors organisms that have successful ways of reproducing. Over time, each species accumulates a set of adaptations related to reproduction. The adaptations may include specific reproductive structures, the particular timing of reproductive behaviors, the number of offspring produced, the behaviors related to the care of offspring, and the methods of identifying and attracting mates. Together these are called a species' reproductive strategy.

   Based on this detailed definition of reproductive strategies, add to or revise your answer to the question in step 6 on whether humans use a reproductive strategy.

2. Think about the following questions. Record your responses in your science notebook.
   a. Is reproduction necessary for the survival of an individual? Explain.
   b. Is reproduction necessary for the survival of a species? Explain.
   c. Explain the relationship between changes in a species' environment and the effectiveness of that species' reproductive strategy.

      Consider whether a species' reproductive strategy might change over time. How might fast or slow changes in the environment affect the strategy?

3. Explain the connection between natural selection and reproduction. In your explanation, describe their importance to the continuation of a lineage or species. Also, explain their connection to the continuation of life on Earth.

Further Challenges

In this activity, you learned about how some plants and invertebrates can reproduce asexually by cloning. You may have also heard that scientists have developed techniques for cloning animals. This kind of cloning represents a new kind of reproductive strategy, one assisted by technology.

To find out more about animal cloning, read the sidebar, *Cloning*. Then answer the following questions in your science notebook.

1. Explain the difference between somatic cell nuclear transfer and fertilization.
2. Discuss your views of the ethical issues involved in
   a. cloning an animal for agricultural purposes,
   b. generating new tissues or organs by cloning cells, and
   c. cloning a human being.

ENGLISH SPANISH

Cloning

Cloning is defined in different ways by various groups and organizations. A commonly used definition is that cloning is the production of genetically identical organisms. Identical twins fit that definition. Yet, accepting identical twins as clones would yield a variety of negative and positive responses. A more widely accepted definition comes from the American Medical Association (AMA): "Cloning is the production of genetically identical organisms via somatic cell nuclear transfer."

Somatic cell nuclear transfer refers to the process of removing the nucleus of an ovum and replacing it with the nucleus of a somatic cell. In that way, the ovum gains a full set of genetic information from the existing organism, without fertilization. The genetic information transferred into the ovum may have no relation to the ovum. The last four words of the AMA's definition gives a much more complete picture of what cloning means to most people today.

One of the world's most famous clones was a sheep named Dolly (figure 10.6). We will use Dolly to illustrate the last four words of the AMA's definition. A cell was removed from the udder of a six-year-old white-faced ewe (a *somatic cell*). An egg cell was removed from a black-faced sheep, and its nucleus was removed. The somatic cell was fused with the egg cell, from which the nucleus had been removed (*nuclear transfer*). Thus, the ovum gains a whole set of genetic information from the existing organism, without fertilization. At this point, the

Figure 10.6 Dolly and her lamb. Dolly, a clone, was able to breed normally to produce her first lamb in April 1998.

egg cell contained its original cytoplasm, including mitochondria and DNA. But it had the nucleus of another sheep. An electric shock was used to stimulate the egg cell to divide and develop. The egg cell developed normally to an early embryonic stage. It was then transplanted into a surrogate, black-faced ewe. On July 5, 1996, 148 days later, Dolly was born. Dolly appeared to have all the traits of the white-faced ewe whose somatic cell had been used in the cloning procedure.

Since Dolly, there have been clones of mice, cattle, and pigs. Does this mean that in the near future there will be human clones?

Few doubt that the biological processes of human cloning could be successful with further research. However, the ethical implications—the "rights" and "wrongs"—of human cloning must be explored. We must develop an acceptable, comprehensive, and intelligent plan before human cloning has a chance to become a reality.

Dr. Arthur Caplan is the director of the Center for Bioethics and professor of bioethics at the University of Pennsylvania. He was asked to describe the ethical pros and cons of cloning. He stated, "The pros are that you might be able to help infertile individuals and couples have children, and by making cloned cells, you might find a way to make tissues and organs to treat diseases. That's called therapeutic cloning. The cons are that human cloning is not safe. Animal cloning has produced many dead, deformed, and diseased animals. However, I do favor making cloned cells for research" (2001). Some data that support Dr. Caplan's objection come from experiences in cloning Dolly. It took scientists 277 tries before Dolly was created. In 277 nuclear fusions, only 29 embryos developed. Only 13 embryos appeared normal enough to implant in 13 ewes. Only Dolly's surrogate mother gave birth. Experts say that the technique that produced Dolly fails 97 percent of the time. In addition, Dolly developed arthritis at age five and a half, raising other concerns.

In 2003, scientists decided to euthanize Dolly because she had a serious lung infection. Dolly was relatively young when she got arthritis and the lung disease. Scientists, however, do not know whether the early onset of disease was a result of the cloning process.

As of this writing, a high percentage of scientists and bioethicists seem to oppose human cloning. However, cloning tissues and organs falls under a different category than cloning humans. The majority think that type of cloning would be beneficial to science.

EXPLAIN

Making Sense of Human Reproduction

In the Explore activity, *Making Sense of Reproductive Strategies*, you explored the wide variety of characteristics that make up an organism's reproductive strategy. How does this relate to humans? What about reproduction in humans? How does it work? What parts of the body are involved? How are they regulated? In this Explain activity, *Making Sense of Human Reproduction*, you will learn more about human reproduction. You will first compare the parts of the male and female reproductive systems. Then you will learn about how gametes are produced. Finally, you will begin to understand the steps that occur when the gametes come together at fertilization.

Materials

Part A
none

Part B
online resource (optional)
scissors
glue or tape
different-colored pens or pencils

Part C
online resource

PROCESS AND PROCEDURES

Part A   Parts of the Reproductive System

To begin making sense of how reproduction works in humans, it is important to understand the structures that are part of the male and female reproductive systems.

1. In your science notebook, create a Venn diagram of the structures involved in the human reproductive system. To help you with your diagram, read the essay, *Human Reproductive Systems*.

   In your Venn diagram, include the following terms related to reproductive systems.

   a. Sperm
   b. Ova
   c. Epididymes
   d. Vasa deferentia
   e. Ovaries
   f. Uterus
   g. Gonads

   h. Penis
   i. Scrotum
   j. Cowper's gland
   k. Prostate gland
   l. Vagina
   m. Gametes
   n. Clitoris

   o. Testes
   p. Labia
   q. Seminal vesicles
   r. Vulva
   s. Oviducts
   t. Urethra

   One circle should be labeled "male" and the other circle should be labeled "female." Terms that describe structures present in both males and females should appear in the overlapping section. For more information on how to create a Venn diagram, see appendix B5, *How to Use and Create Venn Diagrams*.

   HOW TO

2. Compare your Venn diagram with your partner's. Discuss any differences between your Venn diagrams and revise your diagram if necessary.

Human Reproductive Systems

ENGLISH SPANISH

Have you ever wondered how sperm and eggs are produced? Where are they made? What structures in the body and outside the body are involved in human reproduction? The answers to these questions will help form an understanding of the human reproductive system.

Female Anatomy

Did you know that a woman is born with all the ova she will ever have? The ovaries of a female baby contain approximately 2 million ova, or female gametes. Ova are sometimes called eggs, and the two terms are used interchangeably here. **Ovaries** are the human female **gonads**—the organs that produce gametes. Only about 400 of the 2 million ova mature into healthy ova over the course of a

woman's life. Ova begin maturing in the ovaries when a female reaches sexual maturity, or **puberty**. Puberty typically happens between the ages of nine and 14. Once an ovum is mature, it can be fertilized.

Each month, one of the two ovaries (see figure 10.7) releases a mature ovum. Although the ovum is released into the body cavity, it is quickly swept up into a long tube called an **oviduct**. As you can see in figure 10.7, there are two oviducts, one near each ovary. The oviducts are lined with very fine, hairlike structures. These structures help move the ovum down the oviduct. An ovum disintegrates after about 24 hours if it is not fertilized by a sperm. If fertilization does occur, it usually takes place in the oviduct. The oviducts lead to the uterus. The **uterus** is a thick-walled, pear-shaped

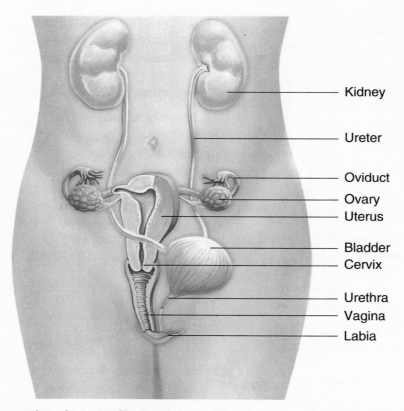

Kidney

Ureter

Oviduct
Ovary
Uterus

Bladder
Cervix

Urethra
Vagina
Labia

Figure 10.7 The human female reproductive system. The illustration shows the internal organs of the female reproductive system. The urinary system is also shown. Notice that the uterus and the vagina are shown in a cross-section view.

organ located between the bladder and the rectum. This organ can stretch to several times its width to make room for a growing baby.

The lower, narrow portion of the uterus is called the **cervix**. It extends into the vagina, the organ that connects the internal and external reproductive organs. The **vagina** is a muscular tube that lies at a 45° angle to the female's back. The vagina is also capable of stretching, which is important when a baby is born. The vagina is also the organ that is penetrated in vaginal intercourse and is the exit for menstrual flow.

The external female reproductive organs, together, are called the **vulva**. This includes the **labia**, which are folds of skin that protect the genitals. These folds cover the clitoris and the openings of the

vagina and the urethra. The **clitoris** is a small, sensitive organ situated at the front of the vulva. The clitoris is developmentally homologous to the male penis. This means that these structures develop in a similar way and from the same type of tissue, even though they perform different functions. Notice that in females the reproductive system is completely separate from the urinary system (see figure 10.7). In females, the urethra only carries urine from the bladder and is not involved in reproduction.

Male Anatomy

Unlike a female child, a male child is born without any gametes in his body. **Sperm**, the male gametes, begin forming in the testes at puberty (see figure 10.8). **Testes** (singular: testis) are the male gonads.

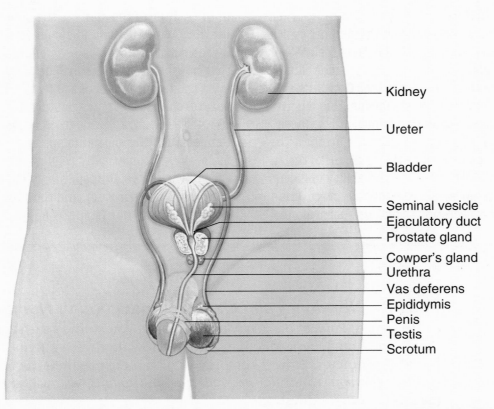

Kidney

Ureter

Bladder

Seminal vesicle
Ejaculatory duct
Prostate gland

Cowper's gland
Urethra
Vas deferens
Epididymis
Penis
Testis
Scrotum

Figure 10.8   The human male reproductive system. The structures that make up the male reproductive system are shown. Some parts lie within the body cavity, while others are external. The parts of the urinary system are also shown.

After sperm are produced in the testes, they are stored in long, coiled tubes lying outside each testis, called the **epididymes** (singular: epididymis). Sperm remain in the epididymes until they are mature, which takes about two weeks. The sperm may stay in the epididymes for several months awaiting ejaculation. If they have not been ejaculated after that time, they will disintegrate. From each epididymis, they pass through a tube called the **vas deferens** (plural: vasa deferentia). Each vas deferens runs from the epididymis, through the body cavity, and up and around the bladder. The sperm then empty into the urethra near the base of the bladder.

Also, at the base of the bladder are two small sacs called seminal vesicles. The **seminal vesicles** contribute to the production of semen. **Semen** is a white, sticky fluid that carries and nourishes the sperm. Semen is added to the sperm as they flow into ejaculatory ducts. These ducts connect the seminal vesicles with the opening of the urethra in the prostate gland. The **prostate gland** produces and adds more fluid to the semen. Another gland, called the **Cowper's gland**, produces an alkaline, or basic, mucus. This mucus is secreted before ejaculation to neutralize traces of urine, which is acidic, and clean the urethra. The mucus also helps neutralize the acidic pH of the vagina. This increases the sperm's ability to move and survive in the female reproductive tract. It is possible for this secretion to pick up sperm along the way. Thus, fertilization can readily take place if a couple relies only on withdrawing the penis before ejaculation for birth control.

In males, the **urethra** is the passageway for both sperm and urine. A muscle near the prostate gland contracts so that no urine can flow through the urethra during ejaculation. **Ejaculation** expels semen from the urethra of the penis during orgasm. During ejaculation, up to 5 mL of semen is released. It contains approximately 300 million sperm cells.

The external male reproductive organs include the penis and scrotum. The **penis** is made up of the shaft and the glans. The **glans** is a rounded gland structure at the tip of the penis. It is covered by the foreskin. The foreskin is sometimes removed (usually in infancy) by a surgical procedure known as *circumcision*. The small opening in the center of the glans is the opening of the urethra where urine and semen are released.

The **scrotum** is a loose sac of skin and muscle that houses the two testes. The scrotum regulates the temperature of the testes. This temperature must be approximately 33°C–34°C (91.4°F–93.2°F, a few degrees cooler than body temperature) for optimum sperm production. The male body automatically regulates the temperature of the testes. It does this by changing the position of the scrotum, and thus the testes, to be closer or farther from the body.

Part B   Hormones and Gamete Production in Humans

In part A, *Parts of the Reproductive System*, you studied the structures of the male and female reproductive systems. How do these systems work to produce gametes? How is the process of gamete production controlled? In part B, *Hormones and Gamete Production in Humans*, you will examine the answers to these questions.

1. Examine figure 10.10a and the *Human Menstrual Cycle* handout with your partner. Cut out graph A from the handout and place it in your science notebook.

2. On graph A, draw arrows and write highlight comments for what you see happening in figure 10.10a. Leave room to fill in comments about "What it means" in step 5.

> Relate the hormone levels shown in the graph to the events in the ovary. For more information on highlight comments, see appendix B6, *How to Write Highlight Comments and Captions.*

HOW TO

3. Cut out graph B from the handout and place it in your science notebook. Which of the 2 hormones do you think has more control over the thickening of the uterine lining? Draw arrows on graph B where you see evidence of which hormone controls the thickness of the uterine lining.

4. Read the essay, *Producing Gametes,* to help you make sense of what the changes in the levels of hormones mean during the ovarian cycle and the uterine cycle. As you read, think about how the changes relate to the graphs you looked at in steps 2 and 3.

> You may also wish to watch the video segment, "Human Menstrual Cycle."

Online Resource

5. Complete the remaining parts of the highlight comments and captions for graph A and graph B.

6. Add the common features and the differences between male and female gamete production to the Venn diagram you created in part A.

7. Discuss the new additions to the diagram with your partner. Revise, as necessary.

Producing Gametes

ENGLISH   SPANISH

In order to reproduce, both males and females need to be able to produce gametes. The production of both eggs and sperm is highly regulated. Hormones are responsible for controlling gamete production in both males and females, though the process is quite different between the two sexes.

Ovum Production

Although a woman is born with all the ova she will release throughout her lifetime, these eggs are not mature, or ready to be fertilized. Beginning at puberty, hormones regulate the maturation and release of, typically, one egg per month. How is the cycle controlled to allow an egg to be released once a month?

If we were able to have an open view into an ovary (see figure 10.9), we would see several structures

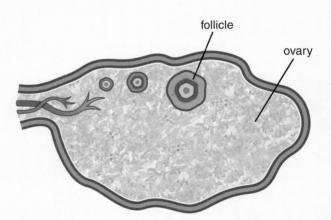

Figure 10.9   Cross section of an ovary. This open view into an ovary shows the dominant follicle with an ovum. Two additional smaller follicles can also be seen. Approximately what day of the ovarian cycle do you think this represents?

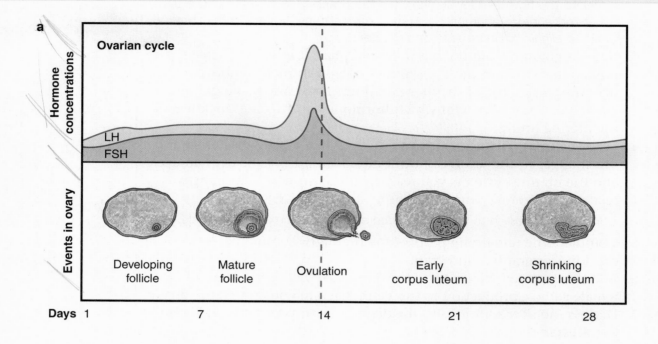

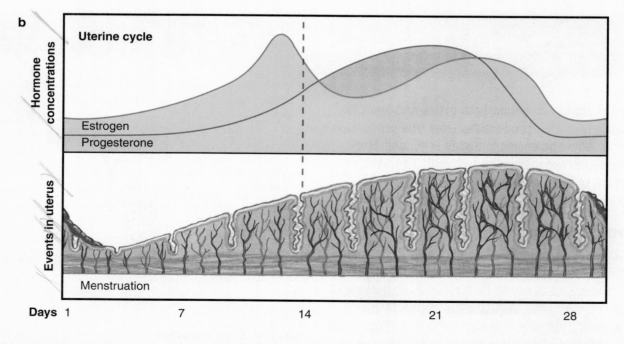

Figure 10.10   The human menstrual cycle. Interactions between the brain, hormones, and the parts of the reproductive system regulate the menstrual cycle. It consists of two parts, (*a*) the ovarian cycle and (*b*) the uterine cycle. The cycle usually lasts about 28 days. Note how the levels of hormones change over the cycle. How do those changes relate to the events in the ovary and in the uterus?

called follicles. A **follicle** is a sac that contains one undeveloped ovum and a number of other cells that support and nourish that ovum. Each month, hormonal signals from the brain instruct several follicles to begin developing, as shown in figure 10.9. Typically, one follicle, and the ovum inside, will complete the maturing process each month. This process is called the **ovarian cycle** (figure 10.10a and graph A). This cycle typically lasts about 28 days, although it may range from less than 24 to more than 35 days.

The ovarian cycle begins with the brain releasing **follicle-stimulating hormone (FSH)**. This is an appropriate name because FSH signals several follicles to begin developing. FSH causes the ovum to divide its genetic material, or chromosomes.

As the follicles begin developing, they release estrogen. Levels of estrogen control the amount of FSH that is released through the rest of the cycle. At times, the estrogen inhibits more FSH from being produced. At other times, such as right before ovulation, the estrogen causes more FSH to be released. Currently, the role of FSH in ovulation, if there is one, is unknown. The estrogen from the follicles also causes the brain to begin releasing **luteinizing hormone (LH)**. A large burst of LH is released right before ovulation. The high level of LH causes one dominant follicle to enlarge quickly. Any remaining follicles stop developing by this point. The rapid increase in LH is known as the **LH surge**. This is the signal that causes **ovulation**, the time when the mature egg is released from the follicle. Ovulation occurs around the middle (day 14) of the ovarian cycle. The monthly cycle can vary a lot between individual women, however, so it is extremely difficult to predict when a woman will ovulate.

Once the ovum is released, it is swept into the oviduct. At this point, there are two possible fates for the egg. It will be fertilized or it will not. If it is fertilized, this will generally happen in the oviduct. The fertilized egg will then be transported into the uterus, where it will implant in the uterine wall and be nourished through pregnancy. If the ovum is not fertilized within 24 hours, it will stop developing and will disintegrate before reaching the uterus.

Hormonal signals not only play a role in the maturation and release of the egg, but also in the **uterine cycle** (figure 10.10b and graph B). A buildup of the uterine lining happens at the same time the ovarian cycle is occurring. The ovarian and uterine cycles together make up the **menstrual cycle**. Remember that estrogen is released from the developing follicle during the first half of the cycle. This estrogen causes the lining of the uterus to thicken. Once ovulation occurs, the empty follicle is known as the **corpus luteum**. The corpus luteum releases both estrogen and progesterone. The progesterone has an important role because it causes the lining of the uterus to thicken even more. This prepares the uterus to cushion and nourish a fertilized egg if pregnancy occurs. If pregnancy does not occur, the absence of a fertilized egg causes the uterus to shed its lining over four to five days in a process called **menstruation**.

During menstruation, a small amount of blood (between 50 mL and 150 mL—between 1/4 cup and 2/3 cup) is expelled through the vagina. Day 1 of the ovarian and uterine cycles is defined as the day that menstruation begins.

Females continue this cycle each month until **menopause**. Just as puberty marks the beginning of sexual maturity, menopause marks the end. After menopause, females no longer have a menstrual cycle and no longer ovulate. The effects and timing of menopause vary widely. Menopause usually takes place between the ages of 45 and 55, although it can occur earlier. Like puberty, its onset is regulated by hormones in the body.

Sperm Production

Sperm begin forming in the testes at puberty (figure 10.11). Millions of sperm mature each day in a healthy, young adult male. The difference

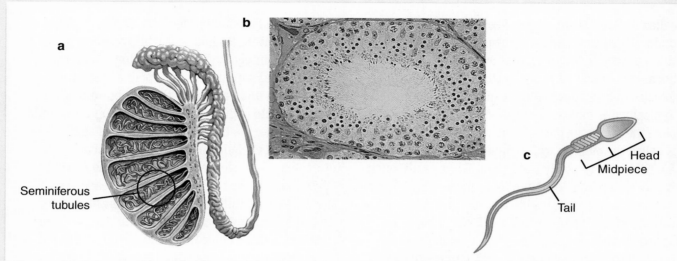

Figure 10.11 **Sperm production in the testes.** (*a*) Each testis is composed of packed coils of tubules, called the seminiferous tubules, in which sperm develop. (*b*) This photograph is a cross section through a seminiferous tubule (100×). Sperm begin developing at the outer edges of the tube and are mostly developed by the time they reach the inner part. Notice the tails of the sperm extending into the open space. (*c*) A mature sperm has three parts: the head, the midpiece, and the tail.

between the number of male and female gametes may surprise you. However, very few sperm survive long enough to reach an ovum.

Hormone signals from the brain cause sperm to be produced. Some of these hormones are the same as those in females. In males, FSH stimulates the testes to produce sperm. LH stimulates the testes to release the major male sex hormone, **testosterone**.

Within the testes are long, coiled tubes called **seminiferous tubules**. These tubes make up about 80 percent of the mass of the testes. The tubules contain developing sperm as well as support cells that will help nourish the sperm as they form.

Sperm production is continuous, meaning that each day new sperm mature. At any given time, there are sperm in varying stages of development within the testes. Those sperm near the outer edges of the tubule are the least developed. As they move

toward the inner part of the tubule, they become more and more mature. The process to become fully developed takes about 70 days.

Sperm are much smaller than ova. Once developed, sperm have three main parts. The head of the sperm contains the genetic material. This material fuses with the genetic material in an ovum at fertilization. The tip of the head contains enzymes that will help the sperm penetrate an ovum. The midsection of the sperm contains many mitochondria. Mitochondria provide the ATP the sperm needs for energy to swim through the female reproductive tract. The sperm's tail whips back and forth to direct its movement.

After developing in the testes, sperm leave the seminiferous tubules and are stored in the epididymes. They remain in the epididymes for up to two weeks to undergo the final steps of maturation, such as gaining the ability to swim.

Part C   *Fertilization*

Once gametes have been formed, they can come together at fertilization to produce new offspring. How do children ensure the continuity of information and of life? Part C, *Fertilization*, will help you understand the process involved in creating offspring.

1. Imagine that a human egg was put in an environment with the sperm from a cat. Would the sperm fertilize the egg? Why or why not? Discuss your ideas with your partner.
2. Watch the video segment, "Conception," to see how fertilization occurs.
3. Write the steps that happen during conception, or fertilization, based on your observations from the video.
4. Read the need to know, *Cultural Aspects of Reproduction*. As you read, think about how the beliefs relate to your scientific understanding of conception.

Online Resource

NEED TO KNOW
ENGLISH   SPANISH

Cultural Aspects of Reproduction

On one of the Trobriand Islands of Papua New Guinea, a woman completes a long labor and delivers a healthy baby boy. Although the woman has a husband, she and the others present at the birth do not congratulate the father. People in the Trobriand Islands emphasize the mother's contribution to a child's development. Not much importance is placed on the biological link between the baby and his father. The islanders believe that ancestral spirits plant the seeds that enable a fetus to grow. This belief establishes a link between the past and the future. The father does have a role to play, however. They expect him to have intercourse with the mother throughout the pregnancy. Trobriand Islanders believe that continued intercourse helps the fetus grow.

One aspect of the Trobriand Islanders' view fits with the scientific view. Like the Trobriand Islanders, we believe offspring are related to their ancestors. However, science has demonstrated that offspring acquire their genetic heritage from both parents. We also know that pregnancy is not caused by spirits planting seeds in the mother. Instead, pregnancy is caused by an ovum and a sperm coming into contact with each other. To understand more fully how humans reproduce, you need to understand how reproductive structures function and are regulated.

5. Write a paragraph on the parts of the story in the need to know, *Cultural Aspects of Reproduction* that conflict with a scientific understanding of conception.
6. Read the essay, *Human Fertilization*, to add to your knowledge about conception. Based on the reading, add any new information to your list of the steps in fertilization from step 3.
7. Look back at the paragraph you wrote in step 5 about the beliefs of the people in the Trobriand Islands. Add to or revise your paragraph based on the information from the essay.
8. Think back to the question posed in step 1 about the human egg and cat sperm. What new ideas do you have about the question? Discuss them with your partner.

Human Fertilization

ENGLISH SPANISH

After the gametes have been produced and are mature, they are ready to come together and fuse their genetic material. This process is called fertilization, or conception. In order for this to happen, a man and a woman first engage in sexual intercourse.

Sexual Intercourse

As a male becomes sexually aroused, the blood flow to the penis increases. Increased blood volume causes the penis to become rigid. This makes it easier to enter the vagina. As the female becomes sexually aroused, blood flow to the vaginal area increases. Glands near the vagina secrete fluids that lubricate the vagina. This eases the movement of the male's penis in the vagina. It also allows the sperm to swim more easily.

The peak of sexual stimulation for both men and women is called **orgasm**. In men, it results from stimulation of sensitive nerve endings in the penis. Male ejaculation occurs during orgasm, releasing sperm-containing semen through the penis. Ejaculation results from involuntary muscle contractions. Female orgasm also causes involuntary muscle contractions. These result from stimulation of sensitive nerve endings in the vaginal area, especially the clitoris. These contractions may help transport the sperm upward through the cervix and into the uterus toward the egg. However, fertilization can take place without female orgasm.

The muscle contractions that happen during both male and female orgasms create pleasurable sensations. From an individual human couple's perspective, these sensations enhance the emotional bond between them. From a human species' perspective, the pleasure derived from sexual intercourse helps ensure continuation of the species.

Fertilization

Fertilization occurs as a result of sexual intercourse. The journey of sperm to the oviducts may take less than an hour; however, sperm can live for several days and fertilization may occur during those days. But only a few thousand sperm may survive the trip. If an ovum is present in one of the oviducts, sperm swarm around it and release enzymes. The enzymes promote changes in the outer layers of the ovum. This allows the sperm to penetrate these layers. The photograph at the beginning of the chapter shows a sperm fertilizing an ovum. Notice how much smaller the sperm is than the egg. Only one sperm actually penetrates the egg during fertilization. As soon as penetration takes place, the cell membrane of the ovum changes to prevent entry of any other sperm.

Chemicals play an important role in fertilization. First, it is believed that the egg releases chemicals that attract the sperm to it. Once a sperm reaches the egg, enzymes are released to help the sperm penetrate the egg. These enzymes are located in a sac called the **acrosome**, found at the tip of the sperm head. Once a single sperm penetrates the egg, chemicals play another role. Certain chemicals are released to make the coat around the egg hard. This prevents additional sperm from fertilizing the egg. The sperm and eggs from different species of animals have different enzymes, chemicals, and receptors. This makes fertilization between different species highly unlikely.

Fertilization usually happens in the oviduct. The single cell that results from the joining of the ovum and sperm is called a zygote. A zygote has genetic material from both the mother and the father. The zygote begins a series of cell divisions to produce an **embryo** (figure 10.12). The embryo develops as it moves through the oviduct and into the uterus. About seven days after fertilization, the embryo consists of a ball of cells containing an inner, flattened cavity. At this stage, it begins to implant into the wall of the uterus. The uterus protects the developing embryo. It stretches and grows as the embryo grows.

After implantation, the developing embryo will obtain the nutrients and oxygen it needs from the mother's blood supply. It does this through an organ called the **placenta**. The placenta attaches to the uterine wall. It is connected to the embryo by a ropelike **umbilical cord**. The placenta exchanges nourishment from the mother and waste products from the embryo through the mother's blood. After eight weeks of growth, the embryo is called a **fetus**.

Birth

Following a nine-month gestation period, contractions of the uterus push the baby through

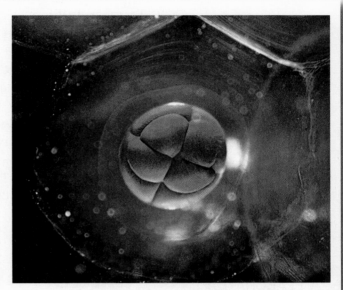

Figure 10.12   An embryo. This computer-generated image of an embryo has eight cells. After fertilization, it takes 3 divisions to reach 8 cells. This takes about 3 days after fertilization.

the cervix and into the vagina. Because the vagina is a muscle, it is able to stretch to accommodate the baby. The time when a woman's body is undergoing contractions to deliver a baby is called *labor*. Hormones and regulatory feedback loops determine when a woman will begin labor. During labor, contractions become more frequent as the baby nears the vagina and the cervix expands. The fetus usually travels head first through the vagina.

The moment when the fetus exits the mother's body is called *delivery*. After delivery, the umbilical cord is cut and clamped near the navel. Finally, mucus is cleared from the baby's mouth, nose, and throat. From that moment forward, the baby's body takes over the processes of maintaining homeostasis. These processes had been taken care of by the mother's body only hours before.

Analysis

1. The word "progesterone" means "to promote gestation." "Estrogen" means "to generate estrus." Estrus is the hormonal cycle that takes place in nonhuman mammals. Explain why these are appropriate names.
2. Estrogen influences both FSH and LH during the menstrual cycle. What would happen if estrogen stayed at a constant level throughout the month?
3. Explain the role that gametes play in sexual reproduction. How do they ensure the *continuity of information* that must take place for a species to survive?
4. Explain how changes to sperm and eggs between 2 different lineages can cause reproductive isolation.

   First think about the reasons that a sperm can only fertilize an egg from the same species. Then consider what would happen if those mechanisms were changed.

ELABORATE

Regulation of Human Reproduction

In most mammals, females and males are drawn to mate by powerful instincts that happen only when the female's body is able to conceive. In humans and some other primates, however, the female may be receptive to sexual activity at any time. Although her body can only conceive during a short period each menstrual cycle, this time is not always predictable. For that reason, humans have long tried to find ways to regulate reproduction.

There is evidence even from ancient times of humans trying to control the size of their families. Some of their reasons were cultural or social. Other families wanted to regulate family size for physical, emotional, or economic reasons. The first evidence of artificial birth control was found on an approximately 4,000-year-old scroll near the source of the Nile River. It showed a recipe for a substance that would be applied to the vagina before intercourse. This substance would harden and block the cervix. The earliest known record of condom use comes from Egyptian illustrations drawn around 3,000 years ago.

Over time, scientists learned more about the biology of the human reproductive system. This allowed them to develop improved birth control methods. Birth control methods are also called **contraceptives**. Today, there are many effective birth control methods that can be used to prevent pregnancy. Certain contraceptives also help protect against sexually transmitted diseases (STDs). As scientists learn more about the human body, they have been able to develop safer, more reliable birth control methods.

Your task in this Elaborate activity, *Regulation of Human Reproduction*, is to explain the *biological basis* for birth control methods. In other words, you will explain how birth control technologies work and *why* they differ in their degree of effectiveness.

Materials (per person)

additional resources on birth control methods
different-colored pens or pencils
art supplies (such as colored paper and markers)

PROCESS AND PROCEDURES

1. Create a 3-column table in your science notebook. Write the title "contraceptives" above the table. Label the headings of the 3 columns as "physical barriers," "chemical methods," and "behavioral methods." Leave room for an additional column on the right.
2. Classify the devices and methods from the *Examples of Birth Control Methods* handout into the categories listed at the top of your table. Write each method in the appropriate column in your science notebook.
3. Review your classification with a partner. Be able to explain why you classified each method the way you did. Make any revisions to your chart in a different-colored pen or pencil.

   For more information about using the TSAR strategy, see appendix B3, *How to Use the Think-Share-Advise-Revise (TSAR) Strategy.*

4. Create a new table similar to the one shown in figure 10.13.
5. In addition to helping prevent pregnancy, certain contraceptives can lower a person's risk of being infected by a sexually transmitted disease. To learn more about STDs, read the essay, *Sexual Activity and Health Hazards.* As you read, complete the information in the table you created in step 4.

Topic: birth control
Code: human4E547

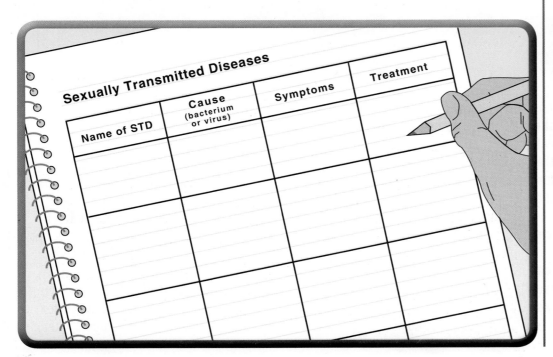

Figure 10.13
Sexually transmitted diseases (STDs).
STDs may be caused by bacteria or by viruses. Some STDs have similar symptoms and treatments. Use the table to record information about each STD.

6. Look back at the 3-column chart you created in steps 1 and 2. Make an additional column with the heading "helps protect against STDs." Place a checkmark (✓) in the column next to each birth control method that can help protect against STDs.

7. Obtain a copy of the handout, *Birth Control Brochure Rubric*. Using the available resources, prepare a brochure describing 1 contraceptive method from each category: physical barriers, chemical methods, and behavioral methods. Your brochure should give the *biological* explanation for how each of the 3 contraceptive methods works.

   You will know you have developed a good brochure when you do each of the following.

   a. Describe how each birth control method interferes with reproduction.

   b. Explain how each method affects the reproductive systems of males or females. (For example, how does the method alter the hormonal levels of the male? The female?)

   c. Explain why each method needs to be used at a particular time.

   d. Explain the differences in the effectiveness of the methods that you chose in each category.

   > You can develop one brochure that describes all the methods or one brochure for each method. Remember, your goal is to show that you understand the *biology* behind these methods. For example, if you choose to create a brochure on birth control pills, you should discuss how they influence the hormone levels during the menstrual cycle.

Sexual Activity and Health Hazards

ENGLISH SPANISH

Sexual behavior involves risks. People who are sexually active run the risk of becoming parents. Sexual behavior can also increase the risk of contracting a **sexually transmitted disease (STD)**. Using birth control methods greatly reduces the possibility of pregnancy. However, not all birth control methods protect against sexually transmitted diseases. Abstinence from all sexual activity is the only way to completely protect against both pregnancy and sexually transmitted diseases.

Sexual behavior usually involves the exchange of body fluids. This exchange provides pathogens with an excellent route of infection. Sexually transmitted pathogens include the viruses that cause AIDS and genital herpes. Other pathogens include the bacteria that cause syphilis, chlamydia, and gonorrhea.

AIDS (acquired immunodeficiency syndrome) is caused by a virus called human immunodeficiency virus, or HIV. Casual contact, such as shaking hands with an infected person, does not transfer HIV. Infection requires a transfer of body fluids such as blood, semen, or vaginal secretions. HIV infection most often occurs during sexual intercourse (heterosexual and homosexual) and through the sharing of needles by drug users. When individuals are first infected by HIV, they usually have no symptoms. However, they can still transmit the virus to others. Symptoms of AIDS accumulate over several years. They include extreme fatigue, weight loss, reduced resistance to other infections, and cancer. A regimen of multiple antiviral drugs can slow the progress of the disease. An understanding of the evolution of HIV has helped researchers work on treatments for AIDS. However, AIDS and HIV cannot be cured.

Another sexually transmitted disease caused by a virus is genital herpes. An estimated 1 in 5 of the total adolescent and adult population of the United States is infected with genital herpes. The virus that causes this disease is related to the viruses that cause chicken pox and cold sores. Symptoms of genital herpes are painful sores on the male's penis or the female's vulva, vagina, or cervix. There is no cure for genital herpes. The sores heal and recur throughout an infected person's life. Genital herpes is transmitted through direct contact with the infected area. Infection can occur whether or not sores are present. Although there is no cure, antiviral drugs help relieve the painful symptoms. Outbreaks of sores also become less frequent and milder over time. Genital herpes may be transmitted to the babies of infected mothers as they pass through the birth canal. In these infants, the herpes virus can cause serious neurological damage. To avoid this, doctors recommend that women with active herpes sores deliver their children by cesarean section. In a cesarean, a baby is delivered through a surgical incision in the mother's abdomen.

Human papillomavirus (HPV) is a group of viruses. Some strains of the virus cause changes in cells, which lead to cervical cancer. Other strains of the virus cause the sexually transmitted disease genital warts. The symptoms of genital warts are flat or raised, flesh-colored warts on the genitals. They may be single warts or groups of warts. Without treatment, the warts sometimes grow in size or increase in number. The strains of HPV that cause genital warts are different from the strains that cause cervical cancer. Many people who have HPV are not aware they are infected because some strains do not cause any symptoms. It is estimated that 50 percent of sexually active people in the United States will have HPV at some point. Recently, a vaccine against the most common strains of HPV was approved by the U.S. Food and Drug Administration.

Syphilis is another sexually transmitted disease. It is caused by a bacterium. The symptoms of syphilis vary depending on the stage of the disease. Each stage is separated by a long period without symptoms. In the early stage, a hard sore called a chancre develops on the male's penis or the female's vagina, or on the hands and lips. Although no symptoms are present after the chancre heals, a blood test would reveal that syphilis bacteria are present. During the second stage, a skin rash develops. This can happen even on the palms and the feet. Individuals are highly infectious during this stage. During the final stage, tissue damage occurs throughout the body, particularly to the nervous system. Untreated, late-stage syphilis causes severe damage to the circulatory and nervous systems, and even death. An estimated 36,000 new cases of syphilis occur annually in the United States. Antibiotics are available that can cure infection by the syphilis bacteria.

The most common sexually transmitted disease is chlamydia. Chlamydia is caused by a very small bacterium. It is estimated that over 2 million people in the United States are infected by chlamydia. Most people who are infected with chlamydia do not have symptoms and, therefore, do not seek treatment. When symptoms are present, females have inflammation of the opening to the vagina or cervix. Males have inflammation of the epididymes and a watery discharge from the penis. Untreated, chlamydia can cause serious reproductive and other health problems. For example, chlamydia may cause pelvic inflammatory disease in females, resulting in infertility. Babies born to women who have chlamydia may be infected and develop eye inflammations or pneumonia. Antibiotics are available that can cure infection by the chlamydia bacteria.

Gonorrhea is a bacterial disease that has afflicted humans since ancient times. Symptoms may or may not be present. If they are, males experience painful urination and pus from the penis. In females, the cervix is infected, causing a discharge from the vagina. If left untreated, gonorrhea may lead to infertility in females. A pregnant woman with untreated gonorrhea may transmit the bacteria that cause the disease to her baby as it passes through the birth canal. The resulting eye infection can lead to blindness, so physicians routinely treat newborns with eyedrops that prevent the disease. An

estimated 700,000 new cases of gonorrhea occur each year in the United States. Antibiotics can cure gonorrhea most of the time. However, there has been a dramatic increase in antibiotic-resistant strains of gonorrhea. Again, an understanding of evolution helps health care workers treat this disease.

The most effective way to avoid contracting a sexually transmitted disease is abstinence. This means that a person avoids all sexual contact. Abstinence is considered the most effective way of preventing STDs because infection is not always obvious or known. The use of latex condoms helps prevent the transmission of many sexually transmitted diseases, although they do not guarantee protection. Other methods of birth control, such as spermicide, diaphragms, and birth control pills, may help prevent pregnancy, but they do not protect a person against STDs.

Analysis

Join the class in a discussion of the following.

1. What do you think the prefix "contra-," as in "contraception," means?
2. Explain why some methods of birth control are not effective at preventing STDs.
3. Consider the natural family planning method (the rhythm method) of birth control. Explain how a couple who desires children could modify and use it to *increase* the chances of conception.

Further Challenges

1. Research and report on current progress in developing oral contraceptives for men.
2. Research and report on the history of syphilis in human culture and science.

Analyzing Reproductive Behaviors

Now you have some understanding of the biological basis of reproduction in humans. However, it is not enough simply to have working reproductive structures and hormonal cycles. Sexual reproduction takes two, and for animals, attracting a mate can be a major endeavor. Throughout the animal kingdom, the males and females of many species put on a show of behavior aimed at attracting a mate. When a peacock wants to attract a peahen, he displays his extravagant plumage, he struts, and he shakes his colorful tail. Similarly, a male elk (bull elk) calls out loudly (bugles) during mating season. The bugling of a bull elk has at least two effects. It attracts potential mates, and it announces his presence to other bulls with the goal of steering them away. Such animal displays often are showy and complicated. Scientists who study animal behavior, including mating behavior, are called **ethologists**.

What about humans? In the first Elaborate activity, *Regulation of Human Reproduction,* you examined the biology of the human reproductive system. Do you think humans also exhibit mating behaviors?

In this Elaborate activity, *Analyzing Reproductive Behaviors*, you will observe some animals' mating behaviors, think about mating behaviors in humans, and explore the costs and the benefits these behaviors have for individuals and populations.

Materials

online resource

PROCESS AND PROCEDURES

1. Study the mating behavior of the animals in the video segment "Animal Mating Behaviors." Record your observations in your science notebook. You may want to make notes about different kinds of behaviors, the behaviors that surprised you, and what might be the value of different behaviors.

2. Read the essay, *Mating Behaviors*. Take brief notes about the mating behaviors described in the essay.
3. Think about the advantages and disadvantages of showy mating behavior. For each behavior you observed in step 1, write at least 1 advantage and 1 disadvantage.
4. Record the similarities and the differences you see between the mating behaviors of humans and those of nonhuman animals.

   Many human mating patterns are influenced by the culture in which a person lives. For more information on the role that culture plays in mating, read the sidebar, *Cultures and Mating Patterns.*

Mating Behaviors

Have you ever seen a male peacock (figure 10.14)? The tails of these individuals are brilliantly colored with bright blues and greens. They have colored eyespots that stand out on each feather of the tail. When the tail is spread open, it is an impressive sight. The fabulous tails of male peacocks seem at odds with natural selection, though. Surely, the bright colors could attract predators to the male. Why would the male peacocks have evolved to have such a tail? The answer is another type of natural selection, called sexual selection. Females prefer to mate with males that display bright colors.

To ensure the continuity of a species, reproduction is essential. For this reason, behaviors that promote mating and reproduction are advantageous. Some behavioral and physical traits give individuals a competitive edge in mating and producing offspring. These traits contribute to sexual selection. **Sexual selection** is a process of natural selection. It involves specific characteristics that one sex prefers in the other. The animal world provides many striking examples. As you will see, there are a wide variety of behaviors used by different animals.

Bighorn sheep provide an example of dramatic mating behavior. They live in the mountainous regions of western North America. The males often engage in competitive sparring, bashing their heads together as shown in figure 10.15. The spars take place only during the winter mating (rutting) season. During this time, the males fight to control the areas where females gather. Massive horns and unique sparring movements may provide an advantage to a particular male. The winners mate more frequently than the losers. This makes it more likely that their traits would be passed on to offspring. However, fighting is expensive in terms of expended energy, lost foraging time, and injury. For this reason, males undergo elaborate rituals before they actually butt heads. The rituals allow the two males to estimate the size and strength of their rival and provide opportunities for the less dominant male to back out before the brutal physical interaction. When two males do fight, the losers do not challenge the winners again that year. Sometimes young males challenge the dominance of older males in later years. Another interesting phenomenon is "sneaker males." These males sometimes take advantage of the fact that two males are fighting to gain access to a female.

In many species, actual fighting may not be part of the competitive strategy to attract or gain access to a mate. Simple behavioral displays may be adequate. Males of certain species of grouse, for instance, dance. They gather on a lek, or dancing ground, and begin a synchronized, elaborate display for the females. The males spread their tail feathers, inflate their neck pouches, and produce a booming call to accompany the dance. Females select a mate from the group of displaying males. A male's plumage and the subtle features of his dance may improve the chance that a female will select him. Males of some species, such as the bird of paradise, have extremely elaborate plumage that enhances their courtship display. The colorful feathers of male birds may become a disadvantage, however, because it makes them more visible to potential predators. This example highlights the

Figure 10.14 **Male peacock.** The brilliant colors on the tail of a male peacock are the result of sexual selection.

Figure 10.15 These male bighorn sheep (*Ovis canadensis*) are in a competitive sparring match.

delicate balance that exists between sexual selection and other forms of natural selection.

Male songbirds frequently express sexual readiness in the form of songs and calls. These vocalizations may announce the male's defense of his territory or his invitation to mate. In wetland areas in the springtime, an evening chorus of male frogs croaks to attract females. In some species of fish, courtship and mating movements mimic aggressive behaviors. Figure 10.16 illustrates courtship and mating in one such fish, the American stickleback.

Most nonhuman mating behaviors only take place periodically. Those periods happen around the times when species are able to reproduce. For example, most nonhuman mammals have cycles known as *estrus*, or "heat." Humans undergo a menstrual cycle instead. Hormones and environmental factors regulate the frequency of the estrous cycle. Unlike the human menstrual cycle, ovulation takes place only *during* estrus. Animals such as deer, elk, and moose enter into estrus once a year. Most dogs go into estrus twice a year. Those nonhuman female mammals that have estrus are receptive to males only during that cycle. This means that mating behaviors only occur around the time of estrus. Mating behaviors are absent or greatly reduced at other times. In addition, the lining of the uterus is often reabsorbed after estrus, rather than being shed in a menstrual cycle. Some animals do have a bloody discharge during estrus, however, this is not the same as a human period.

You may think that humans are very different from stickleback fish or bugling elk. How do human males and females attract each other's attention? Think about the behaviors, attire, and fragrances of people at dances and other social gatherings. Do you see any parallels between human behavior and the patterns of other animals?

In humans, the sexual drive has a genetic and a physiological basis. Certain physical attributes, such as facial features and body shape proportions, may initially attract a mate. Other, less obvious attributes also may attract a mate. Attributes such as good character, good health, and intelligence also may be advantageous to survival and reproduction.

a Male (right) threatens other males.

b Male's red underside attracts female.

c Male starts zigzag dance toward nest; female follows male.

d Male guides female into nest.

e Male taps female near tail; female lays eggs.

f Male bites female; female leaves nest. Male enters nest and fertilizes eggs.

Figure 10.16   The courtship and reproductive behavior of American sticklebacks. Stickleback fish perform a series of behaviors that lead to mating.

ENGLISH SPANISH

Cultures and Mating Patterns

Think about ceremonies in your community such as baby showers, weddings, and funerals. Every culture has characteristic rituals for birth, marriage, and death (figure 10.17). Cultural influences also affect how we approach daily events, such as gathering and preparing food and raising children. There are also cultural factors that play a role in mating.

In some societies, individuals choose their own partners. In this type of culture, people date before getting married. Individuals spend time getting to know each other and, after some period of time, may decide to make their arrangement permanent. In some other cultures, most marriages are arranged. There are different types of arranged marriages. In some societies, parents choose the mate for their son or daughter. There is little contact between the couple before they are married. In other arranged marriages, the parents might only introduce their son or daughter to a potential spouse. After that, it is up to the children to decide whether they want to date and eventually marry.

Cultural patterns may also be seen in the age at which someone marries. In the United States, most states require that individuals be at least 18 years of age to get married without a parent's permission. The average age at which people in the United States get married, however, has increased over time. In 2006, the average age of people getting married for the first time was between 26 and 28 years old. In some cultures, marriage takes place long before a couple is even ready to reproduce. For example, in some parts of rural India, children might be married by age seven. The bride and groom would then be sent home to grow up and would not live together until many years later.

Cultural ceremonies such as marriage promote bonds between males and females. In many cultures, this bond is monogamous. **Monogamy** is a bond between one male and one female. In some cultures, polygamy is practiced. **Polygamy** is a bond between a man or a woman and multiple spouses. In these cultures, the family formed with multiple spouses provides opportunities for support in raising children and sharing household duties.

Other cultural patterns dictate whether the male or female partner is the head of the household and whether marriage can occur between close relatives. Cultural beliefs about mating may change over time. Such changes may be influenced by law, religion, values, and individual choices. By looking at a variety of patterns in different areas, it becomes clear that different cultures can carry out the same rituals in very different ways.

Figure 10.17 A Hmong couple. The traditional marital union of Hmong families includes rituals that resolve any existing conflicts between other families and sets rules for the future. Traditional Hmong marriages are arranged according to customary patterns of authority and respect.

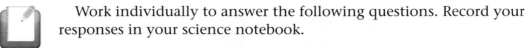
Analysis

Work individually to answer the following questions. Record your responses in your science notebook.

Topic: mating behaviors
Code: human4E556

1. List 3 showy mating behaviors displayed by nonhuman animals that were not used as examples in the essay, *Mating Behaviors*.

2. For each mating behavior example you listed in question 1, explain 1 benefit and 1 cost that the behavior brings to the individual organisms or populations that exhibit the behavior.

   Refer specifically to the behaviors that you have chosen. Explain whether the costs and benefits affect the individual, the population, or both.

3. List 2 mating behaviors that can be observed in humans interacting socially in public (see figure 10.18). Do you think these behaviors also have benefits and costs? Why or why not?

Figure 10.18
Teenage girls getting ready in front of a mirror. What might this image convey about mating behavior in American culture?

Further Challenges

1. An ongoing debate in the scientific community is whether most human sexual behavior is biologically based. Research the scientific literature to learn about this debate. Report the conclusions that your evidence supports.

2. Research and report on cultural influences on human mating and reproduction in a culture other than American culture (see figure 10.19). Include at least 5 different types of cultural influences. Consider both modern influences, such as the subtle messages included in television commercials, and long-standing influences that have been in the culture for many generations.

3. Compare and contrast human mate selection in the United States 200 years ago with mate selection today. Explain 3 specific examples of changes in American culture that contributed to differences in mate selection now and then.

Figure 10.19 A Turkana wedding ceremony. During a Turkana wedding ceremony in northwestern Kenya, the bride's family brings sheep and goats to give to the groom. Men and women dance in the background. What cultural influences do you see in this photo?

A Reproductive Strategy for Your Critter

EVALUATE

When one egg sac of a spider hatches, swarms of tiny spiders emerge. Although huge numbers of spiders are born, as seen in figure 10.20, each one lives a relatively short time and only a few survive to maturity. In contrast, an elephant gives birth to one baby. But this young elephant has the potential to live for almost a century. In both cases, mechanisms exist that provide for a continuation of the species, even though the individual organisms eventually die. In this Evaluate activity, *A Reproductive Strategy for Your Critter*, you will demonstrate and evaluate what you have learned about reproduction.

Figure 10.20 A cluster of newborn spiders. Many spiders are born at one time, but each spider has a short life span.

Materials (per person)

descriptions and diagrams of your critter from chapter 8
online resource
felt-tipped markers (optional)
blank sheet of paper (optional)

PROCESS AND PROCEDURES

1. Revisit the critter that you discovered earlier this year. Think about how it might reproduce. To give you sufficient opportunities to show everything that you have learned from this chapter, your critter must reproduce, either sexually or asexually.

    Consider the habitat where your critter lives and the factors that likely would lead to a successful reproductive strategy. Use your science notebook notes, the essays, and video segments to help you develop complete ideas.

2. Obtain the handout, *Your Critter's Reproductive Strategy Rubric,* from your teacher and study the criteria. Participate in a class discussion about the criteria for this project.

3. Write a detailed description of your critter's reproduction method in your science notebook, or as your teacher directs. You may be creative and invent new reproductive characteristics for your critter. However, you must be able to logically explain the biological basis for the idea and demonstrate your knowledge. Be sure to address the following.

    a. The reproductive structures involved

    b. A description of the role that hormones and other factors play in regulating reproduction

    c. An explanation of the mating behaviors your critter uses to ensure the production of offspring

    d. An analysis of the advantages and disadvantages for the number of offspring produced, their approximate life spans, and the nurturing they receive

    e. How the organism's overall method of reproduction compares and contrasts with human reproduction

       You may want to include a drawing or diagram with your description.

4. Explain the reproductive strategy for your critter to a partner. Think about the similarities and differences to your own critter's reproductive strategy as you listen to your partner's description.

5. Discuss the advantages and disadvantages you see in the reproductive strategy used by your critter and your partner's critter. Write a brief summary of the similarities and differences as well as the advantages and disadvantages.

Analysis

Return to the concept map for reproduction that you started in the Engage activity, *A Zillion Ways to Make More*. Study the ideas and relationships that it represents. Think about how your understanding has increased, and then add 3 or 4 more ideas or relationships to your map. Make any necessary changes so that your concept map accurately shows your current understanding of reproduction and how it allows for the continuity of life. Either add these ideas and changes to your existing diagram or create a new one that your teacher can read and evaluate easily.

11

Gene Action

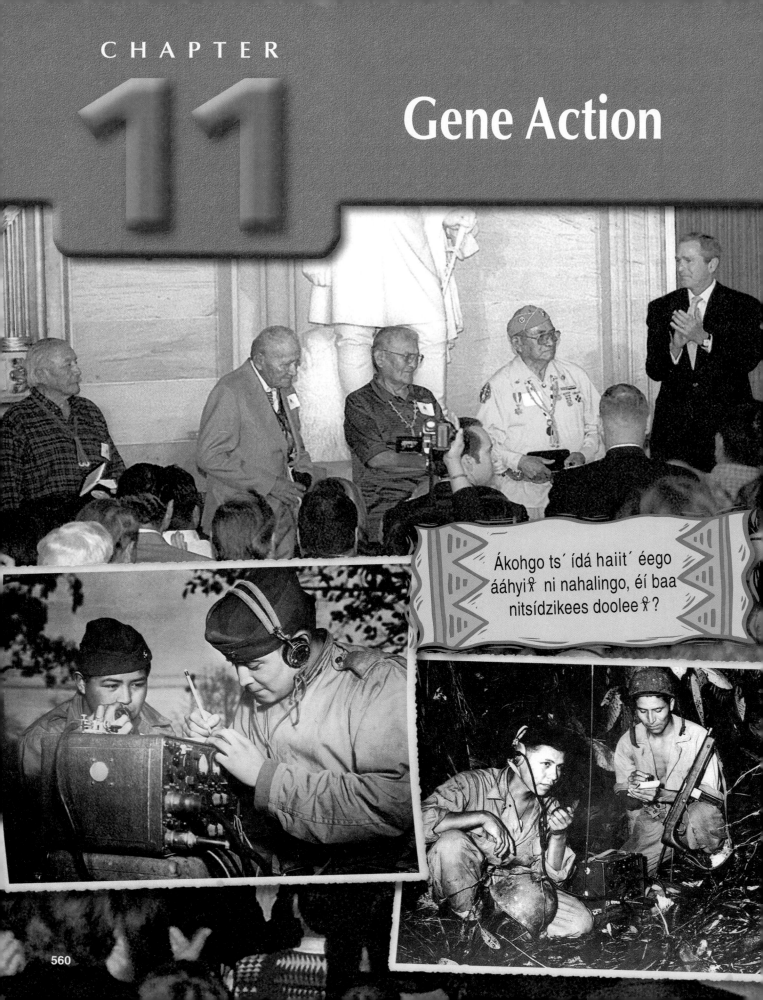

Ákohgo tsʼídá haiitʼéego ááhyiłʼ ni nahalingo, éí baa nitsídzikees dooleeł?

We all have the extraordinary coded
within us, waiting to be released.

Jean Houston

Do you have any idea what the words in the picture inset mean? How might you try to understand information that is stored in an unfamiliar language? Do you think you could use an unfamiliar language to transfer messages?

During World War II, the U.S. Marine Corps sometimes used different languages to transfer information. At that time, there were 29 Navajo, or Diné, men who were members of a special group called the *code talkers*. These men used their language to code and transfer secret military information.

The military chose the Navajo to be code talkers because their language is complex and little known. Imagine how difficult it would be to decode the Navajo words written in the picture inset. In English, they mean, "What does this sentence really mean when you think about it?"

The code talkers made significant contributions to the war and helped secure a victory by transmitting messages. On July 26, 2001, President George W. Bush presented the Congressional Gold Medal to four of the living code talkers and the families of the other 24 men.

In any language, the symbols that make up words function as a code to store and transfer information. Genetic material also functions as a code. Like written language, genetic material stores and transfers information. In chapter 11, *Gene Action*, you will learn about and model the genetic code. You will begin to understand how an organism uses genetic information. You will also consider the effects of advances in genetic engineering.

GOALS FOR THE CHAPTER

In chapter 11, you will work to gain an understanding of the following concepts:

✔ The structure of DNA allows information to be stored in cells, transferred to new generations, and expressed in ways that are useful to an organism.

✔ Mutations are changes in genetic information.

✔ The process of protein synthesis relies on the genetic code.

✔ There are several components, each with a different role, involved in synthesizing proteins.

✔ Genetic technologies have an impact on human societies.

✔ Models are a useful way of visualizing structures and processes that are hard to observe.

To help you develop these understandings, you will complete the following activities.

ENGAGE	Decoding the Message
EXPLORE	The Stuff of Life
EXPLORE / EXPLAIN	Modeling DNA
EXPLAIN	Expression of Genetic Information
ELABORATE	Genetic Technology
EVALUATE	Effects of Mutations

As you work through the chapter, remember to use the chapter organizer to link what you have learned to new concepts.

Decoding the Message

Key Idea: Complex information can be transferred by using a simple code.

Linking Question:
What is an example of a code used by organisms?

Chapter 11

The Stuff of Life

Key Idea: DNA is a simple code that is used to make complex organisms.

Linking Question:
What does DNA look like?

MAJOR CONCEPTS

✔ The structure of DNA allows information to be stored in cells, transferred to new generations, and expressed in ways that are useful to an organism.

✔ Mutations are changes in genetic information.

✔ The process of protein synthesis relies on the genetic code.

✔ There are several components, each with a different role, involved in synthesizing proteins.

✔ Genetic technologies have an impact on human societies.

✔ Models are a useful way of visualizing structures and processes that are hard to observe.

Modeling DNA

Part A: Modeling DNA Structure
Part B: Analyzing a DVD Model
Part C: Modeling DNA Replication
Key Idea: We can create an accurate model of DNA's structure.

Linking Question:
How is information in DNA used by cells?

EVALUATE

Effects of Mutations

Key Idea: Gene mutations can have different effects.

Gene Action

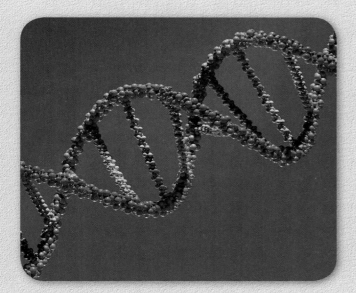

Linking Question:
What information do we have about the expression of particular genes?

ELABORATE

Genetic Technology

Key Idea: Because scientists understand the molecular basis of gene expression, they have been able to develop many genetic technologies.

Linking Question:
How have scientists applied our knowledge about genes and gene expression?

EXPLAIN

Expression of Genetic Information

Key Idea: Cells are able to use information in DNA to synthesize other types of molecules.

Decoding the Message

Imagine that you want to send a note to a friend but you don't want anyone else to know what it says. What could you do? One of your options is to write the note using a code. People often use codes. Bar codes on items at stores include information about the price of the item. Codes are used to control some alarm systems. People who are blind sometimes use the Braille alphabet, which is a type of code, to read. Each of these types of codes is shown in figure 11.1.

In *Decoding the Message*, the Engage activity, you will experience one code that people use to communicate with one another. Later in the chapter, you will relate your understanding of this code to help you explain how a code can direct life's processes.

Figure 11.1 Types of codes. How are codes used in each of these situations? Why is a code necessary?

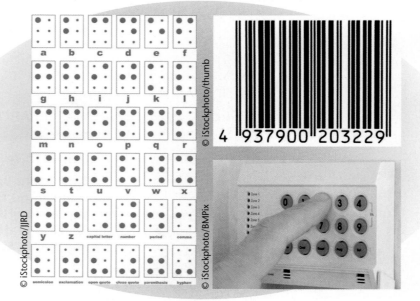

Materials (per person)

coded message

PROCESS AND PROCEDURES

1. Obtain a coded message from your teacher.
2. Try to determine what your message says. Can you figure it out?
3. Read the need to know, *Digital Coding,* to help you decipher your message.
4. Use your coded message and the following information to decipher the code.
   a. If the code says "1," fill in the box. That is your black dot.
   b. If the code says "0," leave the box blank.

   You might find it easier to work with a partner to decipher your message. If so, help each other with both of your codes.

NEED TO KNOW

Digital Coding

Your message was written using digital coding. Digital coding allows us to program computers for many different applications such as games, word processing, and mathematics. Digitally encoded information allows computers to store and display complex information in pictures or video. Modern television is based on interpreting a digital code. Some communication networks, such as cellular phones, are also digitally encoded.

To get a sense of how a digital code can provide information, we can use the first fax machines as an example. Fax machines, like the one shown in figure 11.2, provide us with the technology to send an exact copy of a document across telephone lines. The information is transmitted using a digital code. Simple fax machines use the numbers 0 and 1 as a code. First, an optical device looks for the light and dark areas on the original document. Fax machines see documents as many densely packed dots. For each dot, or small area of the document, the fax machine assigns a number. A white area on a document is coded as 0. Black areas on a document are coded as 1. In the end, the fax machine codes the document as a series of 0s and 1s. It transmits the code over telephone lines to the receiving fax machine. The receiver then prints black dots or leaves blank spots according to the code. When all the code is printed, the document appears exactly like the original.

© Dreamstime/Feng Yu

Figure 11.2   A fax machine. Fax machines use a simple code made up of the numbers 0 and 1 to transmit complex information.

5. When you have revealed your message, record your results on the class list, as directed by your teacher.
6. Copy the class list into your personal glossary. As you encounter each word in the chapter, return to the list and write a brief definition next to the word.

   For additional help, refer to appendix B8, *How to Develop a Personal Glossary.*

Analysis

Work individually to answer these questions. Record your answers in your science notebook.

1. Would you have been able to read the message if guidelines were not provided for you? Why or why not?

2. Digital coding uses only 2 symbols (0s and 1s). How many different words are on the class list? Could the same code be used to make more words? Explain how only 2 symbols can be used to make so many words.

3. This activity showed that a simple code can transmit complex information. How do you think that idea might relate to genetic information?

The Stuff of Life

In the Engage activity, *Decoding the Message*, you saw how codes are used for storing and transmitting information. Do you think a code could be used to store and transmit all the unique characteristics that organisms display? After all, there are millions of species of organisms, each with its own unique characteristics. That is quite a lot of information! A code would be one way to store this information, and then pass it to the next generation.

If there is such a code, where is it found? What does it look like? Is this code found in all organisms? Does it look the same for all organisms? These are some of the questions that scientists such as Barbara McClintock, seen in figure 11.3, have asked. In this Explore activity, *The Stuff of Life*, you will work with a partner to search for the substance that carries the code of life in the cells of some common organisms.

Materials (team of 2)

2 pairs of safety goggles
2 lab aprons
1 5-mL graduated cylinder
1 10-mL graduated cylinder
1 large test tube
1 test-tube rack
1 wooden splint or metal spatula
1 50-mL beaker containing
   20-mL of filtered material
   (from your teacher)

Woolite liquid detergent
meat tenderizer
cold ethanol or isopropanol
bleach solution
dark-colored sheet of paper
   (optional)
clock or timer
supplies for additional
   investigations (optional)

CAUTION: During this investigation, wear safety goggles at all times. Ethanol and isopropanol are very flammable. Make sure there are no open flames or burners turned on nearby. Keep the lids on all the solutions when not in use. Do not inhale any fumes. If you spill any filtered material, wipe up the spill with a dilute bleach solution. Be sure to wash your hands thoroughly after handling the filtered material and also at the end of this investigation.

Figure 11.3 Barbara McClintock, an accomplished geneticist, won the Nobel Prize in Physiology or Medicine in 1983 for her work in genetics.

PROCESS AND PROCEDURES

1. Look at the names of the organisms your teacher has written on the board. What are some things these organisms have in common? Write your ideas in your science notebook.
2. Read *Extracting the Substance of Life Protocol* to learn how you can search for the substance that carries the code of life. To find it, you will need to break open cells of 1 of the organisms provided by your teacher.
3. Gather the materials you need and follow the protocol.
4. Complete the following tasks in your science notebook as you observe the test tube.
   a. What do you see happening in the alcohol layer? Record your observations.
   b. Describe the appearance of the material in the alcohol layer.
   c. This material is **deoxyribonucleic acid (DNA)**. DNA carries the code for all of life. You may have heard of DNA. List 3 things you already know about DNA.
5. Observe other teams' results. Be sure to look at the DNA from all 3 organisms.
6. Discuss the similarities and differences between their results and yours. Does DNA look similar among the organisms your class used? Record your thoughts in your science notebook.
7. Consult with your teacher if you want to perform any further investigations with the DNA. Only perform investigations that your teacher approves.
8. Clean up the materials you used, following your teacher's directions. Wash your hands when you are done.
9. You may wonder how scientists discovered that DNA is "the stuff of life." To find out more about the experiment that showed this, read the sidebar, *Landmark Discovery: DNA May Be the Stuff of Life*.

PROTOCOL

Extracting the Substance of Life Protocol

CAUTION: During this investigation, wear safety goggles at all times. Ethanol and isopropanol are very flammable. Make sure there are no open flames or burners turned on nearby. Keep the lids on all the solutions when not in use. Do not inhale any fumes. If you spill any filtered material, wipe up the spill with a dilute bleach solution. Be sure to wash your hands thoroughly after handling the filtered material and also at the end of this investigation.

1. Obtain a 20-mL sample of filtered material from your teacher. In your science notebook, record the organism that this material came from.

   Your teacher made this material by putting the substance in a blender with salt and water and blending it for 15 seconds. It was then filtered to remove large particles.

CAUTION: Be sure to wear your safety goggles and lab apron.

2. Add 3 mL of Woolite liquid detergent to your sample and swirl the mixture *very slowly* and *gently*.

   The molecule carrying the code of life is fragile, which is why your movements should be slow and gentle.

3. Mark the time in your science notebook and allow the mixture to sit for 10 minutes. *Very gently* swirl the mixture every few minutes.

4. After 10 minutes, *very carefully* and *slowly* pour all the mixture into a large test tube.

5. Using the tip of a wooden splint or spatula, add a small amount of meat tenderizer to the mixture. Stir the mixture *very gently* with the wooden splint just enough to mix in the meat tenderizer.

6. Obtain cold alcohol (ethanol or isopropanol) from your teacher.

7. Carefully tilt the test tube at a 45° angle.

8. *Very slowly* pour the alcohol down the inside of the test tube as shown in the illustration in figure 11.4. The alcohol should form a layer on top of the filtered material. Try not to let the alcohol mix with the bottom layer. Pour until you have about the same amount of alcohol as you have of the filtered material.

9. Wash your hands before returning to your work.

Figure 11.4 Adding alcohol to the filtered material. Slowly pour alcohol into the test tube. Be careful to pour it down the side so that the alcohol forms a layer on top of the mixture. Pour until you have about the same amount of alcohol and filtered material in the tube.

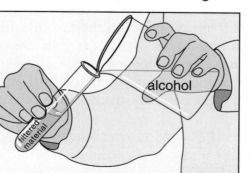

ENGLISH SPANISH

Landmark Discovery: DNA May Be the Stuff of Life

What's New?

NEW YORK (1944)— Scientists have wondered for years what makes up those mysterious particles called genes. The effort to describe the molecular composition of genes has moved a giant step forward this year. More than 10 years ago, Frederick Griffith discovered a "transforming" substance. A new report indicates that a chemical called "deoxyribonucleic acid (DNA)" may be the so-called transforming substance.

Griffith conducted experiments with two strains of a bacterium. When one strain, referred to as R because of its rough surface, was injected into mice, it did not make them sick. The other strain, S, had a smooth coat. When it was injected into the mice, it caused pneumonia and killed the mice. Griffith observed that the mice died when injected with a mixture of live, rough-surfaced, harmless bacteria and dead, smooth-surfaced, harmful bacteria. He then took bacteria from the tissues of the dead mice. The dead bacteria did not show any changes from when they were injected. But Griffith saw that the live bacteria in the tissues of the dead mice had been *transformed*. Now all the live bacteria were also smooth surfaced and harmful. That *transformation* is the change in the characteristics of the living bacteria from rough surfaced to smooth surfaced and from harmless to harmful. This change seems to involve the transfer of some information-rich substance from the dead bacteria to the live bacteria.

The identity of this transforming substance, however, remained unknown until this year. Oswald Avery, Colin MacLeod, and Maclyn McCarty are investigators at the Rockefeller Institute in New York. They reported a set of experiments that demonstrate that the substance causing the transformation actually is DNA. This group was able to isolate DNA and show that it could transform bacteria. Scientists do not know much about this powerful substance. But the announcement is likely to intensify efforts to describe DNA's structure and function. In addition, scientists will work to explain how DNA can cause such important effects in cells.

Analysis

Complete the following tasks individually in your science notebook.

1. Answer questions 1a–c.
   a. Does DNA appear to be the same for all organisms?
   b. What is your evidence?
   c. What could you do to be more certain of your answers?

2. How could you investigate the idea that DNA is found only in living or once-living things?

3. What features do you think DNA might need to have in order to contain a code that directs the processes of life? How do you think DNA allows genetic information to be passed to new generations?

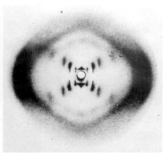

Figure 11.5
Rosalind Franklin's X-ray diffraction photograph of DNA taken in 1953. This photograph helped James Watson and Francis Crick determine the structure of DNA.

Modeling DNA

In the Explore activity, *The Stuff of Life*, you and your classmates extracted DNA from different organisms. You saw that the DNA looked similar, whether it was from a banana or a chicken liver. What if you could see the details of DNA, though? What do you think DNA would look like? In this Explore-Explain activity, *Modeling DNA*, you will build a model of DNA. Your model will help you to explain how this molecule can store genetic information and transfer it accurately to new cells.

As you build your model, keep in mind that modeling is a tool for understanding structures and processes that may be difficult to observe directly. James Watson and Francis Crick are the scientists credited with proposing the first detailed description of DNA's structure. They used model building extensively in their work. When they began developing their DNA model, they had limited information. Their first attempts did not match the actual structure of DNA very well. They then obtained more information from X-ray photographs of DNA taken by Rosalind Franklin and Maurice Wilkins (see figure 11.5). Watson and Crick were able to improve their model with this new information. They also applied their knowledge of chemistry to the model. The more information the scientists had, the more closely their model matched the actual structure of DNA.

Remember also that even the best model has limitations on how accurately it can represent something. Models are useful for showing *some* aspects of an actual structure or process. But they do not portray every characteristic perfectly. The power of models comes from their ability to help us picture structures and processes that we cannot actually see. Keep in mind that people have a tendency to assume that every feature of a particular model is accurate. This activity will help you develop and critique a biological model.

Materials

Part A (team of 4)
pop beads
twist ties
rubber bands
double-sided tape
wire

Part B (team of 4)
online resource (watch as a class)

Part C (team of 8 and 2)
online resource (optional)
pop beads

PROCESS AND PROCEDURES

Part A   Modeling DNA Structure

For part A, *Modeling DNA Structure*, imagine that you are on a team of research scientists involved in an effort to describe the likely structure of the DNA molecule. You have decided to tackle this task by modeling. You will build physical representations of a variety of possible structures. As new information becomes available, you will change these models to reflect the new information, much like Watson and Crick did. Although you will work as a team to share information, each of you should build your own model. This will allow you to compare different ways of representing the same physical characteristics of the DNA molecule.

Model 1

1. Working individually, build your first model out of pop beads, like those in figure 11.6. Use the following observations about the structure of DNA to create your model:
   - DNA is a polymer. A polymer is a very long, chainlike molecule composed of small subunit molecules. Subunit molecules are like the links in a chain. They are attached to each other by covalent bonds.
   - Four different types of subunit molecules exist.
2. Compare your model with those built by the other members of your team. Discuss any differences that you notice. Make any changes to your model that you feel are necessary.
3. In your science notebook, analyze your model by responding to the following.
   a. What features of your model represent the properties of DNA described above?
   b. How do you think this structure of DNA may allow it to encode information?
   c. How might DNA store different information along different parts of its length?

Figure 11.6 Use pop beads to build your model.

Figure 11.7 **A helix is the shape that a pipe cleaner takes when you wrap it around a pencil.**
How do you think two helical chains bonded together would look?

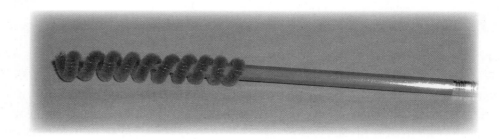

Model 2

4. Modify your DNA model. It should reflect the following additional information:
   - DNA consists of 2 long chains of subunits twisted around each other to form a double helix.

     A helix is a spiral. Think of the shape a pipe cleaner takes when you wrap it around a pencil, as shown in figure 11.7.

   - The 2 helical chains are weakly bonded together. Subunits on one chain or strand bond to subunits on the other strand.
   - The diameter of the DNA molecule is the same along its length.

5. Compare your new model with those built by the other members of your team. Discuss any differences that you notice. Make any changes to your model that you feel are necessary.

6. Analyze your second model by considering how well your pop-bead model represents the 5 characteristics of DNA listed in steps 1 and 4. To do this, complete the following tasks.

   a. Create a 2-column table in your science notebook. In the left column, briefly list the 5 structural characteristics of DNA. In the right column, explain how your model represents each.

   b. Examine the figures that your teacher presents. List the strengths and weaknesses in your science notebook of using a spiral staircase or a zipper to illustrate DNA's structure.

   c. What strengths and weaknesses can you see in using a pop-bead model to represent DNA's structure?

Model 3

7. Now add another layer of detail to your model of DNA. Consider the following observations, then modify your design accordingly:
   - The order of subunits in one strand of DNA determines the order of subunits in the other strand.
   - Subunits are not paired with a subunit of the same type on the other strand.

     For example, a red pop bead on one strand would not be paired with a red pop bead on the other strand.

   - The 2 strands point in opposite directions.

8. Compare your new model with those built by the other members of your team. Discuss any differences that you notice. Make any changes to your model that you feel are necessary.

9. In your science notebook, analyze your third model by responding to the following.

   a. Use your modeling results to describe the relationship between subunits bonded to each other on opposite strands of the DNA double helix.

   b. Think about the characteristic of DNA described in 9a. Consider how the relationship between the subunits on each strand might suggest a means of replicating, or copying, the molecule. Describe your ideas.

   > Before a cell divides, the DNA must be copied so that each new cell has a complete set of genetic information.

Part B Analyzing a Video Model

In part B, *Analyzing a Video Model*, you will watch a video segment about the structure of DNA. This segment will give you even more information about DNA's structure. You will learn the names of the four subunits of DNA as well as how they interact with one another. The segment will also help you understand the importance of this structure to the replication of DNA molecules.

1. With your class, view the video segment, "DNA Structure." As you watch the video segment, look for information that will help you answer the following questions. Take notes in your science notebook. The new information that you gather will help you better understand the structure of DNA.

   a. What characteristic of the subunits allows for a uniform diameter of the double helix?

   b. What type of interaction takes place between the subunits of each strand that encourages a double helix to form?

   c. How does the sequence of subunits on one strand provide a guide for the sequence of subunits on the other strand? Is that important to replication? Explain your answer.

2. Use the new information that you gathered from the video segment and the following tasks to reevaluate your third model.

   a. Write a short paragraph in your science notebook that describes how you would have to modify your third model to reflect this new information.

   b. List 3 ways in which pop beads limit your ability to create a more detailed or more accurate model of a DNA molecule.

3. What materials, other than pop beads, could you use to model DNA more accurately? How would you assemble these materials to make a more accurate model?

4. To learn more about the original modeling of DNA, read the sidebar, *Landmark Discovery: Why the Fuss about Watson and Crick?*

Landmark Discovery: Why the Fuss about Watson and Crick?

What's New?

LONDON, ENGLAND (1953)—The most recent issue of *Nature* hit scientists' desks this week. This issue contains a landmark paper proposing a physical structure for DNA. DNA is the substance that makes up the genetic material of living organisms. The paper is coauthored by James Watson and Francis Crick, with important contributions from Rosalind Franklin's work (see pictures in figure 11.8). This paper already has the scientific world buzzing with enthusiasm and optimism.

To be honest, though, your humble science club's What's New? correspondent didn't see what the fuss was all about. I mean, I thought science was an *experimental* endeavor. How could a paper that only proposes a *model* be exciting? Where is the evidence that these two scientists actually are right? Besides, I think that coming up with a model would be easy. There must be hundreds of different ways to suggest how DNA is put together. So what's the big deal with *their* model?

To get answers to my questions, I called an old friend of mine, Pete, at the university. Wow, did he set me straight! First, he pointed out that a good model *explains* all of the known characteristics of the system that you are studying. Take the Watson and Crick model as an example, he said. It explains how DNA can do all the things the genetic material appears to be able to do. Not only can DNA *encode* information, but it also can store that information in a stable manner through time. DNA can also be copied with very high accuracy.

Then Pete pointed out that a good model also is *consistent* with all the available experimental evidence. In the case of DNA, this includes several pieces of evidence. DNA is shaped like a double helix. The nitrogen bases that make up DNA are stacked inside the molecule in a regular pattern. The big nitrogen bases and the small nitrogen bases are present in the molecule in a 1:1 ratio.

Finally, Pete insisted that a good model is *testable*. He said, "Just look at all the predictions that the new DNA model makes that you could test. For example, you could test whether newly copied

Figure 11.8 Watson, Crick, and Franklin. James Watson and Francis Crick are credited with proposing the first detailed description of the structure of DNA. Their work built on the arrangements of atoms suggested by the X-ray photographs taken by Rosalind Franklin.

DNA contains some of the original DNA. Or you could consider whether the two strands at any point on the molecule are identical."

"OK, OK," I said. So I've learned something about modeling and science. And if Pete and his friends are right about where the study of DNA is going to take us, this is just the beginning of what I'm going to learn. In fact, all of us will be learning a lot in the next few decades. So, hats off to model building. . . . Got any building blocks?

Part C   Modeling DNA Replication

As you saw in part A of this activity, one reason that scientists build models is to help them picture *structures* that are difficult to observe directly. This helps them better understand these structures. Models also can help scientists picture and better understand complex *processes*.

For part C, *Modeling DNA Replication*, imagine that you now have determined the structure of DNA. Your research team has turned its attention to the task of explaining how DNA replicates.

Topic: DNA replication
Code: human4E575

1. To begin thinking about the way information is transferred in living systems, join your teammates to discuss the following questions. Record your answers in your science notebook.

   Think about the idea that information needs to be transferred to new cells when they are made, and also to new organisms when parents have offspring. At this point in the chapter, your answers may be brief and simple.

   a. What ideas do you have about how information is stored in DNA molecules?
   b. What is the role of genetic information in the life of an individual organism?
   c. Why is replication (copying) of DNA important to the continuity of a species?
   d. Why is it important that genetic information be passed on, or transmitted, accurately?

2. According to your teacher's instructions, create a team of 8. Follow your teacher's directions for carrying out the Information Transfer Game.

3. The previous step showed why it is important to transmit a message accurately. When DNA is copied, or replicated, in the cell, it is important that it be done accurately. Otherwise, there may be errors in the new DNA. To study DNA replication, your research team has decided to answer 2 research questions. Read the first research question to understand your first goal.

   Research question 1: DNA allows genetic information to be stored for a long time. It also allows information to be transferred through copying (replication). What are the critical characteristics of DNA that allow these two features?

4. Begin thinking about the critical characteristics of DNA that will help you answer the research question. To help you come up with ideas, read the essay, *DNA Structure and Replication*. As you read, list any information that you think might help you answer the first research question.

   You may also want to watch the video segment, "DNA Replication."

DNA Structure and Replication

ENGLISH SPANISH

Why is DNA important in your life? To answer that question, you need to understand the role that DNA plays. DNA contains information that is critical to the structure and function of your body's cells. When new cells are made in your body, they must contain DNA. Not only do the cells need the DNA, but there needs to be a full set of DNA and it must be transferred accurately.

DNA is not just important when new cells are made, though. In fact, the instructions encoded in DNA play a major role in determining how your body operates. DNA instructions preserve many of the characteristics of a species. A child's life depends on the accurate transmission of genetic information from his or her parents.

DNA structure and the process by which DNA is copied are critical to that transmission. At one level, DNA is responsible for the accurate transmission of genetic information from parents to offspring. At another level, the structure is responsible for accurately transmitting genetic information from a cell to its offspring cells. In other words, DNA is the *molecular* basis of reproduction.

DNA is required for the building, maintenance, and regulation of all living organisms' cells. This means each new cell must receive a copy of the genetic material from its parent cell. How are copies of genetic information made? The process is called **replication**. The process of making a copy of the cell's genetic material is complex. To understand this process, you first need to understand a few things about how a cell's genetic material is structured and organized.

In humans, as in all eukaryotes, the genetic material consists of long DNA molecules. These molecules are packaged tightly in chromosomes, as seen in figure 11.9. To give you an idea of the length of DNA in a chromosome, one of the mid-sized chromosomes contains about 145 million nitrogen bases. In each of your cells (except gametes and red blood cells), you have 23 pairs of chromosomes, for a total of 46 chromosomes.

One set of 23 came from your father and one set of 23 came from your mother. Each chromosome contains one long DNA molecule and many protein molecules. The DNA and proteins pack together tightly and form the structure of a chromosome. This is the compact structure that we see when we look at a dividing cell under the microscope.

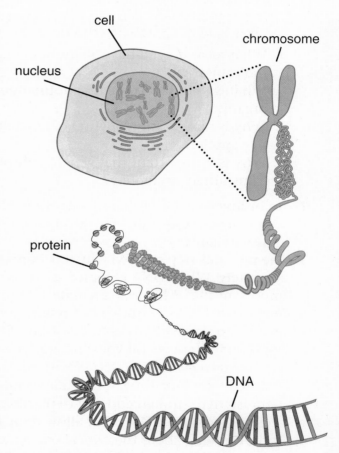

Figure 11.9 Eukaryotic chromosome structure. In eukaryotes, chromosomes are found within the nucleus. Each chromosome consists of a long molecule of DNA. The DNA is wrapped around proteins to help it pack together tightly. Fully extended, the DNA in one human chromosome would be about 5 cm (2 in) long. Prokaryotes, in contrast to eukaryotes, have only one chromosome. This chromosome lacks the bead-like proteins that aid packing. What advantage might efficient packing of DNA offer a cell?

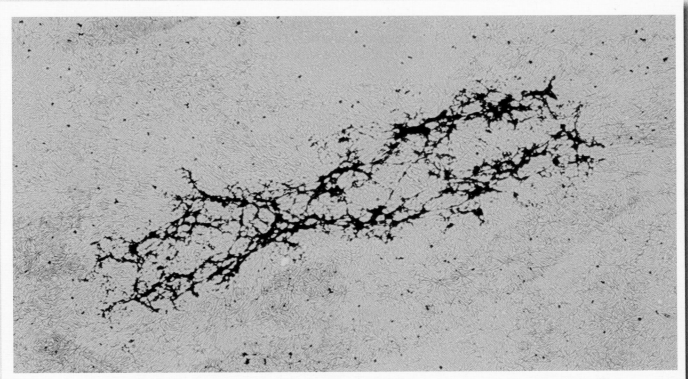

Figure 11.10 Human DNA. This human chromosome is seen through an electron microscope. The chromosome was treated with a substance that disrupted its structure, releasing the DNA.

The ability to store information lies ultimately in the DNA (see figure 11.10). That ability is not due to the protein components that are packed with the DNA inside the chromosomes. So the question of how a cell copies its genetic information during reproduction is actually a question of how the cell copies its DNA. Copying DNA accurately is similar to communicating a message. It is easier when some form of physical template, or pattern, is used. Games such as the Information Transfer Game show how easily inaccurate copying can happen when there is no physical record, such as a written note, of the transmitted message. In fact, using a physical template is exactly how biological systems transmit information. The DNA molecule itself serves as a template for its own replication.

DNA can serve as its own template because its organization is specific. Look at the drawing of DNA shown in figure 11.11a. Note that a single DNA molecule is a double-stranded structure. The two strands twist together in a spiral, or *helical*, form. That aspect of DNA earned it its nickname: the *double helix*.

Examine the two DNA strands more closely. Each strand (figure 11.11b) is made up of a series of smaller molecules called **nucleotides**. A long chain, or strand, made up of nucleotides is called a **nucleic acid**. DNA is one example of a nucleic acid.

A closer look at the nucleotides that make up each strand of DNA (figure 11.11c) reveals even more regularity. Each nucleotide is made up of the same three parts. These are a nitrogen base, a deoxyribose sugar, and a triphosphate group. The sugar and phosphate portions are the same in all nucleotides. However, the nitrogen bases vary. As figure 11.11d shows, a DNA nucleotide may contain

a The structure of DNA is a double helix.

b Strands of DNA are made of nucleotides that are covalently bonded to one another. This creates the backbone of the DNA. A strand of DNA is known as a nucleic acid.

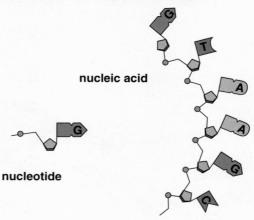

nucleic acid

nucleotide

d Nucleotides may contain 1 of 4 different nitrogen bases. The nitrogen bases on one strand interact with the nitrogen bases on the other strand of DNA. The sequence of nucleotides along the strand encodes the cell's genetic information.

c Nucleotides are made up of 3 parts:
- a triphosphate group,
- a sugar (deoxyribose), and
- a nitrogen base.

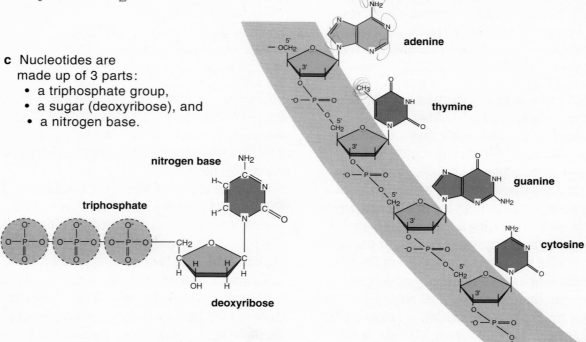

nitrogen base

triphosphate

deoxyribose

adenine

thymine

guanine

cytosine

Figure 11.11 Structure of DNA. The sequence of nucleotides along the strand encodes the cell's genetic information. How many different sequences could be made using just 10 nucleotides in a DNA strand?

one of four different nitrogen bases: adenine (A), cytosine (C), guanine (G), and thymine (T). The four unique bases are like the letters in a word. Consider how the order of letters in a word conveys information to someone reading that word. Similarly, the order of nitrogen bases along one strand of DNA conveys information to certain parts of the cell. The order of bases is called the DNA **sequence**.

How does this structure allow a DNA molecule to be copied to make another identical molecule? The answer to this question is that the nitrogen bases interact with one another in predictable ways. Pairing between nitrogen bases on opposite strands is always the same. Figure 11.12 shows this aspect of DNA structure. Notice that the pairing that takes place between nitrogen bases is specific in DNA strands. Adenine, a large base, bonds with thymine, a small base. Guanine, a large base, bonds with cytosine, a small base. This specific bonding pattern that happens between the nucleotides is called **complementary base pairing**.

Complementary base pairing explains how it is possible for DNA to act as a template for its own replication. Figure 11.13 illustrates the replication process. Specific enzymes are required for replication to take place. Replication begins when those enzymes separate the two DNA strands. Separation of the double helix is critical to replication.

Next, enzymes read the sequence of nucleotides on one strand. Finally, enzymes create a new, complementary strand. They do this by adding one nucleotide at a time to the new strand. Remember, A always bonds with T, and G always bonds with C. This means that the sequence of bases in the old strand *determines* the sequence of bases in the new strand. In other words, during replication, each newly added base must *complement* the base in the old strand with which it will pair. Eventually, there are two molecules of DNA where

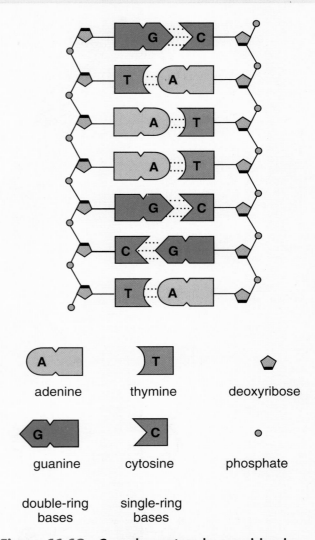

adenine   thymine   deoxyribose

guanine   cytosine   phosphate

double-ring bases   single-ring bases

Figure 11.12 Complementary base pairing in DNA. Notice the pattern of how the bases pair with each other. The dots between base pairs represent hydrogen bonds. These bonds hold the two strands in a double helix together. Are there any differences in hydrogen bonding between guanine (G) and cytosine (C) and between adenine (A) and thymine (T)?

previously there had been one. Once complete, each molecule contains one old strand and one new complementary strand. In this way, any DNA molecule can serve as a pattern for a new copy of the genetic information that it encodes.

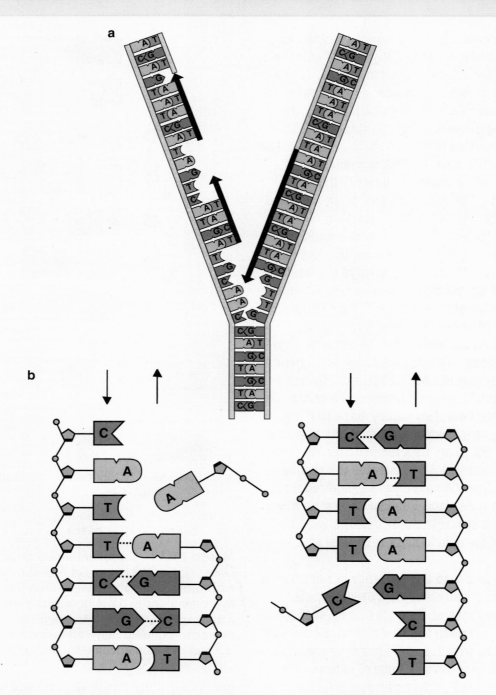

Figure 11.13   DNA replication. (*a*) A replication fork where two new DNA strands are being synthesized. Notice how the two strands are copied in opposite directions. (*b*) Details of nucleotide addition. DNA replication enzymes add nucleotides one at a time to each of the growing strands. In eukaryotic cells, the process of DNA replication takes place in the nucleus. In prokaryotes, replication takes place in the cytoplasm.

 = adenine 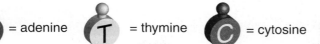 = thymine = cytosine  = guanine

Figure 11.14 What components of DNA do these pop beads represent?

5. Return to your team of 2. Use the pop beads and the key in figure 11.14 to build a model of a molecule of DNA.

   Although you will work as a team to share information, each of you should build and manipulate your own model. You will need to demonstrate to your teacher your *own* understanding of replication.

6. Manipulate your pop-bead model to illustrate the process of replication.

7. Analyze your work in steps 5–6. Then individually develop an answer to research question 1. Record your answer in your science notebook.

   Research question 1: DNA allows genetic information to be stored for a long time. It also allows information to be transferred through copying (replication). What are the critical characteristics of DNA that allow these two features?

8. Your research team has a second question to answer in order to explain how DNA replication works. Read the second research question.

   Research question 2: What are the advantages and disadvantages of an information transfer system that uses a physical pattern, or template? (Remember that a template is a physical pattern.)

9. To help you think about research question 2, read the essay, *Replication Errors and Mutation*. As you read, create a Venn diagram like the one shown in figure 11.15 to compare deletion mutations and substitution mutations. Be sure to label each circle.

   For additional help, refer to appendix B5, *How to Use and Create Venn Diagrams*.

HOW TO

Topic: genetic mutation
Code: human4E581

10. Use your pop-bead model to demonstrate a mutation in your DNA molecule. In the essay, *Replication Errors and Mutation*, you learned about 3 types of mutation. Make sure your team demonstrated each of the 3 types of mutation.

11. Use your pop-bead model to demonstrate what would happen to this mutation as your DNA molecule replicates.

12. In your science notebook, briefly explain whether it makes a difference if the mutation is in a body cell or in a cell that makes gametes. Think about this question as it relates to 1 individual as well as how it relates to the future generations from that individual.

Figure 11.15
A Venn diagram.
Use the Venn diagram to compare and contrast the types of mutations.

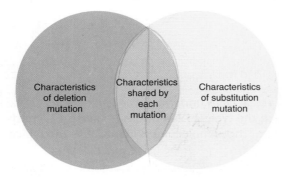

Characteristics of deletion mutation

Characteristics shared by each mutation

Characteristics of substitution mutation

Replication Errors and Mutation

Templates provide a very accurate way of transmitting information. They do this whether the information is a written language or the genetic information in DNA. Even with the use of a template for replication, however, errors do occur. In language, these errors appear as misspellings, deletions, or additions in books and articles. In DNA, these errors are called **mutations**. One type of error takes place when the replication enzymes mistakenly skip a base. In this case, the new strand forms with a missing base. When that strand is replicated, the error is copied onto a new, second strand. This makes a DNA molecule that is missing one or more nucleotides at that position. Such an error is called a **deletion mutation**. In other cases, one or more nucleotides may be added into a DNA molecule at a particular place. This type of error is called an **insertion mutation**.

Another type of error takes place when the replication enzymes mistakenly add the wrong base to a position. Substituting one base for another during replication is called a **substitution mutation**. In this case, the complementary pairing normally seen in DNA is disrupted at the point of substitution. If the DNA is replicated, however, enzymes will read the substitution and put in the complementary base for that substitution. This means that the newly synthesized DNA will contain a different nucleotide pair at that location than the original DNA (figure 11.16). In this way, the mutation is preserved and carried on in all future offspring cells. Usually,

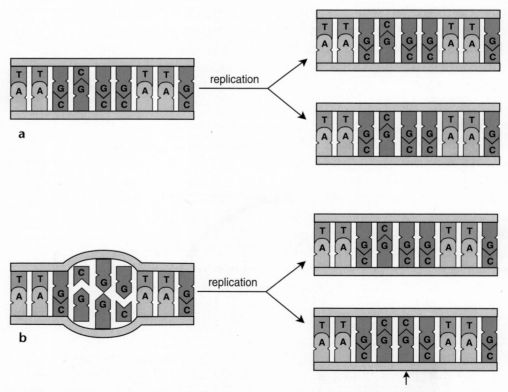

Figure 11.16 Preserving a mutation. (*a*) Typical DNA undergoes replication to produce two identical DNA molecules. (*b*) Mutated DNA (note that a C from the typical DNA has mutated to a G) undergoes replication to produce two new DNA molecules. But only one of those molecules is identical to the typical DNA. In this way, replication preserves the mutation (arrow).

specific repair enzymes detect and repair mutations. Despite the existence of those enzymes, some mutations become a permanent part of a cell's genetic material.

Mutations can take place in the DNA of any cell in the body of an organism. Imagine what could happen if mutations occur in cells that give rise to gametes (sperm and eggs, for example). If those gametes become zygotes and grow, the mutation will be passed along to the offspring.

Once an offspring has the mutation in its DNA, the mutation may continue to be passed down to future generations. An organism might have several offspring, each with a possibility of inheriting the mutation. There is potential for many members of a population to have the mutation after several generations. Then the mutation may become a lasting change in that species' genetic information. Think about this in terms of a single-celled organism. This type of organism makes new individuals by simple cell division. Any mutation may be passed along to new individuals. When those individuals divide, they will also pass along the mutation. Ironically,

the accuracy that results from the template method of copying DNA also means that, once a mutation occurs, *it* copies accurately as well.

Think about those errors that are copied accurately during replication. Some mutations are in areas of DNA that are not used by cells. These mutations have no consequence. Such neutral changes can accumulate in a species due to chance events. Other mutations may cause only mild effects. Sometimes these mild effects are helpful, and sometimes they are harmful. Mild mutations may continue to be passed from generation to generation. This type of mutation helps contribute variation to a species. Other mutations can cause large effects. These may be beneficial, such as a mutation that causes a change in the coloration of an animal. Other mutations can cause serious developmental problems. These mutations are so harmful that they may kill the organism long before it reaches reproductive maturity. In such cases, the mutation is not passed to the next generation. Natural selection acts strongly to keep these types of mutations from accumulating in a species.

13. Discuss the following questions with your team and with your teacher when he or she visits your team. These questions will help you answer research question 2.
    a. Think back to the Information Transfer Game that you played at the beginning of part C of this activity. How did the accuracy of the orally transferred information compare with the accuracy of the written transfer?
    b. Under what conditions might the extremely high accuracy of replication be advantageous to a species?
    c. Under what conditions might such accuracy be disadvantageous?
14. Review your work in steps 12–13. Then individually develop an answer to research question 2. Record your answer in your science notebook.

Research question 2: What are the advantages and disadvantages of an information transfer system that uses a physical pattern, or template? (Remember that a template is a physical pattern.)

Analysis

© Dreamstime/Mrloz

Figure 11.17
How are the steps
you completed similar
to the work that
scientists do?

During this activity, you used some of the same techniques that scientists use (see figure 11.17). You used scientific modeling to explore two important characteristics of DNA: (1) its ability to *store* information and (2) its ability to *transmit* that information to future generations. Fit these characteristics into the big picture of genetic continuity and reproduction by completing the following tasks.

1. Examine the results of each test you conducted in part C, step 2 (the Information Transfer Game). In your science notebook, explain how each set of observations might apply to the genetic mechanisms that are responsible for storing and transferring information.
2. In a paragraph, or in a concept map, briefly describe the relationships among DNA, chromosomes, cells, an organism, and offspring.
3. In your science notebook, explain the relationship between DNA's structure and the following.
   a. Information storage
   b. Accurate information transfer during the reproduction of organisms (meiosis)
   Include a diagram to illustrate your explanations.

EXPLAIN

Expression of Genetic Information

In the last activity (Explore-Explain, *Modeling DNA*), you studied how a DNA molecule can act as a template for its own replication. You should now be able to explain how genetic information maintains the continuity of a species from one generation to the next. But how is the genetic information in DNA used by each organism that possesses it? How do your cells use the information in the sequence of nucleotides in your DNA to build and maintain the physical being that is you?

In this Explain activity, *Expression of Genetic Information*, you will develop your own explanation of the relationship between genetic information and physical characteristics. You will do this by tracing the series of events that lead to sickle cell disease. Sickle cell disease is a potentially fatal condition caused by a mutation that affects a person's blood cells. As you and your partner work through this activity, you will create a poster that illustrates the molecular basis of sickle cell disease.

Materials (team of 2)

online resource
poster board
scissors
assorted construction paper
tape or glue
different-colored felt-tipped markers or crayons

PROCESS AND PROCEDURES

1. Begin your study of the molecular basis of sickle cell disease by reading the information in the need to know, *Hemoglobin and Red Blood Cell Abnormalities in Sickle Cell Disease*. You will learn about this inherited disorder.

2. Discuss the following questions with your partner. Contribute to a class discussion as your teacher directs.

   a. What problem with hemoglobin proteins causes changes in the red blood cells?

   b. What problem in the red blood cells causes changes in an organ system?

   c. What medical symptoms might a person with sickle cell disease experience?

   > Think back to the information you learned about the circulatory system in unit 2, *Homeostasis: Maintaining Dynamic Equilibrium in Living Systems*.

   d. How do the changes in the red blood cells relate to the symptoms experienced?

NEED TO KNOW

ENGLISH   SPANISH

Hemoglobin and Red Blood Cell Abnormalities in Sickle Cell Disease

Each year, about 1 in 625 African American children is born with sickle cell disease. Although the disease may affect other populations, African Americans are the most commonly affected population. This disease is caused by an abnormality in the protein **hemoglobin**. Hemoglobin is present in red blood cells and carries oxygen to body cells. When the oxygen supply in the blood is low, these abnormal hemoglobin molecules stack to form long polymers. Typical hemoglobin molecules remain separate. Figure 11.18a shows the difference between the behavior of sickle cell hemoglobin and typical hemoglobin under conditions of low oxygen.

In a person with sickle cell disease, the stacking of the hemoglobin molecules at low oxygen levels causes the red blood cells to become long and rigid like a *sickle* instead of remaining round and flexible (figure 11.18b). That change in cell shape causes a variety of problems in the body. For example, as cells become sickled, they tend to block small blood vessels (figure 11.18c). The blockage causes pain and damage

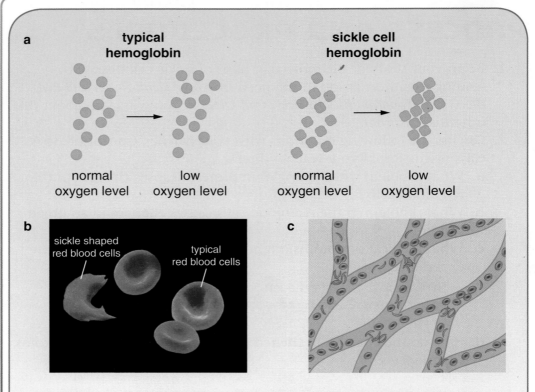

a   **typical hemoglobin**   **sickle cell hemoglobin**

normal oxygen level   low oxygen level   normal oxygen level   low oxygen level

b   sickle shaped red blood cells   typical red blood cells

c

Figure 11.18 (*a*) **Comparison of the behavior of typical and sickle cell hemoglobin under conditions of low oxygen.** Notice how, in low oxygen levels, typical hemoglobin molecules stay separate. Under the same conditions, sickle cell hemoglobin clumps together. This causes the red blood cells to change shape. (*b*) **Comparison of the shapes of typical and sickle cell red blood cells under conditions of low oxygen.** Typical red blood cells are shaped similar to a doughnut, although there is no hole in the middle. In people with sickle cell disease, the red blood cells become long and rigid and are shaped like a sickle. (*c*) **Sickled red blood cells in a blood vessel.** As cells become sickled, they tend to block small blood vessels. This keeps blood from reaching tissues. As a result, people with sickle cell disease have pain and tissue damage.

to the areas that do not receive an adequate blood supply. The long-term effect of repeated blockages may permanently damage a person's internal organs. This includes the heart, lungs, kidneys, brain, and liver. For some people, the damage is so severe that they die in childhood. With good medical care, however, many people with sickle cell disease can live reasonably normal lives.

3. Work in teams of 2 to begin a poster that illustrates the molecular basis of sickle cell disease. Use the materials that your teacher provides and the information in figure 11.19. Your poster should have a place for a title (you will add it later). It should have each of the numbered sections that you see in figure 11.19.

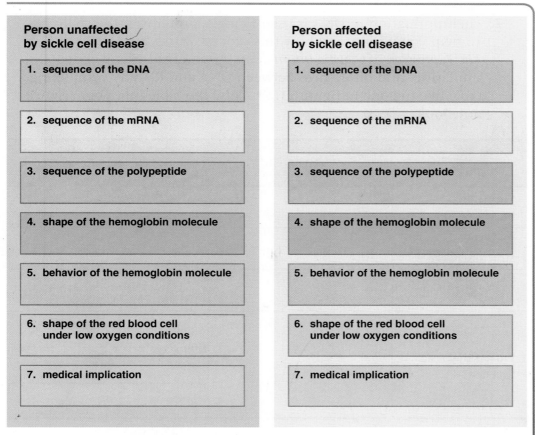

Person unaffected by sickle cell disease

1. sequence of the DNA

2. sequence of the mRNA

3. sequence of the polypeptide

4. shape of the hemoglobin molecule

5. behavior of the hemoglobin molecule

6. shape of the red blood cell under low oxygen conditions

7. medical implication

Person affected by sickle cell disease

1. sequence of the DNA

2. sequence of the mRNA

3. sequence of the polypeptide

4. shape of the hemoglobin molecule

5. behavior of the hemoglobin molecule

6. shape of the red blood cell under low oxygen conditions

7. medical implication

Figure 11.19 Sample poster design. Use this outline as a model for the poster that you will create to explain the molecular basis of sickle cell disease.

4. Use the information that you gathered in steps 1–3 to complete sections 5, 6, and 7 of your poster. Refer to figure 11.19 to determine the information required in each of these sections.

> On your poster, include pictures and words that you think would be appropriate and helpful. Add a descriptive label to each area so that a viewer will understand what each section is displaying.

5. To begin your study of how the information in DNA relates to sickle cell disease, use the DNA sequences that your teacher provides. Complete the following 3 tasks.
   a. Compare the 2 DNA sequences.
   b. Draw an arrow or circle on the sequences, indicating how the DNA sequence is different between the sickle cell DNA and the unaffected DNA.
   c. What type of mutation exists in the sickle cell DNA region?
6. Use the materials provided by your teacher to represent the DNA in a person who is not affected by sickle cell disease and the DNA in a person who is affected. Attach these models to section 1 of your poster.

7. The information in DNA is used to make proteins in the cell. To help you understand how this process works, read the essay, *The Expression of Genetic Information*. As you read, think about the similarities and differences between DNA and RNA by completing a table like the one in figure 11.20. Copy the table into your science notebook.

Figure 11.20 Table to compare DNA and RNA. What are the similarities and differences between these two nucleic acids?

Features of Nucleic Acids	DNA	RNA
What is the backbone sugar?		
What is the overall structure?		
What are the 4 bases?		
What is the basic function?		mRNA
		tRNA
		rRNA

http://www
Online Resource

8. Watch the video segment, "Transcription," to help you visualize how RNA is generated from a molecule of DNA.

9. Transcribe the sequences for the typical hemoglobin allele and the sickle cell hemoglobin alleles. To do this, work with your partner to generate a messenger RNA (mRNA) sequence for the 2 DNA sequences from step 5. Use the materials provided by your teacher.

   Think about complementary base pairing and the characteristics of RNA as you do this.

10. Attach your mRNA models to the appropriate places on your team's poster.

11. Compare the mRNA that results from the transcription of the typical allele of the hemoglobin gene with the mRNA that results from the transcription of the sickle cell allele. On your poster, use an arrow or a circle to indicate the nucleotides in the sickle cell mRNA that differ from those in the sequence for typical hemoglobin.

12. Translate the mRNA sequences for the typical allele and the sickle cell allele into the corresponding amino acid sequences. To do this, use the information in the essay, *Translating the Message in mRNA*, and in the genetic code table (figure 11.25).

   Remember to add words to your personal glossary as you need to.

13. Post your amino acid sequences in the appropriate places on your team's poster.

When an error in replication takes place, the nucleotide sequence of a DNA molecule is altered. The resulting mutations may be passed on during the next round of DNA replication. Knowing how a change in DNA sequence can be preserved and passed to new cells, however, does not tell us what effect the altered DNA structure has on the organism. To see that effect, we must look at the organism's characteristics and discover whether they are also altered. In other words, we must see whether the mutation caused a change in a region of DNA that is used to control some characteristic of the organism.

In order to understand this, we need to know how DNA is organized. You already saw that DNA uses four nucleotides. Particular regions of DNA are called genes. A **gene** is a segment of DNA that will code for a specific product in cells. Genes are the basic units of heredity. Humans are estimated to have 20,000–25,000 genes. Humans have two copies of each gene. One copy is on a chromosome from our mother and one copy is on a chromosome from our father. This means that our two copies of the gene may not be identical. The different versions of a gene are called **alleles**. For example, a person might have one allele that specifies sickle cell disease and one allele that does not have the mutation for that disease.

The process by which a cell *uses* the genetic information in genes is called **gene expression**. Let's look at the first step in understanding how gene expression takes place. Genes contain information that is required to build proteins. Proteins carry out critical biochemical and structural activities inside cells. These activities include a number of housekeeping functions that almost all cells must continuously perform to remain alive. Think about how you must replace burned-out lightbulbs, take out the trash, and grocery shop to maintain a healthy household. Cells must also replace and repair worn-out parts, eliminate wastes, and break down glucose for energy to stay healthy. In addition to those basic chores, however, most cells also conduct very specialized types of activities.

But isn't a protein something you find in meat, nuts, and dairy products? These are all types of proteins. However, in a living organism, proteins are much more than that. Proteins play a role in almost all of life's processes. For example, enzymes are proteins that help reactions take place. Some enzymes in your stomach help break down the food you eat. Replication enzymes help DNA to replicate. Insulin is another protein. It is a type of hormone that aids in controlling the level of sugar in your body. Other proteins produce pigments that determine the color of your eyes and hair. Collagen is a protein that helps make your skin and bones strong. Proteins such as hemoglobin help move oxygen around your body. Antibody proteins help your body fight off illness. Proteins help give cells their structure and shape. Those are just a few examples of the variety of proteins and what they do. DNA contains the original instructions to make all of the different types of proteins in your body.

The first step in expressing the information in DNA is to construct another nucleic acid. This nucleic acid is called **ribonucleic acid** (**RNA**). Structurally, RNA is very similar to DNA, but there are several major differences. RNA contains a ribose sugar instead of a deoxyribose sugar. These sugars are similar, but slight differences in them make DNA able to easily form a double helix while RNA cannot. Because of this, RNA is single stranded. Thymine (T), one of the bases in DNA, does not occur in RNA. Instead, a related base, uracil (U), is found at positions complementary to adenine (A). As with the sugars, thymine and uracil are similar in structure. The small difference in structure, though, helps protect DNA from enzymes that might break it down in the cell. Why do you think it is important that DNA be protected?

RNA is made by copying a DNA template. RNA is produced in the same way for all genes. The process of producing RNA from the DNA template is called **transcription** (figure 11.21). Given that RNA is chemically similar to DNA, can you imagine how DNA serves as a template to make a strand of complementary RNA? A new RNA chain is made by joining RNA nucleotides in an order that is complementary to the DNA template.

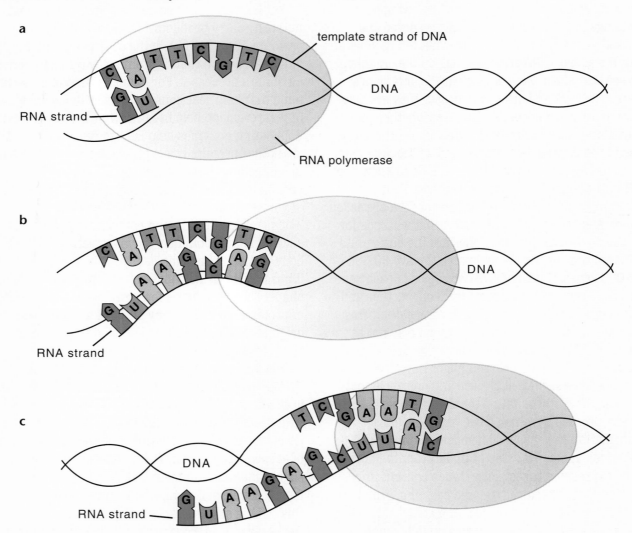

Figure 11.21   Transcription. Note that only the bases that are involved in transcription are shown here. The other bases are represented by the black lines. (*a*) An enzyme called RNA polymerase synthesizes RNA by joining RNA nucleotides in the order specified by a template strand of DNA. The process of transcribing DNA into RNA is very similar to the process of replication. However, only one RNA strand is made. (*b*) Note that as the enzyme moves along the DNA, the double helix is unwound. Specific base-pair interactions form between the DNA and RNA. (*c*) The DNA strands behind the enzyme then interact again to form the double helix. Eventually, the enzyme that is building the RNA reaches the end of the gene. At that point, the DNA and the RNA are released. Transcription, like replication, takes place in the nucleus of eukaryotic cells.

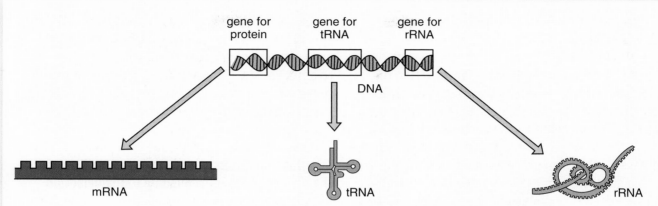

gene for protein   gene for tRNA   gene for rRNA

DNA

mRNA   tRNA   rRNA

Figure 11.22 Types of RNA. DNA encodes three types of RNA. The information encoded in messenger RNA (mRNA) will be translated directly into proteins. The transfer RNA (tRNA) and the ribosomal RNA (rRNA) participate in the reactions that assemble proteins.

As figure 11.22 shows, cells can make three types of RNA. The first type is called **messenger RNA (mRNA)**. It has the crucial role of carrying information from the DNA in the cell's nucleus to the cell's cytoplasm. This is where the proteins will be made. The name messenger RNA comes from the idea that this type of RNA carries the information, or message, from the nucleus to the cytoplasm of the cell.

The second and third types of RNA are called **transfer RNA (tRNA)** and **ribosomal RNA (rRNA)**. These types of RNA function in the actual process of assembling proteins. These two forms of RNA are transcribed from genes that are not expressed as proteins. Instead, as figure 11.22 shows, the final product of these genes is RNA.

During gene expression, the sequence of an mRNA directs the synthesis of a protein through a process called translation. A protein consists of a chain of subunits called amino acids. Just as the mRNA was created based on the DNA sequence, the order of the amino acids that make up a protein is also determined by the gene's nucleotide sequence (A, C, T, and G). The diagram in figure 11.23 illustrates this process. Notice that a set of three nucleotides codes for one amino acid. In the cell, only one strand of the DNA is read to find the set of nucleotides for an amino acid. Amino acids are first put together in a long, linear molecule. Proteins later fold into particular shapes. A given protein's shape is specified by the order of amino acids. Proteins will function properly only when they have folded into a very specific shape.

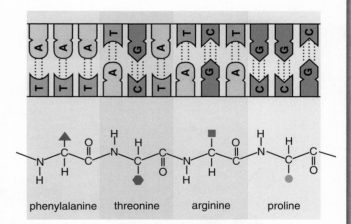

phenylalanine   threonine   arginine   proline

Figure 11.23   Relationship between DNA sequence and protein sequence. Each strand of DNA consists of a series of nucleotides. These nucleotides are bonded together in a particular order (top). Sets of three nucleotides along one strand of DNA direct the order of amino acids (bottom). The amino acids are bonded together to make the protein. The genetic code is examined in more detail in the essay, *Translating the Message in mRNA.*

Translating the Message in mRNA

ENGLISH SPANISH

To express a gene for a protein, the cell first makes a molecule of mRNA. This mRNA then acts like a blueprint for the protein, the same way we have blueprints to guide the construction of buildings or machines. Cells translate the mRNA blueprints into specific sequences of amino acids that make up proteins. Those proteins are the cellular equivalents of buildings and machines (refer to figure 11.24). The process of converting the genetic code in an mRNA sequence into an amino acid sequence is **translation**. Think about how the Navajo code talkers had to translate information from English into another language. In the same way, your cells must translate the information encoded in mRNA into proteins for it to be useful.

When we translate information from one language to another, there are certain characteristics that help us. In the same way, there are basic characteristics of the code that link a nucleotide sequence to the amino acid sequence in a protein. This code is called the **genetic code**. An amazing number of proteins are built from just 20 different

amino acids. Each amino acid must be identified specifically from information in the mRNA. The code cannot be a simple 1:1 pairing of nucleotides to amino acids. If it were, it would only be possible to have four amino acids, one for each nucleotide. Likewise, the code cannot involve a 2:1 relationship (two nucleotides encoding one amino acid). If that were the case, the code could specify only 16 amino acids (four nucleotide possibilities for the first position multiplied by four nucleotide possibilities for the second position). Instead, the code involves a 3:1 relationship. In other words, the genetic code uses three sequential mRNA bases to identify each amino acid. Each triplet (three-nucleotide combination) is called a **codon**.

Unraveling the details of the genetic code involved determining exactly which amino acid is specified by which codon. This was one of the most exciting series of discoveries ever made in the field of biology. The code of life was cracked. Now, scientists know the codons that specify each amino acid.

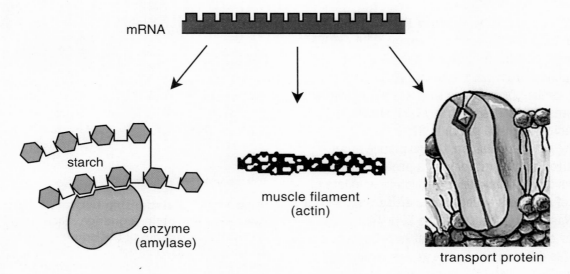

mRNA

starch

enzyme
(amylase)

muscle filament
(actin)

transport protein

Figure 11.24 Translating mRNA into proteins. The information encoded in mRNA is translated into proteins. Proteins carry out the functions of cells, so there are a wide variety of protein types. Some function as enzymes, such as amylase. Amylase breaks down starch. Other proteins function as structural proteins. Actin makes up our muscle fibers. Still other enzymes function to help transport materials across cell membranes.

First letter	Second letter				Third letter
	U	**C**	**A**	**G**	
U	phenylalanine	serine	tyrosine	cysteine	U
	phenylalanine	serine	tyrosine	cysteine	C
	leucine	serine	stop	stop	A
	leucine	serine	stop	tryptophan	G
C	leucine	proline	histidine	arginine	U
	leucine	proline	histidine	arginine	C
	leucine	proline	glutamine	arginine	A
	leucine	proline	glutamine	arginine	G
A	isoleucine	threonine	asparagine	serine	U
	isoleucine	threonine	asparagine	serine	C
	isoleucine	threonine	lysine	arginine	A
	(start) methionine	threonine	lysine	arginine	G
G	valine	alanine	aspartate	glycine	U
	valine	alanine	aspartate	glycine	C
	valine	alanine	glutamate	glycine	A
	valine	alanine	glutamate	glycine	G

Figure 11.25   The genetic code. The code letters represent bases in mRNA. The words in the boxes are the names of the 20 amino acids most commonly found in proteins. To use the code, follow a codon's three nucleotides to arrive at the corresponding amino acid. You do this by using the rows and columns labeled "first letter," "second letter," and "third letter." For example, GGA codes for glycine. How many of the amino acids have more than one codon?

Study the table in figure 11.25 carefully. It lists the triplet codes for each of the amino acids. Did you notice that using all four bases, three at a time, results in 64 possible codon combinations ($4^3 = 64$)? Remember, there are only 20 amino acids. The early genetic code researchers discovered that some amino acids are specified by more than one codon.

Study the table again. You will notice that some of the possible triplet base combinations do not correspond to any amino acid. These signal a *stop* in translation (that is, the end of the protein). Another special codon is AUG. This codon specifies the amino acid methionine. It also is a signal to *start* translation (to begin building the protein).

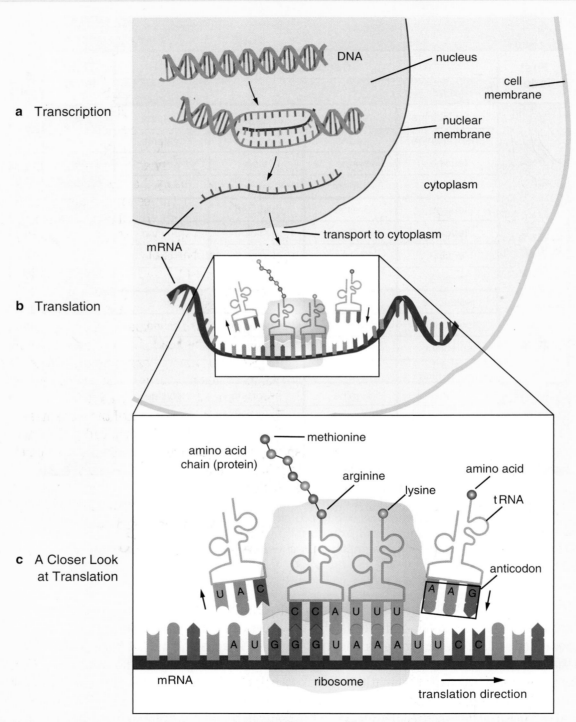

Figure 11.26 **Protein synthesis.** (*a*) Transcription of the DNA takes place in the cell nucleus. The mRNA moves out into the cytoplasm. (*b*) Protein synthesis, or translation, takes place in the cytoplasm. The ribosome reads the mRNA to generate the correct sequence of amino acids. (*c*) shows a more detailed view of translation.

One of the most remarkable aspects of the genetic code is that it is universal. Only a small number of organisms have been discovered that have slight variations on this code. For example, although archaea, eubacteria, and eukaryotes have *many* basic structural differences, they use the same genetic code. That basic similarity is an important piece of evidence that supports the idea that all life-forms evolved from one common ancestor.

How, then, does the actual process of translation take place? The process involves identifying the proper amino acids, aligning them, and joining them together. First, the mRNA from transcription moves out of the nucleus and into the cytoplasm (see figure 11.26a). Then a cellular component called a **ribosome** attaches to the mRNA. Ribosomes are large structures that are made up of both protein and RNA. They are found in the cytoplasm of the cell. Ribosomes can read any mRNA. As the ribosome travels down the mRNA, it provides the site for translation to occur. This process occurs completely within the cytoplasm of the cell.

A ribosome will travel down the mRNA until it reaches the start codon, made up of the bases AUG. This is the beginning of the sequence that specifies the protein. The start codon directs the synthesis of the new protein chain starting with the amino acid methionine. How is methionine put into place?

This is where the tRNA comes into play. tRNAs are able to recognize the codon on the mRNA. The three bases at the bottom of the tRNA, called the anticodon (see figure 11.26b and c), interact with the codon on the mRNA through complementary base pairing. At the other end of the tRNA, there is a region where amino acids can attach. Each tRNA is specific for being able to recognize only one codon. The tRNA is only able to carry the amino acid that is specified by that codon.

The ribosome continues to read down the mRNA. For each codon, the ribosome pauses and waits for another molecule of tRNA to join the complex. Remember that only the tRNA with the correct sequence and amino acid will be able to pair with the codon. Once the two amino acids are side by side, the ribosome will link the amino acids together with a covalent bond. This bond is called a **peptide bond**. As the string of amino acids grows, they are released by the tRNAs. The tRNAs may then pick up another amino acid in the cytoplasm and be used again later.

Translation continues until the ribosome reaches a stop codon. The stop codon does not specify an amino acid. It causes the ribosome to release the mRNA. At this point, the chain of amino acids folds into its final protein shape. The shape is determined by the sequence of amino acids. The protein is now ready to function.

14. Compare the amino acid sequence that results from the transcription and translation of the typical allele for the hemoglobin gene with the amino acid sequence that results from the transcription and translation of the sickle cell allele. On your poster, use an arrow or a circle to indicate the amino acids in the sickle cell protein sequence that differ from those in the unaffected sequence.

15. Read the information in the need to know, *The Sequence of Amino Acids Determines the Hemoglobin Molecule's Shape.* You will learn about the relationship between the sequence of amino acids in a hemoglobin molecule and the molecule's shape.

SC/LINKS®
NSTA

www.scilinks.org

Topic: protein synthesis
Code: human4E595

NEED TO KNOW

ENGLISH   SPANISH

The Sequence of Amino Acids Determines the Hemoglobin Molecule's Shape

Inside the environment of a red blood cell, a molecule of typical hemoglobin consists of four protein chains folded into a globular shape. The four chains in the molecule remain together because of attractive forces. These forces occur between amino acids in different parts of the protein chains.

When there is a particular mutation in the DNA of the sickle cell gene, a change in the amino acid sequence also occurs. This amino acid change has no effect on the overall shape of hemoglobin when oxygen levels are normal. For that reason, sickle cell hemoglobin behaves just like typical hemoglobin when there is plenty of oxygen.

When oxygen levels are low, however, the change in a single amino acid alters the attraction between different parts of the protein. This causes molecules of sickle cell hemoglobin to assume a different shape from the typical hemoglobin protein. As figure 11.27 shows, it is the change in molecular shape under low oxygen levels that causes sickle cell hemoglobin to form rigid, rodlike complexes of proteins. In turn, these protein complexes cause red blood cells to take on a sickle shape.

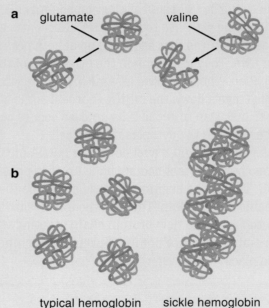

a   glutamate   valine

b

typical hemoglobin   sickle hemoglobin

Figure 11.27   **Typical and sickle hemoglobin.** The difference in the behavior of sickle cell hemoglobin is related to a change in shape that takes place at low oxygen levels. (*a*) The shape change results from the amino acid valine replacing a glutamate. (*b*) Molecules of typical hemoglobin will not associate with each other because of their shape. Molecules of typical hemoglobin remain in solution, even under conditions of low oxygen. In contrast, under the same conditions molecules of sickle hemoglobin associate together to form rigid cells. The shape allows the sickle hemoglobin proteins to associate.

16. Add what you learned in step 15 to the appropriate places on your team's poster.

17. Complete your team's poster by adding a descriptive title. Include any other details that you think would help someone else understand the information that it presents.

> Take this opportunity to check your poster. The information on your poster should reflect what you understand about how human cells use the information stored in the nucleotide sequence of their DNA to build and maintain the human being that those cells compose.

Analysis

Use the information on your poster and in the essays to respond to the following. Record your responses in your science notebook. Your teacher will use your science notebook to evaluate your understanding of gene expression.

1. Create a concept map in your science notebook. Include the following words on your map. Be sure to include linking phrases between the terms.
   a. Amino acid
   b. Nucleotide
   c. DNA
   d. Protein
   e. Chromosome
   f. rRNA
   g. mRNA
   h. tRNA
   i. Gene
   j. Nucleus
   k. Cytoplasm
   l. Physical characteristic
   m. Organism

   > If you need help creating your concept map, see appendix B7, *How to Construct a Concept Map.*

2. Cystic fibrosis is a genetic condition that occurs when both copies of the cystic fibrosis gene are mutated. The gene involved in cystic fibrosis normally codes for a protein that affects the flow of ions and water across cell membranes. When mutated, the faulty version of that protein limits the body's normal ability to secrete fluids into the digestive and gas exchange systems. Think about what you now know about gene expression. Create a flowchart that illustrates how a mutation in the cystic fibrosis gene could cause cystic fibrosis.

   > The poster that you made on sickle cell disease may suggest a general scheme for your outline.

Further Challenges

1. Learn more about the details of translation by watching the video segment, "A Closer Look at Protein Synthesis: Translation." Then complete the following tasks in your science notebook.

   Before watching the video segment, look at the symbols in figure 11.28. You will need to know these symbols to help you explain the events in the video. You may wish to copy the symbols into your science notebook.

   a. Create a diagram to represent the steps of protein synthesis.
   b. Label the parts of your diagram. Be sure to include ribosome, mRNA, tRNA, amino acid, codon, start codon, stop codon, and peptide bond.
   c. Why do you think it might be important for DNA to remain in the nucleus of the cell?
   d. Imagine that a mutation occurred in the DNA for a gene. On your drawing, indicate with an arrow or circle where changes as a result of this mutation would be.

2. Read the sidebar, *Landmark Discovery: White-Coated Sleuths Decipher Genetic Code,* to learn more about the experiment that helped scientists crack the genetic code. Summarize their experiment and discovery in your own words.

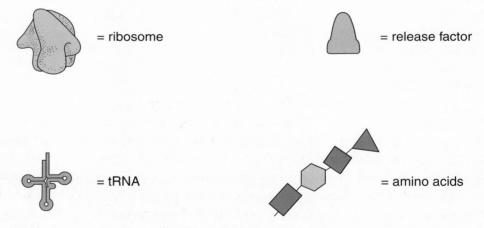

Figure 11.28 The figure lists the symbols used in the video segment, "A Closer Look at Protein Synthesis: Translation."

SIDEBAR

ENGLISH   SPANISH

Landmark Discovery: White-Coated Sleuths Decipher Genetic Code

What's New?

BETHESDA, MARYLAND (1961)—It looks as though one of the greatest challenges in scientific decoding soon will be conquered. Hats off to the pioneering work of two modern-day detectives from the National Institutes of Health: Marshall Nirenberg and Heinrich Matthaei. Nirenberg and Matthaei were intent on cracking the genetic code. They announced last week the first decoded results from their landmark research. The results showed that three mRNA nucleotides in the sequence UUU correspond to the amino acid phenylalanine, and the mRNA triplet CCC corresponds to the amino acid proline.

The genetic code lies at the heart of all living systems. Thus, this break-through truly is a remark-able accomplishment. The existence of a code—the sequence of bases in an organism's DNA—has been known since the mid-1950s. But until now, scientists had no idea how to read it. To decipher the genetic code, Nirenberg and Matthaei built an artificial protein-making system in a test tube. They then gave it an

artificial message. By knowing the message that they gave the system and by analyzing the protein that was made, they were able to decode the code (figure 11.29).

Although the process sounds simple, its execu-tion represents an amazing feat. To read even those first two words (UUU and CCC), Nirenberg and Matthaei had to create a test-tube system that actu-ally built proteins to order. To do that, they extracted enzymes and other neces-sary protein-assembly com-ponents from dead bacteria. For example, their test-tube system contained molecules of rRNA and of tRNA. Both of these molecules are known to be central to the assembly process. In addi-tion, Nirenberg and Matthaei had to build a set of artificial mRNAs. Those mRNAs had to contain known nucleotide sequences. Only after both of those tasks had been

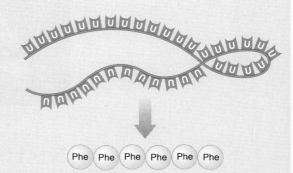

Figure 11.29   Marshall Nirenberg and Heinrich Matthaei were able to design an experiment to determine the genetic code.   These scientists created mRNA with all uracil nucleotides. They used their test-tube system to build a protein from that mRNA. They found that all of the amino acids were phenylalanine. This meant that the UUU codon codes for phenylalanine.

accomplished were they able to start deciphering the code.

What does all of this mean to you? Well, if you have any UUUs or CCCs in your genetic information (and you do), it means that we now know what those codons mean to your cells. We now can *read* them. As we break more and more of the code, who knows? One day we may be able to pull all of the mRNAs out of your cells and read your genes. What would our molecular sleuths say about that?

Genetic Technology

In this Elaborate activity, *Genetic Technology*, you will apply your understanding of the basic principles of gene action. You will learn how scientists study and manipulate genetic material. You also will discuss the potential positive and negative effects of gathering genetic information and manipulating the genes of organisms. When you have completed this activity, you will understand how geneticists have started to identify and document the molecular similarities that make us all human. You will also appreciate the molecular variability that uniquely identifies each of us.

PROCESS AND PROCEDURES

In this activity, you and your partner will study two rapidly growing areas of genetic research and technology. You then will analyze the ethical consequences that may result from those technologies.

1. With your teammate, decide who will study genetic engineering and who will study the Human Genome Project.
2. Working individually, read the appropriate essays for your topic. As you read, make notes about important discoveries, the details of how the technologies work, and examples of what can be accomplished using the genetic engineering technique.

   If you are studying genetic engineering, read the essays, *Landmark Discovery: Extraordinary New Technique Changes Biology Forever* and *Manipulating Genetic Material*.

   If you are studying the Human Genome Project, read the essays, *Landmark Discovery: New Technique Discovered While Driving, Mapping and Sequencing the Human Genome*, and *Genetic Screening: A Dilemma for All of Us*.

Landmark Discovery: Extraordinary New Technique Changes Biology Forever

ENGLISH SPANISH

What's New?

SAN FRANCISCO, CALIFORNIA (1973)—Both the study and practice of biology were radically and irreversibly changed today. Stanley Cohen of Stanford University, California, and Herbert Boyer of the University of California–San Francisco, reported the first successful attempt to build and create copies of a *recombinant* DNA molecule. What makes this accomplishment so remarkable? The recombinant

DNA molecule—made by joining together (or *recombining*) pieces of DNA from two completely different sources—never existed before. Today, it exists. It exists in many thousands of copies, and researchers can make thousands more at will.

When congratulated on their accomplishment, Cohen and Boyer quickly acknowledged their debt to many other scientists whose hard work and important discoveries made creating and cloning a recombinant molecule possible. One key advance in just the last few years was the 1970 discovery of the first restriction enzyme. This discovery was made by Werner Arber of the University of Basel, Switzerland, and Daniel Nathans and Hamilton Smith of Johns Hopkins University in Maryland. **Restriction enzymes** are proteins that can recognize a specific sequence of nucleotides in DNA and cut the DNA in a specific place within or near that sequence.

Another key advance took place in several research labs at the same time. This discovery involves isolating another important protein. The protein is the enzyme **DNA ligase**. DNA ligase functions during the replication and repair of DNA molecules. It repairs nicks that occur in one DNA strand. Isolating DNA ligase allows scientists to use it to fasten back together DNA fragments that restriction enzymes have cut. In

addition, the DNA that scientists stitch together can come from different organisms. For instance, scientists can combine bacterial DNA with yeast DNA to create *recombinant molecules.*

The idea behind Cohen and Boyer's technique is straightforward. They cut DNA from two different sources with the same restriction enzyme. They then mixed the DNA together with DNA

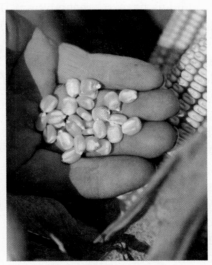

ligase. The DNA ligase caused the cut pieces to stitch together. Then Cohen and Boyer inserted the new, recombinant molecules into living bacteria. As the bacteria reproduced, the tiny recombinant DNA molecules also multiplied. Within hours, their technique produced a colony of reproducing bacteria. They could then extract as many copies of the recombinant molecule as they wanted.

Recombinant DNA techniques are revolutionizing scientific

research and technology. Scientists around the world are isolating and inserting a wide range of human genes into bacteria or other cell types. By doing this, they can harvest the products for which the genes code. Such techniques may lead to a steady supply of human insulin to use in treating diabetes. Or they could produce unrestricted quantities of human growth hormone to use in treating dwarfism. Imagine the benefits of inserting the genes for a wide range of desirable characteristics into crop plants. We might be able to create bigger cucumbers, frost-resistant strawberries, or sweeter corn. One day, we may even be able to replace faulty genes to provide typically functioning proteins.

Of course, new technologies come with potential problems as well. Scientists already are pointing out the need to regulate the technology to allow for only beneficial and safe DNA transfers. The deliberate combining of genes from *different* species, however, involves controlling genes and evolution in a different way than has ever been done before. We may not be able to predict exactly the impact that those changes will have. Our world is a different place today from what it was yesterday. It is important that all of us—scientists and nonscientists alike—be knowledgeable. We must all take part in deciding how we will use our new genetic abilities.

Manipulating Genetic Material

ENGLISH SPANISH

Since the discovery of DNA, science has greatly increased our understanding of the structure and function of genetic material. Also changed is our ability to work with it in the laboratory. In fact, our increasing ability to study and manipulate molecular processes in a variety of species has led to a revolution in the ways that scientists conduct research. That, in turn, has changed how pharmaceutical firms make medicines and how many industries conduct their day-to-day business.

The technologies are new. But our fundamental interest in studying and manipulating genetic information is not new. For centuries, humans have selectively bred plants and animals to produce organisms with desirable combinations of characteristics. Hundreds of years ago, farmers began crossing individual plants that had desirable characteristics. For example, a farmer might cross a pea plant that has a high yield with a pea plant that is less susceptible to disease. Some of the offspring of the cross would show both desirable traits. The farmer would continue to select these plants for reproduction while preventing plants with undesirable traits from reproducing. This is still the primary way that farmers improve their herds of animals. For example, a heavily muscled bull might be crossed with a cow that shows excellent "mothering abilities." Some of the female offspring will receive both traits of good muscles and mothering abilities. These females would be kept as breeding stock. This type of selective breeding was the earliest form of genetic engineering. **Genetic engineering** is a process designed to artificially control the genetic makeup of an organism.

In recent years, scientists have developed more-powerful techniques for examining genetic material at the molecular level. These techniques allow scientists to alter the genetic information of a species. This is more direct and specific than the older methods of selective breeding. It is now possible to introduce genes into an organism that

neither parent possessed. It is even possible for scientists to remove genes from one organism and introduce them into an organism that shared a common ancestor millions of years ago—one that does not normally possess those genes. The new DNA formed through that process is called **recombinant DNA** (see figure 11.30).

One example of how scientists are using recombinant DNA technologies to address a

Topic: genetic engineering/ recombinant DNA
Code: human4E602

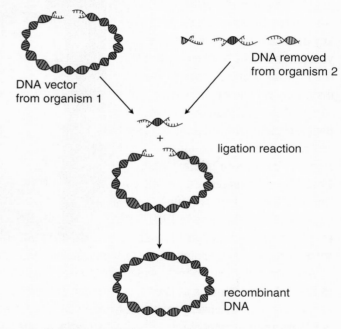

DNA vector from organism 1

DNA removed from organism 2

+

ligation reaction

recombinant DNA

Figure 11.30 Recombinant DNA. Molecular biologists isolate DNA from separate sources and combine them in unique combinations. DNA from organism 2 can be joined to a small circular molecule of DNA from organism 1. This takes place in an enzyme reaction called ligation. The circular DNA molecules are called plasmids or vectors. They are found in many bacteria. Because scientists can move vectors in and out of bacterial cells relatively easily, vectors serve as convenient carriers of DNA. As a result, they allow for the production of recombinant DNA molecules.

specific practical problem involves the cotton plant. Cotton plants are often attacked by a pest called a bollworm. The bollworm damages cotton crops and costs millions of dollars each year to control. Researchers have known for a long time, however, that a bollworm will die if it eats the common bacterium called *Bacillus thuringiensis* (or Bt for short). A protein that the bacteria produce is partially digested in the worm's gut and poisons the worm. Because that protein is so effective, for years farmers have sprayed Bt bacteria on their cotton crops to discourage the bollworms from eating them. This protective measure has its drawbacks, though. Sunlight breaks down Bt, and rainfall easily washes it off the plants.

Through genetic engineering, however, researchers have overcome those drawbacks. Figure 11.31 shows how scientists isolated the gene that codes for the poisonous bacterial protein. They then transferred the gene into the cotton plant. The new cotton plants thus contain recombinant DNA. They can produce the bacterial protein, Bt toxin, in their leaves. These plants are engineered to protect themselves from damage. When a bollworm begins nibbling on the leaves, it eats the Bt protein and dies. Food crop plants also can be engineered to produce the Bt protein because it is not toxic to humans. Farmers can use less insecticide, thereby decreasing the amount of toxic chemicals that enter the water supply and food web.

The technology, however, has not been completely effective. Farmers using the engineered cotton in 1996 reported that many bollworms survived in the new crop. Additional pesticides had to be applied, though the total amount was reduced. The surviving bollworms raise concerns, too. What might prolonged exposure to Bt do to the bollworm's resistance to its toxicity? There also are concerns for the other organisms that will encounter Bt through this technique. Current tests show that the Bt toxin is nontoxic for most animals, including beneficial insects. But the toxin has the potential to harm endangered and threatened species of moths and butterflies.

Plants or animals that contain genes from distantly related species, such as cotton plants containing bacterial genes, are called **transgenic**. Transgenic organisms are used widely in research and industry. Transgenic plants are also used widely in agriculture in the United States. Transgenic corn is used in many products such as some brands of corn chips, tortillas, and canned corn.

Genetic engineering also has a great effect on human health. Insulin is the peptide hormone that is required to help control the levels of sugar in our blood. People who have diabetes do not make insulin and often must take pills or shots to replace the insulin in their bodies. At one time, insulin could only be obtained from the pancreases of cows and hogs. Insulin produced from these animals was available in limited supplies, and it was expensive. Furthermore, insulin from other animals was not as effective for some individuals because it was not similar enough to human insulin. By recombining the human insulin gene with bacterial genes, however, researchers have been able to produce human insulin from bacteria. Because large quantities of bacteria can be grown, this is an economical method for producing authentic human insulin (figure 11.32).

Researchers are currently working on ways to treat certain human genetic disorders. They use recombinant DNA that has been constructed from harmless forms of viruses and functional copies of human genes. Introducing genetically engineered human cells into a human body for curing a genetic defect is called **gene therapy**. The first successful attempt to accomplish gene therapy began on September 14, 1990. Genetically altered white blood cells were introduced into the circulatory system of a four-year-old girl named Ashanti De Silva. Ashanti was born with adenosine

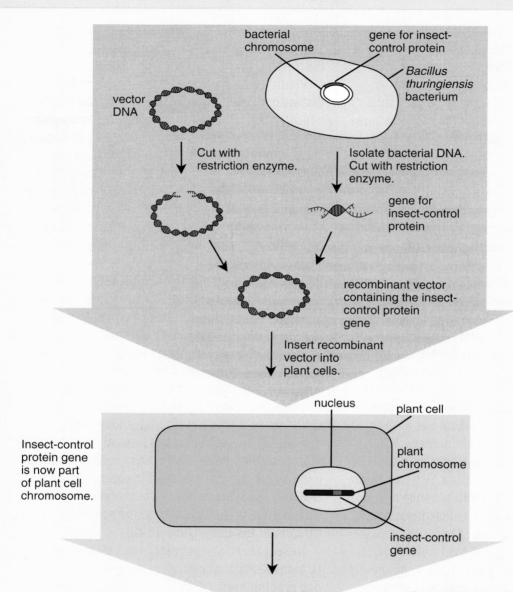

bacterial chromosome

gene for insect-control protein

Bacillus thuringiensis bacterium

vector DNA

Cut with restriction enzyme.

Isolate bacterial DNA. Cut with restriction enzyme.

gene for insect-control protein

recombinant vector containing the insect-control protein gene

Insert recombinant vector into plant cells.

nucleus

plant cell

Insect-control protein gene is now part of plant cell chromosome.

plant chromosome

insect-control gene

A whole cotton plant is grown from 1 altered cell. Every cell in the plant produces the insect-control protein. The plant can now protect itself from bollworm attack.

Figure 11.31 Genetic engineering of cotton. The toxic insect-control protein gene *Bacillus thuringiensis* is isolated. This is done with the same DNA-cutting restriction enzyme that is used to cut the DNA vector. Scientists combine these two pieces of DNA. They then insert the recombinant DNA into a plant cell. An entire plant regenerates from that one cell. The plant can now protect itself from the bollworm.

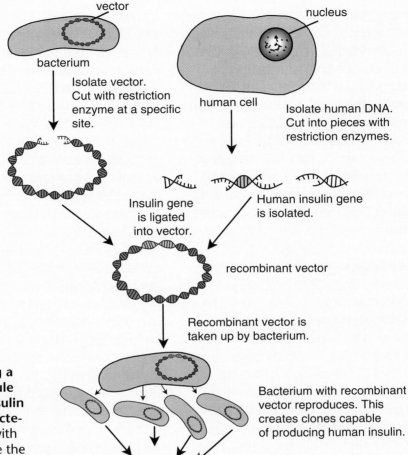

vector

bacterium

Isolate vector.
Cut with restriction
enzyme at a specific
site.

nucleus

human cell

Isolate human DNA.
Cut into pieces with
restriction enzymes.

Insulin gene
is ligated
into vector.

Human insulin gene
is isolated.

recombinant vector

Recombinant vector is
taken up by bacterium.

Figure 11.32 Producing a recombinant DNA molecule containing the human insulin gene for expression in bacteria. The bacteria created with this procedure will produce the human insulin protein.

Bacterium with recombinant
vector reproduces. This
creates clones capable
of producing human insulin.

insulin

deaminase (ADA) deficiency. In this condition, an atypical allele of the ADA gene fails to make a key protein. This key protein is required for the correct functioning of T cells. These cells are critical to an individual's immune response. The absence of this protein meant that Ashanti, like other children who inherit ADA deficiency, could easily die of infections that would scarcely trouble other children.

Physicians treated Ashanti by genetically engineering some of her cells to produce the missing protein. First, they removed T cells from her body. They then used genetic engineering techniques to

insert copies of the typical allele of the ADA gene into them. Next, they allowed cells that started to use the inserted gene (thus producing the typical protein) to undergo mitosis and make many more functional cells. Finally, they inserted all of these genetically engineered cells back into Ashanti's body.

The scientists hoped that once back inside her body, the engineered cells would continue to produce the typical protein. Thus, they would function normally to defend her body from disease. The engineered cells did, in fact, produce typical ADA. Ashanti's immune system function improved. This procedure was repeated a dozen times over the next two years. The level of typical ADA protein in Ashanti's blood eventually stabilized at 20–25 percent of that found in most people. That, along with a small dose of ADA, was enough to protect her. Today, Ashanti is healthy and active.

Despite the early promise of gene therapy, most of these treatments are only in experimental stages of development. Like Ashanti De Silva, some individuals who have participated in gene therapy trials have experienced dramatic health improvements. However, most have shown only modest improvements. Most of those who have had dramatic health improvements require re-administration of the typical gene.

The 1999 death of Jesse Gelsinger, a participant in a gene therapy experiment, has heightened awareness that gene therapy is not risk free. The experiment used a modified cold virus to insert a corrective gene into Jesse's DNA. The modified virus caused an unusual but deadly immune response in him. This led to multiple organ failure and death. For a brief time in 2003, all gene therapy studies were stopped due to illnesses and additional deaths of some study participants. By the end of 2003, gene therapy studies were allowed to proceed, however.

In 2008, scientists announced that they had been successful at using gene therapy to improve the vision of young adults who had a rare type of inherited blindness. The potential promise and excitement of these techniques are causing significant activity in the pharmaceutical industry. Drug companies are investing billions of dollars into identifying genes associated with human disease. Discovering these genes is already leading to the development of commercially produced gene products. It could also result in techniques for gene therapy that effectively treat a range of genetic disorders that are resistant to existing treatments.

As you might expect, gene therapy brings with it a whole series of ethical and legal questions. Some of the most troubling of those questions involve whether such techniques should be used to replace defective genes in a person's *reproductive* cells—her or his so-called *germ line*. Placing typical genes into a person's T cells or lung cells (or other body cells) affects only these cells and the cells' offspring, should they divide. This type of gene therapy does not affect cells in the reproductive organs that produce the eggs or sperm that may carry the defective form of the gene.

On the other hand, replacing genes in a person's germ line is tinkering with that person's genetic legacy, as well as with the genetic legacy of the human species. Suppose this type of gene therapy is successful and is allowed one day (it is currently prohibited). The result would be a permanent change in genetic information. And this change would affect all following generations produced from an individual who experienced the gene therapy.

Not surprisingly, the prospect of germ-line gene therapy has triggered a great deal of controversy. Questions abound. For example, what if gene therapy is used to correct a gene, but it creates other unexpected problems? Do children have a right to inherit an unmanipulated set of genes? Should they be allowed to inherit a set of "corrected" genes? Who will decide which genes need to be corrected and which genes do not? Say we discover the set of genes that controls fast-twitch muscles. Should parents be allowed to manipulate those genes in their germ lines in an effort to conceive children who will be better sprinters or better marathoners than the parents' natural genetic legacy might dictate? What, after all, is "typical" or "preferred"? Who should decide, not only for people today, but for people who are yet unborn? These are difficult issues. The rapid growth in our understanding of the human genome and in our ability to manipulate DNA will only raise the stakes involved in resolving them.

Landmark Discovery: New Technique Discovered While Driving

What's New?

CALIFORNIA (1983)—A young scientist was driving at night to his cabin in northern California. He found his mind moving back and forth between the road and a problem he was dealing with in biochemistry. Suddenly, a flash of insight caused him to pull to the side of the road and stop. He awakened his passenger and excitedly explained to her that he had hit upon a solution. It was not a solution to his original problem, but to one of even greater significance. The scientist, Kary Mullis (figure 11.33), had just conceived of a simple method of producing nearly unlimited copies of a specific DNA sequence in a test tube.

Figure 11.33 Kary Mullis was a scientist working for Cetus Corporation when he discovered how to make nearly unlimited copies of DNA.

When he returned to his laboratory at Cetus Corporation, Mullis asked a librarian to run a literature search on the enzyme DNA polymerase. He was interested in its role in cells, and whether anyone had used it to create copies of DNA in a laboratory. Nothing relevant turned up. For the next several weeks, he described his idea to anyone who would listen. No one had ever heard of it being tried. But no one saw any good reason why it would not work. For a year, he studied and refined his idea. In the spring of 1984, he presented a poster describing his idea at a scientific meeting. Joshua Lederberg, president of Rockefeller University in New York and a Nobel Prize winner in 1946 for his work in genetics, expressed great interest in what Mullis had proposed. After a conversation, Lederberg saw the value of the proposed idea despite its simplicity. His response was, "Why didn't I think of that?" Mullis responded, "Nobody really knows why; surely I don't. I just ran into it one night."

What did Kary Mullis run into that spring night in northern California? His idea is now a well-known process called **polymerase chain reaction (PCR)**. This technique revolutionized the way scientists analyze DNA. It also earned Mullis the 1993 Nobel Prize in Chemistry. Since the development of PCR, as little as a single molecule of DNA can be copied many times to provide sufficient amounts for sequence or mutation analysis. The PCR process uses a DNA polymerase to produce exact copies of a DNA sequence. The term "chain reaction" refers to the fact that the DNA it produces becomes the template for additional DNA synthesis in the next cycle of reactions. This DNA is copied in an exponential way each cycle. The number of copies doubles with each cycle.

Since Mullis made his idea public at a scientific meeting, many developments have been built on the original idea. For example, engineers invented a machine that can automatically control the temperature of the DNA mixture so that it is repeatedly warmed and cooled. This device repeats the procedure shown in figure 11.34 about 30–40 times. First, heating separates the double-stranded

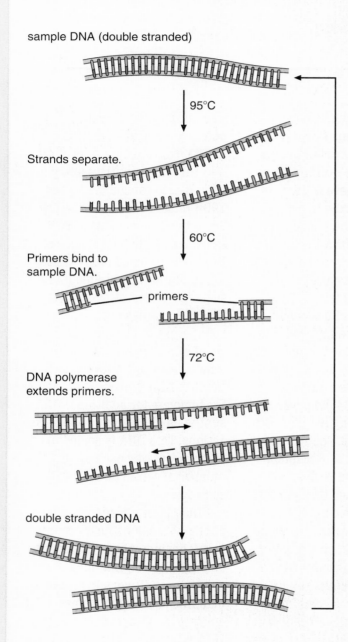

sample DNA (double stranded)

95°C

Strands separate.

60°C

Primers bind to sample DNA.

primers

72°C

DNA polymerase extends primers.

double stranded DNA

Figure 11.34   Polymerase chain reaction (PCR). Each PCR cycle roughly doubles the number of DNA molecules.

DNA molecules. Next, DNA polymerase acts at a lower temperature to make a complementary DNA strand to the single-stranded DNA. The cycle then repeats. The result of all this DNA synthesis is several million copies of the starting DNA.

Each cycle requires only one to four minutes. The entire procedure can usually be completed in a few hours. The success of PCR requires the use of DNA polymerase from the bacterium *Thermus aquaticus* (or Taq for short). This bacterium lives in hot springs. Unlike the enzymes of most organisms, its DNA polymerase is stable at the high temperatures needed to separate double-stranded DNA. Most proteins are destroyed when they are heated even moderately. In PCR, the heating separates the DNA. But this does not damage the Taq DNA polymerase because it has evolved to function at the high temperatures of hot springs. The use of DNA polymerase from Taq in PCR is a good example of the practical application of biological knowledge.

How might PCR affect your life? It has accelerated the study of gene function, gene mapping, and evolution because it is one of the main techniques used in the Human Genome Project. In medicine, PCR is particularly useful in prenatal testing for genetic diseases. Other medical applications of PCR include identifying viruses, bacteria, and cancerous cells in human tissues. In forensic science, PCR has revolutionized the process of criminal identification. PCR can be used to amplify a small sample of DNA enough to make analysis possible. The DNA can come from any cells left at a crime scene. These cells might be from blood, semen, skin, or hair.

During his midnight ride, Kary Mullis was wrestling with a biochemistry problem. He developed a remarkable solution. While it may sound like Mullis made a chance discovery, it is actually a good example of the creativity, imagination, and critical thinking that characterize most scientific discoveries.

Mapping and Sequencing the Human Genome

As technology advances, and our understanding of the mechanism of inheritance increases, more information is being discovered. In 2003, scientists finished mapping the entire human genome. After the completion of the project, the biggest surprise was that the human genome contains fewer genes than scientists had expected.

A **genome** is all of the information coded in the DNA of an organism (see figure 11.35). A genome contains the complete set of genetic instructions for making an organism. Human cells (with the exception of egg and sperm cells) normally contain 22 pairs of autosomes (nonsex chromosomes), plus two sex chromosomes (XX or XY). Remember that these chromosomes are made of DNA. When the Human Genome Project (HGP) was completed, scientists knew the entire sequence of human DNA and the location of each gene on each chromosome.

Two major groups worked independently to sequence the human genome. The public group was the Human Genome Project. This project was funded in the United States primarily by the Department of Energy and the National Institutes of Health. Several other countries were also involved. The other group was a private company called Celera Genomics Corporation.

Human DNA contains approximately 3.2 billion base pairs of DNA. Determining the sequence of that DNA, as shown in figure 11.36, finding genes, and mapping the genes is a tremendous task. If the DNA sequence of the human genome were compiled in books, we would need about 200 volumes

SCILINKS®
NSTA
www.scilinks.org
Topic: Human Genome Project
Code: human4E609

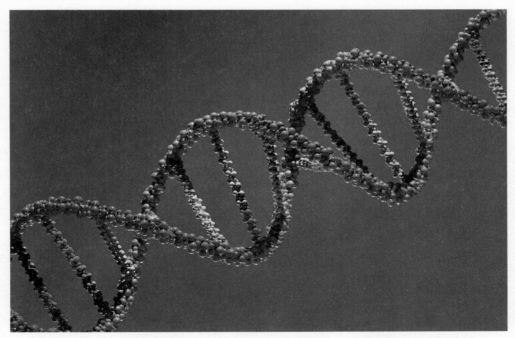

Figure 11.35 DNA molecule. False colors identify the different chemical structures that make up this DNA molecule.

at 1,000 pages each to hold all this information. Through this work, scientists learned that there are approximately 25,000 genes in human DNA.

The major findings of mapping the human genome include the following:

- The small number of genes found surprised scientists. It appears that humans only have a few thousand more genes than the roundworm *Caenorhabditis elegans*.
- Humans are more than 99 percent similar to one another in our DNA. Although the 1 percent difference may seem small, re-member that there are billions of base pairs in our genomes. This means there is still plenty of variation between humans as well.
- Genes appear to be concentrated in certain areas of the human genome. In between these areas, there are large regions of DNA that do not code for proteins.

- Chromosome 1 has the most genes (about 3,000), and the Y chromosome has the fewest (about 230).
- Sperm carry twice as many mutations as eggs. This is interesting because mutations are a major source of genetic changes and also lead to variations in a population.
- The functions of over half of the discovered genes are unknown.
- Statistical tests have shown that many genes were affected by natural selection.
- Ninety-five percent of the human genome does not code for proteins. Originally, scientists thought of this 95 percent as "junk DNA." They now realize that this DNA may play a role in regulating transcription and translation and in the development of embryos.

Because of the Human Genome Project, certain types of studies are now possible. One type of work that scientists are doing looks at variations in the

Figure 11.36 Automated DNA sequencing. Scientists use instruments to help them sequence multiple samples of DNA. Each of the colors on the screen represents one of the four nitrogen bases.

human genome. Scientists are now able to compare the DNA of people affected by a disorder with the DNA of people unaffected by the disorder. From this, they can find areas that are different between the DNAs in the two groups. If there are variations that seem to occur frequently in people affected by the disorder, these changes are thought to be related to the disorder. These regions serve as pointers to the regions of the genome that might contain a change that causes the disorder.

It is important to realize, though, that only a few genetic disorders are caused by just one change in DNA. Most disorders are complex and have multiple genes involved. Comparisons of genomes can give scientists ideas of which genes are involved. Because of the complex nature of disorders, however, scientists will not necessarily be able to pinpoint the exact changes that lead to a disorder.

The process of genome mapping has also given rise to new fields of science. Bioinformatics uses computer science and mathematics to identify and compare genes in the DNA sequences of many organisms. Proteomics is the study of proteins. Scientists in this area look at protein structure, function, and interactions. The research done in proteomics has been enhanced with knowledge from the HGP. Pharmacogenics is the study of how genetic variation affects the body's response to drugs. It might someday lead to the development of drugs customized for a person's genetic makeup.

The mapping of the human genome generated some ethical issues. Individuals and society as a whole will have to address these issues. For example, scientists are developing new technologies that can sequence an individual's genome for less than $1,000. This technology will bring up questions such as these:

- Who will have the right to see a person's genetic information?
- Could this information be used against people in the workplace?
- Could insurance companies have access to genetic information?
- Should families have the right to see the genetic profiles of other family members?

Many further questions arise around these questions. Federal and state governments are working to create laws to protect genetic privacy. In the United States, there are laws that say people cannot be discriminated against based on genetic information. One such bill was passed in 2008. This bill relates to health insurance and employment. The bill protects a person's health insurance and job, regardless of the person's genetic information. It also makes clear what is considered "genetic information." Genetic information includes an individual's genetic tests and the genetic tests of family members. It also includes the family's history of disease. The bill also prevents discrimination against people who ask for genetic testing or counseling about genetic disorders.

There are also questions about what can be changed by using our new information. Should our genes be "fixed"? Should we eliminate certain diseases? At what point should a disease be considered something we should change? What will be the effects of living longer? How will tinkering with genetics affect the human population as a whole?

The ethical issues associated with scientists' ability to map the human genome will affect you in your lifetime. What questions are important to you? What information will you need to make important decisions related to our knowledge on the human genome?

Genetic Screening: A Dilemma for All of Us

Finding the gene for cystic fibrosis (CF) was a major breakthrough in biomedicine. There is new hope that research will produce a cure for the disorder. The CF gene can be detected through DNA analysis. DNA analysis could help identify people who do not have the disease but could pass it on to their children. Once recognized, these people could be advised of the risk of having a child with cystic fibrosis. They might choose alternative methods of having a child such as adoption or using sperm or eggs from a donor. They might choose to have their gametes screened for the CF gene. DNA analysis can also detect cystic fibrosis in developing fetuses. The parents of a fetus diagnosed with cystic fibrosis could choose to end the pregnancy or to carry it to term. This ability to screen an individual or population for a genetic disorder is called genetic screening.

Genetic screening allows for early detection and prevention. It also raises many difficult questions about ethics and public policy. Dorothy Nelkin and Laurence Tancredi are sociologists who study the social impact of medicine. They feel that DNA analysis in genetic screening has caused a shift in the focus of health care. In the past, doctors looked for diseases in individuals. Now, if they have reason to suspect a person might develop a disease, they are able to do genetic tests. Who would have the right to see the results of genetic screening? How could these results be used? Although there is a ban on discrimination against people based on genetic screening, are there other potential problems that could arise from the results?

Neil A. Holtzman, a pediatrician and geneticist at Johns Hopkins University in Maryland, raises another concern about genetic screening. The tests may not always predict with certainty whether a person will develop a particular disorder. This is especially true of the many disorders that are affected by genes and the environment. Some examples are

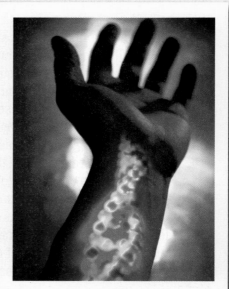

heart disease, cancer, and schizophrenia.

From this, we can see it is important to control how screening is done and what is done with the results. More public education about genetics is important, too. Without regulation and more education about genetics, there is danger that some individuals may lose some control of their lives. Some people might be encouraged to have particular medical treatments based on their genetic information, rather than on their actual health.

Questions are also raised when we think about the complexity of disease. Scientists once thought that many diseases may be controlled mainly by one or a few genes. After the Human Genome Project, however, scientists have realized that most diseases have many genetic components that each contribute a small amount of information to whether a person is affected by the disease. Would it even be possible to screen people for a disease when so many different genes are involved?

Genetic screening has potential benefits. It also raises ethical questions. During the Human Genome Project, 5 percent of the budget was dedicated to identifying ethical issues. It was several million dollars each year. This money supported research, discussion, and public education about ethical questions. Today, scientists, ethicists, philosophers, and lawmakers are still involved in these discussions.

Analysis

1. Use the information from your assigned essays and any other reliable resources to complete the following tasks. Record your responses in your science notebook. Be prepared to explain your topic and answers to your teammate.

   a. Summarize the scientific technologies that you read about in the essays.

   b. Identify and summarize at least 2 major ethical issues related to the technologies associated with your topic.

   c. Explain at least 1 benefit and 1 concern related to each of the major ideas that you summarized in question 1a. Be sure to include discussion of the issue from different views.

   d. Describe how the issues that you explained have already affected or might affect you and others in the future.

   e. Recommend what you think should be done about the issues that you have summarized.

      You may wish to refer back to the essay, *Ethical Analysis*, in chapter 6, *Human Homeostasis: Health and Disease*, to help you think about the issues.

2. With your teammate, take turns teaching each other about your topics.

   Discuss the responses that you wrote in questions 1a–e. Be sure that you respect your teammate's right to have a different opinion from you.

3. In your science notebook, write 2 or 3 paragraphs that summarize your teammate's topic. Include the benefits and concerns that are tied to the related technologies.

Further Challenges

Complete the following tasks individually. Write your answers in your science notebook.

1. "Genetic engineering and genetic screening have the potential to reduce human variability."
   a. Describe whether this statement is true, and why.
   b. What effect could a reduction in variability have on human populations?

2. Genetic engineering is being used to solve problems. How might it create new problems?

3. Do you think there are some genetic technology solutions that are needed and some that are not? If so, what characteristics define whether a technology is needed?

Effects of Mutations

In chapter 11, you have examined the processes that allow genetic information to be used by cells. You have also learned about advances in genetic technology, from the Human Genome Project to polymerase chain reaction to genetic screening.

Throughout this chapter, many of the examples used are related to genetic disorders. Not all mutations in genes cause diseases, though. In this Evaluate activity, *Effects of Mutations*, you will use your knowledge of genetic processes to analyze a mutation that relates to coloration in animals.

Materials

different-colored pens or pencils (optional)
chart paper, poster board, or construction paper (optional)

PROCESS AND PROCEDURES

1. Obtain a copy of the *Gene Expression Rubric* handout from your teacher. Read it over and ask any questions you may have about your project.
2. With your partner, choose which topic you will learn more about: coloration in jaguars, insecticide resistance in mosquitoes, or hemoglobin in geese that live at high altitude. One partner will learn about one topic, and the other partner will learn about a different topic.

   Your teacher may ask you to choose between only the jaguar coloration example and the insecticide resistance in mosquito example.

3. Read the need to know associated with your topic (*Coloration in Jaguars*, *Resistance to Insecticide in Mosquitoes*, or *Geese Living at High Altitude*). This will help you complete your project.

NEED TO KNOW
ENGLISH SPANISH

Coloration in Jaguars

Have you ever seen a jaguar in a zoo? Most jaguars are orange with dark spots. There are also jaguars that are completely black, though. What do you think caused the difference in coloration between these two animals? If you said that it might be a difference in their genes, you are right.

The gene responsible for the coloration of jaguars is called the melanocortin-1 receptor, or *MC1R* for short. The protein made from this gene helps regulate the amount of the pigment **melanin** that is made in many organisms. Melanin is a brown or black pigment. The more melanin that is present in skin, fur, or feathers, the darker these structures appear.

In jaguars, the typical allele produces a moderate amount of melanin. These jaguars appear orange with spots. A small change in the *MC1R* gene can allow higher amounts of melanin to be produced, which results in a black jaguar. The high amount of melanin does not allow the spots to be seen. (The spots on jaguars are caused by a different gene.) The following sequence shows some of the *MC1R* DNA sequence for the typical coloring and for the black coloring. Note that this is just a short portion in the middle of the gene's sequence. The entire *MC1R* gene is made up of several thousand DNA nucleotides, begins with a start codon, and ends with a stop codon:

- Typical jaguar:

   GTG CTG GAG ACG GCC GTC ATG CTG CTG CTG GAG GCG GGC ACC CTG GCC GGC

- Black jaguar:

   GTG CTG GAG ACG GCC GTC ATG CTG CTG ACG GCC GGC

It is interesting to note that the *MC1R* gene is involved in differences in coloration in other animals, too. One change in the DNA sequence of this gene causes the difference between white snow geese and blue-gray snow geese. Changes in *MC1R* also cause the difference between the white and black forms of the black bear and light and dark forms of certain lizards. This gene is also responsible for light and dark rock pocket mice. In humans, most people with red hair have one particular allele of the same gene.

Resistance to Insecticide in Mosquitoes

Malaria is a disease that is common in many tropical locations in the world, such as Africa, Asia, and South America. Malaria is caused by a parasite that is transferred to humans when they are bitten by an infected mosquito. It is a serious disease that can cause a flulike illness with fevers, chills, vomiting, and joint pain. Sometimes malaria can be serious enough to cause death.

In the 1950s, an effort started across the globe to kill the mosquitoes that carried malaria. This was done using insecticides such as DDT. In some places, such as the southeastern United States and in Europe, the effort was successful in wiping out malaria by the late 1970s. In other parts of the world, there was not as much success. As it turned out, a mutation in the DNA of the mosquitoes had caused them to become resistant to insecticides. The live mosquitoes were still able to carry the malaria parasite and continue to infect people.

What effect did the change in DNA that led to insecticide resistance have? Mosquitoes and other organisms have an enzyme called acetylcholinesterase, or AChE, in the synapses between neurons. This enzyme helps remove a chemical called acetylecholine from the synapse. Insecticides cause AChE to work improperly to remove acetylcholine. This results in acetylcholine building up and causing the mosquitoes to become paralyzed and die. The mutation caused a change in AChE, though, that made it resistant to the effects of insecticides. This means the AChE could continue carrying out its typical functions in the cell and the mosquitoes were able to live.

The following sequences show a part of the DNA sequence in the typical AChE allele and the insecticide-resistant AChE allele. Note that this is only a small portion of the DNA sequence. The whole AChE gene is made up of several thousand DNA nucleotides, begins with a start codon, and ends with a stop codon:

- Typical AChE:
    CGG CGG CAG TAC GAC ACC TAG AAG CCC CCA CCG AAG ATG AGG CCC TGA CGG

- Insecticide-resistant AChE:
    CGG CGG CAG TAC GAC ACC TAG AAG CCC CCA TCG AAG ATG AGG CCC TGA CGG

Geese Living at High Altitude

Mount Everest rises above the country of Nepal, its peak soaring at 8,848 m (29,028 ft). Temperatures are so cold that flesh will freeze instantly if it is exposed. Almost all of the few climbers who attempt to reach the top require bottled oxygen as they climb. The amount of oxygen available at that altitude is only about a third of the amount available at sea level. Despite the harsh conditions, bar-headed geese fly over the top of Mount Everest as they migrate from their feeding grounds in India to their nesting grounds in Nepal.

The key to this type of goose being able to fly at such high altitudes is a special type of hemoglobin. In these geese, the hemoglobin in their red blood cells is able to bind oxygen very quickly compared with the hemoglobin found in most geese. When a bar-headed goose breathes in, the oxygen binds to the hemoglobin in red blood cells, even at extreme elevations where the oxygen pressure is low. The oxygen then moves to all parts of the body, carried by the red blood cells. This gives the important systems, such as the gas exchange system and the muscular system, the power to fly at such high altitudes.

What changes have occurred at the protein level that allow the hemoglobin to bind oxygen more quickly? Scientists have found that one change in the protein has caused the hemoglobin proteins to differ between bar-headed geese and geese that live at low altitude. The following protein sequence shows a portion of the hemoglobin protein in bar-headed geese and in greylag geese, a type of goose that lives at lower altitude. Note that this is only a small portion of the protein sequence. The whole hemoglobin gene is made up of several thousand DNA nucleotides, begins with a start codon, and ends with a stop codon. This results in a large protein with many more amino acids than are shown:

- Greylag goose hemoglobin:

  valine valine alanine isoleucine histidine histidine proline serine alanine leucine threonine proline glutamate valine histidine alanine serine

- Bar-headed goose hemoglobin:

  valine valine alanine isoleucine histidine histidine proline serine alanine leucine threonine alanine glutamate valine histidine alanine serine

Some scientists wanted to confirm that this change in amino acid sequence was what caused the change in the hemoglobin. To do this, they took human hemoglobin and made the same amino acid change at the same place in the protein. They found that the modified human hemoglobin bound oxygen more quickly as well.

4. Use the following information to create an illustration of the process of gene expression for your topic. Your teacher will direct you on the materials you may use.

   Your illustration should show the following criteria.
   a. The name of the gene and its location in the cell
   b. The mutation that occurs, labeled with the type of mutation
   c. The mRNA that is transcribed and its location in the cell
   d. The important components of translation and their locations in the cell
   e. The amino acid sequence of the product of translation
   f. A description of how the mutation affects the organism

      If you are studying jaguar coloration or insecticide resistance in mosquitoes, you have been provided the DNA sequence and will be able to work through the steps in order. If you are studying geese at high altitude, you have been given the protein sequence and will work backward to a DNA sequence. Note that because there is more than one codon sequence for some amino acids, you may come up with a different sequence from other students working on this topic.

5. Explain your illustration to your partner. Provide feedback to your partner about his or her illustration.

   Constructive feedback will help your partner improve his or her work. Try to advise your partner about anything that could be improved, rather than just saying, "Nice work."

6. Revise your illustration based on your partner's feedback.
7. Be prepared to turn in your illustration as your teacher instructs.

12

Continuity of Information through Inheritance

> It is certainly desirable to be well descended, but the glory belongs to our ancestors.
>
> Plutarch

Did you know that at one point in history, scientists thought that the trait of "wanderlust"—a strong desire to travel and explore—was inherited from one's parents? Have you ever wondered if your musical ability or athletic ability was something you were born with or something you learned? Today, scientists are making progress toward understanding the degree to which certain characteristics are passed from parents to children.

In chapter 10, *Reproduction in Humans and Other Organisms*, you learned how reproduction contributes to continuity of life. In chapter 11, *Gene Action*, you explored the ways genetic information is stored and used in cells. For a species to continue on Earth, it must be able to pass genetic information from one generation to the next. In this chapter, you will learn about how that happens with humans. You also will learn how the laws of probability make it possible to predict the inheritance of some traits, how cellular processes account for patterns of inheritance, and how our genes contribute to human variation.

GOALS FOR THE CHAPTER

In chapter 12, *Continuity of Information through Inheritance*, you will work to gain an understanding of the following concepts:

✔ The flow of genetic information from one generation to the next provides continuity of life.

✔ The genotype of an organism limits the possible phenotypes.

✔ The environment plays a role in determining phenotypes.

✔ Genetic patterns can be predicted on the basis of biological processes.

✔ Genetics plays a role in variation among organisms, including humans.

✔ Mathematics improves our ability to analyze data, construct explanations, and communicate results.

To help you develop these understandings, you will complete the following activities.

ENGAGE	Gifts from Your Parents
EXPLORE	Inheritance: What's the Chance?
EXPLAIN	A Cellular View of Inheritance
EXPLAIN	Patterns of Inheritance
ELABORATE	Predicting Inheritance by Using Pedigrees
ELABORATE	The Genetic Basis of Human Variation
EVALUATE	Human Genetic Disorders

As you work through the chapter, remember to use the chapter organizer to link what you have learned to new concepts.

Gifts from Your Parents

Key Idea: Genetic information is passed from parents to children.

Linking Question:
How can we make useful predictions about how information is passed from parents to children?

Chapter 12

EXPLORE

Inheritance: What's the Chance?

Key Idea: We can apply the mathematics of probability to make predictions about inherited traits.

Linking Question:
Why is it possible to make predictions about inherited traits?

MAJOR CONCEPTS

✔ The flow of genetic information from one generation to the next provides continuity of life.

✔ The genotype of an organism limits the possible phenotypes.

✔ The environment plays a role in determining phenotypes.

✔ Genetic patterns can be predicted on the basis of biological processes.

✔ Genetics plays a role in variation among organisms, including humans.

✔ Mathematics improves our ability to analyze data, construct explanations, and communicate results.

EXPLAIN

A Cellular View of Inheritance

Part A: Meiosis
Part B: Tracking Genes through Meiosis
Key Idea: The process of meiosis helps explain how we are able to predict the inheritance of traits.

Linking Question:
How can we predict the inheritance of traits?

Human Genetic Disorders

Key Idea: Human genetic disorders have the same characteristics of inheritance as other genetic traits.

Linking Question:
How can our understanding of genetic variation be applied to medicine?

Continuity of Information through Inheritance

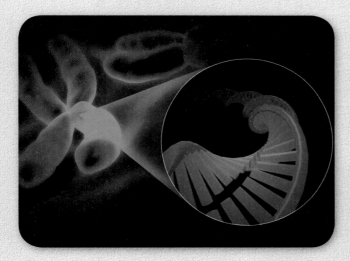

ELABORATE

The Genetic Basis of Human Variation

Key Idea: Genetic information contributes to human variation.

Linking Question:
How can we explain traits that have continuous variation in phenotype?

ELABORATE

Predicting Inheritance by Using Pedigrees

Key Idea: Pedigrees allow us to examine the differences in the inheritance patterns of traits.

Linking Question:
What other patterns of inheritance are there, and what tools help us understand them?

EXPLAIN

Patterns of Inheritance

Key Idea: Geneticists have tools to help predict the ways genetic traits are inherited.

ENGAGE

Gifts from Your Parents

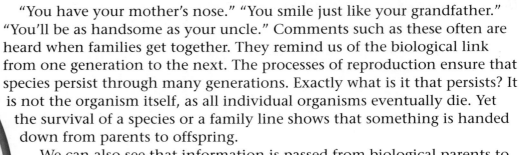

"You have your mother's nose." "You smile just like your grandfather." "You'll be as handsome as your uncle." Comments such as these often are heard when families get together. They remind us of the biological link from one generation to the next. The processes of reproduction ensure that species persist through many generations. Exactly what is it that persists? It is not the organism itself, as all individual organisms eventually die. Yet the survival of a species or a family line shows that something is handed down from parents to offspring.

We can also see that information is passed from biological parents to children when we look at their features. Eyes, noses, and hair color are all examples of traits that might be similar between generations of a family. Did you know that some diseases can be passed down from parents to children as well? Genetic counseling is a service provided to people who are at risk for an inherited disease. Genetic counselors provide information about the chances of having a baby who is affected, as well as about the disease itself. In this Engage activity, *Gifts from Your Parents*, you will be introduced to a high school student doing an internship in a genetic counseling clinic. You will learn about genetic counseling along with this student throughout the chapter.

PROCESS AND PROCEDURES

1. Read the scenario, *The Genetic Counseling Clinic,* for a brief introduction to genetic counseling.
2. Look at the picture that Ms. Gomez gave to Elise (figure 12.1). In your science notebook, make a list of the physical characteristics you can see that might be passed from biological parents to children. Title this list "observable inherited characteristics."

Figure 12.1
A family portrait.
What characteristics can you see that were passed from generation to generation in this family?

The Genetic Counseling Clinic

Elise approached the door to the clinic with some butterflies in her stomach. It was her first day as an intern at the genetic counseling clinic. Elise had spent the last few weeks learning about the field of genetic counseling and was anticipating learning many different things in her semester as an intern. She knew that genetic counselors help educate people about genetic conditions and disorders. She also knew that genetic counselors can help families estimate the risk of inheriting some disorders.

Her high school guidance counselor had explained that during the internship Elise would shadow, or follow, the people who work in the clinic. She would learn about the types of patients they see and the work the genetic counselors do. They might give her tasks to do to help her learn more about genetics and genetic counseling.

As Elise walked into the clinic, she saw Linda Gomez, one of the genetic counselors, waiting for her.

"Good morning, Elise!" Ms. Gomez called out. "I hope you are ready to get started right away. Let's go into my office."

Once they arrived in the office, Ms. Gomez slid a picture across the table to Elise. "First, I'd like you to begin thinking about what characteristics are passed from a parent to a child. Take a look at this picture and see how many features you can name that you think are inherited from one's parents."

3. Create a second list of characteristics that you think might be passed from parents to children that could not be seen in figure 12.1. Title this list "hard-to-observe inherited characteristics."

4. Participate in a class discussion about your lists from steps 2 and 3. Add any additional characteristics to your list.

Analysis

Answer the following questions individually.

1. Think about traits that might not be passed from parents to children, called acquired traits, and then answer the following questions.
   a. What is the difference between an acquired trait and an inherited trait?
   b. What traits can you think of that are acquired traits?
   c. Do you observe any acquired traits in figure 12.1?

EXPLORE

Inheritance: What's the Chance?

Think about flipping a coin. If you flip it one time, what is the likelihood it will land on heads? If you flip it 10 times, how many times do you think it will land on heads? Probability is an area of mathematics that expresses the likelihood or chance that an event will occur. Using probability, it is possible to estimate whether it will rain on a particular day, what a favorite player's baseball batting averages will be, or whether a person will win the lottery. It is important to realize, though, that when we are using probability, we are only making estimations about what might happen, not guaranteeing a result. What we predict by using probability will not necessarily occur.

Genetic counselors use probability to estimate a couple's risk of having a child with a particular disorder. These estimations are based on probability and the couple's family histories. In this Explore activity, *Inheritance: What's the Chance?*, you will learn more about probability. You will think about probability in a biological context to consider how it is possible to make predictions about the inheritance of traits. This will help you make predictions throughout the chapter about genetic events.

Materials (teams of 2)

1 calculator
1 coin
different-colored pens or pencils (optional)

PROCESS AND PROCEDURES

1. Work with your teammate to solve the following problems. Record your ideas in your science notebook.
   a. A pair of rabbits mated and produced a litter of 10 offspring. How many males and how many females do you predict would be in the litter?
   b. Explain how you made your prediction. What knowledge did you use?
   c. Even if you are reasonably confident that your prediction is correct, can you guarantee how many males and females would be born in a litter of 10 offspring? Explain your answer.

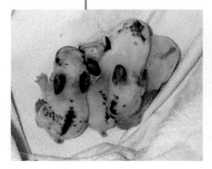

2. Test your prediction by using a coin to simulate the number of males and females among the 10 offspring. Follow step 2a–c to complete the simulation.

   Assume that heads represents a male rabbit and tails represents a female rabbit.

   a. In your science notebook, prepare a 2-column chart with the headings "male" and "female" to record your team's results.
   b. Shake the coin in both hands, and then release it 10 times. Record your results by placing a checkmark (✔) in the appropriate column.
   c. Explain the role of chance in determining your results.

3. Think about how probabilities relate to humans by discussing the following problems with your teammate. Record your ideas in your science notebook. If you are not sure about your answers, write down your best ideas. You will have a chance to revise your ideas later.

   a. A couple is going to have their first child. What is the probability, or chance, that the child will be a female?
   b. Another couple has 3 sons already. They are expecting their fourth child. What is the probability that the child will be a female?
   c. A couple just had their sixth child. How many males and how many females would you predict that they have?

4. Read the information in the need to know, *Probability,* to learn more about probability.

5. Look back at the 3 questions in step 3. Revise your answers if needed and represent each answer using the mathematic equation in the need to know, *Probability*.

NEED TO KNOW

ENGLISH SPANISH

Probability

Imagine that the weathercaster announced that there is a 20 percent chance of rain today. Should you take your umbrella with you? What does it mean that there is a 20 percent chance?

We often make predictions about whether or not events will occur. We use our knowledge of past events and other possible outcomes to say how likely it is that something will happen. Some events we can predict with high accuracy, such as eclipses of the Moon. Other events we can only predict with low accuracy, such as earthquakes. It is often useful to use percentages to show how likely it is that the event will occur. **Probability** is the area of mathematics that expresses the chances that a certain event will occur.

For example, when you flip a coin it can land on either heads or tails. In this example, there are 2 possible outcomes: heads or tails. Out of those 2 outcomes, there is 1 "way" the coin can land on tails. Thus, the probability of the coin landing on tails is

$$\text{probability of landing on tails} = \frac{1 \; way \; of \; landing \; on \; tails}{2 \; possible \; outcomes} = \frac{1}{2} \text{ or } 50\%.$$

In more general terms, probability can be described as

$$\text{probability} = \frac{no. \; of \; ways \; a \; specific \; outcome \; can \; happen}{total \; no. \; of \; outcomes}.$$

Now, think about an example with more than 2 possible outcomes. On a six-sided die (the singular of dice) like the one in figure 12.2, how many possible outcomes are there? In other words, if you rolled the die, how many different answers could you get? If you said 6, you are right. What, then, is the probability of rolling a two? There is 1 way of landing on a two. The probability of rolling a two is 1/6, or 17 percent.

Now, imagine that you rolled a six. You are about to roll the die again. What is the probability that you will roll a six this time? The probability is still 1/6. Events that have already happened do not influence the probability of the next event.

Genetic counselors use probability to make predictions about the risk of inheriting a genetic disorder. It is important to remember, though, that the numbers calculated here are only predictions. These numbers represent what is likely to happen, not what is definitely happen.

© Dreamstime/Picsfive

Figure 12.2   One die has 6 possible outcomes.   What is the probability of rolling a five?

6. Look at the data under the heading "small sample size" in figure 12.3. These data show the results of 3 rabbit matings. Discuss the following with your teammate.
   a. Do these results match your predictions from step 1 or your test results from step 2? Write down your ideas about why the results may be the same or different.
   b. Use the following equation to calculate the percentage of male rabbits for each group of 10 offspring. Record these results in your science notebook.
      percentage males = (no. males / total no. offspring) × 100
   c. The result of each of these 3 trials is not the same. Why do you think the actual outcomes vary from 50 percent males and 50 percent females?
7. Examine the data under the heading "large sample size" in figure 12.3. Note that the total number of offspring is 600. Calculate the percentage of male rabbits for each group of 600 offspring. Record these results in your science notebook.

Small sample size			
Trial	No. of offspring	Males	Females
1	10	4	6
2	10	6	4
3	10	6	4
Large sample size			
Trial	Total no. of offspring	Males	Females
1	600	279	321
2	600	296	304
3	600	316	284

Figure 12.3 The results of rabbit matings. The top table shows the number of male and female rabbits produced in a litter with only 10 rabbit offspring. The bottom table shows the number of males and females when data from many matings were combined to get 600 rabbit offspring.

8. With your teammate, answer the following questions. Record the answers in your science notebook.
   a. Are the results for the large sample size (step 7) generally closer to 50 percent than those for the small sample size (step 6)?
   b. Why do you think you see a difference in the percentages between the large and small sample sizes?
9. Work with your partner to follow these steps to test the accuracy of large sample sizes.
   a. Flip the coin 20 times. Record the results in your science notebook.
   b. What is the percentage of heads for this sample size of 20 flips?
   c. Contribute your data to a class data table.
   d. What is the percentage of heads for this large sample size?
   e. What do these results suggest about the effect of sample size on the match between probable outcomes and actual results?

Analysis

Discuss the following with your teammate. Record your answers in your science notebook.

1. Use your knowledge of probability to answer the following questions.
   a. You have a bag with 4 marbles in it: 1 red, 1 yellow, 1 blue, and 1 green. If you reach in and randomly pull out 1 of the marbles, what is the probability that it will be the blue marble?
   b. You have a bag with 8 marbles in it: 2 red, 2 yellow, 2 blue, and 2 green. What is the probability of pulling out a green marble?
   c. Were the answers to questions 1a and 1b the same or different? Why?

Topic: probability
Code: human4E627

2. A couple has come to the genetic counseling office. They have a child affected by the genetic disorder cystic fibrosis. (You will learn more about cystic fibrosis later in the chapter.) The genetic counselor tells the couple that the risk of having a child affected by cystic fibrosis is 1/4, or 25 percent. Since the couple already has a child with cystic fibrosis, can they have 3 more children without worrying that any of them will be affected by the disorder? Explain your answer.

3. When you pooled your data for the coin toss with the rest of the class's data, what happened to the percentages of heads and tails?

4. Using your observations for question 3, write a "rule" about sample size.

5. The graph in figure 12.4 shows the relationship between the sample size and the margin of error. The margin of error tells you how much your results need to be qualified. For example, imagine a study where you had a sample size of 10 people. Based on the graph in figure 12.4, your margin of error is 31 percent. Your results may indicate that, "50 percent of people had brown hair," based on your data. Because of the margin of error, when you try to talk about all people, your results could be 31 percent higher or lower than your original claim of 50 percent. Use the graph to answer the following 5 questions.

   a. If you had 100 people in your study, what would the margin of error be?

   b. If there were 1,000 people in your study, what would the margin of error be?

   c. If there were 10,000 people in your study, what would the margin of error be?

   d. Look at the margin of error going from a sample size of 100 to a sample size of 1,000 and from a sample size of 1,000 to a sample size of 10,000. Do you see the same benefit from continuing to increase the sample size?

   e. Consider the relationship between margin of error and sample size. Why do you think it is important to pay attention to the number of subjects in a scientific study?

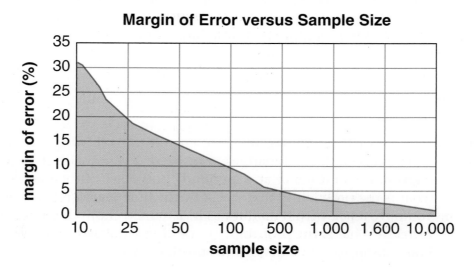

Figure 12.4 Graph of the effect of sample size on margin of error. As the sample size increases, what is the effect on the margin of error?

Further Challenges

Read the following information on probabilities, then answer the questions that follow.

Think about having 2 dice. What is the probability of rolling a 5 and a 6? To calculate this probability, multiply the probabilities of each event. There is a 1/6 chance of rolling a 5 on 1 die. There is a 1/6 chance of rolling a 6 on 1 die. This means that the probability of rolling a 5 and a 6 is $1/6 \times 1/6 = 1/36$, or 3 percent.

1. You have a bag of marbles with 1 red, 1 green, 1 blue, and 1 yellow marble. You draw 1 out, look at the color, and place the marble back in the bag. You then choose another marble. What is the probability that you will draw a red marble on the first try and a blue marble on the second try?
2. Using the information in *Further Challenge* 1, what is the probability you will draw a red marble on the first try and again on the second try?
3. What is the probability that a couple will have a boy child first, followed by a girl child?
4. A couple is expecting fraternal (nonidentical) twins. What is the probability that they will have 2 males?

   Fraternal twins are the result of two different eggs being fertilized by two different sperm.

A Cellular View of Inheritance

In the Explore activity, *Inheritance: What's the Chance?*, you saw that there is about a 50 percent chance of having a male child. Genetic counselors can also make estimations about the chance of a couple having a child with a particular genetic disorder. What happens on a cellular level that allows them to make these estimations? How can genetic counselors make predictions about how alleles might be inherited?

Recall from your work in chapter 10 that in sexual reproduction, genetic information is passed from generation to generation by cells called *gametes*. Gametes such as egg and sperm have only *half* the genetic information of other body cells. If they had more, each zygote would start life with more genetic information than its parents. (See figure 12.5.) For that reason, it is important that the number of chromosomes in gametes be only half the number of chromosomes in other body cells.

How and when does this reduction in chromosome number occur? Do all gametes contain the same genetic information? In this Explain activity, *A Cellular View of Inheritance*, you will use information presented on the video and in an essay to model the mechanism that produces gametes. This model will help you understand how it is possible to make estimations about the probability of inheriting some traits.

Figure 12.5
A zygote results after a sperm fertilizes an egg. The sperm and egg each contributes one-half of the genetic information contained in the nucleus of the zygote.

Materials

Part A   (for the class)
    online resource
    tape or glue
    different-colored pens or pencils

Part B   (per team of 2)
    red and blue modeling clay
    1 large sheet of paper
    small sheet of scratch paper for making labels
    scissors
    different-colored pens or pencils

PROCESS AND PROCEDURES

Part A   Meiosis

When gametes are produced, they need to have only half the amount of genetic information as other body cells. Cells have a mechanism to ensure that this reduction of information happens. The mechanism also explains why some patterns of inheritance are predictable.

Work with your team to complete the following tasks.

1. Write a short paragraph that explains the relationship between the terms "chromosome," "gene," "DNA," and "allele." This will help you keep track of what occurs during the remaining steps in the activity.
2. Watch the video segment, "Meiosis," as a class. As you watch, take notes to help answer the following questions.
   a. How many times is DNA copied, or synthesized, during meiosis?
   b. How many times are the chromosomes pulled to the poles of the cell?
   c. How many times does the cell divide?
   d. How does the number of chromosomes in the gametes compare with the number of chromosomes in the cell at the beginning of the process?

3. Place the *Overview of Meiosis* handout, which includes figure 12.6, into your science notebook. You will use this table to help you keep track of the events in meiosis. On your handout, fill in the boxes with a description of each stage of meiosis.
4. Add to your knowledge about the steps of meiosis by reading the essay, *Meiosis: The Mechanism behind Inheritance.* As you read, fill in the boxes on the right side of your handout with a description for the picture on the left side.

> The pictures on the left side of figure 12.6 and the handout do not represent the stages of meiosis. It is more important here to have an understanding of the overall process than of the individual stages.

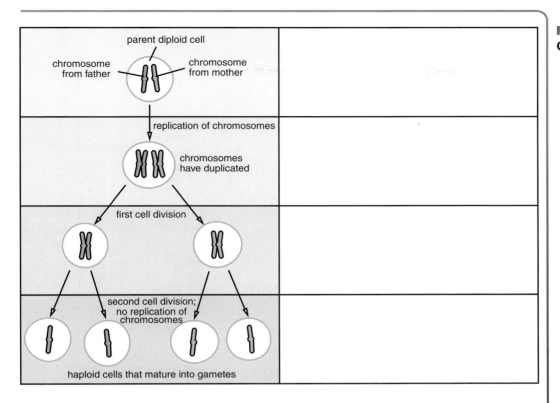

Figure 12.6
Overview of meiosis.

parent diploid cell

chromosome from father

chromosome from mother

replication of chromosomes

chromosomes have duplicated

first cell division

second cell division; no replication of chromosomes

haploid cells that mature into gametes

Meiosis: The Mechanism behind Inheritance

ENGLISH SPANISH

In sexual reproduction, genetic information is passed from generation to generation by the gametes (ovum and sperm). Remember that gametes have only *half* the genetic information of other body cells. That means these cells have half the chromosomes (one copy of each chromosome) and thus half the alleles of other body cells.

The key to achieving this reduction in genetic information is a process called meiosis. **Meiosis** is a type of cell division that produces gametes in male and female organisms. Meiosis accomplishes three major tasks: (1) It forms cells that will allow each parent to contribute equal amounts of genetic information to the offspring. (2) It reduces the number of chromosomes in these cells (gametes) to half the number of chromosomes found in body cells. For example, in humans, the gametes

have 23 chromosomes in each cell. Body cells have 46 chromosomes. (3) It is an important source of variation in offspring.

Following the chromosomes during meiosis provides a way to understand certain patterns of inheritance. In all cells other than gametes, chromosomes occur in matching pairs. For each pair, one chromosome came from the mother's egg cell and one chromosome came from the father's sperm cell. This is called the **diploid** condition. The maternal and paternal chromosomes of each pair contain genes that affect the same traits. As you learned in chapter 11, however, the alleles for each gene may be different.

In contrast, gametes contain *one* chromosome from each matching pair. Gametes are **haploid**: they contain one copy of each chromosome. This is half the number of chromosomes that other body cells such as skin and nerve cells have. In sexual reproduction, a sperm fertilizes the ovum, and then both cells fuse to form a new cell with the correct number of chromosomes found in most cells. The single cell that results from the joining of the egg and the sperm is called a *zygote*. In humans, the zygote will have 23 matching pairs of chromosomes. Each pair is composed of one chromosome from the egg and one chromosome from the sperm. Thus, fertilization restores the diploid number of chromosomes in the zygote. What would happen if chromosome numbers were not halved during meiosis? The number of chromosomes would double with each generation. Such a condition in humans and other animals would lead to the death of the zygote. Plants, however, are able to survive even when their cells contain more than two sets of chromosomes.

SCiLINKS®
NSTA

www.scilinks.org

Topic: chromatid
Code: human4E632

Figure 12.7 provides an overview of what happens during meiosis, using a model cell that has just one pair of chromosomes. Let's examine the process in more detail. Just before meiosis begins, each chromosome pair doubles to make two identical copies. During the first meiotic cell division, the doubled chromosomes separate into two cells. Each of the two new cells contains one doubled chromosome. This chromosome is made up of two sister chromatids joined together by a centromere, as shown in the micrograph in figure 12.8. During the second meiotic cell division, the sister chromatids in each cell separate, and the cell divides into two more cells. This second cell division results in a total of four cells. Each cell contains one chromosome from the original pair, meaning the cells are haploid.

In humans, meiosis results in four sperm cells for males, as seen in figure 12.9. In human females, meiosis results in one large egg cell that

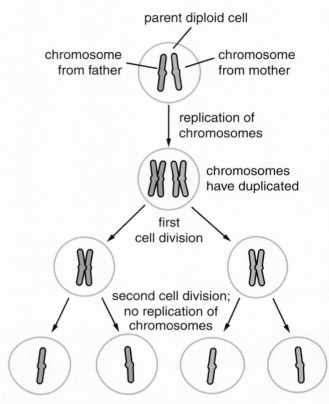

parent diploid cell

chromosome from father

chromosome from mother

replication of chromosomes

chromosomes have duplicated

first cell division

second cell division; no replication of chromosomes

haploid cells that mature into gametes

Figure 12.7 **Meiosis.** Meiosis consists of one replication of chromosomes followed by two cell divisions.

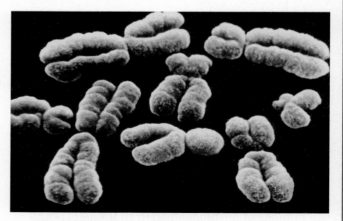

Figure 12.8 **Human chromosomes.** These chromosomes have replicated and are joined to their sister chromatids.

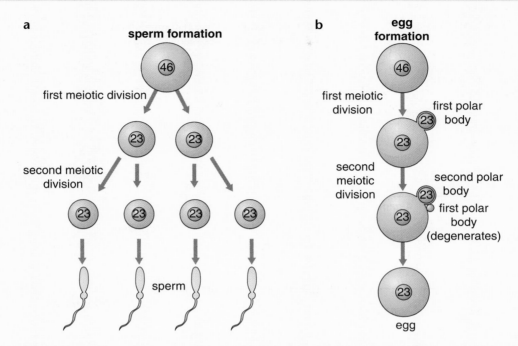

a **sperm formation**

first meiotic division

second meiotic division

sperm

b **egg formation**

first meiotic division

first polar body

second meiotic division

second polar body

first polar body (degenerates)

egg

Figure 12.9 **Human gamete formation.** (*a*) In human males, meiotic division usually results in four equal-sized sperm, each with 23 chromosomes. (*b*) The formation of an egg in females is somewhat different. Two unequally sized cells are formed in the first meiotic division. The larger cell of the two produces another smaller cell in the second division. The result is one large ovum that can be involved in reproduction and two or three small cells, called polar bodies, that will not be involved in reproduction. The polar bodies will eventually disintegrate.

can be involved in reproduction and two or three polar bodies that are not involved in reproduction. Once a fertilized egg implants in the lining of the uterus, the polar bodies disintegrate.

Figure 12.10 shows the detailed stages of meiosis in a cell with two pairs of chromosomes. Notice that the process starts with new copies of the chromosomes being made. These chromosomes line up in the center of the cell. This allows the duplicated chromosomes to be pulled to the poles, or ends, of the cell so that each new cell gets one copy of each homologous (matching) chromosome. During the second half of the meiosis process, the chromosomes line up again in the middle of the cell. The sister chromatids that make up each chromosome are then pulled to the poles, and each resulting cell has a single set of chromosomes.

After the chromosomes are copied at the beginning of meiosis, a special process occurs that is one of the sources of variation in organisms. Remember that mutations are one source of variation. Mutations are rare, though. By themselves, new mutations don't cause a great deal of variation in the next generation. This is where meiosis comes in. A diploid human cell (not a sex cell) has 23 pairs of chromosomes—one of each pair came from the mother and one from the father. Through meiosis, chromosomes from the two parents can be shuffled into new combinations. In a human sex cell, 20 chromosomes may come from the mother, and 3 from the father. Or maybe 15 come from the mother and 8 come from the father. There are many different combinations. This leads to a great deal of diversity.

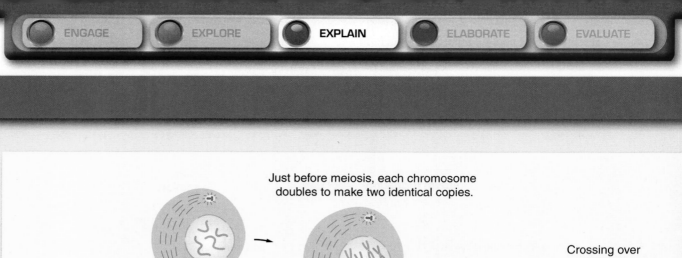

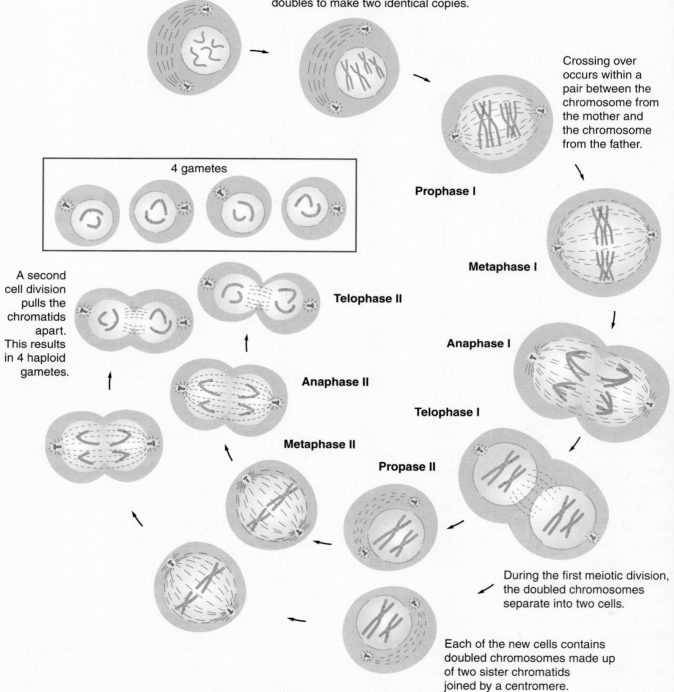

Just before meiosis, each chromosome doubles to make two identical copies.

Crossing over occurs within a pair between the chromosome from the mother and the chromosome from the father.

Prophase I

Metaphase I

Anaphase I

Telophase I

Propase II

During the first meiotic division, the doubled chromosomes separate into two cells.

Each of the new cells contains doubled chromosomes made up of two sister chromatids joined by a centromere.

Metaphase II

Anaphase II

Telophase II

4 gametes

A second cell division pulls the chromatids apart. This results in 4 haploid gametes.

Figure 12.10   The stages of meiosis. This figure illustrates the events of meiosis for a cell that has two pairs of chromosomes.

But making new combinations of parental chromosomes isn't the only way meiosis generates diversity. In the process called crossing-over, part of a chromosome from the mother can swap places with part of a chromosome from the father. The swap also results in new combinations of alleles. Remember that for each pair of chromosomes, one came from the mother and one from the father. During meiosis, chromosomes line up with their matching chromosomes. The arms of the pairs intertwine, or "cross over." At this time, pieces of the chromosome partners exchange places, as shown in figure 12.11. This means one chromosome might have some information from the mother and some from the father. The pieces of chromosome that are exchanged

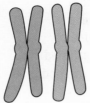

a replicated
   chromosome pair

b crossing-over

c chromosome pair
   after crossing-over

Figure 12.11   Crossing-over generates new allele combinations within chromosomes during the early stages of meiosis.

are equivalent to one another, however, so no information is lost. Crossing-over occurs at least once per chromosome pair. When the chromosome pairs separate later in meiosis, each has a unique combination of alleles.

5. Align the detailed stages of meiosis in figure 12.10 with the overview in figure 12.7 by matching up the events that are listed. For example, can you find where both the overview and the detailed version show that chromosomes have replicated. Add the stages that occur to each of the boxes on your handout of figure 12.6, *Overview of Meiosis.*

6. Study figure 12.10, which shows the stages of meiosis in a cell with 2 pairs of chromosomes. Record your answers to the following in your science notebook.
   a. How many chromosomes do *human* cells have before meiosis?
   b. How many *pairs* of chromosomes do *human* cells have?
   c. How many chromosomes do human cells have after meiosis?
   d. Explain why this is so.
   e. Describe the difference between haploid and diploid cells.

7. Write down your current ideas about why siblings can look very different from one another.

8. Read the essay, *Sorting Genes,* and complete the following task to show your understanding of how offspring of the same parents can have different combinations of alleles.

   Describe how the principle of independent assortment and the principle of segregation help explain the variation that exists within a population of organisms, such as humans or pea plants.

Sorting Genes

ENGLISH SPANISH

Gregor Mendel, shown in figure 12.12, was an Austrian monk who lived in the 1800s. He is often called the "Father of Genetics" because of his work on inheritance in pea plants. He studied several traits in peas, including pod color and pod shape (see figure 12.13).

Based on his work, Mendel understood that offspring receive alleles from each parent. Remember that (1) genes are located on chromosomes and (2) alleles are different versions of the same gene. Think about a gene for seed color in peas. A particular pea plant might have an allele for green seeds on one chromosome and an allele for yellow seeds on the matching chromosome. During meiosis, these two chromosomes will line up in the middle of the cell. When the cell divides, one daughter cell will get the chromosome with the green seed allele. The other daughter cell will get the chromosome with the yellow seed allele. These daughter cells will continue through meiosis and divide again. The product of meiosis will be two gametes with the green seed allele and two gametes with the yellow seed allele.

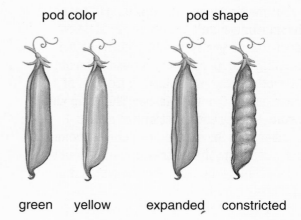

pod color   pod shape

green   yellow   expanded   constricted

Figure 12.13 **Pod color and shape in garden peas.** Most of Mendel's work was on garden peas. Two of the traits he studied were the pod color and the pod shape of the peas.

Alleles on the two chromosomes in a pair segregate (separate) when the two chromosomes separate during meiosis. Each gamete, therefore, receives only one allele for a given gene. So half the gametes that are formed carry one of the parent's alleles and half the gametes carry the other allele. Mendel called this separation the **principle of segregation**. When fertilization occurs, the random combination of alleles in the mother's egg fuse with the random combination of alleles from the father's sperm.

Allele segregation occurs in a regular pattern that makes it possible to predict offspring. If the alleles of the parents are known, then the gametes that result can be predicted as well. For example, if a man has allele A and allele a, 50 percent of his sperm will have allele A and 50 percent will have allele a (see figure 12.14). However, this does not mean 50 percent of his children will have allele A and 50 percent will have allele a.

Another of Mendel's discoveries was that chromosome pairs separate independently during meiosis. Two of the traits Mendel studied were the seed color and seed shape in his pea plants.

Figure 12.12 **Gregor Mendel dedicated his life to experiments in inheritance.** He is often called the "Father of Genetics."

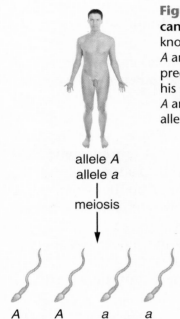

Figure 12.14 Gametes can be predicted. If we know that a man has allele *A* and allele *a*, then we can predict that 50 percent of his sperm will have allele *A* and 50 percent will have allele *a*.

allele *A*
allele *a*
|
meiosis

A   *A*   *a*   *a*

When Mendel looked at multiple traits of pea plants, he found that green seeds were sometimes associated with round seeds. Other times, green seeds were associated with wrinkled seeds. The same was true for yellow seeds. This is because the genes for seed color and seed shape are located on different chromosomes. The movement of one chromosome does not depend on the movement of another chromosome. The idea that chromosomes separate independently from one another during meiosis is called the **principle of independent assortment**.

Segregation of alleles and independent assortment are caused by meiosis. They help explain where variation among individuals comes from. Along with crossing-over and mutation, these processes are the main sources of variation among organisms.

Part B   Tracking Genes through Meiosis

Consider a cell from a male diploid animal that has two pairs of chromosomes. Use figure 12.15, your notes, and modeling clay to track how meiosis affects the distribution of the four chromosomes. You will do this by identifying a specific gene associated with each chromosome. Modeling meiosis will help you reflect on and understand the process. It will also help you remember how meiosis works.

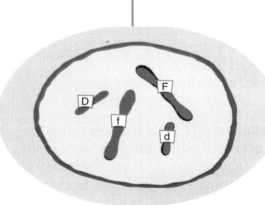

Figure 12.15 These clay models show the chromosomes in a diploid animal cell with two chromosomes.

1. With your partner, develop a plan for simulating meiosis. Your simulation plan should include the following 7 characteristics. These characteristics will help you develop an effective plan on your own. Record your plan in your science notebook.

   The simulation will be your own visual representation of the stages of meiosis. Refer to the essay, *Meiosis: The Mechanism behind Inheritance*, in part A, *Meiosis*, for details about the process.

   a. A diploid animal that has 2 pairs of chromosomes
   b. Circles on a large sheet of paper to represent cells at different stages of meiosis

c. A way to represent *replication* of chromosomes before meiosis begins
d. Modeling clay to represent 2 different pairs of chromosomes
e. Different colors of modeling clay to represent the chromosome of each pair that came from the female parent and the male parent
f. A way to represent crossing-over
g. Labels to represent at least 1 gene on each chromosome (see figure 12.15)

> As in the example, you should have one allele for a particular gene represented by a capital letter and one allele represented by a lowercase letter.

2. Have your teacher approve your plan.
3. Carry out your plan to simulate meiosis by completing the following steps.
   a. Using your cell-diagram circles, move your clay chromosome models through the process of meiosis and into a sperm.
   b. Sketch in your science notebook how you lined up the chromosome models during each meiotic division. Use different colors of pens or pencils in your sketches to accurately depict your model.
4. Think about how you just modeled meiosis, and then answer the following questions with your partner.
   a. In your model, which alleles are present in each of the 4 final sperm cells?

   > Remember that some alleles are represented by capital letters and some are represented by lowercase letters. This allows you to tell them apart.

   b. What other combinations of alleles could have resulted for the sperm cells?
   c. Sketch how you would have to position your chromosome models to obtain the other possible combinations of alleles.
5. Use your model to show what would happen if Mendel's principle of independent assortment were not true. Sketch the results in your science notebook.
6. Write your best explanation about your discoveries in steps 4 and 5. Remember, an explanation should have a claim, supporting evidence, and reasoning.

   > If you need help writing your explanation, see *How to Develop an Explanation* in appendix C4.

7. If you are interested in learning about genetic disorders that can occur when mistakes are made during meiosis, read the sidebar, *When Meiosis Has a Glitch*. After reading, complete the following task in your science notebook.

   > Draw a picture of the gametes that might fuse to create an individual affected by Klinefelter syndrome. Describe any other possible sets of gametes that might lead to this condition.

SCILINKS
NSTA

www.scilinks.org

Topic: meiosis
Code: human4E638

HOW TO

ENGLISH SPANISH

When Meiosis Has a Glitch

"Elise, our next patient in the clinic has a disorder called Down syndrome. Have you ever heard of it?" Ms. Gomez asked.

"Isn't that when you have three of some chromosome, instead of two?" Elise questioned.

"Yes, people with Down syndrome have an extra chromosome in the 21st pair. It is sometimes called trisomy 21. 'Trisomy' means that there are three of a particular chromosome."

Down syndrome affects about 1 in every 1,000 births worldwide. The severity varies from individual to individual. People with Down syndrome have some degree of mental retardation, slow physical development, and organ abnormalities. The most common physical features of those with Down syndrome include short stature, low muscle tone, and altered facial features (see figure 12.16). Often, males with Down syndrome are sterile, but females may be fertile.

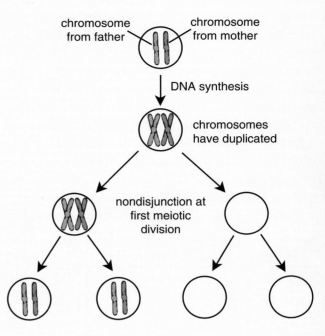

Figure 12.17 Nondisjunction. Compare this sequence of events with normal meiosis in figure 12.7.

The characteristics of Down syndrome are caused by extra genetic material. The disorder results when the partners in a chromosome pair do not separate from each other during the first division of meiosis. As figure 12.17 shows, both of the chromosomes from a pair end up in one offspring cell. The other offspring cell gets neither chromosome. This error in chromosome movement is called **nondisjunction**. At the second division of meiosis, the doubled chromosomes separate in the usual way. The result is two gametes that contain two copies of this particular chromosome and two gametes with no copies of the chromosome. Fertilization of a gamete containing two copies of chromosome 21 with a gamete containing one chromosome 21 from the other parent produces a zygote that is affected by Down syndrome.

Figure 12.16 A girl with Down syndrome. This girl shows the typical facial features of a person affected by Down syndrome.

A different disorder may result if the two X chromosomes do not separate. If a gamete containing no X chromosome is fertilized by a normal gamete, the zygote will only have one X chromosome. Individuals with only one X chromosome and no second X or Y chromosome have Turner syndrome.

Turner syndrome affects approximately 1 out of every 2,500 female live births worldwide. As with Down syndrome, some individuals with Turner syndrome may have only a few characteristics of the syndrome. Others may have many. Almost all people with Turner syndrome have short stature and loss of ovarian function. This loss of function may cause them to be sterile. In general, individuals with Turner syndrome have average intelligence.

Any of the chromosomes in humans can be involved in nondisjunction. However, most embryos with an extra chromosome do not survive. The human embryo can only develop properly with an extra or missing chromosome when only a few genes are involved. Figure 12.18 shows the other situations where a zygote with a trisomy develops into a human.

Trisomy	Disorder	Characteristics of the disorder
13	Patau syndrome	Children born with Patau syndrome usually have severe mental disabilities. They also have physical problems such as small eyes, an opening in the roof of the mouth, problems with the skeleton, and heart defects. Most children affected by Patau syndrome do not live more than a few months.
18	Edwards syndrome	Children with Edwards syndrome have severe intellectual disabilities. They have physical problems such as small, abnormally shaped heads, heart defects, and problems with organs. Only 5–10 percent of children with Edwards syndrome live more than 1 year.
21	Down syndrome	Down syndrome causes some degree of mental disability, altered facial features, and slow development. People with this disorder may also have heart defects and problems with their organs. The majority of people with Down syndrome live well into adulthood.
X	Turner syndrome	Females with Turner syndrome have only 1 X chromosome. They are shorter than average and may be sterile. They are often of average intelligence.
XXX	Triple X syndrome	Females with 3 X chromosomes often have no unusual physical or mental problems. They are sometimes taller than average and may have learning disabilities. Triple X syndrome does not occur in males.
XXY	Klinefelter syndrome	Males with Klinefelter syndrome are often taller than average. They may have learning disabilities and lower levels of testosterone. Klinefelter syndrome does not occur in females.
XYY	XYY syndrome	Most often, XYY syndrome causes no unusual physical or mental problems. Males with this disorder are sometimes taller than average and may have learning disabilities. XYY syndrome does not occur in females.

Figure 12.18 Some trisomy situations allow the development of a human. This table shows the disorders that result from trisomies in humans. Trisomies of chromosomes other than the ones listed here do not allow the zygote to develop.

Analysis

1. One of Mendel's pea plants had green pea pods. This plant had a combination of alleles *GG*. What kind of alleles and how many of each were present in the gametes that gave rise to this organism? You may wish to draw a picture to help you answer the question.
2. Write a paragraph that explains how meiosis is related to the inheritance of traits. Use genetic terminology in your paragraph.

Further Challenges

1. If you have not already, read the sidebar, *When Meiosis Has a Glitch.* Choose one of the trisomies and do research on it. Include information about how often it occurs, symptoms, life expectancy, treatments, and any other interesting information.
2. Write a short essay describing how the genetic variation within a population can change over time due to natural selection. The sidebar, *Variation and Evolution,* will help you make connections between evolution and processes that generate variation.

SIDEBAR

ENGLISH   SPANISH

Variation and Evolution

Have you heard the saying, "Variety is the spice of life"? When you consider life from a genetic and evolutionary standpoint, this point really is true. Diversity in cell structure and function allows cells to specialize. This helps cells work together for complex functions. Differences among individual humans means that you will never meet someone just like you. Differences among human cultures help us realize that there are many ways to be a human. Differences among species are an endless source of fascination for anyone interested in a life of exploration and discovery. In fact, the totality of all the different forms of life, both living and extinct, is called **biodiversity** (see figure 12.19). Humans' daily existence and our future depend critically on biodiversity.

Variation among individuals within populations is the fuel for the fire of evolution. Natural selection would grind to a halt without evolution. Remember why? Charles Darwin and Alfred Russel Wallace demonstrated that natural selection is based on the following observations and conclusion:

- Observation 1: More offspring are born than can survive.

Figure 12.19 A coral reef ecosystem. Coral reefs contain a large number of different species and are an important part of Earth's biodiversity.

- Observation 2: Individual organisms within a population vary from one another in particular characteristics.
- Observation 3: Some variations among individuals can be passed from parents to offspring.
- Conclusion: Individuals that have inherited traits that better enable them to survive and reproduce will leave more offspring. The frequency of these traits will increase in future generations.

Let's explore two of these crucial observations in light of your new understanding of genetics.

Individual Organisms within a Population Vary from One Another in Particular Characteristics

Figure 12.20 shows the variation among individual finches for beak depth. In chapter 2, *Evolution: Change across Time*, you considered what happened to this variation when environmental conditions changed. But you didn't explore deeply what actually causes the variation in the first place. What can cause this variation? First,

changes can occur within an individual due to some factor in the environment. Birds with access to more food will generally be larger, for example. However, such changes that occur within an individual's lifetime are typically not inherited. In the case of the finches, the size of the beaks in finch chicks resembled the size of the parents' beaks. This is evidence that environmental factors were not a major factor in causing the variation in beak size. In this case, the variation was due in large part to changes in genetics. These changes can be inherited. This then leads to the next observation.

Some Variations among Individuals Can Be Passed from Parents to Offspring

What types of genetic changes can occur to cause variation? First and foremost is mutation, or specific changes to the genetic material of an organism (usually DNA). All genetic variation is due to mutation, in one way or another. In the case of the different beaks in finches, scientists are now looking for the specific genes that affect beak shape. Scientists have indentified a protein that affects beak depth and width. They have also identified a different protein that affects beak length. Now they are looking

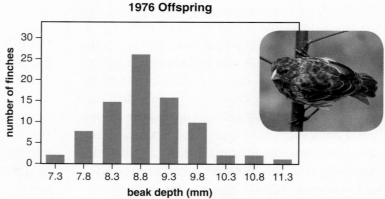

1976 Offspring

Source: Adapted from Grant, B. R., and Grant, P. R. (2003). What Darwin's finches can teach us about the evolutionary origin and regulation of biodiversity. *BioScience, 53* (10): 969. Copyright, American Institute of Biological Sciences.

Figure 12.20   Beak depth of medium ground finch offspring in 1976. The population of birds shows variation for the depth of beaks. What processes lead to variation?

to identify the specific alleles that cause the amounts of these proteins to differ in different birds. The alleles that cause these differences originally arose by mutation.

As you learned in this chapter, however, processes other than mutation contribute to diversity. The processes of meiosis and the union of egg and sperm in sexual reproduction generate new combinations of alleles. In other words, meiosis and sexual reproduction shuffle the diversity present from mutations.

Let's apply our knowledge to a specific case involving genetics and evolution. Have you heard the slogan "Everyone needs milk"? It turns out that, in fact, most adults alive today throughout the world do not "need" milk, as was discussed in chapter 7, *Physical Fitness and Performance*. The majority of humans, like all other mammals, cannot digest milk after infancy.

The ability to digest milk depends on a protein enzyme called lactase. Most of the time, the gene that codes for lactase is "turned off" after infancy. In other words, the gene for lactase is not expressed. However, some people are *lactose tolerant*, meaning they can digest the sugar lactose that is found in milk. Lactose tolerant individuals have a change in their DNA near the lactose gene that keeps the gene "turned on" through adulthood. Populations of humans that domesticated cows in the past show a high frequency of people who are lactose tolerant. Interestingly, the change in DNA that keeps the lactase gene turned on is different in different groups of people. For example, most Europeans who are lactose tolerant have one specific change in their DNA near the lactase gene, but a different change in DNA is found in most Africans who are lactose tolerant. This means that lactose tolerance has evolved multiple times in different populations of humans.

So humans show diversity in the DNA region that controls the lactase gene. The changes in the DNA that allowed the gene to remain turned on first arose by mutation. This mutation must have occurred in a sex cell because it was passed to the next generation. Over time, this gene spread to other individuals through sexual reproduction. As a result, human populations show diversity for the ability to digest milk as adults. Some people can digest it, and some cannot. In populations that domesticated cattle around 7,000 years ago, there were advantages to drinking milk as an adult. As a result, people who were lactose tolerant left relatively more offspring. Lactose tolerance alleles were favored by natural selection and quickly spread through these populations. If you can drink milk today without discomfort, it is likely that you had an ancestor many generations ago from a population who herded cows or goats.

Note what happened to the frequency of the allele that allows lactase to remain "on" in some populations. The frequency of the allele changed over time. This is a more precise definition for **evolution**. In this case, natural selection caused the allele frequency to increase in the population over time. But there are other processes that can cause changes in allele frequencies besides natural selection. Mutation by itself creates new alleles. Therefore, mutation causes an immediate, but small, change in the frequency of alleles in a population. Of course, mutation is the basis for genetic diversity, but by itself it is not a powerful process for changing the genetic makeup of a population from one generation to the next.

One process that is particularly important in small populations is called genetic drift. **Genetic drift** refers to random changes in allele frequencies due to chance. Genetic drift reduces the amount of genetic variation in a population. Because changes due to drift are random, the process can cause different changes in different populations. This contributes to populations becoming different from one another. Another process that can change gene frequencies in a population is migration, or the movement of organisms into or out of a population. If organisms moving into or out of the population have different frequencies of alleles than those in the rest of the population, a change in allele frequency can occur. The movement of genes into or out of a population because of migration is called **gene flow**. Gene flow reduces the genetic differences among populations. In other words, it decreases the amount of variation. In summary, the processes that can change the frequencies of genes, or that can cause evolution, are mutation, natural selection, genetic drift, and gene flow. Natural selection and drift are the two most important causes of evolution.

Understanding the amount of genetic diversity among individuals in a population is important for understanding evolution. But what about diversity at other levels of organization? Knowing how changes to genetic material happen and what the consequences are for phenotypes matters in these cases, too. For example, scientists are very interested in the way mutations accumulate within different cells within individuals. These mutations happen to everyone, but when specific mutations occur, cancers can result. In a very real way, cancer cells evolve within an individual. So an understanding of genetics and evolution helps scientists and doctors treat cancer. Similarly, recall that new species evolve when two lineages become reproductively isolated from each other. Scientists now routinely try to identify the genes that cause one species to differ from other species. Remember the monkeyflowers that you explored in chapter 3, *Products of Evolution: Unity and Diversity*?

Variation, variation everywhere. Variety is the spice of life indeed.

Patterns of Inheritance

Why is it that children look similar to their parents, but not exactly like them? Think of your own family or the families of your friends. In many cases, you can see physical resemblances among family members even when they are different ages.

In the last Explain activity, *A Cellular View of Inheritance*, you looked at how meiosis relates to the inheritance of particular alleles. You know from the last chapter that these different alleles are expressed as proteins in the cells. But are all alleles expressed? How can genetic counselors predict the inheritance of particular traits?

In this Explain activity, *Patterns of Inheritance*, you will work to understand the answers to these questions. You will model the inheritance of a trait by using beans, and then learn why family members often resemble one another. You will also learn about a tool that can help make predictions about the inheritance of traits.

Materials (per team of 2)

online resource
red beans
white beans

PROCESS AND PROCEDURES

1. Continue reading the scenario, *The Genetic Counseling Clinic,* to learn more about how traits are passed from parent to offspring.
2. Select 2 beans randomly from the container that your teacher provides. Your partner will also select 2 beans.
3. In your science notebook, record the color of your beans. Also, note whether your pair is homozygous or heterozygous.

   Each bean represents an allele in one of the parents. If the beans are the same color, the pair is homozygous ("homo-" = "same"). If the beans are different colors, the pair is heterozygous ("hetero-" = "different").

SCENARIO

ENGLISH SPANISH

The Genetic Counseling Clinic, continued

"Ms. Gomez, I understand that there are traits that are passed from parents to offspring, but how does that happen?" Elise asked. "I can see that there are a lot of similarities between all the people in this picture. Then again, one woman in the picture has blue eyes. Does that mean that she isn't related to the family?"

"No, not at all," replied Ms. Gomez. "We will come back to the blue eyes later on. That may seem like a simple question, but there are a few things to understand before we get to the blue eyes. First, it is important to remember that each offspring—whether it is a human or a dog or a rabbit—gets genetic information from both parents. There are two complete sets of information in an individual of any organism. One set of information is from the mother, and one set is from the father. This relates to meiosis because it produces the gametes that contain that set of information.

"Let's think of an example. In humans, there is a trait called hitchhiker's thumb (figure 12.21). If you have hitchhiker's thumb, your thumb bends backward when you give a 'thumbs-up' sign. Whether or not you have hitchhiker's thumb is a trait you've inherited from your parents. Let's try to model the inheritance by using these beans."

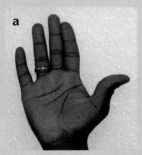 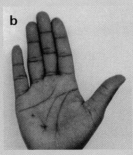

Figure 12.21 Hitchhiker's thumb. (*a*) The thumb of a person with hitchhiker's thumb bends backward when he or she gives the "thumbs-up" sign or holds his or her hand out flat. (*b*) The thumb of a person with a straight thumb does not bend this way.

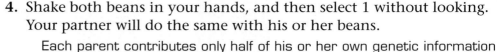
4. Shake both beans in your hands, and then select 1 without looking. Your partner will do the same with his or her beans.

   Each parent contributes only half of his or her own genetic information to each offspring. Parents do not know which half they contribute.

5. Place the bean you selected next to the bean your partner selected.

6. Record the color of the 2 beans in the new combination. Indicate whether the pair is homozygous or heterozygous. The new bean combination represents the genetic information that will determine whether the offspring has hitchhiker's thumbs.

7. Use the trait key that your teacher displays. In your science notebook, list whether each of the following combinations would lead to hitchhiker's thumb or straight thumb.
   a. To which thumb type did your first bean combination correspond?
   b. To which thumb type did your partner's first bean combination correspond?
   c. To which thumb type did the new offspring combination correspond?

8. Record your results on the class chart.

9. Use the trait key once again, along with the shared results of the class, to consider the following.
   a. Describe any patterns of bean colors that relate to hitchhiker's thumb.
   b. Describe any patterns of bean colors that relate to straight thumb.
   c. Did 1 bean color (which represents 1 piece of inherited genetic information) have a greater influence in determining hitchhiker's thumb than the other bean color? If so, which one?

10. Read the essay, *Phenotype and Genotype,* to learn how to relate the patterns you saw with your beans to the inheritance of traits. Add the terminology in bold print to your personal glossary as you read. Also add any other words that are new to you.

    If you need a reminder on how to enter words into your personal glossary, see *How to Develop a Personal Glossary* in appendix B8.

HOW TO

11. In your science notebook, complete the following tasks.
    a. In steps 2–9, were the beans a model for phenotype or genotype?
    b. Label the combinations and traits that you recorded in steps 3, 6, and 7 as phenotype or genotype.

12. Using genetic terminology, write 1 paragraph that describes the inheritance of hitchhiker's thumb. Relate steps 2–9 of the activity to the characteristics described in the essay, *Phenotype and Genotype.*

Online Resource

13. Watch the video segment, "Mendel's Peas," to learn more about a tool that can be used to help you make predictions about the inheritance of traits. As you watch, write the questions and answers presented in the video into your science notebook.

Often, there is more than one combination of alleles that allows for a trait. With thumbs, two different combinations of alleles cause the straight thumb to appear. Only one combination causes hitchhiker's thumb. How can we distinguish whether we are talking about the combination of alleles for a trait or the physical appearance of the trait itself?

Blood type, ear shape, and petal color—these are some physical traits that we observe when an organism's genetic information is expressed. The traits, or characteristics of an organism, are its **phenotype**. As you learned in the Engage activity, *Gifts from Your Parents*, there are both observable and hard-to-observe characteristics. The term phenotype can refer to either a specific trait or to the collection of traits that characterizes an entire organism. For instance, we can say that a collie has a long-hair rather than a short-hair phenotype. We also can say that a collie has a very different overall phenotype from a Great Dane. A collie is smaller, has longer hair, and has shorter legs than a Great Dane. The genetic plan passed from parents to offspring provides the blueprint for the offspring's phenotype. Thus, offspring usually have a phenotype similar to their parents' phenotypes.

But how does the genetic information determine an organism's physical traits? To understand this, let's look at a simple example. In snapdragon plants, one gene determines the color of the flower. In some snapdragons, one of their two alleles codes for red flowers, as shown in figure 12.22. The gene is transcribed into RNA. The RNA is then translated into a protein for red pigment. The red pigment protein causes the flowers to appear red. When the allele for red flowers is not present, no red pigment protein is made. Although many phenotypes depend on more than one gene, all are based on whether or not particular proteins are made.

The genetic plan, or **genotype**, consists of all of the genetic information in an organism. The genotype is the combination of alleles an organism has. For any trait, a person has two alleles. One allele was inherited from the father. The other allele came from the mother. Scientists often use a shorthand way of writing alleles by using a letter for each allele. In this case, the letter t is used for each allele because the trait is thumb type. The particular letter that is used does not matter, but it is usually wise to choose letters in which the capital letter looks different from the lowercase letter.

Let's think about a woman who has straight thumbs. Her genotype might be Tt. She may have

Figure 12.22 **Snapdragon flowers come in different colors.** If a snapdragon has an allele for red flowers, that gene is transcribed, and then translated into red pigment protein.

inherited the *T* allele from her mother and the *t* allele from her father. Or the *T* allele may be from her father and the *t* allele from her mother. Either way, this combination results in a genotype that is **heterozygous** ("hetero-" = "different") for the thumb alleles. Alternatively, a person who inherits two identical alleles (*TT* or *tt*) has a genotype that is **homozygous** ("homo-" = "the same") for thumb type. Here, a person with the *TT* genotype would have the straight thumb phenotype. A person with the *tt* genotype would have the hitchhiker's thumb phenotype. From this we can see that two different genotypes—*TT* and *Tt*—both lead to one phenotype of the straight thumb. How can this be?

Geneticists have discovered that thumb type is controlled by only one gene. One allele is involved in having the straight thumb. A second allele is involved in having hitchhiker's thumb. These alleles interact to determine which type of thumb a person has. An individual who inherits even one allele for the straight thumb (from either parent) will show that phenotype, regardless of the other allele he or she inherits. The straight thumb is a dominant trait. A **dominant trait** presents itself whether the individual is homozygous or heterozygous for that allele. The genotype of a person with two alleles for the straight thumb (*TT*) is "homozygous dominant." A person with two different alleles (*Tt*) has a heterozygous genotype. Dominant alleles, shown by capital letters, are usually written first in a genotype.

A **recessive trait** is observable only in individuals who are homozygous for that allele. This trait is only expressed when a dominant allele is not present. Individuals who do not have straight thumbs did not inherit an allele for straight thumbs from either parent. Instead, they inherited two alleles carrying information for hitchhiker's thumb. This person's genotype (*tt*) is called "homozygous recessive."

When writing genotypes, dominant alleles are always shown using a capital letter. Recessive alleles are written with a lowercase letter.

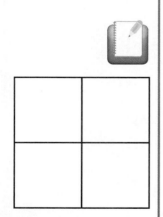

Figure 12.23
Punnett square.
A Punnett square looks similar to a windowpane.

14. Carry out the following steps to predict the thumb type of a child born from a parent who is heterozygous for hitchhiker's thumb and a parent who is homozygous recessive for the trait.
   a. Write down the genotype (the alleles) of each parent.

      Remember that one parent is heterozygous for hitchhiker's thumb and the other is homozygous recessive for the trait.

   b. In your science notebook, sketch a Punnett square like the one shown in figure 12.23.
   c. Write the alleles of one parent across the top of your Punnett square and the alleles of the other parent along the left side of your Punnett square. Make sure you write only 1 allele next to each box. This represents the allele that is in a gamete, which is why there is only 1 allele.

      Only one letter goes above or to the left of each box. It does not matter which parent is on the side or the top of the Punnett square.

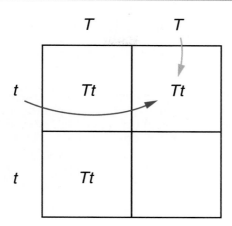

T   T

t   Tt   Tt

t   Tt

Figure 12.24 **Filling in a Punnett square**. In this example, one parent is homozygous dominant for the hitchhiker's thumb trait. This parent is shown across the top of the Punnett square. The other parent is homozygous recessive for the trait and is shown on the left side of the Punnett square. Complete the Punnett square by taking an allele from the top and combining it with an allele from the left.

15. Determine the alleles of the predicted offspring by taking each allele from the parent column and combining it with an allele from the parent row in the corresponding square, as shown in figure 12.24. Remember that each parent contributes 1 allele for each trait to the offspring.

The Punnett square in figure 12.24 shows a cross between a parent with a *TT* genotype and a parent with a *tt* genotype. The predicted alleles of the offspring are the likely outcome of a cross, or mating, between these two parents, not the actual outcome. Once the Punnett square is complete, all four boxes should be filled in.

16. Write the phenotype for each possible offspring underneath the genotype in each square.

Remember, your Punnett square shows a cross between the parents described in step 14.

17. In your science notebook, answer the following questions about your Punnett square.

You may wish to review the information in the need to know, *Probability*, from the Explore activity, *Inheritance: What's the Chance?*

a. What is the probability that an offspring will have a heterozygous genotype?

b. What is the probability that an offspring will have a hitchhiker's thumb phenotype?

c. If the couple shown in your Punnett square has 8 children, how many of them are likely to have a straight thumb?

d. Can you use your answer to step 17c to say with certainty how many children the couple will have with straight thumbs? Explain your answer.

18. Many genetic disorders also show a pattern of dominant and recessive inheritance. In your science notebook, draw a Venn diagram like the one shown in figure 12.25. This will help you study the characteristics of 2 genetic disorders.

If you need help, refer to *How to Use and Create Venn Diagrams* in appendix B5.

HOW TO

Figure 12.25
A Venn diagram showing the shared characteristics of two genetic disorders. This Venn diagram will help you see which characteristics are similar and which are different between Huntington's disease and cystic fibrosis.

unique characteristics of Huntington's disease

shared characteristics of both genetic disorders

unique characteristics of cystic fibrosis

19. Read the essay, *Case Studies of Two Genetic Disorders,* to learn about 2 genetic disorders. This will help you understand how the information you have been learning applies to genetic disorders. As you read, complete the Venn diagram by filling in the characteristics in the appropriate place.

As you work on and discuss questions that involve genetic disorders, be sensitive to the possibility that some of your classmates may have, or be close to someone who has, one of the genetic disorders we are studying or a different genetic disorder. *Anyone* can be born with a genetic disorder.

Case Studies of Two Genetic Disorders

ENGLISH SPANISH

As Elise approaches Ms. Gomez, she says, "Ms. Gomez, for my internship I have been reading some essays about genetic disorders. I found these two case studies on families who came to a genetic counseling clinic. I would like to ask a few questions about these cases."

Ms. Gomez replies, "I would be happy to discuss them with you. Let me read through the two studies you found, and then we can talk about them."

"Great!" replied Elise. "I found one on Huntington's disease and one on cystic fibrosis. Here they are."

Case Study 1: Huntington's Disease

Rita is a 30-year-old woman. She and her husband would like to have a baby. Rita's father died a few years ago of Huntington's disease (HD).

HD is a dominant genetic disorder that causes degeneration of the cells in the brain. This results in uncontrollable movements, changes in behavior, and difficulty swallowing and speaking. People with HD also have confusion and memory loss. The symptoms of the disease usually do not appear until age 35 or older. Currently, there is no effective treatment or cure for HD. The disease worsens for five to 15 years. Then the patient dies. Because Rita's father had HD and it is caused by a dominant allele, she knows that her chance of developing the disease is 50 percent (see figure 12.26).

A genetic test can determine whether Rita carries the allele for HD. It is a simple procedure requiring a small blood sample. The possibility of being tested for a genetic disorder can raise many questions for patients, though. Patients might ask

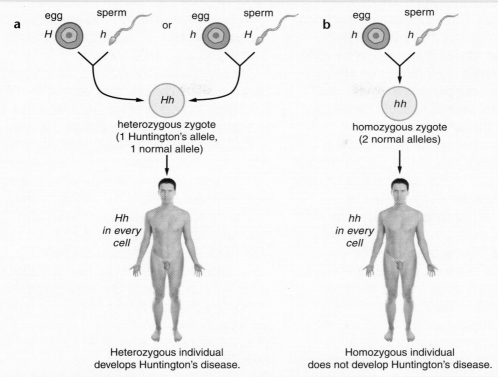

Figure 12.26 **Genotypes in Huntington's disease.** The allele for Huntington's disease is symbolized by a capital *H.* A lowercase *h* indicates the unaffected allele. (*a*) If a person receives the *H* allele in the gamete that came from one parent and the *h* allele in the gamete from the other parent, he or she has the heterozygous genotype *Hh.* People who are heterozygous will eventually develop the disease. (*b*) If a person receives *h* alleles in the gametes from both parents (homozygous *hh*), the person will remain free of the disease. An individual who received *H* alleles from both parents (a relatively rare situation) would have the homozygous genotype *HH.* This person would develop the disease.

questions such as, "Should I have the test? What are the advantages of knowing that I have the allele for HD? What are the disadvantages of knowing? Are there advantages in *not* taking the test?"

HD often puts tremendous psychological and physical stress on the family and the individual. Many affected parents feel guilty because they may have passed the allele on to their children. Should affected people avoid passing on the allele by deciding not to have biological children?

Case Study 2: Cystic Fibrosis

Almost from the time his parents brought him home from the hospital, Richard seemed weaker than other infants. He frequently fell ill with coughs and colds. The doctors finally diagnosed Richard with cystic fibrosis (CF) when he was

nearly a year old. CF causes chronic digestive and respiratory problems. In CF, a person's mucus is much thicker and stickier than normal mucus. His or her mucus clogs the lungs and makes it easy for bacteria to cause infections there. CF is the most common disorder that is caused by a single gene. People with CF live to an average age of 37.

Richard's grief-stricken parents were confused and angry when they learned the diagnosis. They made an appointment with the genetic counseling clinic to learn more about the disease. Here is part of the conversation they had with the genetic counselor:

"How could our son have such a terrible disease when no one in either of our large families has ever had CF?" asked the distraught father.

"The allele for CF is quite common," explained Ms. Gomez. "In fact, about 1 in 25 European

or Jewish Americans, 1 in 48 Hispanic Americans, 1 in 61 African Americans, and 1 in 90 Asian Americans carry an allele for cystic fibrosis. With cystic fibrosis, a person must inherit an allele for cystic fibrosis from both parents to be affected."

"So you mean that both of us could get sick as well?" interrupted Richard's mother.

"No. Neither of you can get CF because it is a recessive trait. You only have the disorder if you are homozygous. The fact that Richard is sick indicates that he is homozygous. Each of you must be heterozygous: each of you carries one allele for CF. We call people who are heterozygous for a recessive trait "**carriers**." Carriers are healthy and do not show symptoms of a trait, but they are able to pass the cystic fibrosis allele to their children.

"Let me indicate the allele for cystic fibrosis with a lowercase f and the unaffected allele with an uppercase F. Only persons with the genotype ff, like Richard, will develop the cystic fibrosis pheno-type. Persons with an Ff or FF genotype will have a normal phenotype. Those with the genotype Ff, like both of you, are carriers of CF.

"As I mentioned, the allele for CF is widespread in the population. The high frequency of the CF allele in the population explains the fact that cystic fibrosis is relatively common, even though it is recessive."

Ms. Gomez helped Richard's parents understand why they could not have known they were carriers without getting a specific genetic test. Richard's parents and his team of doctors were determined to provide him with the best possible care. They gave him antibiotics to help his body fight lung infections. They performed a daily routine of chest-thumping therapies to clear the thick mucous deposits from his lungs. He was a happy child most of the time despite his treatments and reduced life expectancy. Fortunately, recent medical advances offer the promise of a healthier life for people with CF.

20. Elise had several questions about the case studies. First, complete a Punnett square in your science notebook for a cross between a woman who is heterozygous for the Huntington's disease allele and a man who is unaffected by the disorder. This will help you answer the questions.

21. Help Elise answer the following questions related to the couple in step 20. Use the Punnett square you created to help you answer them.
    a. What is the probability that a child of this couple will be affected by HD?
       Remember that the HD allele is dominant.

    b. What is the probability that a child of this couple will have the genotype *HH*?

22. Elise also wanted to know more about the inheritance of cystic fibrosis. Complete a Punnett square for a cross between a man and a woman who are both heterozygous for the cystic fibrosis allele.

23. Use the Punnett square from step 22 to answer the following questions for Elise.
    a. What is the probability that this couple will have a child who is a heterozygote?

    b. What is the probability that this couple will have a child who is affected by cystic fibrosis?
       Remember that the CF allele is recessive.

Analysis

Work individually to develop responses to the following questions. Record your answers in your science notebook.

1. Think back to Elise's question at the beginning of the activity about the woman in the picture who has blue eyes. Eye color is known to be related to multiple genes; however, blue eyes are a recessive trait. How would you explain to Elise how the woman could still be related to the family, even though her eyes are a different color?

Topic: Mendelian genetics
Code: human4E653

2. Although Huntington's disease is a dominant trait, the symptoms do not appear until the middle or late adult years. Imagine that you are the doctor of a young man who has a parent with Huntington's disease. What concerns might you have for your patient and why?

3. Restate the following accurately: One out of every 2 offspring that result from a cross between parents with the genotypes *Hh* and *hh* definitely will have Huntington's disease.

4. Two healthy individuals marry and produce 3 children. The first 2 are healthy. But the third is born with cystic fibrosis, indicating that she is homozygous *ff* for the cystic fibrosis alleles. Use a Punnett square to help you answer the following questions.
   a. What can you conclude about the genotypes of the parents?
   b. What can you conclude about the genotypes of the 2 older children?

5. What is the probability that if the couple in question 4 has another child, he or she will have cystic fibrosis?

6. Imagine that the healthy children in question 4 grow up and have their own children. Could those children be affected by CF? Explain your answer.

© Dreamstime/Thomas Perkins

Predicting Inheritance by Using Pedigrees

ELABORATE

In the second Explain activity, *Patterns of Inheritance*, you learned about genetic traits that may be inherited. You also learned about how to predict inheritance, as well as how to use a Punnett square as a tool to help with those predictions. In the first Explain activity, *A Cellular View of Inheritance*, you saw that the key to inherited patterns is a process called *meiosis*. Meiosis results in the production of gametes. Each gamete carries genetic information from one of the parents. By observing phenotypes of offspring across multiple generations, scientists have been able to identify patterns of inheritance.

In this Elaborate activity, *Predicting Inheritance by Using Pedigrees*, you will learn about another tool, called a pedigree. There are many types of pedigrees, and many types of people who use them. Here, you will begin using a type of pedigree that geneticists and genetic counselors use. You will also work with a partner to use pedigrees to help you identify patterns of inheritance and make predictions.

PROCESS AND PROCEDURES

1. Genetic counselors also use a tool called a pedigree to help them analyze family histories. Read the continuation of the scenario, *The Genetic Counseling Clinic,* to learn more about this tool and how it is used.

SCENARIO

The Genetic Counseling Clinic, continued

"Ms. Gomez, I am beginning to understand more about traits and disorders that are inherited. But I don't really see how scientists figured out which traits were dominant and which were recessive," Elise said one afternoon.

"That is a good question," said Ms. Gomez. "One way to determine the pattern of inheritance for a disorder is to look at its occurrence within a family across multiple generations. The information is drawn up using a tool called a pedigree. Geneticists use pedigrees to study the inheritance of genes in humans. A pedigree is very similar to a family tree, except that a pedigree is a tool that is used to follow a trait through multiple generations of a family. You also might be familiar with the use of pedigrees by dog or horse breeders." (See figure 12.27.)

a Dog Pedigree

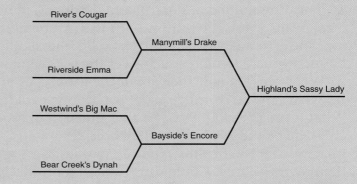

b Family Tree

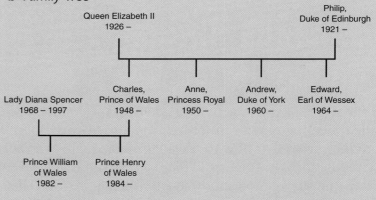

Figure 12.27 **Dog pedigree and family tree.** (*a*) Dog pedigrees show the male's name on the top part of the branches. Females are shown on the bottom part of the branches. You might notice that dogs are often given unusual names that include the name of the kennel that owns the dog. (*b*) Family trees, such as the one shown of the British royal family, often show the birth and death dates for each individual on the tree. Notice that the pedigree and the family tree do not have information about genetics.

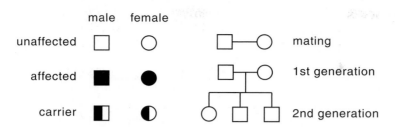

Figure 12.28 Symbols used in pedigrees. Pedigrees make it easier to look at the occurrence of a trait within a family. The trait might be a physical characteristic such as eye color, or the trait might be a disorder. Unaffected individuals do not express the trait. Affected individuals express the trait. Carriers carry the trait, but do not express the trait. In pedigrees, males are indicated by squares and females by circles. A horizontal line between a circle and a square indicates mating. Vertical lines indicate the children from the mating.

2. Study figure 12.28 to learn what each symbol used in a pedigree represents. You will use this information in the steps that follow to interpret pedigrees.
3. Study the 2 pedigrees shown in figure 12.29. Decide which pedigree represents a family with a dominant trait and which represents a family with a recessive trait.

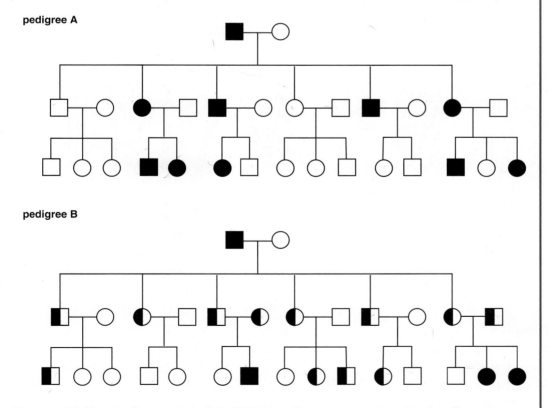

Figure 12.29 Pedigrees A and B. Which pedigree represents a family affected by a dominant trait? Which represents a family affected by a recessive trait?

4. Draw a 2-column table in your science notebook. Label the first column "dominant" and the other column "recessive."

5. In the first column, list patterns you see in the dominant pedigree. In the second column, list patterns you see in the recessive pedigree.

> Examples of patterns you might think about are whether males or females seem to be affected more often, whether affected people appear in each generation, and whether there are carriers of the disorder. You may find additional patterns as well.

6. Read the scenario, *A Royal Tragedy,* to learn more about using pedigrees to identify inheritance patterns. As you read, make notes about the causes and symptoms of hemophilia, as well as the characteristics of its inheritance.

SCENARIO

A Royal Tragedy

"I am beginning to see the patterns in the different types of inheritance!" Elise exclaimed.

"Good," said Ms. Gomez. "Now I'd like you to read a story about another family affected by a genetic disorder. This story has a pedigree at the end of it. See if you can figure out anything about the inheritance from this pedigree." Ms. Gomez gave Elise the following story.

In 1904, a great wave of celebration and public enthusiasm swept through the vast Russian Empire. At long last, after having four daughters, the czar and czarina had produced a son. This son would be the heir to the throne. The little boy was given the name Czarevitch Alexis. It seemed he was destined to have a great future for a number of reasons.

Czarevitch Alexis was born heir to the throne of the world's largest country. He was also related to many royal and aristocratic families in Europe. His great-grandmother, Queen Victoria, had died only three years before. She had been the queen of England for more than half a century. During her reign, the British Empire reached its greatest heights of power and influence. The kings of England and of Spain, the prince of Prussia, and the kaiser of Germany were all cousins of Czarevitch Alexis on different branches of his family tree. His own mother, Czarina Alexandra, was the daughter of one grand duke of Hesse and the sister of another. The huge empire of Alexis's father, Czar Nicholas II, was troubled by unrest; however, everyone expected that the little heir would provide a sense of stability to the country.

Unfortunately, the little boy was not well. He had been born with hemophilia A. In this disorder, the blood clots so slowly that the person can bleed to death from a minor injury. People who are not affected by hemophilia have a number of proteins in their blood that help it clot when they are cut. In hemophilia, one or more of those proteins are not made in the cells. Today, treatments are available that allow people with hemophilia to lead fairly

unrestricted lives. But this was not the case in little Czarevitch Alexis's time. For him, even the most minor childhood accidents meant bouts of painful and potentially fatal illness.

Czar Nicholas was obsessed with the poor health of his only son. As a result, he did not pay enough attention to the many problems of Russia. The boy's mother, Czarina Alexandra, became even more preoccupied than the czar. She may have been tormented by the possibility that her son's illness came to him from her side of the family. A number of male relatives in different branches of her family were afflicted or had been afflicted, including one of her brothers (see the pedigree in figure 12.30).

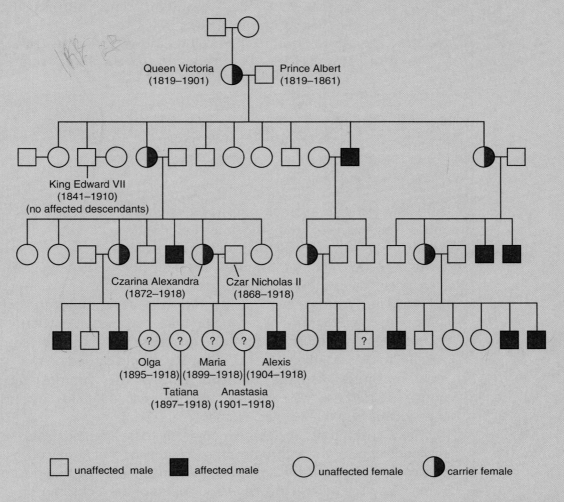

Figure 12.30   Hemophilia in Czarevitch Alexis's family. Several generations of Czarevitch Alexis's family are shown in this pedigree. What patterns do you observe about the inheritance of hemophilia?

The czarina became desperate about her son. She began to consult a series of quacks and mystics. Government officials and the people of Russia became very concerned about the influence of the quacks and mystics on the czarina. Some historians have suggested that the family's preoccupation with Czarevitch Alexis's health may have caused the downfall of Russia. The Russian society became more and more unruly. Finally, the social problems started the

Russian Revolution of 1917. This revolution led to the murder of the entire royal family by agents of the Bolsheviks in July 1918.

The story of young Czarevitch Alexis and his family is filled with drama and tragedy. Because the royal family was in the spotlight, a great deal of information is known about its members. This allows for a fairly complete pedigree. Using this pedigree, we can see a number of features about the inheritance of hemophilia.

7. Determine whether the pedigree from the czar's family fits with the characteristics of dominant or recessive disorders. Write in your science notebook the similarities and differences of this pedigree to the pedigrees you examined in step 5.
8. Read the information in the need to know, *Sex-Linked Traits,* to learn more about traits that are on genes on the sex chromosomes.

NEED TO KNOW

Sex-Linked Traits

Pedigree analyses sometimes show evidence that certain traits are more likely in one sex than the other. Color blindness is one example. When a person is color blind, he or she has trouble seeing differences between certain colors. Most often, the difficulty is in distinguishing red and green. Males show red-green color blindness much more frequently than females. Why is this so? Scientists have discovered that the gene for red-green color blindness is carried on the X chromosome, but not the Y chromosome. Traits that are carried on one of the sex chromosomes are said to be sex linked. Most sex-linked traits are carried on the X chromosome, due to the number of genes on that chromosome (see figure 12.31). These traits are also sometimes called X-linked because of their location on the X chromosome.

With X-linked traits, males are more likely to be affected. Males only have one copy of the X chromosome. This means that if they have just one copy of the allele for a disorder, they are affected by that disorder. Females, on the other hand, have two copies of the X chromosome. If they have one copy of the allele for the disorder, females are only carriers of the disorder, not affected by it.

Remember that the chromosomes that do not determine sex are called autosomes. Traits that are carried on the autosomes are called autosomal traits. The inheritance pattern of these traits is called either autosomal dominant or autosomal recessive. Sex-linked traits may also be dominant or recessive. X-linked recessive disorders are the most common.

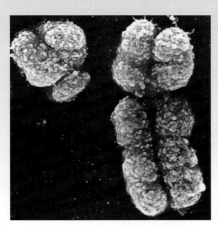

Figure 12.31   Electron micrograph of the X and Y chromosomes. Notice that the X chromosome (right) is much larger than the Y chromosome (left). The X chromosome contains many more genes than the Y chromosome.

9. Write a paragraph to explain the pattern of inheritance of hemophilia. Relate your paragraph to the patterns seen in Czarevitch Alexis's family. Include information about whether males and females are affected with the same frequency, whether members of each generation are affected, and whether a child could be affected without a parent being affected.

   You may wish to add the information about the patterns to the table you created in step 4.

10. Read the following paragraph to learn how to represent the allele for a sex-linked recessive trait by using symbols.

   You just learned that some traits are carried on one of the sex chromosomes. Most of these traits are **X-linked recessive**, meaning that it is a recessive trait controlled by a gene on the X chromosome. One example of an X-linked recessive trait is the color blindness trait discussed in the need to know, *Sex-Linked Traits*. One example of a sex-linked trait is fruit fly eye color. The eye color gene for fruit flies is carried on the X chromosome, making it an X-linked trait. The X chromosome carrying a dominant red eye allele is symbolized by X^R. If the X chromosome carries the recessive white eye allele, it is symbolized by X^r. The Y chromosome is represented with the letter Y. Since the allele for eye color is not found on the Y chromosome, it does not have the superscript R or r. Study figure 12.32 to learn which fruit fly genotypes have the red eye trait and which genotypes have the white eye trait.

Figure 12.32   Fruit fly Punnett square. Eye color in fruit flies is an X-linked trait. The X chromosome carries the allele for eye color.

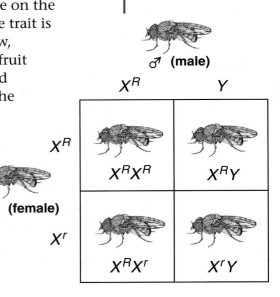

11. To check your understanding, answer the following questions about sex-linked recessive traits.
    a. Why does the male fruit fly with the genotype X^rY have white eyes?
    b. What genotype do you think a female fruit fly would have if she had white eyes?
    c. Why do you think white eyes in fruit flies is called an X-linked recessive trait?

12. Read the following information and, to demonstrate your understanding, complete the task described. Record your answers in your science notebook.

    Ms. Gomez tells Elise that she has learned a lot about patterns of inheritance. She asks Elise to test her knowledge by completing the following task. You should try the task, too. Decide whether each statement describes an autosomal dominant, autosomal recessive, or sex-linked recessive pattern. Some statements might describe more than 1 pattern. Record your answers in your science notebook.
    a. Brothers and sisters are equally likely to have the trait.
    b. Family members from all generations have the trait.
    c. The trait can be inherited from either parent.
    d. Men in the family are more likely to have the trait.
    e. The trait might appear in offspring without appearing in their parents.

Analysis

Be prepared to respond to the following as part of a class discussion.

1. Explain why males are more likely than females to display the phenotypes associated with X-linked recessive traits.
2. In what ways are pedigrees useful tools to illustrate inheritance patterns?
3. What are some differences between the patterns of sex-linked traits and those of autosomal traits?

ELABORATE
The Genetic Basis of Human Variation

In the first Elaborate activity, *Predicting Inheritance by Using Pedigrees,* you looked at a number of genetic traits that show simple inheritance. Either a person has hitchhiker's thumbs or she does not. Either a person is affected by cystic fibrosis or he is not.

Now look around at your classmates. Consider how different they are from one another. Think about the tremendous variety of physical characteristics, such as hair type, skin color, body type, and facial features. Some classmates are a little taller than others. The inheritance of these traits

Figure 12.33 What physical distinctions can you see among these people? How do you know they are all human?

is more complex. We know this because there is more variability among the phenotypes for these traits.

Although traits distinguish one human from another, the degree of variation is limited. Despite the physical distinctions of humans, you easily can recognize a stranger from a distant country as a member of *Homo sapiens* (see figure 12.33). What might be the genetic basis for such variation? How might natural selection affect the variety of characteristics exhibited by humans? In this Elaborate activity, *The Genetic Basis of Human Variation*, you will begin to answer these questions. You will experience some of the nature and range of variation in human populations and acquire additional information about how genotype affects phenotype.

Materials (per person)

1 white 3 × 5-in card   masking tape
1 colored 3 × 5-in card   meterstick

PROCESS AND PROCEDURES

1. Look at the 2 histograms shown in figure 12.34. Notice what the x- and y-axes represent for both of the histograms. Your teacher has created similar axes in or near your classroom.
2. Write "XX" on a white 3 × 5-in card if you are a female. Write "XY" if you are a male. This is your chromosomal sex.
3. Write your height in centimeters on the colored 3 × 5-in card—round off to the nearest 5 cm.

   If you are not sure of your height, ask a partner to help you measure your height. Your teacher can provide you with a meterstick to use.

4. Tape your cards to the proper places in each histogram, according to your teacher's instructions.

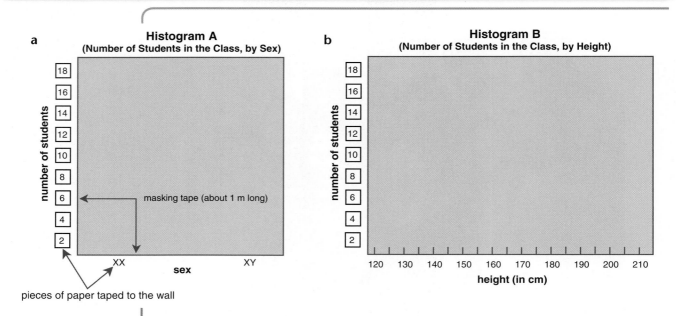

a
Histogram A
(Number of Students in the Class, by Sex)

number of students

18
16
14
12
10
8
6
4
2

masking tape (about 1 m long)

XX   XY
sex

pieces of paper taped to the wall

b
Histogram B
(Number of Students in the Class, by Height)

number of students

18
16
14
12
10
8
6
4
2

120 130 140 150 160 170 180 190 200 210
height (in cm)

Figure 12.34 What information is represented on the *x*- and *y*-axes on (*a*) histogram A and on (*b*) histogram B?

5. When the class histograms are complete, work with your partner to answer these questions. Record your answers in your science notebook.

   Use the data in the histograms and your understanding of genetics to help you.

   a. How many different types of individuals are represented on histogram A?

   b. How many different types of individuals are represented on histogram B?

   c. In your science notebook, draw and label the 2 histograms. Describe how their shapes differ.

   d. What would happen to the shapes of the histograms if you added data from the rest of the students in your school?

   e. Why do you think the shape of histogram A is different from the shape of histogram B?

   f. List 3 other human traits that would result in the same type of pattern as histogram A. Do the same for histogram B.

6. Read the essay, *The Complexity of Inheritance,* to help you understand the shapes of the histograms. As you read, revise or add to your answers in step 5.

7. In your science notebook, answer the following questions.

   a. From what you have learned in units 1–4, why do you think it is important for there to be variation among organisms in a population?

   b. Give an example where a lack of variation in a population would cause problems.

   c. List a trait that is mainly influenced by genetics.

   d. List a trait that is mainly influenced by environment.

Look around your classroom. It is apparent that people look different from one another. Some students are female, while others are male. Some students are tall, and others are short. Try rolling your tongue into a U shape (figure 12.35). Can you do it?

You might be surprised to learn that the ability to roll your tongue is an inherited trait. Being able to roll the tongue is dominant over not being able to roll it. Characteristics such as tongue rolling are called **discrete**, because they tend to fall into distinct, or discrete, categories. Either you can roll your tongue or you cannot. Either you are male or female. Either you have dimples or you do not.

Discrete characteristics tend to be controlled by a single gene. These traits are often used in biology classes to study inheritance patterns. It is important to realize, though, that very few biological traits are determined by a single gene. The majority of traits are determined by complex interactions between multiple genes.

Traits controlled by multiple genes often do not show distinct categories of phenotypes. These show continuous variation. "**Continuous**" means that phenotypes for a particular

trait include a range with no distinct categories. Height, weight, and skin color are traits that demonstrate continuous variation in human populations. Each of these traits is controlled by multiple genes.

You may wonder if anything else contributes to phenotype. Think about the trait of weight, listed above as a continuous trait. Do you think that genes are the only thing that plays a role in determining a person's weight? You may say that the amount a person eats or the amount that person exercises also plays a role in a person's weight. So the genetic blueprint is not always the only factor that determines phenotype. Environmental factors play a critical role as well. Traits that are influenced by both genetic and environmental factors are called multifactorial traits.

For example, the average height of people in Japan increased by several inches in the early and mid-1900s (see figure 12.36). Did the genetic blueprints for the entire population change? No, the environment for the population changed. Many

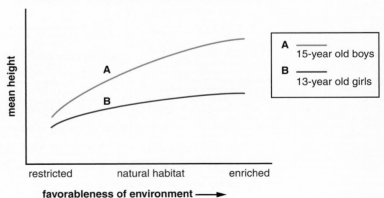

Height versus Environment in Japanese Children

Source: Based on data from Gottesman, I.I., and Heston, L.L. (1972). *Genetics, environment, and behavior.* Academic Press.

Figure 12.36 **Height in Japanese boys and girls in relation to environmental conditions.** Improved environmental conditions led to a phenotype of increased height during the early and mid-20th century. Curve A represents 15-year-old boys. Curve B represents 13-year-old girls. The units for both mean height and environmental conditions are not to scale. Note that, as the environmental conditions became better, the height of the children increased.

Figure 12.35 The ability to roll the tongue into a U shape is genetic.

children in generations before the 1900s had poor diets. Then, during the first part of the century, the diets became more nutritious. Japanese diets began to include dairy products as well as more meat and bread. The poor diets were an environmental limitation for children of earlier generations. This limitation prevented those children from growing to the maximum size permitted by their genetic plans. The Japanese children are one example of how genetic plans and the environment interact to produce a phenotype. This is common for complex traits, such as height and behavior. Many genetic and environmental factors may be involved in how complex traits are expressed.

Analysis

Respond to the following tasks individually. Contribute your answers to a class discussion.

1. Is the variation observed in histogram B of the same type as that which causes genetic disorders such as cystic fibrosis? Explain.
2. In a paragraph, discuss your ideas about the following questions.
   a. How do we define "normal" or "typical" for a continuous trait, such as height?
   b. Where does "short" end and "tall" begin?
   c. How does the idea of "normal" relate to complex behaviors, such as intelligence?
   d. Is "normal" a biological or a social concept?

      For example, what might someone say is "normal" height for your class? Would the idea of normal height be different within a group of Pygmy Africans?

3. Look back at figure 2.13 in chapter 2. When you examined these graphs before, you thought about them from a natural selection perspective. Now that you know more about genetic characteristics, would you say that beak depth is determined by 1 gene or by more than 1 gene? Explain your answer.

Further Challenges

Read the optional sidebar, *The American Eugenics Movement: A Cautionary Tale*, and then answer the following questions.
1. Do you think the traits studied by eugenics researchers represent genetic traits, environmental traits, or both? Explain your answer.
2. In what ways did eugenics represent bad science?

ENGLISH SPANISH

The American Eugenics Movement: A Cautionary Tale

In England during the early 1900s, the birthrate of society's upper class was low. At the same time, the birthrate among the lower-class citizens was high. In addition, Charles Darwin's idea of natural selection had taken root. These ideas caused some scientists to fear that the increasing population of the lower class would cause disastrous problems. Sir Francis Galton, a scientist and explorer, promoted a science he called *eugenics* (meaning "of noble birth"). The aim of eugenics was to improve society by increasing its proportion of healthy and intelligent citizens. This could be accomplished by encouraging people with desirable traits to have more children and by restricting people with undesirable traits from having children.

Eugenics spread quickly to other countries, including the United States. The founder of the American eugenics movement was Charles Davenport. In 1904, Davenport established the Eugenic Record Office (ERO) in Cold Spring Harbor, New York. Workers from the ERO collected information from thousands of families. They used the data to analyze the pedigrees of the families. In this work, the ERO was looking for evidence of inherited traits. Reports from the ERO and other researchers claimed to have identified genes responsible for a wide variety of traits. Some of the traits they thought were caused by genes included shyness, musical ability, feeblemindedness, and even the tendency to run off and become a sea captain. Davenport called this last gene *thalassophilia,* meaning "love of the sea."

Eugenics was supported by many wealthy and influential Americans including Theodore Roosevelt, Calvin Coolidge, John D. Rockefeller, and Alexander Graham Bell. During the 1920s, state fairs in the Midwest held Fittest Families contests. Trophies were awarded to families judged to be the most mentally and physically fit. Eventually, laws were passed to promote eugenics:

- There was concern that mixing races would harm the white race. Laws were passed in the majority of states to ban interracial marriage.
- In 1924, the Immigration Act (the Johnson-Reed Act) was passed. It sharply limited the number of immigrants coming to the United States from areas outside of northern Europe.
- In 1927, the U.S. Supreme Court made its *Buck v. Bell* decision. The decision allowed individuals to be sterilized against their will if it could be shown that they were mentally "defective." Over 60,000 Americans were sterilized.

Before and during World War II, Nazi Germany used eugenics to justify the extermination of millions of people. As these crimes became known to the world, the word "eugenics" lost its appeal. Most countries stopped using the word. Today, eugenics has become a historical footnote. People still remember the idea, however. It remains in people's minds during debates about current genetic and bioethical issues. Hopefully, the world has learned lessons from its mistakes of the past.

EVALUATE

Human Genetic Disorders

In this Evaluate activity, *Human Genetic Disorders*, you will apply your understanding of the basic concepts of genetics by creating an informational brochure about a genetic disorder. You will demonstrate your understanding of the patterns of inheritance, probability, and the tools used by geneticists.

Materials (per student)

art supplies
additional resources (optional)

SC LINKS
NSTA
www.scilinks.org
Topic: genetic diseases/
genetic screening/
genetic counseling
Code: human4E666

PROCESS AND PROCEDURES

1. Read the final episode of the scenario, *The Genetic Counseling Clinic*, to learn about your final project.
2. Obtain a copy of the *Genetic Disorder Brochure Rubric* handout from your teacher. Examine the rubric to see how your brochure will be evaluated.
3. From the following list, choose a genetic disorder for which you would like to create a brochure:
   • Hemophilia: A disorder in which the blood does not clot normally
   • Tay-Sachs disease: A disorder in which a fatty substance builds up in the nerve cells of the brain
   • Neurofibromatosis: A disorder in which tumors grow on nerve cells in the body

SCENARIO

ENGLISH SPANISH

The Genetic Counseling Clinic, continued

"Elise, you are coming to the end of your internship at the genetic counseling clinic. I'd like you to complete one final project before you go," Ms. Gomez said.

"Sure!" replied Elise. "What can I do to help?"

"Patients have been asking for information they can take with them and share with their extended families. I would like you to create a brochure about a particular genetic disorder. This brochure would be something we could give to patients whose lives might be affected by that disorder. It would give them information on the symptoms of the disorder, the number of people affected by the disorder, and the patterns of inheritance. You should use pedigrees and Punnett squares to help explain the information to the patients in terms they can understand."

"That sounds like fun," Elise said. "I will get started right away!"

- Duchenne muscular dystrophy: A disorder in which muscles become progressively weaker over time
- Marfan syndrome: A disorder in which the connective tissue in the body (which provides support to tendons, ligaments, blood vessels, cartilage, and heart valves) is not as stiff as it should be

4. Create a brochure to help patients learn more about the disorder. A good brochure will include each of the following.
   a. A description of the symptoms of the disorder and how many people are affected
   b. The pattern of inheritance of the disorder (autosomal or sex linked, dominant or recessive)
   c. A written description of a sample family who might be affected by the disorder
   d. A pedigree showing information from the sample family
   e. A Punnett square showing a cross between 2 members of the sample family
   f. The probability of the offspring of the cross being affected
   g. A description of how the results of meiosis are used to make a Punnett square
   h. Identification of the gene that contains a mutation and the result of that mutation
   i. Any treatments for the disorder
5. Be prepared to share the information in your brochure with the class.

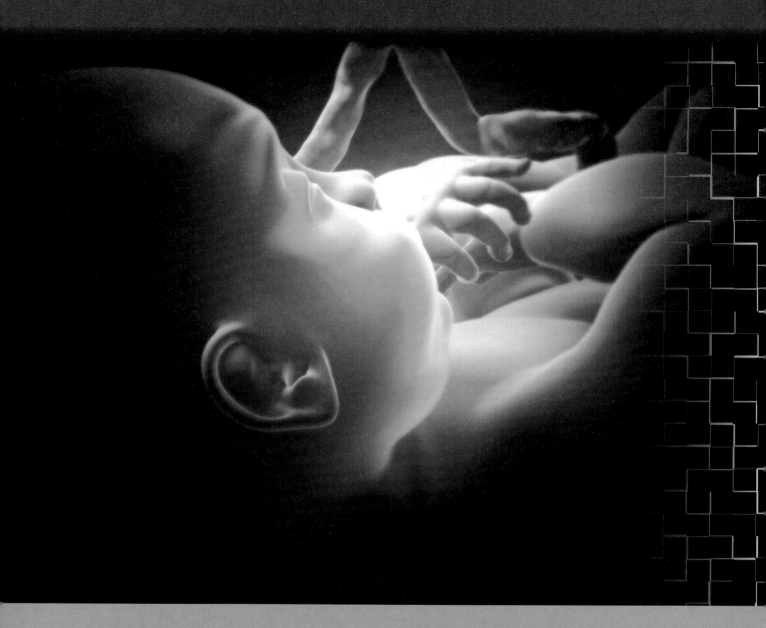

n unit 4, *Continuity: Reproduction and Inheritance in Living Systems,* you learned about genetic processes that allow for continuity from one generation to the next and for change in species over evolutionary time. In unit 5, *Development: Growth and Differentiation in Living Systems,* you will explore developmental processes that allow organisms to slowly change from a fertilized egg to an adult. In chapter 13, *Processes and Patterns of Development,* you will learn how processes that make cells different from one another underlie the development of tissues, organs, and organisms. In chapter 14, *The Human Life Span,* you will focus on changes in human growth and development from birth through old age. You also will explore human life stages in other cultures to learn how culture influences the expression of life stages. In this unit, you will revisit your critter and participate in a multicultural fair.

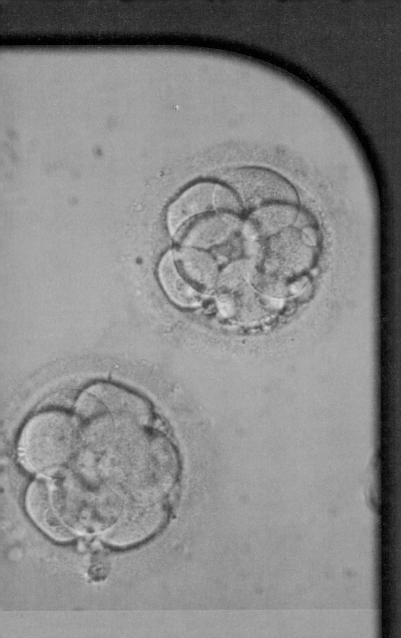

UNIT 5

Development: Growth and Differentiation in Living Systems

By the end of unit 5, you should be able to understand how

- ✔ cells divide through a process known as mitosis;
- ✔ embryonic development involves processes of growth and differentiation;
- ✔ humans grow and develop in different ways through life (physically, cognitively, emotionally, and socially);
- ✔ culture influences how human life stages are interpreted and experienced; and
- ✔ as scientists answer specific questions, knowledge accumulates to address larger questions.

13 14

CHAPTER

13 Processes and Patterns of Development

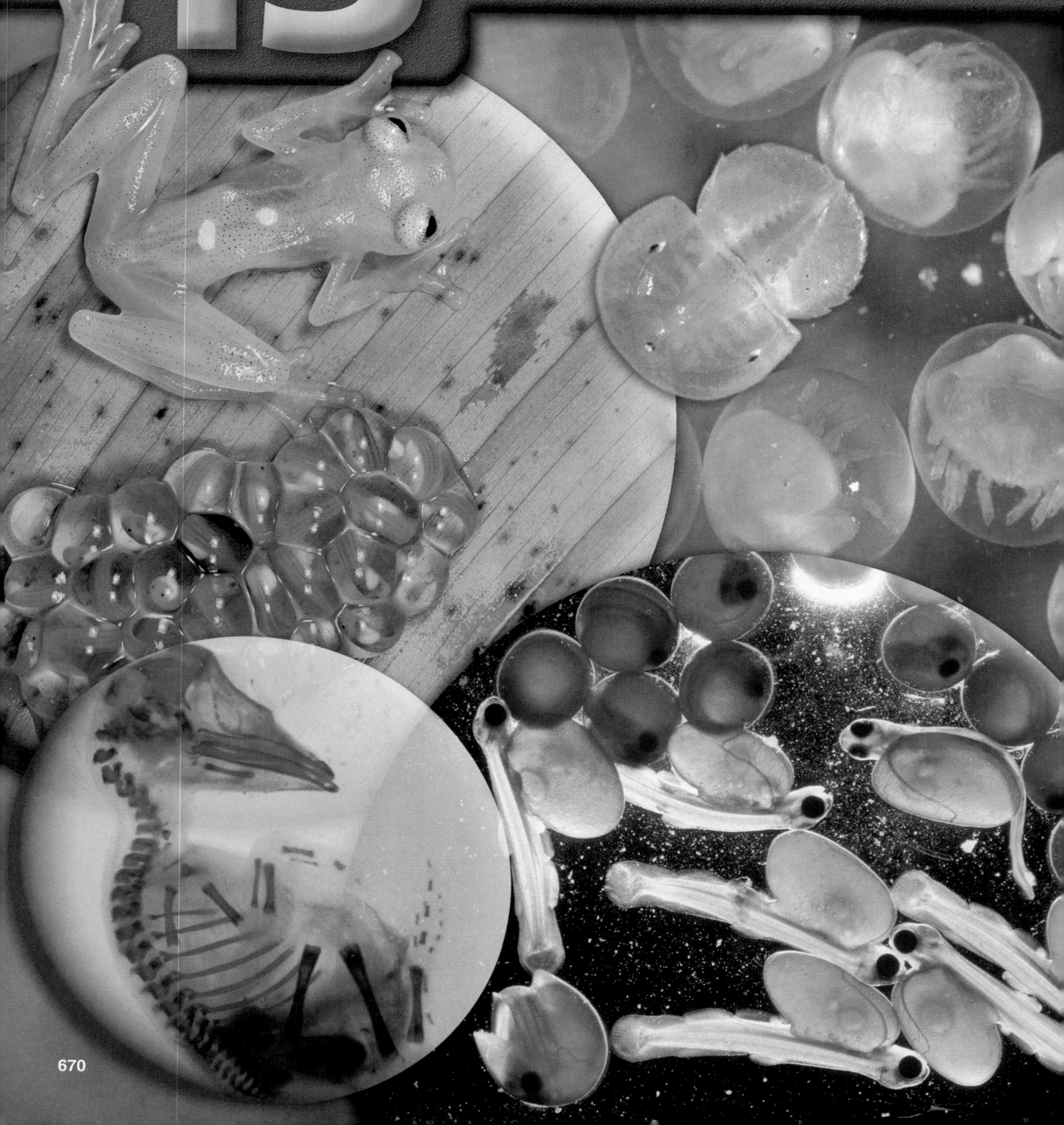

ow organisms grow and develop has long been a question of interest in biology. Watching an animal embryo develop from a single cell into a complex adult seems magical. But we know that biological processes are responsible. How is it that organisms change in precise and predictable ways from fertilized eggs to adults? In chapter 13, you will learn about the processes and patterns of development. You also will be invited to think about how scientists have gathered this knowledge. How might scientists extend their understanding to answer the questions about development that continue to puzzle us today?

People sometimes describe the processes of science as a simple set of steps that you can follow to generate scientific knowledge. Perhaps you have studied the so-called scientific method. It is true that practicing scientists really do generate questions, test hypotheses, and form conclusions. However, they do not necessarily complete exactly those tasks in exactly that order. Instead, "doing science" is a highly creative, long-term search for answers to complicated and fascinating puzzles. Searching for answers is a dynamic process. It requires careful questioning, hypothesis making, and concluding. Scientific searches also involve imagination, persistence, humor, and sometimes luck.

GOALS FOR THE CHAPTER

Throughout chapter 13, *Processes and Patterns of Development*, you will work to gain an understanding of the following concepts:

✔ Development is a progression of long-term changes that occur in an organism from the beginning of life until death.

✔ Development occurs as a result of the coordinated events of growth and differentiation.

✔ Developmental processes are the expression of a genetic plan that can be influenced by the environment.

✔ A relationship exists between the heritable changes in development and evolution.

✔ Developmental biology has progressed because of an accumulation of evidence around several key questions.

To help you develop these understandings, you will complete the following activities.

ENGAGE	One Hundred Years of Questions
EXPLORE / EXPLAIN	A Start in Development
EXPLORE / EXPLAIN	Generating Specialized Cells
ELABORATE	Development Gone Awry
EVALUATE	Development in Your Critter

The chapter organizer can help you keep track of your learning and the flow of ideas across the chapter. Refer to it periodically as you complete the chapter activities.

One Hundred Years of Questions

Key Idea: Developmental biology has a long history of inquiry around several key questions.

Linking Question:
What have scientists learned about the fundamentals of development?

Chapter 13

MAJOR CONCEPTS

✔ Development is a progression of long-term changes that occur in an organism from the beginning of life until death.

✔ Development occurs as a result of the coordinated events of growth and differentiation.

✔ Developmental processes are the expression of a genetic plan that can be influenced by the environment.

✔ A relationship exists between the heritable changes in development and evolution.

✔ Developmental biology has progressed because of an accumulation of evidence around several key questions.

A Start in Development

Part A: Stages of Development
Part B: How Do Cells Divide?
Key Idea: Every organism passes through similar developmental stages. A key process of development is growth by cell division (mitosis).

Linking Question:
How do genetically identical cells develop into different cell types?

Generating Specialized Cells

Key Idea: A second key process of development is cell differentiation. In this process, cells become different from one another in structure and function through differential gene expression.

Development in Your Critter

Key Idea: All multicellular organisms undergo the key processes of growth and differentiation, even though development appears very different among different organisms.

Processes and Patterns of Development

Linking Question:
How does development occur in nonhuman organisms?

 ELABORATE

Development Gone Awry

Key Idea: Genetic and environmental factors can disrupt development.

Linking Question:
What factors can disrupt development?

ENGAGE

One Hundred Years of Questions

How do scientists think of the questions that they would like to investigate? Actually, finding questions to ask is the easy part of science. The hard part is expressing our questions in such a way that we can investigate them. For example, multicellular animals must go through a complex process to develop from a fertilized egg to adult. How can we study this process? In this Engage activity, *One Hundred Years of Questions*, you will make observations and generate questions about animal development. Then you will learn about some of the questions raised and investigated by early developmental biologists.

Materials

online resource

PROCESS AND PROCEDURES

1. View the video segments, "From Egg to Adult" and "A Collection of Eggs: An Assortment of Adults." What questions do the pairs of images you viewed raise in your mind? In your science notebook, record 2 questions about development.

   Feel free to write down any questions you think of. These questions do not have to be testable in your classroom. They could be questions about what kinds of information, matter, or energy the embryo needs for development or how it uses these resources in development. They could be questions about the timing or sequence of events in development. They could be specific to one organism you saw or to all the organisms pictured.

2. View the video segment, "Zebrafish Development." In your science notebook, record 2 more questions regarding development that the time-lapse images lead you to think about.

3. To learn about some of the questions scientists have asked about development, read the scenario, *Changes All Around*. Then record your ideas about the following questions. Be prepared to join the class in a discussion about them.

   a. What was the specific question that Wilhelm Roux tried to answer? How was his question different from the question, "How do organisms develop?" Why was this difference important?

   b. Compare Roux's hot-needle experiment on a frog embryo with Hans Driesch's experiment on sea urchin embryos (figure 13.3). Indicate similarities and differences in each of the following aspects of their experiments.

      1) Experimental design
      2) Results
      3) Conclusion

   c. What was Roux's contribution to the field of developmental biology?

Changes All Around

The fertilized frog egg has just started to develop, dividing to make a two-celled embryo. Under a microscope, it is clear that the two cells are in close contact with each other. The scientist picks up a hot needle. With excruciating care, he pierces just one of the two cells. The other cell remains untouched. Cytoplasm oozes out of the pricked cell, causing the cell to deflate like a flat tire. The scientist wonders if the remaining cell will develop further or if it also will die. The year is 1888. The scientist, a young German biologist named Wilhelm Roux (figure 13.1), is in the process of making a dramatic step forward in the study of living systems.

Why was this experiment so important? Scientists in the late 19th century knew that vertebrates, such as frogs and humans, start life as a single cell, the fertilized egg. Scientists had proposed many ideas to try to explain how an embryo develops after fertilization. Many thought that a fertilized egg contained a tiny, fully formed—or preformed—organism that simply grew larger during development. Some thought that the process was more complex. They thought the structure of an organism formed as the embryo developed.

Figure 13.1 **A portrait of scientist Wilhelm Roux.**

Roux took a big step forward by doing more than just thinking about how development might take place. He asked the large question: "How do organisms develop?" He then identified a simpler, related question that he could test. This question was, "Does each of the first two cells in an embryo contain all of the structures and information needed to grow into an organism? Or does each cell contain only half of the structures and information needed?" Roux hypothesized that if the embryo were preformed, then each cell of the two-celled embryo would contain only half of the necessary information. Roux tested this question by performing the hot-needle experiment described earlier (see also figure 13.3a).

The results of Roux's hot-needle experiment were spectacular. As Roux described them: "[An] amazing thing happened; the one cell developed in many cases into a half-embryo generally normal in structure, with small variations occurring only in the region of the immediate neighborhood of the treated half of the egg."*

---

* Wilhelm Roux wrote these words in 1888. They were translated by Hans Laufer and appeared in Shostak, S. (1991). *Embryology: An Introduction to Developmental Biology.* New York: HarperCollins Publishers.

In other words, the cell that survived gave rise to only half of the embryo. The surviving cell appeared to lack the materials or information needed to produce the other half. Roux interpreted his results as evidence for preformed embryos.

As new evidence came to light, however, Roux's conclusion was challenged. In 1892, another scientist, Hans Driesch, conducted a similar experiment with a different design (figure 13.3b). First, Driesch used a different organism, a sea urchin (figure 13.2). Second, Driesch did not kill one cell. He separated the two cells and watched to see what would develop from each one. Driesch's results supported a conclusion that was the opposite of Roux's. Driesch observed that whole embryos developed from each of the separate cells. This evidence supported the idea that an organism forms during development, not that it is preformed. It also suggested that each cell contains all the information it needs to produce an entire organism.

Driesch was astonished with this observation. How could he account for his results? His first response was that sea urchin eggs are not frog eggs. Perhaps he simply was seeing a difference between the two types of organisms. But he also noted that his and Roux's experiments were slightly different. Roux had killed one cell. But the dead cell remained in contact with the live one. Possibly the dead cell was exerting an influence on the development of the live cell.

In 1910, a scientist named J. F. McClendon tested whether Driesch's results were caused by differences between the species or by the influence of the dead cell. He removed one cell of a two-celled frog embryo by carefully

Figure 13.2 **Sea urchin.** Sea urchins develop from eggs. The eggs develop into a stage where they are called larvae (singular: larva) before becoming adults (see figure 13.36).

sucking it up into a tiny eyedropper. Like Driesch, he isolated one cell of a two-celled embryo. He also found that the remaining cell developed into a normal, although small, frog embryo. This result was the opposite of Roux's original result and suggested that leaving the dead cell in place affected the remaining cell. It strengthened the idea that each cell of the embryo had the genetic potential to become any cell, even if it were destined to be only a specific part of the embryo.

Figure 13.3a illustrates Roux's historic experiment. Why do scientists remember it, despite Roux's incorrect conclusions? In fact, Roux's work began an important new area of biology: experimental developmental biology. Roux's work and the work of other scientists of his time highlighted the importance of asking questions about development that we can answer by doing experiments. Sometimes the questions that we can answer are only parts of larger questions that we wonder about. We gain scientific knowledge from piecing together the answers to small questions. These answers in turn shed light on more-complicated questions.

In 1894, Roux helped start a scientific journal to communicate new discoveries and to air new discussions about development. Today, after more than 100 years of asking questions, performing experiments, and building answers, developmental biologists have a much better understanding of how a fertilized egg develops. We have learned how many other aspects of development happen as well. Yet

Roux's experiment

Driesch's experiment

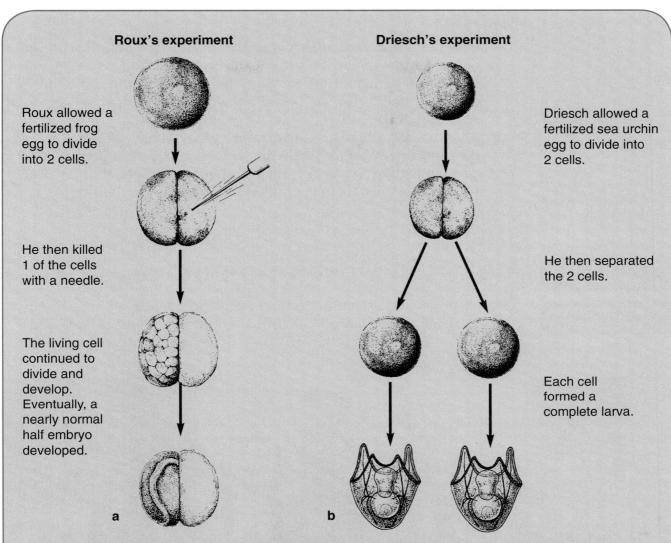

Roux allowed a fertilized frog egg to divide into 2 cells.

He then killed 1 of the cells with a needle.

The living cell continued to divide and develop. Eventually, a nearly normal half embryo developed.

a

Driesch allowed a fertilized sea urchin egg to divide into 2 cells.

He then separated the 2 cells.

Each cell formed a complete larva.

b

Figure 13.3   Early experiments in developmental biology. (*a*) Roux killed one of the first two cells of a frog embryo. The remaining cell developed tissues corresponding to half of a normal frog embryo. The results would have been different if Roux had removed the dead cell. (*b*) Driesch experimented with sea urchin eggs and found that each of the first two cells could form a complete larva. Later, McClendon reconciled these apparently conflicting results by demonstating that the dead cell influenced the development of the live cell.

we still have unanswered questions. In 1994, 100 years after the establishment of Roux's journal, the publishers of *Science* magazine performed a survey. They asked scientists what questions about development were most interesting to them and what questions were most likely to be answered from experiments conducted during the 1990s. The top two questions that scientists named were these:

1. "How are the body's tissues and organs formed?"
2. "What clues does development reveal about the process of evolution?"

Today, scientists continue to explore these questions. As you read this chapter, scientists are devising new experiments and using new technologies to study these complex questions. New data emerge daily that help biologists find answers to the puzzles of development.

Analysis

1. Compare the questions that you recorded in steps 1 and 2 with the questions that scientists in the *Science* survey named as most interesting to them. How are your questions similar to those the scientists asked? How are they different? Record your answers in your science notebook.

2. Scientists are still asking and answering questions about development. What does this fact suggest about the processes of development? What does it suggest about the processes of science? Record your answers in your science notebook.

EXPLORE

EXPLAIN

A Start in Development

Simple observation reveals changes in size and shape as a human baby grows to an adult (see figure 13.4). The 19th-century scientists Roux and Driesch were able to watch the early development of fertilized frog and sea

Figure 13.4   Life stages. What changes happen during development that take place before birth? What changes occur as organisms develop to maturity?

urchin eggs because the technology of microscopes improved their view. Today, more-advanced microscopes and other technological tools, such as fiber optics and ultrasound, give scientists an even closer look at development.

In this Explore-Explain activity, *A Start in Development*, you will use a series of video images to begin your study of animal development. As you do so, consider the question, "What processes are involved in forming tissues and organs during development?"

Materials (per team of 2)

Part A
online resource (watch as a class)

Part B
modeling clay
large sheet of paper
online resource (watch as a class)

PROCESS AND PROCEDURES

Part A   Stages of Development

The video images that you saw in the Engage activity, *One Hundred Years of Questions,* provided basic information about development. However, the images did not reveal which specific events occur as a fertilized egg develops into an adult. The time span that elapses as an organism develops may be from weeks to years, depending on the species. What happens during that time? The video segment, "A Closer Look at Animal Development," will provide clues. The images on that segment were filmed using a combination of technologies. These include fiber optics, high-resolution microscopes, and video recording equipment. Fiber optics allows tiny cameras to record images of hard-to-view areas, such as the human uterus.

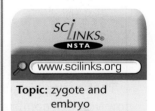

Topic: zygote and embryo
Code: human4E679

1. To help you identify important events in development, make a table in your science notebook that is similar to figure 13.5. Then view the video segment, "A Closer Look at Animal Development," to gather information that will help you complete the table.

    It may help if you focus on making observations of one or two stages for a particular organism, as listed in the table.

2. Compare the images you saw in "A Closer Look at Animal Development" with the images in the video segment, "From Egg to Adult," in the Engage activity, *One Hundred Years of Questions.* In what ways has technology increased scientists' ability to study development?

Figure 13.5 Key stages of development. Use this table to record your observations of different organisms as they develop.

Topic: differentiation of cells during animal development
Code: human4E680

HOW TO

Developmental stage	Focus organism	What I see	What I think it means
Initial cell divisions	Fish		
Gastrulation	Frog		
Organ formation	Chicken		
Growth	Human		

3. To expand your understanding of development, read the essay, *The Long and Short of Development*. As you read, make entries for the terms "cell division" and "cell differentiation" in your personal glossary. Then answer the following questions in your science notebook.
   a. Explain the difference between cell division and cell differentiation.
   b. List specific examples from the video segment, "A Closer Look at Animal Development," that show evidence of each of these processes taking place.

   For more information on completing a personal glossary, see *How to Develop a Personal Glossary* in appendix B8.

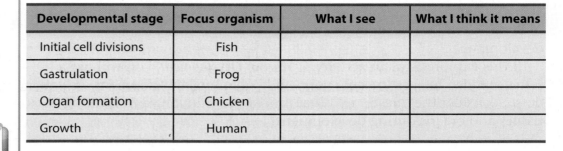

The Long and Short of Development

ENGLISH SPANISH

That nasty pimple finally disappeared, but now you are coming down with a cold. Is it time for lunch yet? Your stomach is growling. Surely, you have noticed changes such as these in your body. Many of these changes are short-term internal adjustments that ensure homeostatic balance. Homeostatic changes tend to be relatively rapid and reversible. They happen in seconds, hours, or days. They allow conditions in our bodies to remain within narrowly defined limits.

Other changes take place at a slower pace and across a longer period of time. These changes are not directly related to homeostasis. They are not rapid or easily reversed. Instead, they are relatively slow and generally permanent. This change process is called **development**. Development is the process by which a fertilized egg transforms into an adult organism. Developmental processes slow dramatically in adults. However, development never completely stops. For example, the body continues to make new skin cells throughout life. In humans, emotional and social growth also continue throughout life.

Some developmental changes are dramatic. A human embryo forms a beating heart at the age of four weeks. Other developmental changes are slow. Features of a child's body are constantly changing size. A child's thinking abilities and coordination also change over time. You are probably familiar with some of the dramatic physical and emotional changes that occur during puberty. Every day, your body is also replacing cells in your digestive system and bloodstream. Old age brings new changes, such as wrinkles. All of these changes are aspects of the developmental process.

Development takes place in all multicellular organisms. Frog embryos turn into tadpoles that grow larger, lose their tails, and become frogs. Trees grow larger and develop branching limb and root systems (figure 13.6). As humans, rats, chimpanzees, and other mammals grow older, their hair (or fur) turns gray and their skin becomes less elastic.

Two key processes in development are cell division and cell differentiation. **Cell division** is a process by which new cells are made. Cell division provides the raw materials for the formation of complex structures. Each one of your body's structures contains many cells. Cell division can also cause an increase in the size of the organism by increasing the number of cells. Finally, cell division can generate new cells to take the place of cells that have died. **Cell differentiation** is a process by which cells acquire specialized shapes and functions. In many cases, cells that have undergone differentiation can no longer divide.

Starting with a fertilized egg, cell division allows for the formation of a multicellular embryo. As the embryo continues to grow, cells differentiate, forming specialized parts. For example, a

Figure 13.6 Development in a piñon pine tree (*Pinus edulis*). What evidence of development do you see in these photographs?

newborn baby has skin, nerve, liver, and blood cells located in specific places. Each cell type performs distinct functions. Figure 13.7 illustrates some of the stages that take place during the development of a mammal.

Cell division and cell differentiation continue after birth or hatching. These processes enable an organism's body to grow and change. The two processes also serve to maintain and repair body systems. This allows recovery from accidents and illness. The developmental process of **senescence**, or aging, is prominent in later life. Developmental biologists recognize that aging leads to a progressive and irreversible loss of function. However, they do not have a complete understanding of the processes of aging. They generally agree that aging is genetically controlled. For example, scientists have identified a gene in fruit flies that appears to limit their life spans. Development can be characterized as a series of biological changes that takes place in an individual organism from fertilization to death.

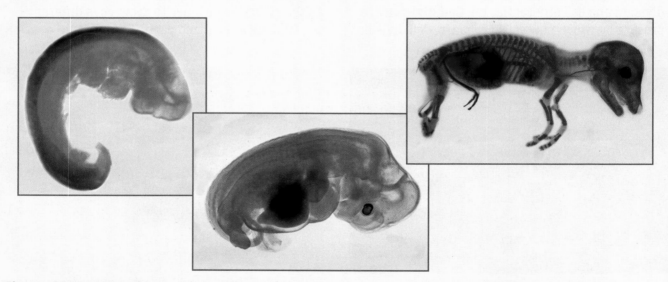

Figure 13.7   Pig embryos. These images of pig embryos show many common features of mammalian development. The embryos are arranged from younger (at left) to older (at right).

Part B   How Do Cells Divide?

In part A, *Stages of Development*, you observed two basic processes involved in development. Part B, *How Do Cells Divide?*, helps you explore one of those processes: cell division. In cell division, one cell becomes two cells.

1. With your partner, think about the kinds of events that would have to happen to make 2 cells from 1 cell. Make a list of your ideas in your science notebook.

It might help to think of an analogy. If you had one bowl of soup, what would you need to do to divide it between you and a friend? Would this process require certain kinds of matter? Would it require energy? Now transfer this thinking to cells. Think about what the new cell would require to function exactly like the original cell. What might the original cell need to "donate" to the new cell? Think also about the physical changes that will take place in the original cell. What kinds of biosynthesis might need to take place?

2. Observe the cells in the video segment, "Cell Division." Watch carefully for evidence of any of the events you listed in step 1. Discuss the following with your class.

   a. What appeared to be happening as the cells in the video and animation divided?

   b. Did you find evidence for any of the ideas that you and your partner wrote down in step 1?

   c. How do you think the process of cell division (figure 13.8) contributes to the changes that take place as humans and other animals develop? Give 2 examples to support your answer.

3. Record the following questions in your science notebook, leaving plenty of room to write answers. Then watch the video segment "Cell Division" again for information that can help you answer the questions. Answer the questions in your science notebook.

   a. What are the dark structures that are very active during cell division?

   b. What are the functions of the structures that you identified in step 3a?

   c. What happens to these structures during cell division? (Answer as specifically as you can.)

4. To clarify your understanding of cell division, read the essay, *The Cell Cycle and Growth Control*. As you read, develop a concept map that relates the following terms.

   a. Cell cycle
   b. Mitosis
   c. Interphase
   d. DNA synthesis
   e. Prophase
   f. Metaphase
   g. Anaphase
   h. Telophase
   i. Cytokinesis

   Remember to add linking verbs along the lines that connect your terms to each other in your concept map. For more information, see *How to Construct a Concept Map* in appendix B7.

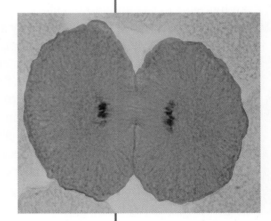

Figure 13.8 Cell division. The process of cell division produces two cells from one original cell. When would your body's cells need to undergo cell division?

HOW TO

The Cell Cycle and Growth Control

Have you ever wondered why beetles are small and whales are large? At hatching or birth, both are smaller than their parents. Yet each grows to a size similar to their parents. What determines their growth and final size?

Because nearly all organisms grow during their lifetimes, growth is regarded as an important developmental process. Understanding development requires that we understand growth. In multicellular organisms, growth takes place primarily through an increase in the *number* of cells, not through an increase in the *size* of cells. Why? Diffusion and osmosis are the processes of cellular transport. These very slow processes place upper limits on how large cells can become. The physical limitations have influenced development in a way that favors *more* cells rather than *larger* cells. As a result, an increase in the size of an embryo reflects an increase in the number of cells that compose it.

Simple observation of your own body suggests that growth is a highly regulated process. Think, for example, of the changes in size and proportion that already have taken place in your body (figure 13.9). In most cases, growth takes place according to a pre-dictable schedule, with most of it happening before birth and during childhood. With some minor exceptions, that growth takes place evenly from one side of the body to the other. Can you imagine if it didn't? Organisms would frequently have legs of different lengths! The production of new cells also allows for the replacement of cells that become damaged or die during the normal events of life. Such replacement activity also is precisely controlled.

Before we consider how cell production is controlled during development, we must look at how new cells arise. In cell division, two cells are produced from one. Cell division that includes the process of **mitosis** produces offspring cells that are genetically identical to the original cell. The term mitosis refers specifically to the way in which chromosomes are divided between the two new cells.

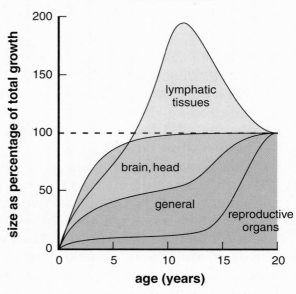

Relative Growth of Body Parts Across Time

Figure 13.9 **Relative growth of body parts over time.** As you look at the graph, notice how the growth of the body parts levels off at age 20. What benefit is associated with the rapid growth of lymphatic tissue?

Figure 13.10 illustrates this process. The chromosomes duplicate before mitosis, during **interphase**, and other essential organelles form as well. During the four phases of mitosis, the duplicated chromosomes coil up, line up, and separate into two newly formed offspring cells. Specifically, the four phases begin with **prophase**, when chromosomes coil tightly, becoming more dense. In this phase, they look somewhat like Xs because each pair of duplicated chromosomes is held together at a midpoint structure called the centromere. The nuclear envelope is broken down during this phase, paving the way for the next phase. During **metaphase**, the duplicated chromosomes, guided by cytoplasmic fibers, form a long line across the middle of the cell. During the third phase, **anaphase**, the cytoplasmic fibers pull apart

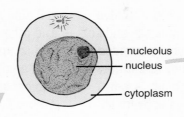

nucleolus
nucleus
cytoplasm

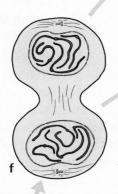

a

During **interphase,** materials required for
the next cell division are synthesized.
(Interphase is a long and active phase
of the cell cycle.) For example, DNA
and chromosomes are duplicated
in the nucleus. Cell structures such as
mitochondria are made in the cytoplasm.
The cell grows.

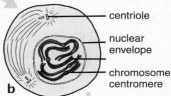

centriole
nuclear
envelope
chromosome
centromere

b

As **prophase** begins, the long thin chromosomes coil
and become shorter and thicker. Each chromosome now
appears as a doubled structure joined at a centromere.
The centrioles were duplicated during interphase. They
now begin to move to opposite ends of the cell. (In plant
cells, there are no centrioles. But the events of mitosis
otherwise take place as described here.)

f

During **telophase,** the chromosomes approach
the opposite ends of the cell and group together.
A new nuclear envelope is synthesized around the
chromosomes. The cytoplasm begins to divide. A
new cell membrane forms. (In plant cells, a new
cell wall is laid down between the two new cells.)
The new cells enter interphase.

centriole-to-
centriole fibers

c

Later in prophase, the nuclear envelope
breaks down. The chromosomes contract
to their shortest lengths. Cytoplasmic fibers
stretch from centriole to centriole. They also
stretch from each doubled chromosome to
both centrioles.

e

The doubled chromosomes
separate during **anaphase.** The
new chromosomes are pushed
and pulled to opposite ends of
the cell by the cytoplasmic fibers.

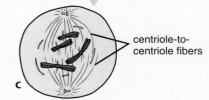

d

centromere-to-centriole fibers

During **metaphase,** the doubled
chromosomes line up along the
middle of the cell. Cytoplasmic fibers
now are attached to each doubled
chromosome at the centromere.

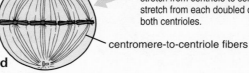

Figure 13.10   The phases of mitosis. How does mitosis compare with meiosis? (Meiosis is the process of
cell division that precedes the formation of gametes.)

the duplicated chromosomes. This action divides and moves the genetic material to opposite ends of the cell. Finally, during **telophase**, chromosomes at each end of the cell clump together and a new nuclear envelope forms around each set. A new cell membrane is made as the two cells begin to divide physically.

Other parts of the cell, such as mitochondria and the endoplasmic reticulum, also are distributed between these offspring cells during cell division. Each new cell contains a copy of the same genetic information and the same types of organelles that were contained in the parent cell.

As shown in figure 13.11, mitosis is only a small fraction of the **cell cycle**, the life cycle of a typical cell. Mitosis takes place during the *M phase* of the cell cycle. The bulk of a cell's life is spent in a phase between cell divisions. During most of this nondividing interphase, the cell carries out any specialized functions it may have. The

cell also grows as it synthesizes the RNA, proteins, and other macromolecules it needs to function and to undergo the next round of mitosis.

If a population of cells does not divide, growth can occur only by a limited increase in cell size. Adipose (fat-storing) tissues are an example of that kind of cell population. Once your body produces a basic number of fat cells, these cells do not multiply in number. However, they can become larger by incorporating more fatty substances.

In the cells of most tissues, controlling growth means controlling the occurrence and rate of mitosis. Two major levels of control regulate mitosis. The first level, called *internal control*, involves substances inside the cell. These critical substances regulate the timing of the specific phases of the cell cycle. That regulation is necessary. What if, for example, a cell entered mitosis before it replicated its DNA? If that happened, there would not be a full set of chromosomes in each offspring cell. Both offspring cells may die as a result.

A second level of *external control* involves factors outside the cell. These external signals trigger internal events in the cell. The internal events initiate or suppress the events of the cell cycle. One example of external control is *contact inhibition*, which causes cells to stop dividing. Contact inhibition takes place when cells reach a certain population density or degree of crowding (figure 13.12). This happens even though nutrients may be plentiful in the environment. Contact inhibition prevents the overcrowding of cells within a particular organ or area of the body. Sometimes this inhibition must be relaxed to allow healing. When your skin is cut, the cells at the edge of the wound begin to divide and slowly cover the bare spot. Once the open wound is repaired, however, cell division and cell movement stops again. Contact inhibition is an important example of growth control. Problems arise when this control is lost. A cell that suffers mutations in the

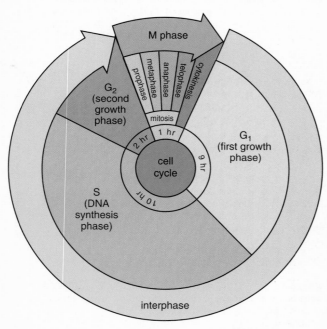

Figure 13.11   The cell cycle. The times given for each phase represent the approximate times for a liver cell grown in the lab.

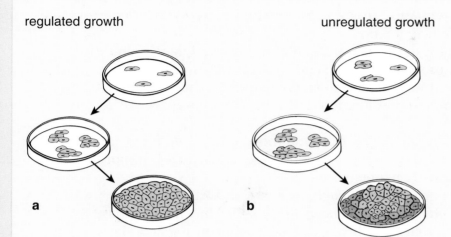

regulated growth

unregulated growth

Figure 13.12 **Contact inhibition.** (*a*) Cells experiencing normal growth regulation stop dividing when they make contact with other cells. (*b*) Cells that have lost this regulation will continue to divide, piling up on one another.

a

b

genes that regulate contact inhibition may divide without regard to external signals. Eventually, a tumor forms.

The actions of hormones represent another form of external growth control. Recall that hormones are produced by one set of cells. But hormones exert their effects on other cells, often in distant locations of the body. For example,

growth hormone coordinates the proportional growth of the body. As its name suggests, growth hormone stimulates cells to divide. An excess of growth hormone before puberty results in gigantism. Likewise, a lack of growth hormone produces some types of dwarfism. The most obvious effects of growth hormone show in the long bones of the limbs. But it affects growth all over the body.

5. To solidify your learning about cell division, make a clay model of the process. Your model should show everything listed here. Be prepared to show and explain your model to your teacher.
   a. A starting cell with 2 pairs of chromosomes (see figure 13.13)
   b. DNA synthesis
   c. All the stages of the cell cycle
   d. The contents of the 2 cells that are formed

   You also may wish to view the video segment, "Cell Division" again. Compare the video segment with the diagrams in figures 13.10 and 13.11. This may help you follow the specific events of the cell cycle more easily.

6. Share your model with your partner, naming the different stages of the cell cycle as you go. Use the TSAR strategy to give and receive advice about parts of the models that can be improved.

Figure 13.13
A model of a cell with modeling clay chromosomes.

http://www
Online Resource

HOW TO

SCI LINKS
NSTA

www.scilinks.org

Topic: cell cycle and mitosis
Code: human4E688

Remember, TSAR stands for think, share, advise, and revise. For more information, see *How to Use the Think-Share-Advise-Revise (TSAR) Strategy* in appendix B3.

7. Arrange your model to display the *anaphase stage* of mitosis and use your observations to answer these questions. Write your answers in your science notebook.

   a. What is important about the number and sizes of chromosomes that move to opposite ends of the cell?

   b. How does the genetic information in the 2 groups of chromosomes at each end of the cell compare with each other?

8. Think carefully about how you moved the components of your clay model. In your science notebook, explain why it is important that the following happens.

   a. The chromosomes *duplicate* before mitosis begins.

   b. The chromosomes *line up in single file* during metaphase.

   c. The duplicated chromosomes *separate* during anaphase.

Analysis

One important skill that successful scientists develop is recognizing contradictions between observations and conclusions. They also must be able to recognize the difference between the results of an experiment and an established scientific principle. Sometimes a contradiction shows that either the observation or the conclusion is wrong. In other cases, however, the contradiction is not real. In those cases, scientists may discover that there only appeared to be a contradiction. This is because they did not understand the bigger context of their investigations.

Read the following statements. Pay attention to any contradictions you find between them. Work individually to answer the questions after the statements and record your answers in your science notebook. Your teacher will collect your science notebook to assess your current understanding of development.

Examine these Statements

- Statement 1: Growth takes place during development because of the mitotic division of cells.
- Statement 2: Mitosis results in daughter cells that are genetically identical to one another and to the parent cell that divided.
- Statement 3: During development, cells appear that are different from each other (such as muscle and nerve cells).

1. To the best of your knowledge, is each statement correct as written? Write a brief explanation for each statement to support your answers.

2. What contradiction do you see between statements 2 and 3? In other words, what is it about statement 2 that does not appear to be consistent with statement 3? Explain your answer.

3. Suppose you were a scientist who recognized the contradiction between statements 2 and 3. Describe an experiment that you might attempt that explains the inconsistency. Answer specifically.

Further Challenges

When you want to arrive at the movie theater at the same time as your friend, what do you do? You have to communicate with each other in some way to coordinate your arrival. Perhaps you agree on a time during biology class or you talk on the phone the night before. Now think about your growing body. How does your left arm grow to the same length as your right arm? Why don't you see many people with bodies having noticeably different sizes of ears, eyes, or index fingers? Just as you coordinate activities with your friends, your body coordinates the growth of different body parts as you develop. Read the sidebar, *Coordinating Growth,* to deepen your understanding of this process.

SIDEBAR

ENGLISH   SPANISH

Coordinating Growth

Imagine engineers and mechanics replacing the engines, wings, and cockpit of an airliner *while the plane is airborne.* As difficult and absurd as that may seem, managing the growth of a living organism is like that. Controls on growth operate during every phase of an organism's development. During the embryonic period, rapid cell division produces millions of offspring cells. These cells slowly give shape and substance to an embryo's arms, legs, and internal organs. The growth must be coordinated constantly. This is because an embryo is not like a machine, which does not work until all of its parts are in place. Instead, an

embryo functions from the very moment that it exists. And it keeps functioning even as it constantly changes.

Coordinating growth requires some complex events as an organism develops. For example, because an embryo's cells are alive, they need a regular supply of oxygen and nutrients. Chicken eggs contain a special set of blood vessels that lie just under the shell. These blood vessels also surround and penetrate the yolk. The blood vessels connect to the developing circulatory system of the growing embryo. They carry oxygen that is absorbed across the shell. They also carry nutrients that are absorbed from

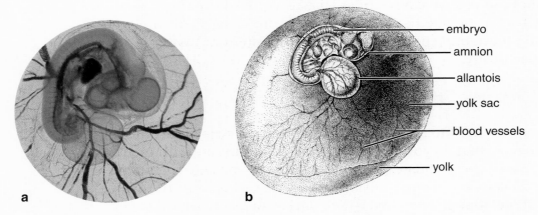

a   b

embryo
amnion
allantois
yolk sac
blood vessels
yolk

Figure 13.14 Which structures are involved in transporting oxygen and nutrients to the embryo and wastes out of the embryo?

the yolk into the body of the embryo where they are needed (see figure 13.14). The umbilical cord and the placenta serve similar functions in the human embryo. They deliver oxygen and nutrients taken from the mother's blood supply.

As an embryo's tissues and organs grow and take shape, its circulatory system also grows and changes. This process is a good illustration of the interaction between internal and external growth controls. Scientists have found that different types of cells divide by mitosis when certain proteins known as **growth factors** are present in the external cellular environment. When the local concentration of the growth factors rises, cells that were not dividing now begin to divide. The division process they follow is directed by signals inside the cell.

For example, as the brain of a vertebrate embryo begins to develop, new brain cells secrete a specific growth factor. This external growth signal promotes internal changes in cells at the tips of nearby blood vessels. These blood vessel cells undergo rapid cell division and grow toward the source of the growth factors. They build a circulatory network to support the new brain tissue. Scientists have discovered a whole set of growth factors that work during embryonic

development and after birth. Typically, these substances have powerful effects even at low concentrations. In addition, these effects are specific to the cells that release the factor and to the tissue that responds. Different tissues may respond to different growth factors.

The constant remodeling, balancing, and regulation of growth continue throughout life. Look again at figure 13.4. Notice how large the newborn boy's head is in proportion to his arms. Then compare the proportions of the newborn with your own (or with those of the young boy in the same figure).

Clearly, your arms and legs *must* have grown much faster than your head. And even after you have achieved your full growth, your cells will still divide in a controlled manner. This means that cells lost through normal wear and tear or through injury are replaced at an appropriate rate. If too little division takes place, injuries go unrepaired. If too much division takes place, a tumor can develop. Scientists still do not understand all the mechanisms involved in the control of cell division. Yet it is becoming increasingly clear that proper regulation happens only when both internal and external mechanisms work together in a coordinated fashion.

Generating Specialized Cells

EXPLORE

EXPLAIN

You have seen that the development of a multicellular organism involves the process of growth. But growth is only half the story of development. Differentiation, the development of specialized cell types, is the other half (see figure 13.15).

Your body, for example, consists of trillions of cells. But those cells include hundreds of different types. Hold your hands up in front of you. Think about how complex they are for a moment. Your fingers and thumbs are different lengths and shapes, capable of thousands of different actions. What about the skin, bone, cartilage, and muscles that make up your hands? These different tissues are packaged together in identical ways, in each hand. There are also hundreds of nerves (bundles of neuron axons) in your hands. These nerves interact with neurons in your spinal cord, which interact with neurons that extend to your brain. Together they form an extensive communications network that offers great sensitivity, precision, and coordination. Now consider the rest of your body: your heart, your brain, your kidneys, and even your big toes. Along with your hands, all of these complicated structures arose from the same single cell.

In this Explore-Explain activity, *Generating Specialized Cells*, you will continue to examine developmental processes. As you work, consider the following questions: "How are the body's different cell types, tissues, and organs formed?" "How can such a wide variety of tissues and organs develop from cells that were originally identical?"

a

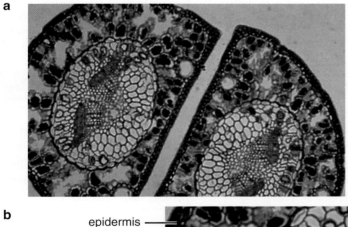

b

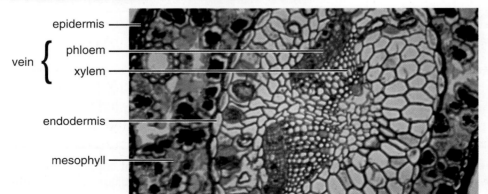

epidermis

vein { phloem

xylem

endodermis

mesophyll

**Figure 13.15
Differentiated tissues in plants.** Both plants and animals have many types of specialized cells. (*a*) How many different tissues can you see in this cross section of pine needles? (*b*) At higher magnification, even more detail is visible. Xylem and phloem function as support and transport tissues. Xylem permits water to move from the roots to the leaves. Phloem, on the other hand, conducts the carbohydrates produced as a result of photosynthesis from the leaves to the stem and roots.

Materials

online resource

PROCESS AND PROCEDURES

1. Observe the video segment, "Cells, Cells, and More Cells." As you watch, make a list of the cell types that are shown and briefly note what those cell types look like.

   As you watch the segment, compare the physical appearance of the cells within specific organisms. Think about what this tells you about development. You may want to organize your observations in a two-column table.

2. What do the observations you made about different cells suggest about the process of development from a single fertilized cell? Write your answer in your science notebook.

3. Examine closely the observations you made of cartilage, epithelium, and brush border cells. Discuss the following questions with your class.

   a. How are these 3 cell types structurally different from one another?

   b. How do these cells compare with one another genetically?

   c. How do your answers in steps 3a and 3b relate to the process of differentiation?

4. Working with your partner, examine the information in figures 13.16 and 13.17 about the cells found in the trachea. In your science

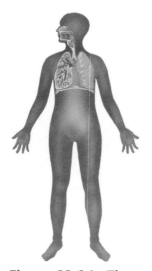

Figure 13.16 The trachea is commonly called the windpipe. It is part of the respiratory system.

Type of cell	Function	DNA	Messenger RNA (mRNA)	Major proteins produced
Goblet cell	Produces mucus	Identical to zygote	mRNA coding for proteins is required for basic cell functioning; also, much mRNA coding is needed for proteoglycans and glycoproteins (complex protein-carbohydrate molecules).	Proteoglycans and glycoproteins, the major types of protein in mucus
Cartilage cell	Produces cartilage	Identical to zygote	mRNA coding for proteins is required for basic cell functioning; also, much mRNA coding is needed for collagen.	Collagen, the major protein in cartilage
Muscle cell	Contracts	Identical to zygote	mRNA coding for proteins is required for basic cell functioning; also, much mRNA coding is needed for actin and myosin.	Actin and myosin, the major proteins in muscle

Figure 13.17 **Cell types found in the human trachea.** The trachea is the tube that connects your nose and mouth to your lungs. It is a tissue made of many cell types, including goblet cells, cartilage cells, and muscle cells. How does a combination of specialized cells enable the trachea to function?

notebook, write down the similarities and the differences among the cell types listed.

> As you examine the information in the table, ask yourself whether the structural differences that you saw among these cells correlate with any molecular differences among them.

5. To deepen your understanding of cell differentiation, read the essay, *Specialized Cells: Identical Genes, Different Gene Expression.* As you read, make notes about possible answers to this question: How does gene expression explain how genetically identical cells become structurally different? After you have finished reading, write a final answer to this question, incorporating specific examples from figure 13.17. Be prepared to share your answer in a class discussion.

Specialized Cells: Identical Genes, Different Gene Expression

Early research into developmental events involved painstaking observations of many types of developing organisms. These observations revealed that all embryos of a particular species go through apparently identical stages in the same sequence. Specific tissues and organs become visible and then functional at specific times. Scientists concluded that developmental changes must be under precise control. We can make the same observation about development that occurs later in life. Although people vary in exactly *when* they reach various stages of life (puberty and old age, for example), most of us go through every stage, and in the same sequence.

These observations raise a question. How are the processes of development regulated and coordinated? In the case of humans, the union of the ovum and the sperm eventually gives rise to an adult made up of trillions of cells. An adult's body continues to change and develop until death. What is it that affects how, where, and when each part of our body develops as it does?

Part of the answer to this question rests in our chromosomes. The 46 chromosomes present in a human zygote (23 from the ovum and 23 from the sperm) contain all the basic instructions needed to produce a complete human. In other words, the basic information by which all cells grow and differentiate is located in the zygote's DNA. Through mitosis, this information is distributed to each offspring cell.

Every cell in a developing organism contains all the genetic instructions for producing a complete organism. Then how do cells become *different* during development? Some human cells, for example, become long and ridged as they develop. They build extended filaments of protein that allow them to contract (muscle cells). Other cells secrete digestive enzymes that can reduce a turkey sandwich and a piece of fruit into useful nutrients (pancreatic cells). Still other cells become flat and scaly looking and produce pigments that absorb ultraviolet light (skin cells). The specialized cells will continue to produce proteins and display functions that are characteristic of that cell type. We don't have to worry that our heart cells suddenly will start growing hair or that our skin cells will start oozing digestive enzymes.

Instead, these cells likely will spend their entire lives working as they always have.

Figure 13.18 shows several types of human cells. If all of these cells have the same genetic information, why do so many different and stable cell types form? The general answer is that different cell types use different subsets of their genes. Signals that are received by a cell during development cause certain genes to turn on and others to turn off. A gene turns on or becomes active when it is transcribed into messenger RNA (mRNA) for protein synthesis. A gene turns off or becomes inactive when it is not transcribed. The particular pattern of on and off genes determines the cell type that a developing cell will become.

As cells become specialized, they use a specific subset of their total genetic information. Therefore, they perform specialized functions and may produce a narrow range of products. A mature skin cell will never send an electrical signal to the brain the way a nerve cell does. The genes required to accomplish this function are not active in the skin cell. Instead of generating electrical signals, the skin cell displays different functions (such as pigmentation) that are encoded by a different subset of genes. The different functions are consistent with the signals that have affected the cell's development.

A great deal of research has focused on understanding the mechanisms of differentiation that turn sets of genes on and off in specific cells. For a long time, scientists have been interested in investigating *how* cells go about differentiating. Initially, scientists worked to answer their questions by manipulating nonhuman embryos.

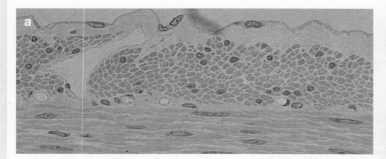

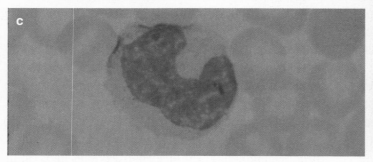

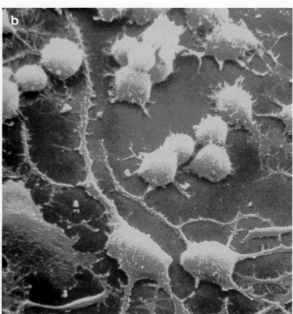

Figure 13.18   Different cells, same DNA. (*a*) Smooth muscle cells (160×). The nearly circular structures near the top of the image are smooth muscle cells in cross section. The long cells at the bottom are in longitudinal section. (*b*) Nerve cells (2,500×). The long cell structure extending toward the top of the photograph from the cell body is an axon. The shorter structures extending downward are dendrites. (*c*) Blood cells (710×). White blood cells such as this monocyte are part of the immune system. What differences do you see among the cells illustrated?

Embryos were shaken, poked at, turned upside down, and treated with chemicals to see how these actions would affect development. The experiments of Wilhelm Roux and Hans Driesch provide good examples of this type of experimental embryology. Today, scientists use more-specific tools to experimentally turn off specific genes and sets of genes and observe the effect on development. The knowledge that scientists have accumulated through more than 100 years of such studies is beginning to answer the central question of differentiation: What processes cause cells to express a specific subset of genes?

One explanation for this question is that the substances *inside* cells differ. The internal makeup of a cell can influence its pattern of gene expression. For example, there may be a substance in one area of a cell's cytoplasm. As a result of cell division, this substance ends up in one offspring cell and not the other. The substance may change the activity of the genes in the cell that received it. Another explanation is that something *outside* the cells differs. A substance secreted by one cell may affect a neighboring cell's pattern of gene expression. In either case, influences from inside or outside the cell may affect the pattern of its gene expression and lead to its specific differentiation.

Experimental results from a wide variety of organisms and laboratories have provided evidence for *both* explanations. In some species, molecules that can regulate gene expression are located in different portions of the zygote's cytoplasm. As mitosis occurs, the division of cytoplasm into offspring cells distributes these regulatory molecules into some cells but not into others. As these molecules begin to influence gene activity, the cells that received them follow one path of development. The cells that did not receive them follow another path. One example of this occurs in early *Drosophila melanogaster* (fruit fly) embryos. The distribution of specific proteins in the embryo affects how it develops a distinct back and front. Figure 13.19 illustrates how differentiation may take place through the mechanism of cytoplasmic regulation.

In other cases, gene products (proteins) released by one group of cells can cause a neighboring group of cells to differentiate in a particular way. Figure 13.20 illustrates this example of outside influence on differentiation, which is known as **induction**. Here, the outpocketing of the brain is an inducing tissue. Molecules secreted by this tissue contact cells that would have become skin tissue and change their developmental path. They are induced

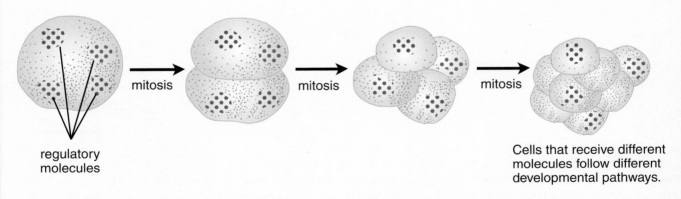

regulatory molecules

mitosis

mitosis

mitosis

Cells that receive different molecules follow different developmental pathways.

Figure 13.19 Cytoplasmic regulation. Regulatory molecules are unequally divided during the development of some organisms. This can lead to different developmental fates for different cells.

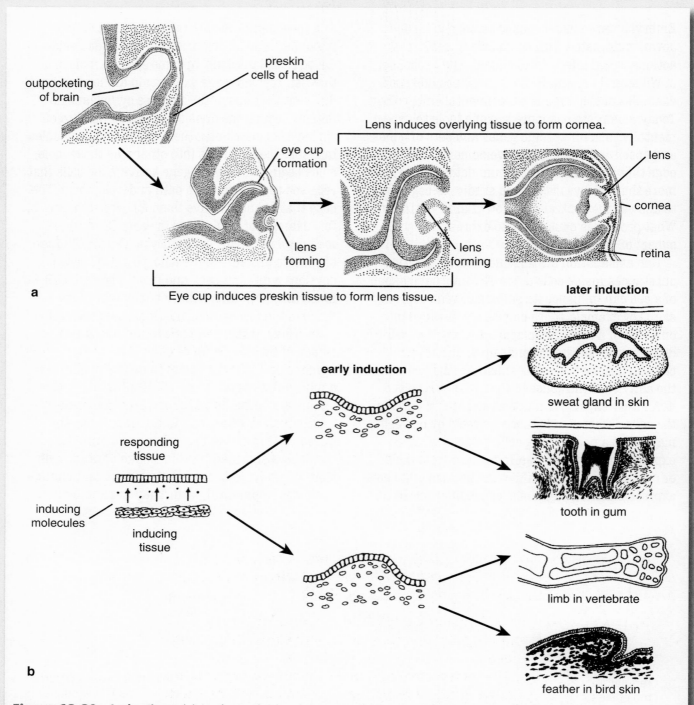

Figure 13.20   **Induction.** (*a*) In the early development of a human's eye, an outpocketing of the brain called the eye cup causes early skin cells of the head to become the lens of the eye. The lens, in turn, causes skin cells to become a cornea. (*b*) Regulatory molecules released by the inducing tissue can affect the responding tissue in different ways.

into becoming eye tissue instead. The development of all human organs and systems, including sweat glands, teeth, and limbs, involves induction.

Development requires a sophisticated system of genetic instructions and controls. What happens when mutations cause these genetic instructions or control systems to change? Sometimes the result is a change in the phenotype of the organism. Across many generations, changes in phenotype within a population can lead to the evolution of a new adaptation or a new species. Evolutionary developmental biologists have made striking progress in this area in the last 20 years. They compare differences in gene expression in the embryos of closely related species or populations. The evidence they collect helps explain the genetic basis for the evolution of different structures. For example, they have identified genes affecting the development of butterfly

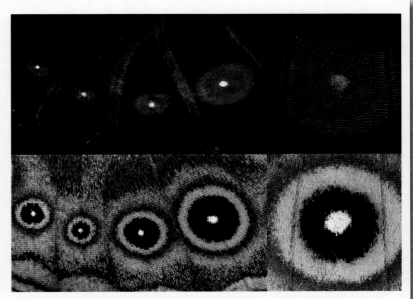

Figure 13.21 **Scientists have developed techniques that allow gene expression to be seen as different regions of color in embryos.** Here, three genes expressed in developing eyespots foreshadow the pattern of spots on adult butterfly wings.

eyespots (figure 13.21), bat wings, and the beaks of Darwin's finches.

Analysis

Review your work in both Explore-Explain activities, *A Start in Development* and *Generating Specialized Cells*, as well as in chapter 11, *Gene Action*. Participate in a class discussion of the following.

1. Explain how genetically identical cells can differentiate into structurally and functionally diverse cells. Describe how this occurs at the molecular level.
2. Write a story from the perspective of a fertilized human egg cell. In your story, explain the different developmental processes that affect how that fertilized egg becomes a baby. Be sure to mention cell division, mitosis, and cell differentiation in your answer.

3. To what extent do you feel that the story you wrote fully explains development? List at least 2 areas of understanding that you would have to know more about to answer this question completely. Explain why this information would be important to explaining the puzzle of how growth and development take place.

Further Challenges

The study of cell differentiation has been important to the area of regenerative medicine. In this field of medicine, doctors try to repair tissue that the body cannot repair by itself. An example is nervous system tissue damaged in spinal cord injuries. To carry out studies in this area, scientists compare the characteristics of differentiated and undifferentiated cells. Undifferentiated cells that can become many different cell types are known as stem cells. However, ethical questions have been raised about the study of stem cells that come from human embryos.

To learn more, read the sidebar, *Stem Cells, Medicine, and Ethics*. Then carry out the following tasks.

1. Identify 2 or 3 questions that you would still like to answer about stem cell research. Search for answers to your questions using resources in the library and the Web.

2. Identify your opinion on this ethical question: Should the government limit funding for studies of stem cells from human embryos? Write down 2 or 3 arguments that you think support your opinion.

   Remember that ethical questions are addressed in a different way from scientific questions. There is no "right answer" to this question, though you should strive to construct an answer that is well reasoned and well supported. As you form your opinion and supporting arguments, it may be helpful to review your notes from the essay, *Ethical Analysis*, which you read in the chapter 6 (*Human Homeostasis: Health and Disease*) Elaborate activity, *What's the Risk?*

3. Write a report on your research and opinion. You will know you have written a complete report when it achieves the following criteria.

   a. Describes what stem cells are and gives examples of their functions in embryonic and adult animals

   b. Describes the ethical dilemma of using embryonic stem cells from humans in scientific research

   c. States your answer to question 2, provides supporting arguments, and makes a specific recommendation for how government funding should be provided or limited for stem cell research

Stem Cells, Medicine, and Ethics

The evolution of differentiated cell types was a key event. From different cell types, complex organ systems evolved. The most complex of these are found in the vertebrates. However, such complexity comes with a downside: vertebrate tissues have a limited ability to regenerate. This is an example of an **evolutionary trade-off**, a limitation that goes hand in hand with an evolutionary advantage. In other words, you can't evolve something for nothing.

In comparison, many organisms can regenerate large parts of their bodies (figure 13.22). They include the fungi, plants, and many invertebrate animals. Wouldn't it be fantastic if the human body could naturally regrow a finger? What if your spinal cord could reconnect if severed? What if your body could reverse a degenerative disease? Because we lack the capacity to do this naturally, we turn to medical science. Regenerating tissue in the laboratory has the potential to help.

Development holds clues about how to reverse permanent injuries. After all, each of our bodies began as a single undifferentiated cell. From this cell, all of our differentiated cell types developed. These cells responded to their cellular environment. They also responded to specific genetic cues. If we

© Dreamstime/John Sfondilias

Figure 13.22 Many organisms can regenerate new parts throughout their lives: (*a*) a starfish regrowing arms, (*b*) a lizard regenerating its tail, and (*c*) a tree growing a new branch.

understood those cues and could reproduce them, we might be able to differentiate cell types in the laboratory.

In fact, developmental biologists have determined many genetic cues required to differentiate a cell. They use a technique for maintaining cells outside the body in petri dishes. This technique is known as **cell culture** (also known as cell lines; see figure 13.23). Cell culturing allows for much medical progress. For example, it is used in vaccine development, the study of cancer, and bone marrow transplants. Cell culturing techniques also led to tissue engineering. For example, scientists can now grow skin grafts using cells cultured from a patient's own healthy skin. The grafts can be used to repair skin damaged by burns or trauma. The patient's immune system recognizes the graft as self tissue and does not attack it, as it would with a skin graft from a different person.

Human skin cells are relatively easy to culture, however. This is because the skin is one of the few organs of the human body that naturally self-repairs. It is more challenging to generate tissues and organs that show little or no self-repair after damage.

These include the heart, limbs, and nervous system tissue. In meeting this challenge, scientists have focused on harnessing the body's natural processes of cell differentiation. In the 1960s, two Canadian scientists named Ernest McCulloch and James Till cultured **stem cells** from mouse bone marrow. These undifferentiated cells divided continuously by mitosis. They also were able to differentiate into different cell types. Scientists discovered that when stem cells divide, one daughter cell remains as a stem cell while the other daughter cell is committed to differentiating.

Over the next few decades, stem cells were cultured from other sources. The sources include human umbilical cord blood (1978), mouse embryos (1981), and human embryos (1998). Stem cells have also been cultured from human tissues including blood, skin, baby teeth, and testes (2000s) and from amniotic fluid (2007). In recent years, scientists used adult stem cells to generate differentiated liver cells. Cartilage cells generated from adult stem cells were used to treat knee injuries. In a striking study, stem cells from mouse

a

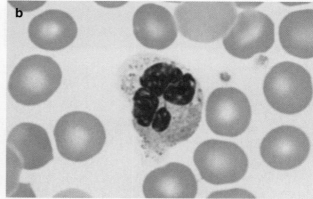
b

© iStockphoto/Mando19

Figure 13.23 Human cell lines can be maintained in (*a*) culture dishes for long periods of time, including (*b*) white blood cells.

embryos were used to produce neurons. When injected into paralyzed rats, these neurons partially restored the rats' ability to move.

Scientists distinguish between stem cells that are from embryos (**embryonic stem cells**) and all others. Stem cells from the tissues of adults or children, including umbilical cord blood, baby teeth, and skin, are known as **adult stem cells**. Embryonic stem cells can develop into hundreds of cell types. Directing their differentiation into one specific cell type can be difficult. Human embryonic stem cells are usually taken from surplus embryos generated by fertility clinics. Usually, the harvesting of embryonic stem cells destroys the donor embryo. However, in 2008, a team developed a nonlethal technique for harvesting human embryonic stem cells.

Adult stem cells can be more difficult to isolate than embryonic stem cells. They differentiate into fewer different cell types. What they differentiate into depends on their tissue of origin. However, in 2007, two teams of researchers reported that they produced adult skin stem cells that can generate nearly any other cell type. Adult stem cells that are generated from an individual patient carry some distinct benefits. Because they are self tissue, they aren't rejected by an individual's immune system. However, the techniques that are used to reverse differentiation in adult stem cells can lead the cells to become cancerous.

The use of human embryonic stem cells in research is controversial. Opponents argue that destroying a human embryo to harvest the cells is unethical. They also point out that adult stem cells provide a good substitute. Proponents argue that the human embryos are not created for research use. But because the embryos are by-products of fertility treatments, it is ethical to put them to use. They also argue that science should not be limited by the presence of a substitute. They say the benefits of researching embryonic stem cells could be different from the benefits of researching adult stem cells. The ethical dilemma around embryonic stem cell research has led many countries to develop policies about it. In 1995, the U.S. Congress passed a law keeping the federal government from funding any research that resulted in the destruction of a human embryo. In 2001, President George W. Bush revised the law, allowing research on existing human embryonic cell cultures. However, the executive order maintained a ban on funding research leading to new human embryonic stem cell lines. In 2009, President Barack Obama reversed course, allowing funding to be allocated for research on any human embryonic stem cell line.

The dilemma over embryonic stem cell research is an ethical one. Because of this, it is an issue for scientists, policy makers, and citizens to resolve together. In many countries, stem cell research policies will affect the pace of science. However, there is no question that research will continue to progress at a galloping pace worldwide. There are many medical therapies that stem cell research may lead to. They include generating artificial organs, reversing paralysis and neural degenerative disease, and repairing the damage caused by heart attacks and strokes. Certainly, progress in these areas will be warmly welcomed by patients.

ELABORATE

Development Gone Awry

© iStockphoto/emyerson

Figure 13.24 Early prenatal care helps assure healthy development during gestation.

You have seen that the growth of cells and their differentiation into specialized tissues are highly regulated events. In this Elaborate activity, you will investigate how sensitive that regulation is. You will also look at what can happen if errors occur during development. A human embryo, for example, can develop improperly if certain environmental influences disrupt the regulation of growth or differentiation (figure 13.24). Similarly, an embryo's growth and development can proceed incorrectly if its genetic plan contains harmful mutations.

Developmental errors are not limited to the growing embryo. They can happen even after birth. For example, sometimes changes in hormonal conditions alter the pattern of growth that normally would take place as an organism matures. Likewise, sometimes body cells accumulate mutations that cause the cells to grow unrestrained. Such uncontrolled growth is known as cancer. As you begin *Development Gone Awry*, apply your understanding of the processes of human development. Consider situations in which human development has gone awry.

Materials (per person)

resource materials that include news articles, essays, and video material
video or audio equipment for recording and playing (optional)
online resource

PROCESS AND PROCEDURES

Imagine that you are a doctor who is handling a case that involves an error in development. Developmental errors fall into two general categories. These are birth defects and cancer (figure 13.25). Follow the steps to write a conversation in which you discuss the disorder with your patient or his or her family and describe what can be done about it. In this conversation, you (the doctor) will need to explain how developmental processes (growth, differentiation, or both processes) have been altered to produce the disorder.

1. Work individually. Choose a disorder to be the topic of your script. Good ways to identify possible topics include the following:
   - Find a news event that relates to either birth defects or cancer. Some birth defects you may have heard of include cleft palate and spina bifida. You may find interesting news bulletins on the Web (be sure to select reputable sites), in newspapers, and in publications such as *Science News* and *Discover.*
   - Interview a person who has experienced a birth defect or cancer or someone who has had a family member with a birth defect or cancer.
2. Discuss your idea with your teacher. Ask him or her to approve your topic and help you identify likely resources where you can find more information.

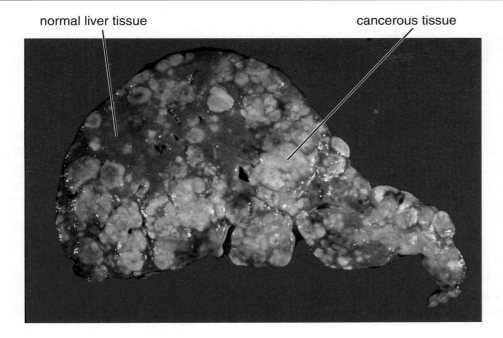

normal liver tissue   cancerous tissue

Figure 13.25 Liver cancer. The extensive cancerous growths in this liver are the result of metastasis. The cancer began in the lungs.

If you are having trouble deciding on a topic, it may help you to read ahead the criteria for a good script or the essays for this activity. The criteria and essays are listed in steps 3 and 4.

3. Using the information you collect, begin making notes in your science notebook about your project. Your final product will be the script of a conversation between a doctor (you) and a patient (or family of a patient) suffering from the disorder you chose in step 1. Your script needs to meet the following criteria.
   a. Describes in detail the disorder you chose
   b. Explains the probable role (if any) of environmental factors in producing the disorder
   c. Explains the probable role (if any) of genetic factors in producing the disorder
   d. Describes how growth, differentiation, or both, have been affected, and at which stage in development it occurred (if this is known for the disorder)
   e. Describes the long-term effects of the disorder
   f. Describes any treatments and how they work to affect the disorder
4. To deepen your knowledge of the mechanisms that can cause birth defects and cancer, read the essays, *Development and Birth Defects* and *Cancer: Unregulated Growth.* As you read, make notes in your science notebook about information that could be incorporated into your script.

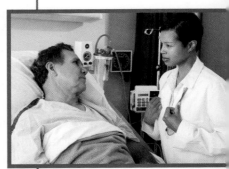

© Dreamstime/ Monkeybusinessimages

Development and Birth Defects

ENGLISH SPANISH

The parents wait while the doctor examines their daughter immediately after she is born. The mother is physically exhausted from hours of labor. The father is mentally exhausted from the tension of waiting and supporting her efforts. They both eagerly wait to hold their baby. The doctor smiles and hands the child to the mother. Everything seems to be fine.

Reproduction does not always go so smoothly. Despite the highly regulated and precise expression of the genetic instructions for development, sometimes things go wrong. Observations of development in nonhuman animals show that many fertilized eggs fail to develop completely. Many human pregnancies result in **miscarriage**, which is a natural, spontaneous abortion of the fetus. Most miscarriages occurring within the first three months of human gestation are related to some genetic abnormality that interferes with development. Up to 20 percent of all pregnancies may end in miscarriage.

However, not all developmental errors result in miscarriage. Each year, about 3 percent of all babies born in the United States have significant problems. Many of these are developmental problems. Often, parents feel guilty about the challenges their newborns face, though many problems are genetic in nature. For other problems, the causes are not well understood. But in some cases, the specific source of a developmental problem can be determined.

Developmental problems can be categorized into two general groups: those that result from errors in the genetic plan and those that result from disruptions in the expression of that plan. In the first category, certain mutations exist in the DNA inherited from either parent. Mutations can also occur in the embryo itself. These mutations can disrupt the growth and differentiation of the embryonic cells, resulting in physical, mental, or both types of challenges in a newborn. Exposure to a mutagenic agent such as radiation can disrupt development in an embryo by causing changes in the DNA (see figure 13.26). When your dental assistant takes an X-ray of your teeth, he or she covers the rest of your body with a leaded apron to block the radiation. Though it's quite small, the radiation level of a dental X-ray presents a risk, especially to pregnant women. Radiation damage to the DNA of developing ova and sperm threatens the future offspring of both men and women.

In the second category, developmental errors can be the result of a disruption in the *expression* of genetic material. A disruption can happen even when the genetic material does not have mutations. Because development is highly regulated, there are many points at which a misstep could have lasting effects. The major organ systems become established during the first three months of development. Early pregnancy, therefore, is a time when the embryo is particularly vulnerable to toxic substances. Exposure to certain chemicals can interrupt tissues from forming properly. The uterus and placenta provide some physical and immune protections for the growing embryo (see figure 13.27). However, toxic substances and even some pathogens that enter the mother's blood supply can reach the embryo through the placenta.

One of the most tragic examples of this vulnerability happened during the early 1960s. An unusually large number of extremely malformed babies were born in Western Europe, Japan, Canada, and Australia. Medical scientists determined that all of the mothers had taken a mild sedative known as thalidomide. Thalidomide was prescribed to help control nausea due to pregnancy. The drug had produced almost no side effects in the mothers. Its devastating effects on the embryo happened only when the drug was taken between the third and fifth weeks of pregnancy. Even a single dose of thalidomide taken during the

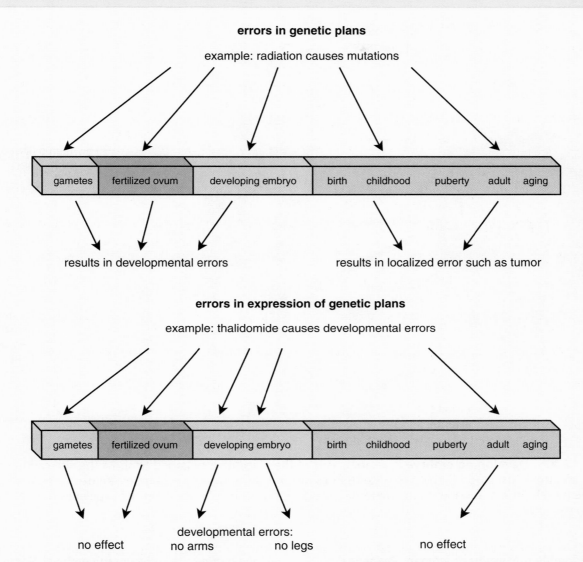

Figure 13.26 **Developmental stages at which errors can take place.** Developing humans are vulnerable to developmental problems at different times and in different ways. Notice that changes may arise from a combination of genetic and environmental factors. Errors can be alterations in the genetic plan for development (in a gamete or in a developing embryo). Or errors can be disruptions in the expression of that plan.

third week of pregnancy resulted in improperly formed or missing arms in the children. As shown in figure 13.28a, exposure during the fourth week caused malformed or missing legs. Other abnormalities were mapped to other periods of development.

By the time doctors realized the effects of thalidomide on development, many children had already been born with serious problems.

In the United States, the Food and Drug Administration (FDA) did not approve the use

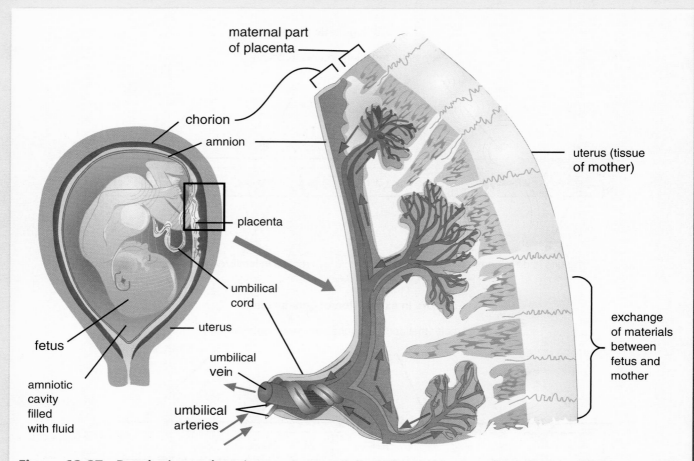

Figure 13.27 Developing embryo in uterus. Part of the placenta is enlarged to show the circulation of the mother and the fetus. Blood in the two systems does not mix. But nutrients and gases are exchanged. They cross the membranes that separate the maternal blood supply in the placenta and the capillaries that deliver blood to the fetus.

of thalidomide for pregnant women. Frances O. Kelsey, a medical officer at the FDA, examined the results of clinical trials on the use of the drug. She decided that there had not been enough testing to conclude that thalidomide did not cause birth defects. She refused to approve this drug for pregnant women. As a result, few children in the United States were born with severe limb defects due to the use of this drug.

This example demonstrates that a developing embryo is not fully protected by the uterus and placenta. Commonly used drugs also can do

serious harm to the developing embryo. Some nonprescription drugs such as aspirin may increase the risk of miscarriage. Diet pills that contain dextroamphetamine have been implicated as a possible cause of birth defects when taken at particular stages of pregnancy.

A mother's exposure to cigarette smoke and alcohol damages a developing embryo. Among mothers who smoke, the effect of nicotine on blood circulation results in generally weakened infants with low birth weights. The developing brain is particularly sensitive to damage from alcohol.

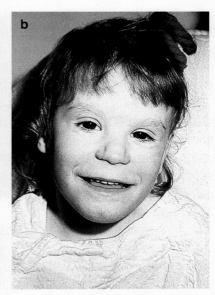

Figure 13.28 (*a*) **The effects of thalidomide on leg development.** (*b*) **Child affected by fetal alcohol syndrome.** Facial abnormalities and mental retardation are typical of children damaged in utero by alcohol.

Amounts of alcohol that an adult can tolerate with limited damage can have an extreme effect on the embryo. Scientists do not know for certain whether there is a minimum amount of alcohol that the mother can drink without harming the baby. Even limited alcohol intake appears to contribute large effects. Many women refrain from drinking any alcohol during pregnancy to protect their unborn children. Damage to a child caused by the mother's alcohol consumption is called fetal alcohol syndrome (FAS). Children who have FAS usually have low birth weights and flattened faces with thin upper lips (see figure 13.28b). They also exhibit a range of mental, behavioral, and developmental problems. These may include mental retardation, hyperactivity, and developmental delays. FAS is the leading known cause of mental retardation in the United States.

You have seen that environmental hazards threaten the health of a newborn in several ways. The hazards may mutate genes in the gametes of the parents or interfere with the expression of normal genes before birth. Some of these errors are beyond the control of the parents. Others are due to their lifestyle choices.

Cancer: Unregulated Growth

A pediatrician invites two parents into her office to discuss the physical examination she has just made of their seven-month-old daughter. The child looks pale and is terribly weak. She has a fever, and the doctor can feel an enlarged spleen.

The doctor tells the parents that the baby will have to be hospitalized for tests to determine which of several possibilities explains their daughter's condition. One possibility is leukemia. As they sit down, the mother looks the doctor squarely in the eyes and asks, "Is leukemia the worst thing it could be?"

"No," the doctor replies. "Leukemia is the best thing it could be."

The parents are shocked because they are old enough to remember a time when leukemia, like almost any cancer, meant certain death. However, they are reassured to learn that many forms of childhood leukemia now can be treated. In fact, the likelihood of success for these treatments is relatively high.

When the tests are done, the diagnosis comes back: their daughter Lauren does have leukemia. Fortunately, the pediatrician also specializes in treating cancer. The doctor treats Lauren with chemotherapy to control the growth of cancerous blood cells.

As you might guess from her photograph (see figure 13.29), Lauren is now a healthy and energetic seven-year-old, free of leukemia. Now her parents worry about whether she is careful while riding her bicycle or hiking in the mountains.

Certainly, pregnancy represents a particularly vulnerable period for development. However, developmental errors can happen throughout life. **Cancer**, one such condition, occurs most often in mature adults. It can occur in any type of tissue. Some of the more familiar forms of cancer include skin cancer, breast cancer, prostate cancer, lung cancer, and leukemia. The name "cancer" comes from the Latin word for crab. Many years ago,

physicians noticed that cancerous growths were often shaped like crabs. The growths had leglike appendages extending from a central mass. Cancer results from cells that grow uncontrollably. Most cancer cells do not show specialized characteristics. Cancerous cells are not inhibited from dividing by contact with other cells (contact inhibition), as normal cells would be. They pile up on one another, forming a tumor.

Figure 13.29 Lauren, a leukemia survivor, is now a healthy, energetic child.

Scavenger cells of the immune system often destroy cancerous cells before they grow into a tumor. However, if some cancerous cells escape the immune system's defenses, they can quickly become too numerous for the immune system to control. A tumor that grows may be benign or malignant. *Benign* tumors remain localized in one area. The cells of *malignant* tumors release enzymes that enable them to invade other tissues. Figure 13.30 illustrates how cancer cells can spread from one part of the body to another. This process is called **metastasis**. It can result in the production of new tumors in additional parts of the body and damage to many organs.

For many years, scientists and physicians have tried to understand the causes of cancer and find effective ways to treat it. Some scientists conduct basic research. That is, they do research studies that explore the cellular and biochemical mechanisms that cause uncontrolled growth or

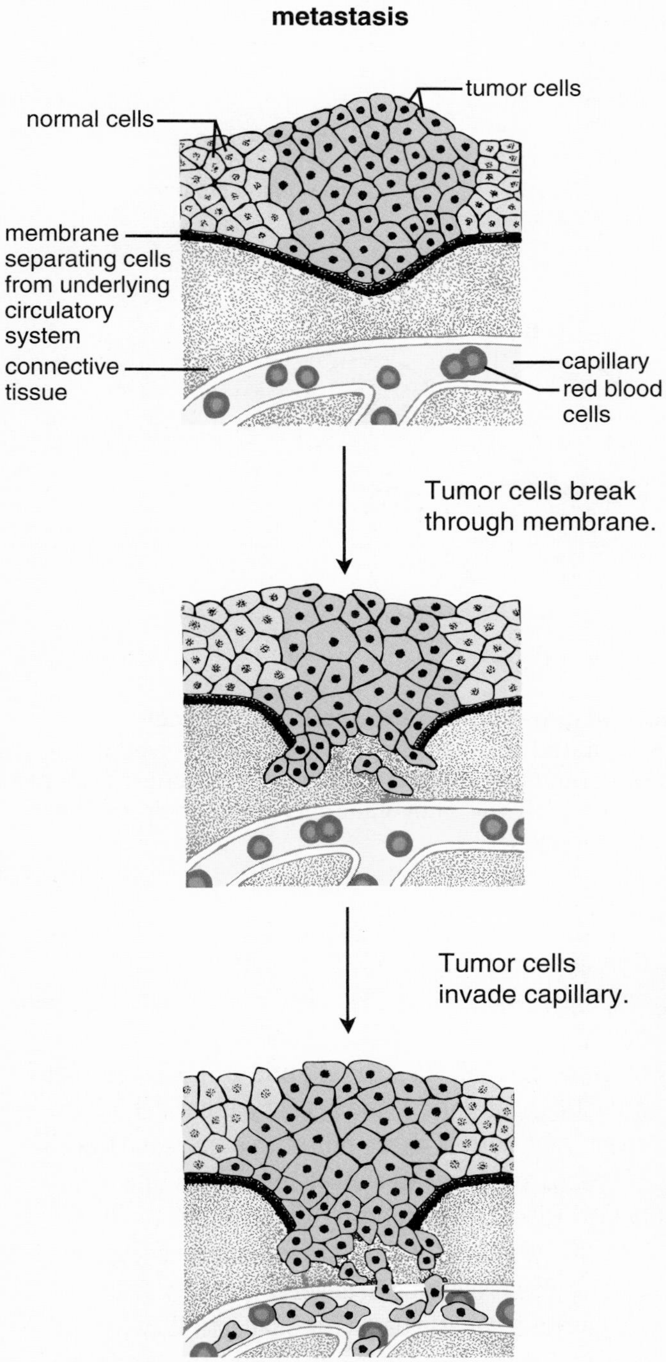

metastasis

normal cells

tumor cells

membrane separating cells from underlying circulatory system

connective tissue

capillary

red blood cells

Tumor cells break through membrane.

Tumor cells invade capillary.

Figure 13.30 Metastasis involves the dangerous spread of cancer cells from a localized tumor to new areas in the body.

malignancy. Other scientists carry out applied research. They use the knowledge gained from basic research to search for new cancer treatments and preventive measures. Through the combination of basic and applied research, we now have both a better understanding of the causes of cancer and better methods for treating it.

In 1911, a young scientist named Peyton Rous performed an experiment to investigate the cause of cancer. He crushed cancerous cells from a chicken tumor and filtered the material. Injecting the filtered liquid into healthy chickens caused them to develop tumors. Today, we know that the liquid contained a virus called *Rous sarcoma virus* (refer to figure 13.31). This virus can infect animal cells and transform them into cancer cells. It took more than 40 years for the scientific community to fully accept this idea. During that time, many other cancer-causing viruses, such as the human papillomavirus, were identified. Fifty years after publishing his work, Rous was awarded a Nobel Prize.

Genetic and biochemical experiments in the 1970s and 1980s led scientists to discover an

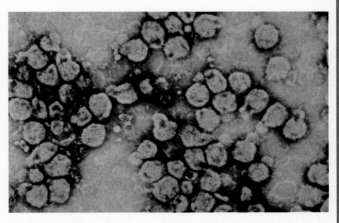

Figure 13.31 *Rous sarcoma viruses* (85,000×). While most viruses (such as the influenza virus) do not cause cancer, the *Rous sarcoma virus* does. Understanding the ways that some viruses cause cancer helps scientists and physicians find ways to prevent and treat cancer.

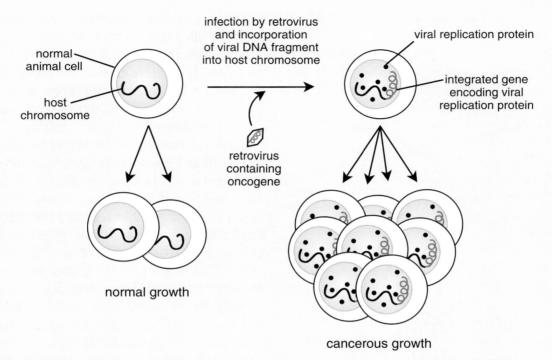

Figure 13.32   Cancer can result from alterations in normal genes whose products regulate cell growth. It can also result from infection by certain viruses. Mutated versions of genes that are involved in the development of cancer are called oncogenes. Oncogenes can originate from changes in normal genes. They can also enter the cell from the genetic material of an invading virus. How might evolutionary theory help explain the similarity between the DNA sequences of viral genes and oncogenes?

unexpected connection between normal cells and the viruses that cause cancer. Surprisingly, genes within many cancer-causing viruses nearly match normal genes found in animal DNA. Furthermore, many of the nearly matching animal genes code for necessary regulatory proteins. Regulatory proteins are gene products that affect normal cell growth (see figure 13.32). They may also affect how cells stick together, also known as adhesion. Regulatory genes that have been mutated by a virus or in other ways that can lead to cancer are called **oncogenes**. Oncogenes are abnormally active versions of normal regulatory genes. Abnormal activity results in abnormal division or altered adhesive properties of the host cell. This can result in a normal cell transforming into a cancer cell.

A number of mutant genes have been identified that appear to play a role in human cancer. For example, researchers identified a mutation in a gene on chromosome 17 (*BRCA1*) and another on chromosome 13 (*BRCA2*). *BRCA1* and *BRCA2* stand for breast cancer gene 1 and breast cancer gene 2, respectively. Both of these mutations increase the risk of breast and ovarian cancer in women. One clue helped researchers identify these mutant genes. The clue was finding that breast cancer occurred among close relatives in several families. This suggested a genetic basis for susceptibility to this cancer. Researchers discovered that the product of the normal *BRCA1* and *BRCA2* genes helps suppress cell growth. Altered genes release this brake on cell growth. The researchers also discovered that both men and women have these genes. Because of this, either the mother or the father can pass down the mutated genes. They also noted, however, that only about 1 in 10 breast cancer cases involves inherited, altered genes. This means that 90 percent of all breast cancers are *not* due to inherited mutations, but instead are due to so-called spontaneous mutations that arise in the individual. Furthermore, some inherited breast cancers involve inherited genes other than *BRCA1* or *BRCA2*.

Genetic testing for *BRCA1* and *BRCA2* simply requires taking a blood sample. Genetic testing raises many questions, however. Who should be tested? Should insurance cover the cost of the test? Should the insurance company then be entitled to know the results? How will the person react to the knowledge that he or she has inherited the gene? Inheriting the altered *BRCA1* or *BRCA2* genes does not guarantee that the disease will occur. Rather, these altered genes increase the *possibility* of developing cancer. One, or more likely several, additional mutations may be needed for cancer to occur. A healthy immune system may also offset the development of cancer.

A similar sequence of mutations is probably required to cause cancer in a person who has not inherited a mutated gene. Cigarette smoke, for example, contains several compounds that greatly increase the risk of cancer. Nicotine and other compounds produce cancer-causing mutations in DNA. In addition, tar and other components of cigarette smoke impair the action of the immune system in the lungs and the esophagus. If the immune system can no longer destroy transformed cells effectively, the risk of developing cancer increases. Sunbathing exposes skin cells to ultraviolet (UV) radiation, which damages DNA. Mutations to the genes that control the cell cycle may result in skin cancer.

As science builds an understanding of the mechanisms that underlie cancer, our culture's view of cancer has changed. People now understand the need to avoid behaviors that either damage the immune system or increase the risk of transforming cells. Using sunblock helps avoid damaging UV radiation and limits the risk of skin cancer. The choice not to smoke greatly reduces the risk of lung cancer (as well as heart disease and emphysema).

Not all forms of cancer can be avoided. Advancements in medical technology, however, have helped make many types of cancer treatable and, in some cases, curable. One treatment involves removing the cancerous tissue surgically. The success of this treatment relies on early detection, while a tumor is still localized. Technologies such as magnetic resonance imaging (MRI), mammography (figure 13.33), and ultrasound offer nonsurgical methods of searching for tumors while they are still small. Low-tech methods such as breast self-exams also are valuable for early detection. Finding a small breast tumor early increases survival rates to nearly 90 percent. Late detection drops survival rates to about 10 percent.

Other approaches for treating cancer rely on therapies that kill potentially cancerous cells. Unfortunately, it is difficult to limit the damage caused by these therapies to only the cancer cells. The challenge of these therapies is to kill more cancer cells than healthy ones. Radiation therapy does this by focusing radiation only on the cancerous tissue. Chemotherapy uses toxic chemicals that specifically kill dividing cells. This strategy relies on the fact that cancer cells divide more often than most normal cells. Some exceptions are normal cells that divide rapidly, such as hair follicle cells and the cells that line the intestinal tract. That is why patients who undergo chemotherapy frequently lose their hair and experience nausea and vomiting. The immune system also may be impaired temporarily by chemotherapy. Researchers continue to search for therapies that target cancer cells more specifically and that have fewer side effects.

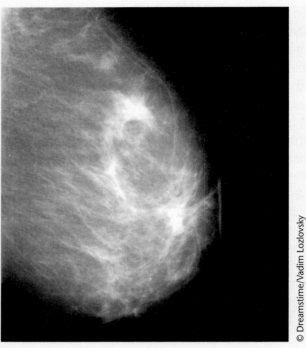

© Dreamstime/Vadim Lozlovsky

Figure 13.33 **Mammography is a type of X-ray technology.** It is used to detect breast cancer. Do you know of other technologies that help to detect or treat cancer?

5. Review the information you have collected and the criteria listed in step 3. Do you have enough information to begin writing your script? If not, write out questions you still need to answer and identify additional resources to consult. Consult with your teacher if you are struggling to find a piece of information.

6. Using the most-relevant information you have collected, write your final script.

> Assume that the patient or the family members of the patient are just learning of the diagnosis and are struggling to deal with it. Your goal is to explain (1) what the disorder is, (2) how it came about (the biological basis), and (3) what can be done about it, if anything. Present the information in a way that meets the criteria listed above, but also in a way that seems realistic. Imagine what questions the patient or family members might ask and how the doctor would respond. Your teacher will tell you if you are to submit your script in writing. You might enlist the help of other students and perform it for your class. Another option is to record your script on video or audio.

Analysis

Your study should have convinced you that development involves the expression of a genetic plan within a set of environmental conditions. These conditions can influence and modify the plan's execution. Write a response in your science notebook to the following questions. After you have written your answers, join the class in a discussion of this topic.

1. Do personal choices influence an individual's risk of developing cancer or causing birth defects? Explain your response.
2. Give 3 examples of developmental errors that scientists believe are largely or entirely genetic in origin.
3. Give 3 examples of developmental errors that scientists believe are largely or entirely environmental in origin.
4. Give 3 examples of developmental errors that scientists believe result from both genetic and environmental causes.
5. Is it possible for a person to make choices that could result in environmentally induced developmental errors? Explain and support your answer with an example.

Development in Your Critter

EVALUATE

How many arms and legs do humans have? Now, how many limbs do oak trees have? You can see from this simple comparison that different species show qualitative differences in their developmental patterns. The basic processes of development are essentially the same in all multicellular species, but the results vary greatly.

If you took a snapshot of an outdoor scene, you would record a moment in the lifetime of a variety of organisms. Some of those organisms likely would be in different developmental stages. For example, in springtime you might see trees with new, bright green leaves, adult animals foraging for food, and a caterpillar eating a leaf to build up its energy stores before changing into a moth. In the diversity captured by such a snapshot, you would see many different developmental stages.

In this Evaluate activity, *Development in Your Critter*, you will apply your knowledge of developmental processes and patterns to a new challenge. You will describe a developmental scheme for the critter that you adopted in chapter 3, *Products of Evolution: Unity and Diversity*. This will be your opportunity to show what you have learned up to this point. Keep in mind that how you apply your knowledge to explain your critter's processes of growth and development will help your teacher determine how much you have accomplished.

Materials (per person)

descriptions and diagrams from your previous critter work
resource materials about developmental stages

PROCESS AND PROCEDURES

1. Summarize what you have learned about how the body's tissues and organs are formed. Write your summary in your science notebook.

   Keep in mind that development involves much more than just getting bigger.

2. To broaden your perspective on development in different organisms, read the essay, *Patterns of Development*. As you read, consider the developmental stages that you might see in your critter and in one other multicellular organism (figure 13.34). Identify as many significant developmental events or stages as you can that might take place in the lifetime of those 2 organisms. Record them in your science notebook. Provide specific examples to illustrate your list.

   As you generate your list, ask yourself when each event typically takes place and what each event or stage accomplishes for the organism. For example, what does flowering accomplish in the developmental pattern of flowering plants?

3. Obtain a copy of the handout *Growth and Differentiation in Your Critter Rubric* from your teacher. Study the criteria. Participate in a class discussion about the criteria for this project.

4. Consult resources that your teacher provides and resources on the Web in order to learn more about your critter's developmental stages. As you accumulate information, make notes in your science notebook.

   Some resources may refer to an organism's development as its "life history" or "life cycle." Use all of these terms as you search for information.

Figure 13.34 Giant water bugs. These male water bugs (*Abedus indentatus*) are caring for the eggs that will produce the next generation. What developmental stages will the offspring pass through before becoming adults?

Think of development as a series of important events that take place during the life of an organism. Some of these events, such as fertilization and death, occur for almost all multicellular organisms. The same is true for cell division and cell differentiation.

Other developmental events are found to occur only in *some* organisms. In fact, development is remarkably diverse. For example, trees never completely stop growing. Biologists say that organisms such as these have indeterminate growth. Other organisms, such as humans, stop growing at some point during their lives. (At least, we stop getting *taller*.) These organisms have determinate growth.

Consider the spectacular growth of the giant sequoia. These huge trees begin life as tiny seeds that weigh only 6 mg. Successful seedlings grow rapidly. Young sequoias, at about 100 years of age, begin producing seeds. At this age, they are about the size of typical pine trees. Healthy sequoias normally attain their full heights at about 1,000 years. They would grow even taller except that they tend to lose their growing tips to lightning. Even so, the 2,500-year-old General Sherman tree at Sequoia National Park in California continues to produce cones, seeds, new wood, leaves, and branches each year. The amount of new mass produced each year by this tree (and others like it) equals the wood of a tree 18 m (59 ft) tall and 0.5 m (about 1.5 ft) in diameter. Other plants such as tomatoes and cucumbers show a similar, if not so spectacular, pattern of continued growth.

Plants grow continuously because they have clusters of undifferentiated cells called **meristems**. Cell division in the meristems located near the tips of branches and roots produces a constant supply of new cells. The cells can differentiate into new structures. Meristem tissue can be removed from a plant to produce a clone. Figure 13.35 illustrates development in a growing plant.

Some animals continue growing for as long as they live. Examples include many types of invertebrates, most types of fish and reptiles, and some mammals. This growth, however, usually slows greatly once the animals attain sexual maturity. Most birds and mammals grow to a relatively defined size.

Other organisms undergo **metamorphosis**. Organisms that undergo metamorphosis start life with one body plan. Later, the organism develops a quite different body plan. In most cases, metamorphosis must take place before the organism is able to reproduce. Metamorphosis occurs in many species of amphibians, such as frogs. Metamorphosis also takes place in a number of invertebrates, such as insects and echinoderms (see the sea urchins in figure 13.36).

Reproduction is the final test of an organism's developmental plan. Developmental patterns that ensure survival and sexual maturity are maintained by natural selection. In contrast, developmental plans that do not assure reproduction are not maintained. In this way, the developmental patterns of species respond to the forces of evolution just as any other characteristic might.

The diversity of development that exists gives rise to an even greater diversity of adult organisms. This observation brings us to one of the major questions about development. What can studies of development reveal about evolution?

We have already begun to answer this question. We have seen that all development involves cell division and cell differentiation. These similar processes reflect the evolutionary relatedness of all life. In addition, we can identify other evolutionary patterns. For example, early embryos of animals have a similar form. The form consists of cells grouped around an internal cavity. As figure 13.37 shows, the exact shape of the cavity varies with the species. In more closely related animals, such as all vertebrates, subsequent developmental

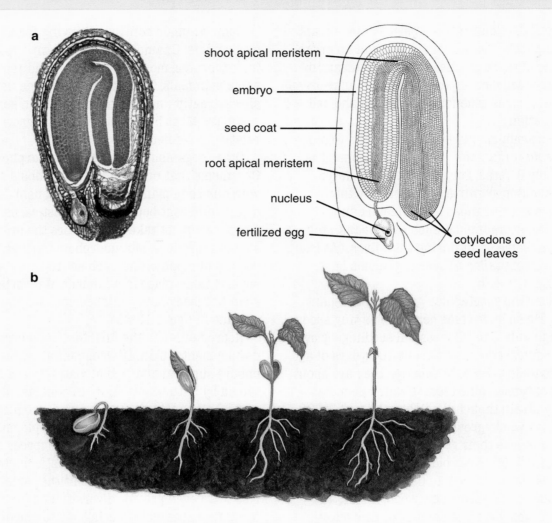

a

shoot apical meristem

embryo

seed coat

root apical meristem

nucleus

fertilized egg

cotyledons or seed leaves

b

Figure 13.35　Development in a flowering plant. (*a*) When pollen grains, which contain sperm cells, come into contact with the female reproductive organs of a flower, fertilization of an egg cell can take place. The zygote then grows and develops into an embryo. In a seed (as shown here), the embryo has temporarily stopped developing. Seeds are well adapted for survival. Many can survive being eaten and eliminated. (*b*) Under favorable environmental conditions, a seed can germinate. When this happens, development resumes. A new plant develops from the embryo. A root develops from the root apical meristem in the embryo. The cotyledons then help provide food for the plant until the leaves develop.

stages also show some similarities. In closely related vertebrates, such as mammals, the developmental similarities are even more obvious.

Such observations suggest that vertebrate embryos share a general developmental plan. Modifications of this plan generate distinctive features.

For example, birds have modified scales that develop into feathers. Mammals have modified scales that develop into fur. There are many questions about how evolution leads to the modification of development: Exactly what types of modifications are possible? How might these changes result in a changed

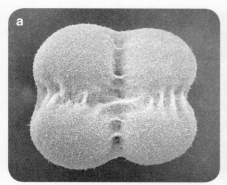

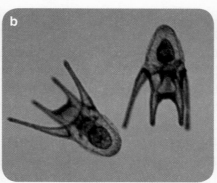

Figure 13.36 **Development in a sea urchin.** (*a*) Sea urchin embryo at the four cell stage (550×), (*b*) sea urchin larvae (150×) before metamorphosis, and (*c*) adult sea urchin (8–20 cm, 3–8 in) across.

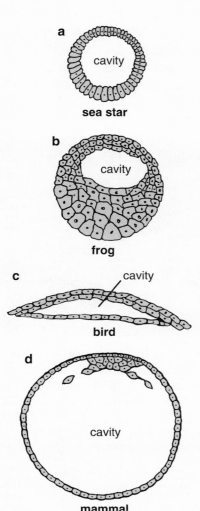

phenotype? Could a modification in development affect speciation?

To answer these questions scientifically, we need to gather evidence. Is there evidence that the same process, occurring in slightly different ways, leads to changes in structures? One way this could happen is to have a change in the *timing* of developmental events.

A much-studied example occurs in the tiger salamander, *Ambystoma tigrinum*. In warm regions, tiger salamanders pass their early lives in creeks. They have gills for breathing under water and flattened tails for swimming. Later, hormonal signals cause the individuals to undergo metamorphosis. They become burrowing land animals. They have lungs and rounded tails. They reproduce only after the metamorphic events.

In colder regions, the same tiger salamanders are adapted to live permanently in water. In these regions, tiger salamanders reach adult size and

Figure 13.37
Developmental patterns. The similarity of the early developmental phase among diverse organisms reflects an evolutionary connection. Which organism would you expect to most resemble the early developmental phases of a salamander? Why?

can reproduce even though they still have gills. They never undergo metamorphosis. They are said to retain their larval form. The warm- and cold-region tiger salamanders have a big developmental difference (see figure 13.38). Do you think it is caused by many or few genetic differences?

The difference turns out to be quite simple. Consider the tiger salamanders that live in warmer regions. Metamorphosis is triggered by a surge of thyroid hormone that takes place before the animals reach sexual maturity. For tiger salamanders that live in colder regions, however, the cold environment prevents production of thyroid hormone. The animals simply continue to grow in size until they become sexually mature. As a result, these tiger salamanders retain gills and other features of the larval form. They remain aquatic organisms throughout their lives.

Some organisms have evolved to respond to environmental conditions during development. Developmental flexibility allows tiger salamanders to exist in both warm and cold environments. In other organisms, developmental pathways are fixed. The life cycle of the Mexican salamander, *Ambystoma mexicanum*, is fixed. These salamanders never undergo metamorphosis in nature. The tiger salamander and the Mexican salamander are closely related species. Perhaps when the developmental pathway in the Mexican lineage became fixed, it was important to the evolution of that species. Remember what you learned in unit 1, *Evolution: Change in Living Systems*, about isolating events and speciation. Changes in developmental timing or features can be isolating events, which can lead to new species formation.

Figure 13.38 **Changes in timing during development can lead to quite different results in the same species.** (*a*) In cold regions, tiger salamanders never receive the developmental signal that triggers metamorphosis. Thus, the salamander retains its aquatic larval form as it sexually matures. (*b*) In warm regions, tiger salamanders produce a hormone that triggers metamorphosis before sexual maturity is reached. This causes the salamander to transform into a land-dwelling organism.

Analysis

1. Use your answers from steps 2 and 4 to help you draw your critter in its various developmental stages. Label the stages with enough detail so that someone looking at the illustration will understand what is happening.

   If you need to use any unfamiliar terminology, be sure to define it in your diagram.

2. Write a detailed description of your critter's developmental processes, including growth and cellular differentiation. Explain how your critter's genetic plan may interact with environmental conditions to direct and regulate development. Describe how errors might cause disruptions in your critter's development.

   Review the essays, particular activities, and notes in your science notebook to meet the goals outlined in the rubric.

Further Challenges

At the beginning of this chapter, you read about two questions regarding development that were of particular interest to scientists in 1994. The first question ("How are the body's tissues and organs formed?") is basically the same question that earlier developmental biologists asked. Early scientists also wondered about the second question ("What clues does development reveal about the process of evolution?"). Throughout this chapter, you have learned about many aspects of development that are related to these two questions. Think about what you know about the processes of science. Then answer the following questions in your science notebook.

1. Years of experimentation have produced much data relating to the events and processes of development. Why, then, do scientists continue to ask these 2 questions:
   - "How are the body's tissues and organs formed?"
   - "What clues does development reveal about the process of evolution?"
2. Most developmental biologists likely would say that we understand the answers to the first question far better than we understand the answers to the second question.
   a. Does this mean that the second question is invalid or unanswerable? Should we stop pursuing answers to it? Explain your reasoning.
   b. What does the history of our attempts to answer the first question suggest about how we should go about answering the second? How long might it take to answer this question? Illustrate your answer with specific references to the history of developmental biology.

It takes courage to grow up and turn out to be who you really are.

Unknown

he photographs that you see here feature the same individual across her century-long lifetime. As you look at them, think of the immense changes this woman experienced in her lifetime. During her childhood, automobiles were just becoming commonly used. As an adult, she saw the development of cars, airplanes, and computers. She watched a man walk on the surface of the Moon and NASA launch the International Space Station. Imagine the different stages of her life. Think about the people who have influenced her, and those she has influenced. In chapter 14, *The Human Life Span,* you will study the stages of life that a human experiences. Essentially, all humans develop physically in much the same way. But life stages also include emotional, cognitive (mental), and social development. A person's genetics and culture influence this development in many ways.

To help you start thinking about human life stages, we put a family's photograph album into motion. During the Engage activity, *A Century of Photographs,* you will think about the stages of life through which an individual has progressed. Next, you will join with your teammates to study a specific life stage by observing and interviewing people. You will continue to develop your understanding of the human life span by participating in a discussion. You will discuss how much your culture, environment, and genetic plan contribute to your development. Finally, you will participate in a multicultural fair. There your team will present information about certain life stages in a different culture.

GOALS FOR THE CHAPTER

By the end of chapter 14, you should be able to understand and appreciate the following:

✔ Human life stages involve physical, cognitive, social, and emotional development.

✔ Physical development may allow for other types of development.

✔ Culture influences the expression of human life stages.

✔ Making observations of people requires ethical considerations.

✔ Maintaining objectivity when studying cultures can be difficult.

To help you develop these understandings, you will complete the following activities.

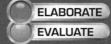

ENGAGE	A Century of Photographs
EXPLORE	Growing Up—What Does That Mean?
EXPLORE	A View of Life
EXPLAIN	Life-Span Development: Examining the Contexts
ELABORATE	Cultural Diversity in the
EVALUATE	Human Life Span

Remember to refer to the chapter organizer frequently as you complete the activities in chapter 14. It will help you gain perspective on the flow of concepts across the chapter and the connections between activities.

A Century of Photographs

Key Idea: Humans pass through a number of life stages as they age.

Linking Question:
What changes do humans undergo through the span of life?

Chapter 14

MAJOR CONCEPTS

✔ Human life stages involve physical, cognitive, social, and emotional development.

✔ Physical development may allow for other types of development.

✔ Culture influences the expression of human life stages.

✔ Making observations of people requires ethical considerations.

✔ Maintaining objectivity when studying cultures can be difficult.

EXPLORE

Growing Up—What Does That Mean?

Key Idea: Humans develop along several dimensions: physical, cognitive, social, and emotional.

Linking Question:
What factors influence human development across the span of life?

EXPLORE

A View of Life

Part A: Interview Preparation
Part B: The Interview
Key Idea: An elder's life reflects cultural and technological influences.

Cultural Diversity in the Human Life Span

Key Idea: Cultures differ in their expression of human life stages.

The Human Life Span

Linking Question:
How are life stages in humans affected by culture?

 EXPLAIN

Life-Span Development: Examining the Contexts

Key Idea: Genetic and environmental influences contribute to all of the dimensions of human development.

Linking Question:
How do nature and nurture each influence human development?

A Century of Photographs

When you look through a photograph album, you are likely to see images of friends and relatives caught in a moment of time (figure 14.1). What would you see if you could put those individual snapshots into motion and watch someone's life progress? What happens to a person during the process of aging? This Engage activity, *A Century of Photographs*, will give you a sense of what that might look like.

Materials

online resource (watch as a class)

Figure 14.1 Many physical, mental, emotional, and social changes take place during the human life span.

PROCESS AND PROCEDURES

1. Read through the *Analysis* questions. Keep them in mind as you view the video segment, "Age Progression."
2. In your science notebook, note 2 or 3 thoughts or additional questions that you had as you viewed the images.
3. Discuss your thoughts and questions with your classmates.

Analysis

You have now discussed some of the changes associated with aging. Answer the following questions and write your answers in your science notebook.

1. What are some of the stages in a human life?
2. What do you think identifies particular life stages?
3. Is each stage clearly distinct from the next? Explain your answer.

Growing Up—What Does That Mean?

In the Engage activity, *A Century of Photographs*, you watched a baby grow into a little girl, then into a mature woman, and finally into an elderly woman. As you watched, did you wonder exactly what happens to people as they grow and develop? In this Explore activity, *Growing Up—What Does That Mean?*, you will make observations of humans in a specific stage of life (figure 14.2). You will then focus on physical, cognitive, emotional, and social aspects of their development. By comparing your findings with those of other groups studying other stages of life, you will start to develop an understanding of what growing up means.

Materials

permission forms
materials for making a class visual representation of human growth
and development

PROCESS AND PROCEDURES

1. With your team of 4 and your teacher, determine which 1 of the following age groups your team will observe:
   - Infancy (birth through 1 year)
   - Early childhood (2 years through 6 years)
   - Middle childhood (7 years through 11 years)
   - Adolescence (12 years through 18 years)
   - Young adult (19 years through 30 years)
   - Prime adult (31 years through 55 years)
   - Middle age (56 years through 70 years)
   - Old age (more than 71 years)

2. Working individually, record your current ideas about the following characteristics for the age group your team will be exploring. Write your ideas in your science notebook.

   a. Three physical characteristics (of your chosen age group)
   b. Two cognitive characteristics
   c. Two emotional characteristics
   d. Two characteristics related to social interaction

   > The term "cognitive" refers to functions of the mind, or thought processes. You can think of cognition as mental functioning. For this step, it may help to think of a person you know in the age group you will study. Then to think about the characteristics he or she displays that are potentially related to the stage of life that person is currently in.

3. Share with the rest of your team your science notebook entries for each category listed in step 2. Note the similarities and differences in your ideas.

4. To help you plan to make observations of people in your chosen age group, read the essay, *Human Development 101*. Take notes about any information that may help you make observations.

   > The essay is a series of journal entries from a fictitious college student who, at the time of the entries, was just beginning her studies in human development. The information in her journal will provide you with some background about aspects of physical, cognitive, emotional, and social development.

Figure 14.2 Making observations. Developmental psychologists learn a lot about patterns of child development by observing children in a variety of settings.

Human Development 101

ENGLISH   SPANISH

Personal Journal Entry: 21 October

I am just about to begin observations for my human development class. I am both excited and apprehensive. I am already tired of reading the textbook and am really excited about getting to observe. It will be a great way to learn. So why am I apprehensive? I guess maybe it's because I won't be observing plants or protozoans, as I'm used to doing in my biology classes. I'll be observing *people*!

My professor has been great about helping us get ready. She has explained to us all the important things to keep in mind. I think it's interesting that public ethical standards for working with children were established only after World War II (1939–1945). Officials discovered the unethical and inhumane experiments that Nazi physicians had conducted on both children and adults. During the war crimes trials that followed, the Nuremburg Code was written and adopted by many governments and institutions. This code was aimed at protecting people who participate in research projects. Then, in the late 1960s, government officials in the United States established their own set of specific guidelines to protect human subjects. And in 1982, the American Psychological Association published a set of ethical standards for conducting research with children.

I think the first important issue is

Keeping an observation record. When making observations, a complete, detailed written record is essential.

respect for all participants. All participation must be completely voluntary. This means that if people do not want us to observe them or to include them in a study, then we must respect their wishes. Also, the participants can decide to drop out of the project at any time. And with children, it's important to remember that even if the parents have given permission, if the child does not want to participate, we must respect the wishes of the child—not just the parent. It seems obvious that you especially shouldn't do anything that would harm a participant physically or emotionally.

I remember that the ethical guidelines also say we must explain the purpose of our research or observations to the participants. Also, the information that we obtain is confidential. This means that we should never discuss personal information about a participant with anyone outside the project. When social scientists publish research papers, they never disclose the participants' identities. The participants also have the right to ask questions about the observations or the research. It's important to remember that they may want to know the results. It's critical to remember that the rights of the participants come before the rights of the researcher.

OK. I think I'm ready for my first day of observations.

Personal Journal Entry: 28 October

Well, I thought I was ready, but I wasn't. I was supposed to make observations of cognitive growth and development. But I didn't even remember what that meant. So I went back to my notebook from class and read through my notes. I found out that **cognitive growth** refers to the changes that take place as we age in how we learn, think, and process information. **Cognition** involves perceiving, remembering, imagining, and reasoning. It makes sense that we get better at that as we grow older. My cognitive skills are better now than when I was five. They were better at five than when I was five months old.

So what exactly do I look for to find examples of cognitive growth? Maybe I need to ask the children to do something, like solve a problem or do a puzzle. Maybe I could just ask certain questions. Let's see, what are some ideas?

For the Youngest Children

- Ask them to point to things of specific colors.
- Ask them to point to pictures of different animals.

For Children a Little Older

- Ask them to write something or draw something.
- Listen to how well they use language, such as how long their sentences are and their pronunciation of words.

For Children in Late Childhood

- Ask them to solve simple math problems.
- Listen to their sentences and their use of language.
- Ask them to read.

For Adolescents

- Ask them to discuss a book they just read or a movie they just saw.
- Ask them to solve a difficult jigsaw puzzle.
- Ask them to solve a more difficult math problem.

For Adults

- Ask them to discuss a book or a movie.
- Ask them to describe what they do in their jobs.

For the Elderly

- Ask them what they remember about their families.
- Ask them about the people in the photographs around the room.
- Ask them to play a board game or card game.

A Special Note on Children

I remember a neat activity about the idea of conservation. First, you hold a tall, narrow container of water. Then, with the children watching, you pour the water into another container having a wider diameter. You ask the children which one had more water. Young children will say that the tall, narrow container had more water in it. But at some point in their cognitive growth, their abstract thinking improves, and the children will realize that the amount of water is the same. I think that is so cool.

Goal: Maybe tomorrow I can try to find out at what age that happens. Complete, clear notes will be important. Maybe I will revise my observation forms so that they are easier to use.

Personal Journal Entry: 29 October

Observing physical development is sort of straightforward. I mean, you actually can watch people do things. I asked the kids if I could measure how tall everyone is. They thought it was great and enjoyed helping me. Sometimes they were even a little bit competitive about who would get to help. (This is when I realized that, although I thought I was recording data about physical development, my partner was recording a lot of stuff about social and emotional behavior. That was great. We didn't even have that planned! It helps to be ready for anything.) Our professor explained that when we observe adolescents, we should measure only height, not weight, because adolescence is a time when people generally are very sensitive about their weight.

Even though I thought observing physical development was more straightforward, I realized that I wasn't getting a very detailed picture. It would be great to be able to observe the kids on the playground. Maybe tomorrow I will ask them to skip and see who can do it and who can't. I should ask my mom how old I was when I started to skip.

Personal Journal Entry: 3 November

I just noticed that my notes on emotional growth and development aren't as complete as I would like them to be. This type of development is a hard thing to observe. Is what I think someone is feeling really what the person is feeling? Or am I misinterpreting her or him? This is hard. I need to try to separate what I see and hear from what I think it means. I need to separate the *observation* from the *interpretation*. My professor has reminded me to place brackets in my notes around any phrases that represent interpretations and to avoid making judgments.

Should I ask or just observe? Maybe I could ask them to explain to me what emotions like anger, excitement, and love mean. This is not the same as *observing* the emotions, and it would give me some different information.

Social growth is pretty easy to observe with children in groups. As I was watching a group of children, it was easy to separate the sociable ones from the reserved ones. But again, I tried to write down my observation, not my interpretation. I could observe how many children were willing to share toys, how often they would make eye contact with others, and how much time they preferred to play alone.

It's really important what size group you are observing. If you don't have a large enough group (at least three), then you really limit the amount of social interaction that happens. But if the group is too large (more than six or seven), then it is too hard to keep track of everybody.

Social behavior will be harder to observe in adolescents and adults. They have more self-awareness. They also are more concerned about how others will perceive them. For these reasons, they are more cautious in their interactions. How can I find out about their social growth? What questions can I ask? Maybe I can ask them to estimate how much time they spend each week (outside of school and work) by themselves and with one, two, or more than two other people.

OK. It looks like I have a place to start again. Observing is fun, but harder than I thought.

5. With your team, develop a plan for making observations that all team members will follow (figure 14.3). To do this, read the need to know, *Guidelines for Observations*, review the sample observation form (figure 14.4), and complete the following steps.

a. With your team, hold a brainstorming session. Create a list of ways to observe and obtain information about people in the age group that you chose to study.

b. Refine your list. Develop an outline with specific strategies, potential questions, and potential tasks that you will use during your observations. Make sure your plans allow each person to spend some time recording observations and some time interacting with participants.

c. When you think your plan is complete, ask your teacher to approve it. Revise it, if necessary, and have your teacher look at it again.

d. Based on your plan, create observation forms that will help you keep track of the information you collect.

Figure 14.3 Collaborate constructively. Work with your team to develop questions and tasks for gathering data about the people you will study.

NEED TO KNOW

ENGLISH SPANISH

Guidelines for Observations

Introduction

1. Introduce yourself to the people you will be observing and to any teachers or supervisors present.

2. Describe your project in a way that is appropriate to the age of your subjects.

3. Reach an agreement with the participants or supervisors on the approximate length of your observation session.

4. Answer any questions that your subjects might have about the observation process. Make certain that each of them is willing to participate.

5. Remember that the participants have the right to stop at any time. You must respect such a request.

Making Observations

6. You must make specific observations in each of the following areas: physical, cognitive, emotional, and social development. In general, you should focus your observations on three different people for about 15 minutes each.

   Some of the things that you observe will cover more than one area. Remember to record your observations (see figure 14.4), not your interpretations of the observations.

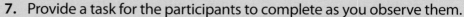
7. Provide a task for the participants to complete as you observe them.
8. Ask questions as needed to obtain the information that you want.
9. Ask the participants to perform tasks that will help you obtain the information that you want.
10. If you are observing two- through six-year-olds, ask the participants to draw something that you can take back to your classroom with you. You might ask them to draw a pet, a favorite toy, a friend, or their family. (Refer to those drawings as you read the essay, *Physical Growth Influences Cognitive, Social, and Emotional Growth*, in the Explain activity, *Life-Span Development: Examining the Contexts*.)
11. Record your observations clearly and completely.
12. Before you conclude your observations, look over your observation forms. Make sure they are as complete as possible.

Conclusion

13. Thank the participants and supervisors for their time and cooperation.

6. Work in pairs to conduct your observations.

    You likely will conduct these observations after school or on the weekends. Your teacher will set up the structure and arrangements. When the observations are complete, each pair should have observed at least three people.

7. Meet with the rest of your team to share and summarize your observations. Include information about each type of development (physical, cognitive, emotional, and social). Discuss the following questions.
    a. How do your actual observations compare with the ideas you wrote down in step 2?
    b. Between the 2 pairs of teammates, what were the similarities in your observations?
    c. What were the differences you found between different people in the same age group? How might you explain the differences in what you observed?
    d. Do you think that your presence influenced the behaviors of the people you studied? If so, does this influence your conclusions?
8. To gain perspective on your observations, read the essay, *Growing Up through Life's Stages*. As you read, make notes that you think would enhance your team's summary.
9. With your team, decide which pieces of information from the essay (if any) you will include in your team's summary. Be clear about which information comes from your observations, and which comes from what you learned from the essay. Decide how each member of the team will contribute to reporting to the class.

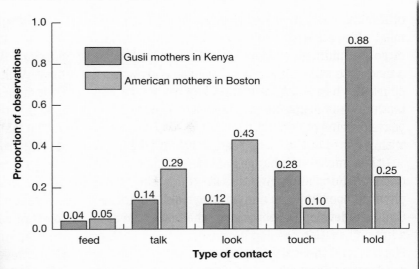

Figure 14.7 **Interacting with infants.** The way parents interact with their infants reflects greater cultural patterns.

Source: Data from Richman, A. et al. (1988). Maternal behavior to infants in five cultures. In R.A. LeVine et al. (eds.). *Parental Behavior in Diverse Societies: New Directions for Child Development.* San Francisco: Jossey-Bass.

Figure 14.6 In the United States, an infant's first unassisted steps usually happen at about one year.

size by the end of the second year. An important aspect of brain development is the infant's awareness of caregivers. This interaction results in *attachment*, the development of close emotional ties to the regular caregivers. The cultural setting influences the way in which attachment takes place.

In 1988, a group of researchers studied parenting patterns in five different cultures. Figure 14.7 demonstrates some of the differences they found between a group of Gusii parents in Kenya and a group of Boston parents in the United States. Gusii mothers, like mothers in many developing societies, are primarily concerned with the physical survival of their young. By holding them and keeping them close, the mothers help keep their children safe. In addition, the Gusii

believe that children cannot understand language until they are close to two years old. Therefore, they rarely talk to their babies. Gusii people generally do not look at each other. They avert their gaze when talking with someone. Similarly, Gusii mothers make very little eye contact with their babies. In Boston, on the other hand, infants spend more time in infant seats and playpens than in their mothers' arms. This practice may reflect the mothers' need for independence during the day and perhaps also the value of teaching independence to their young. Boston parents, however, provide more visual, aural, and motor stimulation for their babies. They make frequent eye contact with the babies and talk or read to them.

Childhood is the next stage of life. Most human societies use one or more specific terms to refer to individuals in this period of life as well. English-speaking people say "child." Trobriand Islanders say *gwadi*. The French say *enfant*. The Ainu people of Northern Japan say *ki yakka pirika*, which means "it eats with adults now." During the decade or so of childhood, physical growth continues at a moderate pace. Children experience a growth spurt just before adolescence. The first permanent teeth usually erupt during the fifth to seventh years. During childhood, the skull grows mostly within bones of the facial region (figure 14.8).

Other important changes also take place during childhood. During this stage, a child's physical coordination and language skills improve. Children develop in response to the teachings of adults. They also develop in response to what they observe and their play experiences. Playing physical games, telling jokes, and listening to stories are all important experiences. In the United States, parents have many face-to-face interactions with their young children. Young children in such settings are likely to begin talking and interacting socially earlier than children growing up in less interactive cultures.

A growing child continues to develop his or her own unique personality. The child discovers personal likes and dislikes in foods and hobbies. A healthy child begins to develop skills in judgment. Over time, children gain an internal sense of what is and is not appropriate behavior.

The major type of work in a society influences its child-rearing values and practices. In hunting-and-gathering societies, adults work independently much of the time. Such societies value self-reliance and autonomy. Parents are observed to exercise little control over their children and rarely punish them. In agriculturally based societies, however, adults work under close supervision. Parents learn that obedience is rewarded in the workplace. In these societies, parents demonstrate a more restrictive child-rearing style.

When puberty occurs, the period called *adolescence* begins. Most human societies recognize adolescence as a distinct milestone. Biologically, secondary sexual characteristics appear.

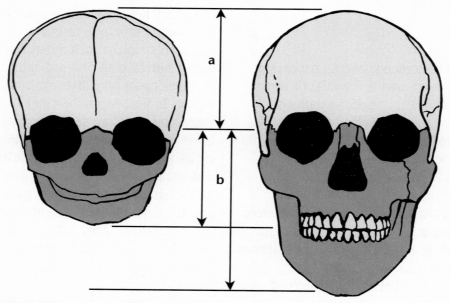

Figure 14.8 Facial development in childhood. The heights of the cranium in the infant and the adult are indicated by distance a. Distance b indicates the length of the bones of the facial region. It is clear that after infancy, most of the growth of the skull takes place in the facial bones, especially the jawbones.

Adolescents notice that hair begins to appear in the pubic region and under the arms. The pelvic area of females broadens and breasts develop. The shoulders of males broaden, facial hair grows, and the voice deepens. Girls are initially taller than boys due to a growth spurt just before puberty. However, males are eventually about 13 cm (5 in) taller than females. The physical changes associated with puberty are summarized in figure 14.9. Puberty varies a lot among individuals. Puberty is primarily under hormonal control. But it can be influenced by environmental conditions, such as nutrition. As adolescents experience the obvious changes associated with the onset of sexual development, a number of other physical alterations take place.

Mental capacity changes during adolescence as well. Thinking skills improve. This includes the ability to deal with abstract concepts and to engage in critical thinking. In the United States, adolescents begin to challenge the ideas of their parents as they develop cognitively. Socially, many adolescents have a strong desire to gain acceptance from their peer group. They become concerned about presenting the "right" appearance and behavior. Adolescents struggle with striking a balance between questioning and conformity. But it marks a key step in the development of each person's identity.

Adulthood begins when individuals stop growing, usually in their late teens. Adulthood does not mark the end of development, however. Social, emotional, and cognitive development continues throughout adulthood. Several key events take place during adulthood. Many individuals develop a long-term pair-bond with another individual. Adults learn and practice working skills. These skills bring financial independence. Many adults create a new household. They may produce and parent children. Each of these activities clearly calls for the development of many social and cognitive skills. Individuals can only acquire these skills gradually. In traditional societies, people often engage in the same work

Physical Development in Adolescents			
Boys	**Age span**	**Girls**	**Age span**
Beginning of growth spurt; growth of scrotum, testes, and penis; sparse, light-colored, slightly curled pubic hair	11–13	Beginning of growth spurt; breasts and nipples elevated (breast buds); sparse, light-colored, slightly curled pubic hair	10–11
Rapid physical growth; deepening of voice; maturation of scrotum, testes, and penis; ejaculation of semen; sparse facial hair; pubic hair darker, denser, and more curled	13–16	Rapid physical growth; deepening of voice; further breast enlargement; rapid growth of uterus, vagina, and ovaries; vaginal secretion acidic; menstruation begins; pubic hair darker, denser, and more curled	11–14
Slowdown or cessation of physical growth; further deepening of voice; penis adult size; darkening of scrotum; increased body and facial hair; adult-type pubic hair	16–21	Slowdown or cessation of physical growth; breasts adult size; clitoris mature; adult-type pubic hair	14–18

Figure 14.9 The characteristics of physical development in adolescents are summarized in this table.

throughout their adult life and establish their family near their relatives. In contemporary Western societies, however, people may change their homes, work skills, and even family affiliations throughout their adult years.

Biologically, the adult years represent the period of aging. The aging process begins when adults are in their 20s. Aging involves a very slow deterioration of all the body's systems. Muscles slowly lose strength and mass. Skin becomes less resilient, and wrinkles form. Cuts heal more slowly. Bones and tendons gradually become more brittle. The peak performance of major organ systems declines. For people whose physical gifts allow them to become professional athletes in vigorous sports, these changes usually compel retirement from top-level competition by age 40. For most people, however,

the changes of aging are so slow and gradual that they can maintain much the same level of activity from their 20s through their 40s or 50s.

By the age of 50 or 60, most humans have completed raising their immediate family if they chose to reproduce or adopt. During this stage of life, however, the elderly play an important role in maintaining the continuity of cultural practices across the generations. The active involvement of grandparents, great-aunts, and great-uncles in the upbringing of grandchildren or other youth plays a major role in many cultures. This segment of the community also contributes to many other domestic and volunteer activities. The important contribution of the elderly is a unique outcome of the fact that the human life span is relatively long.

Analysis

Complete step 1 below as a class. Next, complete step 2 individually.

1. Create a visual representation of human growth and development based on the aspects of development that you and your classmates observed. Your representation should
   - be chronological;
   - include aspects of physical, cognitive, emotional, and social development; and
   - include a written component.

   Use any supplies that your teacher provides. Be creative!

2. In your science notebook, write a short, reflective entry that describes your current understanding of development during the human life span. Address the following questions in your entry.
   a. Which characteristics of development do you think are specific to the culture that your team observed?
   b. Which characteristics of development do you think are found in most cultures? In other words, which do you consider "universal"?
   c. What other questions come to mind that you hope to answer as you continue with this chapter?

© iStockphoto/digitalskillet

A View of Life

Can you imagine what it would be like to have experienced all the stages of life? With a healthy lifestyle, the chances of a young person living an active life extending seven or more decades are much greater today than they were several generations ago. In this Explore activity, *A View of Life*, you will have an opportunity to have an elderly guest visit your class and answer interview questions that you and your teammates develop. This will give you a look back in time from the point of view of someone who has experienced most of life's stages. The type of interview you will be doing is an *autobiographical oral history*. That is the most personal type of interview. It should be relaxed and free ranging.

PROCESS AND PROCEDURES

Part A   Interview Preparation

1. Assemble into your team of 4 from the previous Explore activity, *Growing Up—What Does That Mean?*

2. Refer to the class project that you completed in the previous activity. Make a list of any additional information that would help you construct a more complete representation of human life stages.

   > Think about the insights that an interview could provide. What insights were not apparent from your observations in the previous activity? For example, you collected information about various stages of life. But you learned little about experiencing all of them.

3. With your team, develop at least 5 interview questions for your guest. Use your list from step 2, along with advice in the need to know, *Guidelines for Interviews*.

   > You also might find the questions in step 2 of the *Analysis* helpful as you develop your interview questions.

4. Order your questions with respect to importance (1 = what you feel is most important).

5. Have a representative from your team record your first question on the board or flip chart.

   > If there is already a question that is similar to yours, go to the next question on your list.

6. Continue to record questions in this manner until your class has about 15 questions listed. Work as a class to decide the final order of these 15 questions.

   > With your class, suggest improvements for clarifying the wording or eliminating repetitive questions.

NEED TO KNOW

Guidelines for Interviews

A primary goal for an interviewer is to create a suitable environment in which to carry out the interview. You should make the guest feel comfortable, and you and your fellow interviewers should be active listeners. The following tips should help you conduct a successful interview:

1. A good interviewer is not the star of the show; the guest is. The objective is to get the guest to tell his or her story.
2. Ask questions that give the guest an opportunity to tell stories.

   For example, "What was the most exciting time of your life?" is a better question than, "Did you have an exciting life?"
3. Ask only 1 question at a time. Keep the questions brief.
4. Do not begin with controversial or sensitive questions. Save those for later when the guest warms up to the class.
5. Allow plenty of time for your guest to reflect on and to respond to your questions. Be patient. Allow your guest to pause before answering.
6. Allow time at the end of the interview for the guest to add whatever he or she would like.

Part B   The Interview

1. Choose a spokesperson from your team. As your teacher calls on your team, have that person pose 1 of the prepared questions to the guest.
2. You may pose follow-up questions that your guest's responses might raise. Your teacher will invite these questions periodically throughout the interview.

3. In your science notebook, record the major ideas from your guest's responses.

   You will have access to a recording of the interview. This will allow you to review the responses and add detail to your notes. Make sure that you collect word-for-word quotations as *data* to support your inferences.

Analysis

Revisit the project that your class developed in the *Analysis* of the previous Explore activity, *Growing Up—What Does That Mean?* Then complete step 1 below as a class and step 2 individually.

1. Determine what new information about human physical, cognitive, social, and emotional development emerged from the interview. Add it to your class project.

2. Use the information from the interview to respond to the following. Write your responses in your science notebook.

   a. How did the guest's culture influence his or her growth and development?

      Explain how a different cultural setting might have had an impact on this person.

   b. Provide examples of how technological change during the individual's lifetime influenced his or her development at each life stage.

Life-Span Development: Examining the Contexts

You have investigated how people develop through the major stages of life on their dramatic journey from birth to old age. Where we are along that journey frequently determines how we see those stages. By completing the previous activities in this chapter, you have had an opportunity to broaden your perspective through observation, an interview, and some analysis. In this Explain activity, *Life-Span Development: Examining the Contexts*, you will further develop your understanding of human life stages. You will prepare for and participate in a discussion about the relative contributions that a genetic plan and the environment make to each individual.

Materials

resource materials that your teacher provides

PROCESS AND PROCEDURES

1. With your teammates, discuss the following 2 questions. With help from your teacher, decide which question your team would like to focus on.
   a. How much of the variation that we see among individuals can be attributed to variation in specific genetic plans?
   b. How much of the variation that we see among individuals can be attributed to their experiences or other environmental influences?
2. Copy the table shown in figure 14.10 into your science notebook. As you complete the next step, fill in only the column of the table corresponding to the question your team chose.

   You will fill in the other column of the table as you engage in the class discussion at the end of the activity.

Topic: human growth and development
Code: human4E739

3. Fill in 1 of the columns in your table with examples you find in the essays, *Twin Studies* and *Physical Growth Influences Cognitive, Social, and Emotional Growth.*

Human cognitive, social, or emotional trait	How genes may affect the trait's development	How the environment may affect the trait's development
Novelty-seeking behavior		
Spoken language		

Figure 14.10 **Sample table of information about the contribution of genes and the environment to various human traits.** A table such as this will help you and your team organize your ideas for the class discussion.

Twin Studies

ENGLISH SPANISH

Have you heard the phrase "nature or nurture"? Scientists no longer talk about traits as the result of *either* genes or the environment. This is because *both* genes ("nature") and the environment ("nurture") influence the development and expression of traits to varying degrees. When scientists talk about the environment as an influence, they include conditions such as habitat, climate, and temperature, but also all the experiences organisms have, including what they may have learned. Today, scientists are interested in understanding the *relative* contribution that genes and the environment make to developmental processes.

To discover the relative contribution of genes and environment to various human traits, scientists have compared identical and fraternal twins. Identical twins are genetically the same because they originate from the same fertilized egg that splits apart early in development. Fraternal twins, on the other hand, develop from two different fertilized eggs, so they share only 50 percent of their genes. This is the amount of genetic similarity found between any two siblings. Often, scientists

measure the traits of identical twins raised apart and compare them with the traits of fraternal twins of the same sex that are raised apart. Such a comparison helps the scientists tease apart the contributions of genes and environment on the same trait.

Topic: behavior
Code: human4E740

Let's take a simple example from a study of height. If genes influence height more strongly than the environment does, then we would predict that identical twins raised apart are more similar in height than fraternal twins raised apart. Since all of the study participants were raised apart from their siblings, we can assume they have all experienced different environments. Therefore, if a greater similarity in height is found between identical twins (compared to fraternal twins), that similarity is likely to be genetic. If identical twins were found to be no more similar in height than fraternal twins, then we would conclude that environmental factors are an important factor

Figure 14.11 Identical twins. Would you expect identical or fraternal twins to be more similar in height?

© iStockphoto

in determining height. Think of the identical twins you know, the fraternal twins you know, and consider figure 14.11. What do your observations suggest about whether height is more determined by genes or the environment?

Studies show that the height between identical twins is more similar than the height between fraternal twins, for those who are raised apart. This suggests that height differences are more strongly influenced by genes than by the environment. In fact, 80–90 percent of height differences among people have been found to be due to genetic variation.

Twin studies are especially helpful in gaining a better understanding of human behavior. Often, behavior has both genetic and environmental components. For example, scientists have compared how identical and fraternal twins raised apart seek new experiences. Their "novelty-seeking" behaviors were given a score, and the scores are graphed in figure 14.12. Do you see any pattern between the identical twins? How about between the fraternal twins? You

may notice that the scores of the identical twins fall roughly along a line that angles upward. This indicates that the novelty-seeking scores of identical twins tend to match each other. On the other hand, the fraternal twins do not show such a pattern. This indicates that the score of one twin is not likely to match the fraternal sibling's. Overall, the comparison between the identical and fraternal twins indicates that there is a genetic component to a person's tendency to seek new experiences.

Scientists actively debate the extent to which different human behaviors are genetically based. However, twin studies show that at least some complex human behaviors are influenced by genes as well as by the environment. People's ability to learn language appears to be influenced by specific genes that direct the development of the language centers of the brain. A baby's environment, specifically the language that the baby hears from his or her parents, however, determines which language he or she will learn. This type of flexibility in certain behaviors, such as language, is a characteristic of humans.

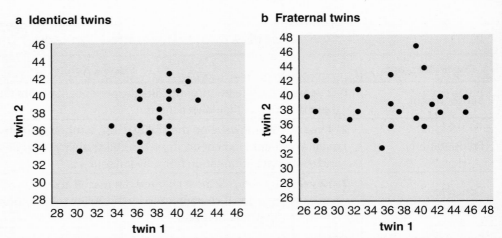

Figure 14.12 Scatter plots of twins' novelty-seeking behavior. These scatter plots compare the novelty-seeking scores between pairs of (*a*) identical twins and (*b*) fraternal twins raised apart.

Physical Growth Influences Cognitive, Social, and Emotional Growth

ENGLISH SPANISH

Physically, humans are animals possessing the same basic biological functions and organs as their primate relatives. Humans also are highly social creatures. Because of this, growth and development in humans is not just a physical process. It is also a cognitive, social, and emotional one. Because human development is slow, there is much opportunity for the genetic plan to be influenced by the environment. As development progresses, some human cognitive, social, and emotional traits are influenced more by genes than by the environment, while others are influenced more by the environment than by genes.

Cognitive Growth in Humans

Biology explains much of humans' capacity for cognitive growth (also known as mental growth). Because the human birth canal would not be big enough to accommodate a baby's head if its brain were full sized, the human brain continues to grow after birth. This allows humans to acquire the capacity for more-complex cognition and learned behavior than they would have otherwise.

The frontal lobes of the cerebrum grow rapidly around age two, with another increase between ages five and seven. Accordingly, the circumference of the head also increases. An insulating myelin sheath develops around each neuron in the cerebrum by age seven. These sheaths speed neural transmission between different parts of the brain and between the brain and the body. By this age, children's brains generally are as complex as adults' brains.

Cognitive growth refers to the changes that take place as we age in how we learn, think, and process information. Cognitive growth appears to parallel the physical growth of the brain. Most developmental psychologists agree that cognitive growth occurs in stages. Not surprisingly, they hold different opinions about the precise order and length of the stages in the process.

As an example of one scientist's theory of cognitive development, let's examine the ideas of Jean Piaget. Piaget was a 20th-century Swiss scientist who became interested in human

Cognitive Stages Developed by Piaget	
Cognitive stage	**Description**
Sensorimotor	**0–2 years:** infants learn through direct experience; have limited understanding of things that exist outside their own actions
Preoperational	**2–7 years:** children develop the ability to use symbols; sometime between 5–7 years, a qualitative improvement occurs in the child's ability to organize information logically and coordinate information from several sources
Concrete Operational	**7–12 years:** by age 7–8, most children can reason about objects and events that they can perceive; this stage is characterized by the ability to solve problems involving cause and effect, ordering, and numbers
Formal Operational	**12+ years:** adolescents begin to think logically about abstract or imagined concepts

Source: Fogel, L. and G. Melson (1988). *Child Development: Individual, Family, and Society.* St. Paul, MN: West Publishing Company.

Figure 14.13   A series of cognitive stages developed by Jean Piaget.

development by observing young children. He suggested that all complex thinking develops through the interaction between the individual and the environment. He divided childhood into a series of stages defined by a series of increasingly complex thought processes, as summarized in figure 14.13. Other scientists, such as the Russian psychologist Lev Vygotsky, have pointed out that culture may influence the order or length of these stages. Vygotsky's theories emphasize the role of adult-child interactions in cognitive development over the role of biology.

Language development is a good example of cognitive growth in children. Language development requires more than learning vocabulary. Language appears to develop by a similar series of steps in children of many different cultures. At around one year, infants begin to utter single words. Most of these are nouns that simply identify things the infant sees. These nouns can represent names, questions, or demands, depending on the intonation, as in "toy," "Toy?," or "*Toy*!" By about two years of age, children begin to make short utterances. These might include "Book here," "Sit chair," "All gone milk," and "*My* ball." As language acquisition continues, children begin to learn the particular grammatical rules of their own language.

Interestingly, the developing human brain appears to be able to acquire language most easily very early in life. Teens and adults experience more difficulty in learning a new language. Moreover, studies on the rare cases of children not exposed to language suggest that they missed their opportunity to develop complex language skills.

Cognitive growth also can be studied through children's artwork. For example, children appear to move through similar stages of representing the human body as they learn to draw (figure 14.14). As children age, their drawings tend to become more detailed and complex.

Genetic disorders, developmental disorders, and accidents can delay or limit a child's capacity for cognitive growth. Shaken baby syndrome illustrates how an injury can cause brain damage. Shaken baby syndrome can take place when someone severely shakes an infant. The brain injury often results in permanent retardation and can be fatal. As humans age, mental abilities deteriorate. Known reasons include Alzheimer's disease, stroke, and injuries.

Social Growth in Humans

Human social interactions also become increasingly complex from infancy to maturity. Psychologists note that humans begin life relating to others only in terms of their own wants and needs. As they grow socially, humans increasingly see themselves within give-and-take relationships. Social growth has a physical basis, however. Children with brain damage frequently cannot develop mature social skills. For example, the consumption of alcoholic beverages during pregnancy disrupts

When children of 2 years are given a drawing tool, they generally use simple repetitive movements to draw scribbles. Children of 3 begin to control their scribbling by observing the lines and concentrating on where they put them. Soon after this, most children begin to realize that their scribbles can represent things. "That's my cat" or "This is the Sun." They often begin drawing first and only name it as they work. Often, they will say the same drawing "represents" something different if asked about it later.

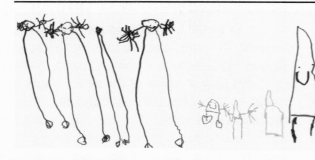

Children of 3½–4 begin to use particular symbols to represent the same thing every time they draw. A common example is when a child draws a person with only a head and limbs and no body.

Children of 5 begin to add other features to their drawings of humans and even then might not always include a body. As children begin to depict real activities in their drawings, they often exaggerate particular features that are important for the action they are representing.

Around 6 or 7, children begin to represent actual scenes and add more detail such as stripes on clothing and shoelaces. Even at this point, their drawings tend to be built of simple geometric shapes. In one experiment, children were asked to represent a person using different media such as clay, precut paper shapes, and various drawing instruments. The children's representations were similar regardless of the medium they used.

Figure 14.14   A set of drawings made by children of different ages.

Figure 14.15 **The play years.** Play is so central to the life of a young child that the years from two through five are often referred to as the play years.

fetal brain growth, resulting in fetal alcohol syndrome. Affected children frequently cannot develop mature social skills or other types of advanced mental functions.

Bonding—or its absence—with parents and other family members characterizes the first social interactions in an infant's life. As children grow, their social contacts reach beyond the family to include playmates and other adults (refer to figure 14.15). As they reach maturity, most individuals develop an extensive circle of friends and acquaintances. The circle includes teachers and other authority figures. People acquire appropriate social skills by interacting with others. These social skills include not only a desire to please and help relatives and friends, but also a sense of social responsibility toward all people.

Interestingly, a specific portion of the human brain appears to govern socially responsible behavior. Individuals who experience accidents that damage only a region located in the frontal lobes sometimes retain normal cognition. But they lose all sense of social responsibility and appropriate behavior toward others. Phineas Gage, an engineer who lived in the 1800s, experienced such a tragic accident. While at work, a metal rod shot through the frontal lobes of his brain (refer back to figure 1.9). Although he survived and could take care of himself, the once friendly, dependable worker became irresponsible and foulmouthed.

Emotional Growth in Humans

Like cognitive and social growth, emotional growth in humans has a biological basis and takes place progressively as a child's brain matures. Mental retardation may delay or limit emotional growth. Affected individuals may become physically mature, but remain somewhat childlike in their emotional development. Moreover, older individuals affected by disorders such as Alzheimer's disease frequently undergo emotional regression and become childlike.

Emotional growth normally begins in a child's relationship with his or her parents or caregivers and gradually extends to a wider circle of individuals. With successful emotional growth, a child learns to express negative feelings in a nondestructive manner. The child learns to accept that some of his or her wishes and desires cannot be satisfied immediately—or at all. A key point in the process of emotional growth takes place at puberty. This is when individuals begin to experience the very powerful drives and emotions connected with sex. Adolescents learn to control sexual behavior in order to maintain personal health and social acceptance. For some young people, the realization that their sexual orientation is different from most of those around them presents an additional emotional challenge. Most adolescents emerge from puberty able to express their emotions with greater subtlety and sensitivity to social context. As humans age, they often continue to gain awareness of their emotional states and those of others.

4. Join with the other teams that selected the same question as your team. Prepare for a class discussion of the 2 questions from step 1 by completing the following steps.

   a. Choose a recorder for your new team.

   b. Summarize what you already know.

   > Take turns describing the examples you wrote down in your tables. Write down new information in your organizing table. Make sure that you can logically support each statement.

   c. Make a list of other information that you would like to have. Explore the resources that your teacher has available to determine whether you can answer your questions.

   d. Think about what the other group might say about the traits you have collected information about, and how you might explain your reasoning.

5. Participate in a class discussion of the 2 questions from step 1.

   > As the discussion progresses, record notes and questions in your science notebook. Fill in the other column in your table in your science notebook with examples from the teams that focused on the other question.

Analysis

With your classmates, discuss the findings from the discussion. Briefly summarize the best responses of different teams to the questions in step 1. Then, individually, write a short essay in your science notebook that summarizes the contributions of genes and the environment to the development of different human physical, cognitive, social, and emotional traits. Relate how heredity and environment interact to influence human development.

ELABORATE

EVALUATE

Cultural Diversity in the Human Life Span

In this activity, *Cultural Diversity in the Human Life Span*, you will explore life stages in a culture different from your own. In doing so, you will elaborate on what you have learned in this chapter. Each team will explore a different culture. You will then create a display and a presentation for a multicultural fair. At this fair, you and your classmates will display what you have learned about growing up and living in a specific culture. You also will present some feature of that culture for the rest of the class.

After you have studied a culture, you will evaluate your understanding of human development over a life span. You will do this by reflecting on the similarities and differences in the process of development as it takes place in different cultures. You also will explain the characteristics of biological

development that underlie those similarities and differences. The focus question of this activity is, "How do developmental processes interact with cultural factors to affect the physical, cognitive, social, and emotional growth of humans?"

Materials

resource materials that your teacher provides
materials needed to complete your multicultural fair entry

PROCESS AND PROCEDURES

1. To prepare for the multicultural fair, do the following.
   a. Identify a culture in which you might want to explore human life stages.

      Your teacher will have a list of suggestions as well as some resources for you to look through to help you choose.

   b. Join with other classmates who have chosen to explore the same or a similar culture. Share with them your reasons for being interested in this particular group of people.

2. You will study this culture on your own, and then work with a team to create a multicultural fair entry about the culture. To prepare to study the culture you chose, make a list of information you hope to find out about the culture.

   Remember, you are to focus on how biology and culture interact to shape human development. Consider the focus question of the activity as you make your list: "How do developmental processes interact with cultural factors to affect the physical, cognitive, social and emotional growth of humans?" To help you with this task, you may wish to read the sidebar, *Culture: A Great Shaper of Life*. As you read, notice the kinds of information that are included about each culture.

Culture: A Great Shaper of Life

Personal Journal Entry: 5 April

Well, I'm getting the hang of observing humans. I think I probably make the best observations with infants and young children and then with older adults. I think it is probably hardest to observe people closest to my own age. I find myself comparing my own thinking and behaviors with theirs too much, and so I forget to focus on them. Sometimes I find myself judging their actions, when in fact my job is simply to document what I am observing.

I just got a letter from Malcolm, a friend who is in graduate school in California. He has an even bigger challenge. He is studying anthropology and is doing some fieldwork in Papua New Guinea and the surrounding area. He was describing to me how hard it is to study people from another culture. He says that when you are just beginning to learn about another culture, it is natural to fill in the gaps in your understanding with what is familiar from your own culture. He points out, however, that by doing so, you often develop an inaccurate picture of the culture you are trying to learn about.

I remember from my anthropology course last semester that it is important to try to put your own cultural values aside. This is called cultural relativism. Cultures are not better or worse than other cultures, just different. You need to learn about another culture from the perspective of how certain behaviors and attitudes work within that other culture—to

whatever extent that is possible. Of course, this is tricky. But Malcolm explained in his letter how cool it is to learn not just about the differences, but that, in spite of those differences, humans from all over Earth have many things in common. On the other hand, when cultures are studied in depth, we also learn that there is a lot of variation in behavior and attitudes even within one group. I also remember learning about the work of Urie Bronfenbrenner. In 1979, he proposed an ecological approach to the study of development (see figure 14.16). Bronfenbrenner points out that an individual is embedded in a set of nested environments. The environments influence each other, and together influence the development of an individual.

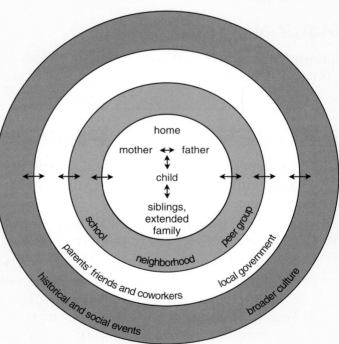

Source: Kopp, C. and J. Krakow. J. (1982). *Child Development in the Social Context.* Reading, MA: Addison-Wesley Publishing Company. Reprinted by permission of Addison-Wesley Publishing Co., Inc.

Figure 14.16 This diagram represents a simplified version of Urie Bronfenbrenner's ecological approach to development. As a child develops, he or she is influenced by each of these environments.

Personal Journal Entry: 15 May

I just got another letter from Malcolm. He now is spending time with the modern-day Trobriand Islanders (see figure 14.17) of Papua New Guinea. That reminded me of the traditional Trobriand society that we had studied in our class, so I sent him the following copy of my notes from class last semester.

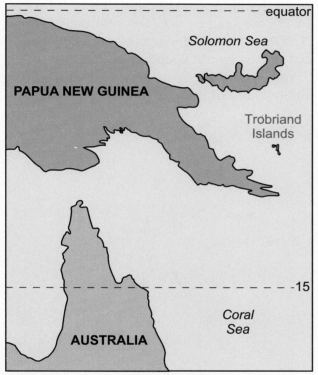

Figure 14.17 The Trobriand Islands.
The Trobriands are a group of small islands off the east coast of Papua New Guinea.

Anthropology 220, 11 November Trobriand Islanders

In general, traditional societies are societies that have not been influenced by the modern or Western cultures around them. Because we live in an extremely mobile world, most traditional cultures have had contact with modern cultures. But the timing and the extent of this contact have varied.

In traditional Trobriand society, children are usually weaned from breast-feeding by the time they are two. They usually are weaned by being sent to sleep with their father or their maternal grandmother. When the children turn four or five, they begin to spend time with a children's group that has quite a bit of independence. They stay with this group until puberty. On any given day, the children might remain with their parents or go with their group, as they chose.

When the children stay at home, the parents give the children miniature tools and show them how to plant crops and do other adult work. When the boys reach the age of six, their maternal uncles (their mothers' brothers) take more charge over their training. After the boys reach puberty, they still eat at home, but they begin sleeping in special bachelors' huts with several other boys their own age. This also is the time when the boys begin to participate in the regular occupations of adult men.

After girls reach puberty, they begin to do more adult women's work in the home. They often join their boyfriends in the bachelors' huts at night, but they can still sleep at home whenever they would like.

After spending several years in informal relationships, a pair of Trobriand adolescents might form a long-term relationship and begin to appear together in public. This act is a signal that they are ready to marry. If both young people consent, the family might build them a hut of their own near a maternal uncle of the boy, and the couple would begin adult life together.

In cases of divorce, which are usually at the woman's request, all of the children would stay with their mother. In this society, grandparents have little to do with the training of children, and respect for elders is not highly valued.

Personal Journal Entry: 16 May

As I was looking through the notes from my class to send to Malcolm, I came across notes about other cultures as well. I read through them and again was struck by the different ways in which people approach life. The following is a copy of those notes.

Anthropology 220, 18 November
Ainu: People of Northern Japan

The Ainu are a traditional hunting and fishing people who once lived in many small coastal settlements in far northern Japan (see figure 14.18). Today, most descendants of the Ainu take part in the predominant Japanese culture. It is reported that only 15 fluent speakers of the Ainu language are alive, and no traditional Ainu settlements exist.

Traditionally, Ainu mothers breast-fed their children until the age of four or five, and families traced their descent through the female side. Small children played with carved fish, toy boats, and other toys that resembled objects that they would use later when they became adults. Older boys played with miniature hunting weapons, and girls played with dolls. Both girls and boys lived at home during childhood. Usually, the grandparents would instruct the children in the proper behavior and the duties expected of people in Ainu society. One of the most important behaviors was respect for elders.

When boys were about five, they were allowed to watch the men prepare for fishing expeditions. At about 12 or 13, they began going out in the ocean with the adult men. When boys turned 15, they started wearing their hair as the adult men did. They began to let it grow long and grew a mustache and beard as well. Girls began learning household chores when they turned five or six. At 13, the girls began to receive facial tattoos. A few years later, when the tattoos were complete (see figure 14.19), they put on adult women's clothing. (The Ainu believed that tattoos in conspicuous places would keep evil spirits at bay.)

Young couples usually courted with little involvement of their parents and usually

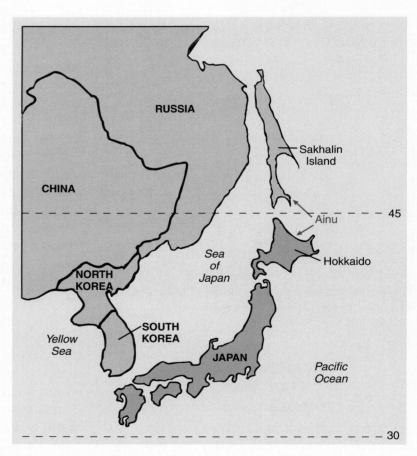

Figure 14.18 Ainu location. The Ainu traditionally lived in small coastal settlements in far northern Japan and on the southern tip of Sakhalin Island.

Figure 14.19 **Ainu girls dancing.** When Ainu girls began to mature, they started receiving tattoos. The Ainu believed that the tattoos would keep evil spirits away.

married by the time they were 16 or 17. When a child was born, both the new father and new mother would spend a period of time at home and would not engage in their usual activities. Either partner could end the marriage if she or he wanted. If this happened, the daughters would live with their mother, and the sons would live with their father.

Gusii: People of Kenya

Among the traditional Gusii of Kenya (see figure 14.20 for location), people live in farming homesteads as extended families. Usually, one man is the head of these extended families. The family might include his wives and their children as well as his married sons and their wives and children. People trace their descent entirely through the male line.

Generally, children are weaned when their mother becomes pregnant again, which might be anywhere from one to three years. Children stay close to home and have duties to perform. As soon

as they turn five, the girls begin to take care of the infants, and the young boys help with the cattle. Both girls and boys work in the fields from the time they are about six or seven years old.

The grandparents generally are friendly and good humored. But the children's own father is a strong authority figure whom the children both respect and fear. When the boys turn seven or eight, they begin living in a separate house on the homestead.

Girls are formally initiated into womanhood when they are only eight or nine, as soon as they begin to show a strong interest in women's duties. Boys are formally initiated into manhood when they are between 10 and 12. After special initiation ceremonies involving the removal of the clitoris (for girls) or foreskin (for boys), there is a period of seclusion and then a formal public appearance. At this point, the boys and girls are welcomed as adult members of Gusii society.

After a few years of brief relationships, a young man might choose a young woman as a prospective wife. He sends someone to

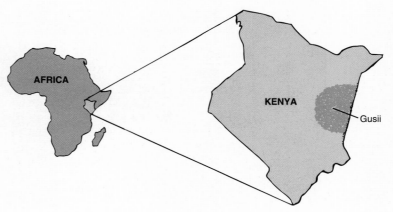

Figure 14.20 **A map of the Gusii region of Kenya.**

inquire about her background. This person also finds out the formal price (in cattle) that her family expects in return for her hand in marriage. If everyone agrees and the young man's family pays the price, the groom and his family then come and take the bride to his home. It is a tradition that the bride pretends to put up a fight rather than go willingly.

After a young woman is married, she remains with her new husband for a month. But then she returns to her father's home for about two months. During this time, she can request that the marriage be dissolved if she is truly unhappy. She also might leave her husband later, especially if she does not become pregnant within a year or so. In all cases, the children from a marriage legally belong to the father.

The Amish in America

The Amish keep a traditional culture in North America side by side with modern American culture (refer to figure 14.21). The Amish are of Swiss and German descent and speak both English and a particular dialect of German. They refer to all members of the modern American culture as "the English."

The Amish reject many aspects of the dominant culture and prefer simplicity. In general, Amish people avoid any use of electric power other than some batteries they use in the home. They travel in horse-drawn buggies and do not own or operate automobiles. However, they will hire or accept rides in cars and buses when necessary. They farm using horse-powered cultivating methods or else are carpenters or craftspeople.

Amish children dress almost as miniature adults as soon as they are old enough to be out of diapers (see figure 14.22). They are regarded with great affection by the adults. Children are encouraged to play but also to be responsible for many chores around the farmstead.

At around five, the children begin formal schooling. In the United States, the Supreme Court has recognized the right of the Amish to run and administer their own system of schools. These teachers are usually young Amish women who are not yet married.

The children study English, practical arithmetic, High German (which is necessary

Figure 14.21   Amish man plowing. Amish communities like this one in Lancaster County, Pennsylvania, exist throughout North America.

Figure 14.22   Amish man and child. At a very young age, Amish children are dressed in styles similar to the adults.

to read their religious books), geography, basic science, and several other subjects. The goal of all of their studies is to provide the children with the knowledge that they will need to function successfully in Amish society and to deal with the surrounding culture. The Amish consider their society a community of equals and they frown on pride. In school, then, they expect the bright students who finish their lessons quickly to help the slower schoolmates with their work so that the whole group can advance together. The Amish believe that formal education should end with the eighth grade to avoid the possibility of the children becoming too worldly.

When Amish children are not in school, they spend time playing and learning about the skills of adult life. It is not unusual to see a young Amish boy of 10 driving a five-horse hitch of big draft animals and plowing a field by himself. And Amish girls of the same age are expected to handle a big garden or care for a group of younger children.

When their formal education is over, Amish youngsters work full-time at home, where they learn agricultural skills. The Amish believe that a person must be a mature

adult, usually in his or her early 20s, in order to freely choose to accept formal baptism into the Amish community. Formal baptism includes a commitment to completely reject the forbidden aspects of the outside culture. Therefore, young people between 16 and 22 have more freedom to experiment with the outside culture than either young children or baptized adults. This period is described by a Germanic term that roughly translates as "running-around time." Young Amish men often decorate their buggies and may dress in clothes like those of the "English" teenagers. These young men often work at town jobs in construction. Some may even own a car, which they generally keep somewhere other than at home.

During the running-around time, girls often make and wear brightly colored dresses that older women would not wear. They may hold jobs as restaurant workers or store clerks. Groups of young people or courting couples may travel into cities to attend films, sporting events, or even dances. Their elders are aware of what is going on but, in general, regard it as a necessary period in the young people's development.

Those who finally decide not to receive baptism, but instead join the mainstream culture, usually remain on good terms with their families and often return to visit. Those who accept baptism but later decide to leave, however, are shunned (avoided).

When young Amish people marry, they take up a lifestyle like their parents' and raise a family of their own. Amish elders are highly respected and generally turn over the responsibility of running the farm when the youngest child is old enough to take over. At this time, the elders move from the main house into a small one that is located nearby. They take an active role in raising and teaching their grandchildren and are always on hand to lend advice and help around the farm.

Personal Journal Entry: 19 May

Because I have been making observations of humans and learning about many related aspects of human growth and development, it has been interesting to read over my notes from anthropology. It has been clear to me that fundamental aspects of human biology are responsible for both similarities and differences in the way humans develop. This is because all humans are very closely related. It now is becoming clear to me that all human cultures have developed ways of responding to developmental milestones and the processes involved as humans develop. Cultural influences lend an additional layer of diversity to the expression of human life stages.

3. Begin your study of another culture.
   a. Look through the resources that your teacher has as well as additional resources that you might want to find.
   b. With your team, divide the responsibility of reading and reviewing the resources. Then work together to write a general overview of the culture.

   > You may want to find additional resources of your own. Remember, you are not limited to books and magazines. You may want to look for Web sites, films, videos, music, or art. You may even know someone from the culture you have chosen who might be willing to share ideas with you.

   c. Share what you have learned so far with your team. Exchange resources if you wish.

4. Obtain the handout *Multicultural Fair Presentation Rubric* for the multicultural fair entry from your teacher. Participate in a class discussion about the criteria that your teacher will use to assess your entry and knowledge.

5. With your team, develop a specific design for your entry in the multicultural fair. Refer to the guidelines in the need to know, *Guidelines for Creating Your Entry for the Multicultural Fair.*

> Remember to divide the work for researching and constructing your entry fairly among all teammates. For example, each team member could work on one life stage listed in step 2 of the need to know, and one cultural aspect listed in step 4. Keep in mind that your job is not just to learn about the life stages in another culture, but to teach your classmates about them as well.

6. Prepare your entry for the multicultural fair.

> Be as creative as you want, but remember to follow the guidelines provided. Also, clearly illustrate how your culture provides an example that can help answer the focus question of the activity: "How do developmental processes interact with cultural factors to affect the physical, cognitive, social, and emotional growth of humans?" Remember, your entry provides the evidence for all that you have learned in this chapter.

7. Practice the presentation portion of your entry.

> You may want to schedule additional practice time outside of class. You will participate in the fair as both a visitor and an exhibitor.

NEED TO KNOW

Guidelines for Creating Your Entry for the Multicultural Fair

   Your team's entry for the fair should include a combination of visual displays and written support material. You may want to include an audio portion as well. Displays may be arranged in any way that you want, within the boundaries that your teacher establishes. You also will need to create or develop some type of presentation that includes all team members.

   As you create your entry, your team should do the following.

1. Provide an overview of the culture that you studied. Include where this group of people lives or lived and a description of their way of life.

2. Present information about each of the following life stages.
   a. Infancy and childhood
   b. Adolescence
   c. Adulthood
   d. Old age
      1) Describe the physical and social setting that is predominant at each life stage.

      Who is around the individuals at each stage? What do the individuals do at each stage?

      2) Describe the cultural practices for the individuals at each stage.

      What is expected of the individual at each stage?

      3) Describe the cultural values surrounding each stage.

      How are the individuals in each stage perceived?

3. Explore some aspect of cognitive development that seems particularly significant in the culture that you are studying. For example, in American culture, the point at which a child begins to speak is considered significant. Explain why you think this particular cognitive development is highly valued. Describe the underlying biology that allows for this aspect of development.

4. Choose and complete each of the following.
   a. Describe the different forms of cultural expression that seem to be significant during any life stage, for example, music, art, dance, mythology, religion, or dress.
   b. Describe the celebration of at least 1 of the following rites of passage:
      - Birth
      - Puberty
      - Marriage
      - Death
   c. Describe the differences in growing up male from growing up female in the culture you are studying.

5. Some part of your entry should be a presentation. You may, for example, decide to portray in detail 1 life stage that you found most interesting. You may want to incorporate music, literature, art, dress, or dance.

Analysis

After you have completed step 6, record in your science notebook your reflections on the following questions. Work individually.

1. Imagine that you are a young woman or man living in the culture that you have just studied. Write 2 or 3 paragraphs that describe how he or she might view modern American culture. Which aspects of your life experience would seem similar to his or her experiences? Which aspects would seem different?

2. Reflect on the focus question of the activity with respect to all the cultures you have learned about. What have you learned about biological development in humans that may help explain both the similarities and the differences between different human cultures?

What happens when someone cuts down the trees along a riverbank? The trees are gone, you say. But what effect does the loss of these trees have on the river's ecosystem? What about the birds that depend on the trees for nesting or the insects that use the leaves for food? How will the loss of shade affect water temperature and the fish that live in the river? Many organisms depend on these trees in different ways. So, how has this complex web of interactions been altered? In this unit, you will explore the concepts of interaction and interdependence in living systems. You will also investigate the issue of human influence on ecosystems.

Ecology:
Interaction and Interdependence in Living Systems

By the end of unit 6, you should understand that

✔ a community of organisms interacts with the abiotic environment to form ecosystems;

✔ ecosystems are complex, but it is possible to analyze them;

✔ populations are limited in size by the amount of available resources;

✔ ecosystems can be modified by human actions; and

✔ human actions follow from decisions, which are made within a cultural context.

UNIT CONTENTS

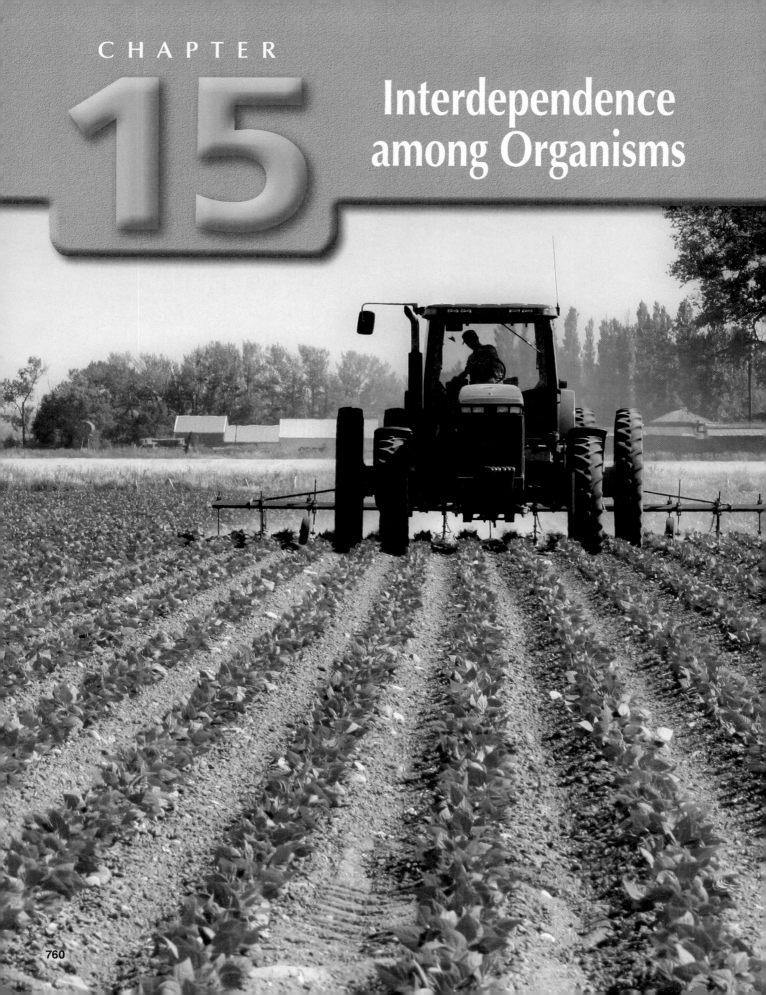

We do not inherit the land from our ancestors; we borrow it from our children.

Haida Tribe Saying

Life along a bustling city street. Life in a forest. Life in the oceans. Life in a refugee camp in Africa. Life on a farm in rural Ohio. Think of an organism that lives in one of these settings. In what ways does this organism depend on other organisms for survival? How can such interdependence among these organisms be described? What factors influence their interdependence?

An **ecosystem** is made of all the living (biotic) and nonliving (abiotic) components in an environment. In this chapter, you will learn about the interdependence of organisms in various ecosystems. First, you will seek evidence of interactions in your own school yard or neighborhood. Next, you will study interactions in ecosystems throughout the world. You will further explore ecosystems by considering the types of resources that exist in them. You will then analyze the influences those resources have on communities of organisms. You will apply your understanding of communities and resources to different types of "island" ecosystems. During your study of island ecosystems, you will analyze patterns of population growth in a real group of people who lived on an island off the coast of South America. You will also examine how global climate change is affecting organisms living in specialized habitats, in this case, the tops of mountains, or so-called islands in the sky. Finally, you will evaluate your understanding by describing how your critter will use resources and interact with other organisms in a particular ecosystem.

GOALS FOR THE CHAPTER

By the end of chapter 15, *Interdependence among Organisms*, you should understand the following concepts:

- ✔ Organisms interact and are interdependent.
- ✔ Interactions occur among biotic and abiotic parts of an ecosystem.
- ✔ Factors such as climate and carrying capacity affect the interdependence of organisms.
- ✔ Humans influence the biosphere in many different ways.

To help you develop these understandings, you will complete the following activities.

ENGAGE / EXPLORE	Observing the World around Us
EXPLORE	Interactions in the World around Us
EXPLAIN	The Pasture Story
ELABORATE	Mystery on Easter Island
ELABORATE	Islands in the Sky
EVALUATE	Critters and Interdependence

The chapter organizer can help you keep track of your learning and the flow of ideas across the chapter. Refer to it frequently as you complete the chapter's activities.

Observing the World around Us

Key Idea: Organisms interact with other organisms.

Linking Question:
What are the different ways organisms interact with each other and with the environment they live in?

Chapter 15

 EXPLORE

Interactions in the World around Us

Key Idea: Organisms interact with their environment in complex ways.

MAJOR CONCEPTS

✔ Organisms interact and are interdependent.

✔ Interactions occur among the biotic and abiotic parts of an ecosystem.

✔ Factors such as climate and carrying capacity affect the interdependence of organisms.

✔ Humans influence the biosphere in many different ways.

Linking Question:
How do interactions that involve the use of shared resources influence the number of organisms an environment can support?

 EXPLAIN

The Pasture Story

Key Idea: The use of an environment's resources influences carrying capacity.

Linking Question:
Does the concept of carrying capacity apply to humans?

EVALUATE

Critters and Interdependence

Part A: Resources and Ecosystems
Part B: Critters in Ecosystems

Key Idea: Every organism depends upon abiotic factors in the environment and interacts with other organisms.

Interdependence among Organisms

Linking Question:
How is my critter limited by abiotic and biotic factors in its ecosystem?

ELABORATE

Islands in the Sky

Key Idea: Multiple limiting factors can operate to affect population levels.

Linking Question:
How do limiting factors affect nonhuman organisms?

ELABORATE

Mystery on Easter Island

Key Idea: Human population growth is restricted by limiting factors.

 ENGAGE

 EXPLORE

Observing the World around Us

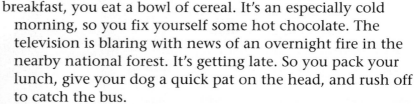

Imagine crawling out of bed in the morning. You flip on a light and your radio, and stroll to the bathroom as music plays in the background. For breakfast, you eat a bowl of cereal. It's an especially cold morning, so you fix yourself some hot chocolate. The television is blaring with news of an overnight fire in the nearby national forest. It's getting late. So you pack your lunch, give your dog a quick pat on the head, and rush off to catch the bus.

This scenario describes a typical morning for many teenagers. Think about how you interact with your environment during your morning routine. In this Engage-Explore activity, *Observing the World around Us*, you will make observations of organisms in their environment and you will consider what interactions you see in the natural world.

Materials

drawing pencil

PROCESS AND PROCEDURES

Go outside as your teacher directs. In your science notebook, record the following observations and answers to the questions.

1. Look carefully at all the organisms around you. Find 2 or more different organisms that are interacting with each other.

   Remember to consider all the living things you observe, not just animal life.

2. Create a quick drawing of the interacting organisms from step 1. Add labels or a brief explanation for the interactions.

3. Listen for sounds made by living organisms. Write a brief description for how 1 organism is using sound to interact with other organisms.

4. Focus on the smells of the natural world. Write a brief description for how 1 odor you smell may be evidence for an organism interacting with other organisms in its community.

5. Name and describe or draw 2 different organisms near you that may be prey for other organisms.

6. Name and describe or draw 2 different organisms that have a distinguishing texture.

7. Write a brief description for how each texture may encourage or discourage other organisms to touch it.

8. Name and describe or draw 1 organism that appears to be living in isolation from all other organisms.

Analysis

Discuss the *Analysis* questions with a partner. Write all answers to the questions in your science notebook.

1. Does the organism observed in step 8 require any interactions with other organisms to survive? Why do you think so?
2. During this activity, do you think the class was able to observe all of the different types of organisms present in the study area? Explain your answer.

Interactions in the World around Us

Think about the different organisms you observed in the Engage-Explore activity, *Observing the World around Us*. How were the various organisms interacting? Do both organisms benefit from an interaction? Is one organism harmed while the other benefits? Are both organisms harmed by the interaction? These are just some of the questions an ecologist might ask when studying the interactions among organisms in a certain area.

Ecologists (figure 15.1) attempt to describe and understand the interrelationships that exist between organisms and their environments. First, they gather information about organisms and their environment in a particular area. They might compare this area with different regions to look for similarities, differences, and patterns. Finally, they try to explain the patterns they observe. They might run experiments to test their hypotheses.

In this Explore activity, *Interactions in the World around Us*, you will consider the questions posed above as you practice thinking like an ecologist. You will look for patterns and analyze the interactions you observed in the Engage-Explore activity, *Observing the World around Us*. You also will have the opportunity to compare your observations with images from around the world. The images you will see on the video represent a wide variety of interactions in many different settings.

www.scilinks.org
Topic: ecosystem
Code: human4E765

Figure 15.1 Some ecologists analyze the complexity of an ecosystem by concentrating on the changes in the quantity and the quality of one particular component of the ecosystem.

Materials (per team of 2)

online resource (watch as a team)
1 task card

PROCESS AND PROCEDURES

1. With your partner, share the observations you recorded during the Engage-Explore activity, *Observing the World around Us*, and discuss the following questions. Be prepared to share your ideas with the rest of your class.
   a. What types of interactions did you see between organisms in which only 1 organism appeared to benefit from the interaction?
   b. What types of interactions seemed to benefit all organisms involved?
   c. Give examples of how odor, taste, and sound can lead to interactions that either attract or repel other organisms.
   d. Name at least 5 living and 3 nonliving components that are part of the area where you made your observations.
2. Participate in a class discussion about your observations and answers, as your teacher directs.

   When sharing your ideas, consider how you might describe the ecosystem where you made your observations.

3. In your science notebook, use your own words to write a definition for the term "ecosystem."
4. Obtain a task card with a set of 4 tasks from your teacher. These tasks will help guide your observations as you watch the video segment, "Images from around the World."
5. In your science notebook, make an organizing table to help you take brief notes about the examples you will see in the video.

   If you wish, you may split up the tasks with your partner. You may want to set up columns for each task you need to complete and enter examples in the rows of your table. For help with this task, you may want to refer to *How to Use and Create Organizing Tables* in appendix B4.

HOW TO

6. Watch the video segment, "Images from around the World." Provide examples of the influences assigned on your task card.

   Be sure to record examples in your table.

7. Create a new 3-column table in your science notebook and title it "interactions among organisms."
   a. Label the first column "one organism benefits and the other organism is harmed."
   b. Label the second column "both organisms benefit."
   c. Label the third column "both organisms are harmed."
8. Join another pair of students who had a different set of tasks. Discuss your video observations as a team. Choose at least 2 observations from your discussion to record in each column of your *Interactions among Organisms* table.
9. Study the table in figure 15.2 to learn more about how ecologists classify interactions among organisms. Add the terms from figure 15.2 to appropriate locations on your *Interactions among Organisms* table.

Interaction	Effect of the interaction	Description
Mutualism	+ / +	In this interaction among organisms, both organisms benefit. For example, lichens consist of an alga and a fungus that live in close association. The alga produces food through photosynthesis, and the fungus provides moisture and nutrients. Another example is the interaction between flowering plant species and insects that pollinate them.
Predator-prey	+ / −	One organism (predator) eats another (prey). This interaction harms the prey (often killing it) but benefits the predator.
Parasitism	+ / −	One organism (the parasite) lives on or in another organism (the host), using it as a habitat and a food source (figure 15.3). The interaction may or may not kill the host species over time.
Herbivory	+ / −	This interaction involves the consumption of living plant material by a consumer. The interaction is not necessarily lethal to the plant, but it can be.
Competition	− / −	Organisms may compete for such things as food, space, sunlight, nutrients, or water. Competition often limits the growth of populations of organisms. In competition, both organisms may be harmed through the effort necessary to obtain a limited resource.
Commensalism	+ / 0	One organism benefits from the interaction, and the other organism is unaffected. For example, many orchids use trees as surfaces upon which to grow. The trees are not harmed or helped by the orchids. The orchids, however, benefit by growing near the top of the tree, where they can collect more sunlight and rain. True commensalism is relatively rare in nature.

Figure 15.2   Interactions in ecosystems classified by the effects of the interaction. The survival or reproduction of a species may benefit from the presence of another species (+) or be harmed by it (–). In the table, "+ / +" indicates that both species benefit from an interaction; "+ / –" indicates that one species benefits and the other is harmed; benefits; "– / –" indicates that both species are harmed; and "+ / 0" indicates that one organism benefits and the other is unaffected.

10. Individually, read the scenario, *Early Morning Reflections*. As you read, record additional examples of interactions that fit into your *Interactions among Organisms* table.

11. In your science notebook, write 1 or 2 general statements about the interactions of organisms (see figure 15.3) with each other and with the environment.

Think about the interactions you recorded in your *Interactions among Organisms* table, your observations from the Engage-Explore activity, *Observing the World around Us*, and the video images.

Figure 15.3 The mistletoe growing on this pine tree branch is a parasitic plant.

SCENARIO

Early Morning Reflections

Dear Senator Wilks,

I just returned from an interesting stay at a ranch in northern Nevada. I would like to share with you some reflections about my visit to your part of the state.

The landscape of northern Nevada is spacious and stark. Yet there is still something splendid about the place. I spent the weekend with my good friend and his family at their ranch on the Marys River floodplain. I was inspired by their down-to-earth approach to life and genuine concern for the fragile river ecosystem that is part of their vast, 7,000 acre (about 2,800 hectare) ranch.

Marys River winds its way through the ranch. As my friend showed me around, I noticed a group of willow trees lining the riverbank. But farther upriver and downriver, there were almost no willows. I wondered what caused this pattern. When I asked, I saw a faint smirk cross my friend's face, followed by a touch of sadness. He told me that back in the 1970s, many of the farmers along the river began cutting down the willows because they thought the trees sucked up too much water. They thought that by cutting down the willows, they would increase their crop yields. My friend explained that it may have worked that way for a while, but there were unintended consequences when the river

flooded. It flooded in 1983 and 1984, after the willows on most farms along the river had been long gone. My friend's family never cut the willows, and their ranch had the least damage of any along the river. Others, where the willows were cut, had great damage. The willows, along with the native hay meadow vegetation, helped stabilize the riverbanks and the floodplain soils. Together, they reduced erosion and other flood damage. But my friend said there was even more to the story. To show me what he meant, he took me down to the riverbank.

The variety of lush vegetation that I saw in addition to the willows amazed me. I tried to figure out why there was so much vegetation there. I saw beaver dams built across the river at various places and, although I didn't see any beaver, I did see two otters.

Soon, my friend began to give me the whole story. He explained that the willows and other vegetation along the river provide material with which the beavers can build their dams. With the dams in place, the water becomes somewhat deeper just upriver from the dam. The amount of groundwater increases in these areas. This additional water is what supports the lush vegetation. As he talked, I made mental notes of all the evidence I saw. My friend explained that the willows and other overhanging plants also shade the river so that it stays cooler. This keeps the level of oxygen higher.

I started nodding my head. I was beginning to get the picture. Willows for shade. More oxygen in the water. Deeper water levels. With these things, the river could support more life, including aquatic plants and fish. This affects the entire food chain to the level of the beaver (an herbivore) and the otter (an omnivore that loves fish).

Without the willows, the ranchers lost out during the spring floods. But the beaver also lost out because without willows there was no material for building dams. Without the dams and the shade from vegetation, the river was too shallow and warm to support much aquatic life. So the fish lost out. Without the fish, the otter lost out, too, because it had almost nothing to eat.

The river environment surrounding this ranch is quite barren, especially to the west. But my friend and his family have been stewards of the river and the land—and their stretch of the river is fertile and beautiful. I would like to encourage you to consider how the government can reward and encourage good stewardship.

Sincerely,

Jada Cameron

Analysis

1. Do you think that humans have more or less influence on the environment than other organisms have? Provide reasoning for your answer.
2. Do you think that humans have a responsibility to monitor how we influence the environment? Provide reasoning for your answer.

The Pasture Story

In the Explore activity, *Interactions in the World around Us*, you studied some of the complex interactions that take place in a variety of ecosystems. One organism's actions influence those of another. Populations influence one another as well. Humans influence other humans, other species, and the nonliving components of the ecosystems where we live. In some situations, we feel that we can control the influence that other humans have on our lives. In most situations, the decisions made by other people in our communities have significant influence on our lives. In this Explain activity, *The Pasture Story*, you will study a historical dramatization of farmers grazing cows on a shared pasture. This will help you think about the factors that influence how individuals share resources.

Materials (per team of 2–4)

online resource
computer with Web access

PROCESS AND PROCEDURES

1. View the video, "The Pasture Story." Work in teams as your teacher directs.
2. What happened to the pasture that the farmers shared?
3. In your science notebook, write your ideas about why this happened to the pasture. Discuss these ideas with your teammates.
4. Divide your team into 2 groups. Each group will make the decisions for 1 of the dairy farmers (Sondra or Jason) in the "Pasture Profits" simulation.
5. Go to the "Pasture Profits Simulation" and run your first simulation.

   Follow your teacher's instructions to simulate managing the pasture's resources while maximizing your profits. If time permits, you may be able to run the simulation again to try a different management strategy.

6. Print the individual and summary reports that appear after you have completed the simulation. With your teammates, graph the 4 sets of data found on the summary reports onto the *Pasture Profits* handout.
7. Analyze your graphs with your teammates. Discuss the following questions.
   a. Which management scenario best protected the pasture?
   b. What is the relationship between the amount of food available per cow and the number of cows?
   c. What is the relationship between the amount of food available and the production of milk per cow?
   d. Using your graphs, determine the maximum number of cows the pasture can support and still have the ability to renew itself.

      You may want to look at other teams' graphs for additional information that may help with this task.

   e. Read the following paragraph for information that will help you answer this question: Do you think different management strategies affect the carrying capacity for the pasture? Record your answer in your science notebook, citing evidence from your simulations.

      Carrying capacity is the maximum number of individuals of a certain species that a habitat can support. The carrying capacity for a habitat can change over time if the habitat changes in size or if resources within the habitat change in abundance or quality. In the pasture example, carrying capacity was the maximum number of cows that the pasture could support without destroying its ability to renew itself.

Topic: carrying capacity
Code: human4E770

8. Read the background information provided in "The Abundant Earth" segment. On the basis of your reading, use your own words to define the following concepts. Record your definitions in your science notebook.
   a. Natural resource
   b. Renewable resource
   c. Nonrenewable resource

9. What is the best management option for the commonly owned pasture in the "Pasture Profits" simulation? Why do you think so? In your science notebook, write your claim and support it with evidence and reasoning.

10. Contribute your ideas about steps 7 and 9 to a class discussion.

Analysis

With your team, consider the following questions. Record your answers individually in your science notebook.

1. What specific types of interactions among organisms were present in the pasture simulation?

   You might find it helpful to refer to the *Interactions among Organisms* table in your science notebook, which you completed in the Explore activity, *Interactions in the World around Us*.

2. List 3 examples of resources in the modern world that humans use that are like the commonly owned pasture in "The Pasture Story" video. Describe how people manage each example.

3. Are renewable resources more likely to be biotic or abiotic resources? Explain your answer.

4. Write a paragraph that summarizes the challenges you and your teammates faced in maximizing personal profits on a pasture owned in common. In your summary, include a response to this question: What kinds of information made it easier for your team to make decisions about how to best manage the pasture?

5. Like every model, the simulation "Pasture Profits" has realistic and unrealistic features when compared to an actual pasture. Explain at least 2 realistic and 2 unrealistic aspects of the "Pasture Profits" model.

Mystery on Easter Island

Islands are good places to study ecosystems because they are somewhat isolated. Because they are isolated, their resources are much easier to measure. It is especially interesting to study the patterns of population growth for animals on islands. Such is the case for a human population that lived on Easter Island from the year 500 to the present. This Elaborate activity, *Mystery on Easter Island*, will give you an opportunity to examine the mystery that surrounds Easter Island. You will study data about the history of its human population. You will then reflect on some of the interactions that took place in that ecosystem.

Materials (per team)

online resource
computer with Web access
different-colored pens or pencils

PROCESS AND PROCEDURES

1. Read the need to know, *The Mystery*, to learn more about Easter Island.

NEED TO KNOW

ENGLISH SPANISH

The Mystery

Noted writer Jared Diamond called Easter Island "the world's most isolated scrap of habitable land." Easter Island is located in the Pacific Ocean, more than 3,218 km (2,000 mi) west of South America. The island has an area of about 166 km² (64 mi²). Its subtropical location gives it a mild climate. And its volcanic origin provides fertile soil. Despite its mild climate and fertile soil, when Europeans first reached the island in 1722, their first impression was of a barren wasteland. The island was without a single tree or bush more than 3 m (10 ft) tall. There were no native animals larger than insects. The people had no real source of firewood to warm themselves. Chickens were their only domestic animals. Yet the evidence indicates that at one time in its history the island offered abundant food and building materials. This was when the first Polynesian colonists arrived, some 1,400 years earlier. What happened?

The first colonizers traveled to the island in double canoes. They arrived at the roughly triangular island (see figure 15.4) in approximately CE 450. When they came to the island, it was covered by a forest dominated by a now-extinct species of giant palm tree (see figure 15.5). These abundant palm trees were an important resource for the colonizers. In fact, ancient Easter Islanders created rock art showing images of palm trees and other important island resources such as birds, fish, turtles, and dolphins (see figure 15.6).

The giant palm is similar in appearance to the Chilean wine palm. We can look at the Chilean wine palm and make inferences about the

SCI*LINKS*
NSTA
www.scilinks.org
Topic: habitat
Code: human4E772

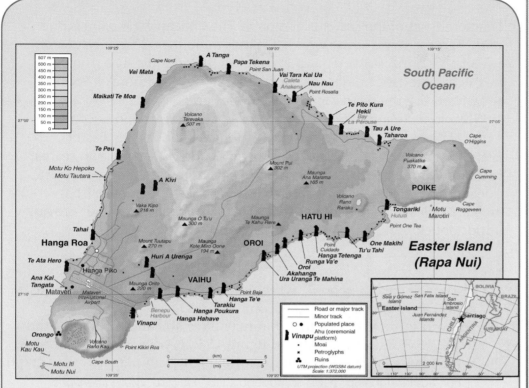

Figure 15.4 Easter Island is located more than 3,218 km (2,000 mi) west of South America. It is roughly triangular, with sides of 18, 18, and 24 km (11, 11, and 15 mi). How would you calculate the surface area of Easter Island?

Figure 15.5 This Chilean wine palm is similar to the now-extinct species of giant palm that was abundant when humans first arrived on Easter Island.

Figure 15.6 These petroglyphs were carved by ancient Easter Islanders.

characteristics of the Easter Island palm. The Chilean wine palm is one of the largest palms in the world. It stands more than 20 m (about 65 ft) tall and has a trunk diameter of 1 m (about 3 ft) or more. The trunk has a characteristic bulge, and the large leaves are featherlike. South Americans use the palm sap to make honey and wine.

Why did the giant palms that once covered Easter Island become extinct? What happened to the population of colonizers on Easter Island? Visitors to Easter Island have been asking these and many other questions about the mysterious island for hundreds of years. For some questions, we can only speculate answers. However, evidence from archaeological digs and inferences based on population studies provide important clues for uncovering Easter Island's history.

2. In your science notebook, write down what you think caused the giant Easter Island palm to become extinct.
3. To learn more about factors that may have affected the palm, study figure 15.7. Draw the graph in figure 15.7 in your science notebook.
4. Follow steps 4a–e to help you make highlight comments on your graph.

HOW TO

For additional help, refer to appendix B6, *How to Write Highlight Comments and Captions.*

a. What do you see when you compare the years 400 and 850?
b. What do you see when you compare the years between 850 and 1250?
c. What do you see when you compare the years between 1250 and 1600?
d. What do you see when you compare the years between 1600 and 2000?

Figure 15.7
Population growth for the first Easter Island inhabitants.
Researchers Paul Bahn and John Flenley used historical studies and population formulas to infer population levels on Easter Island over time.

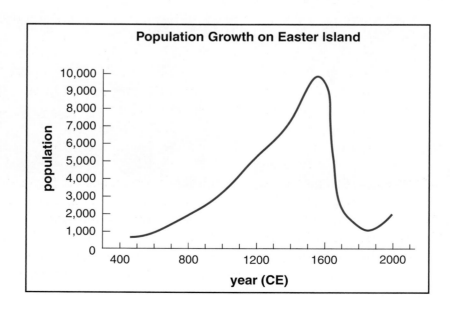

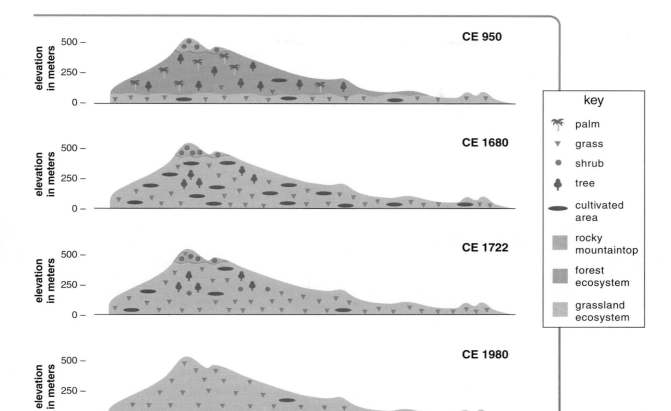

Figure 15.8 Easter Island vegetation distribution between CE 950 and CE 1980.
Biologists study ancient pollen and spore samples to determine the historical vegetation distribution.

   e. Write 2 or 3 sentences that describe what your observations about the graph mean.
5. Share your answers for step 4e with your teammates. What was similar among all your ideas? What was different?
6. With your teammates, study the vegetation charts and information in figure 15.8. Write a brief description of the Easter Island ecosystem. Include at least 3 examples of biotic and 3 examples of abiotic resources on the island that likely influenced the human population.
7. View the "Easter Island" segments. You will learn more about the islanders, the mysterious stone statues (figure 15.9), the land, and the vegetation. As you view these segments, think about this question: How did the presence of humans affect the Easter Island ecosystem?
8. Discuss with your partner the changes that took place on Easter Island after the first humans arrived. Write 1 or 2 paragraphs that summarize the changes in vegetation on Easter Island between 950 and 1980. Also, include your ideas about what you think caused those changes.

   Consider the interactions and interdependence that took place among the people as well as among the people and the shared biotic and abiotic resources.

Figure 15.9 These monoliths (called *moai*) were carved from compacted and hardened volcanic ash by using stone tools. They stand up to 11 m (about 36 ft) tall and weigh up to 77 metric tons (85 short tons).

9. Participate in a class discussion of steps 5–8.
10. To get additional ideas to help you explain the mystery on Easter Island, read the essays, *Interdependence Involves Limiting Factors and Carrying Capacity* and *Growing, Growing, Grown*. You may want to preview the questions in steps 11–16 before you read.
11. What limiting factor or factors slowed the growth of the human population on Easter Island? What other factors might limit the growth of a population of organisms? Give at least 3 specific examples.

Interdependence Involves Limiting Factors and Carrying Capacity

Newspapers report continued famines in Africa. New animals are being added to the endangered species list. What are the causes of these events? Are they caused by human mismanagement, or do some happen naturally?

We can find some of the answers by studying the concepts of carrying capacity and limiting factors. Carrying capacity is the maximum number of individuals of a certain species that a habitat can support. It is influenced by biotic (living) and abiotic (nonliving) factors. A **limiting factor** is anything that slows, or limits, population growth. Limiting factors can be biotic or abiotic. They influence the carrying capacity of an environment. Take the Easter Island ecosystem as an example. Biotic factors include the giant palms, rats, and humans. Abiotic factors include space, sunlight, freshwater, nutrients, and temperature.

Climate is the average weather conditions in a given area over long periods of time. Climatic conditions are abiotic and include temperature; sunlight intensity; precipitation in the form of rain, snow, and fog; wind; and humidity (the amount of moisture in the air). The combination of climatic factors, along with individual weather events, partly determines the kinds of organisms that can live in a particular region. Along with individual weather events, climate also influences the carrying capacity for those organisms.

How does something like temperature limit population size? One example involves the mosquito and the organisms that feed on it. A cold day in the fall in temperate regions will kill almost all mosquitoes. The decrease in temperature directly affects the ability of the mosquito to survive. However, the effects don't stop with the mosquitoes. The organisms that feed on the mosquito, such as bats, now have a smaller food supply. The decline of the mosquito population due to cooler temperatures now lowers the carrying capacity for other populations until temperatures warm in the spring.

The same type of interactions takes place between various wildflower populations and the insects that pollinate them. As temperatures drop in the autumn, wildflowers die, leaving the seeds of the next generation in the soil. The insects then either die, become dormant, or migrate. In both examples, temperature causes limited population growth for a period of time.

What about water? How can it affect population size? Since water is needed by all living organisms, it is a limiting factor that influences the carrying capacity of many ecosystems. Look at figure 15.10. Water limits the carrying capacity of a savanna in East Africa. Also, because different organisms have different water needs, the location of water sources influences how populations are distributed throughout an ecosystem.

Figure 15.10 Water is a limiting factor in the savanna in East Africa. Here, only grasses and scattered trees can grow. These plants in turn support grazing animals. The grazing animals move on when the rainfall in their location decreases.

Light also can be a limiting factor. The penetration of light into the ocean determines the depth to which organisms that photosynthesize can grow. This is generally not beyond the depth of 180 m (590 ft). If silt reduces the water clarity in a pond or lake, plant growth is limited. In dense rain forests, the tallest trees spread their leaves and take most of the light. The ground below them is shaded. The shade prevents other plants from reaching great heights. Light affects animals indirectly. The amount of light influences the number of plants that can grow. This then influences the carrying capacity of the environment for organisms that feed on the plants.

Space is another abiotic limiting factor. Every individual needs living space, but some need more than others. For example, individual corn plants grow well when they are planted close together. A mountain lion requires many square kilometers of space to find enough food. However, the availability of this space is affected by population density. **Population density** is the number of individuals in relation to the space a population occupies. An increase in density can have a drastic effect on a population. For example, think about the experiment described in figure 15.11. Researchers gave caged mice more food than they needed each day. As the mice reproduced, the cages became very crowded. Because of this, some female mice stopped caring for their young. Mice continued to be born, but many newborn mice died from neglect. Eventually, the death rate of young mice reached 100 percent. Space, as a limiting factor, affects all living populations and the carrying capacity of particular ecosystems for those populations.

Figure 15.11 **Experiments involving population growth of mice.** (*a*) In one population experiment, researchers provided mice with more than enough food. (*b*) As a result, the population grew dramatically. Space then became a limiting factor that resulted in a high death rate among young mice.

Growing, Growing, Grown

ENGLISH SPANISH

SCiLINKS
NSTA
www.scilinks.org

Topic: population
Code: human4E778

Why did the human population on Easter Island grow and grow and suddenly crash? Do all populations of organisms grow in this way? Thomas Malthus (pictured in figure 15.12) spent many years thinking about how populations grow. In 1798, he put forth an idea about this topic. He indicated that under ideal conditions both the total population size and the rate the population increases rise steadily across time. This is called **exponential growth**. A simpler way to think about exponential growth is that the larger a population gets, the faster it grows. During exponential growth, a population can reach a very large size in a short amount of time. However, a population must have an unlimited supply of resources to do this. These resources include limiting factors such as food, water, space, and protection from other organisms.

When graphed, an exponentially growing population takes on a J-shaped appearance (figure 15.13). This growth principle applies to all species—both fast-breeding species such as the housefly and slow-breeding species such as the elephant. Just one adult female housefly could increase the fly population to 5.5 *trillion* in just one year (figure 15.14). Charles Darwin calculated that a mating pair of elephants could grow to 19 *million* elephants in only 750 years.

If all species can grow exponentially,

Figure 15.12 Thomas Malthus was an English economist who lived from 1766 until 1834. He gave serious thought to how populations grow.

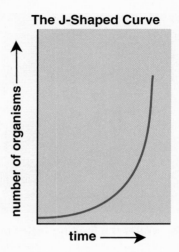

The J-Shaped Curve

number of organisms

time ——▶

Figure 15.13 The J-shaped curve is characteristic of populations that are growing exponentially.

why isn't the entire Earth buzzing with flies or being trampled by elephants? The answer has to do with limiting factors such as food supply.

Generation	Population size
1	120
2	7,200
3	432,000
4	25,920,000
5	1,555,200,000
6	93,312,000,000
7	5,598,720,000,000

Source: Data from E. J. Komondy (1984). *Concepts of Ecology,* third edition. Englewood Cliffs, NJ: Prentice Hall Publishers.

Figure 15.14 Predicted population growth of the common housefly in one year. This prediction is based on the following observations and assumptions. An average female fly lays 120 eggs at a time. About half the eggs develop into females. There are seven generations in one year. Individual flies live for one generation.

Malthus indicated that populations tend to increase in size exponentially (that is, 1, 2, 4, 8, 16, 32, 64, 128). However, food supply tends to increase only arithmetically (for example, 1, 2, 3, 4, 5, 6, 7). This means there is not enough food to sustain exponential growth. As the number of individuals increases, competition over resources such as food, water, and space also increases. It may cause death rates to increase. Exponential growth ceases. Since limiting factors are present in all ecosystems, exponential growth cannot be sustained. So, if exponential growth is restricted by limiting factors, what type of population growth occurs in the natural world?

In nature, conditions are not ideal and resources are in limited supply. Because of this, populations undergo a pattern of **logistic growth**. Scientists have observed this type of growth in populations of different organisms under natural conditions. The logistic growth curve looks like a flattened S (see figure 15.15). In logistic growth, the population levels off at the carrying capacity of the environment.

After all this talk of population growth, you might be wondering how the human population is growing. To help answer this question, let's look back in time. The world's human population was at 1 billion people in 1820. By 1930, it had reached 2 billion. In 1960s, the world's population was over 3 billion people. In less than 40 years, the population doubled to 6 billion people in 1999. The number of humans is expected to increase to 9 billion people by 2040.

By reading and thinking about those population figures, you have likely figured out that the human population is growing at an exponential rate. This raises interesting and timely questions. How will continued rates of human population growth affect global resources? What happens to the humans when the population exceeds Earth's carrying capacity? How will the quality of life for future generations be affected by unchecked population growth? None of these questions is easily answered. Yet future generations depend on us not only answering these questions but taking appropriate action as well.

The S-Shaped Curve

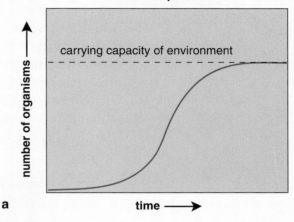

a

Population Growth of *Paramecium*

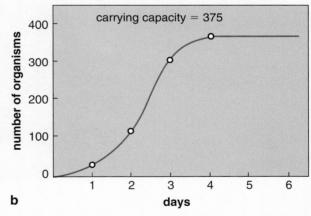

b

Source: From G.F. Gause (1934). *The Struggle for Existence.* Baltimore: Williams and Wilkins.

Figure 15.15 (*a*) **An idealized S-shaped growth curve. (*b*) A population growth curve for the single-celled organism *Paramecium*.** Limiting factors force this population of organisms to level off.

12. Color-code the population growth graph (figure 15.7) you drew in your science notebook in step 3, so that each significant trend in the rate of growth is a different color.

13. Add a line to this graph that shows where you think the island's carrying capacity for people was when the colonizers first landed on Easter Island. Label this line "initial carrying capacity." Why did you draw your line there?

    You might find it helpful to compare the vegetation distribution graphic in figure 15.8 with the population growth graph in figure 15.7 as you think about where this line should go.

14. What evidence can you point to on the population growth graph that suggests that the number of people on the island exceeded its carrying capacity?

15. Add another line to your graph. Show where you think the island's carrying capacity for people was around the year 1690. Label this line "later carrying capacity." Why did you draw your line there?

16. Using terminology from the essay, *Growing, Growing, Grown*, identify which type of population growth the human population on Easter Island experienced between the years 450 and 1250.

Analysis

With your partner, discuss and answer the following questions. Record your answers in your science notebook.

1. Think about the growth in the human population on Easter Island between 1000 and 1600. Compare that with the rate of growth during the first years that the colonizers were on the island. What might account for this large increase?

2. What does the example of Easter Island tell you about unchecked population growth?
3. Think about the relationship between Easter Island's population size and the resources available per individual. How is that relationship similar to the relationship between the number of cows and the common pasture from the previous activity (Explain, *The Pasture Story*)? What does each relationship demonstrate?
4. In what ways is the Earth system as a whole similar to an island ecosystem such as Easter Island? Use specific examples of resource consumption and interactions to explain your answer.

Islands in the Sky

In the previous Elaborate activity, *Mystery on Easter Island*, you studied the ecosystems on Easter Island. Organisms that live on Easter Island are surrounded by many miles of ocean. The situation causes the majority of plants and animals to be isolated from mainland populations. This Elaborate activity is titled *Islands in the Sky* because plants and animals living on the tops of mountains are nearly as isolated as those living on islands in the ocean. They are adapted to cold and sometimes arid conditions. These organisms may not have an easy way to move from one mountaintop to another. This activity will focus on one sky island resident from the mountains of the western United States: a small mammal called the American pika. You will use your understanding of the interactions among organisms, limiting factors, and scientific inquiry to gain a better understanding of why pika populations have been changing.

PROCESS AND PROCEDURES

1. Read the scenario, *Mystery Mountain Mammal* to become familiar with the star of this activity, the American pika.
2. Copy figure 15.18 from the scenario into your science notebook and study it. Write highlight comments on your data table. Share your ideas with your partner.

   Remember, highlight comments include "What you see" as well as "What it means." Compare the numbers between the time periods, as well as between the two elevation categories. For additional help, refer to appendix B6, *How to Write Highlight Comments and Captions*.

3. Write a final caption under the data table, basing it on your highlight comments.

   The caption should describe whether the number of pika populations is stable, increasing, or decreasing over time.

4. With your partner, brainstorm a list of all of the limiting factors that you think might affect pika populations. Create a 2-column table in your science notebook to organize the list into abiotic and biotic factors.

SCENARIO

ENGLISH SPANISH

Mystery Mountain Mammal

This past fall, Malcolm and his family moved from a large city to a small town in the Rocky Mountains. It was difficult for Malcolm to adjust to small town living at first. He was so used to the lights and sounds of the city that the cool, quiet nights were a bit unnerving. However, by early summer, the snow was almost done melting, and Malcolm began to feel that he was starting to fit in. To celebrate the start of summer vacation, Malcolm and his new friend, Dylan, decided to hike up Mount Princeton and enjoy the warm summer day.

During the hike, the boys passed through dense forests of aspen, spruce, and fir trees, crossed an alpine meadow with a small stream, and scrabbled up rocky slopes. As the sights and smells of a warm mountain day filled their senses, they began to feel calm and peaceful. They decided to take a break on some sunny boulders by the trail. All of a sudden, a loud sound startled them. It sounded like a raspy chirp: "chee, chee, chee." Malcolm couldn't

actually see the animal making the noise and wondered what it could be. Dylan had never heard an animal make that sound either. It didn't sound like a bird. They thought it might be a small mammal, like a squirrel or a chipmunk. As the boys continued climbing higher up the mountain, over loose rocky slopes, the sound became more frequent.

Back at Dylan's house late that afternoon, Dylan called his aunt Sandy, who works nearby as a ranger for the National Park Service. She suggested that they might have heard a pika, but she was not certain. She invited the boys to come to her office in the morning to talk more about the pika populations in the area. Before hanging up the phone, she suggested the boys look up information about the pika on the Web.

Back at home, Malcolm decided to do a search about pikas. He came across an interesting article about the pika's mountain lifestyle.

---

http://www   What's a Pika?

The American pika (*Ochotona princeps*) is a small mammal that looks like a cross between a large hamster and a rabbit with short ears (figure 15.16).

The best place to catch a glimpse of a pika is on rocky slopes or in boulder fields. However, you would be more likely to hear the American pika than to see one. The pika uses a series of calls to communicate with others nearby. To avoid predation and the heat of summer, pikas retreat to the cracks and spaces between the rocks. They also use these spaces to store food for winter. During the summer, small piles of grass, flowers, and other plant parts drying in the Sun provide evidence of pika activity. Pikas consume these dried piles of vegetation during the winter months. This interesting behavior has earned the pika the nickname "haymaker."

The American pika is most closely related to rabbits and hares. Its most common predator is the weasel. Unlike other small animals, pikas don't hibernate during the winter. To withstand the cold, pikas have a thick coat of fur. Although fur insulates them from the cold, it inhibits cooling. Pikas can overheat and have been observed to die when trapped in temperatures over 25°C (77°F) for more than a few hours. Pikas thrive at high elevations where temperatures never get too high, rocks provide shade in the summer, and there is enough snow cover to provide insulation over the winter.

Pikas live in many mountaintop regions around the western United States. Each mountaintop may be home to one or several pika populations living on rocky slopes. Pikas from different populations may not encounter one another very frequently, because they tend to stay close to the rocks where they are born. The maximum distance that pikas are known to travel from their place of birth is about 3 km (1.86 mi).

Figure 15.16 The American pika is related to rabbits and hares.

In the mountains surrounding the Great Basin region of the United States (figure 15.17), which is made up of the state of Nevada and parts of the states of Utah, Idaho, Oregon, and California, a number of pika populations have been discovered by hikers and scientists over the years. Records of pika discoveries date back to 1898 (figure 15.18). More recently, a survey of pika populations in this area was carried out by Erik Beever and his colleagues. They went to locations where pikas had been known to live. In each location, they looked for pikas and also searched for indirect evidence of pika activity such as calls, feces, and hay piles.

Beever compared their observations with records of pikas dating back to the 1800s. His results show how many pika populations were found historically, compared with 1998 (figure 15.18). Beever and other scientists say that these numbers cause them concern about the American pika's long-term outlook in its sky island habitat.

Figure 15.17 Pikas can be found in the mountains of the Great Basin region of the western United States.

Dates of population records	Higher-altitude populations	Lower-altitude populations
1898–1956	18	6
1990–1998	16	2

Figure 15.18 **Pika populations discovered between 1898 and 1956, and re-observed between 1990 and 1998.** Higher-altitude populations are defined as those living above 2,000 m (6,560 ft). Populations found below 2,000 m are called lower-altitude populations.

Malcom stopped reading to ponder. It must have been a pika that he and Dylan heard. Not only did they hear the calls, but Malcom also remembers seeing small hay piles around some of the rocks. Malcom looked at the table of population numbers in the article and thought, "What do these numbers mean for the pika's future?"

5. With your partner, choose 2 or 3 factors on your list that you think are most likely to lead to the extinction of pika populations. Write a sentence explaining how changes in each factor could negatively affect pika survival or reproduction.

6. With your partner, think about how changes to multiple limiting factors at the same time could affect pika populations. Describe 1 way that a changing abiotic factor could cause a change in a biotic factor, which could, in turn, negatively affect pika survival or reproduction. Write your description in your science notebook.

7. Imagine you and your partner are scientists investigating the cause of pika declines. Brainstorm your ideas about the following questions with your partner, then record your ideas in your science notebook. Be prepared to share your ideas in a class discussion.
   a. What data would you want to collect about pikas?
   b. How would you go about collecting the data?
   c. On the basis of your ideas about limiting factors, what patterns do you predict you would see in the data?

8. On your own, read the scenario, *Investigating Pika Declines*. The reading will help you learn how some factors might affect pikas.

9. Reflect on the list of factors that you made in step 5, which you thought might contribute to pika population extinctions. Did Beever's team investigate any of the factors you listed? Write an entry in your science notebook about 1 of the following:
   • If Beever's team studied a factor you listed, describe your reaction at learning the result.
   • If Beever's team did not study a factor you listed, describe how you think scientists should study the factor that interests you.
   • Describe another factor that you think Beever's team could have studied, and how.

SCENARIO

Investigating Pika Declines

The next morning, Malcolm headed off to meet Sandy, the park ranger. He couldn't wait to tell her what he learned about the pika and ask questions. Sandy agreed that he probably heard pikas calling to one another. She also told Malcolm that the pika declines he read about led the U.S. Fish and Wildlife Service to look into whether the pika qualifies for protection under the Endangered Species Act. Then she gave Malcolm a news brief summarizing recent research into pika declines in the United States.

How might scientists determine which factors are causing pika declines? In 2003, Erik Beever's team tested several different hypotheses concerning pika populations in the Great Basin region. The team thought many different factors could logically contribute to pika population extinctions. They hypothesized that abiotic climate factors such as average summer temperature might affect how hot pikas get in the summer. Abiotic factors could also affect biotic factors, such as the abundance or water content of the vegetation that the pikas rely on. They also thought biotic factors including human activity and grazing cattle could affect pikas by disturbing the pika's habitat. Beever's team went to each location where pikas had lived or were living and collected data on as many potentially limiting factors as possible.

Why did some populations survive while others went extinct? To test their hypotheses, the team compared living and extinct populations for each biotic and abiotic factor of interest. Then Beever's team ran a statistical analysis comparing all factors at the same time. This model allowed the team to determine which factors most likely impact Great Basin pika population extinctions. A sample of their results is found in figure 15.19.

Abiotic factors	Is this factor related to pika extinction?	Biotic factors	Is this factor related to pika extinction?
Elevation of habitat	Yes, extinctions are more likely to occur at lower elevations.	How heavily livestock graze the location	Yes, extinctions are more likely to occur in heavily grazed areas.
Maximum summer temperature	Yes, extinctions are more likely to occur in locations with higher summer temperatures.	Distance from the habitat to the nearest major road	Yes, extinctions are more likely to occur in habitat that is close to main roads.
—	—	Distance to the nearest neighboring pika population	No, more-isolated pika populations are not more likely to go extinct.

Figure 15.19 This table provides a sample of the results of Erik Beever's study of abiotic and biotic factors and their effect on pika extinctions.

10. To deepen your understanding of inquiry, create a 2-column table in your science notebook. In the first column, use the *Scientific Inquiry Diagram* in figure 15.20 to make a list of the scientific processes that Beever's team used while carrying out their study. In the second column, give examples of how Beever's team used each scientific process you listed.

Figure 15.20 The processes of scientific inquiry are multifaceted. Which elements of this process do you think Beever's team engaged in?

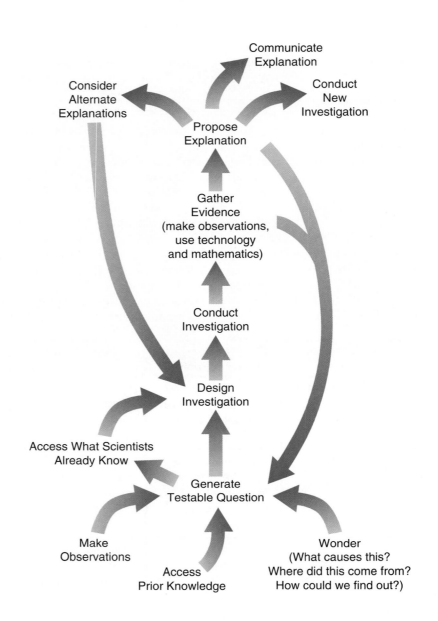

11. In your science notebook, make a list of the factors from figure 15.19 that Beever's team found to be related to pika extinctions. Do you think any of these changing factors suggest a connection between pika extinctions and global climate change? Circle factors you think may be related.

12. To gather information to answer the question of whether pika extinctions could be related to climate change, read the essay, *Climate Change and Its Impacts on the Western United States.*

Climate Change and Its Impacts on the Western United States

"Climate change" is a term used to describe long-term changes in the average temperature and precipitation over a region or across the globe. Across geologic time, climates have changed in a regular pattern, resulting in periodic ice ages and warm periods. More recently, the term climate change has become particularly associated with a warming trend observed over just the past century, also known as global warming (figure 15.21). This recent warming trend has been linked to a number of additional changes, including the melting of glaciers, ice sheets, and permafrost; sea level rise; changes in regional precipitation patterns; and changes in ecosystems. The speed at which some of these changes have occurred, particularly in arctic regions, is unprecedented.

What factors could cause Earth's climate to become warmer? There are three possible mechanisms: (1) a variation in Earth's orbit around the Sun; (2) an increase in the Sun's intensity; and (3) an increase in the amount of greenhouse gases in Earth's atmosphere. The first mechanism provides the best explanation for Earth's climate changes over geologic history. A number of variations in Earth's orbit occur in regular patterns, causing shifts in climate known as Milankovitch cycles. Taking only these cycles into account, scientists have predicted that Earth's average temperature should remain about the same or begin to fall over the next 50,000 years. The second mechanism, a change in the Sun's intensity, appears to be responsible for another historical event, the Little Ice Age (1650–1850). The Sun's energy output has very gradually increased over the last century, but the increases are too small to explain the recent warming trend.

So, does an increase in greenhouse gases in the atmosphere explain the warming trend of the past 100 years? First, let's explore how this mechanism works. Greenhouse gases are a group of gases whose physical properties allow them to absorb infrared radiation from Earth and change the direction of that radiation. The action of the greenhouse gas molecules spread throughout the atmosphere effectively creates a heat barrier or "blanket" around Earth. This greenhouse effect

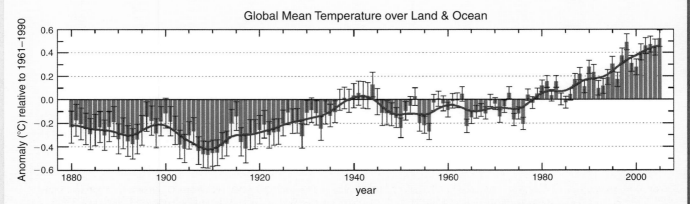

Figure 15.21 **Global mean temperature over land and ocean.** The graph pictured here shows yearly average global temperature (red bars) and five-year averages (blue line) compared with the average temperature for the 30-year period from 1961 to 1990. Gray bars indicate the extent of possible error in the measurements. What trends do you see?

is extremely important, for without greenhouse gases in the atmosphere, Earth would be too cold to support life as we know it. On the other hand, increasing the amount of greenhouse gases in the atmosphere has long been predicted to cause additional warming.

Where do greenhouse gases come from? Greenhouse gases include water vapor, carbon dioxide, and methane. One greenhouse gas that has increased significantly in the atmosphere over the past 100 years is carbon dioxide (figure 15.22). Carbon dioxide is released by a number of processes including cellular respiration and the combustion of wood, oil, and gas fuels. The fact that the recent warming trend began after the industrial revolution suggests that the trend has been driven by human-generated greenhouse gas emissions.

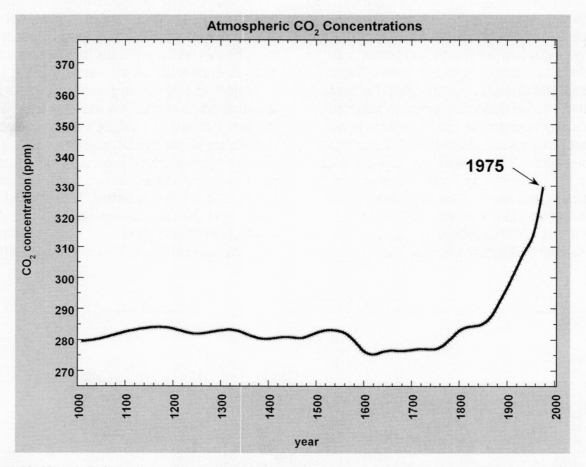

Source: D.M. Etheridge, L.P. Steele, R.L. Langenfelds, R.J. Francey, J.M. Barnola and V.I. Morgan. 1998. Historical CO_2 records from the Law Dome DE08, DE08-2, and DSS ice cores. In *Trends: A Compendium of Data on Global Change.* Carbon Dioxide Information Analysis Center, Oak Ridge National Laboratory, U.S. Department of Energy, Oak Ridge, Tenn., U.S.A.

Figure 15.22   Changes in the concentration of the greenhouse gas carbon dioxide in the atmosphere between the years 1000 and 1975. The amount of carbon dioxide (CO_2) is given in parts per million (ppm) and was collected from bubbles trapped in ice cores from Antarctica. In 2009, the amount of carbon dioxide in the atmosphere reached 385 ppm.

Scientists have studied and compared these different possible mechanisms for recent climate change. In 2007, a group of over 2,000 scientists from across the world assembled the findings of thousands of other scientists. This group is called the Intergovernmental Panel on Climate Change (IPCC). Its task was to compare all the findings and summarize the most important findings into a document about climate change that could help guide future science and policy-making. The IPCC clearly identified human-generated greenhouse gas emissions as the most likely factor causing the recent warming trend and other climatic changes. The entire team was awarded the Nobel Peace Prize in 2007 for its work.

In addition to causing warmer winters and hotter summers across most of the regions of the globe, climate change has other impacts. In the western United States, temperatures have been rising since around 1970 and climate change has been linked to decreased amounts of precipitation—less rain and less snow. There is also evidence of impacts to ecosystems. Trees have been dying at a faster rate during recent decades. An epidemic of pine bark beetle infestations in western forests has been attributed to two climate-related changes. First, the stress that forest trees experience from drought causes them to be more vulnerable to beetle infection. Second, beetle populations are not being limited by severely cold winters as much as they were in the past.

Because recent climate change has been driven mostly by human activities, humans have the opportunity to tackle the problem. We can take many actions to reduce our emissions of greenhouse gases by reducing our consumption of energy. Simple ways to become more fuel efficient involve riding the bus or bicycling to school, changing to energy-efficient compact fluorescent or LED lightbulbs, making sure car tires are properly inflated, drying clothes outside rather than using a dryer, and combining errands into a once-a-week shopping trip rather than shopping every day.

13. Write a paragraph addressing the question of whether pika declines may be related to climate change. You will know you have written a complete paragraph when it includes the following.
   a. What you have learned about the factors affecting pika extinctions
   b. How those factors are changing due to climate change
   c. Reasons supporting your opinion about whether climate change is likely to lead to the extinction of pikas on sky islands

Analysis

1. Several lines of evidence collected by Erik Beever and other scientists suggest that pika populations went extinct without migrating elsewhere. Use what you know about pikas and sky island habitats to develop an explanation for why pika populations did not migrate to another mountaintop habitat.

2. American pikas live in areas other than the Great Basin. In the Rocky Mountains, some pika populations live at elevations higher than they do in the mountains of the Great Basin. Populations living at higher elevations are subjected to much cooler summer and winter temperatures than the Great Basin pikas. These locations historically have much snowfall in the winter. A layer of snow keeps the ground temperature near freezing (0°C, or 32°F), even when air temperatures plunge far below freezing. In the Rocky Mountains, snowfall has been declining, and this trend is thought to result from climate change. What impact do you think decreased winter snow cover might have on pikas in the Rocky Mountain region?

> You may want to refer back to the pika characteristics described in the *Mystery Mountain Mammal* scenario to help answer these questions.

EVALUATE

Critters and Interdependence

It's time to evaluate what you have learned about interdependence among living organisms and the complex interactions that take place in communities and ecosystems. In this Evaluate activity, *Critters and Interdependence*, you will work in teams to create a story that describes interactions among various organisms and resources in a particular habitat. These organisms will include your critter, other classmates' critters, humans, and other native organisms.

Materials

Part A
online resource

Part B
descriptions and diagrams of your critter

PROCESS AND PROCEDURES

Part A   Resources and Ecosystems

1. Identify the habitat card you had in chapter 3, *Products of Evolution: Unity and Diversity*, for the Evaluate activity, *First Encounter with the Critter*. Do this by referring to your science notebook.
2. Watch the video segment, "Ecosystems of the Earth." As you watch, perform the following tasks.
   a. In your science notebook, record the name of each ecosystem.
   b. List at least 4 limiting factors presently found in each ecosystem.
      > Remember, include both biotic and abiotic factors.

3. Participate in a class discussion that your teacher guides. You will summarize the interactions and resources that characterize each of the ecosystems depicted in the video segment.

Think about the main ideas of this chapter and how they relate to those ecosystems.

Part B Critters in Ecosystems

1. Join with classmates who had the same habitat card as you.
2. Obtain a *Critters and Interdependence Rubric* handout from your teacher. Discuss the criteria with your teammates.

Ask your teacher to clarify any questions that come up during your discussion that your team cannot answer fully.

3. Introduce your new teammates to your critter and respond to any questions that your teammates might have.

Be sure to describe all the features of your critter in detail.

4. Imagine that you, your teammates, and each teammate's critter are living together in the assigned habitat from chapter 3. Brainstorm ideas about the following.
   a. Possible interactions among the organisms that inhabit this ecosystem
   b. The biotic and abiotic resources that might exist
   c. The ways the different critters might be interdependent
   d. The adaptations that might evolve over time, as these critters interact
   e. How humans from a variety of cultures might interact with other organisms in this environment
5. Individually, write a story that features some of the ideas that your team suggested. Make sure it follows the criteria outlined in the rubric.

Remember, your teacher will assess what you have learned from this chapter by reading your story.

Analysis

Reflect on the process you used to think about and write your story. Participate in a class discussion of the following questions.

1. What was the most challenging part of writing your story? Explain.
2. Which of the major concepts in this chapter did you have the most difficulty incorporating into the story? Explain.
3. You wrote about the interactions and interdependence of your critter with other organisms. You also wrote about the limiting factors at work and the carrying capacity of the environment. Which was easier to write about? Explain why.
4. What adaptations did you consider adding to your critter? Explain why you did or did not add them.

16

Decision Making in a Complex World

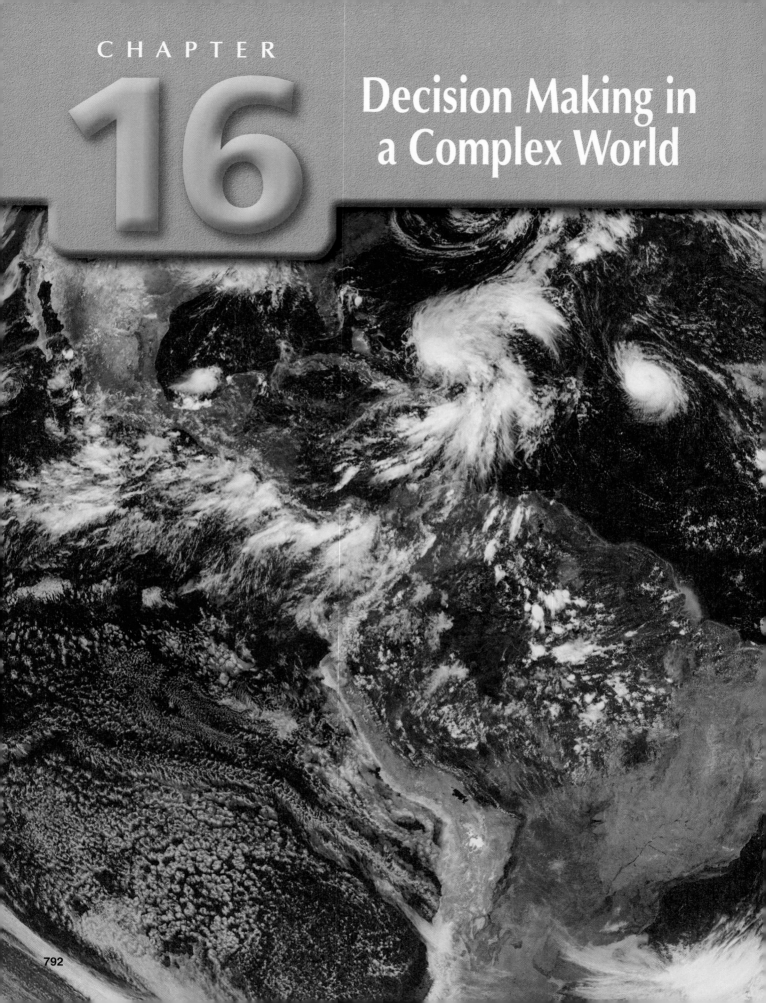

Enjoy present pleasures in such a way as not to injure future ones.

Seneca the Younger

What do you think about when you look at this picture? From space, Earth might seem so large that humans' influence on the planet is tiny. But don't be fooled. In *BSCS Biology: A Human Approach,* you have explored the tremendous diversity of life on Earth. By now, you probably appreciate that a vast number of interactions connect living organisms. Think about the interactions and interdependence among living organisms and between those organisms and the environment. These connections make possible the evolutionary processes that characterize Earth's biodiversity. Unfortunately, the complexity of these interactions makes it difficult for humans to predict how their actions will affect other organisms and the environment.

In this chapter, you will investigate human decision making in a complex world. You will analyze some consequences of human actions on ecosystem interactions and resource distribution.

GOALS FOR THE CHAPTER

By the end of chapter 16, *Decision Making in a Complex World,* you should understand the following concepts:

✔ Ecological interactions are complex.

✔ Humans interact with and affect ecosystems.

✔ Systems analysis is a tool that we can use to study complex interactions.

✔ Complex issues are difficult to analyze thoroughly and to resolve fully.

✔ Environmental policy emerges from the interaction of scientific understanding and human decision making.

To help you develop these understandings, you will complete the following activities.

ENGAGE	Tri-Lakes: Asking Questions
EXPLORE EXPLAIN	Tri-Lakes: An Initial Study
EXPLAIN	Tri-Lakes: Identifying Causes of Change
ELABORATE	The Gulf of Maine
EVALUATE	Tri-Lakes: Public Policy

Review the chapter organizer frequently to gain insight into the flow of concepts throughout chapter 16.

ENGAGE

Tri-Lakes: Asking Questions

Key Idea: Understanding a complex ecosystem often requires answering many questions.

Linking Question:
What approaches might shed light on the Tri-Lakes ecosystem and its bass population?

Chapter 16

MAJOR CONCEPTS

- ✔ Ecological interactions are complex.
- ✔ Humans interact with and affect ecosystems.
- ✔ Systems analysis is a tool that we can use to study complex interactions.
- ✔ Complex issues are difficult to analyze thoroughly and to resolve fully.
- ✔ Environmental policy emerges from the interaction of scientific understanding and human decision making.

 EXPLORE   **EXPLAIN**

Tri-Lakes: An Initial Study

Part A: Exploring a Complex Ecosystem
Part B: Conducting a Limited Systems Analysis

Key Idea: By applying the principles of systems analysis, scientists can test hypotheses related to the behavior of more-complex ecosystems.

Linking Question:
How can we integrate the results of a limited systems analysis with other information to provide a more complete explanation of a complex ecosystem?

EVALUATE

Tri-Lakes: Public Policy

Key Idea: Policy decisions about the environment must take into account interactions and interdependence among organisms, including humans.

Decision Making in a Complex World

Linking Question:
How can we apply our knowledge to suggest policy for the Tri-Lakes problem?

ELABORATE

The Gulf of Maine

Key Idea: It is important to consider both scientific findings and stakeholder perspectives when generating public policy, because ecosystems and human societies are complex.

Linking Question:
What complex interactions exist in real aquatic ecosystems, and how do they respond to human activities?

EXPLAIN

Tri-Lakes: Identifying Causes of Change

Key Idea: Scientists synthesize many sources of information when they are formulating explanations about complex ecosystems.

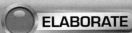

Tri-Lakes: Asking Questions

If you are cold, you can probably identify the cause of your discomfort pretty easily. Perhaps your clothes aren't well suited to the weather. Maybe a cold wind is blowing around a leaky door onto your feet. If a baby cries, you can often figure out the problem by feeding, changing, or holding the infant. When a computer crashes, you may go through a series of steps to determine the cause and make the necessary repairs.

These are examples of situations where figuring out the cause of a given problem is relatively straightforward. You engage in that type of troubleshooting every day. Many situations that affect your life, however, are much more complex. What about determining the causes for diseases or changes in Earth's atmosphere, for example? These situations involve many possible interacting influences. When researchers study complex systems, they must identify the many parts of the system. They must then try to limit the study to a few parts of the system that can be managed or controlled.

Figure 16.1
Tri-Lakes is a fictional lake system, but there are many lakes similar to it in the world.

You will practice skills related to studying and making decisions about a complex system through several activities about the Tri-Lakes region in this chapter. The Tri-Lakes is a fictional model ecosystem (figure 16.1). But it is similar to the situations faced in many communities. Residents around Lake Erie have successfully revitalized one of the Great Lakes that many thought was dying due to industrial pollution. The citizens of Sweden, Canada, Germany, and the northern United States have been studying the acidification of lakes in their countries. In some places, professional and citizen scientists have been able to reverse what some thought was an irreversible course of events affecting lakes. The types of questions raised by the Tri-Lakes Association could be asked in any community about many science and technology issues.

In this Engage activity, you will learn about the problem at Tri-Lakes and identify what you need to know to better understand the issues involved.

PROCESS AND PROCEDURES

1. To learn about recent observations about the Tri-Lakes region, listen to or read to yourself the scenario, *The Problem at Tri-Lakes*.
2. In your science notebook, write a list of at least 5 biotic and 5 abiotic components in the Tri-Lakes ecosystem.
3. Think about how the components you listed may directly or indirectly affect the bass population. Circle several components that you think may be changing in ways that affect the bass population in the Tri-Lakes.

The Problem at Tri-Lakes

Tri-Lakes Association

Dear Biology Students at Tri-Lakes High School:

The members of the Tri-Lakes Association are very concerned about a confusing problem we have in the Tri-Lakes region. In general, the fishing is good, especially for bass. But people are not catching as many bass as they did years ago. As a result, our reputation as the bass-fishing capital of the world is suffering. Reservations at local resorts are down by 25 percent. This has had disturbing financial consequences for our area.

I know that the biology classes at Tri-Lakes High have kept records on the water quality of the lakes for many years under the leadership of your very dedicated teacher. The members of the association have noticed a change in the number of bass being caught. This change seems to have happened along with, or as a result of, a number of other changes around the area. We hope that your data about the lake and your scientific abilities will help us determine what is happening, or at least give us a sense of what questions we need to study.

The members of the association, some of whom are scientists, have made the following observations. We hope this information helps:

- Small invertebrate animals such as *Daphnia magna* and *Gammarus* are less common in the lake than they used to be.
- The lake is greener for more of the year than it used to be.
- Like the bass, perch in the lake seem smaller, and they are less colorful than in previous years.

In addition to those observations, I am sending data packets with information gathered from local papers and lake study records. These packets contain information that the association members pulled together in an attempt to understand what might be happening to our region. Some of the data may look familiar. We pulled some information from your annual report to the association. We hope that this combination of local, national, and historical data will provide enough clues for you to identify our problems so that we can begin working on solutions.

Our next association meeting is in two weeks. We look forward to hearing from you at that time. Because many of you and your families are involved in the fishing and resort industries, I am sure you understand the seriousness of this situation. I eagerly await your response.

Sincerely,

Chris Tackle

Chris Tackle
President, Tri-Lakes Association

4. Discuss with your partner the components you circled, along with your reasoning about why you think they may be important. Also, discuss information you think you may need to better understand the Tri-Lakes problem.

> Focus your discussion on particular components that you and your partner think may be key to understanding the Tri-Lakes situation.

Analysis

For most of this chapter, you will be working on the Tri-Lakes problem. You will think of questions, search for answers, and draw logical conclusions. As questions occur to you, be sure to record them in your science notebook. Leave space to add any possible explanations you may develop as you gather information.

1. In your science notebook, record questions about the Tri-Lakes problem that you think could be useful to answer. The questions could be answered either by gathering known information or by conducting investigations.

> Use information from Chris Tackle's letter and your own knowledge to come up with logical questions about the problems with the Tri-Lakes bass population. Record each question as precisely as possible. After you have written at least two questions on your own, discuss them with your partner. Add to your list any additional questions that you and your partner agree are interesting.

2. Write a brief paragraph in your science notebook that describes your hypothesis for what you think may be causing the Tri-Lakes problem.

> Remember, these are early ideas that are based on minimal evidence. You likely will revise your ideas as you gather more information.

Tri-Lakes: An Initial Study

Imagine yourself as an ecologist. You lower various instruments into the water, sample water quality at different places and depths, and observe system components as you investigate the lake's ecosystem. You measure many factors, because ecosystems are complex. But what do you do with all these data? One of the essential steps for analyzing a complex system is to limit the components that you are studying. A simplified investigation of a complex system can help provide some initial explanations. Then, by comparing a number of simple investigations, an ecologist can begin to construct a more complex explanation.

In this Explore-Explain activity, *Tri-Lakes: An Initial Study*, you will first gather a broad range of information about the Tri-Lakes. Then you will learn about how ecologists use systems analysis to help them handle large amounts of information. You will then apply the ideas of systems analysis to design a limited experiment that may help you gain an understanding of the factors affecting the bass population in Tri-Lakes. You will then compare your findings with those of others in the class, which may help you develop a more complete explanation of the situation. Keep in mind the focus question of this activity: "How can we apply systems analysis to better understand the Tri-Lakes problem?"

Materials (per team of 2)

Part A
data packet

Part B
2 pairs of safety goggles
1 dropping pipet
1 10-mL graduated cylinder
1 petri dish
1 beaker labeled "culture water," containing small invertebrate animals (*Daphnia magna* or *Gammarus*)
1 beaker labeled "used culture"
1 petri dish half
flat toothpicks
thermistor or nonmercury thermometer
pH indicator strips
forceps
1 hand lens
vinegar in dropping bottles
warm water in a dropping bottle
stopwatch with a second hand

PROCESS AND PROCEDURES

Part A   Exploring a Complex Ecosystem

1. To explore the history and complexity of the Tri-Lakes ecosystem, review the titles of the handouts available in the data packet. The titles are listed in the need to know, *Tri-Lakes Data Packet*.

   This packet contains information about trends in abiotic factors in the ecosystem, populations of fishes and other organisms in the lakes, kinds of human activities happening around the Tri-Lakes region, and the impact of pesticides and acid rain on ecosystems in general.

2. Choose 1 or 2 handouts to review that you think may be useful for answering questions you have about the Tri-Lakes. Your partner should also read 1 or 2 handouts. Read these and briefly share what you learned with your partner.

   You and your partner do not have to read everything in the data packet. Compare the titles of the handouts with the questions you raised in the Engage activity, *Tri-Lakes: Asking Questions*. Which information sheets

NEED TO KNOW

ENGLISH SPANISH

Tri-Lakes Data Packet

1. *Tri-Lakes Advertisement*
2. Tri-Lakes Tribune *Article, Tri-Lakes Area Diversifies!, January 29, 2002*
3. Tri-Lakes Tribune *Article, Does Anyone Know What's Going On?, June 17, 2006*
4. *Location of Tri-Lakes Resorts and Industries*
5. *Zone Map of the Average Temperature*
6. *Largemouth Bass*
7. *Yellow Perch*
8. *Total Number of All Species of Fish Caught Annually, 1988–2008*
9. *Number of Largemouth Bass and Yellow Perch Caught Annually, 1988–2008*
10. *Average Length of Bass Caught Compared with the Legal Limit, 1988–2008*
11. *Abiotic Factors Measured for Tri-Lakes, 1988–2008*
12. *Algae and Cyanobacteria*
13. Daphnia
14. Gammarus
15. *Pesticides*
16. *Acid Precipitation*

are likely to be helpful for answering your questions? Critically sort through the large quantity of information to find the important pieces. This is a valuable scientific skill.

3. Keeping the information you have just explored in mind, review your list of questions from the Engage activity, *Tri-Lakes: Asking Questions*. Add to or revise this list of questions.

   At this point, it is typical to feel a bit overwhelmed by the amount of information available to study. You will develop skills for managing this information over the course of the chapter. Remember that at this point in the exploration, you only need to familiarize yourself with the kinds of information that are available to you. Do particular pieces of information stand out for you?

4. To learn about skills you can apply to the Tri-Lakes problem, read the essay, *Systems Analysis*. As you read, write in your science notebook at least 3 characteristics of a study that uses systems analysis to study a complex ecosystem. Also, write down any ideas you may have about how to study the Tri-Lakes ecosystem.

In nature, many situations arise that are very difficult to predict. When that happens, scientists turn to a method of analysis called systems analysis. In **systems analysis**, scientists try to understand a great deal about the interactions within a complex system. This knowledge can help them reliably predict the effect that certain changes will have on the system.

Weather provides an example of a complex system that is sometimes easy to understand in the short term. For example, dark, black clouds usually lead to rain. But predicting weather across great distances or time is much more difficult. Many different types of interactions affect weather at these scales (see figure 16.2). So weather is a complex system. An ecosystem is another example of a complex system.

The first step in analyzing any complex phenomenon is to identify the components of the system under study. The **components**, or collection of parts, that make up an ecosystem are both living (biotic) as well as nonliving (abiotic). For example, an ecologist might describe a pond in terms of its biotic components (figure 16.3). These would be its microscopic organisms, plant life, and fish. She also might describe the pond in terms of its abiotic components. A few examples are the pH of the pond water, the nutrient and oxygen levels, and the depth of sunlight penetration. These components also include elements outside of the pond. Thus, the pond system is not isolated from the world around it. In this case, the pond's pH is influenced by the pH of rainwater and the pH of anything that might wash into the pond. The nutrients are determined by the amount and type of food that washes or falls into the pond and the types of organisms that decay there. The temperature of the water is affected by how much the pond is shaded by vegetation such as trees. How far sunlight penetrates the water is affected by the amount of particles in the water. All of these components influence and define the ecosystem.

Once the components of a system are identified, most scientists try to make the system more manageable. They do this by *limiting* the number of components that are included in the analysis. For instance, a pond ecologist might focus her investigation only on the effects of several nutrients on the number of perch in the pond. The scientist who sets such a structure knows that other factors, such as pH and sunlight, also influence the fish. However, she might choose not to take those factors into consideration. She would tend to exclude factors she has reason to think have a smaller impact than others.

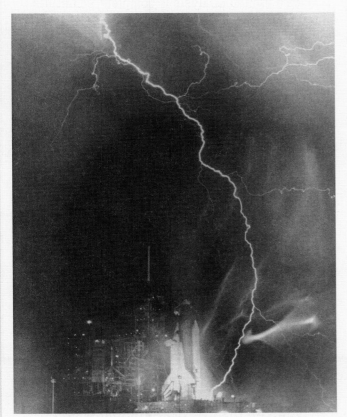

Figure 16.2 Predicting the weather can be difficult because it involves a complex system.

Figure 16.3 A lake or pond is a good example of a complex system that interacts with the world outside of it.

Scientists like to limit the number of components because it allows them to focus on one area of interest. When the focus is narrow, it is easier to develop and test hypotheses. On the other hand, a limited study may lack the power to explain everything. Most systems analysts try to develop manageable studies that are still complex enough to provide important insights.

A second important step in system analysis is to learn as much as possible about the current behavior of the system. If the initial behavior is not understood, then it is difficult to interpret how the system will react when one of its components is altered. In the pond example, say the ecologist does not already know that perch populations decline each fall. This happens because a food source that they require becomes scarce. In this case, she might mistakenly attribute the decline to the success of a new fishing guide in the area. The fishing guide might have an effect on the perch population. However, this effect may be small compared with the annual decline in the perch population caused by declines in nutrient levels.

Once a limited analysis is complete, scientists may try to compare and combine the results of several analyses. For example, the pond ecologist in this example might look for other scientists' work. She might discover that studies have been written about the effects of pH and sunlight on the pond ecosystem and on perch. This way, she can construct a more complex, and more accurate, understanding of the whole ecosystem.

To understand how an ecosystem works, ecologists collect large amounts of data. Their data help them understand how one set of interactions affects another. Ecologists realize that they will never know enough to make a perfect prediction. As a result, many ecologists are conservative in their predictions and recommendations. Scientists generally assume that intervening in ecosystems may have unpredictable consequences.

5. Work with your partner to compare the lists of components you developed in steps 2 and 3 of the Engage activity, *Tri-Lakes: Asking Questions.* If the essay led you to identify additional components that may be important to the Tri-Lakes ecosystem, add them to your lists.

6. Contribute your ideas about how to study important components in the Tri-Lakes system to a class discussion. In your science notebook, write down ideas you think would be good approaches.

Part B Conducting a Limited Systems Analysis

1. Read the need to know, *Investigating Tri-Lakes*, which is about the process you will use to develop a limited analysis of the Tri-Lakes ecosystem.

NEED TO KNOW

ENGLISH SPANISH

Investigating Tri-Lakes

A limited system analysis involves testing an idea about how the system will react when one of its components is altered. For the Tri-Lakes ecosystem, you may have already realized that it may be important to understand the role of the small invertebrates that Chris Tackle mentioned. You might have also noticed that two abiotic factors have been changing over time in the Tri-Lakes ecosystem. This investigation will help you learn more about these particular biotic and abiotic factors. Your class will investigate how changes in two abiotic components of the Tri-Lakes ecosystem (pH and temperature) may affect two important biotic components of the Tri-Lakes food web (two tiny crustacean animals, *Daphnia magna* and *Gammarus*).

You and your partner will focus your analysis on just one abiotic and one biotic component and develop an initial explanation of your findings. By reviewing the findings of all teams, you will begin to develop a more complex explanation of how changes in these components may affect the Tri-Lakes bass population. As you conduct this investigation, keep this focus question in mind: "How are organisms in the lake responding to abiotic changes in the Tri-Lakes ecosystem?"

2. Listen carefully while your teacher reviews the materials available for teams to use in this activity.

   Remember that protocols for the safe and humane handling of organisms should be followed for any organism in the classroom, no matter how small. See appendix A, *Laboratory Safety*, for more information.

3. Read the need to know, *Helpful Background Information*. On the basis of what you have learned about the Tri-Lakes, the materials available to you, and *Helpful Background Information*, develop a testable question and a hypothesis that will guide your investigation. Write your question and hypothesis in your science notebook.

NEED TO KNOW

ENGLISH   SPANISH

Helpful Background Information

pH

Recall from chapter 5, *Maintaining Balance in Organisms*, that pH is a measure of how acidic or basic a solution is. The pH scale goes from 0 to 14. The lower the number, the more acidic the solution is.

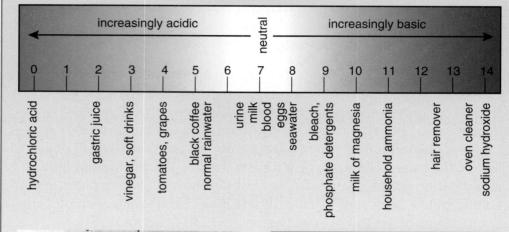

increasingly acidic   neutral   increasingly basic

| 0 | 1 | 2 | 3 | 4 | 5 | 6 | 7 | 8 | 9 | 10 | 11 | 12 | 13 | 14 |

hydrochloric acid — gastric juice — vinegar, soft drinks — tomatoes, grapes — black coffee / normal rainwater — urine / milk / blood — eggs / seawater — bleach, phosphate detergents — milk of magnesia — household ammonia — hair remover — oven cleaner / sodium hydroxide

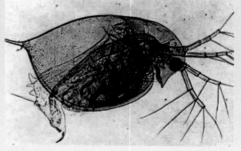

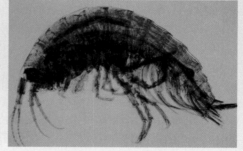

Daphnia

Can you find the heart, gut, and brood pouch for the *Daphnia magna* in your classroom? *Daphnia magna* are about 1 mm (about 0.04 in) long.

Gammarus

Gammarus are about 4 mm (about 0.16 in) long. What features of this animal are easier to see because the photograph is enlarged?

If necessary, you may want to review the information in the data packet about *Daphnia magna* and *Gammarus* before finishing your question. Your question should be testable given the materials available for this activity and be limited to one abiotic and one biotic component. Make sure the testable question you choose is related to the focus question, "How are organisms in the lake responding to abiotic changes in the Tri-Lakes ecosystem?"

4. Review the 2 protocols, *Protocol 1: Small Invertebrates and pH* and *Protocol 2: Small Invertebrates and Temperature,* to help you develop ideas about how you might test your question.

> These protocols provide examples of methods for studying the invertebrate crustaceans *Daphnia magna* and *Gammarus.* Don't forget, a protocol is not a replacement for your own experiment. However, it may provide a valuable technique for you to incorporate into your work.

5. With your partner, develop a procedure to gather data about your testable question. After you have written the procedure, ask your teacher to approve it.

> As you discuss procedures, consider what features of *Daphnia magna* or *Gammarus* you can compare under different abiotic conditions. What might you observe about the organisms that could change as an abiotic condition changes? If you can, develop a way to measure differences in what you observe by counting something.

PROTOCOL

Protocol 1: Small Invertebrates and pH

SAFETY: Put on your safety goggles.

1. Place about 15 mL of culture water in a petri dish.
2. Use a dropping pipet to carefully transfer 1 or 2 organisms from the culture to the petri dish.
3. Observe the organisms with a hand lens or stereomicroscope for long enough to determine their behavior.
4. Record this behavior in your science notebook.
5. Measure the pH of the water in the petri dish. Record this value in your science notebook but not in your table.
6. Use the dropper to add 1 drop of vinegar at a time. Stir the water after each drop of vinegar. Wait 30 seconds before adding the next drop. With pH strips, measure the pH each time you stir in 1 drop of vinegar. Do not allow the pH to drop below 3.5.

CAUTION: Vinegar is a *mild irritant*. Avoid eye contact. If contact occurs, flush affected area with water for 15 minutes. Call the teacher.

7. Record observations. Look for changes in the organisms' behaviors.
8. Continue observing the organisms for 1 minute after the last addition of vinegar. Record your observations in your science notebook.
9. Transfer the organisms to the container labeled "used culture" when you are finished.

PROTOCOL

Protocol 2: Small Invertebrates and Temperature

SAFETY: Put on your safety goggles.

1. Place about 10 mL of culture water in a petri dish.
2. Use the dropping pipet to carefully transfer 2 or 3 organisms from the culture to the petri dish.
3. Observe the organisms with a hand lens or stereomicroscope long enough to make an initial measurement of their behavior.
4. Record this behavior in your science notebook.
5. Measure the temperature of the water in the petri dish.
6. Gradually add warm water to the petri dish with a dropper. Stop when the temperature is 2°C different from the starting temperature.

   > You may need to remove some water to keep the petri dish from overflowing.

7. Observe the organisms for 1 minute. In your science notebook, record your measurements of their behavior.
8. Repeat steps 5–7 until you have changed the temperature of the water 10°C from its starting temperature.
9. Transfer the organisms to the container labeled "used culture" when you are finished.

6. In your science notebook, create a data table to organize and record your experimental data and observations.

   > For help in developing a data table, refer to appendix B4, *How to Use and Create Organizing Tables.*

HOW TO

7. Conduct your experiment with your partner. Record your observations and data in your science notebook.
8. Consider your data, then write a claim about whether changes in the abiotic factor you studied affect the invertebrate crustaceans you studied. Support your claim with specific evidence and reasoning.

   > At this point, limit your explanation to only the data that you and your partner have collected. For help in developing this explanation, refer to appendix C4, *How to Develop an Explanation.*

HOW TO

9. Follow your teacher's directions to present your team's explanation and learn about the explanations that other teams developed. Ask other teams questions about what they have learned from their experiments.

Analysis

Work individually to answer the following questions. Record your answers in your science notebook.

1. Think about all the different explanations that the teams in your class developed. Some teams gathered data about abiotic and biotic components that you did not study. Using all the information available to you at this point, write a paragraph in your science notebook that answers the question, "How are organisms in the lake responding to abiotic changes in the Tri-Lakes ecosystem?" Support your claim with evidence from multiple teams' experiments as well as from the data packet. Include the reasoning that ties this evidence to your claim.
2. Review the hypothesis you wrote in the Engage activity, *Tri-Lakes: Asking Questions* (*Analysis* question 2). How has your thinking changed since you wrote that hypothesis? Do you think it would change again if you had more information about the Tri-Lakes ecosystem? How might it change?

Tri-Lakes: Identifying Causes of Change

As an ecologist studying the Tri-Lakes system, you have developed an explanation of how some abiotic changes in the Tri-Lakes ecosystem can affect some organisms. How can you develop a fuller explanation of what is causing these changes and how these changes may affect the bass population? It will help to synthesize your initial explanation with information from a variety of sources. Reviewing what is already known about the Tri-Lakes and some of the organisms that live there may help you answer some of the questions you developed in the first two activities of the chapter. After spending more time discussing the information available about Tri-Lakes, you will construct an explanation that synthesizes your findings from the laboratory and the literature.

Remember, keep asking questions and thinking critically. Don't accept an explanation that sounds simplistic. As you work on this Explain activity, *Tri-Lakes: Identifying Causes of Change*, it may help to remember the following two focus questions: "How has the ecosystem as a whole changed over the past 10 years?" and "What caused the bass population within the lake to change?"

Materials (per team of 3)

data packet from the Explore-Explain activity, *Tri-Lakes: An Initial Study*
poster board
sticky notes
different-colored felt-tipped markers

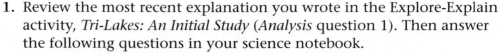
PROCESS AND PROCEDURES

1. Review the most recent explanation you wrote in the Explore-Explain activity, *Tri-Lakes: An Initial Study* (*Analysis* question 1). Then answer the following questions in your science notebook.
   a. Does this explanation address what may be causing the bass population to decline?
   b. Does this explanation address what may be causing the abiotic components of the Tri-Lakes ecosystem to change?
   c. What information can you review that might help you formulate a more complete explanation of the Tri-Lakes problem?

2. Look again at the handouts in the data packet you received at the beginning of the previous activity. With your team, choose a subset of handouts to study closely. Choose handouts that you think will most likely be helpful for constructing a more complete explanation of the bass decline in Tri-Lakes.

   It will probably be helpful to study handouts that you did not initially review during the previous activity, particularly if you think they will help you come to a more complete understanding.

3. Divide the handout reading work in thirds. Study your third of the documents that you think are important to understand; your teammates will study the other two-thirds. As you read, take notes in your science notebook and record questions you have about the information.

   In the Explore-Explain activity, *Tri-Lakes: An Initial Study*, you chose only a few handouts to read, based on the limited information you had learned about Tri-Lakes. Now, with more information from your laboratory experience, you have the opportunity and time to review all the available information you think is pertinent. Scientists commonly cycle in this way between the processes of searching for known information and conducting new studies.

4. When you are finished studying your handouts, meet with your teammates and share what you have learned. Focus your discussion around the 2 focus questions for this activity: "How has the ecosystem as a whole changed over the past 10 years?" and "What has caused the bass population within the lake to change?" Record all ideas in your science notebook.

   Do your best to accurately represent the information you learned and clearly explain it. Listen to and carefully consider the perspectives of your teammates. Ask as many questions as you need to in order to understand their reasoning. At the end of this activity, you will rate yourself and your teammates on how well you taught one another about your information.

5. Develop a concept map in your science notebook that describes your team's current thinking about how different abiotic and biotic components in the Tri-Lakes ecosystem are changing and

affecting one another. Along the arrows connecting the different components, write short sentences to indicate how changes in some components cause increases or decreases in other components. For each component that you think is changing, try to list a factor that you think is causing that change or indicate that the cause is unknown.

> For example, you might draw an arrow labeled "causes" between "increasing temperature" and "decreasing *Daphnia* population."

> It is OK if different members of your team develop different-looking concept maps.

6. With your team, come to a consensus about the factors that you think best explain the decline in the bass population in the Tri-Lakes ecosystem. On a piece of poster board, write your team's best explanation. Make separate sections listing your claim, evidence, and reasoning. Write large enough for your work to be read several feet away.

> Remember to include in your explanation the evidence from both the laboratory activity and the handouts. You may find it difficult to come to consensus if different team members have different ideas about what is affecting the lakes. Remember, your task is to determine what you all agree are the most important factors likely causing the change in the bass population. It is OK to leave factors that seem less important, or that not everyone can agree upon, out of your final explanation.

7. Following your teacher's directions, post your team's explanation on a wall of the classroom and begin to review other teams' explanations. Use sticky notes to leave a constructive question or comment on the posters of at least 2 other teams.

> On the sticky notes, include comments or questions that will provide specific feedback. For example, if you notice that a team did not get a result similar to your team's, describe your team's result and suggest a possible reason for the difference. If a team did not word its statement clearly, point out the most unclear portion of its statement and maybe even suggest how to reword it.

8. When the review time is over, collect your team's poster board and sticky note comments. Review each comment with your team. Sort them into "helpful" and "off-target" piles. Discuss the comments that are helpful and how they can be used to revise your explanation. Make notes in your science notebook of your discussion.

> You may need to review some of the handouts in your data packet in order to answer questions that the comments raise for your team's explanation.

Topic: technology and human culture
Code: human4E810

Analysis

1. Review your team's discussion and your observations of other teams' explanations. Then write in your science notebook a final explanation of the factors causing the bass population in the Tri-Lakes to decline.

2. Rate yourself and your teammates on how well you taught one another about the packet of information. Use a scale of 1 = not very well to 5 = very well. In your science notebook, record your ratings and 2 sentences of justification.

3. Review the concept map you made in step 5. What changes to the components in the Tri-Lakes ecosystem are not completely explained by the information you have? What suggestions would you make to Tri-Lakes High School students interested in collecting additional data?

4. Review the characteristics for a systems analysis that you wrote down in step 4 of the Explore-Explain activity, *Tri-Lakes: An Initial Study*. How did you use systems analysis in developing an explanation for the Tri-Lakes problem?

The Gulf of Maine

Complexity is a characteristic of many parts of our world. You have just learned how to manage many sources of information to arrive at a better understanding of a complex ecosystem. There are other types of complex systems, however. Some of these systems are ecosystems, such as the ocean ecosystem you will study in this activity. Other examples of complex systems are cells, businesses, governments, and social programs. People manage large amounts of information from many sources to arrive at decisions about complex systems. Systems analysis can be applied to all of these to help humans make decisions.

In *The Gulf of Maine*, you will learn how different people can have different perspectives about the ways to manage a common resource. Though the Tri-Lakes ecosystem you have studied is fictional, the Gulf of Maine is real (see figure 16.4). Many organisms and communities of people

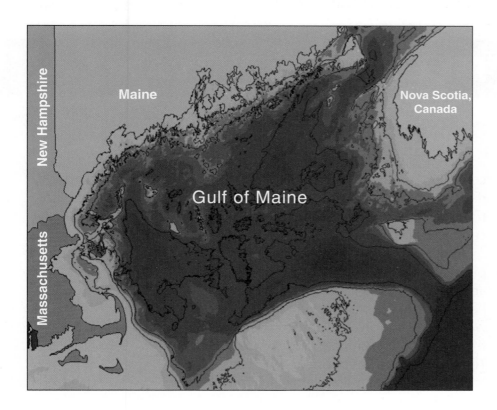

Figure 16.4 A map of the Gulf of Maine.

depend on this aquatic ecosystem. In this Elaborate activity, you will assume the role of one of the various stakeholders involved with that resource. Using the online resource, you will research policy options for the Gulf of Maine and participate in a debate about them.

Materials (per team of 2–4)

online resource
computer with Web access

PROCESS AND PROCEDURES

1. With your team or class, read the need to know, *Fishing in the Gulf of Maine*. Participate in a short class discussion about the idea in this reading.

2. Read the information provided on the handout titled *Gulf of Maine Occupations*. Follow your teacher's directions for determining which role your team will assume in the upcoming role play. In your science notebook, record information about your team's occupation.

   > Your team will assume one of the following roles: large-boat owners, small-boat owners, resource economists, marine biologists, fisheries scientists, or policy makers.

NEED TO KNOW

ENGLISH SPANISH

Fishing in the Gulf of Maine

In 1995, science writer Michael Parfit wrote, "The unthinkable has come to pass: the wealth of the oceans, once deemed inexhaustible, has proven finite." In saying this, Parfit is recalling data that indicate that most of the world's major fisheries are either in decline or are not commercially profitable. There are fewer and fewer fishes to catch.

In the Gulf of Maine off New England, for example, fish catches have plummeted in the last 40 years. Compared with 1965, catches of cod are down 40 percent, yellowtail flounder are down 90 percent, and haddock are down a shocking 96 percent. Fishermen have been paid with taxpayer money to destroy their boats. Yet only a century ago, these legendary fishing grounds provided a bountiful supply of fishes. The unthinkable has happened.

How should we manage the Gulf of Maine fisheries? Your answer may depend on your point of view. Many individuals—fishing-boat owners, fisheries scientists, marine biologists, resource economists, and policy makers—depend on or work with the fisheries.

3. With your team, learn about the Gulf of Maine with the following online resources. As you work through and interact with these segments, discuss with your team what you are learning and take notes about information that is particularly relevant to your team's role. The segments you should view follow.
   a. "Fish: A Renewable Resource"
   b. "On the Dock"
   c. "Crisis in the Gulf"
   d. "The Straw Model"
   e. "Different Voices"
4. Discuss the following questions with the members of your team.
   a. What is the controversy surrounding the Gulf of Maine fisheries?
   b. Which kinds of occupations have a stake in the health of the fisheries?
5. Read the need to know, *Science and Public Policy,* to learn more about how science can inform decision makers in the Gulf of Maine. As you read, take notes about the differences between science and public policy.

6. In your science notebook, make a table similar to the one in figure 16.5. It will help you organize information about the different management options for the Gulf of Maine fisheries. Make a number of columns to

NEED TO KNOW

Science and Public Policy

What is the appropriate role of science in human decision making? Scientists are responsible for interpreting scientific findings and reporting them to the public. Once scientists have reported their research, it is up to policy makers to analyze the information and suggest public policy (such as laws) that uses the scientific knowledge in the best way. Scientists themselves do not make policy nor do they enforce policy. The results of scientific work may lead to recommendations about what to do about a complex system, but science cannot tell us what we should do about a particular problem.

You might wonder, "Can public policy really affect a complex environmental problem?" The answer is yes. The Clean Air Act first introduced in the 1960s led to an improvement in U.S. air quality. This improvement resulted from requiring the use of catalytic converters on automobiles and the use of unleaded gasoline. When you become old enough to vote, you, too, will become part of the process of making decisions about public policy. Your career may lead you to become a policy maker. When the time comes, you can apply what you have learned about complex systems to help you make decisions.

record information, such as a column for a brief description of each option, one for data supporting the adoption of each option, and one for the advantages and disadvantages of each option for the role your team has been assigned.

Turn your science notebook so that your table can be as wide as possible and use a full page. Leave additional space to the right of the first few columns to add additional columns later. For help in developing a data table, refer to appendix B4, *How to Use and Create Organizing Tables*.

Management option	Description	Data supporting option	Advantages or disadvantages for my team's role	Short- and long-term effects of option
Close the fisheries				
Open the fisheries				
Manage the fisheries				

Figure 16.5 In your science notebook, create a table similar to this one to keep track of different management options for the Gulf of Maine fisheries.

7. With your team, go to "Surfing the Gulf" on the online resource. In this segment, search "Management Strategies" for information about 3 management options for the fisheries in the Gulf of Maine. Make notes in your table of the information you find.

   Your challenge will be to decide which of the three options is best *from the perspective of your assigned role.* Use keyword searches and the Web sites of the organizations that are listed to gather information about management options and the perspectives of different stakeholders about those options. Identify the files that will be most useful. Remember, in "Management Strategies" the Web sites are fictitious. But you can search the Web for real Web sites about those issues, as well.

8. Discuss all 3 management options with the members of your team. During your discussion, consider the following questions. Add new information to your table as needed.
   a. Who benefits from each option? Who doesn't?
   b. Who is responsible for managing each option? How difficult is it to manage?
   c. What data support each option?
   d. What assumptions is each option based on? Are the assumptions correct?
   e. What short- and long-term effects is each option likely to have on the fish population?
   f. What short- and long-term effects is each option likely to have on the region's economy and on people's lives?

9. Choose 1 management option with your team. You will support this option in a class discussion about the best management option for the Gulf of Maine fisheries.

10. Choose 1 or 2 representatives from your team, as your teacher directs. The representatives will present a brief (3–4-minute) explanation to the class for the option your team has chosen. Help your representatives prepare and practice this explanation. Also, identify other ways you can ask questions or make comments to support your team's explanation in the class discussion.

    Take turns practicing explaining the information you found with "Management Strategies" to support the adoption of the option you prefer. Be sure to provide relevant data and logical arguments. Be ready as a team to answer questions and respond to comments from other teams. If you need to, conduct an additional search in "Management Strategies" or on the Web to find additional information. Concentrate on locating information and building arguments that support the management option that benefits your assigned role.

11. Participate in the class discussion of the following questions.
    a. What management option is the most appropriate for the Gulf of Maine? How should it be enacted and enforced?
    b. Why is it difficult for communities to resolve how to manage natural resources?

12. Individually, reflect on all of the teams' arguments for managing the fisheries. On the basis of your own reasoned opinion (rather than on your assigned role), vote on the best management option for the Gulf of Maine fisheries.

Analysis

1. Write a paragraph in your science notebook that explains your vote.
2. Does the situation in the Gulf of Maine contain principles that apply to all of Earth's natural resources? Record at least 3 important ideas that emerged from your study of the Gulf of Maine ecosystem and the human decision making around it.
3. Describe how the science of ecology differs from the development of public policy around environmental issues. Use the Gulf of Maine as an example.
4. Write a paragraph comparing the similarities and the differences between the Gulf of Maine ecosystem and the fictional Tri-Lakes ecosystem. Does the Gulf of Maine suggest any additional factors that could help explain the Tri-Lakes bass population decline? Could the policies you explored be applied to the Tri-Lakes ecosystem?

Further Challenges

Use your knowledge of systems thinking to investigate the effects of human activities on an ecosystem in your local community. You may wish to begin your investigation by interviewing someone whose job it is to manage a river, stream, or body of water in your area, or someone working with forest or park natural resources. Then seek out additional perspectives on the problem you have identified. Summarize your findings and make policy recommendations based on those findings.

Tri-Lakes: Public Policy

The sheer number of humans on Earth complicates our interactions with the environment. To preserve the environment, we must consider many economic and political aspects to gain support for public policies. Situations such as those of Tri-Lakes or the Gulf of Maine involve complex interactions among all the people involved. These interactions are in addition to the interactions among humans, other organisms, and resources in the ecosystem (figure 16.6).

In this Evaluate activity, *Tri-Lakes: Public Policy*, you will combine the results of all the systems analyses from this chapter to communicate your understanding of the Tri-Lakes system. In a letter to the Tri-Lakes Association, you will describe how the components in the Tri-Lakes system interact under

Figure 16.6 Lakes like the ones described in the Tri-Lakes scenario are complex systems that are affected by many human decisions.

normal conditions. Then you will state your best explanation for the changes that have taken place. Finally, you will recommend policy decisions you think must be made. From this activity, you and your teacher will evaluate what you have learned about interactions and interdependence in living systems.

PROCESS AND PROCEDURES

1. Think about what you have learned about balancing the needs of various stakeholders and using scientific data to help guide decision making. Work with your team to apply this learning to a discussion of the following questions.
   a. Who are the stakeholders in the Tri-Lakes region?
   b. What should the Tri-Lakes community do about the declining bass population?

   > Remember that you considered different management options for an ecosystem previously in the Explain activity, *The Pasture Story*, in chapter 15, *Interdependence among Organisms*, and the Elaborate activity, *The Gulf of Maine*, in chapter 16.

2. Obtain a *Tri-Lakes Letter Rubric* handout for this activity from your teacher. Following this rubric will help you write a strong letter to the Tri-Lakes Association. Discuss the criteria with your partner and ask any clarifying questions you need to.

3. Develop a response to the letter from the Tri-Lakes Association. You will know that your letter is developed fully when it meets the criteria in the rubric, including the following.
   a. Showing how complex interactions and interdependence are evident in the Tri-Lakes ecosystem
   b. Explaining how a systems approach can assist in analyzing the problems in the Tri-Lakes
   c. Identifying and explaining the causes of at least 2 problems in the Tri-Lakes ecosystem

   d. Supporting your explanation with specific observations from your lab work and the data packet

   e. Identifying missing information that would be valuable to the continued analysis of the problem or would better identify the initial causes of the problem

   f. Showing an understanding about the different viewpoints within the Tri-Lakes community about how to manage the Tri-Lakes ecosystem

   g. Making specific policy recommendations based on your findings

4. Exchange letters with another student, as your teacher directs. Analyze the letter you received according to the rubric.

5. Provide the student whose letter you analyzed with at least 4 specific constructive comments about his or her letter.

> Your feedback should be a mix of statements. Provide at least one positive statement that indicates the strengths of the letter. Other statements should identify weak areas that need to be revised and how you think those areas could be strengthened.

6. Revise your letter to reflect the feedback that you received.

7. Participate in a class discussion. Using the information in your letter, talk about the changes in particular components that likely affected the Tri-Lakes ecosystem and the recommendations for public policies to address the problems.

8. Reflect on the laboratory investigation you completed in the Explore-Explain activity, *Tri-Lakes: An Initial Study*. Compare your thinking at the end of that investigation with your current thinking about the causes and remedies for the Tri-Lakes problem. In your science notebook, describe the changes in your thinking, using any method that makes sense for you.

© istockphoto/track5

> You could choose to write notes, write a paragraph, or organize your prior and current thinking into a two-column table.

Analysis

1. From your notes from step 8, write a paragraph summarizing the difference between an explanation based on a single, limited analysis and one based on a combination of related analyses. Add 1 or 2 sentences explaining how this difference should affect the way you interpret scientific studies that are reported in the news.

2. Write a general statement that assesses our ability to predict the consequences when humans introduce abiotic or biotic components into the environment. Provide examples and reasons that support your statement.

> Examples of components that humans introduce into the environment include microbes, animals, and plants that are moved from one region or continent to another; gases and particles that are released into the atmosphere from the combustion of fuels and from industrial processes; fertilizers, herbicides, and pesticides that are applied to agricultural land; and waste material or waste heat that is released into waterways or buried.

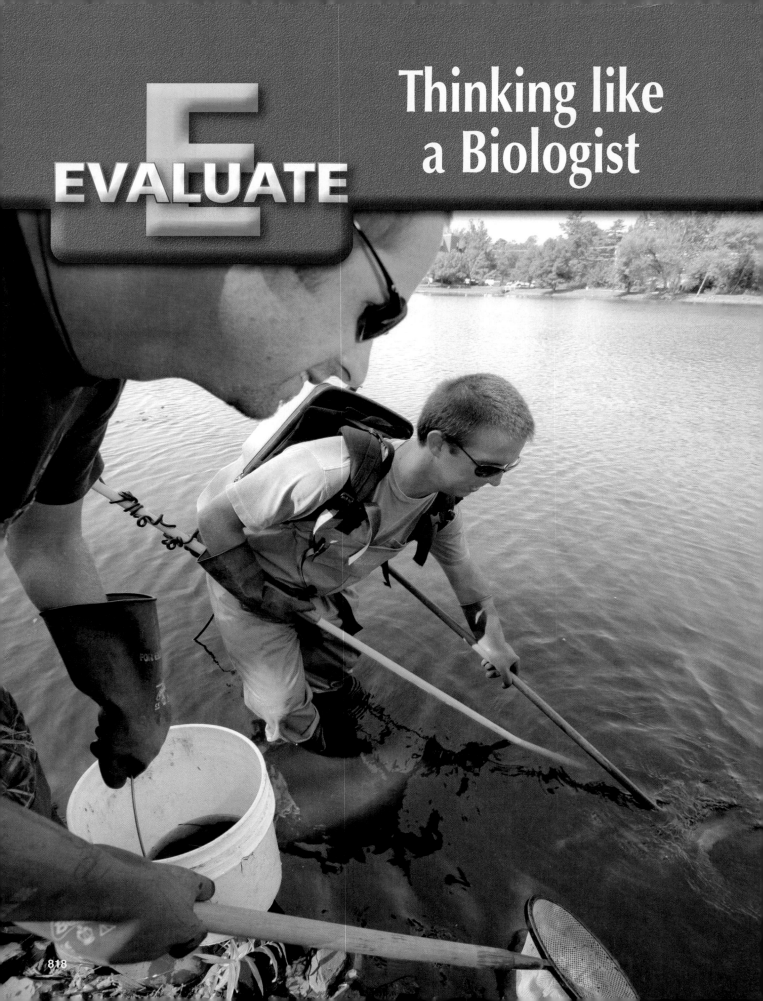

EVALUATE

Thinking like
a Biologist

The important thing in science is not so much to obtain new facts as to discover new ways of thinking about them.

Sir William Bragg

The final section in *BSCS Biology: A Human Approach, Thinking like a Biologist,* helps you evaluate what you have learned. You will examine your learning about biology and about the process of scientific thinking. Now that you have completed this course, we hope that you are better able to ask questions about the world around you. We hope you are able to reason scientifically to find answers. As you continue to learn and become an independent citizen, you will encounter many situations to which you can apply your understanding of biology. Remembering the six unifying principles of biology that we used to organize this program may help you understand those situations.

In this *Evaluate* section, we will revisit the six unifying principles of biology. You will have several ways to demonstrate your understanding of the principles. These ways include analyzing two scenarios based on actual events, answering a series of questions about the key concepts in each chapter, and creating a portfolio that your teacher may assign as an additional or an alternative activity.

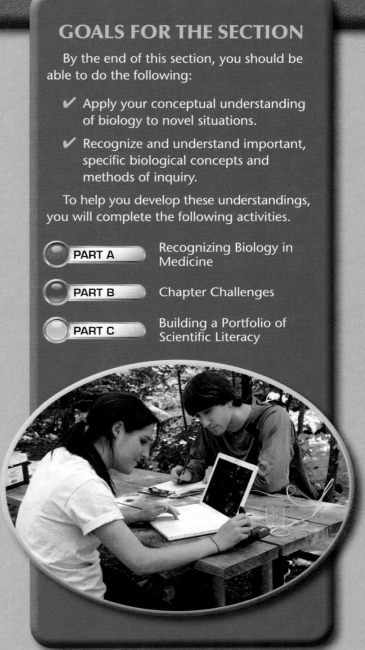

PART A

Recognizing Biology in Medicine

Each unit in *A Human Approach* focuses on one of the six unifying principles that unite the biological sciences. Each principle illustrates a different aspect of biology. But remember, all of these principles are present in all living systems. For example, when we become infected by a bacterium, it presents a challenge to our homeostasis. We may have been more susceptible to infection because of our genetic makeup. And, if we take antibiotics, we generate a selective pressure that may lead the bacterium to evolve. If you learned the concepts associated with each principle, you now should be able to think about any biological topic in light of these principles. Doing so will help you understand the world from a biological point of view. In this activity, *Recognizing Biology in Medicine,* you will identify unifying principles within articles written about medical science.

PROCESS AND PROCEDURES

1. Obtain the handout *Recognizing Biology in Medicine Rubric* from your teacher. Study the requirements for completing this activity successfully.

   This rubric will help you during the *Analysis* section of this activity. Discuss the scoring rubric with your partner. Ask your teacher to answer any questions that you have about the project.

2. In your science notebook, list each of the 6 unifying principles. Write a statement describing what each one means.

   The unifying principles of biology are the foundation for this course. They are in the title of each unit. Refer to the need to know, *Unifying Principles of Biology,* for a list of the principles.

NEED TO KNOW
ENGLISH SPANISH

Unifying Principles of Biology

These principles should look very familiar by now. They are the basis for organizing the ideas of *A Human Approach*.

Evolution: Change in Living Systems
Homeostasis: Maintaining Dynamic Equilibrium in Living Systems
Energy, Matter, and Organization: Relationships in Living Systems
Continuity: Reproduction and Inheritance in Living Systems
Development: Growth and Differentiation in Living Systems
Ecology: Interaction and Interdependence in Living Systems

3. To prepare to demonstrate your understanding of how the unifying principles of biology are evident in biological phenomena, review the following 2 scenarios, *Scenario 1: Iguanas and Aspirin, Shots and Antibiotics* and *Scenario 2: Cystic Fibrosis and Cholera*. Choose 1 that interests you. You will use this scenario to complete the *Analysis*.

4. Describe at least 2 interesting things that you learned from reading the scenario you chose. Write your description in a few sentences in your science notebook.

SCENARIO

ENGLISH   SPANISH

Scenario 1: Iguanas and Aspirin, Shots and Antibiotics

"I hate going to the doctor. It's probably just a cold anyway," Miguel complained as he sat in the waiting room with his father.

"Oh, come on, seeing the doctor isn't so bad," his father replied. "Besides, there's been a lot of flu going around, so I don't want to take any chances."

Just then, the nurse called, "Miguel Hernandez, Dr. Chen can see you now."

Before seeing the doctor, Miguel was examined by a nurse who took some measurements and asked him a few questions. The nurse recorded Miguel's data for the doctor (see figure Ev.1).

The doctor then examined Miguel. She looked in his throat and ears and listened to his heart and lungs as he breathed slowly.

When finished, the doctor began to explain her analysis and treatment plan to Miguel.

"I suspect you have strep throat—a *Streptococcus* bacterial infection. I'll give you a prescription for penicillin. But first we need to take a throat swab and a blood sample for the staff in the lab. They'll grow bacteria from the swab on an agar plate and test the bacteria for antibiotic resistance. They'll also check your blood for antibodies that would indicate a strep infection."

"How do you know it isn't just a cold?" Miguel asked.

"The virus that causes a common cold usually doesn't cause a fever. And you don't have congestion. Also, the spots on your throat look like a strep infection to me."

"Are you sure it's not the flu?" Miguel's dad asked. "Maybe he should have had a flu shot. He wasn't vaccinated for German measles either."

"Flu is caused by an infection of body cells by *Influenzavirus*," Dr. Chen said. "It infects humans and some other animals such as ducks.

Patient	Miguel Hernandez
Temperature	38.3°C (101°F)
Blood Pressure	122/80 mm Hg
Pulse	77 beats/min
Mass/weight	52.3 kg (115 lbs)
Comments	Complains of sore throat, headaches, lack of appetite

Figure Ev.1 Miguel Hernandez's vital signs data, as recorded by the nurse.

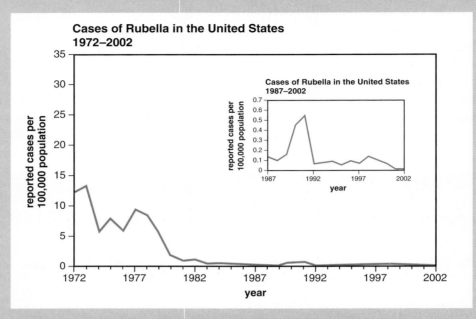

Cases of Rubella in the United States
1972–2002

Cases of Rubella in the United States
1987–2002

Figure Ev.2   Rubella occurrence in the United States. A vaccine for rubella became available in the United States in 1969. The data show slight increases in the number of cases of rubella in 1990–1991 and again in 1998–1999. What might have caused these increases? Why hasn't rubella been eliminated?

Influenza does produce fever, but it also causes extreme body aches and many other symptoms that Miguel doesn't have. I don't think Miguel has the flu, but if he wants to get a flu shot just in case the flu goes around his school, we can arrange that. Vaccination against *Rubella virus*, which causes German measles, is even more important for youngsters, though the danger of infection is much lower than it used to be. Let me see if I can find those data . . . here we are. Look at these data (figure Ev.2) showing the recent history of rubella cases."

"Rubella vaccination is most important, however, for girls because of the risk of infection later in life. If a pregnant woman gets rubella, it can seriously damage her developing fetus. For reasons like these, there is a push to make sure everyone is vaccinated against rubella."

"Anyway, if it were the flu, the penicillin would wipe it out, right, Dr. Chen?" Miguel asked.

Dr. Chen shook her head. "No, penicillin works by interfering with the production of the bacterial cell wall as the bacterial cells divide. Because viruses such as *Influenzavirus* live inside the host's cells and don't have a cell wall, antibiotics don't affect them. Also, it's a bad idea to use antibiotics when they aren't needed. This is because some bacteria carry genes whose products make the bacteria resistant to the action of a particular antibiotic. Those resistant bacteria are usually only a tiny percentage of the population infecting you. Remember, you should always finish all of the antibiotics you are given when prescribed. If you stop taking them early, you could give resistant bacteria a chance to reproduce and repopulate your tissues."

"Should Miguel take aspirin or a cold medicine containing aspirin to reduce his fever?" Mr. Hernandez asked. "Is the fever bad for him?"

"Well, it certainly makes him feel bad," Dr. Chen said. "But his fever is not at a dangerous level." Dr. Chen pointed to a wall chart showing the ranges of temperature for humans (see figure Ev.3).

"As long as his fever is at a reasonable level and appears to be caused by an infection instead of a head injury or overheating, it won't hurt him. Aspirin and over-the-counter cold and flu medicines that contain aspirin can be effective in reducing fevers. But they shouldn't be given to children or teenagers who have flulike symptoms. Aspirin is associated with increasing the risk for Reye's syndrome when it is given to children or teenagers who have fever-causing viral infections such as chicken pox or influenza. Reye's syndrome affects many organs, especially the liver, and can trigger life-threatening pressure on the brain.

"In Miguel's case today, it's difficult to say whether it's helpful or harmful to lower his fever. Fever may be helping him fight his infection. Read this interesting research report." Dr. Chen showed the account called *Fever in Animals* to Miguel and his father.

"What about the old saying, 'Starve a fever, feed a cold'?" Mr. Hernandez asked.

"Well, I wouldn't recommend starving, but don't force too much food. Do drink lots of juices and water to keep hydrated. You use energy to produce the fever. But you have some body stores of glycogen and fat to

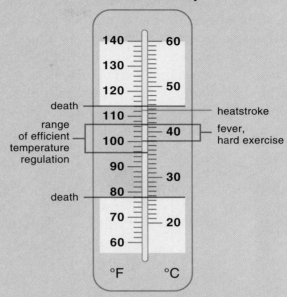

Figure Ev.3 This chart shows the temperature ranges of the human body.

use for energy. You may suffer from diarrhea as the antibiotic kills off the bacteria that normally live in your intestines. If so, you can eat yogurt, which contains lactobacillus cultures, or take tablets containing normal intestinal bacteria to help stop the diarrhea. Those bacteria also help keep the growth rate of pathogens low by competing for resources."

NEED TO KNOW

Fever in Animals

Fever is an above-normal increase of body temperature. Does fever act as a defense mechanism against disease? Several studies have shown that infections may last longer and be more severe when people are treated with drugs such as aspirin. Aspirin reduces fever. But it also blocks pain and reduces inflammation. Scientists have conducted experiments with animals to try to isolate the effects of fever. Rabbits treated with drugs that reduce fever are more likely to survive bacterial infections if they also receive an "artificial fever" by being exposed to an external heat source. These experiments suggest that fever does act as a defense mechanism.

In humans and other mammals, fever is produced when the chemical signals of infection cause the brain to increase the set point for body temperature. The rate of the body's metabolism increases. The organism shivers to warm its body, and blood vessels near the skin constrict, thus reducing heat loss. Fever may enhance the immune system's response. It also induces sleepiness and pain, so the sick organism is less active, making more energy available for fighting the infection. When the infection is over, sweating occurs, and the body temperature returns to normal.

Some animals, such as reptiles, do not rely on internal metabolic warming to produce fever (see figure Ev.4). They rely on behavioral changes to help adjust their body temperature. For example, they can move to warm or cool locations. In one study, scientists infected desert iguanas (*Dipsosaurus dorsalis*) with the bacterium *Aeromonas hydrophila*. The iguanas moved to locations that increased their temperature above normal. When scientists prevented the infected iguanas from moving to the warmer, fever-inducing locations, the infections worsened.

Figure Ev.4   Reptiles, such as the iguana, do not produce fevers from metabolic warming. They rely on behavioral changes and interactions with the environment to regulate temperature.

SCENARIO

ENGLISH   SPANISH

Scenario 2: Cystic Fibrosis and Cholera

Most harmful genetic disorders are quite rare within human populations. In many cases, the most serious mutations never show up in adults. This is because the changes are so harmful that the embryo does not survive early development. So it may seem surprising that cystic fibrosis (CF) is much more common than many other serious genetic disorders. CF is a recessive inherited disease that causes severe problems with the gas exchange and digestive systems. People with CF experience chronic coughs, lung infections, pneumonia, and digestion difficulties. Those problems generally become worse as patients become older. On average, CF patients live into their mid- to late 30s, although new treatments are helping to extend patients' lifetimes.

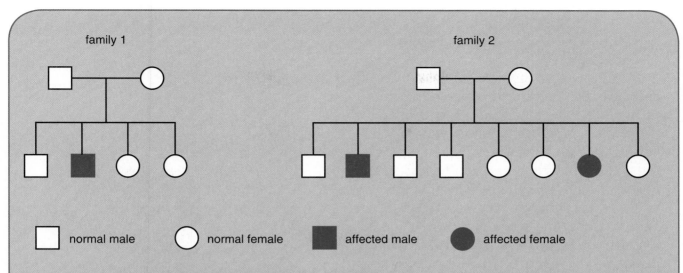

family 1

family 2

normal male   normal female   affected male   affected female

Figure Ev.5 These pedigrees show the incidence of cystic fibrosis in two families.

Why is the mutant gene for CF found in some human populations at a relatively high frequency? One possibility is that it provides some advantage in addition to the problems it causes. If so, it would be a good example of an evolutionary trade-off. Scientists examined the mechanism by which the CF mutation causes disease. They looked for the possibility that the mutation also could cause beneficial effects. One way to investigate that was to consider what happens in heterozygotes, people who carry only one copy of the CF allele (and so do not have any disease symptoms). The pedigrees, or family trees, in figure Ev.5 show two possible inheritance patterns for CF.

This is what the scientists found. Cystic fibrosis is caused by mutations in the gene for a protein. The protein is known as the cystic fibrosis transmembrane conductance regulator protein, or CFTR protein. This protein normally has 1,480 amino acids and is found in the membranes of lung and intestinal cells. The normal form of the CFTR protein is a *transport protein*. It acts as a gate in certain membranes, similar to a gate that allows people to go in and out of a stadium. That protein controls the exchange of chloride ions (Cl⁻) across the membranes

of cells in the gas exchange and digestive systems (figure Ev.6).

In patients with cystic fibrosis, the protein is altered and does not function properly. For example, one particular mutation causes the deletion of just one amino acid. This is the phenylalanine at position 508 in the amino acid sequence of the CFTR protein. This mutation, called F508, is found in both copies

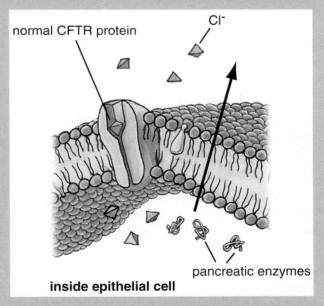

Figure Ev.6 The normal CFTR protein regulates chloride ion (Cl⁻) flow across the membrane. This indirectly affects the secretion of pancreatic enzymes.

of the *CFTR* genes carried by 75 percent of all CF patients.

The CF allele results in only a small change in the amino acid sequence of the CFTR protein. But it has a large effect on the protein's ability to function. Mutant versions of the CFTR protein cannot regulate the exchange of chloride ions. The loss of chloride ion regulation means that the regulation of water balance is lost as well. This is because the concentration of chloride ions outside of the cell affects the amount of water moving into or out of the cell. (This movement takes place by the process of osmosis.) When people are homozygous for the CF allele, they do not have any functional CFTR proteins. As a result, thick mucous secretions build up outside the cells of the gas exchange and digestive systems in people with CF.

Mucus in the digestive ducts of the pancreas interferes with the release of certain digestive enzymes, as shown in figure Ev.7. Mucus in the lungs interferes with breathing and makes people with CF more vulnerable to lung infection. That susceptibility occurs because the immune system cells that normally move to the site of an infection cannot pass through the mucus. Normally, these cells destroy harmful invaders. Without the help of the immune system, even relatively minor infections can become quite serious.

You may wonder, as many scientists have, how an allele that can cause such harmful symptoms would persist over time in some human populations. Evidence obtained from studies of another disease, cholera, suggests a possible reason why CF continues to be relatively common today. Cholera is an infectious disease spread by bacteria that infect the intestines. The disease causes severe diarrhea that, in humans, often leads to death if medical treatment is not available. It is possible that individuals who

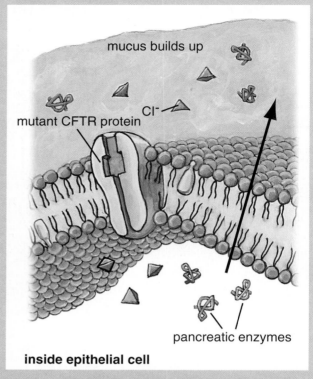

Figure Ev.7   The effect of cystic fibrosis on the pancreas. The mutant CFTR protein interferes with Cl⁻ movement across the membrane. This, in turn, interferes with water movement across the membrane. Pancreatic enzymes get stuck in mucus that builds up outside the cell.

are heterozygous for the CF allele may be more likely to survive cholera than those individuals who are homozygous normal for the *CFTR* gene.

The first step in understanding the possible relationship between CF and cholera was to consider what causes cholera's symptoms. The invading pathogen is the bacterium *Vibrio cholerae*. It produces a toxin called cholera toxin, CT. Scientists found that this toxin interferes with the normal CFTR protein. The toxin CT causes the normal CFTR protein to change its regulatory activity and secrete too much chloride ion and water from intestinal cells. That change causes diarrhea and dehydration in otherwise healthy mice and humans.

Once the cause of cholera's symptoms was understood, scientists set up a model using mice that had mutant *CFTR* genes and could be infected with cholera. With that model, the scientists tested how mice with different genotypes for the CF allele would react to cholera. They knew that heterozygous mice would probably have only half as much normal CFTR protein as homozygous normal mice. This is because they only had one allele for normal CFTR. The other allele produces nonfunctional (mutant) CFTR protein. They measured the amount of normal CFTR protein in mice with different genotypes for the CF allele. They also measured the severity of diarrhea in the same groups of mice after they were infected with cholera. The data from their studies are shown in figure Ev.8.

When infected with the cholera pathogen, the heterozygous mice secrete only about two-thirds as much fluid (diarrhea) as normal (non-CF) mice. Their diarrhea is less severe than that of normal mice, as shown in figure Ev.8b. The mice that are heterozygous for CF do not become as sick from cholera as do mice lacking the mutant CF allele.

The scientists concluded that their data supported the hypothesis that the presence of the CF allele may increase the ability to survive cholera. They also concluded that these data suggest that the high incidence of CF in some human populations may be related to an increased resistance to cholera. They submitted a report of their experiments to the journal *Science*. Their report was reviewed by a panel of scientists who decided that their results and conclusions were worthy of publication. As a result, the science and medical community had access to this new information.

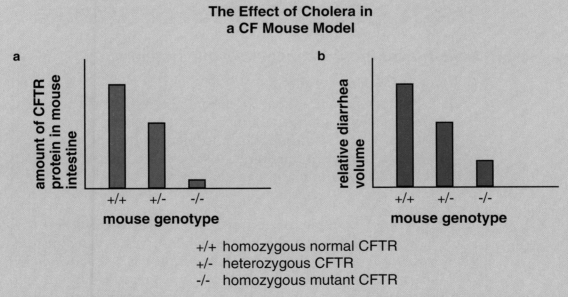

The Effect of Cholera in a CF Mouse Model

+/+ homozygous normal CFTR
+/- heterozygous CFTR
-/- homozygous mutant CFTR

Figure Ev.8 **The effects of cholera in relation to the presence of the CF allele.** (*a*) This graph shows the amount of CFTR protein in normal mice, mice with one copy of the CF allele (heterozygotes), and mice with two copies of the CF allele (homozygotes). (*b*) This graph shows how these groups of mice react to having cholera.

Analysis

Write an essay that describes how each of the 6 unifying principles is evident in the scenario you chose. Describe how the scenario shows how multiple unifying principles interact in living systems.

> Remember, all six unifying principles are represented either directly or indirectly whenever you study living systems. Be sure to use specific examples from the scenario that you chose to illustrate each principle.

Chapter Challenges

In part B, *Chapter Challenges*, you will find at least one challenging question or problem for each chapter in *A Human Approach*. You can use these questions to test your understanding of the specific ideas in the chapters you studied. Keep in mind that although a question may be listed under a particular chapter heading, you can respond by including material from other chapters. You may also need to conduct research outside your student book to complete your answers.

Materials

resource materials (optional)

PROCESS AND PROCEDURES

Unit 1: Evolution: Change in Living Systems

Chapter 1: The Human Animal

1. Discoveries about animal cognition have led to new perspectives on what makes us uniquely human. Read the need to know, *Dolphin Self-Recognition*. Consider this information, then write a paragraph describing some of the unique features of humans, particularly with respect to cognition and consciousness.

Chapter 2: Evolution: Change across Time

1. Describe 2 examples of how evolution has happened over the last 5,000 years. You may discuss the evolution of any organisms, and you may consider those whose evolution has been affected by humans. Your answer may include 1 well-reasoned hypothetical example, if you wish. Explain whether the examples you chose are still evolving today.

> A hypothetical example is one that you or others have made up. In this case, however, any example you give should involve real organisms, and the evolutionary changes you propose should be based on sound reasoning.

NEED TO KNOW

Dolphin Self-Recognition

The ability to recognize one's self in a mirror was once thought to be a feature shared only by humans and other great apes. This idea was challenged in 2001 with a report of dolphin self-recognition (figure Ev.9). The study was designed to eliminate any competing hypotheses about the use of a mirror by dolphins. A dolphin was marked with a nontoxic marker on its head. In subsequent trials, other marks were placed on different parts of its head and body. In all cases, the dolphin could not see the marks without the use of a mirror. In other trials, the dolphin was marked with the same marker filled with water that left no visible trace. The dolphin's behavior around the mirror was monitored. The dolphins oriented the marked area on their bodies to the mirror and spent a much greater amount of time at the mirror when they had actually been marked, compared to when they had only had the sensation of being marked. The authors concluded that the ability to self-recognize is present in dolphins. They speculated that this is likely an example of convergence with the evolution of self-recognition in great apes.

Figure Ev.9
Experiments with marked dolphins have shown that they are capable of recognizing themselves in a mirror.

2. How does technology play a role in helping scientists collect evidence of evolution?

Chapter 3: Products of Evolution: Unity and Diversity

1. Scientists have hypothesized that modern whales are descended from land mammals that moved into the water environment 60–50 million years ago. A number of recent discoveries have improved scientists' explanations of the evolution of whales. Read the need to know, *Whale Evolution,* and study figure Ev.10 to learn more.

   a. Determine the order in which scientists hypothesize that the following whale adaptations developed over the course of evolution. Write these in a column starting with the oldest.
      1) A fluke (tail flipper)
      2) All time spent in water
      3) Nostrils on top of snout
      4) Loss of the hind limbs
      5) Some time spent in water

      In a second column, list the name of the most ancient species or group known to show each adaptation. In a third column, list the evidence linking that adaptation to the species you listed.

b. Explain how scientists could collect additional fossil, genetic, or embryonic evidence to investigate a question that could still be answered about whale evolution.

2. Develop a reasonable scientific explanation for this statement: "Birds are related to dinosaurs."

You may need to access resources outside your student text to develop your explanation.

NEED TO KNOW

Whale Evolution

For many years, paleontologists hypothesized that the most closely related mammal to modern whales was an extinct hyena-like mammal with a slender tail known as a mesonychid. They based their hypothesis on skeletal similarities between this fossil and whales. However, genetic comparisons made between the DNA of living groups of mammals suggested that modern whales are most closely related to hoofed mammals known as artiodactyls, which include pigs and hippos. Also, no fossils had been found that would help link the mesonychids or any other land-dwelling animal to the most-well-known whale fossil, *Basilosaurus*. This fossil contains vestigial hind limbs that would not have been strong enough to support the body on land. *Basilosaurus* also has flippers and a tail fluke.

But in 1994, some major fossil discoveries were made. One fossil is named *Ambulocetus*, which is a mammal that appears to have lived a semiaquatic lifestyle. It has four short legs, large feet, and a thick tail similar to an otter's. Analysis of the isotopes in the fossil indicated that the animal spent some time in freshwater. A second major discovery is named *Rhodocetus*. This fossil bears features intermediate between *Ambulocetus* and *Basilosaurus*. For example, *Rhodocetus* has nostrils on the top of its snout, suggesting that it spent time in water. Furthermore, the *Rhodocetus* skeletons have anklebones that are shaped like those found in hoofed animals. Bones of this shape are not found in mesonychids.

Additional fossil discoveries have led scientists to a much greater understanding of the events that took place as the ancestors of modern whales adapted to a fully aquatic lifestyle. Like all evolutionary trees, the tree of whale evolution is a hypothesis that may be revised (figure Ev.10). But like the piecing together of the edge pieces of a jigsaw puzzle, the outlines of whale evolution now appear to be in place.

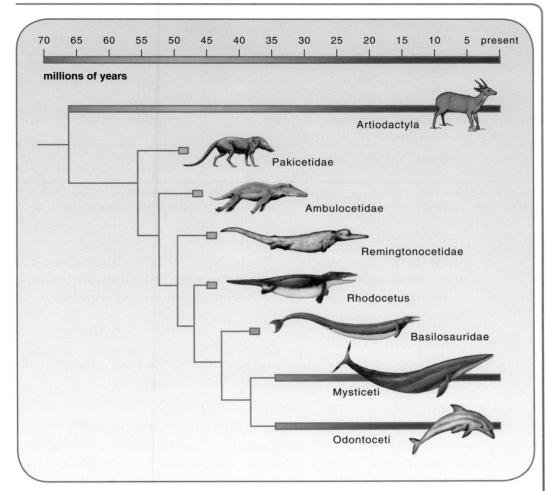

Figure Ev.10
Evolutionary tree of whales and dolphins (in the suborders Mysticeti and Odontoceti) and the extinct groups with which they share common ancestry.

3. The Nature Conservancy is an example of a conservation organization that seeks to protect land from human development. How could the activities of an organization such as this have an effect on biological diversity? Give specific examples using this organization or a similar one.

Unit 2: Homeostasis: Maintaining Dynamic Equilibrium in Living Systems

Chapter 4: The Internal Environment of Organisms

1. An astronaut in space depends on a space vehicle or a space suit to create an environment that can support his or her life. The data in figure Ev.11 show the average daily dietary and metabolic needs of an astronaut in space.
   a. Draw the table in figure Ev.11 into your science notebook. Then complete the third column of the table. Do this by listing the types of waste products that the astronaut would produce given the inputs shown. (You do not need to use numerical values.)

Figure Ev.11
An astronaut's daily dietary and metabolic needs. What do these data tell you about an astronaut's needs?

Input	Amount needed per day	Waste products
Oxygen	0.84 kg/day	
Food solids	0.62 kg/day	
Dietary water (includes drinking water and water in food)	2.77 kg/day	
Water for washing and food preparation	25.26 kg/day	

Source: From Wieland, P.O. (1994), *Designing for Human Presence in Space: An Introduction to Environmental Control and Life Support Systems* (NASA Reference Publication 1324). Huntsville, AL: George C. Marshall Space Flight Center.

    b. Consider the inputs listed in figure Ev.11. What technologies allow the space traveler to maintain these inputs in balance in his or her body during the journey? What do you do to keep these inputs in balance in your body?

Chapter 5: Maintaining Balance in Organisms
    1. What roles does the brain have in maintaining the body's balance of temperature, water, gas exchange, and blood pressure?

Chapter 6: Human Homeostasis: Health and Disease
    1. A human body is continuously subjected to minor disruptions and changes in its external environment. Use 1 or 2 examples to explain why these changes normally do not cause problems for the body. For these examples, under what circumstances can homeostasis become disrupted in a dangerous way?

    2. How do diseases cause disruptions of homeostasis in the human body? Choose AIDS or an autoimmune disease as an example to use when answering this question.

Unit 3: Energy, Matter, and Organization: Relationships in Living Systems

Chapter 7: Physical Fitness and Performance
    1. Have you ever watched someone racewalk? The unusual twisting motion of the hips makes it look as if it would be so much easier for the racers to pick up their feet and run. What is the difference between running and walking? Humans, like many other vertebrates including horses, dogs, cats, and deer, have different ways of moving their legs for locomotion. If you ever have watched a dog break into a run, you know it changes its gait dramatically to go faster. Use the data displayed in figure Ev.12 to answer these questions about energy and locomotion.

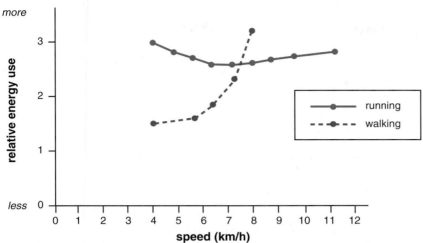

Energy Use and Locomotion

Source: From McNeill, A. R. (1992). *Exploring biomechanics: Animals in motion.* New York: Scientific American Library.

Figure Ev.12
Energy use in different modes of human locomotion. The energy data were calculated based on the amount of oxygen consumed by study participants when running and walking.

   a. At a speed of 5 km/h (about 3 mph), is running or walking more energy efficient? Is the same true at 8 km/h (about 5 mph)? Explain how the data in figure Ev.12 support your answers.

   b. During very fast running, above 16 km/h (10 mph), some of the muscles of the body are transforming energy only from glycolysis, because oxygen is limited. In this case, would the study used to generate figure Ev.12 be an appropriate way to determine energy efficiency? Explain your answer.

Chapter 8: The Cellular Basis of Activity

  1. Metabolism includes the series of chemical reactions that break down macromolecules. These include glycolysis, fermentation, and aerobic respiration. It also includes the reactions that build up macromolecules, such as protein synthesis or (in plants and certain prokaryotes) photosynthesis.

   a. Can both types of reactions (breakdown and biosynthesis) happen in the same cells of the same organism? Explain your answer. You may wish to draw a diagram of an example cell to illustrate your work.

   b. Describe several specific examples that show how biosynthesis and breakdown reactions contribute to the metabolism of an organism.

  2. To grow and develop, a seed must germinate (sprout) as the embryonic plant begins to grow. Germination requires water. For example, lettuce seeds germinate in about 48 hours after being soaked in water. Germination also may be sensitive to light. Some seeds require light to germinate. In other species, light inhibits germination.

a. Design and, if your teacher directs, carry out a controlled experiment to test the question of whether light affects the germination of common garden seeds. You will need to use seeds that germinate quickly, such as Grand Rapids lettuce seeds.

    b. If you carried out your experiment, then report your hypothesis, results, and conclusions. Include a possible explanation of why the seeds you tested behaved as they did.

    c. Imagine a seed germinating underground. Explain the sources of energy and matter for the activities of germination *before* the seedling emerges from the ground. Do the same for *after* the sprout is aboveground and the leaves are open.

Chapter 9: The Cycling of Matter and the Flow of Energy in Ecosystems

    1. Explain the flow of energy in a compost pile. What happens to the matter? What is the connection between the flow of energy and the changes in the matter? You may wish to draw a diagram to help illustrate your explanation.

    2. Identify a population of organisms that lives in your community. Draw or construct a food web that shows the connections among the organisms in that population. Include a discussion of what happens to the energy as you move to higher trophic levels. Illustrate those relationships.

Unit 4: Continuity: Reproduction and Inheritance in Living Systems

Chapter 10: Reproduction in Humans and Other Organisms

    1. Explain how reproductive strategies and reproduction contribute to the continuity of a species and to the continuation of life on Earth.

    2. The behavior of animals such as crickets plays an important role in reproductive success. Read the need to know, *Modeling Behavior,* about the results of a research project, reported in *Science* magazine, that used a robot model of a cricket. Then explain how these results relate to what you know about mating behavior in animals, including humans.

    3. Say you were to invent 2 new types of contraceptives for humans, one hormonal and the other physical. What would they be and how would they work?

Chapter 11: Gene Action

    1. How is the molecular structure of genetic information important to the replication and expression of genes? In your response, describe the similarities and differences among the following molecular processes: replication, transcription, and translation.

    2. How is it possible that a change in a single nucleotide of a gene can produce a mutant protein? Will such a change in a nucleotide always produce a mutant protein? Explain.

NEED TO KNOW

ENGLISH SPANISH

Modeling Behavior

A psychologist in the United Kingdom, Barbara Webb, used a robot cricket to model the way crickets use call songs to find mates (see figure Ev.13). Webb had hypothesized that a cricket's complex behavior of moving toward a calling mate may result from simple reflexes that could be mimicked in a robot cricket that had sound sensors. The robot was programmed to respond to a specific set of syllables from a recording of a male cricket's song. When the recording was played, the robot moved toward the speakers. When the syllables of the recorded cricket song were altered, the robot became "confused." And when key syllables were separated between two speakers, the robot went to a spot halfway between the speakers before "choosing" one and heading toward it.

© Dreamstime/Mauhorng

Figure Ev.13 Modeling the behavior of even relatively simple organisms such as crickets has proven difficult. Why do you think this is so?

Chapter 12: Continuity of Information through Inheritance

1. In the laboratory, scientists can use enzymes to remove the cell walls from plant cells in growing tissue. The resulting cells are called protoplasts. Protoplasts then can be placed on a growth medium in a petri dish. If the medium contains the proper mixture of plant hormones, a single, isolated protoplast can divide and eventually produce a whole plant.

   a. What does this information tell you about the genetic material of a plant cell?

   b. Compare and contrast the role of genetic material between sexually and asexually reproducing organisms.

Unit 5: Development: Growth and Differentiation in Living Systems

Chapter 13: Processes and Patterns of Development

1. Plants and animals adjust to environmental changes in many ways. Read the need to know, *Adaptations to Change,* for a brief description of several adaptations to annual seasonal changes. Then describe how either deciduous trees or insects have a pattern of development that represents an adaptation for extreme seasonal differences in temperature.

2. A tumorous disease of tomato and tobacco plants known as crown gall can result from the action of a bacterium, called *Agrobacterium tumefaciens.* This bacterium can infect any wound on the plant (see figure Ev.14). These bacteria contain copies of a circular piece of DNA, called a plasmid. The plasmid contains special genes that affect

NEED TO KNOW

ENGLISH SPANISH

Adaptations to Change

We are bothered much less by flying insects, such as flies and mosquitoes, in the winter than in the summer. What happens to those insects in the winter months? There are regions where winters are very cold and the land often is covered by snow or lakes are frozen over. There, organisms display a wide variety of adaptations that help them survive the harsh conditions. For example, the sap in broad-leaved deciduous trees, such as maple, apple, and oak, withdraws into the roots and trunk. Leaves fall off and new ones grow in the spring. Animals may migrate, as do many birds. They may slow their activity and enter a prolonged sleep (as do bears and skunks). Or they may enter a dormant state of hibernation (as do ground squirrels). In this state, metabolic activity and body temperature drop significantly.

Adult insects have hard exoskeletons. Their bodies are filled with a bloodlike liquid in which their organs are suspended. Insects cannot easily regulate body temperature and can be damaged by freezing. With their small size, migration is difficult. Monarch butterflies, however, manage to use this strategy successfully. Some insects bury themselves in a protected place. But most insects in harsh climates survive winter in an immature developmental stage. These species lay eggs before the cold season, and then the adults die. The eggs, larvae, or pupae spend the winter in a protected spot. They become active and continue their development in the spring.

Figure Ev.14
Crown galls growing on (*a*) tomato plant and (*b*) laurel tree.

the growth regulation of plant cells. The bacterial genes incorporate into the plant's genetic material. There, the bacterial genes direct plant cells to make specialized amino acids that are useless to the plant but serve as food for the bacteria. A mass of undifferentiated tissue at the infected site soon grows into a tumor. The tumor can affect further growth of the plant, can affect the plant's ability to reproduce, and can even cause death.

Describe how a bacteria-induced crown gall tumor compares with cancer in humans. How is the tumor different from cancer?

Chapter 14: The Human Life Span

1. People go through the same life stages. Each generation, however, does so at a different time in history. A high school student named Rachel was 15 years old in 2003. Her parents were 15 in 1974. They listened to music by the Beatles and the Rolling Stones recorded on large vinyl records. Rachel's grandparents were 15 in 1949, shortly after World War II. They liked to dance to a big band sound and listen to shows on the radio.

   a. Make a table that compares the physical biology and the cultural setting for a single life stage for 3 humans from different generations. For example, your table could include you, your parents at your age, and your grandparents at your age. Alternatively, you could profile a family that you know about or have read about. You can use any life stage as long as you have information that corresponds to each generation.

   b. Make 2 columns. Label one "physical biology" and the other "cultural setting." Under each column, describe the characteristics that apply to each of your individuals.

   c. Label a third column "historical setting." In this column, write how the historical setting may have affected the characteristics of your individuals.

© Dreamstime/Darko Novakovic

Unit 6: Ecology: Interaction and Interdependence in Living Systems

Chapter 15: Interdependence among Organisms

1. An instrument aboard NASA's *Nimbus-7* satellite records data from the surface water of the Atlantic Ocean off the U.S. coast. This instrument is called a Coastal Zone Color Scanner, or CZCS. It measures infrared radiation and concentrations of chlorophyll pigments that are housed in phytoplankton. Phytoplanktons are photosynthetic microorganisms that drift with ocean currents. The pattern of infrared radiation corresponds to water temperature. The patterns of both radiation and chlorophyll correspond to currents and tidal mixing. The highest concentrations of chlorophyll pigments are found near the shore. The lower concentrations are found in the relatively unmixed waters of the warm Gulf Stream current.

   To answer the following question about interdependence, keep in mind that some places in the ocean have high concentrations of phytoplankton. Other places have very low concentrations of phytoplankton. Reflect on the place of phytoplankton, which provide food for many fish, in the food web of the ocean. How might data from *Nimbus-7* be useful for managing commercial fisheries?

   You may find it useful to review the discussion of photosynthesis in chapter 8, *The Cellular Basis of Activity.*

2. Population growth rates are easy to display on graphs. They typically have a characteristic shape that reflects the involvement of limiting factors. Use your knowledge of these types of graphs to complete the following tasks.

   a. Draw a graph that illustrates the growth of any population of organisms over a period of at least 10 generations. The organisms must live in an environment that includes 1 or more limiting factors. You may pick any type of organism, such as flies or cats, for your graph.

   b. Label your graph. Make sure the reader can tell how many generations have passed and what type of organism is represented.

   c. Pick 3 distinct points on different parts of your graphed line. Label them "A," "B," and "C." Describe what is happening to the population at points A, B, and C. Include a discussion of limiting factors to help explain your answer.

   d. Does any point on the graph represent the carrying capacity for your population? Explain why your population reached carrying capacity, or why not.

Chapter 16: Decision Making in a Complex World

1. A panel of lawmakers has met to consider zoning for 200 acres of land near a large forest that currently includes wetlands and a meadow. One development company wants to build a shopping center and apartments on most of this land. Another company proposes building a manufacturing plant there. Conservation groups want to protect the wetlands. Various specialists have provided reports that mention the following observations:

   • Nitrogen acts as a fertilizer for leafy parts of plants and for some microorganisms. Too much of this fertilizer causes plants to grow large tops and insufficient roots.

   • Forests may help protect the world from global warming by converting the greenhouse gas carbon dioxide to plant mass, by way of photosynthesis.

   • Fertilizers used to enhance landscaping and gardens tend to contain large amounts of nitrogen.

   • Acid rain results from certain air pollutants that industrial processes produce. Its effects on living systems are complex.

   • Nitrogen cycling is the conversion of atmospheric nitrogen into nitrogen that living organisms can use (see figure Ev.15). When an organism dies, different microorganisms (called denitrifying bacteria) decompose the organism's body. This releases some of its nitrogen back into the atmosphere. Many denitrifying bacteria live in boggy wetland environments.

The panel is ready to make a decision, but now a new finding is presented. (See the need to know, *Nitrates*.)

NEED TO KNOW

ENGLISH   SPANISH

Nitrates

In Germany, acid rain is a serious problem. Acid rain occurs when industrial pollutants such as nitrogen oxides react with water in the atmosphere, leading to rain with a very low pH. In a study of the effects of acid rain, scientists used radioisotope labels to trace nitrates from air pollution leaving a forest through runoff water. Figure Ev.15 shows what happened to the nitrates in different stands of trees. Two stands

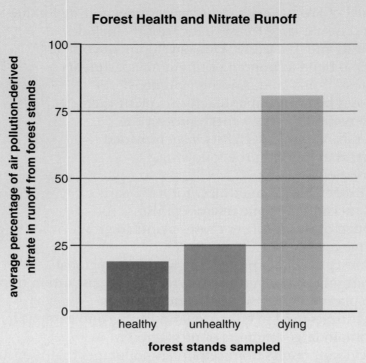

Forest Health and Nitrate Runoff

Source: From Raloff, J. (1995, February 11). When Nitrate Begins, *Science News, 147,* pp. 90–91.

Figure Ev.15   Tracking nitrate pollution. Researchers measured the amount of nitrogen in runoff bearing the nitrogen-15 isotope, a marker of air pollution. They compared the amount with the nitrogen-14 isotope, a marker of normal soil decomposition. The average amount of nitrogen in runoff originating from air pollution is shown for different stands of forest.

were dying and three stands were unhealthy. For a control, the scientists compared their results with two stands of healthy forest undisturbed by human habitation.

The study's authors explained some of the consequences of air pollution–derived nitrate runoff on an ecosystem. If nitrates move through soil without being taken up by living systems, then plants are deprived of the benefits of nitrogen. In addition, the free nitrates can remove other important nutrients that plants need, such as calcium and magnesium. The soil left behind is acidic enough to harm tree roots and kill microorganisms. In these conditions, old trees may die and young trees grow very slowly and may be stunted.

Your task is to discuss the following.
  a. How do the data in figure Ev.15 support the concerns of scientists who claim that acid rain and excessive nitrates from pollution cause damage to trees?

b. Make a 2-column table. In the left-hand column, list all of the possible biological and nonbiological consequences of developing the land. In the right-hand column, list the consequences of not developing the land.

   c. Think about the findings reported in figure Ev.15 and those from the earlier reports. How might these findings influence the panel's decision about how or whether the land in question should be developed?

   d. Would you decide to develop the land or not? If you would develop the land, how would you develop it? Explain the reasoning for your answers.

Building a Portfolio of Scientific Literacy

PART C

   In this activity, *Building a Portfolio of Scientific Literacy*, you will prepare a portfolio that displays evidence that you are a scientifically literate citizen. To fill the job, you need to be able to reason, use evidence to support your ideas, and think conceptually about biology. This means you need more than just facts about biology. You must demonstrate that you understand those facts and how to use them. You will choose samples of your work from throughout the year. You may want to improve some of those samples to accurately show your progress. In addition, you may create new work to make your presentation the best show of your success.

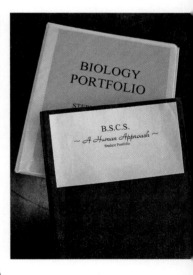

Materials

   samples of your work from this program
   resources and materials to revise your work or create new work

PROCESS AND PROCEDURES

1. Obtain a *Biology Portfolio Rubric* handout from your teacher. Read the scoring rubric carefully. Discuss the criteria with your partner.

   Ask your teacher any questions about the project that you or your partner cannot answer from the rubric.

2. Review all the chapters of your student text. Record in your science notebook what you think the main concepts are from each chapter. Do this by making a table. Create 1 column for the titles of the chapters in each unit. Add a second column to record the main concepts or ideas from each chapter.

3. Let your teacher review your table of concepts before you prepare your portfolio.

4. Look over your work for each chapter. Follow the criteria in the scoring rubric and these steps to select pieces of your work.
   a. Decide how to display your work samples to make a portfolio.
   b. Find a sample of work to illustrate the key concept or concepts of each chapter. Use samples of your work just as they are. Or make corrections or additions if you think you understand the concepts and the particular activity better than when you did it.

   > Remember, you can use additional resources to help you improve an existing activity. Use the essays, your science notebook, your teammates, or outside references.

   c. If you are missing good samples of work from some chapters, add new work to your portfolio. For example, you could choose to answer questions from the collection of questions in the previous activity, part B, *Chapter Challenges*.

   > You can put this new work in the portfolio along with the samples of your previous work.

5. Prepare a caption for each sample in the portfolio. Each caption should include the information explained in the "explanation" section of the scoring rubric.

   > Include a caption for all work in the portfolio, both existing work and new work. The caption should show that you have reflected on what you learned from doing each piece of work.

Analysis

1. When you think your portfolio is complete, take time to look through it. Reflect on whether it is persuasive evidence that you are a scientifically literate citizen. Be sure that you have organized your portfolio so that any reader can easily find and understand your work samples.
2. Have your portfolio reviewed as your teacher directs.
3. Revise your portfolio based on the feedback that you receive.

APPENDIX A
Laboratory Safety

The laboratory has the potential to be either a safe place or a dangerous place. The difference depends on how well you know and follow safe laboratory practices. It is important that you read the information here and learn how to recognize and avoid potentially hazardous situations. Basic rules for working safely in the laboratory include the following:

1. Be prepared. Study the assigned activity before you come to class. Resolve any questions about the procedures before you begin to work.
2. Be organized. Arrange the materials you need for the activity in an orderly way.
3. Maintain a clean, open work area. This area should be free of anything except those materials you need for the assigned activity. Store books, backpacks, and purses out of the way. Keep laboratory materials away from the edge of the work surface.
4. Tie back long hair and remove dangling jewelry. Roll up long sleeves and tuck long neckties into shirts. Do not wear loose-fitting sleeves or open-toed shoes in the laboratory.
5. Wear safety goggles and a lab apron whenever you work with chemicals, hot liquids, lab burners, hot plates, or apparatuses that could break or shatter. Wear protective gloves when working with preserved specimens, toxic and corrosive chemicals, or when otherwise directed to do so.
6. Never wear contact lenses while conducting any experiment involving chemicals. If you must wear them (by a physician's order), inform your teacher *before* conducting any experiment involving chemicals.
7. Never use direct or reflected sunlight to illuminate your microscope or any other optical device. Sunlight focused through a microscope can cause serious damage to your retinas.
8. Keep your hands away from the sharp or pointed ends of equipment, such as scalpels, dissecting needles, or scissors.
9. Observe all cautions in the procedural steps of the activities. **CAUTION** and **WARNING** are signal words used in the text and on labeled chemicals or reagents. These words tell you about the potential for harm and/or injury. They remind you to observe specific safety practices. ***Always read and follow these statements***. They are meant to help keep you and your fellow students safe.

CAUTION statements advise you that the material or procedure has *some potential risk* of harm or injury if directions are not followed.

WARNING statements advise you that the material or procedure has a *moderate risk* of harm or injury if directions are not followed.

10. Become familiar with the caution symbols identified in the need to know.

NEED TO KNOW

ENGLISH SPANISH

Safety Symbols Used in This Program

Caution
The caution symbol alerts you to procedures or materials that may be harmful if directions are not followed properly. You may encounter the following common hazards during this course:

Sharp object
Sharp objects can cause injury, either a cut or a puncture. Handle all sharp objects with caution. Use them only as your teacher instructs you. Do not use them for any purpose other than the one intended. If you do get a cut or puncture wound, call your teacher and get first aid.

Irritant
An irritant is any substance that, on contact, can cause reddening of living tissue. Wear safety goggles, lab apron, and protective gloves when handling any irritating chemical. In case of contact, flush the affected area with soap and water for at least 15 minutes. Call your teacher. Remove contaminated clothing.

Reactive
Reactive chemicals are capable of reacting with another substance, including water. They can cause a violent reaction. *Do not* mix a reactive chemical with any other substance, including water, unless directed to do so by your teacher. Wear your safety goggles, lab apron, and protective gloves.

Corrosive
A corrosive substance injures or destroys body tissue on contact by direct chemical action. When handling any corrosive substance, wear safety goggles, lab apron, and protective gloves. In case of contact with a corrosive material, immediately flush the affected area with water. Call your teacher immediately.

Biohazard
Any biological substance that can cause infection through exposure is a biohazard. Before handling any material so labeled, review your teacher's specific instructions. *Do not* handle in any manner other than as instructed. Wear safety goggles, lab apron, and protective gloves. Any contact with a biohazard should be reported to your teacher immediately.

Safety goggles

Safety goggles are for eye protection. Wear goggles every time you see this symbol. If you wear glasses, be sure the goggles fit comfortably over them. If a material from the laboratory splashes into your eyes, flush your eyes (including under the lid) at an eyewash station for 15–20 minutes. If you wear contact lenses, remove them *immediately* and flush your eyes as directed. Call your teacher.

Lab apron

A lab apron is intended to protect your clothing. Whenever you see this symbol, put on your apron and tie it securely behind you. If you spill any substance on your clothing, call your teacher.

Gloves

Wear gloves every time you see this symbol or whenever your teacher directs you to do so. Wear them when using *any* chemical or reagent solution. Do not wear your gloves for an extended period of time. Wash your hands after wearing gloves.

Flammable

A flammable substance is any material capable of igniting under certain conditions. Do not bring flammable materials into contact with open flames or near heat sources unless instructed to do so by your teacher. Remember that flammable liquids give off vapors that can be ignited by a nearby heat source. Should a fire occur, *do not* attempt to extinguish it yourself. Call your teacher. Wear safety goggles, lab apron, and protective gloves whenever you handle a flammable substance.

Poison

Poisons can cause injury by direct action within a body system through direct contact with skin, inhalation, ingestion, or penetration. Always wear safety goggles, lab apron, and protective gloves when handling any material with this label. If you have any preexisting injuries to your skin, inform your teacher before you handle any poison. In case of contact with a poison, call your teacher immediately.

11. Never put anything in your mouth. Never touch or taste substances in the laboratory unless your teacher specifically instructs you to do so.
12. Never smell substances in the laboratory without specific instructions from your teacher. Even then, do not inhale fumes directly. If you are directed to sniff a substance in the laboratory, wave the air above the substance toward your nose and sniff carefully.
13. Never eat, drink, chew gum, or apply cosmetics in the laboratory. Do not store food or beverages in the lab area.
14. Know the location of all safety equipment. Learn how to use each piece of equipment.

15. If you witness an unsafe incident, an accident, or a chemical spill, report it to your teacher immediately.
16. Use materials only from containers labeled with the name of the chemical and the precautions to be used. Become familiar with the safety precautions for each chemical by reading the label before use.
17. To dilute acid with water, *always add the acid to the water*, pouring slowly and carefully. Diluting acid in another way can cause droplets of acid to splash into contact with you.
18. Never return unused chemicals to the stock bottles. Do not put any object into a chemical bottle, except the dropper with which it may be equipped.
19. Clean up thoroughly. Dispose of chemicals. Wash used glassware and instruments according to the teacher's instructions. Clean tables and sinks. Put away all equipment and supplies. Make sure all water, gas jets, burners, and electrical appliances are turned off. Return all laboratory materials and equipment to their proper places.
20. Wash your hands thoroughly after handling any living organisms or hazardous material. Do this *before* leaving the laboratory.
21. Never perform unauthorized experiments. Do only those experiments your teacher approves.
22. Never work alone in the laboratory. Never work without your teacher's supervision.
23. Approach laboratory work with care and maturity. Move deliberately and cautiously. Never run, push, or engage in horseplay or practical jokes of any type in the laboratory. Use laboratory materials and equipment only as directed.

In addition to observing these general safety precautions, you need to know about some specific categories of safety. Before you do any laboratory work, familiarize yourself with the following precautions.

Heat

1. Use only the heat source specified in the activity.
2. Never allow flammable materials such as alcohol near a flame or any other source of ignition.
3. When heating a substance in a test tube, point the mouth of the tube away from other students and you.
4. Never leave a lighted lab burner, hot plate, or any other hot objects unattended.
5. Never reach over an exposed flame or other heat source.
6. Use tongs, test-tube clamps, insulated gloves, or potholders to handle hot equipment.

Glassware

1. Never use cracked or chipped glassware.
2. Use caution and proper equipment when handling hot glassware. *Hot glass looks the same as cool glass.* Touching hot glass can cause serious burns.
3. Make sure glassware is clean before you use it and when you store it.
4. To put glass tubing into a rubber stopper, moisten the tubing and the stopper. Protect your hands with a heavy cloth when you insert or remove glass tubing from a rubber stopper. Never force or twist the tubing.
5. Immediately sweep up broken glassware. Discard it in a special, labeled container for broken glass. *Never pick up broken glass with your fingers.*

Electrical Equipment and Other Apparatuses

1. Before you begin any work, learn how to use each piece of apparatus safely and correctly in order to obtain accurate scientific information.
2. Never use equipment with frayed insulation or loose or broken wires.
3. Make sure the area in and around the electrical equipment is dry and free of flammable materials. Never touch electrical equipment with wet hands.
4. Turn off all power switches before plugging an appliance into an outlet. Never jerk wires from outlets or pull appliance plugs out by the wire.

Living and Preserved Specimens

1. Be sure that specimens for dissection are properly mounted and supported. Do not cut a specimen while holding it in your hand.
2. Wash your work surface with a disinfectant solution both before and after using live microorganisms.
3. Always wash your hands with soap and water after working with live or preserved specimens.
4. Care for animals humanely. General rules for their care are listed below.
   a. Always follow carefully your teacher's instructions about the care of laboratory animals.
   b. Keep the animals in a suitable, escape-proof container in a location where they will not be disturbed constantly.
   c. Keep the containers clean. Clean cages of small birds and mammals daily. Provide proper ventilation, light, and temperature.
   d. Provide clean water at all times.
   e. Feed regularly, depending on the animals' needs.
   f. Treat laboratory animals gently and with kindness in all situations.

g. If you are responsible for the regular care of any animals, be sure to make arrangements for their care during weekends, holidays, and vacations.

h. Your teacher will provide a suitable method to dispose of or release animals, if it becomes necessary.

5. Many plants or plant parts are poisonous. Work only with the plants your teacher specifies. Never put any plant or plant parts in your mouth.

6. Handle plants carefully and gently. Most plants must have light, soil, and water, although the specific requirements differ.

7. Wear the following personal protective equipment when handling or dissecting preserved specimens: safety goggles, lab apron, and plastic gloves.

Accident Procedures

1. Report *all* accidents, incidents, and injuries, and all breakage and spills, no matter how minor, to your teacher.

2. If a chemical spills on your skin or clothing, wash it off immediately with plenty of water. Have a classmate notify your teacher immediately.

3. If a chemical gets in your eyes or on your face, wash immediately at the eyewash fountain with plenty of water. Flush your eyes for at least 15 minutes, including under each eyelid. Have a classmate notify your teacher immediately.

4. If a chemical spills on the floor or work surface, do not clean it up yourself. Notify your teacher immediately.

5. If a thermometer breaks, do not touch the broken pieces or any spilled liquid with your fingers. Notify your teacher immediately for instructions about disposal.

6. In case of a lab table fire, notify your teacher immediately. In case of a clothing fire, drop to the floor and roll. Use a fire blanket if one is available. Have a classmate notify your teacher immediately.

7. Report to your teacher all cuts and abrasions received in the laboratory, no matter how small.

Chemical Safety

All chemicals are hazardous in some way. A hazardous chemical is defined as a substance that is likely to cause injury. Chemicals can be placed in four hazard categories: flammable, toxic, corrosive, and reactive.

In the laboratory investigations for this course, we have made every effort to minimize the use of dangerous materials. However, many "less hazardous" chemicals can cause injury if not handled properly. The following information will help you become aware of the types of chemical hazards that exist and of how you can reduce the risk of injury when using chemicals. Before you work with any chemical, be sure to review safety rules 1–23 described at the beginning of this appendix.

Flammable substances. Flammable substances are solids, liquids, or gases that will burn. The process of burning involves three interrelated components—fuel (any substance capable of burning), oxidizer (often air or a specific chemical), and an ignition source (a spark, flame, or heat). The three components are represented in the diagram of a fire triangle in figure A.1. For burning to take place, all three components (sides) of the fire triangle must be present. To control fire hazard, one must remove, or otherwise make inaccessible, at least one side of the fire triangle.

Flammable chemicals should not be used in the presence of ignition sources, such as lab burners, hot plates, and sparks from electrical equipment or static electricity. Containers of flammables should be closed when not in use. Sufficient ventilation in the laboratory will help to keep the concentration of flammable vapors to a minimum.

Toxic substances. Most of the chemicals you encounter in a laboratory are toxic, or poisonous to life. The degree of toxicity depends on the properties of the specific substance, its concentration, the type of exposure, and other variables. The effects of a toxic substance can range from minor discomfort to serious illness or death. Exposure to toxic substances can occur through ingestion, skin contact, or inhalation of toxic vapors. Wearing a lab apron, safety goggles, and plastic gloves is an important precautionary measure when using toxic chemicals. A clean work area, prompt spill cleanup, and good ventilation also are important.

Corrosive substances. Corrosive chemicals are solids, liquids, or gases that by direct chemical action either destroy living tissue or cause permanent changes in the tissue. Corrosive substances can destroy eye and respiratory-tract tissues. The consequences of mishandling a corrosive substance can be impaired sight or permanent blindness, severe disfigurement, permanent severe breathing difficulties, and even death. As with toxic substances, wear a lab apron, safety goggles, and plastic gloves when handling corrosive chemicals to help prevent contact with your skin or eyes. Immediately wash off splashes on your skin or eyes while a classmate notifies the teacher.

Reactive substances. Under certain conditions, reactive chemicals cause violent reactions. A chemical may explode spontaneously or when it is mechanically disturbed. Reactive chemicals also include those that react rapidly when mixed with another chemical, releasing a large amount of energy. Keep chemicals separate from one another unless they are being combined according to specific instructions in an activity. Heed any other cautions your teacher may give you.

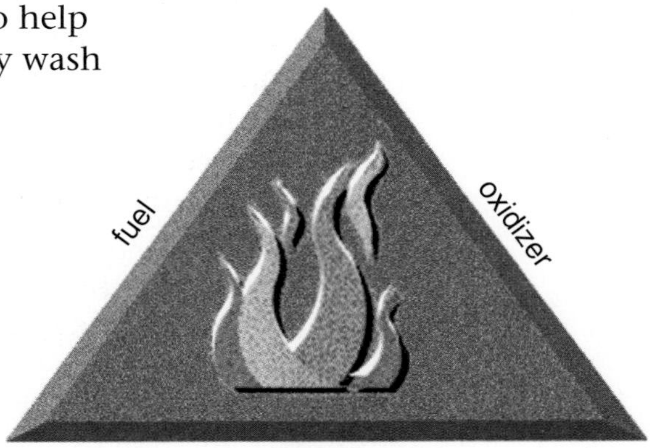

Figure A.1 The fire triangle. To control a fire, one must remove, or make inaccessible, at least one side of the fire triangle.

APPENDIX B1
How to Use the Science Notebook

In *BSCS Biology: A Human Approach*, you will use a science notebook on a regular basis. Science notebooks have many purposes: they provide a place to record data, take notes, reflect on your progress, and respond to questions. This science notebook will become your permanent record of your work, and you will refer to it often during discussions and assessments. The more complete your science notebook is, the more valuable it will be for you. Your science notebook should be a spiral notebook or a hardcover book that is permanently bound. (Do not use a loose-leaf notebook or a spiral notebook with perforated pages that tear out.) A notebook with square-grid (graph paper) pages will make any graphing that you do much easier. The following sections describe the major ways in which you will use your science notebook in this program.

Recording Data

Science depends on accurate data. No one—not even the original observer—can trust the accuracy of confusing, vague, or incomplete data. Scientific record keeping is the process by which you maintain neat, organized, and accurate records of your observations and data. Use a pen to record data. Although your interpretation of data may change, *the original data are a permanent record*. If you learn new or additional things and your thinking changes, make changes in your science notebook in a different-colored pen or pencil. That way, you and your teacher have a record of your ongoing learning.

Keep records in a diary form and record your name and the date at the beginning of each entry. Keep the records of each activity separate. Be brief but to the point when recording data in words. It may not be necessary to use complete sentences, but single words seldom are descriptive enough to represent accurately what you have observed or done.

Sometimes the easiest way to record data is in the form of a drawing or sketch. Such drawings need not be works of art, but they should be accurate representations of what you have observed. Place your sketches or drawings in the middle of the page, leaving room for captions, revisions, and highlights. Keep the drawings simple, use a hard pencil, and include clearly written labels. Often, the easiest way to record numerical data is in the form of a table. When you record data for counts or measurements with numbers, include the units of the measurements you used, for example, degrees Celsius or centimeters.

Do not record your data on other papers and then copy them into your science notebook. Doing so may increase neatness, but it will decrease accuracy. Your science notebook is your book, and cross outs and stains are normal circumstances of field and laboratory work.

You will do much of your laboratory work as a member of a team. Your science notebook, therefore, will contain data that other team members have contributed. Keep track of the source of observations by circling (or recording in a different color) the data that others reported.

Responding to Questions

When you answer discussion or activity questions from your science notebook, record the date and the activity title. Then number each response. You also may find it useful to record the questions. Sometimes you will respond to questions individually and sometimes with your team; indicate whether your responses are your own or your team's. As you are writing your responses, practice writing in complete sentences; this will help you when you synthesize and present ideas. After each answer that you write, leave a blank space where you can add questions or comments that arise as your understanding grows.

Taking Notes

When you need to record notes about information you wish to remember, always begin with the date. Then record the source of information. Often, this is a person or a book, but it could be a video, a Web site, or a computer program. When you are recording notes, start each new idea on a new line. Try to group related ideas under broad headings that will help you remember the important ideas and how they are connected. Write down more than you think you will need; it is hard to make sense of a few words when you look back at them later. Include diagrams and charts to clarify ideas.

It is often valuable to take notes during team and class discussions as well as when your teacher is presenting ideas or instructions. In addition, taking notes in your science notebook as you read essays or sidebars helps you better absorb the written information.

You can use the information in your science notebook to prepare for discussions or to review what you have learned. At times, you also will use the information that you have recorded to complete assessment activities.

Keeping Track of Your Questions

Often, as you read or work through an activity, a question will come to mind or you will find that you are confused about something. If you are not able to talk with your teammates or your teacher right away, jot down your question or what you find confusing in your science notebook so that you will remember to ask about it when you have the opportunity. You also may use this technique to record questions that you want to answer yourself.

Keeping Track of Your Responsibilities

Because you will use your science notebook every day in science class, it is a good place to record your class assignments and responsibilities. Each day you may want to record these in red in the upper corner of your science notebook page.

Using Your Science Notebook During Assessment

At times throughout this program, you will use your science notebook during assessments—both ongoing assessments, such as class discussions and team presentations, and more formal, end-of-unit assessments. Your teacher will collect your science notebook periodically to assess your progress. Using a science notebook for assessment will be a rewarding experience if your entries are complete, detailed, and well organized. Remember to make it easy for someone else reading your science notebook to understand what you have recorded. Using blank space to separate activities, notes, and data will make your science notebook easier to assess, and it will provide space for you to add new information if needed. Keep this in mind as you make entries in your science notebook.

APPENDIX B2
How to Use Chapter Organizers

Some of the skills you will improve upon this year will be your skills of organization. You will work this year at organizing your thoughts and knowledge in a science notebook. In addition, you will learn to use the organizational tools that the student book provides. You will see that we have included a chapter organizer at the beginning of each chapter. This organizer will help you see the big picture. Your understanding will deepen and strengthen as you see that what you have learned today connects to what you will learn tomorrow.

To familiarize yourself with the chapter organizer tool, work with a partner to complete the following tasks. Record your answers and thoughts in your science notebook under the title "Using the Chapter Organizers."

1. Look through the table of contents of your student book and find a chapter title that most interests you. Do not turn to your chapter yet; just look at the title. Make sure that you and your partner choose *different* chapters. If you both like the same one, work out a plan to have 2 different chapters. Learning to compromise in a group is another skill you will develop this year. Complete the following tasks based on the chapter you selected.

    a. Explain to your partner why you think this chapter will be interesting to you. Listen as your partner explains his or her thinking to you. Record the title of your chapter and at least 1 statement explaining why you think this chapter will be interesting.

    b. Think of as many concepts and ideas as you can that might be included in your chapter. List these concepts in your science notebook.

    c. Share your list with your partner and listen as your partner shares with you. Think about your partner's chapter selection. Can you add to his or her list of topics? Add new topics to your list that emerge during this discussion.

2. Find the chapter organizer for your chapter. It is found at the beginning of the chapter. Look at it carefully. All the chapters in this book follow the BSCS 5E instructional model. The 5Es provide a structure for active learning that will have you *doing* and *understanding* science, not just reading about it. Taken together, the 5Es will help you build a strong understanding of science. Can you find each of the 5Es included in your chapter organizer? List them in your science notebook.

3. What do you think each *E* represents in the learning sequence? Record your ideas in your science notebook.

    Include in your answer what you think you should be doing in each activity. For example, in the Explore activity, what will you be doing? How will you be interacting with your teacher and your teammates?

4. Every *E* is an activity that builds on the previous one and helps prepare you for the next one—the next *E*. Do you notice that between each activity there is a linking question? Discuss with your partner what you think the purpose of the linking question might be. Record your best ideas in your science notebook.

5. Look back at your original ideas about concepts you thought would be included in your chapter.
   a. Circle the ones that appear to be covered in this chapter.
   b. Look at other chapters in this same unit. Highlight topics that will be covered in other chapters.
   c. What feature of the chapter organizer helped you determine the topics covered in your chapter?

6. Discuss with your partner how this chapter organizer can help you with your learning. Record at least 3 ways that you can use the chapter organizers to enhance your learning.

7. Using the chapter organizer you chose as a guide, record what you think the main idea of that chapter is. Try to sum it up in 1 sentence.

8. What part or parts of the chapter organizer did you use to write your main idea sentence? What part of the organizer helped you the most?

APPENDIX B3

How to Use the Think-Share-Advise-Revise (TSAR) Strategy

Does learning stop when your paper comes back with a grade on it? It shouldn't. The same is true for experiences *during* class. That is, you get the most out of school when you get ongoing feedback on your thinking, then revise your original ideas to reflect what you've learned. This cycle of thinking on your own, sharing your ideas, getting advice from others, and revising what you think is essential in the workplace as well as in school. Work with a partner to learn about the think-share-advise-revise (TSAR) strategy.

1. Chapter 1, *The Human Animal*, has an example of using the TSAR strategy. Find it in the first Explore activity, *Primates Exploring Primates*, step 10.
2. Match each of the following steps, tailored to carrying out step 10 of *Primates Exploring Primates,* to the descriptions listed in the table in figure B3.1. You'll see generalized tasks in the table and specific examples in the steps below. The combination of the tasks and the examples provides you with why, what, and how to use the TSAR process. Use this strategy for any problem, especially in team situations.

   a. Review silently and *think* about whether each of the questions you and your partner wrote in step 8 of *Primates Exploring Primates* is testable. Think about how you can use the criteria from the need to know, *Testable Questions* to back up your ideas. Write down your reasoning.

   b. *Share* your opinion about the testability of the first question with your partner. Read your reasoning aloud as you wrote it.

   c. Ask for *advice* on whether your partner thinks your reasoning is sound, and if there are additional reasonings he or she thought of.

   d. *Revise* your work if you think your partner's advice makes good sense and improves your understanding.

   e. Switch roles and listen carefully to your partner's reasoning for the same question.

   f. Repeat this cycle for each of the questions you listed.

Figure B3.1
TSAR table.

Step	What you do	What others do
Think	• access what you already know and understand and the skills you already have • work individually • pinpoint what you do and don't know • generate questions • document your thoughts in your science notebook	• respect your private thinking time
Share	• read aloud your thinking to a teammate • explain any diagrams, charts, or sketches • respond to requests for clarification	• listen attentively • ask questions respectfully
Advise	• offer suggestions, elaborations, or alternative explanations to what your teammate read • respond to questions about your advice	• listen to your advice without interruption • ask for clarification if needed
Revise	• record what you changed in your original answer in response to advice • record why you changed your original answer in response to advice (remember, not all advice leads to changes)	• respect your private time to revise your first thoughts

APPENDIX B4
How to Use and Create Organizing Tables

Organizing information helps you see patterns and better understand text materials. There are many different kinds of organizing tables. For example, you can use tables to organize data in an investigation, to make comparisons and analogies, and to show relationships between information in reading passages. Here are three common organizing tables you might use.

1. *Information tables* can show relationships between information listed in the horizontal rows (figure B4.1). These tables can have 2, 3, or even 4 columns. You can use tables to show similarities or differences, or to organize what you know before or after you read. In this program, sample information tables are often given to help you start developing your own. But you can use this table format anytime you have information to organize, for example, while reading essays or reviewing for tests.

Reading about Genetics	
Fact or idea I read	**Questions I have about the fact or idea**

Figure B4.1 T-table example. This is an example of a T-table you could use as you read about genetics. As you read a passage, record your ideas in a table to help you organize your thoughts.

Feature of a road trip	is like . . .	aspect of scientific inquiry . . .	because . . .
A detour on the road	is like . . .	getting unexpected results from an investigation	when you encounter something you do not expect, you change the way you approach your investigation.
Circling back on a portion of the road to look for a turn	is like . . .	adjusting the design of an investigation	you return to your design and adjust it to get the results you need to answer your question.
Trying different routes on a road trip	is like . . .		
Encountering car trouble and returning home	is like . . .		
Abandoning your car on the road	is like . . .		
Starting your trip and changing the destination	is like . . .		

Figure B4.2   Analogy map example. This analogy map is one you could use to compare a road trip you might take with the process of scientific inquiry.

2. *Analogy maps* are a special type of table that allows you to connect new ideas with ideas you are familiar with (figure B4.2).
3. *Data tables* provide a place to record observations or data from an investigation. You can create graphs from the information in these tables or interpret your data directly from the tables themselves (figure B4.3).

Material	Volume of liquid sample (mL)	Mass of cylinder with liquid sample (g)	Mass of cylinder alone (g)
Sample A	100	142.54	2.54
Sample B	100	93.21	2.54
Sample C	100	83.44	2.54

Figure B4.3   Data table example. Data tables are a place to record both qualitative and quantitative observations and data from an investigation. This data table shows data recorded as students conduct an investigation about density. The data can be used to make a graph or do calculations.

APPENDIX B5
How to Use and Create Venn Diagrams

Venn diagrams are a powerful strategy for comparing topics or concepts. You can use them to visually show similarities and differences. A Venn diagram is made up of two or three overlapping circles. Each circle represents one topic or concept. The region inside each circle lists characteristics of that topic or concept. The part of the circle that overlaps contains characteristics common to both concepts. See the example in figure B5.1. Then try creating your own Venn diagrams using steps 1–5 to help you.

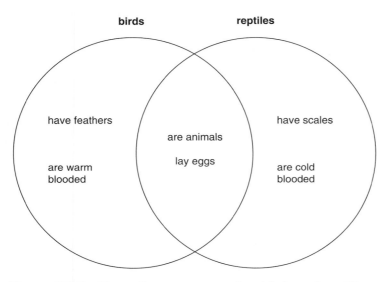

Figure B5.1   **Venn diagram comparing birds and reptiles.**

Venn Diagram Guidelines

1. Draw 2 overlapping circles like the ones shown in figure B5.1. Use at least a half sheet of paper for the circles to give you enough room to write inside the circles.
2. Label each circle with the topic or concept you are comparing.
3. Identify the important characteristics of each topic or concept.
4. Write the characteristics that are specific to only 1 of the 2 topics or concepts inside the circle, but outside the overlapping area.
5. Write the characteristics that are common to both topics or concepts inside the area where the circles overlap.

APPENDIX B6

How to Write Highlight Comments and Captions

How do you make sense of charts, diagrams, graphs, and sketches? You do what scientists have been doing for centuries. You note what you see, then you try to say what it means. This process helps you connect evidence to interpretations, a hallmark of scientific inquiry.

Highlight comments help you link observations from graphs, charts, and other spatial forms of representation to possible interpretations. Captions assemble highlight comments into sentences that form a coherent paragraph. This paragraph tells the story of the graph, chart, or sketch, and communicates a summary of the essential understandings displayed. The combination of highlight comments and captions helps you communicate scientific information with increasing effectiveness, improving your performance and deepening your understanding of the natural world.

Suppose you investigated the uptake of a nutrient by a tree over 24 hours. How would you make sense of the data? Follow the steps in figure B6.1 and use them as a general guide for any graph, chart, diagram, or sketch you make.

Figure B6.1 Steps for writing highlight comments and captions.

1. Look for changes, trends, or differences. Draw an arrow to each of these you notice in the graph.

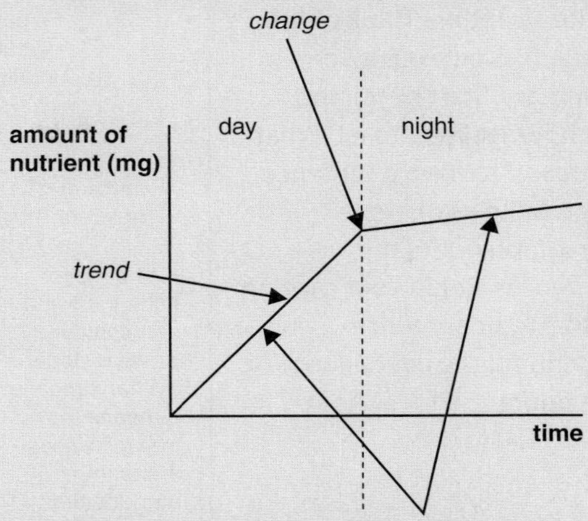

change

trend

amount of nutrient (mg)

day   night

time

2. Write what you see. Each arrow has a different description. Be concise. Write only the essence, or *highlights*, of what you see.

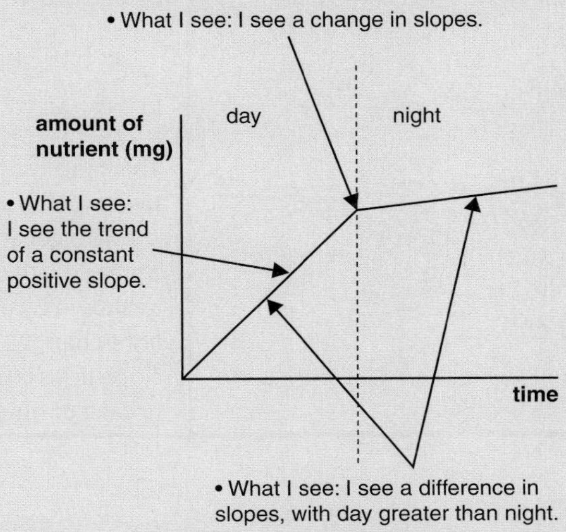

• What I see: I see a change in slopes.

amount of nutrient (mg)

day   night

• What I see: I see the trend of a constant positive slope.

time

• What I see: I see a difference in slopes, with day greater than night.

3. Interpret what you see. Write what each observation means. Don't interpret the entire figure at once, just one observation at a time.

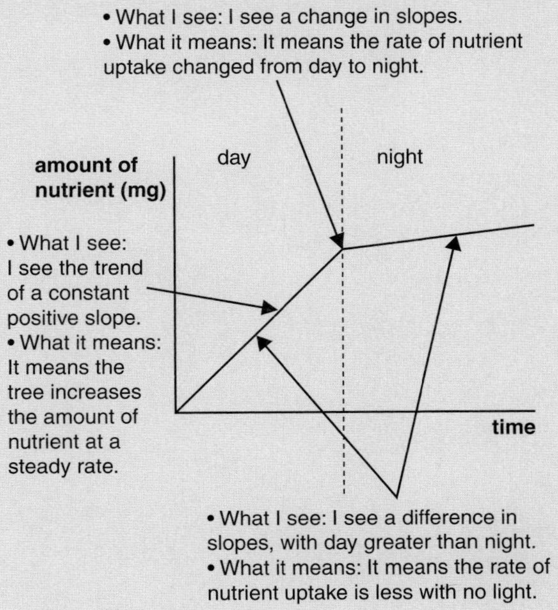

• What I see: I see a change in slopes.
• What it means: It means the rate of nutrient uptake changed from day to night.

amount of nutrient (mg)

day   night

• What I see: I see the trend of a constant positive slope.
• What it means: It means the tree increases the amount of nutrient at a steady rate.

time

• What I see: I see a difference in slopes, with day greater than night.
• What it means: It means the rate of nutrient uptake is less with no light.

4. Write a caption. Think of the caption as an executive summary. Start by joining each "What I see" to its "What it means" to form a sentence. Then build a coherent paragraph out of the sentences. Begin your caption with a topic sentence describing the overview of the figure.

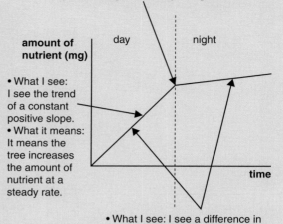

• What I see: I see a change in slopes.
• What it means: It means the rate of nutrient uptake changed from day to night.

amount of nutrient (mg)   day   night

• What I see: I see the trend of a constant positive slope.
• What it means: It means the tree increases the amount of nutrient at a steady rate.

time

• What I see: I see a difference in slopes, with day greater than night.
• What it means: It means the rate of nutrient uptake is less with no light.

This graph shows the uptake of nutrients in a tree over a 24-hour period. During the day, the graph shows a constant, positive slope, meaning there is a steady rate of uptake. At night, the rate changes as shown by a change in slopes. This suggests that light changes the rate of uptake. Finally, the night slope is less than the day slope, meaning the uptake of nutrients slows at night.

APPENDIX B7

How to Construct a Concept Map

Concept maps are tools that help you organize ideas in a way that shows the relationships among them. There is no single correct concept map for a body of information. But together, the concept words, connecting lines, and linking words should be an accurate representation of the content. To create a concept map, follow these steps.

Concept Map Guidelines

1. Identify the major concept that you will map. Then list several words or phrases that are important to understanding this concept. These should be words or phrases that identify parts of your major concept, such as parts of a system, a key idea, or an important process.

2. On a new page in your science notebook, write the major concept that you will map at the top of the page and draw a box around it. Choose related words or phrases from your original list below this box. Leaving plenty of space around your original concept, arrange these related words so that the bigger ideas are near the top and the more specific ideas are near the bottom. Draw boxes around these words, too.

3. Draw lines between the boxes to show relationships between the concept words. Lines can crisscross to show complex relationships.

4. Label the lines with linking words that describe the relationships.

Study the sample concept map of AIDS concept words in figure B7.1. Identify the connecting lines and linking words on the map. Can you see how this concept map was generated by following the four steps in these guidelines?

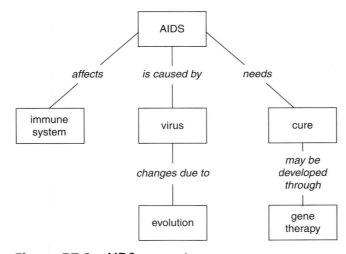

Figure B7.1   AIDS concept map.

APPENDIX B8
How to Develop a Personal Glossary

It is often said that biology students learn more new vocabulary than students studying a new foreign language. Sometimes the amount of terminology can feel overwhelming or hard to remember. A personal glossary can help you build your understanding and memory for terms that will be used throughout *BSCS Biology: A Human Approach*. Your personal glossary is designed to serve as a resource to you. It is a reference bank that you will build yourself, in your own words. Once you start building this glossary, you can refer to it as you re-encounter terms in your reading across the year.

Some activities in *BSCS Biology: A Human Approach* suggest that you add terms to your personal glossary as you read, or give a sample list of terms that you can choose to enter. Keep an eye out for additional words to add to your personal glossary. Words that are unfamiliar or bold are good candidates. The more you make it a habit to use your glossary, the more it will help you understand and use the language of biology.

Personal Glossary Guidelines

Complete your personal glossary in a way that best supports your understanding of the terms. We recommend using a chart similar to the one shown in figure B8.1 for each activity or reading that includes new terms. You may only need to fill in one or two of the columns of the chart for terms you find easy to understand. We suggest that you reserve the last 25 pages of your science notebook to allow you to add to your personal glossary over time, and start a new page for each new chapter you begin in the program.

1. **Title** your chart and include a page reference to your textbook.
2. List the **term** you wish to understand or remember in the left-most column.
3. Add the **pronunciation** if you like. For some terms, this may not be necessary.
4. Write **your definition** of the term based on information in the essay, the definition in the text, and other resources. Use your own words.
5. Draw a **picture** that will either help you define or remember the term if you can.
6. Add a personal connection to help you.

Term	Pronunciation	Definition	Picture	Personal Connection
Limiting factor		Anything that can slow or limit the growth of a population.		Time I spend doing homework is like a limiting factor—for my grades!
Carrying capacity		The maximum population of one species that a habitat can support.		
Biotic	bī ät'ik	Living		Example: my brother
Abiotic	ā bī ät'ik	Nonliving	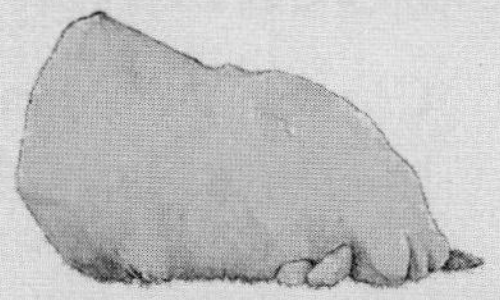	Example: my pet rock
Population density		The number of individuals per unit of habitat.		Mosquitoes by the school pond have high population density in spring.

Figure B8.1 Sample student personal glossary for terms included in the chapter 15 essay, *Interdependence Involves Limiting Factors and Carrying Capacity.*

APPENDIX B9
How to Conduct an Effective Web Search

Searching for information on the Web can be rewarding as well as frustrating. It may take hours to sift through the thousands of sites that pop up from a poorly designed search. It can also be difficult to know which information on the Web is credible, especially when conflicting information is found on different Web sites. *How to Conduct an Effective Web Search* gives you a few pointers for using any search engine to look for credible information on the Web. There are times when you want to broaden the search to include more documents, and there are times when you will want to narrow the search to return fewer documents. The following steps will give you 1) ways to conduct a balanced search that returns documents that pertain to your topic and 2) a method to analyze whether Web information comes from credible sources.

Web Searching Guidelines

1. *Choose your keywords carefully.* You will type keywords that relate to your topic into a search engine. Choose nouns and objects as your keywords. For example, if you were searching for information about new planets discovered outside our solar system, using the keyword *planet* or *planets* would be a good start. Verbs, adjectives, adverbs, and similar will either be thrown out by the search engine or will be too variable to be useful.
2. *Use several keywords in your search.* Using 6 to 8 appropriate keywords can greatly reduce the number of documents that are returned with your search. Using the same example as before, the keywords *new*, *planet*, *solar*, *system*, and *discovery* would return useful documents.
3. *Use appropriate variations in your words connected by* **OR.** For example, use *planet OR planets* to make sure the search engine picks up both variations of the word "planet."
4. *Use synonyms connected by* **OR** *where possible. Discovery OR find* is an example of using 2 synonyms connected by *OR* that will cover the different ways a concept can be described.
5. *Combine words into phrases where possible and place phrases in quotation marks (" ").* For example, *"solar system"* is a phrase in our example that should be combined and put in quotation marks. This will restrict the search to exact matches of the phrase.
6. *Combining 2 or 3 concepts in 1 search, distinguished by parentheses, will narrow your results and possibly give you just what you want.* For our current example, using *("solar system")("new planet")(discover OR find)* would be the best selection.

7. *Order your concepts with the main subject first.* Search engines tend to rank documents that match the first keywords in the search higher than those that match the later keywords. For our example search, you would order the concepts as *("new planet")(discover OR find)("solar system")*.

Identifying Credible Web Sites

1. *Know what* credible *means.* The word credible means you can reasonably believe the information that is presented. Credible information tends to be written by respected authorities or experts with a long history of studying a particular topic. It also tends to be consistent across different sources of information or patterns of reasoning. It is based in a presentation of evidence followed by reasoning that explains that evidence. Where opinion is an important part of the information, it is clearly identified as opinion rather than evidence. Historically, opinion-oriented articles in newspapers have been identified as "Op-Ed" columns. Today, entire Web sites may be based on opinion. In particular, Web logs ("blogs") tend to be used to express opinion, frequently intermixed with facts used to support the opinion expressed.

2. *Identify the author of the information.* Most Web sites authored by organizations include the organization logo and a link to their home page at the top of every Web page. By clicking on the logo, you can find out more about the organization that sponsors the Web page. Most Web sites authored by individuals include the author name at the top or bottom of the Web page. They may also include whether the author holds an advanced degree, like an MA, MS, or PhD in the field that he or she has written about. Many Web sites have additional links to biographies of the staff that wrote the content of the site, or to the organization(s) that funded their work. Web sites that lack identifying or funding information are less credible than those that contain this information.

3. *Choose information based on credibility.* Most often, you will find several Web sites that offer information on the topic of your search. Review Web sites that you consider to be credible first. Credible sources tend to come from scientific, governmental, and major nonprofit organizations. Government Web sites always end with ".gov." Examples include the National Institutes of Health and the National Science Foundation. Major nonprofit organizations frequently operate nationally or internationally and their Web sites always end with ".org." Examples include the American Heart Association and the National Center for Science Education. Scientific Web sites are usually associated with the publication of a scientific journal, a university, a museum, or a national conference of scientists. An example includes the American Association for the Advancement of Science, which publishes *Science* and *Science News*.

Another example is the Web site called Understanding Evolution, which is associated with the University of California Museum of Paleontology. Credible information is also contained on the Web sites of smaller organizations, individuals, and sites presenting blogs or community-editable wikis. However, the credibility of this information is harder to determine. One way to determine whether such sources are credible is to check to see if the information contains citations. Citations are marked by parentheses or placed in superscript next to individual pieces of information, and they link to a set of references that can be traced back to credible sources. Web sites that contain reference information are more credible than those that lack this information.

APPENDIX C1

How to Use a Compound Microscope

The human eye cannot distinguish objects much smaller than 0.1 mm in diameter. The compound microscope is a tool often used in biology to extend vision. It allows observation of much smaller objects. The most commonly used compound microscope is monocular (that is, it has one eyepiece). Figure C1.1 shows a binocular microscope. Light reaches the eye after it has passed through the objects being examined. In this appendix, you will learn how to use and care for a microscope.

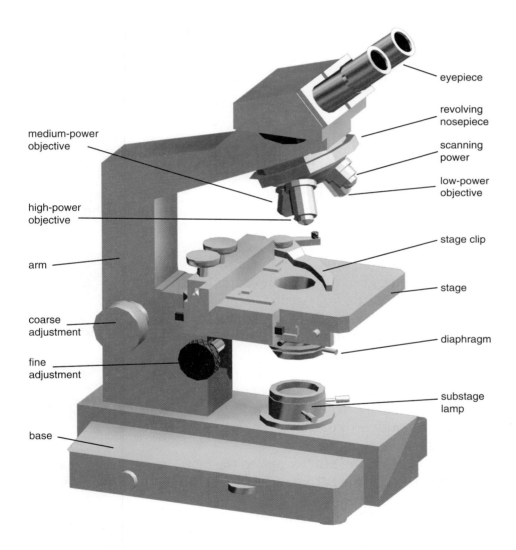

Figure C1.1 Compound microscope. Use this figure to help locate the parts of a compound microscope.

Part I Setting Up the Microscope

Materials (per team of 2)

3 coverslips
3 microscope slides
1 100-mL beaker or small jar
1 dropping pipet
1 compound microscope
1 pair of scissors
lens paper
newspaper
water

PROCESS AND PROCEDURES

1. Read *Care of the Microscope* to learn how to properly care for a microscope.

Care of the Microscope

- The microscope is a precision instrument that requires proper care. Always carry the microscope with both hands. Put one hand under its base, the other on its arm (see figure C1.2).
- Keep the microscope away from the edge of the table. If a lamp is attached to the microscope, keep its cord out of the way. Move everything not needed for microscope studies off your lab table.
- Avoid tilting the microscope when using slides made with water.
- The lenses of the microscope cost almost as much as all the other parts put together. Never clean lenses with anything other than the lens paper designed for this task.
- Always return the microscope to the low-power setting before putting it away. The high-power objective extends too close to the stage to be left in place safely.

Figure C1.2   How to carry a microscope. Always place one hand under the base and the other hand on the arm.

2. Rotate the low-power objective into place if it is not already there. When you change from one objective to another, you will hear the objective click into position.

3. Move the mirror so that you obtain even illumination through the opening in the stage. Or turn on the substage lamp. Most microscopes are equipped with a diaphragm for regulating light intensity. Some materials are best viewed in dim light, others in bright light.

CAUTION: Never use a microscope mirror to capture direct sunlight when illuminating objects under a microscope. The mirror concentrates light rays, which can permanently damage the retina of the eye. Always use indirect light.

4. Make sure the lenses are dry and free of fingerprints and debris. Wipe lenses with lens paper only.

Part II Using the Microscope

Materials (per team of 2)

supplies from Part I

PROCESS AND PROCEDURES

1. In your science notebook, draw a data table similar to the one in figure C1.3.

Object being viewed	Observations and comments
Letter *o*	
Letter *c*	
Letter *e* or *r*	

Figure C1.3 **Microscope observations.**

2. Cut a lowercase letter *o* from a piece of newspaper. Place it right side up on a clean slide. With a dropping pipet, place 1 drop of water on the letter. This type of slide is called a wet mount.

3. Wait until the paper is soaked before adding a coverslip. Hold the coverslip at about a 45° angle, with the bottom edge of the slide touching both the slide and the drop of water. Then slowly lower the coverslip. Figure C1.4 shows these first steps.

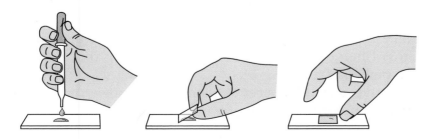

Figure C1.4 Preparing a wet mount. This figure shows the steps to prepare a wet mount with a microscope slide and coverslip.

4. Place the slide on the microscope stage. Clamp it down with the stage clips. Move the slide so that the letter is in the middle of the hole in the stage. Use the coarse-adjustment knob to lower the low-power objective to the lowest position.
5. Look through the eyepiece. Use the coarse-adjustment knob to *raise* the objective slowly, until the letter *o* is in view.
6. If you cannot find the *o* on the first try, start the process again by repeating steps 4 and 5.
7. Once you have the *o* in view, use the fine-adjustment knob to sharpen the focus. Position the diaphragm for the best light. Compare the way the letter looks through the microscope with the way it looks to the naked eye. Record your observations in your data table.
8. To determine how magnified the view is, multiply the number inscribed on the eyepiece by the number of the objective lens being used. For example:

   eyepiece (10×) × objective lens (10×) = total (100×).

9. Follow the same procedure with a lowercase *c*. Describe in your data table how the letter appears when viewed through a microscope.
10. Make a wet mount of the letter *e* or the letter *r*. Describe how the letter appears when viewed through the microscope. What new information (not revealed by the letter *c*) is revealed by the *e* or *r*?
11. Look through the eyepiece at the letter as you use your thumbs and forefingers to move the slide slowly *away* from you. Which way does your view of the letter move? Move the slide to the right. Which way does the image move?
12. Make a sketch of the letter as you see it under the microscope. Label the changes in image and in movement that take place under the microscope.

Part III Using High Power

Materials (per team of 2)

supplies from Part I
1 light-colored hair
1 dark-colored hair

PROCESS AND PROCEDURES

1. Make a wet mount of 2 different-colored hairs, 1 light and 1 dark. Cross 1 hair over the other. Sketch the hairs as they appear under low power.
2. With the crossed hairs centered under low power, adjust the diaphragm for the best light.

3. Turn the high-power objective into viewing position. Do *not* change the focus.

4. Sharpen the focus with the *fine-adjustment knob only. Do not focus under high power with the coarse-adjustment knob.* The high-power objective will touch the slide if the objective is in its lowest position. So you must not make large adjustments toward the slide. *Doing so can damage the objective and the slide by driving the objective into the slide.*

5. Readjust the diaphragm to get the best light. If you are not successful in finding the object under high power the first time, return to step 2. Repeat the entire procedure carefully.

6. Using the fine-adjustment knob, focus on the hairs at the point where they cross. Can you see both hairs sharply at the same focus level? How can you use the fine-adjustment knob to determine which hair is crossed over the other? Sketch the hairs as they appear under high power.

Analysis

Work with your partner to answer the following questions in your science notebook.

1. Summarize the differences between an image viewed through a microscope and the same image viewed with the unaided eye.

2. When you view an object through the high-power objective, not all of the object may be in focus. Explain why.

APPENDIX C2
How to Design an Investigation

An important and exciting part of science is setting up your own investigation to answer your own questions. But some people are hesitant to set up their own experiments. Maybe they don't know where to start. Maybe they don't know what types of data to collect. Maybe they don't consider themselves capable of *doing* science.

One of the major goals of *BSCS Biology: A Human Approach* is to help you develop the skills and abilities to *do* science. As a student of inquiry, you often find yourself considering some problem or aspect of a problem that requires scientific thinking. You often develop a question and then set out to answer your question by carefully designing an investigation. You then conduct your investigation and record and analyze your results. Your results might help you answer your question and they might present you with new questions to investigate. Your experience with activities in this program should convince you that the careful design of your investigation is critical to obtaining information that is useful for developing an explanation.

Scientists propose explanations based on the evidence they collect during their research. This dynamic practice of wondering and asking questions, of designing investigations, of making detailed observations, and of developing explanations based on those observations and evidence is the process of *scientific inquiry*. It is not always a straightforward process. Look at figure C2.1 to see the different paths scientific inquiry can take. These are some of the possible ways scientists study the natural world.

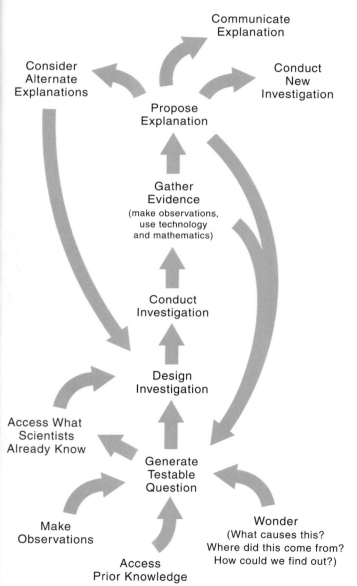

Figure C2.1 Process of scientific inquiry. Inquiry is a dynamic and exciting practice used to study the world around you. Where would controlled experiments fit onto this diagram?

Designing Your Own Investigation

Though the whole process of scientific inquiry is not prescribed and sequential, careful consideration and attention to detail must accompany the designing and conducting of investigations. You want to make sure that your design will give you the information you are seeking. When scientists focus on the design of an investigation, they have to make sure that the design itself guides them to the answer to their question and controls for error. If the design is poor, the results are not valid.

When you find yourself pondering a question in science, you may find it useful to go through the following checklist of questions. If you can answer these questions well, you will know you have a useful experimental design:

❑ What is your question or the problem you are trying to solve?

> Design an investigation that answers the question in the most appropriate and direct manner. Make sure you understand how the question ties into the major concept you are studying.

❑ Are you sure that your question is testable?

❑ What variables can change to affect the result?

❑ What are the dependent variables?

❑ What are the independent variables?

❑ What is one variable that you can change using the materials available?

❑ Do you need a control for the experiment? If so, describe it.

> Some experiments have independent and dependent variables. Some also have control conditions and experimental conditions. However, studies based only on observations have neither of these. All of these variations on scientific inquiry are valid ways of collecting evidence.

> In a controlled experiment, scientists try to control as many variables as possible while changing only one independent variable. One group is not exposed to the variable you are testing, but is similar with respect to other variables. This "control group" serves as a comparison group to determine that the results were due to the tested variable and not to some other factor. In other words, changes in a dependent variable caused by an independent variable can be understood. For example, if scientists are studying the effectiveness of a new arthritis medicine, one group of individuals does not take the medicine. Scientists compare this group with the group taking the medicine. Not all experimental designs involve a control, but many do.

❑ What materials do you need for the investigation?

❑ What procedures will you follow to conduct your investigation?

> You should write the steps down and describe them in sufficient detail that someone else in the class can replicate your experiment using only these steps. It is a good idea to read over your procedure and have a classmate read it over as well, to see if you missed an important step. It is very helpful to provide diagrams for setting up the equipment and carrying out the investigation. You should have your teacher review your procedure before you begin. Think about whether or not you have enough time to complete the experiment as designed. If you start the experiment and notice that you need to modify the procedures, make sure you document the changes and justify why you made them.

❏ What data will you collect?

> You should ask yourself, "How will the data help me answer the question?" and "Will the data I collect help me understand how the variable I am testing affects the outcome?"

❏ What result do I predict?

❏ How will I record and organize the data I collect? How will I represent the data when the investigation is complete?

> Data tables often make the work of collecting data more efficient and better organized. Graphing data often helps reveal patterns and trends.

❏ How many trials are needed so that I can be confident in the results?

APPENDIX C3
How to Interpret Patterns and Trends

A graph tells a story about data. The story evolves as you discover patterns and trends in the graph. The story will have more meaning when you can describe relationships among the variables plotted on the graph. To tell an accurate story, you must learn to recognize patterns and trends. You must also be able to describe both what patterns you see in the data and what you think the patterns mean.

Noticing patterns and trends is something you do naturally. You noticed that over time your friends got taller in elementary school—a trend in the growth rate of your friends. You also noticed that every school day started with the same kinds of activities and that pattern continued each school day. Being able to recognize patterns and trends is a skill that is very useful in using evidence to support explanations in science. Often, patterns or trends among variables are easier to see on a graph. And if these patterns or trends occur, then some underlying relationship among the variables that are graphed may exist.

Trends are changes that move in a particular direction. Begin identifying trends in graphically displayed data by looking for

- what kinds of data the graph is showing;
- an overall change (increase or decrease) in the data across the entire data set;
- changes (increases or decreases) over smaller sections of the data; and
- no change.

These trends tell part of the story. It is important to describe the trend in the graph with precise wording. Avoid saying simply "it increases" or "it decreases" in your description because "it" is vague and could be interpreted to refer to different things. Remember that you want your story to be clear. So for the graph in figure C3.1, you might say that as the mass of the material increases, the volume also increases.

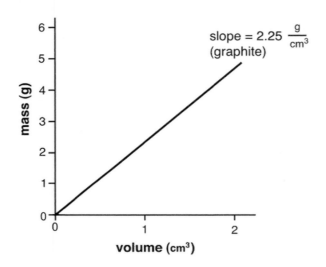

Figure C3.1 Mass versus volume. As the mass of the material increases, the volume also increases. This graph shows a direct relationship between variables.

Figure C3.2
Temperature data for Denver, Colorado. You can see a pattern of increasing and decreasing temperatures in this graph. The temperature in Denver, Colorado, increases during the summer months and decreases during the winter months.

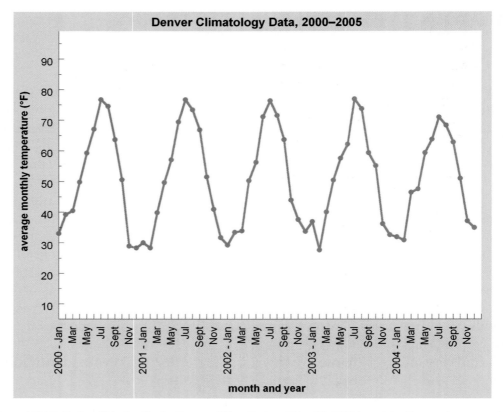

Source: NOAA's National Weather Service Forecast Office. Retrieved May 15, 2008 from: http://www.crh.noaa.gov/den/cli/climo.php

Patterns are changes that repeat periodically. You can recognize patterns in graphs by looking for increases or decreases that occur regularly. Look at the graph in figure C3.2. What repeating pattern do you see? Patterns tell another part of the story in a graph. Again, you want to be precise in your description of patterns. Avoid describing the pattern as "it goes up and down." A clearer description would be that the temperature in Denver, Colorado, increases during the summer months and decreases during the winter months.

You may identify no pattern or trend on a graph. This information is important, too. One variable may not be affected by the other variable if you see no pattern or trend. This would indicate that there is no dependency among the data plotted in the graph. An example of a graph that shows no relationship is figure C3.3. Can you see how the lack of a relationship between these variables can be informative?

In *BSCS Biology: A Human Approach*, you are asked many times to interpret what you see on a graph. Sometimes you may use the highlight comments and captions strategy (see appendix B6, *How to Write Highlight Comments and Captions*). Use the strategies you have learned here to help you write clearer and more descriptive comments and captions for your graphs or to answer questions related to the data. Work through the following exercises to develop your skills at interpreting patterns and trends in data.

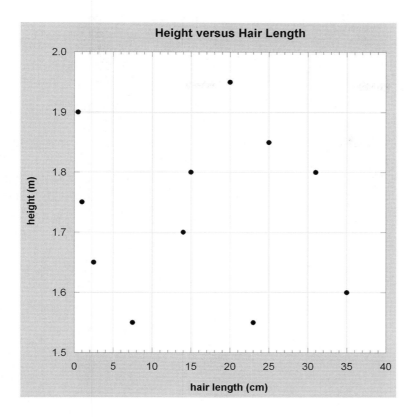

Figure C3.3 Height versus hair length. This graph shows no pattern or trend—the data points are scattered randomly across the graph. You can infer from this graph that there is no relationship between a person's hair length and his or her height.

Analysis

1. Analyze the graph in figure C3.4. This graph shows the number of paramecia, a microscopic protist, in a population over time. Complete the following steps, using the graph.
   a. Sketch this graph in your science notebook.
   b. What trends do you see?

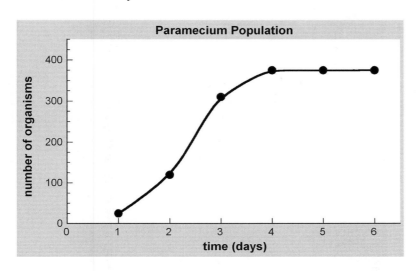

Figure C3.4 Paramecium population. Use this graph to complete steps 1a–f.

c. What patterns do you see?

d. What do you notice about the shape of the graph? Record your observations as the "What I see" portion of the highlight comments.

> Describe any trends and patterns on this graph that you notice.

e. Interpret what you see by recording the "What it means" portion of the highlight comments.

f. Summarize your analysis by writing a caption below your graph.

2. Use figure C3.5 to analyze both patterns and trends.

a. Sketch the graph in figure C3.5 into your science notebook.

b. Describe patterns and trends you see on the graph by using highlight comments and captions.

c. Summarize your ideas by combining your comments into a caption for the graph.

Figure C3.5
Carbon dioxide (CO₂) concentrations at Mauna Loa, Hawaii. Use this graph to complete steps 2a–c.

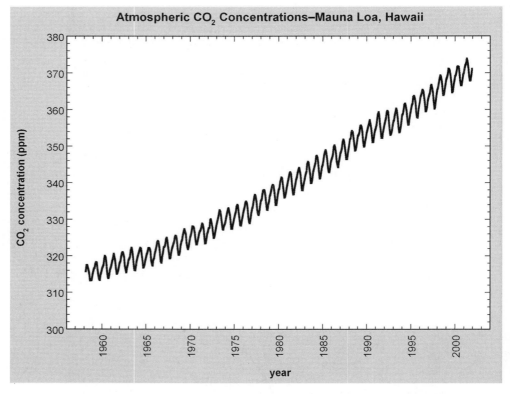

Source: Keeling, C.D. and T.P. Whorf. 2005. Atmospheric CO₂ records from sites in the SIO air sampling network. In *Trends: A Compendium of Data on Global Change.* Carbon Dioxide Information Analysis Center, Oak Ridge National Laboratory, U.S. Department of Energy, Oak Ridge, TN, USA.

APPENDIX C4
How to Develop an Explanation

Scientists support their claims and conclusions about how the natural world works by using data and evidence about the topic they are studying. As you learn about the processes of science as inquiry, you will learn to support your claims and conclusions with evidence. This evidence may come in the form of data that you have collected or that someone else has collected. The evidence may be from work that you have done. You may also use evidence from reports and summaries from scientists or even from other students. These data provide you with the evidence you need to support your ideas, conclusions, and claims in science.

The explanation template (figure C4.1) provides you with a framework to structure your claims, evidence, and reasoning in a way that makes the most sense to someone who will be reading about your work. There are many ways to use this tool, and each situation may call for a slightly different approach to using it. Don't think of this tool as a rigid structure that must be followed precisely for every situation. Rather, think of it as a template to help you organize your ideas.

Question to answer:		
Evidence	**Claim(s)**	**Reason/Rationale**
Explanation:		

_____ results in _____ because _____ .
     (evidence)   (my claim)   (reason/rationale)

Figure C4.1 Explanation template. This explanation template can help you formulate an explanation from a claim, evidence, and reasoning.

Notice that the explanation template tool in figure C4.1 has five basic parts. It can also have several additional features that you and your teacher may decide to use for different circumstances. Following is a summary of the basic parts of the tool:

1. **The question that you are trying to answer.** Science centers on answering questions about the natural world. You will conduct investigations and research to answer questions. Testable questions in science are those that can be answered by investigations. The questions that you ask guide the forms of data you will collect. Ultimately, you will use data to try to explain the answers to the questions.

2. **The evidence that you gather.** This part of the template includes a list of all of the evidence you have collected. Do not list individual data points but rather write a summary of the data. This evidence may come from a number of sources. The data (evidence) should relate to the given claim.

3. **Your claim or claims.** What does the evidence say about the question you are trying to answer? You will write your claims, or your answer to the question, in this section of the template. Your claim should make an assertion or conclusion that addresses the original question or problem. This may be in the form of a statement of trend, a behavior, or a generality that is based on the evidence presented.

4. **The reason or rationale.** In this section, explain why each piece of evidence supports your claim. Your reasoning is a justification that logically links the claim and evidence. These statements show why the data count as evidence that supports the claim according to the appropriate scientific principles.

5. **The explanation.** A template for your summary statement is included at the bottom of the tool. Use the template to connect each piece of evidence and reasoning to your claim. This explanation will likely be more than one complete sentence long. The goal is to write a coherent explanation or conclusion that is supported with your evidence and reasoning.

Study the example in figure C4.2 to develop your understanding of how the explanation template can be applied to a set of data, like the mass and volume data graphed here.

Figure C4.2
Sample explanation template. The graph (*a*) was reviewed to complete the sections of the (*b*) explanation template. You should strive for complete explanations to connect evidence and reasoning to support your claim.

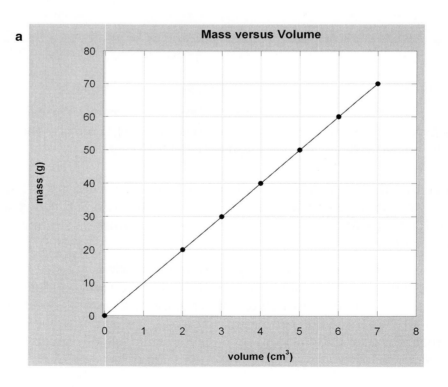

b

Question to answer:		
What is the relationship between the mass and volume of a substance?		
Evidence	**Claim(s)**	**Reason/rationale**
Data points for mass and volume make a straight line with a constant positive slope.	Mass and volume are directly proportional.	A constant positive slope means the variables plotted on each axis are directly proportional.
Add rows for additional evidence and their reasons or rationales.		

Explanation

_____ results in _____ because _____.
    (evidence)   (my claim)   (reason/rationale)

A constant positive slope for my mass versus volume graph *results in* my claim that mass and volume are directly proportional. This is *because* linear graphs represent variables that are directly proportional.

APPENDIX D1
How to Use Very Large and Very Small Numbers

Astronomers have to work with numbers in the billions—and bigger—all the time. For example, how many stars are in the sky? Are there more stars that you cannot see? All stars that you see are part of the galaxy in which we live, the Milky Way Galaxy. A galaxy is an enormous group of stars in a massive cluster. The Milky Way has more than 100 billion stars. The universe contains hundreds of billions of different galaxies, many of which are made up of hundreds of billions of stars. Such large numbers can be difficult to manage. It would be awkward for astronomers to use terms such as a million billion billion or to write out numbers like 1,000,000,000,000,000,000,000,000. Rather, astronomers (and other scientists) use a special way of expressing numbers called scientific notation. In this appendix, you will learn about and practice using scientific notation.

Part I Big Numbers

Materials

calculators

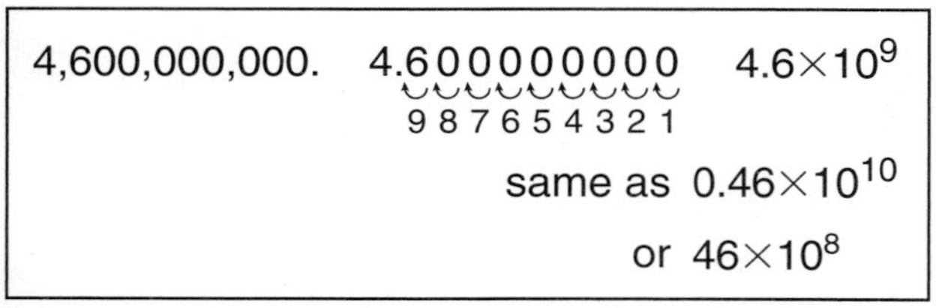

Figure D1.1
Example of moving decimals for positive exponents. This diagram shows the conversion of the number 4,600,000,000 to scientific notation, 4.6×10^9. The illustration in the center shows the decimal place moving left nine times. The table in figure D1.2 explains why 4.6×10^9 is the same as 4.6 billion.

Scientific notation is a way to abbreviate numbers to make them easier to work with. To show numbers with scientific notation, you must first be comfortable with exponents. Exponents are shorthand for the number of times a number, called the base, is multiplied by itself. A base with an exponent is said to be "raised to the power" of that exponent. For example, the number 2^4 means $2 \times 2 \times 2 \times 2$, or 16. Here, 2 is the base and 4 is the exponent. In scientific notation, the base number is always 10. Having 10 as the base works well because the exponent shows how many zeros you would need to write out in the long form of the number. So, 10,000 is expressed as 10^4, because $10 \times 10 \times 10 \times 10 = 10,000$.

In the previous example, you may have noticed that with scientific notation, you simply move the decimal point of a number to obtain a more manageable number. Then you write the number of places you moved the decimal as an exponent of 10. For example, you would write the number 4,600,000,000 as 4.6×10^9 with scientific notation. The second number is a lot simpler, and it says the same thing as the first. You write it like this because you moved the decimal nine places to the left to get to the numeral 4.6. This is shown in figure D1.1.

Pronounced	Number	Powers of ten (scientific notation)	Unit prefix in the metric system (SI)
Trillion	1,000,000,000,000.	10^{12} or 1×10^{12}	tera-
Billion	1,000,000,000.	10^9 or 1×10^9	giga-
Million	1,000,000.	10^6 or 1×10^6	mega-
Thousand	1,000.	10^3 or 1×10^3	kilo-
Hundred	100.	10^2 or 1×10^2	hecto-
Ten	10.	10^1 or 1×10^1	deka-
One	1.	1×10^0 or 10^0	
Three hundred twenty-seven thousand	327,000.	3.27×10^5	

Figure D1.2   Table for large numbers.

Other large numbers are also easy to write using scientific notation. You would write the number 34,000 as 3.4×10^4. You would write the number 286,000,000 as 2.86×10^8. You might remember that the metric system is based on multiples of 10. The table in figure D1.2 shows how large numbers convert to powers of 10. It also shows prefixes for these numbers in the metric system. With the example above, 286,000,000 is also the same as 286×10^6, or 286 million.

Analysis

Work through these problems individually and write your answers in your science notebook. When you finish, join with another student and compare your answers. Discuss and resolve any differences you have in your answers.

1. One kilometer (km) is the same as 1,000 meters (m). How would you write 1,000 m using scientific notation?
2. A googol is one of the biggest named numbers. It is written as the number 1 followed by 100 zeros. Write this number using scientific notation.
3. The speed of light is 3.0×10^8 meters per second (m/sec). What is this value written without using scientific notation?
4. Use scientific notation to write $87 billion and 248 million stars.

Part II Small Numbers

Materials

calculators

Biologists work with large numbers, especially when studying fossil life-forms. They also work with extremely small numbers, especially when working with microscopes. A key property of working with microscopes is

$$0.00000035 \quad 0\underset{1\,2\,3\,4\,5\,6\,7}{\underbrace{0000003}}.5 \quad 3.5\times10^{-7}$$

$$\text{same as } 0.35\times10^{-6}$$

$$\text{or } 350.\times10^{-9}$$

Figure D1.3
Example of moving decimals for negative exponents. This diagram shows the conversion of the number 0.00000035 to scientific notation, 3.5×10^{-7}. The illustration in the top center shows the decimal place moving to the right seven times.

the wavelength of light, which is a key feature of colors. Wavelengths of light are commonly about 1 billion times shorter than a meter.

You write numbers less than 1.0 in scientific notation in the same general way that you write large numbers. The key difference is that the power of 10 is a negative exponent. The exponent still tells you how many places the decimal is from the number 1.0, but the decimal is moved in the other direction (to the right). When writing small numbers using powers of 10, you imagine moving the decimal to the right. The number of places you move the decimal is the power of 10 expressed as a negative number. We would write the number 0.0000001 in scientific notation as 1×10^{-7} because the decimal moves seven places to the right to get to the number 1.0. Another example is shown in figure D1.3 for 0.00000035, which is the same as 3.5×10^{-7}.

Analysis

Work through these problems individually and write your answers in your science notebook. When you finish, join with another student and compare your answers. Discuss and resolve any differences you have in your answers.

1. A micron is an abbreviation for the term micrometer (μm). How would you express 1 μm using scientific notation? Look at the prefixes in the table in figure D1.4.
2. How many meters are in 1 millimeter (mm)?
3. Scientists often measure wavelengths of light in units called nanometers (nm). A nanometer is 0.000000001 m. Write this number using scientific notation.

Figure D1.4
Prefixes for small numbers.

Pronounced	Number	Powers of ten (scientific notation)	Unit prefix in the metric system (SI)
Tenth	0.1	10^{-1} or 1×10^{-1}	deci-
Hundredth	0.01	10^{-2} or 1×10^{-2}	centi-
Thousandth	0.001	10^{-3} or 1×10^{-3}	milli-
Millionth	0.000001	10^{-6} or 1×10^{-6}	micro-
Billionth	0.000000001	10^{-9} or 1×10^{-9}	nano-

APPENDIX D2
How to Convert Measurements

Units of Measurement

When you measure something, it is important to record what units you used for your measurement. For example, suppose someone told you that her cat had a weight of "20"; that number doesn't mean much without units. Does the cat weigh 20 pounds, 20 newtons, 20 ounces, or 20 tons?! Distance measurements (length) also need units such as feet, inches, meters, kilometers, and miles. If you are measuring time, you use units such as seconds, minutes, hours, and years.

Scientists measure things according to the *Système international d'unités* (International System of Units), more commonly referred to as "SI." SI is a modification of the older metric system. It was used first in France, and now is the common system of measurement throughout the world.

Among the basic units of SI measurement are the meter (length), the kilogram (mass), the Kelvin (temperature), and the second (time). All other SI units are derived from these four. Some of these units are described in the following sections. You will use some of these units in your laboratory work.

Length

1 kilometer (km)	=	1,000 meters	=	10^3 m
1 hectometer (hm)	=	100 meters	=	10^2 m
1 dekameter (dkm)	=	10 meters	=	10^1 m
1 meter (m)				
1 decimeter (dm)	=	0.1 meter	=	10^{-1} m
1 centimeter (cm)	=	0.01 meter	=	10^{-2} m
1 millimeter (mm)	=	0.001 meter	=	10^{-3} m
1 micrometer (µm)	=	0.000001 meter	=	10^{-6} m
1 nanometer (nm)	=	0.000000001 meter	=	10^{-9} m

The meter is the basic unit of length. Its increments increase or decrease by the power of 10. For example, measurements under microscopes often are made in micrometers, which is one-millionth of a meter. Still smaller measurements are made in nanometers. You might use nanometers to measure wavelengths of light that plants use in photosynthesis. The units of length you will use most frequently in the laboratory are centimeters (cm) and millimeters (mm).

Units of area are derived from units of length by multiplying two lengths. One hectometer squared is one measure that often is used in ecological studies. It commonly is called a hectare and equals 10,000 m^2. Measurements of area made in the laboratory most frequently are in centimeters squared (cm^2).

Mass

1 kilogram (kg)	=	1,000 grams	=	10^3 g
1 hectogram (hg)	=	100 grams	=	10^2 g
1 dekagram (dkg)	=	10 grams	=	10^1 g
1 gram (g)				
1 decigram (dg)	=	0.1 gram	=	10^{-1} g
1 centigram (cg)	=	0.01 gram	=	10^{-2} g
1 milligram (mg)	=	0.001 gram	=	10^{-3} g
1 microgram (μg)	=	0.000001 gram	=	10^{-6} g
1 nanogram (ng)	=	0.000000001 gram	=	10^{-9} g

Measurements of mass are based on the gram. Like the meter, the basic units of mass also increase or decrease by the power of 10. In the biology laboratory, measurements usually are made in kilograms, grams, centigrams, and milligrams.

Volume

1 kiloliter (kL)	=	1,000 liters	=	10^3 L
1 hectoliter (hL)	=	100 liters	=	10^2 L
1 dekaliter (dkL)	=	10 liters	=	10^1 L
1 liter (L)				
1 deciliter (dL)	=	0.1 liter	=	10^{-1} L
1 centiliter (cL)	=	0.01 liter	=	10^{-2} L
1 milliliter (mL)	=	0.001 liter	=	10^{-3} L

SI units of volume are derived from units of length by multiplying length by width by height. One meter cubed (m^3) is the standard unit. Although not officially part of SI, liters are often used to measure the volume of liquids. There are 1,000 liters in 1 meter cubed (m^3). In other words, it is 1 L = 0.001 m^3. One milliliter equals 1 centimeter cubed (1 mL = 1 cm^3).

Because 1 meter cubed (m^3) is too large for practical use in the laboratory, we use centimeters cubed (cm^3). Volume measurements in the laboratory usually are made in glassware marked for milliliters and liters.

Temperature

Units of temperature that you will use in this course are degrees Celsius. On the Celsius scale, 0°C is the freezing point of water, and 100°C is the boiling point of water. Figure D2.1 illustrates the Celsius scale alongside the Fahrenheit scale, which still is used in the United States. On the Fahrenheit scale, 32°F is the freezing point of water and 212°F is the boiling point of water. Figure D2.1 is useful for converting from one scale to the other.

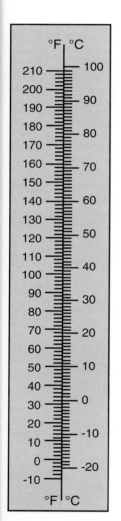

Figure D2.1
A comparison of Fahrenheit and Celsius temperature scales.

Another type of measurement you will encounter is molarity (labeled with the letter *M*). Molarity measures the concentration of a dissolved substance in a solution. A high molarity indicates a high concentration. Some of the solutions that you will use in the activities are identified by their molarity.

If you wish to learn more about SI measurement, check out the Web site of the National Institute of Standards and Technology (NIST).

Calculating Unit Conversions

What if a friend told you that he would phone you in 86,400 seconds? What time would that be on the clock? When faced with a problem like this, you need to be able to convert from one unit to another. After this activity, you will be able to use the technique of unit conversion to show that 86,400 seconds is the same as one day.

Unit conversions are also important for comparing two measurements made with different units. For example, suppose a person who is 5 feet 8 inches tall has a hat on that is 0.30 meters tall. What is the total height of the person, including the hat? Unfortunately, you cannot simply add the lengths. You must convert all of them to the same unit, and then you can add the lengths. You may have to convert again to a more reasonable unit. The total height of the person would be 79.8 inches, 6 feet 7.8 inches, or 2.03 meters tall.

How do you make these conversions? The method is called unit analysis (or dimensional analysis). These terms may sound complicated, but the method is pretty simple. The method uses conversion factors to convert units step-by-step, canceling units at each step. Using the guidelines in the protocol, unit analysis is simple.

PROTOCOL

PROTOCOL

Unit Analysis Guidelines

1. Conversion factors relate different units and are different ways of expressing the number 1. For example, because there are 12 inches (in) in 1 foot (ft), and 12 in = 1 ft, we can say that $\frac{12\,in}{1\,ft} = 1$. This fraction, which contains two different units and equals 1, is the conversion factor for distances measured in inches or feet.

2. Conversion factors can be flipped (inverted) as long as the units stay with the number. For example, you can write
$$\frac{12\,in}{1\,ft} = 1, \text{ or } \frac{1\,ft}{12\,in} = 1.$$

3. Units behave as numbers do in fractions. For example, the units in the numerator of fractions will cancel the same units in the denominator of fractions. For example,

$$\frac{12 \, \cancel{in}}{3 \, \cancel{in}} = 4.$$

4. In unit analysis, your goal is to cancel the same units in the numerators and denominators until you end up with the units you are striving for.
5. When you convert between units, follow these steps.
   a. Identify the units that you have.
   b. See which units you want.
   c. Note the conversion factors that you can use to convert the measurement from the unit in step 5a to the unit in step 5b.
   d. Set up your conversion similar to the examples found in this appendix.

Work through the following three conversions to practice using the guidelines for unit analysis from the protocol box.

1. How many inches are there in 1 mile (mi)?

   To convert miles to inches, start with what you know (1 mi) and use conversion factors (figure D2.2) to cancel units as you go until you get to the units that you want (inches). When the same units are on both the bottom and top, they cancel. Work with your teacher to see how to cancel these units on the top and bottom.

$$(1 \, \cancel{mi}) \times \left(\frac{(5,280 \, \cancel{ft})}{1 \, \cancel{mi}} \right) \times \left(\frac{12 \, in}{1 \, \cancel{ft}} \right)$$

Figure D2.2
Conversion table for miles to inches.

Conversion step (from Protocol Step 5)	Answers
What unit do you have now?	1 mi
What unit do you want?	"How many inches"
What are the conversion factors?	1 mi = 5,280 ft, or $\left(\frac{5,280 \, ft}{1 \, mi} \right) = 1$ 1 ft = 12 in, or $\left(\frac{12 \, in}{1 \, ft} \right) = 1$

The units cancel, so you are left with units of inches. You can then multiply the numerator numbers together for the answer in inches.

$$(1\text{ mi}) \times \left(\frac{5{,}280\text{ ft}}{1\text{ mi}}\right) \times \left(\frac{12\text{ in}}{1\text{ ft}}\right) = \left(\frac{1 \times 5{,}280 \times 12\text{ in}}{1 \times 1}\right) = 63{,}360\text{ in}$$

2. Work through a more complicated example. Suppose that you want to convert 75 miles per hour (mph) into feet per second (ft/sec).

   Now what? Take your conversions (figure D2.3) one step at a time, canceling units as you go until you arrive at the units you want.

$$\left(\frac{75\text{ mi}}{1\text{ hr}}\right) \times \left(\frac{5{,}280\text{ ft}}{1\text{ mi}}\right) \times \left(\frac{1\text{ hr}}{60\text{ min}}\right) \times \left(\frac{1\text{ min}}{60\text{ sec}}\right) = \left(\frac{75 \times 5{,}280\text{ ft} \times 1 \times 1}{1 \times 1 \times 60 \times 60\text{ sec}}\right)$$

$$= \left(\frac{396{,}000\text{ ft}}{3{,}600\text{ sec}}\right) = \left(\frac{110\text{ ft}}{1\text{ sec}}\right) = 110\ \frac{\text{ft}}{\text{sec}}$$

Conversion step (from Protocol Step 5)	Answers
What unit do you have now?	$75\ \frac{\text{mi}}{\text{hr}}$ (mph)
What unit do you want?	$\frac{\text{ft}}{\text{sec}}$ (ft/sec)
What are the conversion factors?	1 hour (hr) = 60 minutes (min) 1 minute (min) = 60 seconds (sec) 1 mi = 5,280 ft

Figure D2.3
Conversion table for miles per hour to feet per second.

3. Try the following conversions on your own. Use the following conversion factors for steps 3a–c. Show your calculations for each.

$$1\text{ slink} = 7\text{ zips}$$
$$1\text{ sliff} = 5\text{ zips}$$
$$4\text{ voles} = 3\text{ sliffs}$$
$$8\text{ lampos} = 7\text{ flies}$$
$$12\text{ voles} = 1\text{ lampo}$$

   a. How many sliffs are in 1 lampo?
   b. One vole is how many zips?
   c. How many flies are in 1 slink?

APPENDIX D3
How to Create Graphs

Graphs are visual representations of numerical data. They help us see patterns that we might not see if we looked at numbers alone. Graphs make it easy to see at a glance what happened in an experiment. We also can use the patterns we observe in graphs to predict future changes or events.

Different graphs serve different purposes. For example, a line graph is a good way to show the relationship between two sets of numbers. Figure D3.1 shows a line graph that relates the number of days and the number of individuals in a laboratory population of microorganisms. A bar graph is a good way to show the frequency of measurements that fall into different categories. Figure D3.2 shows a bar graph of shoe sizes among the girls in a high school biology class. In this case, the different categories are the shoe sizes. A histogram is similar to a bar graph, but it shows data that occur over particular intervals. Figure D3.3 shows a histogram of student scores on a geology test, where the scores are grouped into 5-point intervals. These groups are known as bins.

Figure D3.1 Line graph. A line graph shows the relationship between two sets of numbers. Line graphs are frequently used to show how something changes over a period of time. This line graph shows the growth and decline of a population of microorganisms over 30 days.

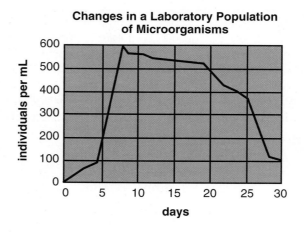

Figure D3.2 Bar graph. A bar graph shows the frequency of a set of observations. This bar graph shows how many girls in a biology class wear shoes of different sizes.

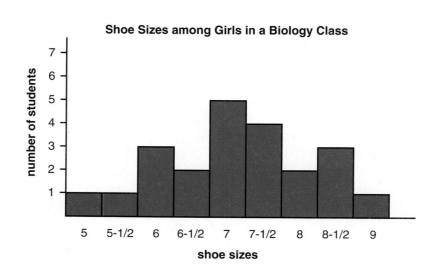

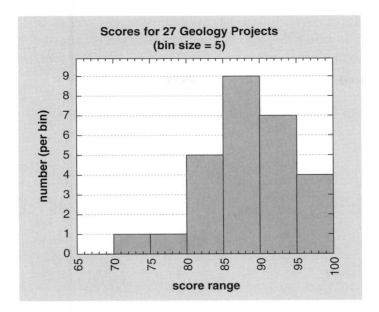

Figure D3.3
Histogram.
A histogram is a bar graph where observations are "binned" into particular intervals. This histogram shows the scores on a geology test by grouping them into 5-point intervals.

There are many types of graphs. In addition to line and bar graphs, you have probably seen pie graphs. These are often used to show percentage data. For example, you could use a pie graph to show the percentage of students in your class with brown, blonde, red, and black hair. You may also have seen a scatter plot. These graphs are often used to visualize a large number of data points. Lines are not used to connect each data point to the others. For example, you might use a scatter plot to show the time of day that students in your class started a particular homework assignment. Next time you look at a newspaper or a science magazine, pay attention to how graphs are used to represent information. Can you find examples of line, bar, and pie graphs, and scatter plots?

In this activity, you will practice making line graphs, bar graphs, and histograms because they are so commonly used in biology. These graphs have two major lines. One runs horizontally, and one runs vertically on the page. These lines are called the *axes* (singular: axis). The horizontal line is the *x*-axis; the vertical line is the *y*-axis. The point at which these two lines meet is the place where the graph begins, or the origin.

Both axes often include a sequence of numbers called a *number scale*. The numbers on the *x*-axis read from left to right; those on the *y*-axis read from bottom to top. The number scale is not necessarily the same on both axes. Look at figure D3.1. The number scale on the *x*-axis reads from 0 to 30; the *y*-axis reads from 0 to 600. What are the number scales on the graph in figure D3.2?

On some graphs, one or both axes show categories, rather than numbers. However, regardless of what a graph's axes represent, graphs are always clearly labeled to help the reader understand them. Look again at figures D3.1, D3.2, and D3.3. Each axis is labeled to explain to the reader what the numbers represent. Furthermore, each graph has a title that describes the relationship that the graph displays.

Making a graph involves several important steps. The steps in part I, *Line Graphs,* will help you draw any line graph. The steps in part II, *Bar Graphs,* will help you draw any bar graph. The steps in part III, *Histograms,* will help you draw any histogram.

Materials (per person)

2 sheets of graph paper
ruler

PROCESS AND PROCEDURES

Part I   Line Graphs

1. Review the data in figure D3.4.

   Before you can make a graph using data that you have collected, you need to organize your data into a data table. For this practice in graphing, you can use the data in figure D3.4 or data that you have collected over some interval of time.

Number of mice caught in a field	
Day	Number of mice caught per 100 traps per night
0	25
30	45
60	38
90	30
120	20
150	14
180	13
210	8
240	7
270	11
300	4
330	13

Figure D3.4   Table showing the number of mice caught over three months of time.

2. Draw the *x*-axis and the *y*-axis for the graph.

   Use a ruler and graph paper so that your lines will be straight and perpendicular (see figure D3.5a).

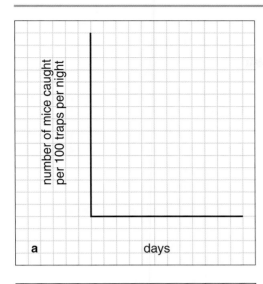

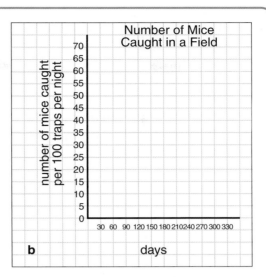

Figure D3.5 How to draw a line graph.

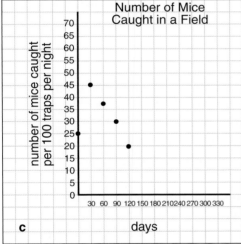

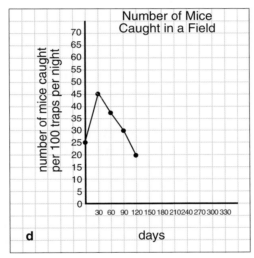

3. Identify what information will go on the *x*-axis and what information will go on the *y*-axis.

> Information on the *x*-axis is usually predictable in nature. For example, this information might be a series of dates, numbers, distances, or sizes. Information on the *y*-axis is usually variable in nature. For example, this could be the number of mice caught, the number of people of a certain height, or the number of butterflies captured.

4. Label each axis of the graph according to what each represents. Remember to include the units for measurements.

> The headings of the data table you are using can be a good place to start when thinking about how to label axes.

5. Set up the number scales on each axis.

> Allow space on each axis for a range of numbers just a bit greater than the numbers that are included in the data table (see figure D3.5b). Note that a number scale does not have to start with the number 1, but the numbers do need to be spaced in equal increments.

6. Give your graph a descriptive title.
7. Plot the data on your graph by doing the following.
   a. Read 1 row of data from the data table, for example, day 0 and 25 mice caught.
   b. Find the number on the *x*-axis where the piece of corresponding data fits (for example, 0).
   c. Move up from the number on the *x*-axis to the place on the *y*-axis where the corresponding piece of data fits (for example, 25).
   d. Draw a dot, called a *data point*, at that place.
   e. Repeat steps a–d for all the pieces of data in the data table.

   > Figure D3.5c illustrates five data points. Can you determine where the remaining data points go?

8. Draw a smooth line from left to right that connects the data points. This should help you see the relationship between the data points.

   > In this case, the line illustrates how the number of mice caught changed throughout the year (figure D3.5d).

Part II   Bar Graphs

1. Review the data in figure D3.6.

   > Alternately, use data that you have collected. Remember that bar graphs are used to show data that fall into different categories.

2. Draw the *x*- and *y*-axes for the graph.
3. Decide which information goes on each axis (refer to figure D3.7a).
4. Label each axis according to what each represents. Remember to include the units for measurements.
5. Decide on the number scales or category labels for each axis. Position the categories on the *x*-axis so that you can draw bars in the spaces between the lines. Place the numbers on the vertical axis next to the lines so that you can end a bar between 2 numbers, if necessary. Figure D3.7b will help you with this step.

Population of heath hens, Martha's Vineyard, MA	
Year	**Population size**
1900	90
1905	45
1910	280
1915	2,010
1920	550
1925	40
1930	10

Figure D3.6   Table showing the population of heath hens.

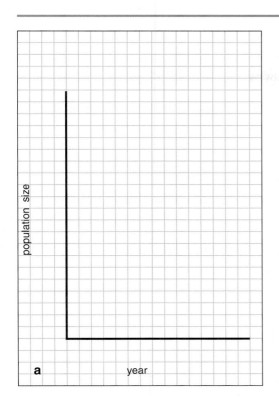

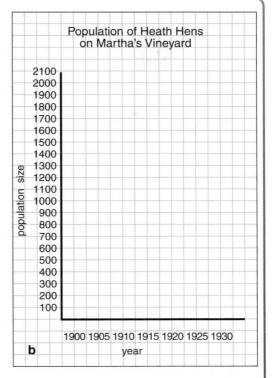

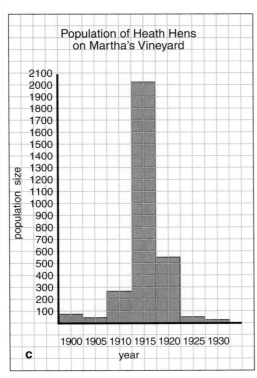

Figure D3.7 **How to draw a bar graph.**

6. Add a title to your graph.
7. Plot the data by following these steps.
   a. Read 1 row of data from the data table in figure D3.7, for example, year 1900 and population size 90.
   b. Find the corresponding category label on the *x*-axis scale of the graph (for example, 1900).
   c. Move up the column above the *x*-axis number you found, until you get to a point at the level of the appropriate number for that piece of data on the *y*-axis (for example, 90).
   d. Draw a horizontal line at that number to make the top of the bar.
   e. Color in the bar from that line down to the *x*-axis number you identified in step 7b.
   f. Repeat steps a–e for all the pieces of data in the data table (see figure D3.7c).

Part III   Histograms

1. Review the data in figure D3.8.
2. Draw the *x*- and *y*-axes for the graph.
3. Decide which information goes on each axis.

   Refer to the example in figure D3.3 if you are not sure.

4. Label each axis.

Height (meters)	Number of aspen trees
0–.5	15
.6–1	10
1.1–1.5	7
1.6–2.0	3
2.1–2.5	3
2.6–3.0	1

Figure D3.8   Table showing the heights of a group of aspen trees in 0.5 m intervals.

5. Decide on the number scales for each axis. Position the numbers on the x-axis so that you can draw bars in the spaces between the lines. Place the numbers on the vertical axis next to the lines so that you can end a bar between 2 numbers, if necessary.

   When writing in the intervals, you can choose to either write the full interval (for example, 0–0.5) or just the end point of the interval (for example, 0.5).

6. Add a title to your graph.
7. Plot the data by following these steps.
   a. Read 1 row of data from the data table, for example, height 0–0.5 m and number of trees 15.
   b. Find the interval for the corresponding piece of data on the x-axis of the graph (for example, 0–0.5 m).
   c. Move up the column above the x-axis interval you found, until you get to a point at the level of the appropriate number for that piece of data on the y-axis (for example, 15).
   d. Draw a horizontal line at that number to make the top of the bar.
   e. Color in the bar from that line down to the x-axis.
   f. Repeat steps a–e for all the pieces of data in the data table.

APPENDIX E

Tables

Periodic Table of Elements

Figure E1.1 Periodic table of elements.

© Kendall Hunt Publishing Company

Vitamins

Important vitamins for human health			
Vitamin *fat-soluble*	**Sources**	**Functions**	**Deficiency symptoms**
A (retinol)	Liver, green and yellow vegetables, fruits, egg yolks, butter	Forms eye pigments; helps cell growth, especially of epithelial cells	Night blindness, flaky skin lowered resistance to infection, growth retardation
D (calciferol)	Fish oils, liver, action of sunlight on lipids in skin, fortified milk, butter, eggs	Increases calcium absorption from gut; is important in bone and tooth formation	Rickets (defective bone growth)
E (tocopherol)	Oils, whole grains, liver, mayonnaise, margarine	Protects red blood cells, cell membranes, and vitamin A from destruction; helps maintain muscles; synthesizes DNA and RNA	Fragility of red blood cells, muscle wasting, sterility
K (menadione)	Synthesis by intestinal bacteria; green and yellow vegetables	Assists liver in synthesis of clotting factors	Internal hemorrhaging (deficiency can be caused by oral antibiotics, which kill intestinal bacteria)
Vitamin *water-soluble*	**Sources**	**Functions**	**Deficiency symptoms**
B_1 (thiamine)	Whole grains, legumes, nuts, liver, heart, kidney, pork, macaroni, wheat germ	Facilitates carbohydrate metabolism, nerve transmission, and RNA synthesis	Beriberi, loss of appetite, indigestion, fatigue, nerve irritability, heart failure, depression, poor coordination
B_2 (riboflavin)	Liver, kidney, heart, yeast, milk, eggs, whole grains, broccoli, almonds, cottage cheese, yogurt, macaroni	Forms part of electron carrier in electron transport system; aids production of FAD; activates B_6 and folic acid	Sore mouth and tongue, cracks at corners of mouth, eye irritation, scaly skin, growth retardation
Pantothenic acid	Yeast, liver, eggs, wheat germ, bran, peanuts, peas, fish, whole grain cereals	Facilitates energy release and biosynthesis; stimulates antibodies and intestinal absorption	Fatigue, headaches, sleep disturbances, nausea, muscle cramps, loss of antibody production, irritability, vomiting
B_3 (niacin)	Yeast, liver, kidney, heart, meat, fish, poultry, legumes, nuts, whole grains, eggs, milk	Serves as coenzyme in energy metabolism; is part of NAD^+ and NADP	Pellagra, skin lesions, digestive problems, nerve disorders, diarrhea, headaches, fatigue

Table E1.2   Important vitamins for human health.

Important vitamins for human health			
Vitamin	**Sources**	**Functions**	**Deficiency symptoms**
B$_6$ (pyridoxine)	Whole grains, potatoes, fish, poultry, red meats, legumes, seeds	Serves as coenzyme in amino acid and fatty acid metabolism and in the synthesis of brain chemicals, antibodies, red blood cells, and DNA; is essential to glucose tolerance	Skin disorders, sore mouth and tongue, nerve disorders, anemia, weight loss, impaired antibody response, convulsive seizures
Biotin	Cauliflower, liver, kidney, yeast, egg yolks, whole grains, fish, legumes, nuts, meats, dairy products; synthesis by intestinal bacteria	Serves as coenzyme in fatty acid, amino acid, and protein synthesis; promotes energy release from glucose; facilitates insulin activity	Skin disorders, loss of appetite, depression, sleeplessness, muscle pain, elevated blood cholesterol and glucose levels
Folate (folic acid)	Liver, yeast, leafy vegetables, asparagus, salmon	Serves as a coenzyme in nucleic acid synthesis and amino acid metabolism; is essential for new cell growth	Failure of red blood cells to mature, anemia, intestinal disturbances, diarrhea
B$_{12}$ (cobalamin)	Liver, organ meats, meat, fish, eggs, shellfish, milk; synthesis by intestinal bacteria	Serves as coenzyme in nucleic acid synthesis; helps maintain nervous tissues; plays a role in glucose metabolism	Pernicious anemia, fatigue, irritability, loss of appetite, headaches
C (ascorbic acid)	Citrus fruits, tomatoes, green leafy vegetables, peppers, broccoli, cauliflower	Is essential to formation of collagen, an intercellular substance that holds cells together; protects against infection; maintains strength of blood vessels; increases iron absorption from gut; plays important role in muscle maintenance and stress tolerance	Scurvy, failure to form connective tissue, bleeding, anemia, slow wound healing, joint pain, irritability, premature wrinkling and aging

Table E1.2 (continued)

Essential Elements

Name	Food	Function	Deficiency symptoms	Excess symptoms
Calcium (Ca)	Dairy products, green vegetables (broccoli, greens), legumes, tofu (bean curd), small fish (with bones)	Helps in bone and tooth development; facilitates muscle contraction, blood clotting, nerve impulse transmission, and enzyme activation	Osteoporosis, stunted growth, poor quality bones and teeth, rickets, convulsions	Excess blood calcium (rare), loss of appetite, muscle weakness, fever
Chlorine (Cl)	Table salt, soy sauce, processed foods	Helps maintain acid/base balance; assists hydrochloric acid formation in stomach; promotes bone and connective tissue growth	Metabolic alkalosis (rare), constipation, failure to gain weight (in infants)	Vomiting
Magnesium (Mg)	Whole grains, liver, kidneys, milk, nuts, dark green leafy vegetables, seafood	Serves as a component of chlorophyll, bones, and teeth, and as a coenzyme in carbohydrate and protein metabolism	Infertility, menstrual disorders	Loss of reflexes, drowsiness, coma, death
Phosphorous (P)	Soybeans, dairy foods, egg yolks, meat, whole grains, shrimp, peas, leafy green vegetables	Serves as component of bones, teeth, nucleic acids, phospholipids, proteins, and ATP	Bone fractures (rare), disorders of red blood cells, metabolic problems, irritability, weakness	Decreased levels of calcium, muscle spasms, jaw erosion
Potassium (K)	Whole grains, meats, fruits, vegetables, milk, peanut butter	Helps maintain body water and pH balance; plays important role in nerve and muscle activity, insulin release, glycogen and protein synthesis	Muscle and nerve weakness, poor digestion	Abnormalities in heartbeat or heart stoppage, muscle weakness, mental confusion, cold and pale skin (all are rare)
Sodium (Na)	Table salt, soy sauce, processed foods, baking soda, baking powder, meat, vegetables	Helps maintain body water and pH balance; plays role in nerve and muscle activity and glucose absorption	Weakness, muscle cramps, diarrhea, dehydration, nausea	High blood pressure, edema, kidney disease
Sulfur (S)	Dairy products, nuts, legumes, garlic, onions, egg yolks	Serves as component of some amino acids; plays role in enzyme activation and in blood clotting	None known; protein deficiency would occur first	Excess sulfur-containing amino acid intake leads to poor growth

Figure E1.3   **Important elements for human health.**

APPENDIX F1

Microorganisms

Diseases Result from Interrelationships

Disease is a condition that interferes with an organism's ability to perform a vital function. An infectious disease involves a disease-causing agent, or **pathogen**. The disease results from the interaction between an organism, or **host**, and the pathogen. The pathogen infects the host. If the pathogen harms the host, symptoms of disease may appear.

How serious a disease becomes depends on the characteristics of both the host and the pathogen. The ability to cause disease is called **virulence**. The ability of an infected host to cope with a pathogen is called **resistance**. A pathogen with high virulence may cause death in a host with low resistance. A host with high resistance, however, may show only mild symptoms of the same disease. Sometimes, a moderately virulent pathogen may produce serious illness. During a famine, for example, more people die from disease than from starvation. This is because a poorly nourished host may have much less resistance than a well-fed host.

Although genetics does play a role in the ability of an organism to resist disease, much of an individual's resistance is acquired during the lifetime of the individual, rather than having been inherited. Resistance, whether acquired or inherited, is called **immunity**. When a pathogen infects a human host, the host produces proteins called **antibodies** that can help destroy the pathogen. In addition to antibodies, certain cells of the body's defense, or immune system, have a chemical memory. If the host survives the initial infection, these cells retain the ability to produce the same antibodies. If the same pathogen infects the host a second time, the host's body can act against it more rapidly, preventing symptoms from developing or reducing their severity.

Each type of antibody is effective against only the particular pathogen that brought about its production, or pathogens that are very similar. For example, a person can have chicken pox only once, because antibodies produced during the first infection usually prevent symptoms from developing after a second infection. These antibodies are not effective against measles, however. Because there are many types of pathogens that cause colds, immunity to one type does not confer immunity to all the others.

Many diseases can be prevented by vaccines. A **vaccine** contains only enough of the killed or weakened disease-causing agent to stimulate production of antibodies by the immune system, usually without producing symptoms of the disease. Memory cells keep later infections, by the same pathogen, from causing disease. Vaccines first were used by Edward Jenner, an English physician (see figure F1.1).

Figure F1.1 The English physician Edward Jenner demonstrated in 1796 that by inoculating patients with a vaccine made of cowpox viruses he could protect them from the more serious disease of smallpox.

Disease may result from a variety of causes. The pathogens involved in infectious diseases may be viruses, eubacteria, or other organisms. For example, athlete's foot, ringworm, potato blight, and corn smut are caused by fungi. Different protists cause malaria, African sleeping sickness, and amoebic dysentery. Many worms and insects cause diseases of plants and animals, and are important vectors, or carriers, of disease. Other diseases, such as scurvy, are the result of diet deficiencies; still others are a result of advancing age; and some, such as asthma, are brought on by reactions to substances or pollutants in the environment. Finally, some disorders, such as cystic fibrosis or Huntington's disease, are hereditary.

Some Eubacteria Are Pathogens

Although the vast majority of microbes are beneficial or at least harmless to other organisms, some eubacteria are pathogenic. At the present time, however, no archaebacteria are known to cause disease.

Eubacterial diseases may be spread through water, food, or air. Many plant diseases are caused by eubacteria, and almost all types of plants are susceptible to one or more types of eubacterial disease. Fire blight, shown in figure F1.2, is a common eubacterial disease that can destroy fruit trees. In Florida in 1984, an outbreak of a eubacterial disease called citrus canker led farmers to destroy more than 4 million citrus seedlings in an effort to halt the spread of the disease. Citrus canker is caused by one of more than 100 distinct varieties of the gram-negative eubacterium *Xanthomonas campestris*. Other varieties of this eubacterium cause diseases with similar symptoms in beans, cabbages, peaches, and other plants. Citrus canker is a continuing threat to the existence of the Florida citrus industry, an annual $8.5 billion business.

Eubacteria also cause human diseases such as cholera, leprosy, tetanus, eubacterial pneumonia, whooping cough, and diphtheria. Many eubacteria multiply in the human digestive tract and leave the body in the feces. If untreated feces enter the water supply, the eubacteria may enter another organism when it drinks the water. Waterborne diseases such as typhoid kill 6 million children each year worldwide. Most cases of food poisoning are due to eubacteria. In some cases, the eubacteria produce poisonous

Figure F1.2 Fire blight is a disease of apples, pears, and related trees. It is caused by the bacterium *Erwinia amylovora*.

Figure F1.3
Droplets from a sneeze carry disease-causing agents through the air.

substances, or toxins, that are released in the food. These toxins can cause nausea, vomiting, and diarrhea within a few hours of ingestion. In the case of botulism, even a small amount of the toxin can be fatal. In other cases, eubacteria ingested with food multiply in the intestine, causing symptoms even several days after ingestion.

Many eubacteria are airborne. Whenever you open your mouth and exhale, you release droplets of moisture, each of which may contain one or two eubacteria. With a sneeze, you release many thousands of droplets at great speed. Droplets from a sneeze, visible in figure F1.3, have been clocked at 200 miles an hour. Droplets from a cough travel at about half that speed. Each time you sneeze, you can expel from 10,000 to 100,000 individual eubacteria. The eubacteria travel through the air without being killed and may infect another person standing close to you.

Group A streptococcus (GAS) eubacteria commonly infect people and cause a variety of health problems. Scientists believe that there are more than 120 different strains of GAS that each produces its own set of proteins. Some infections caused by GAS are minor, but some can be life-threatening. For example, some people may have been infected with the bacteria but don't have any illness or symptoms. These people can pass the infection to others; GAS infections are spread by direct contact with saliva or nasal mucus.

One of the more common diseases caused by GAS is strep throat; people who have strep throat have a sore throat, white patches on their tonsils, swollen lymph nodes, fever, and headache. GAS can also cause minor skin infections. Medical experts estimate that more than 10 million mild GAS infections occur each year. These minor infections can normally be treated effectively with antibiotics. However, some GAS bacteria cause severe, or invasive, infections. Severe infections include infections of the bloodstream, streptococcal toxic shock syndrome (not the same illness that is associated with tampon use in menstruating females, although that disease is also caused by a bacterium), and necrotizing fasciitis (sometimes referred to as the flesh-eating disease). All of these severe infections can lead to shock, organ failure, and even death. Although illnesses such as the flesh-eating disease are scary because of their severe nature, they are fairly rare. Approximately 10,000 to 15,000 cases of invasive GAS diseases occur each year in the United States, compared with millions of cases of strep throat and minor skin infections caused by GAS.

Scientists continue to learn more about how GAS bacteria cause such a wide range of diseases. In recent years, scientists have found that a strain of the GAS bacteria that causes rheumatic fever, the most common infectious cause of childhood heart disease, contains gene sequences that appear to come from a bacteriophage, a virus that infects bacteria. The viral genetic sequences that were inserted into the bacterial DNA cause the bacteria to produce new toxic proteins. A strain of GAS without the viral genes does not cause rheumatic fever. Continuing scientific research will help scientists understand how GAS bacteria can cause such a wide variety of illnesses in humans.

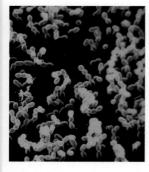

Figure F1.4
Streptococcus mutans is a bacterium associated with tooth decay.

Even dental caries, or tooth decay, is an infection caused by eubacteria. The decay begins on the surfaces of the teeth in a biofilm known as dental plaque. This biofilm consists of large numbers of eubacteria in a complex sugar matrix (shown in figure F1.4), and builds up on unbrushed teeth and in crevices not reached by a toothbrush. Sugars and carbohydrates in the diet serve as food sources for the eubacteria (*Streptococcus mutans*) that are present in the mouth. The eubacteria break the sugars and carbohydrates down into simple sugars and produce lactic acid as a waste product. The acid then causes the tooth enamel to lose minerals, thus causing tooth decay. Fluoride makes the teeth more resistant to decay because it retards the loss of minerals, including calcium and phosphate, from the teeth. It also promotes the replacement of these minerals to help keep the teeth healthy.

Viruses Are Unusual Pathogens

What do AIDS, hepatitis, measles, mumps, influenza, colds, and polio have in common? These diseases all are caused by viruses such as those shown in figure F1.5. A virus is an infectious agent that contains a nucleic acid (either DNA or RNA) and a protein coat. Viruses are so small that they can be seen only with an electron microscope. In fact, viruses can pass through most bacteriological filters. Viruses may play one of two roles when they enter a host cell. As agents of disease, viruses enter the host cells, disrupt the cells' normal functioning, and sometimes kill them. As agents of heredity, viruses can enter cells and cause permanent, heritable changes. Often, the role the virus plays depends on the host cell and environmental conditions.

SCI LINKS
NSTA

www.scilinks.org

Topic: virus
Code: human4E907

Viruses differ from living things in several important ways. They are able to produce copies of themselves only inside a living organism. Outside the host cell, viruses do not reproduce, feed, or grow. They have no metabolism of their own. They do not take in and use energy. They do not have cell parts. Some can be crystallized and survive for years in that state. Only

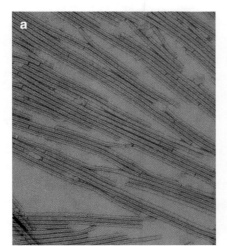
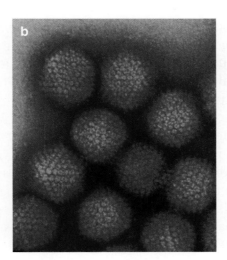
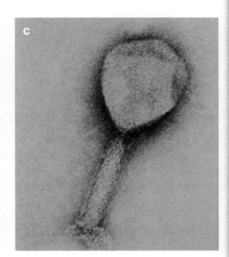

Figure F1.5 All viruses are pathogenic. Tobacco mosaic virus (*a*) causes a disease of plants (185,000×); adenovirus (*b*) causes respiratory illnesses in humans (11,000×); T4 bacteriophage (*c*) (240,000×) infects and kills bacterial cells.

when they enter the appropriate host cells can they resume reproduction. Viruses infect plants (see figure F1.6). Viruses also infect bacteria, as shown in figures F1.7 and F1.8. To reproduce, a virus first attaches to a host cell and then injects its viral DNA or RNA into the host cell. The viral nucleic acid takes over the machinery of the host cell (the proteins that replicate host DNA and that make host cell proteins). Viral proteins direct the host cell to make more viral protein and viral nucleic acid. The proteins and nucleic acids then are assembled into new virus particles, and the infected cell ruptures, releasing hundreds of newly made viruses. Each new virus has the ability to infect a single new host cell.

Usually, genetic information is stored in DNA, transcribed into mRNA, and then translated into protein. In many viruses, genetic information is stored as DNA. In some viruses, however, the viral genetic information actually is stored as RNA. Certain RNA viruses, known as retroviruses, must go through an additional step before they can reproduce. Retroviruses must make copies of DNA from their RNA, the reverse of the normal flow of stored information in biological systems. Like other viruses, a retrovirus binds to the surface of a host cell and injects its RNA into the cell. Reverse transcriptase, a special enzyme associated with the RNA, allows the retrovirus to make a complementary DNA copy of its RNA (see figure F1.9). The newly formed viral DNA then can be integrated into the host cell DNA, replicated at the same time, and transmitted to offspring cells. When the cell produces RNA from its own DNA, it also produces viral RNA, which becomes the source of new viral particles, thus continuing the infection.

Retroviruses are known to cause cancer in some animals and have been associated with certain types of cancers in humans. Human oncogenes have similarities to genes in these retroviruses; both can result in cancerous growth when they are somehow disturbed. The virus that causes AIDS is a retrovirus that attacks and kills certain cells of the immune system. Once these cells are killed, the immune system is unable to perform its normal function of defending the organism against disease.

Figure F1.6 **TYMV (turnip yellow mosaic virus) in a young cabbage plant.**

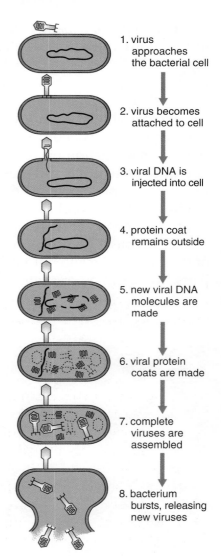

1. virus approaches the bacterial cell

2. virus becomes attached to cell

3. viral DNA is injected into cell

4. protein coat remains outside

5. new viral DNA molecules are made

6. viral protein coats are made

7. complete viruses are assembled

8. bacterium bursts, releasing new viruses

Figure F1.7 **A bacterial virus (called a bacteriophage or simply, a phage) reproducing within a single eubacterium.**

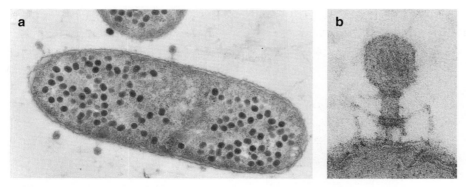

Figure F1.8 The eubacterium *Escherichia coli* (*a*) with T4 phage viruses attached to the surface and inside (50,000×). T4 phage (*b*) attached to the eubacterium after the phage has injected its DNA (200,000×).

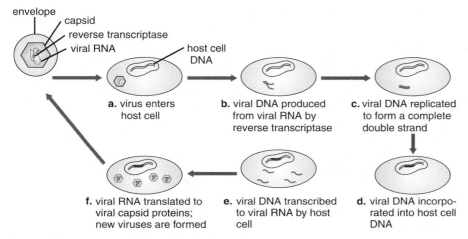

envelope
capsid
reverse transcriptase
viral RNA
host cell DNA

a. virus enters host cell

b. viral DNA produced from viral RNA by reverse transcriptase

c. viral DNA replicated to form a complete double strand

d. viral DNA incorporated into host cell DNA

e. viral DNA transcribed to viral RNA by host cell

f. viral RNA translated to viral capsid proteins; new viruses are formed

Figure F1.9 Retroviruses are composed of an envelope (from the plasma membrane of a host cell), a protein coat, viral RNA, and the enzyme reverse transcriptase. Retroviruses use the enzyme reverse transcriptase to make a DNA copy of their RNA. The viral DNA then is incorporated into the host cell DNA, and the host cell directs production of new viruses.

Analysis

1. Describe the interaction between host and pathogen that may result in disease.
2. Distinguish between infection and disease.
3. What is immunity? How can a vaccine bring about the development of immunity?
4. Describe, using examples, the major ways by which eubacterial diseases can be spread.
5. What is the role of eubacteria in dental caries?
6. What is the structure of a virus, and how does it infect a host cell?
7. How does a virus direct the formation of other virus particles?
8. How does a retrovirus differ from a virus?

APPENDIX F2

Plants

Several hundred million years ago, the land surface of Earth was barren. Life existed only in the water. One-celled algae colored the surface waters of the oceans shades of green. Some algae joined together into multicellular organisms and evolved a degree of cell specialization. These organisms share common ancestry with today's modern plants.

This appendix examines several of the characteristics that enabled plants to invade the land and describes a few examples of modern plants. Today, plants adapted to life on land are found in most habitats, from prairies to tundra and in the forests and deserts of the world. They come in the widest possible range of sizes. The largest organisms in the world are the giant redwoods in California, such as those shown in figure F2.1. Some of these trees are more than 100 m tall and 7 m in diameter. From a simple multicellular green alga in the ancient sea to a giant California redwood tree with billions of cells, the differences in structure and function are tremendous. The evolution of such a complex land organism from a relatively unspecialized multicellular ancestor did not occur overnight. It took millions of years.

Figure F2.1 The giant sequoias, *Sequoiadendron giganteum*, are the largest organisms in the world.

The Evolution of Land Plants

Two Major Groups of Land Plants Evolved

Most plants that we observe around us today are multicellular, photosynthetic organisms adapted primarily for life on land. The evolution of multicellular green algae that had some division of labor among their cells produced many adaptations that allowed plants to live in this environment. The oldest known plant fossils are simple, branched structures that had several important adaptations.

Because the climate on land may vary from hot to freezing and from wet to dry, water is the major limiting factor for any organism. On land, the only reliable source of water is underground, where it is too dark for photosynthesis. What possible advantages of living on land could overcome such a major disadvantage?

Without the presence of other organisms, plants that were able to tolerate the dry conditions that exist on land would have had little competition for food, minerals, living space, and the other necessities of life. Another advantage would have been the abundance of carbon dioxide and oxygen present in the air. A third advantage for these plants would have been increased light levels, because the air does not absorb as much light as water does. Finally, there would have been plenty of space, and minerals would have been readily available in the soil.

A multicellular alga tossed onto the shore would have had a better chance of surviving than would a one-celled alga. The outer cells of the organism could provide some protection against drying out for the inner cells, and the inner cells might have been efficient at photosynthesis. Other cells of the same organism might have specialized in collecting water or nutrients from the environment. The resulting division of labor would have enabled the alga to exploit the resources in its new environment. A specialized multicellular alga, the *Chara* in figure F2.2, is a modern day example of plants that seem to have made this adjustment to land, living and reproducing on land where ocean spray and tides keep it moist.

There is ample evidence that two plant groups share common ancestry with multicellular green algae. The less complex group, the **bryophytes**, are not aquatic, yet they possess few adaptations for life on land. This group includes the true mosses, hornworts, and liverworts. Bryophytes are called nonvascular plants because they do not have vascular tissue. The more complex group, which includes fossils of the oldest land plants, has many adaptations to life on land, including **vascular tissue**—cells joined into tubes that transport water and minerals throughout the body of the plant. These plants are called vascular plants. Vascular plants likely evolved from a common ancestor shared with bryophytes.

Figure F2.2 **The multicellular green alga *Chara*.** The fossil record of *Chara*-like algae extends back about 400 million years. Why is *Chara* considered to be a model of the ancestors of land plants?

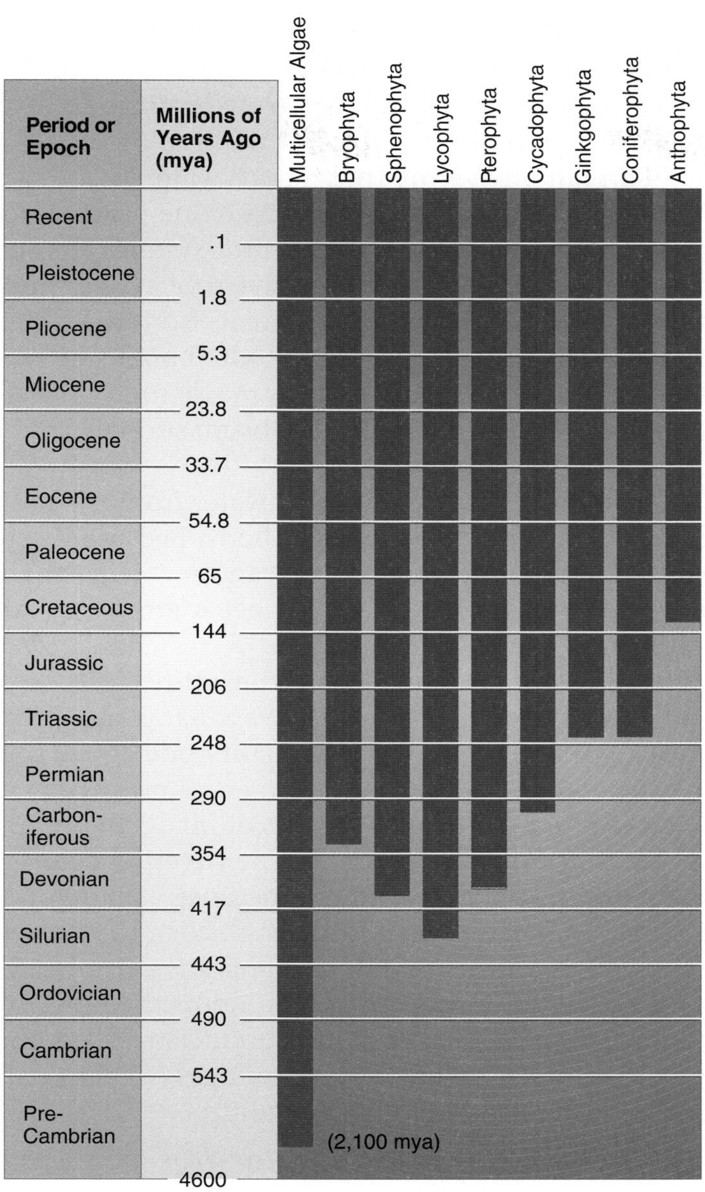

Figure F2.3   The evolutionary history of plants. What evidence was used to construct this history?

Vascular plants can be divided into two groups: those that produce seeds, and seedless plants such as ferns that reproduce with spores. Vascular plants that produce seeds can be divided further into two groups. One group is those, such as pine trees, that produce naked seeds in cones (the Cycadophyta, Ginkgophyta, and Coniferophyta). The second group is flowering plants (Anthophyta), which produce seeds enclosed in a fruit. Figure F2.3 represents an evolutionary history of plants.

Vascular Plants Have Adaptations That Conserve Water and Permit Gas Exchange

The success of plants on land depends largely on their ability to absorb and hold water. Structures that enable them to do so include roots, vascular tissue, and an outer covering that retards water loss.

Vascular plants such as ferns, conifers (cone-bearing plants), and flowering plants have well-developed root systems that penetrate into many parts of the soil. An extensive root system provides an efficient way to collect water and minerals from the soil and bring them to the main body of the plant. Rooted plants offer a good example of division of labor: The cells in the roots collect water and minerals, and the aboveground cells absorb sunlight and produce food through photosynthesis.

Figure F2.4 Plants such as this stonecrop (*Sedum adolphic*) have very thick cuticles. How are thick cuticles adaptive?

Tall plants require cells that can transport water from the roots to the leaves and cells that can support an upright body. Because vascular tissue serves both these functions, vascular plants can grow taller than bryophytes and thus capture more sunlight. Bryophytes never grow very tall because they lack an efficient water transport system.

In bryophytes, water can evaporate from the entire surface, so a moss plant, for example, dries out quickly. Vascular plants produce a waxy covering, or **cuticle**, that covers the plant body above the ground, reducing the amount of water that can evaporate from its surface. The cuticle is often thick on the leaves of plants living in dry places, such as the stonecrop in figure F2.4. The covering does not prevent gas exchange with the environment, because vascular plants have slitlike openings, or **stomates**, in the surface of their leaves. Stomates (figure F2.5), found in the oldest fossil plants, permit carbon dioxide and oxygen to enter or leave the plant. Roots that absorb water,

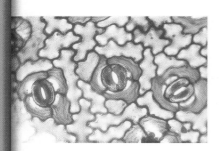

Figure F2.5 Stomates are found on the surface of a leaf.

vascular tissue that supports the plant and conducts water, a cuticle that prevents evaporation, and stomates that permit gas exchange are characteristics that enable plants to live on land.

Bryophytes Require Water for Reproduction

Reproductive adaptations also enabled plants to survive on land. Bryophytes are restricted to moist areas because their sperm are flagellated (have whiplike appendages), as are those of animals and algae. For sexual reproduction to occur, the plants must be bathed in water so the sperm can swim to the egg. Thus, bryophytes reproduce sexually only where water sprays them or after they are wet with dew or rain. Like all sexually reproducing plants, bryophytes have a life cycle in which a haploid (n) phase alternates with a diploid ($2n$) phase. This type of life cycle is called **alternation of generations**.

The carpet of moss shown in figure F2.6a actually is many individual plants. These small plants are haploid, and each is called a **gametophyte**. As the name implies, gametophytes produce gametes, usually in special structures near the tips of the plants. In wet conditions, sperm are produced in male gametophytes. The sperm swim in a film of water to the egg cell in the female gametophyte, where fertilization occurs and a diploid zygote is

produced. In some species, both eggs and sperm are produced on the same gametophyte.

The zygote divides by mitosis and develops into a diploid embryo. Eventually, the embryo grows out of the female gametophyte into a stalk-like structure, the **sporophyte**. The diploid sporophyte is visible above the small haploid individuals shown in figure F2.6b. Meiosis occurs within the capsule at the end of the sporophyte, and haploid spores are formed. The capsule helps protect the spores. Once the spores are released, they are carried wherever wind or water transports them. Most spores fall onto unfavorable habitats and die. If a spore reaches a favorable environment, usually a moist soil surface, its wall can burst open. The cell within begins to divide by mitosis, producing long green threads that resemble the filaments of many aquatic algae. The gametophyte moss plant develops from these threads. When a spore germinates and grows into another gametophyte plant, the life cycle diagrammed in figure F2.7 is complete.

Figure F2.7
Which generation is predominant in the life cycle of a moss?

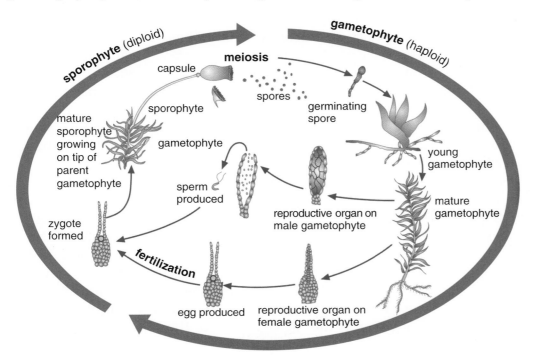

Flowering Plants Have Special Reproductive Adaptations

Unlike bryophytes and seedless vascular plants, which require water to be present for fertilization, seed plants produce special structures called **pollen grains** (figure F2.8), in which nonflagellated sperm develop. The pollen grains may be blown by wind or may be carried by animals from one plant to another. This efficient means of transferring sperm to the egg under dry conditions is most highly developed in the flowering plants. Brightly colored or scented flowers attract a variety of animals, such as hummingbirds, bats, and insects. Many brightly colored flowers contain nectar that these animals drink and use as an energy source. As the animal drinks, it picks up pollen from one flower and carries it to another flower while searching for more nectar. Because seed plants are not restricted to moist conditions, sexual reproduction can occur whenever the sperm and egg are fully developed. Like bryophytes, flowering plants have a life cycle with alternation of generations, but the gametophyte generation of flowering plants is smaller and protected, at least while it is attached to the sporophyte generation.

Flowering plants are considered to be the most complex of the vascular plants. Their reproductive structures are found in flowers. A flower is actually a short branch bearing groups of specialized leaves. Some of these leaves may resemble ordinary leaves in many ways, but others are so different in structure that it is hard to think of them as leaves at all. If you closely examine a flower such as the buttercup illustrated in figure F2.9, you will see a number of green, leaflike structures called **sepals** on the underside of the flower. Before the bud opens, the sepals cover and protect the other parts of the flower. The most conspicuous parts of a flower are the colorful **petals.** Although petals are often leaflike in shape, they are not usually green.

Just inside the circle of petals of a typical flower is a ring of male reproductive structures, the **stamens.** In the center of the flower is the **carpel,** the female reproductive organ. Although most plants have both male and female organs within the same flower, a few plants produce flowers with only female parts or only male parts. Stamens usually have an enlarged tip, the anther, whereas the carpel tip (the **stigma**) is more pointed. Despite their shape, however, both stamens and carpels are thought to be modified leaves that have been adapted for reproductive roles.

Figure F2.10 shows the relationship between reproductive structures and the life cycle of one type of flowering plant. At the base of the carpel is an enlarged portion, the ovary, that contains one or more small structures called **ovules.** Meiosis occurs in a special cell in each ovule, resulting in the formation of four haploid cells, the female spores. These spores do not separate from the sporophyte as they do in mosses. Instead, three of the spores disintegrate. The fourth spore divides three times by mitosis, forming eight nuclei. The nuclei, with their surrounding cytoplasm, form seven cells, one of which is the egg cell. (One of the cells contains two

Figure F2.8
Scanning electron micrograph of pollen grains from dandelion (2,500×).

Topic: plant adaptations
Code: human4E916

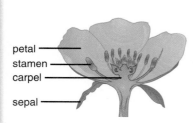

petal
stamen
carpel
sepal

Figure F2.9 The flower structure of a buttercup is shown in a cutaway diagram.

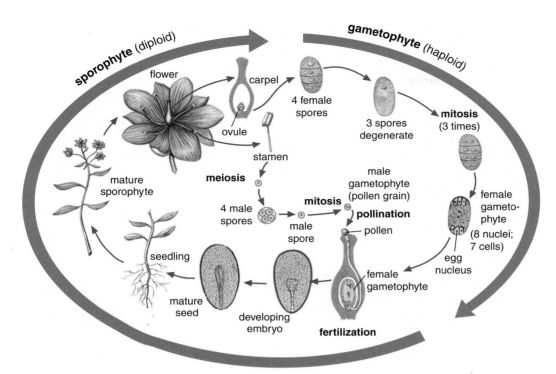

sporophyte (diploid)

flower

carpel

ovule

stamen

meiosis

4 male
spores

mature
sporophyte

male
spore

mitosis

gametophyte (haploid)

4 female
spores

3 spores
degenerate

mitosis
(3 times)

male
gametophyte
(pollen grain)

female
gameto-
phyte
(8 nuclei;
7 cells)

pollination

pollen

egg
nucleus

female
gametophyte

fertilization

developing
embryo

mature
seed

seedling

Figure F2.10 Which generation predominates in the life cycle of a flowering plant? (The parts are drawn to different scales.)

nuclei, the polar nuclei.) Figure F2.11a shows these seven cells, which constitute the female gametophyte.

In the stamens, cells in the anthers undergo meiosis, each giving rise to four haploid cells, the male spores. Each spore contains one haploid nucleus that divides by mitosis, forming two nuclei (see figure F2.11b). A spore wall thickens around each nucleus, forming a pollen grain. A single stamen may contain thousands of pollen grains. Each pollen grain is a single-celled male gametophyte containing two nuclei.

Pollination is the transfer of pollen from the stamens to the carpel, either within a flower, between flowers of the same plant, or between plants of the same species. The sticky stigma at the top of the carpel can trap

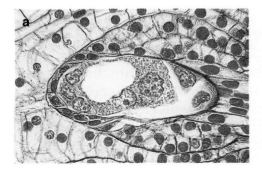
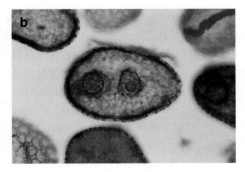

Figure F2.11 These two micrographs show the gametophytes of a lily. (*a*) We see the female gametophyte of a lily. This is a mature ovule ready to be fertilized; the egg nucleus is one of those on the left. (*b*) A pollen grain, the male gametophyte of a seed plant, is shown at the two-nucleate stage.

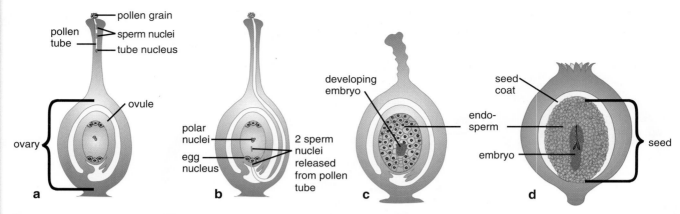

Figure F2.12 The events of pollination (*a*), fertilization (*b*), and development of the embryo (*c*) and seed (*d*) in a flowering plant are drawn here.

pollen grains carried to it by wind, water, or a visiting animal. Only pollen grains from flowers of the same species are useful in fertilization.

The hard wall of the pollen grain protects the haploid cell until the grain lands on a stigma. Once there, a thin finger of tissue, the pollen tube, grows from the grain into the carpel. Within the pollen tube, one nucleus, the tube nucleus, leads the way. The other nucleus divides to form two sperm nuclei. The **pollen tube** grows down the carpel, transporting the sperm nuclei to the ovule. Fertilization occurs when one sperm nucleus unites with the egg, forming a zygote. This diploid cell gives rise to the embryo. The other sperm nucleus unites with the polar nuclei, leading to the formation of **endosperm**, a mass of food-storing cells that will later nourish the developing embryo. The endosperm is triploid; it has three sets of chromosomes: one set from the sperm and two from the polar nuclei. Figure F2.12 summarizes the stages of fertilization and embryo development in a flowering plant.

The life cycle of a flowering plant is similar to that of a moss in two ways. First, meiosis occurs just before spore formation. Second, there is alternation of generations between the sporophyte and gametophyte portions of the life cycle. There are, however, several differences. First, abundant surface water is not necessary for fertilization in flowering plants. Second, the gametophytes are smaller than the sporophytes. Third, the gametophyte that produces an egg and the spore that produces the female gametophyte do not separate from the sporophyte plant. Thus, these structures are better protected from the environment than are their counterparts in an embryonic moss. Finally, the embryo (young porophyte) grows for a short time, then becomes dormant. The embryo and its endosperm are surrounded by a protective coat formed from ovule tissues. This package is a **seed**, diagrammed in figure F2.13. The seed protects the young sporophyte, which remains dormant until environmental conditions are suitable for germination. Moss embryos, on the other hand, cannot tolerate dry conditions. Also, moss spores contain no embryos and only a small amount of food.

Figure F2.13 A bean seed, cut in half, shows the embryo and endosperm. The endosperm of the bean seed, as shown here, is found in structures known as the seed leaves.

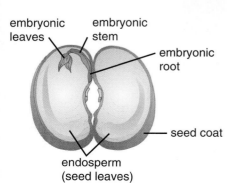

Land plants show a trend toward increasing specialization of the sporophyte and decreasing specialization of the gametophyte, as shown in figure F2.14. Seed plants are more abundant and more diverse than mosses because of their adaptations to the changing environment on land. Flowering plants are well suited to life on land because of the cuticle, vascular tissue, root systems, sperm carried in pollen, spores protected on sporophytes, and embryos protected in seeds.

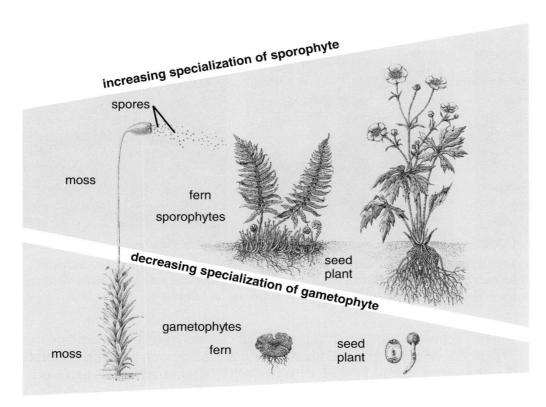

Figure F2.14 The differences between mosses and land plants can be shown by diagramming the evolution and specialization in sporophytes and gametophytes.

Analysis

1. Describe the limiting factors and advantages of life on land for the first land plants.
2. What types of adaptations were necessary for plants to live on land, and why were they important?
3. Briefly distinguish between the different types of land plants.
4. Compare and contrast gametophytes and sporophytes.
5. Compare and contrast the life cycles of bryophytes and flowering plants.
6. Explain the roles of the reproductive structures of flowering plants.
7. Describe the origin of the embryo, the endosperm, and the seed.

Bryophytes and Seedless Vascular Plants

Bryophytes Have No Roots, Stems, or Leaves

Most bryophytes (division *Bryophyta*) are relatively small. Few of them exceed 20 cm in height. Although they have structures resembling stems and leaves, these terms are not used in describing bryophytes because they lack the vascular tissue of other land plants. There are three classes of bryophytes: true mosses, the largest class; liverworts; and hornworts. Figure F2.15 shows several bryophytes.

Figure F2.15 These are examples of varieties of bryophytes: (*a*) moss, *Polytrichium;* (*b*) liverwort, *Marchantia polymorpha;* (*c*) hornwort, *Anthoceros punctatus.* How do bryophytes and seedless vascular plants differ in structure and habitat?

True mosses often grow in clumps or small clusters in rock crevices and on the shady side of trees. An individual moss plant from such a clump is simply an upright, green, stem-like stalk with threadlike structures called **rhizoids**, which perform the function of roots by aiding in absorption and helping to hold the plant in place. Many flat, green, leaf-like structures are attached spirally along the stalk. Water and nutrients are absorbed throughout the body of the bryophyte, so most grow in fairly damp places, and a few grow in water. Under dry conditions, many mosses become dormant. When dormant, the life processes slow down, and the plant appears dead. Normal activities resume when the plant comes in contact with water. Because many bryophytes can photosynthesize in limited light, they often are found on the ground in forest ecosystems, where other plants cannot grow.

One important group of mosses is found in boggy places in the cold and temperate parts of the world. These plants, from the genus *Sphagnum,* form peat bogs—small lakes and ponds completely filled with living and dead mosses. Sphagnum produces a very acidic condition in the water that keeps decomposers such as bacteria and fungi from growing, thus allowing these plants to build up through time, layer on layer. People in Ireland and other countries cut blocks of peat, dry it, and use it for fuel or to build small enclosures. Dry peat absorbs water quickly and holds the water well, characteristics that make peat attractive to gardeners, who add it to their soil to lower the pH and to increase the water-holding capacity.

Liverworts and hornworts grow in very moist areas, such as on the banks of streams where water spray keeps the soil wet. Bryophytes are less complex than vascular plants and are likely the ancestors of vascular plants. The fossil record for bryophytes is small. The earliest bryophyte fossils are only about 350 million years old, but genetic reconstructions of the evolution of plants would predict that older fossils should exist. The first fossils of vascular plants appear 50–100 million years earlier than bryophytes in the fossil record.

Club Mosses and Horsetails Are Seedless Vascular Plants

The roots, stems, and leaves of vascular plants contain the vascular system through which water, sugar, and dissolved nutrients move from one place to another in the plant.

Rhynia major, shown in figure F2.16, best represents the oldest land plants. *Rhynia* had an underground stem that probably anchored the plant and absorbed water. From this underground stem grew upright branched stems that had stomates. At the tips of the stems were sporangia, which split open to release thick-walled spores. A living relative of *Rhynia* is the whisk fern, *Psilotum*, shown in figure F2.17.

The club mosses (division *Lycophyta*) are evergreen plants that seldom grow more than 40 cm tall. Although the word "moss" is a part of their name, they are not true mosses. Their branching, horizontal stems grow on the surface of the soil or just below it. The most noticeable part of a club moss plant is an upright branch growing from one of these stems. Club mosses reproduce by spores, which are produced on modified, specialized leaves. In many species, these leaves form club-shaped cones at the tips of short, upright stems. The name "club moss" is derived from this feature. Club mosses are rather common in the eastern and northwestern United States and often are used to make Christmas wreaths. They rarely grow in the dry states of the Southwest.

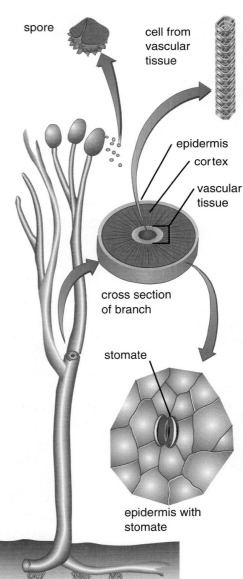

Figure F2.16 The extinct plant *Rhynia* is reconstructed here. It had no leaves or roots and stood about 30 cm high. Sporangia were produced at the tips of the upper branches. The presence of stomates indicates that photosynthesis occurred in the branches. The cells of vascular tissue (upper right) were oblong and sometimes hollow. Thick-walled spores were produced in fours in the sporangia, an indication that the spores were produced by meiosis.

Figure F2.17 Note the sporangia along the stems of the whisk fern, *Psilotum*.

Horsetails (division *Sphenophyta*) have hollow, jointed, upright branches that grow from horizontal underground stems. Their small, scalelike leaves grow in a circle around each stem joint. Spores are produced in conelike structures at the tips of some of the upright branches, such as those shown in figure F2.18. In middle latitudes, horsetails rarely reach a height of 2 m, but in the American tropics one species may grow several meters tall. They are found in moist places, such as along streams. Horsetails are harsh to the touch; their tissues contain silica, a compound present in sand. Because Native Americans and the pioneers scrubbed pots and pans with them, they are commonly called scouring rushes.

Relatives of the club mosses and horsetails can be traced back about 430 million years. During the Coal Age, about 300 million years ago, great parts

Figure F2.18 (*a*) Spores of *Equisetum* (horsetail) are produced in these conelike structures. The vegetative stage of *Equisetum* (*b*) is characterized by hollow, jointed, upright branches.

×1/350

Lepidodendron

×1/250

Sigillaria

×1/350

Cordaites

×1/77

seed fern

×1/151

Calamites

Figure F2.19   These are some examples of the trees of the Coal Age forests: *Lepidodendron* and *Sigillaria* were club mosses. *Cordaites* were primitive cone-bearing plants. The seed ferns have no living species. *Calamites* were horsetails.

of North America were covered by shallow swamps and seas. The warm and wet environment allowed plants to grow year-round. Under these conditions, giant relatives of today's club mosses, horsetails, and ferns, as well as seed-producing plants, covered the land. Some of these plants were more than 20 m tall (figure F2.19). As they died, their large stems were covered with mud and soil before they completely decayed. A tremendous number of plants from the Coal Age were compressed over long periods of time and under high temperature and great pressure. Eventually, they became fossil fuels, mainly coal and some natural gas.

Fern Leaves Grow from Underground Stems

Ferns (division *Pterophyta*), like the club mosses and horsetails, reproduce by spores. At certain times of the year, small brown spots develop on the undersides of fern leaves, as shown in figure F2.20. Each spot consists of a cluster of sporangia. Each sporangium produces a large number of spores, which are almost microscopic in size.

When a sporangium is mature, it opens and the spores are thrown out into the air. Spores are very light and can be carried for

SCiLINKS
NSTA

www.scilinks.org

Topic: ferns
Code: human4E923

Figure F2.20   The dusty-looking spots on the underside of a Christmas fern leaf, *Polystichum acrostichoides*, are sporangia.

Figure F2.21 You may never have seen a fern gametophyte (*a*), but you are probably familiar with the fern sporophyte (*b*).

incredible distances by wind. If a spore falls in a suitably moist place, it germinates and develops rapidly into a thin, green, heart-shaped plant that is rarely more than 1 cm in diameter (see figure F2.21a). This small gametophyte plant, which is completely different from the familiar fern with its large leaves, is seldom noticed in the woods. The gametophyte produces the sperm or eggs, or in some cases, both. Like the moss sperm, the flagellated fern sperm must swim in a film of water to fertilize the egg. The zygote produced by that fertilization eventually grows into the conspicuous spore-bearing fern plant that most people recognize. This large plant is the sporophyte generation of the fern, seen in figure F2.21b.

The ferns native to most of the United States are shade-dwelling plants with underground roots and stems. From these stems, roots grow downward and new sets of upright leaves appear above the ground each spring. In Hawaii and elsewhere in the tropics, many species of ferns have stems that grow upright. These tree ferns may reach a height of 20 m with leaves 5 m long, as figure F2.22 illustrates. Most fern species are found in the tropics, but many can be found in forest ecosystems around the world.

Figure F2.22 Tree ferns grow on the island of Sumatra.

Analysis

1. How do bryophytes differ from vascular plants?
2. How does reproduction in seedless vascular plants differ from that in bryophytes?
3. What events must occur for a fern sporophyte to be produced from a gametophyte?
4. In what type of environment must ferns and horsetails grow in order to reproduce?

Pioneers

Evolutionary Geologist

Dr. Geerat Vermeij (pronounced Ver May) is a paleontologist and a professor at the University of California, Davis. As a paleontologist, he studies life-forms from the ancient past by examining fossils. Dr. Vermeij specializes in the natural history of molluscs and their relationships with ancient predators. According to his research, molluscs have adapted to the presence of ever-more-efficient predators by developing progressively heavier and more protective shells. Dr. Vermeij feels that this reaction to natural enemies provides a better explanation of how molluscs evolved than the usual explanations based on climatic changes and other large-scale physical factors.

Dr. Vermeij was born in the Netherlands and raised in New Jersey. His proximity to the Atlantic seaboard allowed him to pursue his early interest in shell collecting. He has developed this interest through worldwide travel and extensive field study. He has traveled widely in the South Pacific, Central and North America, and Africa. His research on predatory patterns on molluscs has involved investigating shell geometry, breakage patterns, scarring, hole patterns, and evidence of repair following encounters with their marine enemies.

A graduate of Princeton and Yale Universities, Dr. Vermeij holds a particular distinction among paleontologists. He has been completely blind since age three and has never actually seen a single organism he has studied. Instead, he uses his fingers to feel the subtle features of the ancient marine creatures he investigates. His sense of touch is so refined that he often is able to identify molluscs to the subspecies based on the most minor changes in the shapes, textures, and thickness of shells. Dr. Vermeij works closely with his wife and professional colleague, Dr. Edith Zipser, also of the University of California, Davis. Together, they have collected shells from their extensive travels and formulated their ideas on the evolutionary patterns of molluscs. Dr. Vermeij has risen above his physical restrictions and opposition from skeptical peers to be a premier-level paleontologist.

Figure F2.23 These are examples of conifers and related plants: (*a*) ponderosa pine, *Pinus ponderosa*; (*b*) cycad, *Dioon edule*; and (*c*) maidenhair tree, *Ginkgo biloba*. Seeds of these plants are not enclosed in tissues as are those of flowering plants. How are seed plants adapted to life on land?

Seed Plants

Many Conifers Are Evergreens

Humans have used plants for food, clothing, shelter, and medicines. The conifers (division *Coniferophyta*) are woody vascular plants with seeds borne in cones. Conifers provide most of the paper pulp and much of the lumber used in home construction and furniture. They include pines, firs, spruces, and junipers, among many other species. Figure F2.23 shows several conifers and related plants.

Almost all conifers are trees or shrubs, and all are at least somewhat woody. Many have leaves that are like needles or scales, such as those in figure F2.24, and most of these plants are evergreen. An evergreen tree or shrub appears green throughout the year because it always maintains most of its leaves. A few leaves die at different times of the year and drop to the ground. Although the number of conifer species is small, the number of individual conifers is enormous.

Figure F2.24 Many conifer leaves are needlelike or scalelike. (*a*) The needles of Douglas fir, *Pseudotsuga menziesii*, are single and needlelike, while the leaves of juniper, *Juniperus chinensis pfitzerii*, (*b*) are scalelike.

Many common conifers are well adapted to life in dry habitats. For example, although pine trees may grow where there is much snow, the snow is really frozen water and is not available for growth. In the spring, much of the snow evaporates, and the melted snow may run off into streams before it soaks into the soil. The leaves of pines are well adapted for growth in dry places. The long, narrow needles reduce the amount of water lost by evaporation. In addition, a pine needle often is covered by a thick, waxy cuticle that further reduces water loss.

Conifers reproduce by seeds that are attached to the upper surface of cone scales. A seed developing in a cone may be protected by the scales. If two scales are separated slightly, you can see the seed between them, as shown in figure F2.25. Thus, the seeds in cones are not completely covered as they are in the fruits of flowering plants.

Conifer spores are of two types and are produced in different cones, illustrated in figure F2.26. Typically, pollen develops from spores in the

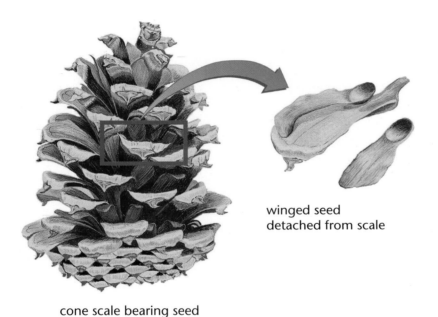

winged seed
detached from scale

cone scale bearing seed
on its upper surface

Figure F2.25 The winged seed of this pine tree is tucked inside the scales of the pinecone.

Figure F2.26 These photographs show the difference between the male cone (*a*) and the female cone (*b*) of the piñon pine, *Pinus edulis*.

Table F2.1
Seed Development in a Pine.

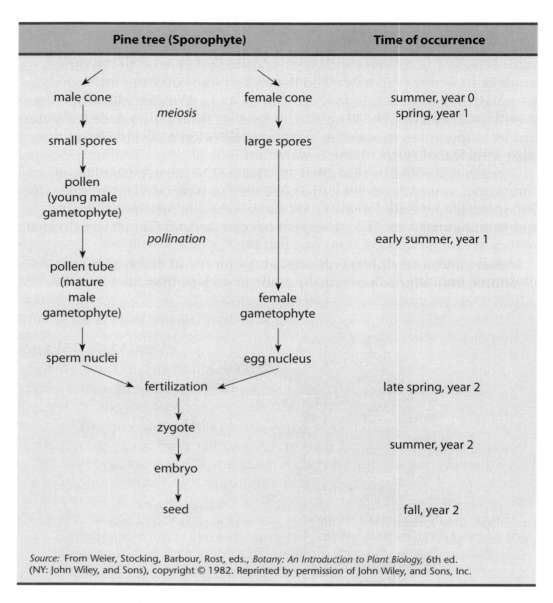

Pine tree (Sporophyte)		Time of occurrence
male cone	female cone	summer, year 0
meiosis		spring, year 1
small spores	large spores	
pollen (young male gametophyte)		
pollination		early summer, year 1
pollen tube (mature male gametophyte)	female gametophyte	
sperm nuclei	egg nucleus	
fertilization		late spring, year 2
zygote		
embryo		summer, year 2
seed		fall, year 2

Source: From Weier, Stocking, Barbour, Rost, eds., *Botany: An Introduction to Plant Biology,* 6th ed. (NY: John Wiley, and Sons), copyright © 1982. Reprinted by permission of John Wiley, and Sons, Inc.

small male cone, and pollination occurs in the spring when the pollen is blown onto a female cone. The larger, more familiar female cones contain the ovules. Pollen grains, the male gametophytes, lodge in a sticky substance secreted by the ovule. Once lodged, the grains develop pollen tubes within which the sperm are formed. Within the ovule, the female gametophytes develop and produce eggs. Fertilization occurs approximately a year after pollination, and the seed requires an additional year to mature. Table F2.1 summarizes these events.

Many Flowering Plants Have Special Pollinators

Flowers are the distinguishing feature of the most successful division in the plant kingdom, the *Anthophyta*. Although we commonly appreciate flowers for their beauty, their major role is in reproduction. When a flower opens, it reveals the reproductive structures, the stamens and carpels. Insects, birds, bats, or other animals that visit the flower may pick up pollen from the anther and carry it to the next flower they visit. When

Figure F2.27 Here are a few colorful examples of the diversity of flowers. (*a*) Indian paintbrush; (*b*) water lily; (*c*) elephantheads; and (*d*) bougainvillea.

pollen is transferred from a flower of one plant to a flower of another in the same species, the process is called cross-pollination. The main pollinators of flowers are insects. Pollen also may be transported from flower to flower by wind. In some plants, the pollen falls on the stigma of the same flower. These flowers are self-pollinating. Many plants, however, have evolved devices that prevent self-pollination.

The sepals and petals are not directly involved in seed formation, so a flower can function without them. In fact, in a few plants a flower may consist of only a single stamen or a single carpel. Petals and their adaptations, however, usually play a major role in flower pollination. Much of the diversity among flowering plant species lies in their flowers (see figure F2.27). This diversity usually is related to the way pollination occurs. If pollen is transferred from stamen to carpel by insects, the petals of the flower often are large and brightly colored, as in figure F2.28a, and often have small glands that produce a sugar solution called **nectar**. These adaptations attract pollinating insects. On the other hand, flowers in which

Figure F2.28 Insect-pollinated flowers such as the aster in (*a*) usually are brightly colored. Windpollinated flowers often lack petals and sepals and produce an abundance of pollen. Shown in (*b*) is the male catkin of a willow, *Salix*; note the many stamens.

pollen is transferred by wind usually have small sepals and petals, or none at all. These flowers often are located high on the plant, where they are accessible to wind currents and produce an abundance of pollen (figure F2.28b). Their carpels commonly have large, long, or feathery structures at the tips, which are covered with a sticky fluid. These adaptations increase the likelihood that some pollen will stick to the carpels.

The great variety of flowers has come about, in part, by the coevolution of flowers and pollination agents. For example, hummingbirds have evolved with plants that produce large quantities of nectar. Research has shown that while hummingbirds do not have a good sense of smell, they can see the color red very well. Flowers pollinated by hummingbirds usually are well adapted to their pollinators, as you see in figure F2.29. The columbine flowers shown in the illustration are red, have little or no scent, and produce copious amounts of nectar. The nectar is found at the bottom of a long tube formed by the red petals, a shape that makes it difficult for other organisms to rob the flower of nectar.

Hummingbirds, however, have long beaks that can probe the flower and reach the nectar. The stamens stick out in such a position that the hummingbird's head is dusted with pollen when it visits these flowers. When the hummingbird flies to another flower of the same species, the tip of the carpel is in a perfect position to have pollen from the hummingbird's head scraped onto it. Thus, the flower is pollinated while the hummingbird drinks nectar. Interactions of this type, in which both organisms become uniquely adapted to each other, have helped shape the way flowering plants have evolved.

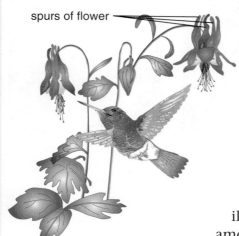

spurs of flower

Figure F2.29 The columbine and hummingbird are uniquely adapted to each other.

Flowering Plants Produce Fruits with Seeds

After pollination and fertilization, seeds begin to develop. The carpel (or carpels in a compound ovary), often with other parts of the flower, develops into a protective fruit around the seed, as shown in figure F2.30. There may be many seeds in a fruit. Each seed began its development when an egg cell in one ovule was fertilized by a sperm from one pollen grain. In flowering plants, then, an embryo is protected within a seed, and seeds are protected within a fruit.

Part of the embryo in the seed consists of one or two modified leaves called **cotyledons**. Another part is a beginning of a root. Each seed also contains a supply of food that is used when the embryo starts to grow. The food may be stored in the endosperm, or it may be stored in the embryo itself, usually in the cotyledon (look back at figure F2.13). Beans and peas are examples of seeds. They

Figure F2.30 These stages occur as tomato fruit develops from flowers.

are enclosed in protective pods, which are just one of many types of fruits. Each bean or pea contains a small embryo and a supply of stored food for its early development. The entire bean or pea can act as food for humans. Beans and peas can be germinated easily, and each embryo gives rise to a plant that, in turn, gives rise to new flowers and fruits. Apples and oranges are examples of fruit that contain a number of seeds. Under natural conditions, these fruits eventually decay, or are eaten by animals leaving their seeds behind to germinate and give rise to the next generation.

Fruits show as much diversity as flowers, as indicated in figure F2.31. This diversity is related to the method of dispersal of the fruits and their seeds, that is, how they are scattered from the parent plant. In Investigation F2.3, *Fruits and Seeds*, you will observe some of the structures that aid in seed dispersal. In many cases, part of the carpel becomes thick and fleshy, as in the fruits of the peach, plum, and tomato. Fleshy fruits, often red in color, may be eaten by birds or mammals. The seeds in many such fruits have thick coats that permit the seeds to pass through an animal's digestive system unharmed. The seeds are dropped later at some distance from the parent plant. Many fruits are not fleshy but have other adaptations that aid in scattering their seeds. These fruits may have spines that catch on the fur of an animal that brushes up against the plant. The fruit is carried from the plant and later falls off or is brushed off by the animal. Many fruits and seeds are lightweight and have special winglike projections that help them to be carried away from the plant by wind. An entire plant, such as the tumbleweed, can be broken off near the ground and blown about by the wind. As the tumbleweed bounces about, it drops its fruits (and the seeds within) all along its path.

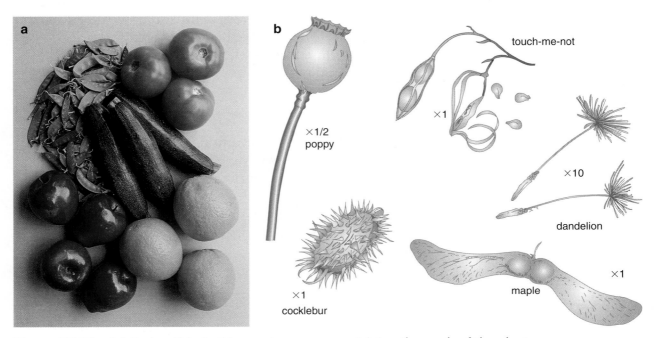

Figure F2.31 (*a*) Each edible fruit is a mature ovary containing the seeds of the plant. (*b*) Many fruits have structural adaptations for seed dispersal. Can you describe them?

Flowering Plants Are the Most Diverse Group of Land Plants

There is great diversity in the size of flowering plants and in the life span of their shoots—the parts that appear above the ground. Many flowering plants are trees. A tree bears leaves well above the ground where they are likely to receive more light than do the leaves of shorter plants. Because of their size, trees can store large reserves of food in trunks and roots and can survive through bad years. Trees have relatively long life spans. A tree species may survive even if a year's seed crop is destroyed. Most species of flowering plants are not trees, however. Some, such as roses and raspberries, are woody shrubs. Others, such as ivy, grapes, and hundreds of tropical species, are woody vines that grow on rocks, walls, or other plants. Most, however, are neither trees, shrubs, nor vines. Instead, they are nonwoody, or **herbaceous**, plants such as those in figure F2.32.

Flowering plants are divided into two large classes—the **monocots** and the **dicots**. In monocots (monocotyledons), the embryo contains a single cotyledon. The monocots include grasses and grain-producing plants such as wheat, rice, and corn—the chief food plants of the world. The pasture grasses that feed cattle, another source of human food, are also monocots. Evidence suggests that the human population could not have evolved to its present state without monocots.

The seeds of the dicots (dicotyledons) have two seed leaves. This class is larger than the monocot class. Most fruits and vegetables, such as carrots, lettuce, apples, and grapes, are dicots. In addition, the so-called hardwoods used in furniture, flooring, hockey sticks, and baseball bats come from dicot trees. Almost all shade trees are dicots, also. Figure F2.33 illustrates the major differences between monocots and dicots.

Figure F2.32
Herbaceous plants include marigolds, common garden flowers.

Analysis

1. How are conifers adapted to dry conditions?
2. How do conifers differ from flowering plants?
3. What role does flower color play in the reproduction of flowering plants?
4. How are fruits related to seed dispersal?
5. In what ways do monocots and dicots differ?

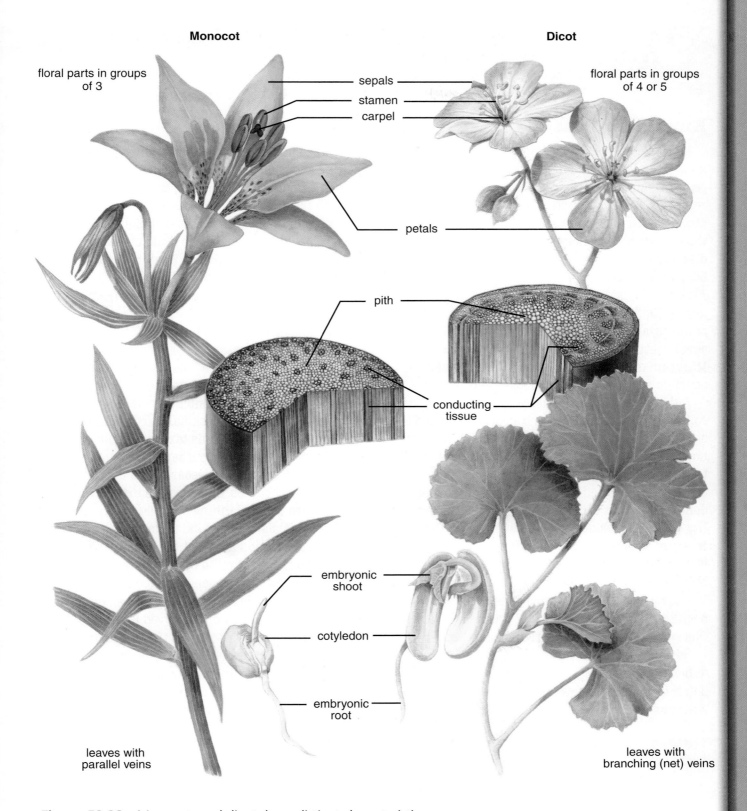

Monocot

floral parts in groups of 3

Dicot

floral parts in groups of 4 or 5

sepals

stamen

carpel

petals

pith

conducting tissue

embryonic shoot

cotyledon

embryonic root

leaves with parallel veins

leaves with branching (net) veins

Figure F2.33   Monocots and dicots have distinct characteristics.

Biological Illustrator

Marjorie Leggit is a freelance biological illustrator. Biological illustrators illustrate reports, journal articles, and books prepared by researchers. Many illustrators work in natural history museums, painting and constructing the background scenery for different types of displays. These artists may recreate Alaskan ice floes to show off a group of polar bears or a South American hillside for a display of llamas. Marjorie's family is composed of writers, sculptors, painters, and woodcarvers, so an interest in art comes naturally to her. Her interest in science, Marj thinks, may have developed because she could do so much drawing in science classes.

Although a biological illustration course in college sparked her interest, Marjorie continued to study fine arts. After studying for a year in Europe, however, she realized she missed science and the technical art that goes with it. She returned to college and designed her own program of independent studies that led to a degree in scientific art. Her program included an internship at the Denver Museum of Natural History in Denver, Colorado. While searching for a full-time job after graduation, Marj illustrated a professor's botanical field guide. Her persistence was rewarded eventually with a position at the Field Museum of Natural History in Chicago, Illinois. Marj later returned to Denver.

Reestablishing her career there proved to be difficult because opportunities for biological illustration were far fewer than in very large cities where more research is conducted. For seven years, she worked at art-related jobs, including geological drafting and computer-aided graphics. Although she learned a whole new field of art, Marj was not satisfied with the direction of her career.

To keep in touch with the field of biological illustration, she contacted the Guild of Natural Science Illustrators (GNSI) in Washington, DC. Knowing Colorado had nothing similar, she founded the Colorado Chapter of GNSI and made friends with a group of local illustrators.

In 1986, Marj went into business for herself as a biological illustrator and graphic artist. She contacted old and new local clients as well as publishers throughout the country. She spent many hours researching the possibilities for assignments and marketing her skills. Marj did many of the illustrations used in this textbook, including figure F2.33. To ensure accuracy in her work, Marj does a great deal of research and uses many references and photos. She consults extensively with authors when planning an illustration. It is essential that she understand the author's intent, what the illustration is meant to portray, and how it relates to the text and to other illustrations. Proper interpretation depends on good communication between author and artist. Marj strongly believes that the hard work involved in creating illustrations has its rewards. At times, the hours are long, the deadlines close to impossible, and the challenges seemingly insurmountable. However, she is doing exactly what she wants to be doing: full-time biological illustration.

Summary

Plants share common ancestry with multicellular algae. A multicellular organism has many advantages over a single cell, including size, division of labor, and ability to conserve water. Other adaptations that permit plants to absorb and hold water are roots, vascular tissue, and the cuticle. All plants have a life cycle that alternates between two different generations, a gametophyte and a sporophyte. In flowering plants, however, the egg cell (the gametophyte that produces the egg), and the spore that produces the gametophyte all remain protected in the flower. Mosses are nonvascular plants that lack roots, stems, and leaves. They possess some adaptations to life on land, but they still require a moist environment. Club mosses, horsetails, and ferns are seedless vascular plants, and many of their ancestors produced today's fossil fuels. Conifers and flowering plants are seed-producing vascular plants, but flowering plants have a fruit that encloses their seeds. The great diversity of flowers and fruits is the result of the coevolution of plants and their agents of pollination or dispersal.

Applications

1. Which organisms in this appendix would you consider to be less complex? Which would you consider to be more complex? Explain your answer.
2. Why are nonvascular plants short?
3. The fossil record reveals that the diversity of flowering plants and the diversity of certain insect groups increased at the same time. How might you explain this?
4. Explain the following statement: The plant parts that furnish the greatest amount of human food are either seeds, roots, or underground stems.

Problems

1. Desert plants are land plants adapted to extremely dry conditions. What adaptations allow these plants to live with little water? Make a collection of desert plants or find out about them from a plant ecology text.
2. Fruits come in many sizes and shapes and with diverse appendages. Collect different fruits and try to identify their plants. Identify the methods of dispersal for the different fruits and their seeds.
3. Bring to the classroom different pieces of furniture, tools, sculptures, or other objects made from wood. What qualities of the wood make it useful for each object? Can you identify which tree provided the wood? Are some woods better than others for certain tasks?
4. Throughout history, plants have played religious and cultural roles in different societies. Many of these roles have been captured in paintings, sculptures, and tapestries. Find artwork that contains a plant or plants as an important part of the composition. What does the plant signify?

Investigation F2.1

Increasingly Complex Characteristics

Biologists sometimes use pairs of terms such as "less complex" and "more complex" when discussing diversity among organisms. A species that has changed little from its ancestors is said to be less complex than organisms that differ greatly from their ancestors. Conversely, a species that has few of the characteristics of its ancestors is said to be more complex. After studying many types of evidence in the fossil record and in living organisms, scientists have reached fairly general agreement about which characteristics have been in existence for a long time and which are more recent. Table F2.3 in step 2 of the investigation is based on such studies. Because there may be many degrees of complexity, the terms "less complex" and "more complex" are not absolute, but they are useful for making the types of comparisons you will make in this investigation, *Increasingly Complex Characteristics*.

Materials (per team of 6)

stereomicroscope or 10× hand lens
10 labeled specimens of organisms of various kingdoms and divisions
microscope slides
compound microscope
coverslips
pens

PROCESS AND PROCEDURES

1. In your science notebook, draw a table similar to table F2.2, with enough lines for all 10 specimens.

Name of organism	Numerical values of choices made	Total complexity score	Rank
1.			
2.			
etc.			

Table F2.2

2. Determine the complexity score for each of the labeled specimens. More-complex organisms such as plants are represented at each station, as well as some less-complex organisms from other kingdoms. Start at the left of table F2.3. Arrows from the starting point lead to 2 descriptions. Choose the one that fits the organism you are scoring.

Key for determining the complexity score for an organism

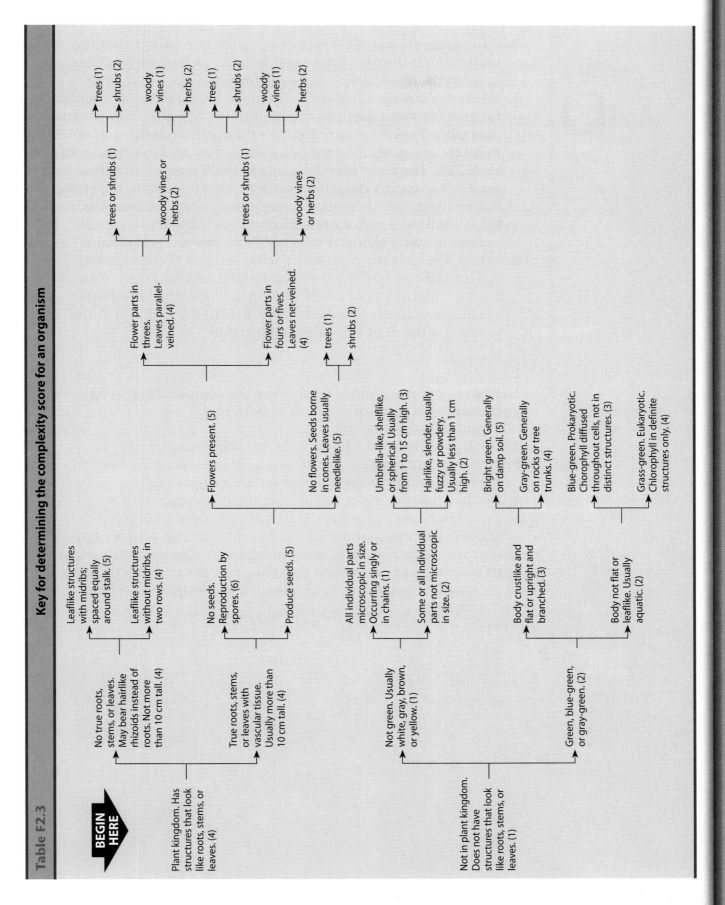

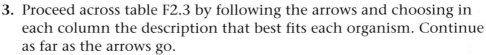

3. Proceed across table F2.3 by following the arrows and choosing in each column the description that best fits each organism. Continue as far as the arrows go.

4. With each description there is a number. As you proceed, record the numbers of your chosen descriptions in the second column of your data table. The complexity score for the organism is the sum of all the numbers appearing after the descriptions you used in working through table F2.3. The more alike 2 organisms are, the more alike their scores will be. The greater the difference between 2 organisms, the greater will be the difference in their scores. More-complex organisms, such as plants, will have high scores (maximum 26), and less-complex organisms, such as prokaryotes, will have low scores (minimum 3).

5. When you have the complexity score for each of the organisms, give the organism with the lowest score a rank of 1 and the organism with the highest score a rank of 10. Then rank the rest of the organisms according to their scores. Record the rankings in the column at the right side of your data table.

Analysis

1. Basing your conclusions on the way the complexity score key was designed, list some of the most important differences among the organisms you observed.

2. What are some of the less important differences?

3. Using the information in table F2.3, list the characteristics you would expect to find in one of the less-complex organisms.

4. Do the same for one of the more-complex plants.

5. Evidence exists that today's land plants evolved from water-dwelling ancestors. Plants that live on land are in constant danger of drying out. Suggest how each of the following characteristics found in a more-complex plant would help the plant live on land: (1) roots; (2) stems that contain vascular tissues; (3) seeds; and (4) flowers.

Investigation F2.2

Reproductive Structures and Life Cycles

Although their reproductive organs differ, as do the environments in which they live and reproduce, the basic principles of sexual reproduction are the same in a moss, a flower, a bee, and a human. In this investigation, *Reproductive Structures and Life Cycles,* you will learn how the structures of a moss and a flower serve reproductive functions in their respective environments.

Mosses form mats on logs and on the forest floor, growing best in damp, shaded environments. Sporophytes grow out of the tops of the gametophytes and often look like hairs growing out of the mat of moss. Mosses cannot reproduce sexually unless they are wet. Flowering plants, on the other hand, are found in many different environments and climates. They need water to live but not to reproduce.

Materials (per team of 2)

compound microscope
stereomicroscope or 10× hand lens
3 microscope slides
3 coverslips
dissecting needle
scalpel
forceps
15% sucrose solution
moss plant with sporophyte
prepared slide of filamentous stage of moss
fresh moss
prepared slide of moss male and female reproductive organs
gladiolus flower
fresh bean or pea pod
other simple flowers for comparison
modeling clay
water in a dropping bottle
petri dish with moistened cotton
pens

PROCESS AND PROCEDURES

Part A   Moss

1. Examine a moss plant with sporophyte attached. The sporophyte consists of a smooth stalk terminated by a little capsule. Separate the 2 generations by pulling the sporophyte stalk out of the leafy shoot of the gametophyte.

2. Using a dissecting needle, break open the capsule of the sporophyte into a drop of water on a slide.

CAUTION: Needles are sharp; handle with care.

3. Add a coverslip and examine under the low power of a compound microscope. What structures do you observe? How are these structures dispersed? How are they adapted for life on land?

4. Most moss spores germinate on damp soil and produce a filamentous stage that looks like a branching green alga. Examine a prepared slide of this stage.

5. The filamentous stage gives rise to the leafy shoot of the gametophyte. Using forceps, carefully remove a leafy shoot from the fresh moss. How does this shoot obtain water and nutrients for growth?

6. The reproductive organs of the gametophyte are at the upper end of the leafy shoot. Examine a prepared slide of these organs under the low power of a compound microscope. The male sex organs are saclike structures that produce large numbers of sperm cells. The female sex organs are flask-shaped and have long, twisted necks. An egg is formed within the base of the female organ. How does a sperm reach the egg? Would you expect to find moss plants growing where there was little or no water? Explain. The union of the egg and sperm results in a cell called the zygote. Where is the zygote formed? What grows from the zygote?

Part B   Flowers

1. Examine the outside parts of a gladiolus flower. The outermost whorl of floral parts may be green and leaflike. These green sepals protected the flower bud when it was young. In some flowers, such as lilies, the sepals look like an outer whorl of petals. Petals are usually large and colored and lie just inside the sepals. Both sepals and petals are attached to the enlarged end of a branch. These parts of the flower are not directly involved in sexual reproduction. What functions might petals have?

2. Strip away the sepals and petals to examine the reproductive structures. Around a central stalklike body are 5–10 delicate stalks, each ending in a small sac, or anther. Together, the stalks and the anthers form the male reproductive organs, or stamens. Thousands of pollen grains are produced in the anther. The number of stamens varies according to the type of flower. How many stamens are present in the flower you are using? How is pollen carried from the anthers to the female part of the flower?

3. If the anthers are mature, shake some of the pollen into a drop of 15% sucrose solution on a clean slide. Add a coverslip and examine with the low power of a compound microscope. What is the appearance of the pollen? How is the pollen adapted for dispersal?

4. Make another pollen preparation on a clean coverslip. Use modeling clay to make a 5-mm-high chamber, slightly smaller than the coverslip, on a clean slide. Add a small drop of water to the chamber

and invert the pollen preparation over it. Examine after 15 minutes and again at the end of the lab period. What, if any, changes have occurred? (If no changes have occurred, store the slide in a covered petri dish containing a piece of cotton moistened with water, and examine it the next day.)

5. The central stalk surrounded by the stamens is the female reproductive organ, or carpel. It is composed of an enlarged basal part, the ovary, above which is an elongated part, the style, ending in a stigma. How is the stigma adapted to trap the pollen grains and to provide a place for them to grow?

6. Use a scalpel to cut the ovary lengthwise.

CAUTION: Scalpels are sharp; handle with care.

7. Using a hand lens or stereomicroscope, look at the cut surface. How many ovules can you see? Each ovule contains 1 egg. To what stage of the moss life cycle is the ovule comparable? How close to the egg can the pollen grain get? If the pollen grain cannot get to the egg, how do the sperm produced by the pollen reach it? To what stage of the moss life cycle is a pollen grain comparable?

8. The union of egg and sperm causes extensive changes in the female reproductive parts. Fertilization of the egg stimulates the growth of the ovary and the enclosed ovules. Carefully examine a fresh bean or pea pod. Open the pod to find the seeds. What part of the female reproductive apparatus is the pod of a bean or pea? What is the origin of a seed? If you plant ripe bean or pea seeds and water them, to what will they give rise? What can you conclude develops within a seed as a result of fertilization?

9. If time permits, examine other types of flowers. Compare the numbers of various parts and the ways the parts are arranged with respect to one another.

10. Wash your hands thoroughly before leaving the laboratory.

Analysis

1. In alternation of generations in a moss, which is the predominant, independent generation? Which is the less conspicuous generation?

2. Compare the life cycle of a moss (with alternation of generations) with your life cycle (with no alternation of generations).

3. Would you expect the most variation in flowering plants or in those plants reproducing by asexual means? Explain.

4. Compare and contrast the life cycle of a moss with that of a flowering plant.

5. Do flowering plants represent more or less adaptation to a land environment than mosses? Explain.

Investigation F2.3

Fruits and Seeds

The survival of plants depends on their ability to reproduce. In seed producers, the most-complex plants, reproductive ability is enhanced by mechanisms that protect and disperse the seeds (and fruits) so the seeds do not compete with the parent plants for nutrients, light, and water. Dispersal increases the likelihood that some seeds will not be eaten. In flowering plants, seeds are protected by the tissues of the mature ovary, or fruit. (Conifers, which lack an ovary, produce naked seeds on cone scales.)

In this investigation, *Fruits and Seeds,* you will try to determine how seeds of various fruits are dispersed. You also will use the fruits to make a dichotomous key, which can help you distinguish between objects by focusing on their similarities and differences.

Materials (per team of 3)

set of fruits
pens

PROCESS AND PROCEDURES

Part A   Seed Dispersal

1. Blow gently at the fruits. What happens? Why? What parts of the fruits are important in allowing them to be wind-dispersed?
2. Gently rest the sleeve of your blouse or shirt on the fruits and then lift up your arm. Which fruits are lifted? What parts of these fruits are important in allowing them to be dispersed by animals?
3. Some fruits attract birds and other animals that eat the fruits but do not damage the seeds inside. What characteristics of the fruits might serve as attractants?
4. Some fruits contain a chemical that acts as a laxative. How might this function in seed dispersal? How might the contents of bird droppings assist in the survival of the new seedlings?

Part B   Dichotomous Key

1. Design a dichotomous key using the fruits from part A. Your dichotomous key should separate all the available fruits into individual categories. Assemble the fruits and review the characteristics you observed in part A.
2. To form a dichotomous key, use characteristics that some fruits have and some do not, rather than characteristics that all the fruits share. For example, *fruits with spines* versus *fruits without spines* might be a good characteristic to use in building your key. On the other hand, *fruits that contain seeds* would not be a good characteristic because almost all fruits contain seeds.

3. To divide the fruits into 2 groups, choose 1 major characteristic not shared by all the fruits. Separate your fruits into 2 groups, one group that possesses the characteristic and another group that does not. In your science notebook, prepare a table similar to table F2.3 in Investigation F2.1, *Increasingly Complex Characteristics,* but with the lines only. Write the characteristic on the table as shown below:

fruits with spines

4. Focus on all the fruits in just 1 of your 2 groups. Choose another characteristic that separates those fruits into 2 groups. Write this characteristic in the second column of the key as shown below:

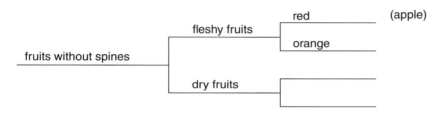

5. Continue to select characteristics and write them on the key until you have produced a key that separates all the fruits into individual categories. In other words, your key should split the fruits into smaller and smaller groups until each fruit is in a group by itself. Once this is done, place the name of the fruit (maple, ash, etc.) next to the appropriate line on the right side of the key.
6. Exchange keys with another team. See if you can follow their key and they can follow yours.
7. Wash your hands thoroughly before leaving the laboratory.

Analysis

1. What are some of the ways seeds/fruits are dispersed?
2. Describe how a dispersal mechanism that relies on the presence of other organisms might develop in a plant species.
3. What would happen to the distribution of plants that produce cockleburs if the plants lived on an island having no animals?
4. Explain how poplar trees might come to inhabit an island in the middle of a large lake.
5. What is the purpose of a dichotomous key?
6. What characteristics did you use to develop your dichotomous key? What characteristics did your class as a whole use?
7. Could you develop a dichotomous key for organisms that looked identical to one another? Explain.

APPENDIX F3

The Body's Organization

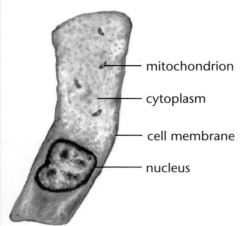

Figure F3.1
Epithelial cell. This epithelial cell contains all of the parts of a typical eukaryotic cell.

labels: mitochondrion, cytoplasm, cell membrane, nucleus

We can think of the entire body as a large compartment that is physically separate from the outside environment. But your body also contains smaller compartments, with still smaller compartments inside of them. Let's examine the body's organization by looking at the structure of some of these compartments. We begin by considering the structure and significance of one of the body's smallest compartments—the cell.

The **cell** is the basic unit of structure and function in living things (figure F3.1). All organisms are made of one or more cells. The exterior border of the cell is the **cell membrane**, a structure that separates the inside of the cell from the outside. The basic material within the cell is called **cytoplasm**, which consists of a complex mixture of water, salts, proteins, and other substances.

Suspended in the cytoplasm are numerous smaller compartments called **organelles**. Different types of organelles perform different functions in the cell. Chief among these is the **nucleus**, which contains the information required to operate the cell. Other important organelles include **mitochondria**, which provide most of the energy that powers activities within the cell.

The human body contains several hundred different types of cells, such as muscle cells, nerve cells, liver cells, and blood cells. Different types of cells have different structures and functions.

A **tissue** is a group of similar cells that are organized together and perform a specific function. The human body contains four types of tissues (figure F3.2). The cell in figure F3.1 is from epithelial tissue; the other three types are connective tissue, nerve tissue, and muscle tissue.

An **organ** is a group of tissues that are organized together to form a structural and functional unit. Every organ contains all four types of body tissue (figure F3.3). Examples of organs include the heart, the kidney, and the stomach.

The tissues of an organ work together, bringing about the organ's function. For example, the stretching that occurs when food enters the stomach activates nerve tissue. The nerve tissue, in turn, stimulates epithelial tissue cells, which then secrete digestive substances that help break down the food. Contractions of muscle tissue cells mix food with digestive substances and move it into the next organ in the system. The connective tissue provides an elastic and supportive framework that holds all of the tissues together.

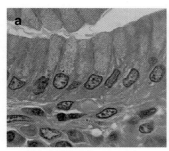

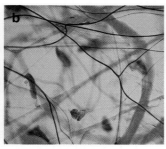

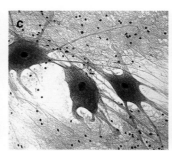

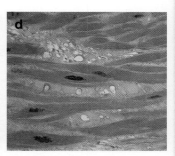

Epithelial tissue covers external and internal body surfaces. Examples of epithelial tissue include the skin and the linings of the digestive tract. Epithelial tissues protect the body's surfaces and produce secretions such as sweat and mucus.

Connective tissue binds, supports, and protects body structure. Connective tissue cells secrete nonliving material that forms a matrix. The matrix may be liquid (as in blood) or solid (as in bone and cartilage).

Nerve tissue is made up of nerve cells, or neurons, which are specialized to transmit nerve impulses (essentially information in the form of electrical signals) from one part of the body to another. The brain and spinal cord are made of nerve tissue.

Muscle tissue consists of cells that are able to contract in response to stimulation. Muscle tissue gives shape and support to the body and produces heat by shivering. It also helps move the whole body, as well as its individual parts.

Figure F3.2   Tissue types. The human body contains four types of tissues: (*a*) epithelial tissue, (*b*) connective tissue, (*c*) nerve tissue, and (*d*) muscle tissue. The structures of different cells support the function of the tissues they are a part of.

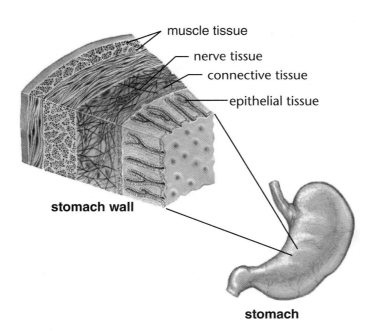

muscle tissue
nerve tissue
connective tissue
epithelial tissue

stomach wall

stomach

Figure F3.3   Organ. An organ such as the stomach functions as a result of all four types of body tissue working together and organized in a specific way.

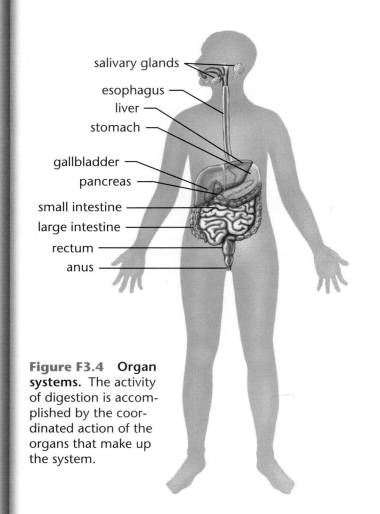

salivary glands
esophagus
liver
stomach
gallbladder
pancreas
small intestine
large intestine
rectum
anus

Figure F3.4 Organ systems. The activity of digestion is accomplished by the coordinated action of the organs that make up the system.

Groups of organs form **organ systems** that carry out major body activities such as circulation, gas exchange, and digestion. These activities are accomplished by the coordinated action of the organs that make up the system. The digestive system, for example, breaks down food into small molecules (figure F3.4). This breakdown begins with mechanical and chemical processes in the mouth and continues with further chemical processes in the stomach and small intestine. Several organs in the digestive system contribute the chemicals needed for digestion. The nutrients that result are absorbed from the small intestine into the blood and transported by the circulatory system to all cells of the body.

Thinking about the structure of the body in this way should help you see that the function of a whole organism is the result of the coordinated action and interaction of all of its parts. For example, the function of a cell results from the coordinated action of its organelles, the function of a tissue results from the coordinated action of the cells that make it up, and so on. Thus, the function of the body results from the action and interaction of all of its parts.

GLOSSARY

A

abiotic [abiótico]: Nonliving. In ecosystems, this is used to refer to nonliving components such as sunlight, wind, nutrients, and minerals.

acrosome [acrosoma]: The structure at the tip of a sperm cell, containing enzymes used to dissolve away the jellylike substance surrounding the egg cell.

activation energy [energía de activación]: The smallest amount of energy necessary to allow a chemical reaction to occur.

active transport [transporte activo]: The movement of a substance across a biological membrane against its concentration gradient with the help of energy input and specific transport proteins.

adaptation [adaptación]: In natural selection, a hereditary characteristic of some organisms in a population. The characteristic improves the organisms' chances for survival and reproduction in their environment compared with the chances of other organisms in the population.

adult stem cells [células madre adultas]: Cells derived from adult tissues that, under specific conditions, can differentiate into more than one cell type.

aerobic (eh ROH bik) [adaptación]: Taking place or living in the presence of free or dissolved oxygen.

allele (al LEEL) [alelo]: One of two or more possible forms of a gene. Each affects the hereditary trait somewhat differently.

allergies [alergia]: An overreactive immune response to foreign matter also known as allergens, which can be touched, inhaled, eaten, or injected.

amino acids [aminoácidos]: The molecular building blocks of proteins, which are each composed of an amino group, a carboxyl group, and a side chain. There are 20 different amino acids.

amylase (AM el ase) [amilasa]: A digestive enzyme found in saliva.

anaerobic (an eh ROH bik) [anaeróbico]: Taking place or living in conditions without free oxygen.

analogous structures [estructuras análogas]: Structures that have similar function, but do not derive their similarities from common ancestry. Frequently, analogous structures arise due to convergent evolution.

anaphase [anafase]: A stage in mitosis or meiosis, during which chromosomes move to opposite sides of the dividing cell.

antibody [anticuerpo]: A blood protein produced in response to an antigen, with which it combines specifically. Antibodies block the ability of pathogens or foreign material to injure the body.

antibody-mediated response [respuesta inmune mediada por anticuerpos]: Immune response in which B cells produce antibodies to bind with and mark antigens for destruction by nonspecific defenses; initiated by helper T cells.

antigen (AN tih jen) [antígeno]: Any material, usually a protein, that is recognized as foreign and raises an immune response.

antihistamine (an tih HIST uh meen) [antihistamínico]: A drug found in medicines used to counteract the histamine response.

artery [arteria]: A blood vessel through which blood flows away from the heart.

artifact [artefacto]: Material remains, such as pieces of pottery, tools, and textiles, that are cultural evidence.

artificial selection [selección artificial]: A process whereby humans allow only those variants of a population or species carrying desirable traits to reproduce.

asexual reproduction [reproducción asexual]: Any method of reproduction that requires only one parent or one parent cell. This type of reproduction leads to offspring that are genetically identical to one another.

atom [átomo]: The smallest particle of an element. In turn, an atom is made of smaller particles that do not separately have the properties of the element.

ATP (adenosine triphosphate [uh DEN oh seen try FOS fayt]) [ATP (trifosfato de adenosina)]: A compound that has three phosphate groups and is used by cells to store energy.

autoimmune disease [enfermedad autoinmune]: A response in which antibodies are produced to attack some of the body's own cells.

autosome (AW tow sowm) [autosoma]: A chromosome that is not directly involved in determining sex.

autotroph (AW toh trohf) [autótrofo]: An organism able to make and store food, using sunlight or another nonliving energy source.

axon [axón]: A structure that extends out from a neuron and conducts impulses away from the cell body.

B

B cell [linfocito B]: A type of lymphocyte that develops in the bone marrow and later produces antibodies.

behavioral responses [respuestas conductuales]: Actions taken by an organism in response to some stimulus.

binary fission [fisión binaria]: A type of asexual reproduction where a cell divides into two identical cells. It is the chief means of asexual reproduction in prokaryotic cells.

binomial nomenclature [nomenclatura binomial]: The scientific system of naming organisms, where each species is given a Latin genus and species name.

biodiversity [biodiversidad]: The number and variability of organisms found within a community, ecosystem, or Earth.

biological classification [clasificación biológica]: The scientific system of classifying organisms into nested groups, generally along the lines of their evolutionary relationships.

biomass [biomasa]: The dry weight of organic matter that makes up a group of organisms in a particular habitat.

biosphere (BY oh sfeer) [biosfera]: The outer portion of Earth—air, water, and soil—where life is found.

biosynthesis (by oh SIN thuh sis) [biosíntesis]: The process of putting together or building up the large molecules characteristic of a particular type of cell or tissue.

biotic [biótico]: Living. In ecosystems, biotic components include all living things.

bipedal [bípedo]: Capable of walking erect on the hind limbs, freeing the hands for other uses.

bladder [vejiga]: An organ in the urinary system that collects urine produced by the kidneys. Urine leaves the bladder through the urethra.

blood pressure [presión sanguínea]: The fluid pressure created by heart contractions; allows blood to circulate.

blood type [grupo sanguíneo]: A class of inherited traits that describe a set of proteins or antigens on the outside of blood cells. Different blood types are frequently not immunologically compatible. Also known as blood group.

body temperature [temperatura corporal]: The internal temperature of an animal's body; for humans, this is typically 37°C (98.6°F).

brain stem [tronco encefálico]: A portion of the base of the brain that controls many involuntary body functions such as breathing and heart rate and some reflexes.

breathing rate [frecuencia respiratoria]: The number of times a terrestrial animal inhales and exhales per minute.

budding [gemación]: A type of asexual reproduction where new individuals begin as outgrowths on the body of a single parent. The offspring eventually separates from the parent and becomes independent. Offspring are genetically identical to the parent.

buffer [tampón]: A solution of weak acids and bases that resists changes in its pH level when an acid or base is added to it.

C

calorie [caloría]: The amount of heat required to raise the temperature of one gram of water 1°C.

calorimeter [calorímetro]: A scientific device used to measure heat.

cancer [cáncer]: Malignancy arising from cells that are characterized by profound abnormalities in the plasma membrane and in the cytosol, and by abnormal growth and division.

capillary [capilar]: A small blood vessel found between the end of an artery and the beginning of a vein. Capillaries are the sites of much gas and nutrient exchange in the human body.

carbohydrates [carbohidratos]: A group of organic compounds composed of carbon, oxygen, and hydrogen that form major portions of plants and are important food sources for all living things.

carbon [carbono]: A element found in all organic molecules that frequently forms bonds with hydrogen and oxygen, having an atomic weight of 12.011 and the atomic number 6.

carbon cycle [ciclo del carbono]: The chemical cycle in which carbon compounds made by some organisms (such as plants) are digested and decomposed by others. The carbon is released in small inorganic molecules that can be used again by more organisms to synthesize carbon compounds.

carbon fixation [fijación del carbono]: Incorporating atmospheric carbon into carbohydrates through photosynthesis.

carrier [portador]: A person who has one typical and one affected allele for a recessive disorder. These people do not show symptoms of the disorder, but can pass it to their offspring.

carrying capacity [capacidad de carga]: The maximum population size that can be supported by the available resources of a given area.

cell culture [cultivo celular]: The process of maintaining and growing cells outside an organism's body, usually supported by a substrate, dissolved gases, and nutrients in liquid form.

cell cycle [ciclo celular]: An ordered sequence of events in the life of a dividing cell, composed of the M, G_1, S, and G_2 phases.

cell differentiation [diferenciación celular]: The process by which embryonic cells develop specialized structures and functions.

cell division [división celular]: The process by which the genetic material and cytoplasm of a cell are divided between daughter cells. Meiosis and mitosis are two types of cell division.

cell-mediated response [respuesta inmune mediada por células]: Immune response in which highly specialized lymphocytes circulate in the blood and lymphoid organs and attack and destroy cells that carry specific surface antigens.

cellular respiration [respiración celular]: The series of chemical reactions by which a living cell breaks down food molecules and obtains energy from them.

cell wall [pared celular]: A nonliving covering around the plasma membrane of certain cells, as in plants, many algae, and some prokaryotes. In plants, the cell wall is constructed of cellulose and other materials.

cerebellum [cerebelo]: A structure of the brain that is important for coordination and motor control, as well as attention and the processing of language and music. It is located at the base of the brain and is characterized by a pattern of small folds.

cerebrum [cerebro]: The largest portion of the brain, which controls voluntary thought and action. It is made of a left and right hemisphere and is characterized by large folds.

cervix [cuello uterino]: The narrow, lower portion of the uterus, which connects the uterus to the vagina.

chemical bond [enlace químico]: The attraction between two atoms that results from the sharing or transfer of outer electrons from one atom to another.

chemical digestion [digestión química]: The breakdown of food molecules in the body with the help of chemical and enzymatic secretions, such as stomach acid.

chlorophyll (KLOR uh fil) [clorofila]: The green pigments of plants and many microorganisms; converts light energy (via changes involving electrons) to chemical energy that is used in biological reactions.

chloroplast (KLOR oh plast) [cloroplasto]: An organelle found only in plants and photosynthetic protists; contains chlorophyll, which absorbs the light energy used to drive photosynthesis.

chromatography (KROM uh toh gra fee) [cromatografía]: Various techniques that scientists can use to separate mixtures of molecules based on their mass, charge, or ability to bind to other molecules.

chromosome (KROH moh sohm) [cromosoma]: A long, threadlike group of genes found in the nucleus of all eukaryotic cells and most visible during mitosis and meiosis; chromosomes consist of DNA and protein.

circulatory system [sistema circulatorio]: An organ system consisting of a muscular pump (heart), blood vessels, and blood; the means by which materials are transported to and from cells. In many animals, it also helps stabilize body temperature and pH.

clade [clado]: A group or lineage of organisms that shares a single common ancestor.

class [clase]: The fourth most inclusive grouping, after domain, kingdom, and phylum or division, in the biological classification system.

classification [clasificación]: An organizing process that focuses on the characteristics that different living systems share by virtue of their common ancestry. This places the millions of different types of life into large categories of similar organisms.

climate [clima]: The prevailing weather conditions of a region, including temperature and precipitation, averaged over many years.

clitoris (KLI tor iss) [clítoris]: An external reproductive organ of the female situated at the front of the vulva. It is homologous to the male penis.

clone [clon]: A cell or organism that is genetically identical to the parent organism from which it was made.

cloning [clonación]: A type of asexual reproduction that produces genetically identical individuals from a single cell or set of cells. This type of reproduction is used in prokaryotes and plants.

closed system [sistema cerrado]: A region or area that is isolated; no matter or energy moves into or out of it.

codon (KO don) [codón]: The basic unit of the genetic code made up of a sequence of three adjacent nucleotides on one strand of DNA or mRNA.

cognition [cognición]: Acts or processes related to perceiving, knowing, or learning.

cognitive growth [crecimiento cognitivo]: An individual's development of knowledge and the ability to learn.

community [comunidad]: All the organisms that inhabit a particular area.

competition [competencia]: Interaction between members of the same population or of two or more populations to obtain a mutually required resource in limited supply.

complementary base pairing [apareamiento de bases complementarias]: Predictable interactions between nitrogen bases on opposite strands of DNA and between DNA and RNA; consists of adenine-thymine and guanine-cytosine (adenine-uracil in RNA) base pairing.

components [componentes]: The collection of things that makes up an ecological system, including biotic and abiotic factors.

concentration gradient [gradiente de concentración]: A difference in the concentration of certain molecules over a distance.

conditioning [condicionamiento]: Training that modifies a response so that it becomes associated with a stimulus different from the stimulus that originally caused it.

conservation of energy [conservación de energía]: The principle that energy within a closed system is constant, though it undergoes changes in form.

consumable biomass [biomasa consumible]: The portion of biological matter at a trophic level that is available for consumption by organisms at higher trophic levels.

consumer [consumidor]: A heterotroph; an organism that feeds on other organisms or on their organic wastes.

continental drift [deriva continental]: A hypothesis proposed in 1912 suggesting that Earth's landmasses had at one time been joined in a supercontinent that has broken up to form the present continents. Continental drift is now considered to be part of a broader theory of plate tectonics.

continuous variation [variación continua]: Occurs when the possible phenotypes for a trait occur as a series of intermediates rather than falling into two distinct categories. One example is human height.

contraceptive [anticonceptivo]: A substance or device that can prevent pregnancy.

control [control]: A treatment within a scientific experiment, also known as the experimental control, that features all characteristics of the experiment except the experimentally manipulated variable.

controlled experiment [experimento controlado]: A scientific experiment that is designed so that the influence of the experimental variable can be detected by preventing other conditions from varying across treatments. This design helps to eliminate alternative explanations of the results generated.

corpus callosum (KOR pus KAL o sum) [cuerpo calloso]: A bundle of nerve fibers that connects the right and left hemispheres of the brain.

corpus luteum (KOR pus LOOT ee um) [cuerpo lúteo]: The structure that forms from the tissues of a ruptured ovarian follicle and secretes female hormones.

covalent bond [enlace covalente]: A chemical bond formed by two atoms sharing a pair of electrons.

Cowper's (KAU perz) gland [glándula de Cowper]: Gland in the male reproductive system that produces an alkaline mucus. This mucus is secreted before ejaculation to protect sperm from the acidic vagina.

crossing over [encruzamiento cromosómico]: During prophase I of meiosis, it is the breakage and exchange of corresponding segments of chromosome pairs at one or more sites along their length. This results in genetic recombination.

cultural adaptation [adaptación cultural]: An adaptation to new pressures or situations resulting from cultural innovation.

cultural evolution [evolución cultural]: The change of cultural features over time, which are transmitted not through inherited traits but through social structures and learning. Cultural evolution operates through different processes than biological evolution.

culture [cultura]: A system of learned behaviors, symbols, customs, beliefs, institutions, artifacts, and technology characteristic of a group and transmitted by its members to their offspring.

D

decomposer [descomponedor]: An organism that lives on decaying organic material, from which it obtains energy and its own raw materials for life.

deletion mutation [deleción (o delección)]: Mutation that results when replication enzymes mistakenly skip a base. The new DNA strand forms missing a base.

dendrite [dendrita]: A structure that extends out from a neuron and transmits impulses toward the cell body.

deoxyribonucleic (dee OK sih ry boh noo KLEE ik) acid (DNA) [ácido desoxirribonucleico (ADN)]: The hereditary material of most organisms. DNA makes up the genes and chromsomes. The subunits that make up DNA are nucleotides, which contain the sugar deoxyribose, a triphosphate group, and one of four bases.

development [desarrollo]: Cell division, growth, and differentiation of cells from embryonic layers into all the tissues and organs of the body; later changes with age, including reproductive maturity, with its effects on appearance and body function.

developmental biologist [biólogo del desarrollo]: A scientist who studies the development of organisms.

dialysis tubing [tubo de diálisis]: A tube made of material that allows some substances, such as water, to pass across while preventing substances of a certain molecular size from crossing. This material is used in dialysis treatments for patients with kidney problems because it can be used to filter out toxic materials from the blood that their kidneys are no longer able to process.

diastole (dy AS tuh lee) [diástole]: The stage of the cardiac cycle in which the heart muscle is relaxed, allowing the chamber to fill with blood. (Compare with *systole*.)

diastolic pressure [presión diastólica]: The blood pressure that occurs during diastole; this is the lowest pressure that occurs during a cardiac cycle.

differentiation [diferenciación]: The process by which cells develop specialized structures and functions, also known as cell differentiation.

diffusion [difusión]: The movement of a substance down its concentration gradient from a more concentrated area to a less concentrated area.

digestion [digestión]: Processes that break down food molecules into smaller units.

dihybrid (DI HI brid) cross [cruza dihíbrida]: A genetic cross between individuals differing in two alleles.

diploid (DIH ployd) [diploide]: A cell containing two copies of every chromosome. The copies may not be identical.

discrete variation [variación discreta]: Occurs when the phenotypes for a trait fall into two distinct categories. One example is human sex, where the phenotype may be male or female.

diuretic (di yer RET ik) [diurético]: Any substance or agent that promotes the increased formation and excretion of urine.

division [división]: The third most inclusive grouping, after domain and kingdom, in the biological classification system for plants.

DNA [ADN]: See *deoxyribonucleic acid*.

DNA ligase [ADN ligasa]: Enzyme that functions during the replication and repair of DNA molecules to bond nucleotides together.

domain [dominio]: The most inclusive grouping in the biological classification system.

dominant trait [rasgo dominante]: A trait that is visible in a heterozygous organism.

E

ecology [ecología]: The study of living and nonliving components of the environment and of the interactions that affect biological species.

ecosystem [ecosistema]: A biological community in its abiotic environment.

ectotherms [ectotermos]: Organisms whose body temperature tends to be similar to their surroundings; also known as poikilotherms. These organisms can regulate their temperature behaviorally, but not physiologically.

ejaculation [eyaculación]: Expulsion of semen (sperm-bearing fluid) from the urethra.

electron transport system [cadena de transporte de electrones]: The process in which electrons are transferred from one carrier molecule to another in photosynthesis and in cellular respiration; results in storage of some of the energy in ATP molecules.

electrophoresis (eh LEC tro for EE sis) [electroforesis]: Any of several techniques for separating large molecules, such as proteins or DNA fragments, based on their ability to move through a gel medium subjected to an electric field.

embryo (em BREE o) [embrión]: An organism in its earliest stages of development after ferilization.

embryonic stem cells [células madre embrionarias]: Cells derived from embryonic tissues that have the potential to differentiate into any cell type of an organism's body.

emigration [emigración]: Departure of individuals from a population; decreases the size of the population.

endocrine (EN doh krin) system [sistema endocrino]: The system of glands that secretes their products from their cells directly into the blood.

endoskeleton (EN doh SKEL eh tun) [endoesqueleto]: A hard skeleton buried in the soft tissues of an animal, such as the spicules of sponges and bony skeletons of vertebrates.

endothermic reaction [reacción endotérmica]: A chemical reaction that involves the absorption of heat energy.

endotherms [endotermos]: Organisms capable of generating their own heat to maintain a stable body temperature, primarily through physiological but also through behavioral mechanisms. Also known as homeotherms.

enzyme (EN zime) [enzima]: A protein or part-protein molecule made by an organism and used as a catalyst in a specific biochemical reaction.

epididymis (eh pih DID ih mus) [epidídimo]: A coiled structure along the surface of the testis that provides for the storage, transmission, and maturation of sperm.

essential elements [elementos esenciales]: Elements that are necessary for the growth or maintenance of organisms.

estrogen (ES troh jen) [estrógeno]: A hormone that stimulates the development of female secondary sexual characteristics.

ethical analysis [análisis ético]: A process by which situations related to right and wrong can be examined to facilitate decision making and the development of understanding.

ethical dilemma [dilema ético]: A situation in which a decision related to right and wrong is needed, but which is complicated by other nonethical concerns, such as survival or well-being.

ethologist [etólogo]: Scientist who studies animal behavior.

eukaryote (yoo KAIR ee oht) [eucariota]: An organism whose cells have a membrane-enclosed nucleus and organelles; a protist, fungus, plant, or animal. (Compare with *prokaryote*.)

evidence [evidencia]: Reliable information that can be used to support a conclusion; in science, this information has been generated in accordance with scientific practices and methods.

evolution [evolución]: Changes in the genetic information and the traits encoded by genetic information across generations of a population or species of organisms due to the processes of mutation, selection, or genetic drift.

evolutionary biologist [biólogo evolutivo]: A scientist who studies how organisms change over time and are related to one another through common ancestry.

evolutionary trade-off [compensación evolutiva]: A change in a trait that offers some advantages for an organism's survival or reproductive success, but which is linked to changes in a second trait that results in some disadvantages for survival or reproduction.

evolutionary tree [árbol filogenético]: A branching diagram that illustrates patterns of relationships between a group of living and/or extinct organisms, where common ancestors are indicated at the nodes between branches. These diagrams are generated from data from physical characteristics of living or fossil organisms, such as molecular sequences or body structures.

exoskeleton (EK soh SKEL eh tun) [exoesqueleto]: A hard encasement deposited on the surface of an animal, such as the shell of a mollusk, that provides protection and points of attachment for muscles.

exothermic reaction [reacción exotérmica]: A chemical reaction that is characterized by the release of heat energy.

exponential growth [crecimiento exponencial]: A type of population increase observed when every individual is able to reproduce, characterized by a constant rate of growth and a rapidly increasing population size.

extinction [extinción]: The process by which a population or species dies out, eliminating the genetic material unique to that group.

F

facilitated diffusion [difusión facilitada]: The process by which molecules are transported across membranes with the help of carrier molecules.

family [familia]: The sixth most inclusive grouping after domain, kingdom, phylum or division, class, and order in the biological classification system; a group of related genera.

feedback system [sistema de realimentación]: A relationship in which one activity of an organism affects another, which in turn affects the first, yielding a regulatory balance.

fermentation (fer men TAY shun) [fermentación]: The incomplete breakdown of food molecules, especially sugars, in the absence of oxygen.

fertilization (fer til iz AY shun) [fertilización]: The union of an egg nucleus and a sperm nucleus. The result is one nucleus in a zygote.

fetus [feto]: A vertebrate embryo in later stages of development when it has attained the recognizable structural plan and features of its type.

filtration [filtración]: In vertebrate kidneys, filtration takes place when blood pressure forces the blood into the glomerulus of the nephron where blood cells and plasma proteins are separated from the blood's water, nitrogenous wastes, and ions. Most of the liquid filtrate is reabsorbed, but some wastes are secreted from the body in the urine.

follicle [folículo]: A cluster of cells found in the ovary that contain a single egg. Generally, one follicle grows and develops each month during the menstrual cycle.

follicle-stimulating hormone (FSH) [Hormona foliculoestimulante (FSH)]: A substance secreted by the anterior lobe of the pituitary that stimulates the development of an ovarian follicle in a female or the production of sperm cells in a male.

food [alimento]: A substance containing energy-rich organic compounds made by organisms and used as a source of energy and matter for life.

food web [red alimentaria]: Food chains in an ecosystem taken collectively, showing partial overlapping and competition for many food organisms.

fragmentation [fragmentación]: A type of asexual reproduction. Here, a piece broken from a parent organism grows into a new individual.

G

gamete (GAM eet) [gameto]: A sex cell, either an egg or a sperm, formed by meiosis, having half the number of chromosomes as body cells.

gas exchange system [sistema de intercambio de gases]: A body system that primarily functions to draw in oxygen for use in the energy-releasing processes of cells, and to remove the carbon dioxide by-product of these reactions from the body. In humans and other mammals, the primary organ of this system is the lungs.

gene [gen]: The fundamental physical unit of heredity, which transmits a set of specifications from one generation to the next. A segment of DNA that codes for a specific product.

gene expression [expresión genética]: The process by which genetic information is used to synthesize a functional product, such as an RNA or protein.

gene flow [flujo genético]: Changes in the frequency of alleles or entire genes in a population due to crossbreeding with other populations; the immigration of genetic material into a population.

gene therapy [terapia génica]: The introduction of a gene into a cell to correct a hereditary disorder.

genetic code [código genético]: The "language" of the genes in which the nucleotide sequence of DNA (in codons) specifies the amino acid sequences of proteins.

genetic drift [deriva genética]: Changes in the frequency of alleles in a population due to the chance survival or reproduction of individuals with particular traits. This mechanism of evolution acts independently of natural selection and is particularly important for small populations.

genetic engineering [ingeniería genética]: The experimental technology developed to alter the genome of a living cell for medical or industrial use.

genome [genoma]: The full set of genetic information in an organism.

genotype (JEE noh tipe) [genotipo]: The genetic makeup of an organism.

genus (JEE nus) [género]: A group of related species; the seventh most inclusive grouping after domain, kingdom, phylum or division, class, order, and family in the biological classification system.

geologic time [tiempo geológico]: Time periods related to the formation of Earth and its approximately 4.5-billion-year history.

gestation (je STAY shen) [gestación]: Development period between conception and birth that takes place in the uterus.

glans [glande]: Rounded gland structure at the tip of the penis, covered by the foreskin.

glial (GLEE ul) cells [células gliales]: Protection, support, and insulation for neurons.

glomerulus (glah MER yoo lus) [glomérulo]: A ball of capillaries surrounded by a capsule in the nephron and serving as the site of filtration in the kidneys.

glucose [glucosa]: A common 6-carbon sugar.

glucose test strips [tiras reactivas de glucosa]: Diagnostic materials used to quickly determine the pH of a liquid or semiliquid substance.

glycogen (GLY ko jen) [glucógeno]: The chief carbohydrate used by animals for energy storage.

glycogenesis [glucogénesis]: The process by which glycogen, an energy storage molecule, is formed.

glycolysis (gly KA luh sis) [glucólisis]: The initial breakdown of a carbohydrate, usually glucose, into smaller molecules at the beginning of cellular respiration.

gonads [gónadas]: The gamete-producing organs. These are the testes in males and ovaries in females.

growth [crecimiento]: Increase in size. In development, the successive rounds of cell division that produce a multicellular organism.

growth factors [factores de crecimiento]: Molecules that trigger cell division or the organization or maintenance of tissues. These factors are frequently expressed during the development of an embryo but are also found in specific adult tissues.

H

habitat (HA bih tat) [hábitat]: Place where an organism lives. Even in the same ecosystem, different organisms differ in their habitats.

haploid (HAP loyd) [célula haploide]: A cell containing only one member (n) of each chromosome pair characteristic of a species.

helper T cell [linfocitos T colaboradores]: A type of T cell required by some B cells to make antibodies, by other T cells to respond to antigens, or by other T cells that secrete lymphokines.

hemoglobin (HEE moh gloh bin) [hemoglobina]: The pigment in red blood cells responsible for transporting oxygen.

heritable trait [rasgo heredado]: A feature of an organism that is at least partly determined by genetic material inherited from parents; also known as an inherited trait.

heterotroph (HET er oh trohf) [heterótrofo]: An organism that obtains carbon and all metabolic energy from organic molecules previously assembled by autotrophs; a consumer.

heterozygous (HET er oh ZY gus) [heterocigoto]: Having two different alleles for a given trait.

histamine (HISS tuh meen) [histamina]: A substance released by injured cells that causes blood vessels to dilate during an inflammatory response.

homeostasis (hoh mee oh STAY sis) [homeostasis]: A fundamental characteristic of living systems; maintaining a stable number of individuals within a population (social); the tendency of an organism to maintain a stable, constant internal environment (physiological).

hominid (HOM ih nid) [homínido]: A primate of the family Hominidae, which includes modern humans, earlier subspecies, and australopithecines.

homogenate (ho MAH jeh nate) [homogenato]: A material with uniform consistency.

homologous structures [estructuras homólogas]: Organismal traits, structures, or molecular sequences that share characteristics due to common ancestry, but may not necessarily have the same function.

homozygous (HOH moh ZY gus) [homocigoto]: Having two identical alleles for a given trait.

hormone [hormona]: A substance, secreted by cells or glands, that has a regulatory effect on cells and organs elsewhere in the body; a chemical messenger.

hyperthermia (HI pur THUR mee AH) [hipertermia]: An abnormally elevated body temperature; fever.

hypertonic (HI pur TAHN ik) [hipertónico]: A solution where the concentration of solutes outside a cell is greater than the concentration inside.

hypothalamus (HI po THAL uh muss) [hipotálamo]: A part of the brain. In humans, it links the nervous system to the endocrine system. (The endocrine system controls the hormones that regulate many body functions.)

hypothermia (HI po THIR mee ah) [hipotermia]: An abnormally lowered body temperature.

hypothesis (hy PA thih sis) [hipótesis]: A statement that suggests an explanation for an observation or an answer to a scientific problem.

hypotonic (HI po TAHN ik) [hipotónico]: A solution where the concentration of solutes outside the cell is less than the concentration inside.

I

immigration (im ih GRAY shun) [inmigración]: Arrival of new individuals into a population; increases the size of a population.

immunity [inmunidad]: Disease-resistance, usually specific for one disease or pathogen.

impermeable (im PUR mee uh bul) [impermeable]: Not permeable; not possible to pass through.

incomplete dominance [dominancia incompleta]: Pattern of gene expression in which the phenotype of a heterozygous individual is intermediate between those of the parents.

independent assortment [surtido independiente]: Independent inheritance of the alleles for a trait.

indicator [indicador]: A chemical that has a variable physical property, such as color, depending on the materials with which it interacts.

induction [inducción]: A developmental process by which one part of an embryo (or a molecule generated in one embryonic region) influences the differentiation of another embryonic region.

inductive reasoning [razonamiento inductivo]: The process of developing a generalization or general principles from detailed facts.

inference [inferencia]: Conclusions that follow logically from some form of direct evidence.

inherit [heredar]: To receive from genetic material.

innate behavior [comportamiento innato]: Actions that organisms take that are not learned, such as instincts. These tend to be governed by inherited traits of the nervous system.

insertion mutation [mutación por inserción]: A change in a DNA sequence involving adding a new nucleotide or sequence of nucleotides.

interphase [interfase]: The phase of the cell cycle in which division is not occurring.

in vitro (in VEE tro) [in vitro]: Literally means "in glass"; refers to laboratory procedures done in test tubes or in petri dishes.

ion [ión]: An atom or a molecule that has either gained or lost one or more electrons, giving it a positive or negative charge.

ionic bond [enlace iónico]: A chemical bond formed by the attraction between oppositely charged ions.

isotonic (I suh TAH nik) [isotónico]: A solution where the concentration of solutes outside a cell equals the concentration inside.

K

kidney [riñón]: An organ of the urinary system that regulates the balance of water and ions, and produces urine.

killer T cell [linfocito T citotóxico]: A lymphocyte that is produced in the bone marrow but matures in the thymus. These cells recognize and destroy infected cells, limiting the spread of infection.

kilocalorie (kil o KAL er ee; kcal) [kilocaloría]: A measure of food energy equal to 1,000 calories.

kinetic (KIN et ik) energy [energía cinética]: Active energy.

kingdom [reino]: The second most inclusive grouping in the biological classification system, following domain.

Krebs cycle [ciclo de Krebs]: The energy-releasing cycle in cellular respiration that completes the breakdown of intermediate products of glycolysis; also a source of carbon skeletons for use in biosynthesis reactions.

L

labia (LAE be uh) [labios (genitales)]: Folds of skin that protect the female genitals and cover the clitoris and the vaginal and urinary openings.

larva (LAR vuh) [larva]: An immature stage of development in offspring of many types of animals.

learned behavior [comportamiento aprendido]: The responses an organism develops as a result of specific interactions with the environment.

LH surge [pico de LH]: An increase in luteinizing hormone that occurs near the middle of the menstrual cycle and signals the follicle to release the ovum.

limiting factor [factor limitante]: An environmental condition such as food, temperature, water, or sunlight that restricts the types of organisms and population numbers that an environment can support.

lineage [linaje]: A group or clade of organisms that is related by common ancestry.

linkage [ligamiento]: In inheritance, the association of different genes due to their physical proximity on chromosomes.

lipid bilayer [bicapa lipídica]: The arrangement of molecules in cellular membranes.

lipids [lípidos]: A group of organic compounds that includes fats, oils, waxes, triglycerides, and steroids, which do not dissolve in water and make up important parts of cells, such as portions of the cell membrane.

logistic growth [crecimiento logístico]: A type of population increase frequently observed in natural conditions.

luteinizing (LEW tee ih NY zing) **hormone (LH)** [hormona luteinizante (LH)]: A hormone secreted by the anterior lobe of the pituitary gland that controls the formation of the corpus luteum in females and the secretion of testosterone in males.

lymphocyte (LIM foh site) [linfocito]: A type of white blood cell important in the immune response.

lysosome (LY soh zohm) [lisosoma]: A cell vesicle that contains digestive enzymes.

M

macrophage (MAK roh fayj) [macrófago]: A large white blood cell that ingests pathogens and dead cells.

meiosis (my OH sis) [meiosis]: Special process of cell division in eukaryotes that produces the gametes. Two successive nuclear divisions (with corresponding cell divisions) produce gametes that have one-half of the genetic material of the original cell.

melanin [melanina]: A dark-colored pigment that can cause darker coloration or spots in some organisms.

memory cell [linfocito de memoria]: B or T lymphocyte produced in response to a primary immune response. The lymphocyte remains in the circulation and can respond rapidly if the same antigen is encountered in the future.

menopause (MEN oh pawz) [menopausia]: In human females, the cessation of menstruation, usually taking place between the ages of 45 and 50.

menstrual (MEN strew al) **cycle** [ciclo menstrual]: The female reproductive cycle that is characterized by regularly recurring changes in the uterine lining. One cycle lasts approximately 28 days.

menstruation (men strew AY shun) [menstruación]: Periodic sloughing of the blood-enriched lining of the uterus when pregnancy does not occur.

meristem [meristemo]: A portion of a plant that contains embryonic tissue and actively dividing cells, from which new roots, stems, leaves, or reproductive structures can grow.

messenger RNA (mRNA) [ARN mensajero (ARNm)]: The RNA complementary to one strand of DNA. It is transcribed from genes and translated by ribosomes into protein.

metabolism (meh TAB oh liz um) [metabolismo]: The sum of all the chemical changes taking place in an organism.

metamorphosis [metamorfosis]: A major change in the body of an organism as it passes from one life history stage to another.

metaphase [metafase]: A stage in mitosis or meiosis, during which chromosomes are lined up along the middle of the dividing cell.

metastasis [metástasis]: The spread of cancerous cells from the tumor where they developed to other parts of the body.

metastasize [metastatizar]: To spread, as in the spread of cancer cells.

miscarriage [aborto espontáneo]: The natural and spontaneous expulsion of a fetus before it is capable of surviving independently, usually between the third and seventh month of pregnancy.

mitochondria (my toh KON dree uh) [mitocondrias]: The organelles in eukaryotic cells that carry on cellular respiration, releasing energy from food molecules and storing it in ATP.

mitosis (my TOH sis) [mitosis]: The replication of the chromosomes and the production of two nuclei in one cell that is usually followed by cell division. Each new cell that results from a mitotic division has the same genetic makeup as the original cell. This process is used to make new cells to replace damaged or dying cells.

model [modelo]: In science, these are representations of specific aspects of a natural phenomenon, built from available evidence and used to gain understanding of the phenomenon or make predictions about it.

molecules [molécula]: The smallest unit of a substance made of two or more atoms that retains the chemical and physical properties of the substance.

monogamy (moh NOG ahm ee) [monogamia]: A bond between two individuals.

monohybrid (mon o HI brid) cross [cruza monohíbrida]: A genetic cross between individuals differing in one allele.

mons pubis (MONS PYOO bis) [monte de Venus]: A pad of tissue covering the female pubic bone that becomes covered with hair.

mortality (mor TAL ih tee) [mortalidad]: Death rate, measured as the proportion of deaths to total population over a given period; often expressed as number of deaths per 1,000 or 10,000 individuals.

motor cortex [corteza motriz]: The region of the cerebral cortex of the brain which transmits information to voluntary muscles to generate movement.

motor neuron [motoneurona]: A nerve cell that conducts information to muscles or glands.

mRNA [ARNm]: See *messenger RNA*.

mutation (myoo TAY shun) [mutación]: A hereditary change to the nucleotide sequence of a gene. A mutation may result in a new allele or a change in a regulatory sequence for a gene. Changes can lead to an increase or decrease in the amount of RNA or protein product made by the affected gene; can alter the function of the gene's product; can eliminate the production of the gene's product; or can have no effect on the gene's product. Whether a mutation is beneficial, detrimental, or has no effect on an organism depends on the change to the gene product and the organism's current environmental conditions.

mutualism (MYOO tyoo ul is um) [mutualismo]: Symbiotic relationship that mutually benefits two species.

N

negative controls [controles negativos]: A type of experimental treatment in which all of the conditions of the experiment are replicated except the experimental variable. A negative control treatment is expected to not show the condition predicted in the experimental treatment.

negative feedback [realimentación negativa]: A kind of feedback that creates equilibrium between input and output in a system or process.

nephron (NEF rahn) [nefrona]: The functional unit of a kidney. It consists of a long, coiled tubule. One end forms a cup that encloses a mass of capillaries. The other end opens into a duct that collects urine. The entire nephron is surrounded by a network of capillaries.

nervous system [sistema nervioso]: A coordinating mechanism in all multicellular animals, except sponges, that regulates internal body functions and responses to external stimuli. In vertebrates, it consists of the brain, spinal cord, nerves, ganglia, and parts of receptor and effector organs.

neurobiologist [neurobiólogo]: A scientist who studies the nervous system of animals.

neuron (NOOR ahn) [neurona]: A nerve cell; a name usually reserved for nerve cells in animals that have a complex brain and specialized associative, motor, and sensory nerves.

neurotransmitter (NOOR oh TRANS mit er) [neurotransmisor]: A chemical messenger that diffuses across the synapse and transmits a nerve impulse from one neuron to another.

niche (NITCH) [nicho]: The sum total of all the adaptations an organism uses to survive in its environment. This includes its role in the community, what it eats, and what interactions it has with other organisms and with its environment.

nondisjunction (non dis JUNG shun) [no disyunción]: The failure of a pair of homologous chromosomes to separate during meiosis or mitosis.

nonspecific barriers [barreras no específicas]: In immunity, these include general barriers to infection such as the skin, mucus, earwax, and colonies of harmless bacteria.

nucleic (noo KLEE ik) acid [ácido nucleico]: DNA or RNA. An organic compound composed of nucleotides, it is important in coding instructions for cell processes.

nucleotide (NOO klee oh tide) [nucleótido]: A subunit or building block of DNA or RNA. It is chemically constructed of a 5-carbon sugar, a nitrogen base, and a triphosphate group.

nucleus (NOO klee us) [núcleo]: In eukaryotic cells, it is the membranous organelle that houses the chromosomal DNA. In atoms, the central core containing positively charged protons and (in all but hydrogen) electrically neutral neutrons.

O

oncogene [oncogén]: A gene found in viruses or as part of the normal genome that is crucial for triggering cancerous characteristics.

order [orden]: A group of related families; the fifth largest grouping, after domain, kingdom, phylum or division, and class, in the biological classification system.

organelle (or guh NEL) [orgánulo]: An organized structure within a cell, with a specific function. Chloroplasts and mitochondria are examples.

organic molecules [moléculas orgánicas]: Matter naturally found within organisms, typically composed of a carbon backbone or ring connected to atoms of other elements such as oxygen, nitrogen, and hydrogen.

organ system [sistema orgánico]: A group of organs that carries out an interrelated set of functions, such as gas exchange, the elimination of wastes, or the circulation of blood.

orgasm [orgasmo]: Sensory and motor events at the peak of sexual stimulation that result in ejaculation for the male and involuntary contraction of the muscles surrounding the vagina in the female.

osmosis (os MOH sis) [ósmosis]: The movement of water across a selectively permeable membrane.

ova (singular: ovum) [óvulos]: Mature female gametes. Also known as eggs, ova are larger than sperm.

ovarian cycle [ciclo ovárico]: The events of the menstrual cycle that occur in the ovary, including the maturation and release of ova in response to hormonal changes.

ovary (plural: ovaries) [ovarios]: The primary reproductive organs of a female; egg-cell-producing organs.

oviduct (OH vi dukt) [trompa de Falopio]: A tube leading from an ovary to the uterus.

ovulation (ahv yoo LAY shun) [ovulación]: In vertebrates, the release of one or more eggs from an ovary.

P

paleobiologist [paleobiólogo]: A scientist who studies relationships between fossil and living organisms.

paleontologist (PAY lee on TOHL oh jist) [paleontólogo]: A scientist who studies fossils to gain insight into the history of life on Earth.

parasitism (PAIR uh sih tiz um) [parasitismo]: An ecological niche in which one organism is the habitat and the food for another. A parasite lives and feeds on the host organism, usually without killing it.

passive transport [transporte pasivo]: The diffusion of a substance across a biological membrane through a transport protein in the membrane.

pathogen (PATH oh jen) [patógeno]: A disease-causing organism.

penicillin (pen ih SIL lin) [penicilina]: Any of several antibiotic compounds obtained from penicillium mold and used to prevent or treat a wide variety of diseases and infections.

penis [pene]: In vertebrates, the male organ through which sperm are passed to the female and through which wastes from the kidneys—in the form of urine—are discharged outside the body.

peptide bond [enlace peptídico]: The type of bond that links amino acids together to form a protein.

permeable [permeable]: Open to passage or penetration.

pH [pH]: A measure of how acidic or basic a solution is, based on the concentration of hydrogen ions in that solution.

phenotype (FEE noh tipe) [fenotipo]: The expression of a genotype in the appearance or function of an organism; the observable traits of an organism.

pheromone (FARE oh mohn) [feromona]: A small chemical signal that animals produce that can stimulate and influence the physiology and behavior of other individuals of the same species; acts much like hormones.

photosynthesis (fo toe SIN thus sis) [fotosíntesis]: The process by which living cells that contain chlorophyll use light energy to make organic compounds from inorganic materials.

phylum (FY lum) [filo]: The third most inclusive grouping, after domain and kingdom, in the biological classification system. A phylum is assigned to all organisms except plants, which are classified in divisions.

physical anthropologist [antropólogo físico]: A scientist who studies the biological evolution of humans.

physical digestion [digestión física]: The breakdown of food molecules through the movement of the mouth, stomach, and other parts of the digestive system.

physiological (fiz ee OH laj ih kul) processes [procesos fisiológicos]: Related to functions of an organism or its parts.

physiological response [respuesta fisiológica]: An automatic change generated by the body of an organism that is triggered by an external or internal stimulus.

pituitary (pih TOO ih ter ee) [pituitaria]: A part of the brain that produces and secretes hormones that regulate a variety of body functions. The pituitary also stores and then releases two hormones produced by cells in the hypothalamus.

placenta (pluh SEN tuh) [placenta]: A structure in the pregnant uterus for nourishing a fetus with the mother's blood supply; formed from the uterine lining and embryonic membranes.

plasma (PLAZ muh) [plasma]: The liquid portion of the blood in which cells are suspended.

plasma cell [célula plasmática]: An antibody-producing cell that forms as a result of the proliferation of sensitized B lymphocytes.

plate tectonics (tek TON iks) [tectónica de placas]: The theory and study of the movement of the plates that make up Earth's crust.

polygamy (puh LIG uh me) [poligamia]: Mating strategy whereby one individual mates with more than one individual of the opposite sex.

polymerase (pah LIH mur ayse) chain reaction (PCR) [reacción en cadena de la polimerasa (PCR)]: A technique for copying a DNA molecule. After 20 cycles of PCR amplification, more than a million copies of a DNA molecule will have been made. Extremely important in biotechnology and research.

polysaccharide [polisacárido]: A carbohydrate molecule made up of three or more sugar or monosaccharide subunits.

population [población]: A group of organisms of one species that lives in the same place at the same time.

population density [densidad de población]: Number of organisms per unit of habitat area.

positive controls [controles positivos]: A type of experimental treatment in which all of the conditions of the experiment are replicated plus a variable known to reliably elicit the expected experimental results. Positive controls are used to test that the experimental setup worked as designed.

positive feedback [realimentación positiva]: A kind of feedback that disturbs or prevents equilibrium between input and output in a system or process.

potential energy [energía potencial]: The energy of an object deriving from the position of that object in space.

predation (pred EH shun) [depredación]: The killing and consumption of prey.

predator-prey relationship [relación depredador-presa]: The relationship between organisms in which one, the predator, feeds on the other, the prey.

principle of independent assortment [principio de distribución independiente]: The inheritance of alleles for one trait does not affect the inheritance of alleles for another trait.

principle of segregation [principio de segregación]: During meiosis, chromosome pairs separate so that each of the two alleles for any given trait appears in a different gamete.

probability [probabilidad]: The relative possibility that an event will occur or is likely to occur.

producer [productor]: An autotroph. Any organism that produces its own food using matter and energy from the nonliving world.

progesterone (proh JES tuh rohn) [progesterona]: A female hormone secreted by the placenta and the corpus luteum that acts to prepare and maintain the uterus for pregnancy and to prepare the breasts for lactation.

prokaryote (pro KAIR ee oht) [procariota]: An organism whose cells do not have membrane-enclosed organelles, such as nuclei, mitochondria, and chloroplasts; a bacterium. (Compare with *eukaryote*.)

prophase [profase]: A phase of mitosis or meiosis in which the nuclear membrane breaks down and chromosomes condense.

prostate (PRAH stayt) gland [próstata]: Male reproductive gland located near the bladder and urethra that produces and adds more fluid to the semen.

protein [proteína]: An organic compound composed of one or more polypeptide chains of amino acids. Most structural materials and enzymes in a cell are proteins.

protocol [protocolo]: A plan or procedure for a basic investigation that can answer a testable question; serves as a standard for controlling variables.

puberty (PYOO bur tee) [pubertad]: The stage of development in which the reproductive organs become functional.

pulse [pulso]: The regular pressure change in the arteries generated by the contractions of the heart.

R

radioactive isotope [radioisótopo]: A form of a chemical element that emits energetic particles (such as electrons) by the decay of its atomic nucleus.

reabsorption (REE ab ZORP shun) [reabsorción]: In the kidney, this takes place in capillaries outside the glomerulus (in the renal tubule). Water and some dissolved substances that had been filtered from the blood are returned (reabsorbed) to the filtered blood.

reactants [reactivos]: The substances that undergo a chemical change in a chemical reaction.

receptor (ree SEP ter) [receptor]: A specialized sensory cell, as in the eye or the skin, that is sensitive to a particular type of stimulus.

recessive (ree SESS iv) [recesivo]: A term used to describe an allele or trait that is masked by a dominant allele or trait.

recessive trait [rasgo recesivo]: A trait that is only observable when a person inherits two recessive alleles from his or her parents.

recombinant (re KOM bin ent) DNA [ADN recombinante]: DNA that incorporates parts of different parent DNA molecules, as formed by natural recombination mechanisms or by recombinant DNA technology.

recombination (re KOM bin EH shun) [recombinación]: The regrouping of genes in an offspring caused by the crossing over of chromosomes during meiosis.

reflex [reflejo]: An involuntary reaction or response to a stimulus.

reflex arc [arco reflejo]: A nerve pathway that forms the structural and functional basis for a reflex.

replication (rep li KAY shun) [replicación]: The process of making a copy of the genetic information in a cell nucleus.

reproduction [reproducción]: The process by which organisms generate new individuals.

reproductive isolation [aislamiento reproductivo]: A state in which two populations of organisms are unable or strongly limited in their ability to reproduce with each other. Reproductive isolation can, over time, lead to speciation.

reproductive strategy [estrategia reproductiva]: The combination of characteristics used by an organism to ensure success in reproduction.

restriction enzyme [enzima de restricción]: An enzyme that recognizes specific nucleotide sequences in DNA and breaks the DNA chain at those points.

ribonucleic (ry boh noo KLEE ik) acid (RNA) [ácido ribonucleico (ARN)]: The hereditary material coded by the DNA of cells to carry out specific genetic functions; for example, messenger RNA and transfer RNA. Also the hereditary material of some viruses.

ribosomal (RY boh SOHM ul) RNA (rRNA) [ARN ribosómico (ARNr)]: A class of RNA molecules found, together with characteristic proteins, in ribosomes.

ribosome (RY boh SOHM) [ribosoma]: The cellular organelle that serves as the site for protein synthesis.

rRNA [ARNr]: See *ribosomal RNA*.

S

scientific theory [teoría científica]: A general principle or system of principles that provides the best logical explanation for a group of related natural phenomena. Scientific theories generally develop from the work of many scientists through the synthesis of multiple lines of experimental and observational evidence, and can be used to predict natural phenomena and provide direction for new areas of investigation.

scrotum [escroto]: A pouch of skin that encloses the testes.

secretion [secreción]: In the kidney, this takes place near the end of the renal tubule. Unfiltered wastes are passed from the blood (secreted) into the filtrate, a process that adjusts the blood pH.

selectively permeable [selectivamente permeable]: A property of biological membranes that allows some substances to cross and prevents others from crossing.

semen (SEE men) [semen]: In mammalian males, the thick fluid that transports sperm.

seminal vesicles (SEM in ul VES ih kuls) [glándulas seminales]: In the male reproductive system, two small sacs that contribute to semen production.

seminiferous tubules [túbulos seminíferos]: Long, coiled tubes found in the testes that serve as the site of sperm production.

senescence [senescencia]: Aging, or growing old.

sensory cortex [corteza sensorial]: The region of the cerebral cortex of the brain that receives and integrates sensory information from the body.

sensory neurons [neuronas sensoriales]: Nerve cells that transmit information from a sense organ to the brain.

sequence [secuencia]: The order of the subunits that make up certain molecules; for example, the order of nucleotides that make up DNA or the order of amino acids that make up a protein.

sexually transmitted disease (STD) [enfermedad de transmisión sexual (ETS)]: A disease that may be contracted through sexual contact; for example, herpes, chlamydia, gonorrhea, HIV, and others.

sexual reproduction [reproducción sexual]: Reproduction involving the contribution of genetic material from two parents. Because each parent contributes information, the offspring of sexual reproduction are not genetically identical to either parent.

sexual selection [selección sexual]: Selection based on variation in secondary sexual characteristics, leading to the enhancement of individual reproductive fitness.

shock [shock]: A condition of profound disturbance of the body's vital processes, characterized by failure of the circulatory system to deliver adequate amounts of blood to vital organs.

solute (SAWL yoot) [soluto]: The dissolved substance in a solution.

solution [solución]: Two or more substances combined to make a homogeneous mixture.

solvent [solvente]: The liquid in which the solute is dissolved.

somatic cell [célula somática]: Any nonreproductive cell in an organism.

speciation [especiación]: The process by which a new species evolves from an ancestral species due to factors that generate the new population reproductively isolated from the original population.

species (SPEE sheez) [especie]: All individuals and populations of a particular type of organism, maintained by biological mechanisms that result in their breeding mostly with their type.

specific immune response [respuesta inmune específica]: A portion of the immune system of vertebrates that responds to specific foreign matter, known as antigens, in such a way that usually eliminates that matter from the body. Components of the specific immune response include B cells and the antibodies they generate; memory B cells, which are stored following the generation of a new antibody type; and T cells, which attack and remove identified foreign matter.

sperm [espermatozoides]: The gametes produced by males. They are often motile and consist of a compact nucleus surrounded by a membrane, a flagellum for propulsion, mitochondria that provide energy, and a small sac at the tip containing enzymes that help penetrate the ovum.

spores [esporas]: One-celled reproductive bodies that are usually resistant to harsh environmental conditions and may remain dormant, in a dry covering, for long periods. In some organisms, spores are asexual and may initiate the growth of a new organism under favorable conditions. In other organisms, spores are sexual and must unite with spores of the other sex before producing a new organism.

sporulation [esporulación]: The process of reproducing asexually by producing spores that grow directly into new individuals.

starch [almidón]: A polysaccharide carbohydrate derived from plants and composed of glucose.

stem cell [célula madre]: A cell that can divide continuously and generate cells capable of differentiating into any cell type of an organism's body.

stimulus (STIM yoo lus; plural: stimuli) [estímulo]: A change or signal in the internal or external environment that causes an adjustment or reaction by an organism.

stomate (stow MATE; plural: stomata) [estoma]: The opening between two guard cells in the epidermis of a plant leaf through which gases are exchanged with the air.

stop codon (KO don) [codón de terminación]: A special codon in messenger RNA that does not specify an amino acid. When present, the synthesis (translation) of the growing amino acid chain stops.

strata (STRA tuh; singular: stratum) [estratos]: Layers, usually of deposited earth sediments carried by erosion. Many strata become mineralized into rock layers and they may contain fossils.

stratigraphy (stra TIG ra fee) [estratigrafía]: A branch of geology that is concerned with the systemized study, description, and classification of stratified rocks.

stressor [situación estresante]: A factor capable of stimulating a stress response.

stroma (STROH muh) [estroma]: The colorless substance in a chloroplast surrounding the thylakoids. The enzymes of the Calvin cycle also are in the stroma.

substitution mutation [mutación por sustitución]: Mutation caused by substituting one nucleotide for another nucleotide during replication.

substrate (SUB strayt) [sustrato]: A molecule on which enzymes act.

symbiosis (sim by OH sis) [simbiosis]: An ecological relationship between organisms of two different species that benefit from living together in direct contact.

synapse (SIN aps) [sinapsis]: An open junction between neurons, across which an impulse is transmitted by a chemical messenger, a neurotransmitter.

systems analysis [análisis de sistemas]: A process by which limited portions of a complex phenomenon are studied, perhaps multiple times with variation, to gain insight about the phenomenon.

systole (SIS toh lee) [sístole]: The stage of the cardiac cycle in which the heart muscle contracts and the chambers pump blood. (Compare with *diastole*.)

systolic pressure [presión sistólica]: The blood pressure that occurs during systole; this is the highest pressure that occurs during a cardiac cycle.

T

T cell [linfocito T]: A lymphocyte that matures in the thymus stimulated by the presence of a particular antigen. It differentiates and divides, producing offspring cells (killer cells) that attack and kill the cells bearing the antigen.

technology [tecnología]: The application of scientific knowledge for practical purposes.

telomere [telómero]: A specific segment of DNA found at the end of a chromosome.

telophase [telofase]: The last phase of a mitotic or meiotic cell cycle in which daughter cells are divided and the nuclear membrane forms around the genetic material.

testis (plural: testes) [testículo]: The primary reproductive organ of a male; sperm-cell-producing organs.

testosterone (tes TOS ter ohn) [testosterona]: A male sex hormone secreted by the testes.

theory [teoría]: See *scientific theory*.

thylakoid (THY luh koyd) [tilacoide]: A flattened sac in a chloroplast. Many of the thylakoids are arranged in stacks known as grana. The pigments and enzymes for the light reactions of photosynthesis are embedded in the sac membrane.

toxin [toxina]: A substance produced by one organism that is poisonous to another.

trachea (TRAY kee uh) [tráquea]: The windpipe of an air-breathing vertebrate, connecting the air passage in the throat with the lungs.

transcription (tran SKRIP shun) [transcripción]: The assembly of an RNA molecule complementary to a strand of DNA. The product may be messenger RNA, transfer RNA, or ribosomal RNA.

transfer RNA (tRNA) [ARN transferente (ARNt)]: The RNA responsible for transporting amino acids to the ribosome during protein synthesis.

transgenic (trans JEN ik) [transgénico]: Plants or animals that contain genes from unrelated species.

translation [traducción]: The assembly of proteins on ribosomes, using messenger RNA to direct the order of amino acids.

triage (TREE azh) [triage]: A sorting out and classification of patients according to the seriousness of injuries, urgency of treatment, and place for treatment. Carried out as an emergency procedure during an influx of large numbers of victims of a disaster.

tRNA [ARNt]: See *transfer RNA*.

trophic level [nivel trófico]: A group of organisms in a community that occupies the same position in the food web, such as producers or primary consumers.

U

umbilical (um BIL ih kul) cord [cordón umbilical]: In placental mammals, a tube connecting the embryo with the placenta.

ureter (yoo REE ter) [uréter]: A muscular tube that carries urine from the kidney to the urinary bladder.

urethra (yoo REE thruh) [uretra]: In vertebrates, the tube through which urine is carried from the bladder to the outside of the body.

urinary system [sistema urinario]: An organ system that functions to generate and eliminate urine and includes the kidneys, ureters, bladder, and urethra.

uterine cycle [ciclo uterino]: The events of the menstrual cycle that take place in the uterus, including the shedding of the uterine lining in response to hormonal changes.

uterus (YOO ter us) [útero]: A hollow muscular organ, located in the female pelvis, in which a fetus develops.

V

vaccine [vacuna]: A medical preparation used to stimulate the specific immune response of an organism's body into producing antibodies against a pathogen, without generating an infection.

vacuole (VAK yoo ohl) [vacuola]: A membrane-enclosed structure in the cytoplasm of a cell or a unicellular organism. Different types of vacuoles serve different functions.

vagina (vuh JI nuh) [vagina]: A tubular organ that leads from the uterus to the opening of the female reproductive tract.

variable [variable]: A condition that varies from one organism to another (size, shape, color) or is subject to change for an individual organism (humidity, temperature, light intensity, fatigue).

vas deferens (vas DEF er enz) [conducto deferente]: A tube that leads from the epididymis to the urethra of the male reproductive tract.

vasopressin (vas O press in) [vasopresina]: Hormone released by the pituitary in response to the signal of dehydration sent from the hypothalamus.

vegetative reproduction [reproducción vegetativa]: Asexual reproduction involving parts of an organism that detach and form new organisms. Offspring are genetically identical to the parent. Examples include budding as the "eyes" on potatoes do, sprouting from roots as aspen trees do, or sprouting from runners as strawberries do.

vein [vena]: A blood vessel through which blood flows toward the heart.

vestigial (ve STIJ ee uhl) [rudimentario]: Describes a structure of an organism's body that has little or no apparent function, though homologous structures in related organisms or a common ancestor had some function.

vitamins [vitaminas]: A group of organic substances essential for the metabolism of living organisms. They are found in very small quantities in foods and some are produced synthetically.

vulva (VUL va) [vulva]: External female reproductive organs including the labia and clitoris.

W

white blood cells [glóbulos blancos]: A group including many types of immune system cells that circulate in the blood and provide specific functions related to the response to and elimination of foreign matter.

X

X-linked recessive [recesivo ligado al cromosoma X]: A pattern of inheritance for a trait that is carried on the X chromosome. In females, two atypical alleles are necessary for the trait to be expressed. In males, only one atypical allele is necessary for the trait to be expressed because males have only one X chromosome.

Z

zygote (ZY goht) [cigoto]: The cell that results from the fusion of gamete nuclei when egg and sperm unite. Zygotes contain a full set of genetic information.

GLOSARIO

A

abiótico [abiotic]: No viviente. En los ecosistemas, se usa para referirse a componentes no vivientes como luz solar, viento, nutrientes y minerales.

aborto espontáneo [miscarriage]: Expulsión natural y espontánea del feto antes de que sea capaz de sobrevivir en forma independiente, usualmente entre el tercer y el séptimo mes del embarazo.

ácido desoxirribonucleico (ADN) [deoxyribonucleic acid (DNA)]: Material hereditario de la mayoría de los organismos. Los genes y los cromosomas están compuestos de ADN. Las subunidades que componen el ADN son nucleótidos, los cuales contienen un azúcar (la desoxirribosa), un grupo trifosfato y una de cuatro bases.

ácido nucleico [nucleic acid]: ADN o ARN. Compuesto orgánico formado por nucleótidos; tiene un papel importante en la codificación de instrucciones para procesos celulares.

ácido ribonucleico (ARN) [ribonucleic acid (RNA)]: Material hereditario codificado por el ADN de las células para llevar a cabo funciones genéticas específicas; por ejemplo, el ARN mensajero y el ARN transferente. También se refiere al material hereditario de algunos virus.

acrosoma [acrosome]: Estructura ubicada en el extremo del espermatozoide, que contiene enzimas para disolver la sustancia gelatinosa que rodea el óvulo.

adaptación [adaptation]: En la selección natural, se refiere a una característica hereditaria de ciertos organismos de una población. Dicha característica mejora las probabilidades de supervivencia y reproducción del organismo en su ambiente en comparación con las probabilidades de otros organismos de la población.

adaptación cultural [cultural adaptation]: Adaptación a nuevas presiones o situaciones que se producen a causa de una innovación cultural.

ADN [DNA]: Ver *ácido desoxirribonucleico*.

ADN ligasa [DNA ligase]: Enzima que actúa durante la replicación y reparación de las moléculas de ADN para unir nucleótidos.

ADN recombinante [recombinant DNA]: ADN que incorpora partes de distintas moléculas de ADN progenitoras, formado por mecanismos de recombinación naturales o por tecnología de ADN recombinante.

aeróbico [aerobic]: Que tiene lugar o que vive en presencia de oxígeno libre o disuelto.

aislamiento reproductivo [reproductive isolation]: Estado en el cual dos poblaciones de organismos no pueden reproducirse una con la otra o tienen grandes limitaciones para hacerlo. Con el tiempo, el aislamiento reproductivo puede conducir a la especiación.

alelo [allele]: Una de dos o más formas posibles de un gen. Cada uno afecta el rasgo hereditario de manera levemente distinta.

alergia [allergies]: Respuesta inmune exagerada a una materia extraña conocida como alergeno, la cual puede tocarse, inhalarse, ingerirse o inyectarse.

alimento [food]: Sustancia producida por organismos que contiene componentes orgánicos ricos en energía y que se utiliza como fuente de energía y materia para la vida.

almidón [starch]: Carbohidrato polisacárido derivado de plantas y compuesto de glucosa.

amilasa [amylase]: Enzima digestiva que se encuentra en la saliva.

aminoácidos [amino acids]: Componentes moleculares esenciales de las proteínas, cada uno de los cuales está compuesto por un grupo amino, un grupo carboxilo y una cadena lateral. Existen 20 aminoácidos distintos.

anaeróbico [anaerobic]: Que tiene lugar o que vive en condiciones en las que no existe oxígeno libre.

anafase [anaphase]: Etapa de la mitosis o la meiosis durante la cual los cromosomas se mueven a lados opuestos de la célula que se divide.

análisis de sistemas [systems analysis]: Proceso a través del cual se estudian partes limitadas de un fenómeno complejo, a veces múltiples veces con algunas variaciones, para obtener información acerca del fenómeno.

análisis ético [ethical analysis]: Proceso por el cual se pueden examinar situaciones relacionadas con el bien y el mal a fin de facilitar la toma de decisiones y el desarrollo del entendimiento.

anticonceptivo [contraceptive]: Sustancia o dispositivo que previene el embarazo.

anticuerpo [antibody]: Proteína sanguínea producida en respuesta a un antígeno, con el cual se combina específicamente. Los anticuerpos bloquean la capacidad que tienen los patógenos o los materiales extraños de causar daño al cuerpo.

antígeno [antigen]: Cualquier material, generalmente una proteína, que se reconoce como extraño y provoca una respuesta inmune.

antihistamínico [antihistamine]: Fármaco utilizado en los medicamentos para contrarrestar la respuesta histamínica.

antropólogo físico [physical anthropologist]: Científico que estudia la evolución biológica de los humanos.

apareamiento de bases complementarias [complementary base pairing]: Interacción predecible entre bases de nitrógeno en hebras opuestas de ADN y entre ADN y ARN; consiste de apareamiento de bases de adenina-timina y guanina-citosina (adenina-uracilo en el ARN).

árbol filogenético [evolutionary tree]: Diagrama ramificado que ilustra patrones de relaciones entre un grupo de organismos vivos y/o extinguidos, en el que los ancestros comunes se indican en los nodos ubicados entre las ramas. Estos diagramas se generan a partir de datos relativos a las características físicas de organismos vivos o fósiles, como la secuencia molecular o las estructuras corporales.

arco reflejo [reflex arc]: Trayecto del impulso nervioso que constituye la base estructural y funcional para un reflejo.

ARN mensajero (ARNm) [messenger RNA (mRNA)]: ARN que complementa una hebra de ADN. Se obtiene después de la transcripción y es traducido en los ribosomas a la estructura de una proteína.

ARN ribosómico (ARNr) [ribosomal RNA (rRNA)]: Tipo de moléculas de ARN que, junto con proteínas características, se encuentran en los ribosomas.

ARN transferente (ARNt) [transfer RNA (tRNA)]: ARN responsable de transportar aminoácidos al ribosoma durante la síntesis de proteínas.

ARNm [mRNA]: Ver *ARN mensajero*.

ARNr [rRNA]: Ver *ARN ribosómico*.

ARNt [tRNA]: Ver *ARN transferente*.

artefacto [artifact]: Restos materiales, como trozos de cerámica, herramientas y artículos textiles, que constituyen evidencia cultural.

arteria [artery]: Vaso sanguíneo a través del cual la sangre fluye desde al corazón a las demás partes del cuerpo.

átomo [atom]: Partícula más pequeña de un elemento. A su vez, un átomo está compuesto de partículas más pequeñas que individualmente no tienen las propiedades del elemento.

ATP (trifosfato de adenosina) [ATP (adenosine triphosphate)]: Compuesto que tiene tres grupos fosfatos y que es utilizado por las células para almacenar energía.

autosoma [autosome]: Cromosoma que no participa directamente en la determinación del sexo.

autótrofo [autotroph]: Organismo que puede producir y almacenar alimento utilizando la luz solar u otra fuente de energía no viviente.

axón [axon]: Prolongación de la neurona que conduce impulsos hacia afuera de la célula. Se lo llama también cilindroeje o neurita.

B

barreras no específicas [nonspecific barriers]: En inmunidad, éstas incluyen barreras generales contra infección, como la piel, las mucosas, la cera del oído y colonias de bacterias inocuas.

bicapa lipídica [lipid bilayer]: Ordenamiento de las moléculas en membranas celulares.

biodiversidad [biodiversity]: Número y variedad de organismos que se encuentran en una comunidad, un ecosistema o en la Tierra.

biólogo del desarrollo [developmental biologist]: Científico que estudia el desarrollo de los organismos.

biólogo evolutivo [evolutionary biologist]: Científico que estudia de qué manera los organismos cambian a lo largo del tiempo y cómo se relacionan unos con otros a través de ancestros comunes.

biomasa [biomass]: Peso seco de la materia orgánica de la que se compone un grupo de organismos en un hábitat particular.

biomasa consumible [consumable biomass]: Porción de materia biológica a un nivel trófico que está disponible para ser consumida por organismos de niveles tróficos superiores.

biosfera [biosphere]: Parte externa de la Tierra—aire, agua y suelo—en la que existen seres vivientes.

biosíntesis [biosynthesis]: Proceso de reunir o fabricar las moléculas grandes características de un tipo específico de célula o tejido. Se lo llama también anabolismo.

biótico [biotic]: Viviente. En los ecosistemas, los componentes bióticos incluyen todos los seres vivientes.

bípedo [bipedal]: Capaz de caminar erguidamente sobre las extremidades posteriores, dejando libres las manos para realizar otras funciones.

C

cadena de transporte de electrones [electron transport system]: Proceso en el cual los electrones se transfieren de una molécula portadora a otra en la fotosíntesis y en la respiración celular; tiene como resultado el almacenamiento de parte de la energía en las moléculas ATP.

caloría [calorie]: Cantidad de calor requerida para aumentar 1°C la temperatura de un gramo de agua.

calorímetro [calorimeter]: Dispositivo científico utilizado para medir calor.

cáncer [cancer]: Conjunto de enfermedades caracterizada por la proliferación de células malignas con crecimiento y división anormales, en las que se producen graves anormalidades en la membrana plasmática y en el citosol (o hialoplasma).

capacidad de carga [carrying capacity]: Tamaño máximo de la población que puede mantenerse con los recursos disponibles en un área determinada.

capilar [capillary]: Vaso sanguíneo pequeño que se encuentra entre el extremo de una arteria y el comienzo de una vena. En los capilares se produce gran parte del intercambio de gases y nutrientes en el cuerpo humano.

carbohidratos [carbohydrates]: Grupo de compuestos orgánicos formados por carbono, oxígeno e hidrógeno que constituyen partes considerables de las plantas y son importantes fuentes de energía para todos los seres vivientes. Se los llama también hidratos de carbono.

carbono [carbon]: Elemento que se encuentra en todas las moléculas orgánicas y que suele unirse al hidrógeno y al oxígeno; tiene un peso atómico de 12.011 y su número atómico es 6.

célula haploide [haploid]: Célula que contiene sólo un miembro (n) de cada par de cromosomas característicos de una especie.

célula madre [stem cell]: Célula que puede dividirse continuamente y generar células capaces de diferenciarse y convertirse en cualquier célula del cuerpo de un organismo.

célula plasmática [plasma cell]: Célula productora de anticuerpos que se forma como resultado de la proliferación de linfocitos B sensibilizados.

célula somática [somatic cell]: Cualquier célula no reproductora de un organismo.

células gliales [glial cells]: Células que desempeñan la función de protección, soporte y aislación de las neuronas. Se las conoce también como glía o neuroglía.

células madre adultas [adult stem cells]: Células derivadas de tejido adulto, las cuales, en determinadas condiciones, pueden diferenciarse y producir más de un tipo de célula.

células madre embrionarias [embryonic stem cells]: Células derivadas de tejidos embrionarios que tienen el potencial de diferenciarse y formar cualquier tipo de célula del cuerpo de un organismo.

cerebelo [cerebellum]: Estructura del encéfalo que es importante para la coordinación y el control motriz, así como para la atención y el procesamiento del lenguaje y de la música. Está ubicado en la base del encéfalo y se caracteriza por un patrón de pequeños pliegues.

cerebro [cerebrum]: Parte más grande del encéfalo, que controla los pensamientos y las acciones voluntarios. Está formado por dos hemisferios: izquierdo y derecho, y presenta pliegues grandes.

ciclo celular [cell cycle]: Secuencia ordenada de eventos en la vida de una célula que se divide, compuesta de las fases M, G_1, S y G_2.

ciclo de Krebs [Krebs cycle]: Ciclo de liberación de energía que se produce durante la respiración celular y el cual completa la descomposición de productos intermedios de la glucólisis; es también una fuente de esqueletos de carbono para uso en reacciones de biosíntesis.

ciclo del carbono [carbon cycle]: Ciclo químico en el cual los compuestos de carbono hechos por ciertos organismos (como las plantas) son digeridos y descompuestos por otros. El carbono se libera en forma de moléculas inorgánicas pequeñas que pueden ser utilizadas otra vez por más organismos para sintetizar compuestos de carbono.

ciclo menstrual [menstrual cycle]: Ciclo reproductivo femenino caracterizado por cambios recurrentes regulares en el endometrio (mucosa que cubre el interior del útero). Un ciclo dura aproximadamente 28 días.

ciclo ovárico [ovarian cycle]: Proceso que tiene lugar en el ovario durante el ciclo menstrual, incluyendo la maduración y liberación de óvulos en respuesta a cambios hormonales.

ciclo uterino [uterine cycle]: Acontecimientos del ciclo menstrual que tienen lugar en el útero, incluyendo el desprendimiento del recubrimiento del útero en respuesta a cambios hormonales.

cigoto [zygote]: Célula que se forma a partir de la fusión de los núcleos de los gametos cuando se unen el óvulo y el espermatozoide. Los cigotos contienen un juego completo de información genética.

clado [clade]: Grupo o linaje de organismos que comparten un único ancestro común.

clase [class]: Cuarto grupo en el sistema de clasificación biológica, después de dominio, reino y filo o división.

clasificación [classification]: Proceso organizativo de acuerdo con las características que comparten distintos sistemas vivientes en virtud de sus ancestros comunes. Millones de tipos de vida diferentes se organizan en categorías grandes de organismos similares.

clasificación biológica [biological classification]: Sistema científico utilizado para clasificar organismos en grupos anidados, generalmente de acuerdo con las relaciones evolutivas entre los organismos.

clima [climate]: Condiciones de tiempo atmosférico prevalentes de una región, incluyendo temperatura y precipitaciones, teniendo en cuenta los promedios de muchos años.

clítoris [clitoris]: Órgano reproductor externo femenino ubicado en el frente de la vulva. Es homólogo del pene en los machos.

clon [clone]: Célula u organismo que es genéticamente idéntico al organismo progenitor del cual proviene.

clonación [cloning]: Tipo de reproducción asexual que produce individuos genéticamente idénticos a partir de una célula o un conjunto de células. Este tipo de reproducción es utilizado en procariotas y plantas.

clorofila [chlorophyll]: Pigmentos verdes de plantas y de muchos microorganismos; convierte la energía luminosa (a través de cambios que involucran electrones) en energía química que se usa en reacciones biológicas.

cloroplasto [chloroplast]: Orgánulo que se encuentra sólo en las plantas y en protistas fotosintéticos; contiene clorofila, la cual absorbe la energía luminosa utilizada en la fotosíntesis.

código genético [genetic code]: "Idioma" de los genes en el cual la secuencia de nucleótidos del ADN (en los codones) especifica las secuencias de aminoácidos de las proteínas.

codón [codon]: Unidad básica de código genético formada por una secuencia de tres nucleótidos adyacentes en una cadena de ADN o ARNm.

codón de terminación [stop codon]: Codón especial del ARN mensajero que no especifica un aminoácido. Cuando está presente, se interrumpe la síntesis (traducción) de la cadena de aminoácido en formación.

cognición [cognition]: Acciones o procesos relacionados con la percepción, el conocimiento o el aprendizaje.

compensación evolutiva [evolutionary trade-off]: Cambio en un rasgo que ofrece algunas ventajas para la supervivencia o el éxito reproductivo de un organismo, pero que está relacionado con cambios en un segundo rasgo que produce algunas desventajas para la supervivencia o la reproducción.

competencia [competition]: Interacción entre los miembros de la misma población o de dos o más poblaciones a fin de obtener un recurso mutuamente requerido que está disponible en cantidades limitadas.

componentes [components]: Conjunto de las cosas que forman un sistema ecológico, incluyendo factores bióticos y abióticos.

comportamiento aprendido [learned behavior]: Respuestas que un organismo desarrolla como resultado de interacciones específicas con el ambiente.

comportamiento innato [innate behavior]: Acciones realizadas por organismos que no son aprendidas, como el instinto. Suelen ser controladas por rasgos heredados del sistema nervioso.

comunidad [community]: Todos los organismos que habitan un área particular.

condicionamiento [conditioning]: Entrenamiento que modifica una respuesta a fin de que se asocie a un estímulo diferente del estímulo que la causaba originalmente.

conducto deferente [vas deferens]: Tubo que conecta el epidídimo con la uretra del tracto reproductor masculino.

conservación de energía [conservation of energy]: Principio por el cual la energía dentro de un sistema cerrado es constante aunque sufra cambios en su forma.

consumidor [consumer]: Heterótrofo; organismo que consume otros organismos y los desechos orgánicos de otros organismos.

control [control]: Tratamiento dentro de un experimento científico, también conocido como control experimental, que presenta todas las características del experimento excepto la variable manipulada experimentalmente.

controles negativos [negative controls]: Tipo de tratamiento experimental en el que todas las condiciones del experimento se reproducen excepto la variable experimental. En un tratamiento con controles negativos no deberían darse las condiciones previstas en el tratamiento experimental.

controles positivos [positive controls]: Tipo de tratamiento experimental en el que todas las condiciones del experimento se reproducen con el agregado de una variable conocida para producir en forma confiable los resultados experimentales esperados. Los controles positivos se usan para probar que el experimento funcionó tal como se diseñó.

cordón umbilical [umbilical cord]: En los mamíferos con placenta, tubo que conecta el embrión a la placenta.

corteza motriz [motor cortex]: Región de la corteza cerebral que transmite información a los músculos voluntarios para generar movimiento.

corteza sensorial [sensory cortex]: Región de la corteza cerebral del encéfalo que recibe e integra la información sensorial del cuerpo.

crecimiento [growth]: Aumento en tamaño. Con referencia al desarrollo, se refiere a las rondas sucesivas de división celular que producen un organismo multicelular.

crecimiento cognitivo [cognitive growth]: Desarrollo del conocimiento y la habilidad de aprendizaje de un individuo.

crecimiento exponencial [exponential growth]: Tipo de aumento de la población que se observa cuando todos los individuos son capaces de reproducirse; se caracteriza por una tasa de crecimiento constante y un aumento rápido del tamaño de la población.

crecimiento logístico [logistic growth]: Tipo de crecimiento de la población frecuentemente observado en condiciones naturales.

cromatografía [chromatography]: Diversas técnicas utilizadas por científicos para separar mezclas de moléculas de acuerdo con la masa, la carga o la habilidad de unirse a otras moléculas.

cromosoma [chromosome]: Grupo de genes largo que asemeja una maraña de hilos; se encuentra en el núcleo de todas las células eucariotas y es particularmente visible durante la mitosis y la meiosis; los cromosomas están compuestos de ADN y proteínas.

cruza dihíbrida [dihybrid cross]: Cruza genética entre individuos con dos alelos diferentes.

cruza monohíbrida [monohybrid cross]: Cruza genética entre individuos con un alelo diferente.

cuello uterino [cervix]: Parte angosta inferior del útero, que conecta el útero a la vagina.

cuerpo calloso [corpus callosum]: Haz de fibras nerviosas que conectan los hemisferios derecho e izquierdo del cerebro.

cuerpo lúteo [corpus luteum]: Estructura que se forma a partir de los tejidos del folículo ovárico roto y segrega hormonas femeninas.

cultivo celular [cell culture]: Proceso de conservar y cultivar células fuera del cuerpo del organismo, generalmente realizado en un sustrato, con gases disueltos y con nutrientes líquidos.

cultura [culture]: Sistema de comportamientos aprendidos, símbolos, costumbres, creencias, instituciones, artefactos y tecnología característicos de un grupo y transmitidos por los miembros del grupo a sus descendientes.

D

deleción (o delección) [deletion mutation]: Mutación que se produce cuando las enzimas duplicadoras accidentalmente se saltean una base. La nueva hebra de ADN que se forma tiene una base faltante.

dendrita [dendrite]: Prolongación de la neurona que conduce impulsos hacia el cuerpo de la célula.

densidad de población [population density]: Número de organismos por unidad de área de hábitat.

depredación [predation]: Matanza y consumo de la presa.

deriva continental [continental drift]: Hipótesis propuesta en 1912 que sugiere que las masas terrestres de la Tierra en un momento estaban unidas en un supercontinente que se separó para formar los actuales continentes. La deriva continental se considera actualmente parte de una teoría más amplia de tectónica de placas.

deriva genética [genetic drift]: Cambios en la frecuencia de los alelos dentro de una población debidos a la probabilidad de supervivencia o reproducción de individuos con rasgos particulares. Este mecanismo evolutivo actúa independientemente de la selección natural y es particularmente importante para poblaciones pequeñas.

desarrollo [development]: División, crecimiento y diferenciación de células de capas embrionarias para formar todos los tejidos y órganos del cuerpo; cambios posteriores de acuerdo con la edad, incluyendo madurez reproductiva, que afectan la apariencia y la función del cuerpo.

descomponedor [decomposer]: Organismo que vive de materiales orgánicos en descomposición, de los cuales obtiene energía y sus propias materias primas para vivir.

diástole [diastole]: Etapa del ciclo cardíaco en la cual el músculo cardíaco se relaja y permite que la cámara se llene de sangre. (Comparar con *sístole*.)

diferenciación [differentiation]: Proceso por el cual las células desarrollan estructuras y funciones especializadas; se la conoce también como diferenciación celular.

diferenciación celular [cell differentiation]: Proceso por el cual las células embrionarias desarrollan estructuras y funciones especializadas.

difusión [diffusion]: Movimiento de una sustancia en el gradiente de concentración desde un área más concentrada a un área menos concentrada.

difusión facilitada [facilitated diffusion]: Proceso por el cual las moléculas son transportadas a través de membranas con la ayuda de moléculas portadoras.

digestión [digestion]: Procesos que descomponen moléculas de alimentos en unidades más pequeñas.

digestión física [physical digestion]: Descomposición de moléculas de alimento a través del movimiento de la boca, el estómago y otras partes del sistema digestivo.

digestión química [chemical digestion]: Descomposición de los alimentos en moléculas dentro del cuerpo con la ayuda de secreciones químicas y enzimáticas, como el ácido estomacal.

dilema ético [ethical dilemma]: Situación en la que es necesaria una decisión relacionada con el bien y el mal, pero que se complica por la presencia de preocupaciones no relacionadas con la ética, como la supervivencia o el bienestar.

diploide [diploid]: Célula que contiene dos copias de cada cromosoma. Las copias pueden no ser idénticas.

diurético [diuretic]: Cualquier sustancia o agente que promueve un aumento en la formación y eliminación de orina.

división [division]: Tercer grupo en el sistema de clasificación biológica de las plantas, después de dominio y reino.

división celular [cell division]: Proceso en el cual el material genético y el citoplasma de una célula se dividen entre las células hijas. La meiosis y la mitosis son dos tipos de división celular.

dominancia incompleta [incomplete dominance]: Patrón de expresión genética en el que el fenotipo de un individuo heterocigoto es intermedio entre los de los progenitores.

dominio [domain]: Categoría más alta en el sistema de clasificación biológica.

E

ecología [ecology]: Estudio de los componentes vivientes y no vivientes del ambiente y de las interacciones que afectan a las especies biológicas.

ecosistema [ecosystem]: Comunidad biológica en su ambiente abiótico.

ectotermos [ectotherms]: Organismos cuya temperatura suele ser similar a la de su entorno; se los conoce también como poiquilotermos. Estos organismos pueden regular la temperatura a través del comportamiento, pero no fisiológicamente.

electroforesis [electrophoresis]: Cualquiera de varias técnicas para separar moléculas grandes, como proteínas o fragmentos de ADN, con base en la habilidad de moverse a través de un medio de gel sometido a un campo eléctrico.

elementos esenciales [essential elements]: Elementos que son necesarios para el crecimiento o el mantenimiento de organismos.

embrión [embryo]: Organismo en las etapas iniciales de desarrollo después de la fertilización.

emigración [emigration]: Partida de individuos de una población; reduce el tamaño de la población.

encruzamiento cromosómico [crossing over]: Durante la profase I de la meiosis, consiste en la ruptura y el intercambio de segmentos correspondientes de pares de cromosomas en uno o más sitios de su longitud. Tiene como resultado recombinación genética.

endoesqueleto [endoskeleton]: Esqueleto duro que se encuentra dentro de los tejidos blandos de un animal, como las espículas de las esponjas y los esqueletos óseos de los vertebrados.

endotermos [endotherms]: Organismos capaces de generar su propio calor para mantener una temperatura corporal estable, principalmente a través de mecanismos fisiológicos pero también a través del comportamiento. Se los conoce también como homeotermos.

energía cinética [kinetic energy]: Energía activa.

energía de activación [activation energy]: Cantidad mínima de energía necesaria para permitir que se produzca una reacción química.

energía potencial [potential energy]: Energía de un objeto debida a la posición de dicho objeto en el espacio.

enfermedad autoinmune [autoimmune disease]: Respuesta en la cual se producen anticuerpos que atacan algunas de las propias células del cuerpo.

enfermedad de transmisión sexual (ETS) [sexually transmitted disease (STD)]: Enfermedad que se puede contraer a través del contacto sexual; por ejemplo, herpes, clamidia, gonorrea, VIH y otras.

enlace covalente [covalent bond]: Enlace químico formado por dos átomos que comparten un par de electrones.

enlace iónico [ionic bond]: Enlace químico formado por la atracción entre iones con cargas opuestas.

enlace peptídico [peptide bond]: Tipo de enlace que conecta aminoácidos para formar una proteína.

enlace químico [chemical bond]: Atracción entre dos átomos que se produce a causa de compartir o transferir electrones externos de un átomo a otro.

enzima [enzyme]: Proteína o molécula compuesta en parte por proteína producida por un organismo y usada como catalizador en una reacción bioquímica específica.

enzima de restricción [restriction enzyme]: Enzima que reconoce secuencias de nucleótidos específicas en el ADN y rompe la cadena de ADN en esos puntos.

epidídimo [epididymis]: Estructura con forma de espiral que se encuentra en la superficie de los testículos y permite el almacenamiento, la transmisión y la maduración de los espermatozoides.

escroto [scrotum]: Saco de piel que rodea los testículos.

especiación [speciation]: Proceso por el cual evoluciona una nueva especie a partir de una especie ancestral debido a factores que generan una nueva población que presenta aislamiento reproductivo con respecto a la población original.

especie [species]: Todos los individuos y poblaciones de un tipo particular de organismo mantenidos por mecanismos biológicos que les permiten entrecruzarse principalmente con organismos de su mismo tipo.

espermatozoides [sperm]: Gametos producidos por los machos. Suelen tener motilidad y consisten de un núcleo compacto rodeado por una membrana, un flagelo para propulsión, mitocondrias que suministran energía y un saco pequeño en la punta que contiene enzimas para ayudar a penetrar en el óvulo.

esporas [spores]: Cuerpos reproductores unicelulares que suelen ser resistentes a las condiciones ambientales extremas y pueden permanecer aletargados, bajo una cubierta seca, durante largos períodos. En algunos organismos, las esporas son asexuales y pueden dar inicio al crecimiento de nuevos organismos dadas las condiciones favorables. En otros organismos, las esporas son sexuales y deben unirse a esporas del sexo opuesto antes de producir un nuevo organismo.

esporulación [sporulation]: Proceso de reproducción asexual que consiste en producir esporas que se convierten directamente en individuos nuevos.

estímulo [stimulus (plural: stimuli)]: Cambio o señal en el ambiente interno o externo que provoca un ajuste o reacción por parte de un organismo.

estoma [stomate (plural: stomata)]: Abertura entre dos células guardianas en la epidermis de la hoja de una planta a través de la cual se intercambian gases con el aire.

estrategia reproductiva [reproductive strategy]: Combinación de las características usadas por un organismo para asegurar el éxito en la reproducción.

estratigrafía [stratigraphy]: Rama de la biología que se dedica al estudio sistematizado, la descripción y la clasificación de rocas estratificadas.

estratos [strata (singular: stratum)]: Capas generalmente formadas por sedimentos de tierra depositados que son arrastrados por la erosión. Muchos estratos se mineralizan y forman capas de rocas, las cuales pueden contener fósiles.

estrógeno [estrogen]: Hormona que estimula el desarrollo de las características sexuales secundarias femeninas.

estroma [stroma]: Sustancia incolora en un cloroplasto que rodea los tilacoides. Las enzimas del ciclo de Calvin también se encuentran en el estroma.

estructuras análogas [analogous structures]: Estructuras que tienen una función similar, pero cuyas similitudes no derivan de ancestros comunes. Con frecuencia, las estructuras análogas surgen debido a evolución convergente.

estructuras homólogas [homologous structures]: Rasgos, estructuras o secuencias moleculares de organismos que comparten características debido a que tienen ancestros comunes, pero que no tienen necesariamente la misma función.

etólogo [ethologist]: Científico que estudia el comportamiento animal.

eucariota [eukaryote]: Organismo cuyas células tienen un núcleo y orgánulos recubiertos por una membrana; un protista, hongo, planta o animal. (Comparar con *procariota*.)

evidencia [evidence]: Información confiable que puede usarse para respaldar una conclusión; en las ciencias, esta información ha sido generada de acuerdo con prácticas y métodos científicos.

evolución [evolution]: Cambios en la información genética y en los rasgos codificados por información genética a lo largo de generaciones de una población o especie de organismos debidos a los procesos de mutación, selección o deriva genética.

evolución cultural [cultural evolution]: Cambios en las características culturales a lo largo del tiempo, los cuales se transmiten a través de estructuras sociales y aprendizaje y no a través de rasgos hereditarios. La evolución cultural tiene lugar a través de procesos diferentes a los de la evolución biológica.

exoesqueleto [exoskeleton]: Recubrimiento duro depositado en la superficie de un animal, como la concha de un molusco, que suministra protección y puntos de sujeción para los músculos.

experimento controlado [controlled experiment]: Experimento científico diseñado para que la influencia de la variable experimental pueda ser detectada al evitar que otras condiciones varíen en los tratamientos. Este diseño ayuda a eliminar explicaciones alternativas de los resultados generados.

expresión genética [gene expression]: Proceso por el cual la información genética se usa para sintetizar un producto funcional, como ARN o una proteína.

extinción [extinction]: Proceso por el cual una población o especie desaparece y debido al cual se pierde el material genético exclusivo de ese grupo.

eyaculación [ejaculation]: Expulsión del semen (líquido que contiene espermatozoides) de la uretra.

F

factor limitante [limiting factor]: Condición ambiental, como alimento, temperatura, agua o luz solar, que restringe los tipos de organismos y las cantidades de población que un ambiente puede sostener.

factores de crecimiento [growth factors]: Moléculas que provocan divisiones celulares o la organización o el mantenimiento de tejidos. Estos factores suelen expresarse durante el desarrollo de un embrión pero también pueden encontrarse en tejidos adultos específicos.

familia [family]: Sexto grupo en el sistema de clasificación biológica, después de dominio, reino, filo o división, clase y orden; grupo de géneros relacionados.

fenotipo [phenotype]: Expresión de un genotipo en la apariencia o la función de un organismo; rasgos observables de un organismo.

fermentación [fermentation]: Descomposición incompleta de moléculas de alimento, especialmente azúcares, en ausencia de oxígeno.

feromona [pheromone]: Señal química pequeña producida por los animales, la cual puede estimular y afectar la fisiología y el comportamiento de otros animales de la misma especie; funciona de manera similar a las hormonas.

fertilización [fertilization]: Unión del núcleo de un óvulo y el núcleo de un espermatozoide. El resultado es una célula llamada cigoto.

feto [fetus]: Embrión vertebrado en las etapas tardías de desarrollo cuando ya ha alcanzado el plan estructural y las características reconocibles de su tipo.

fijación del carbono [carbon fixation]: Incorporación del carbono atmosférico a los carbohidratos a través de la fotosíntesis. Se lo llama también ciclo de Calvin.

filo [phylum]: Tercer grupo en el sistema de clasificación biológica, después de dominio y reino. Se asigna un filo a todos los organismos excepto a las plantas, que se clasifican en divisiones.

filtración [filtration]: En los riñones de los vertebrados, la filtración se produce cuando la presión sanguínea empuja la sangre hacia el glomérulo de la nefrona donde las células sanguíneas y las proteínas plasmáticas se separan del agua de la sangre, los desechos nitrogenosos y los iones. La mayor parte del líquido filtrado se reabsorbe, pero algunos desechos se eliminan del cuerpo a través de la orina.

fisión binaria [binary fission]: Tipo de reproducción asexual en la que una célula se divide en dos células idénticas. Es el principal medio de reproducción asexual de las células procariotas.

flujo genético [gene flow]: Cambios en la frecuencia de los alelos o genes enteros de una población debido a la cruza con otras poblaciones; la inmigración de material genético en una población.

folículo [follicle]: Acumulación de células que se encuentran en el ovario y contienen un solo óvulo. En general, se forma y se desarrolla un folículo cada mes durante el ciclo menstrual.

fotosíntesis [photosynthesis]: Proceso por el cual células vivas que contienen clorofila usan energía luminosa para formar compuestos orgánicos a partir de materiales inorgánicos.

fragmentación [fragmentation]: Tipo de reproducción asexual en la cual un trozo del organismo progenitor se convierte en un nuevo individuo.

frecuencia respiratoria [breathing rate]: Número de veces que un animal terrestre inhala y exhala por minuto.

G

gameto [gamete]: Célula sexual —ya sea un óvulo o un espermatozoide— formada por meiosis, que tiene la mitad de los cromosomas de una célula corporal.

gemación [budding]: Tipo de reproducción asexual en la que un nuevo individuo se origina como prominencia, o yema, sobre el cuerpo de un organismo progenitor. El individuo descendiente termina separándose del progenitor y adquiere independencia. Los descendientes son genéticamente idénticos al progenitor.

gen [gene]: Unidad física fundamental de la herencia, que transmite una serie de especificaciones de una generación a la siguiente. Segmento de ADN que codifica un producto específico.

género [genus]: Grupo de especies relacionadas; séptimo grupo en el sistema de clasificación biológica, después de dominio, reino, filo o división, clase, orden y familia.

genoma [genome]: Conjunto completo de información genética de un organismo.

genotipo [genotype]: Composición genética de un organismo.

gestación [gestation]: Período de desarrollo entre la concepción y el nacimiento que transcurre en el útero.

glande [glans]: Estructura glandular redondeada ubicada en la punta del pene, cubierta por el prepucio.

glándula de Cowper [Cowper's gland]: Glándula del sistema reproductor masculino que produce una mucosidad alcalina. Esta mucosidad se segrega antes de eyacular para proteger los espermatozoides de la acidez de la vagina.

glándulas seminales [seminal vesicles]: En el sistema reproductor masculino, dos sacos pequeños que contribuyen en la producción del semen. Se las llama también vesículas seminales.

glóbulos blancos [white blood cells]: Grupo que abarca muchos tipos de células del sistema inmunitario que circulan en la sangre y tienen funciones específicas relacionadas con la respuesta contra materias extrañas y con la eliminación de materias extrañas.

glomérulo [glomerulus]: Red de vasos capilares rodeados por una cápsula que se encuentra en la nefrona y constituye el sitio de filtración en los riñones.

glucogénesis [glycogenesis]: Proceso por el cual se forma el glucógeno, una molécula que almacena energía.

glucógeno [glycogen]: Principal carbohidrato usado por los animales para almacenar energía.

glucólisis [glycolysis]: Descomposición inicial de un carbohidrato, generalmente la glucosa, en moléculas más pequeñas al comienzo de la respiración celular.

glucosa [glucose]: Azúcar común de 6 carbonos.

gónadas [gonads]: Órganos que producen gametos. Son los testículos en los machos y los ovarios en las hembras.

gradiente de concentración [concentration gradient]: Diferencia en la concentración de ciertas moléculas a lo largo de una distancia.

grupo sanguíneo [blood type]: Clase de rasgos heredados que describen un conjunto de proteínas o antígenos que se encuentran en la parte exterior de las células sanguíneas. Los diferentes grupos sanguíneos suelen no ser inmunológicamente compatibles.

H

hábitat [habitat]: Lugar en el que vive un organismo. Incluso dentro del mismo ecosistema, distintos organismos tiene hábitats diferentes.

hemoglobina [hemoglobin]: Pigmento que se encuentra en los glóbulos rojos y es responsable del transporte de oxígeno.

heredar [inherit]: Recibir de material genético.

heterocigoto [heterozygous]: Que tiene dos alelos diferentes para un rasgo determinado.

heterótrofo [heterotroph]: Organismo que obtiene carbono y toda la energía metabólica de moléculas orgánicas previamente formadas por un autótrofo; consumidor.

hipertermia [hyperthermia]: Temperatura corporal anormalmente alta; fiebre.

hipertónico [hypertonic]: Solución en la que la concentración de solutos fuera de una célula es mayor que la concentración dentro de la célula.

hipotálamo [hypothalamus]: Parte del encéfalo. En los seres humanos, conecta los sistemas nervioso y endocrino. (El sistema endocrino controla las hormonas que regulan muchas funciones del cuerpo.)

hipotermia [hypothermia]: Temperatura corporal anormalmente baja.

hipótesis [hypothesis]: Proposición que sugiere una explicación para una observación o una respuesta a un problema científico.

hipotónico [hypotonic]: Solución en la que la concentración de solutos fuera de una célula es menor que la concentración dentro de la célula.

histamina [histamine]: Sustancia liberada por células heridas que hace que los vasos sanguíneos se dilaten durante una respuesta inflamatoria.

homeostasis [homeostasis]: Característica fundamental de sistemas vivientes; mantenimiento de un número estable de individuos en una población (sociedad); tendencia de un organismo de mantener un ambiente interno estable y constante (fisiología).

homínido [hominid]: Primate de la familia Hominidae, la cual incluye a los seres humanos modernos, subespecies anteriores y australopitecinos.

homocigoto [homozygous]: Que tiene dos alelos idénticos para un rasgo determinado.

homogenato [homogenate]: Material de consistencia uniforme.

hormona [hormone]: Sustancia segregada por células o glándulas que tiene un efecto regulador sobre células y órganos en otra parte del cuerpo; mensajero químico.

hormona foliculoestimulante (FSH) [follicle-stimulating hormone (FSH)]: Sustancia segregada por el lóbulo anterior de la pituitaria que estimula el desarrollo de un folículo ovárico en la hembra o la producción de espermatozoides en el macho.

hormona luteinizante (LH) [luteinizing hormone (LH)]: Hormona segregada por el lóbulo anterior de la glándula pituitaria que controla la formación del cuerpo lúteo en las hembras y la secreción de testosterona en los machos.

I

impermeable [impermeable]: No permeable; que no puede atravesarse.

in vitro [in vitro]: Literalmente significa "en vidrio"; se refiere a procedimientos de laboratorio realizados en tubos de ensayo o en placas de Petri.

indicador [indicator]: Sustancia química que tiene una propiedad física variable, como el color, dependiendo de los materiales con los que interactúa.

inducción [induction]: Proceso de desarrollo por el cual una parte del embrión (o una molécula generada en una región embriónica) influye en la diferenciación de otra región embriónica.

inferencia [inference]: Conclusiones que derivan lógicamente de algún tipo de evidencia directa.

ingeniería genética [genetic engineering]: Tecnología experimental desarrollada para alterar el genoma de una célula viviente con fines médicos o industriales.

inmigración [immigration]: Llegada de nuevos individuos a una población; aumenta el tamaño de la población.

inmunidad [immunity]: Resistencia a una enfermedad, generalmente específica a una enfermedad o patógeno.

interfase [interphase]: Fase del ciclo celular en la que no se produce división.

ión [ion]: Átomo o molécula que ha obtenido o perdido uno o más electrones, lo cual le ha otorgado una carga positiva o negativa.

isotónico [isotonic]: Solución en la que la concentración de solutos fuera de una célula es igual a la concentración dentro de la célula.

K

kilocaloría [kilocalorie]: Medida de poder energético de los alimentos equivalente a 1,000 calorías.

L

labios (genitales) [labia]: Pliegues de piel que protegen los genitales femeninos y cubren el clítoris y las aberturas vaginal y urinaria.

larva [larva]: Etapa de desarrollo inmadura en los descendientes de muchos tipos de animales.

ligamiento [linkage]: Con relación a la herencia, se refiere a la asociación de genes diferentes debido a su proximidad física en los cromosomas.

linaje [lineage]: Grupo o clado de organismos que están relacionados por ancestros comunes.

linfocito [lymphocyte]: Tipo de glóbulo blanco (leucocito) que tiene un papel importante en la respuesta inmune.

linfocito B [B cell]: Tipo de linfocito que se desarrolla en la médula ósea y que luego produce anticuerpos.

linfocito de memoria [memory cell]: Linfocito B o T producido en respuesta a una respuesta inmune primaria. El linfocito permanece en la circulación y puede responder rápidamente si se encuentra el mismo antígeno en el futuro.

linfocito T [T cell]: Linfocito que madura en el timo estimulado por la presencia de un antígeno específico. Al diferenciarse y dividirse produce células descendientes (células citotóxicas) que atacan y matan células que llevan el antígeno.

linfocito T citotóxico [killer T cell]: Linfocito que se produce en la médula ósea pero madura en el timo. Estas células reconocen y destruyen células infectadas, y limitan la propagación de la infección.

linfocitos T colaboradores [helper T cell]: Tipo de linfocito T requerido por ciertas células B para producir anticuerpos, por otros linfocitos T para responder a antígenos, o por otros linfocitos T que segregan linfocinas. Se los llama también linfocitos T efectores.

lípidos [lipids]: Grupo de compuestos orgánicos que incluye grasas, aceites, ceras, triglicéridos y esteroides, los cuales no se disuelven en agua y constituyen una parte importante de las células, como porciones de la membrana celular.

lisosoma [lysosome]: Vesícula celular que contiene enzimas digestivas.

M

macrófago [macrophage]: Leucocito grande que fagocitan patógenos y células muertas.

meiosis [meiosis]: Proceso especial de división celular en células eucariotas que produce los gametos. Dos divisiones nucleares sucesivas (con las correspondientes divisiones celulares) producen gametos que tienen la mitad del material genético de la célula original.

melanina [melanin]: Pigmento oscuro que puede provocar un color más oscuro o manchas en algunos organismos.

menopausia [menopause]: En las hembras humanas, el cese de la menstruación, que tiene lugar generalmente entre los 45 y los 50 años.

menstruación [menstruation]: Muda periódica de la capa sanguinolenta del endometrio cuando no se produce un embarazo.

meristemo [meristem]: Parte de una planta que contiene tejido embrionario y células que se dividen activamente, a partir de las cuales pueden crecer nuevas raíces, tallos, hojas o estructuras reproductivas.

metabolismo [metabolism]: Suma de todos los cambios químicos que se producen en un organismo.

metafase [metaphase]: Etapa de la mitosis o la meiosis durante la cual los cromosomas están alineados en la parte media de la célula que se divide.

metamorfosis [metamorphosis]: Cambio significativo en el cuerpo de un organismo al pasar de una etapa histórica de la vida a otra.

metástasis [metastasis]: Propagación de células cancerosas del tumor donde se desarrollaron a otras partes del cuerpo.

metastatizar [metastasize]: Propagarse, como en la propagación de células cancerosas.

mitocondrias [mitochondria]: Orgánulos de las células eucariotas que llevan adelante la respiración celular; liberan energía de las moléculas de alimento y la almacenan en moléculas ATP.

mitosis [mitosis]: Reproducción de los cromosomas y producción de dos núcleos en una célula que suele ser seguida por la división celular. Cada célula nueva producida tras una división mitótica tiene la misma constitución genética de la célula original. Este proceso se usa para producir nuevas células para reemplazar células dañadas o células que están muriendo.

modelo [model]: En la ciencia, se refiere a representaciones de aspectos específicos de fenómenos naturales, construidas a partir de evidencia disponible y usadas para mejorar el entendimiento del fenómeno y realizar predicciones sobre el mismo.

molécula [molecules]: Unidad más pequeña de una sustancia formada por dos o más átomos que retiene las propiedades químicas y físicas de la sustancia.

moléculas orgánicas [organic molecules]: Materia que se encuentra en estado natural dentro de los organismos, compuesta generalmente de una estructura o anillo de carbono conectado a los átomos de otros elementos como oxígeno, nitrógeno e hidrógeno.

monogamia [monogamy]: Vínculo entre dos individuos.

monte de Venus [mons pubis]: Almohadilla de tejido que cubre el pubis femenino y se recubre de vello en la pubertad.

mortalidad [mortality]: Indicador de la cantidad de muertes, medido como proporción de muertes en una población total durante un período determinado, generalmente expresado como número de muertes cada 1,000 o 10,000 individuos.

motoneurona [motor neuron]: Célula nerviosa que conduce información a los músculos o glándulas.

mutación [mutation]: Cambio hereditario en la secuencia de nucleótidos de un gen. Una mutación puede producir un nuevo alelo o un cambio en una secuencia reguladora de un gen. Los cambios pueden provocar un aumento o una disminución en la cantidad de producto génico (ARN o proteína) producido por el gen afectado; pueden alterar la función del producto génico; pueden eliminar la producción del producto génico o pueden no tener ningún efecto sobre el producto génico. Una mutación puede ser beneficiosa, perjudicial o puede no tener ningún efecto sobre un organismo dependiendo del cambio que tenga lugar en el producto génico y en las condiciones ambientales actuales del organismo.

mutación por inserción [insertion mutation]: Cambio en una secuencia de ADN que consiste en añadir un nucleótido nuevo o una secuencia de nucleótidos nuevos.

mutación por sustitución [substitution mutation]: Mutación causada por el reemplazo de un nucleótido por otro durante la replicación.

mutualismo [mutualism]: Relación simbiótica entre dos especies en la cual las dos especies se benefician mutuamente.

N

nefrona [nephron]: Unidad funcional del riñón. Consiste en un túbulo largo en forma de espiral. Un extremo forma una cápsula que rodea un ovillo de capilares. El otro extremo está comunicado con un conducto que recoge orina. La nefrona entera está rodeada por una red de capilares.

neurobiólogo [neurobiologist]: Científico que estudia el sistema nervioso de los animales.

neurona [neuron]: Célula nerviosa; el término se usa generalmente para referirse a células nerviosas de animales que tienen un encéfalo complejo y nervios sensitivos, motores y sensoriales especializados.

neuronas sensoriales [sensory neurons]: Células nerviosas que transmiten información del órgano responsable de alguno de los sentidos al encéfalo.

neurotransmisor [neurotransmitter]: Mensajero químico que se difunde en la sinapsis y transmite un impulso nervioso de una neurona a otra.

nicho [niche]: Suma total de todas las adaptaciones que usa un organismo para sobrevivir en su ambiente. Esto incluye su papel en la comunidad, los alimentos que ingiere y las interacciones que tiene con otros organismos y con su ambiente.

nivel trófico [trophic level]: Grupo de organismos de una comunidad que ocupan la misma posición en la cadena alimenticia, por ejemplo, productores y consumidores primarios.

no disyunción [nondisjunction]: Error en la separación de un par de cromosomas homólogos durante la meiosis o la mitosis.

nomenclatura binomial [binomial nomenclature]: Sistema científico utilizado para denominar a los organismos, en el que cada especie recibe un nombre de género y un nombre de especie en latín. Se lo llama también nomenclatura binaria o sistema de clasificación binomial.

núcleo [nucleus]: En células eucariotas, es el orgánulo rodeado de una propia membrana que alberga el ADN que contiene los cromosomas. En los átomos, es la parte central que contiene protones con carga positiva y (en todos menos el átomo de hidrógeno) neutrones con carga eléctrica neutra.

nucleótido [nucleotide]: Subunidad o componente de ADN o ARN. Químicamente, está formado por un azúcar de 5 carbonos, una base de nitrógeno y un grupo trifosfato.

O

oncogén [oncogene]: Gen que se encuentra en virus o en el genoma normal y es responsable de transformar una célula normal en una con características cancerosas.

orden [order]: Grupo de familias relacionadas; quinto grupo en el sistema de clasificación biológica, después de dominio, reino, filo o división y clase.

orgánulo [organelle]: Estructura organizada dentro de una célula, con una función específica. Ejemplos de orgánulos son los cloroplastos y las mitocondrias.

orgasmo [orgasm]: Reacciones sensoriales y motrices que tienen lugar en el momento culminante de estimulación sexual; en el hombre, tiene como resultado la eyaculación y, en la mujer, la contracción involuntaria de los músculos que rodean la vagina.

ósmosis [osmosis]: Movimiento de agua a través de una membrana selectivamente permeable.

ovarios [ovary (plural: ovaries)]: Órganos reproductores primarios de la hembra; órganos que producen óvulos.

ovulación [ovulation]: En los vertebrados, se refiere a la liberación de uno más óvulos de un ovario.

óvulos [ova (singular: ovum)]: Gametos femeninos maduros. Son más grandes que los espermatozoides.

P

paleobiólogo [paleobiologist]: Científico que estudia las relaciones entre los organismos fósiles y vivientes.

paleontólogo [paleontologist]: Científico que estudia los fósiles para investigar la historia de la vida en la Tierra.

parasitismo [parasitism]: Nicho ecológico en el que un organismo es el hábitat y el alimento de otro. Un parásito vive en el organismo huésped y se alimenta de él, generalmente sin matarlo.

pared celular [cell wall]: Cobertura no viviente que rodea la membrana plasmática de ciertas células, como en plantas, en muchas algas y en algunos procariotas. En las plantas, la pared celular está compuesta de celulosa y otros materiales.

patógeno [pathogen]: Organismo que causa enfermedad.

pene [penis]: En los vertebrados, órgano masculino a través del cual los espermatozoides pasan a la hembra y a través del cual se eliminan del cuerpo los desechos de los riñones convertidos en orina.

penicilina [penicillin]: Cualquiera de varios compuestos antibióticos obtenidos del moho penicillium; se usan para prevenir o tratar una amplia gama de enfermedades e infecciones.

permeable [permeable]: Abierto al paso o a la penetración.

pH [pH]: Medida de acidez o alcalinidad de una solución, según la concentración de iones de hidrógeno encontrados en la misma.

pico de LH [LH surge]: Aumento de la hormona luteinizante que se produce cerca del momento medio del ciclo menstrual y que hace que el folículo libere el óvulo.

pituitaria [pituitary]: Parte del encéfalo que produce y segrega hormonas que regulan una gama de funciones corporales. La pituitaria también almacena y reserva dos hormonas producidas por células del hipotálamo.

placenta [placenta]: Estructura del útero que se forma durante el embarazo para nutrir al feto con la sangre de la madre; se forma a partir del recubrimiento uterino y las membranas embrionarias.

plasma [plasma]: Porción líquida de la sangre en la cual se encuentran suspendidas las células.

población [population]: Grupo de organismos de una especie que viven en el mismo lugar al mismo tiempo.

poligamia [polygamy]: Estrategia de apareamiento en la que un individuo se aparea con más de un individuo del sexo opuesto.

polisacárido [polysaccharide]: Molécula de carbohidrato constituida por tres o más subunidades de azúcar o monosacáridos.

portador [carrier]: Persona que tiene un alelo típico y un alelo afectado de un trastorno recesivo. Estas personas no presentan síntomas del trastorno, pero pueden transmitírselo a sus descendientes.

presión diastólica [diastolic pressure]: Presión sanguínea que se produce durante la diástole; es la presión más baja durante el ciclo cardíaco.

presión sanguínea [blood pressure]: Presión ejercida por las contracciones del corazón; permite que circule la sangre.

presión sistólica [systolic pressure]: Presión sanguínea que se produce durante la sístole; es la presión más alta durante el ciclo cardíaco.

principio de distribución independiente [principle of independent assortment]: Herencia de alelos de un rasgo que no afecta la herencia de alelos de otros rasgos.

principio de segregación [principle of segregation]: Durante la meiosis, los pares de cromosomas se separan de manera tal que cada uno de los dos alelos de un rasgo determinado aparece en un gameto diferente.

probabilidad [probability]: Posibilidad relativa de que un acontecimiento ocurra o pueda ocurrir.

procariota [prokaryote]: Organismo cuyas células no tienen orgánulos rodeados de membrana, como los núcleos, las mitocondrias y los cloroplastos; una bacteria. (Comparar con *eucariota*.)

procesos fisiológicos [physiological processes]: Procesos relacionados con las funciones de un organismo o sus partes.

productor [producer]: Autótrofo. Cualquier organismo que produce su propio alimento usando materia y energía del mundo no viviente.

profase [prophase]: Fase de la mitosis o la meiosis en la cual la membrana del núcleo desaparece y se condensan los cromosomas.

progesterona [progesterone]: Hormona femenina segregada por la placenta y el cuerpo lúteo, la cual actúa para preparar y mantener el útero para el embarazo y para preparar los senos para la lactancia.

próstata [prostate gland]: Glándula reproductora masculina que se encuentras cerca de la vejiga y la uretra y produce y añade líquido al semen.

proteína [protein]: Compuesto orgánico formado por una o más cadenas polipeptídicas de aminoácidos. La mayor parte de los materiales estructurales y las enzimas de la célula son proteínas.

protocolo [protocol]: Plan o procedimiento para una investigación básica que puede responder una pregunta demostrable; se utiliza como estándar para controlar las variables.

pubertad [puberty]: Etapa del desarrollo en la cual comienzan a funcionar los órganos reproductores.

pulso [pulse]: Cambio de presión regular en las arterias causado por las contracciones del corazón.

R

radioisótopo [radioactive isotope]: Forma de un elemento químico que emite partículas de energía (como electrones) debido a la inestabilidad de su núcleo atómico. Se lo llama también isótopo radioactivo.

rasgo dominante [dominant trait]: Rasgo visible en un organismo heterocigoto.

rasgo heredado [heritable trait]: Característica de un organismo que es determinada al menos en parte por material genético heredado de los progenitores.

rasgo recesivo [recessive trait]: Rasgo que sólo es observable cuando la persona hereda dos alelos recesivos de sus progenitores.

razonamiento inductivo [inductive reasoning]: Proceso que consiste en desarrollar generalizaciones o principios generales a partir de datos detallados.

reabsorción [reabsorption]: En el riñón, tiene lugar en los capilares fuera del glomérulo (en el túbulo renal). El agua y algunas sustancias disueltas que fueron filtradas de la sangre se devuelven a la sangre filtrada (se reabsorben).

reacción en cadena de la polimerasa (PCR) [polymerase chain reaction (PCR)]: Técnica para copiar una molécula de ADN. Después de 20 ciclos de amplificación PCR, se obtienen más de un millón de copias de una molécula de ADN. Es extremadamente importante en biotecnología e investigación.

reacción endotérmica [endothermic reaction]: Reacción química caracterizada por la absorción de energía calórica.

reacción exotérmica [exothermic reaction]: Reacción química caracterizada por la liberación de energía calórica.

reactivos [reactants]: Sustancias que sufren un cambio químico durante una reacción química.

realimentación negativa [negative feedback]: Tipo de realimentación que crea equilibrio entre la entrada y la salida en un sistema o proceso.

realimentación positiva [positive feedback]: Tipo de realimentación que altera y evita el equilibrio entre la entrada y la salida en un sistema o proceso.

receptor [receptor]: Célula sensorial especializada, como las células del ojo o de la piel, que es sensible a un tipo de estímulo determinado.

recesivo [recessive]: Término usado para describir un alelo o rasgo que no puede manifestarse en presencia de un alelo o rasgo dominante.

recesivo ligado al cromosoma X [X-linked recessive]: Patrón hereditario de un rasgo que se transmite a través del cromosoma X. En las hembras, se necesitan dos alelos atípicos para que el rasgo se exprese. En los machos, se necesita un alelo atípico para que el rasgo se exprese porque los machos tienen un solo cromosoma X.

recombinación [recombination]: Reagrupación de genes en los descendientes causada por la cruza de cromosomas durante la meiosis.

red alimentaria [food web]: Cadenas alimentarias de un ecosistema consideradas colectivamente en las que se observa la superposición y la competencia por muchos organismos que constituyen alimentos.

reflejo [reflex]: Reacción o respuesta involuntaria a un estímulo.

reino [kingdom]: Segunda categoría más alta en el sistema de clasificación biológica, después de dominio.

relación depredador-presa [predator-prey relationship]: Relación entre organismos en la que uno de ellos, el depredador, se alimenta del otro, la presa.

replicación [replication]: Proceso de realizar una copia de la información genética del núcleo de una célula.

reproducción [reproduction]: Proceso por el cual los organismos generan nuevos individuos.

reproducción asexual [asexual reproduction]: Cualquier método de reproducción que requiere un solo progenitor o una sola célula inicial. Este tipo de reproducción tiene como resultado descendientes que son genéticamente idénticos al progenitor.

reproducción sexual [sexual reproduction]: Reproducción que involucra contribución de material genético de dos progenitores. Debido a que cada progenitor contribuye información, los descendientes creados por reproducción sexual no son genéticamente idénticos a ninguno de los dos progenitores.

reproducción vegetativa [vegetative reproduction]: Reproducción asexual en la que partes de un organismo se separan y forman organismos nuevos. Los descendientes son genéticamente idénticos al progenitor. Por ejemplo, los brotes de una papa, el crecimiento a partir de la raíz como en el caso de los álamos, o el brote a partir de raíces rastreras como en el caso de las fresas.

respiración celular [cellular respiration]: Serie de reacciones químicas por medio de las cuales una célula viva descompone moléculas de alimento y obtiene energía de éstas.

respuesta fisiológica [physiological response]: Cambio automático generado por el cuerpo de un organismo a causa de un estímulo externo o interno.

respuesta inmune específica [specific immune response]: Parte del sistema inmunitario de los vertebrados que responde a materias extrañas específicas, conocidas como antígenos, de manera tal que suele eliminar del cuerpo dichas materias extrañas. Los componentes de la respuesta inmune específica incluyen linfocitos B y los anticuerpos que estos generan; linfocitos B de memoria, que se almacenan después de la generación de un nuevo tipo de anticuerpo; y linfocitos T, que atacan y eliminan la materia extraña identificada.

respuesta inmune mediada por anticuerpos [antibody-mediated response]: Respuesta inmune en la que los linfocitos B producen anticuerpos que se unen a los antígenos y los marcan para ser destruidos por defensas no especificadas; el linfocito B se activa al ser estimulado por linfocitos T cooperadores.

respuesta inmune mediada por células [cell-mediated response]: Respuesta inmune en la cual linfocitos altamente especializados circulan en la sangre y en los órganos linfáticos y atacan y destruyen células portadoras de antígenos de superficie específicos.

respuestas conductuales [behavioral responses]: Acciones tomadas por un organismo en respuesta a un estímulo.

ribosoma [ribosome]: Orgánulo celular que sirve como sitio para la síntesis de proteínas.

riñón [kidney]: Órgano del sistema urinario que regula el equilibrio de agua y iones, y produce orina.

rudimentario [vestigial]: Describe una estructura del cuerpo de un organismo que tiene poca función o ninguna función aparente, pero que es homóloga de estructuras que en organismos relacionados o en un ancestro común tienen alguna función.

S

secreción [secretion]: En el riñón, tiene lugar cerca del extremo del túbulo renal. Los desechos sin filtrar pasan de la sangre al producto filtrado; este proceso ajusta el pH de la sangre.

secuencia [sequence]: Orden de las subunidades que forman ciertas moléculas; por ejemplo, el orden de los nucleótidos que forman el ADN o el orden de los aminoácidos que forman una proteína.

selección artificial [artificial selection]: Proceso a través del cual los seres humanos permiten que sólo se reproduzcan variantes de una población o especie que tienen rasgos deseables.

selección sexual [sexual selection]: Selección basada en la variación de las características sexuales secundarias, la cual conduce a favorecer la aptitud reproductiva del individuo.

selectivamente permeable [selectively permeable]: Propiedad de las membranas biológicas que permite que algunas sustancias pasen e impide que otras lo hagan.

semen [semen]: En los mamíferos machos, líquido espeso que transporta los espermatozoides.

senescencia [senescence]: Envejecimiento.

shock [shock]: Estado de alteración grave de los procesos vitales del cuerpo, caracterizado por la falta de circulación sanguínea adecuada a los órganos vitales.

simbiosis [symbiosis]: Relación ecológica entre organismos de dos especies diferentes que se benefician por vivir juntos en contacto directo.

sinapsis [synapse]: Unión abierta entre neuronas, a través de la cual un mensajero químico (un neurotransmisor) transmite un impulso.

sistema cerrado [closed system]: Región o área asilada; no penetran en ella ni salen de ella materia o energía.

sistema circulatorio [circulatory system]: Sistema de órganos compuesto de una bomba muscular (el corazón), vasos sanguíneos y sangre; el medio a través del cual se transportan materiales hacia y desde las células. En muchos animales, también ayuda a estabilizar la temperatura corporal y el pH.

sistema de intercambio de gases [gas exchange system]: Sistema corporal que funciona principalmente para atraer oxígeno a fin de usarlo en los procesos celulares que liberan energía y para eliminar del cuerpo el dióxido de carbono producido por estas reacciones. En los seres humanos y en otros mamíferos, los órganos principales de este sistema son los pulmones.

sistema de realimentación [feedback system]: Relación en la cual una actividad de un organismo afecta a otra, la cual a su vez afecta a la primera y se obtiene un equilibrio regulador.

sistema endocrino [endocrine system]: Sistema de glándulas que segregan sus productos directamente de sus células a la sangre.

sistema nervioso [nervous system]: Mecanismo coordinador que se encuentra en todos los animales multicelulares, excepto las esponjas; regula las funciones internas del cuerpo y responde a los estímulos externos. En los vertebrados, está formado por el encéfalo, la médula espinal, los nervios, los ganglios y partes de órganos receptores y efectores.

sistema orgánico [organ system]: Grupo de órganos que realizan funciones interrelacionadas, como intercambio de gases, eliminación de residuos o circulación de la sangre.

sistema urinario [urinary system]: Sistema de órganos que funciona para generar y eliminar orina e incluye los riñones, los uréteres, la vejiga y la uretra.

sístole [systole]: Etapa del ciclo cardíaco durante la cual el músculo cardíaco se contrae y las cámaras bombean sangre. (Comparar con *diástole*.)

situación estresante [stressor]: Factor capaz de estimular una respuesta de estrés.

solución [solution]: Dos o más sustancias combinadas que forman una mezcla homogénea.

soluto [solute]: Sustancia disuelta en una solución.

solvente [solvent]: Líquido en el que se disuelve el soluto.

surtido independiente [independent assortment]: Herencia independiente de los alelos de un rasgo.

sustrato [substrate]: Molécula sobre la cual actúa una enzima.

T

tampón [buffer]: Solución de ácidos suaves y bases que resiste cambios en el nivel de pH cuando se le añade un ácido o base.

tecnología [technology]: Aplicación del conocimiento científico para fines prácticos.

tectónica de placas [plate tectonics]: Teoría y estudio del movimiento de las placas que forman la corteza terrestre.

telofase [telophase]: Última fase de un ciclo celular mitótico o meiótico en la cual las células hijas se dividen y se forma la membrana nuclear alrededor del material genético.

telómero [telomere]: Segmento específico del ADN que se encuentra en el extremo de un cromosoma.

temperatura corporal [body temperature]: Temperatura interna del cuerpo de un animal; en los seres humanos, suele ser 37°C (98.6°F).

teoría [theory]: Ver *teoría científica*.

teoría científica [scientific theory]: Principio general o sistema de principios que suministra la explicación más lógica para un grupo de fenómenos naturales relacionados. Las teorías científicas suelen desarrollarse a partir del trabajo de muchos científicos por medio de la síntesis de múltiples fuentes de evidencia experimental y observacional, y pueden usarse para predecir fenómenos naturales y brindar orientación hacia nuevas áreas de investigación.

terapia génica [gene therapy]: Introducción de un gen en una célula para corregir un trastorno hereditario.

testículo [testis (plural: testes)]: Órgano reproductor primario del macho; órgano que produce espermatozoides.

testosterona [testosterone]: Hormona sexual masculina segregada por los testículos.

tiempo geológico [geologic time]: Períodos de tiempo relacionados con la formación de la Tierra y su historia de aproximadamente 4,500 millones de años.

tilacoide [thylakoid]: Saco aplanado que se encuentra en un cloroplasto. Muchos tilacoides forman pilas que se conocen como grana. Los pigmentos y las enzimas para las reacciones de la fotosíntesis se encuentran en la membrana del saco.

tiras reactivas de glucosa [glucose test strips]: Materiales de diagnóstico usados para determinar rápidamente el pH de una sustancia líquida o semilíquida.

toxina [toxin]: Sustancia producida por un organismo que es venenosa para otro organismo.

traducción [translation]: Formación de proteínas en los ribosomas, usando ARN mensajero para dirigir el orden de los aminoácidos.

transcripción [transcription]: Formación de una molécula de ARN que complementa una hebra de ADN. El producto puede ser ARN mensajero, ARN transferente o ARN ribosómico.

transgénico [transgenic]: Plantas o animales que contienen genes de especies no relacionadas.

transporte activo [active transport]: Movimiento de una sustancia a través de una membrana biológica contra su gradiente de concentración con la ayuda de energía y proteínas de transporte específicas.

transporte pasivo [passive transport]: Difusión de una sustancia a través de una membrana biológica por medio de una proteína de transporte en la membrana.

tráquea [trachea]: En los vertebrados que respiran aire, tubo que conecta la laringe con los pulmones.

triage [triage]: Ordenamiento y clasificación de pacientes de acuerdo con la gravedad de las heridas, la urgencia del tratamiento y el lugar de tratamiento. Se realiza en procedimientos de emergencia cuando se presentan grandes números de víctimas durante un desastre.

trompa de Falopio [oviduct]: Tubo que conecta un ovario al útero. Se lo llama también oviducto.

tronco encefálico [brain stem]: Parte de la base del encéfalo que controla muchas funciones corporales involuntarias, como la respiración, la frecuencia cardíaca y algunos reflejos. Se lo llama también tronco del encéfalo, tronco cerebral o tallo cerebral.

tubo de diálisis [dialysis tubing]: Tubo hecho de un material que permite que pasen algunas sustancias, como el agua, pero impide que pasen otras sustancias de determinado tamaño molecular. Este material se usa en tratamientos de diálisis para pacientes con problemas de los riñones porque puede usarse para filtrar materiales tóxicos de la sangre que los riñones de estos pacientes ya no pueden procesar.

túbulos seminíferos [seminiferous tubules]: Tubos espiralados y alargados que se encuentran en los testículos y en los cuales se producen los espermatozoides.

U

uréter [ureter]: Tubo muscular que lleva la orina del riñón a la vejiga urinaria.

uretra [urethra]: En los vertebrados, tubo a través del cual sale del cuerpo lo orina desde la vejiga.

útero [uterus]: Órgano muscular hueco, que en encuentra en la pelvis femenina, en el cual se desarrolla el feto.

V

vacuna [vaccine]: Preparación médica usada para estimular la respuesta inmune específica del cuerpo de un organismo para que produzca anticuerpos contra un patógeno, sin generar una infección.

vacuola [vacuole]: Estructura recubierta de una membrana que se encuentra en el citoplasma de una célula o en un organismo unicelular. Distintos tipos de vacuolas tienen funciones diferentes.

vagina [vagina]: Órgano tubular que conduce del útero a la abertura del tracto reproductor femenino.

variable [variable]: Condición que varía de un organismo a otro (tamaño, forma, color) o que está sujeta a cambio en un organismo individual (humedad, temperatura, intensidad de la luz, fatiga).

variación continua [continuous variation]: Se produce cuando los fenotipos posibles para un rasgo ocurren como una serie de intermedios en lugar de dividirse en dos categorías distintas. Un ejemplo es la altura del ser humano.

variación discreta [discrete variation]: Se produce cuando los fenotipos de un rasgo pertenecen a dos categorías distintas. Un ejemplo es el sexo humano, en el que el fenotipo puede ser masculino o femenino.

vasopresina [vasopressin]: Hormona liberada por la pituitaria en respuesta a la señal de deshidratación enviada por el hipotálamo.

vejiga [bladder]: Órgano del sistema urinario que recibe la orina producida por los riñones. La orina sale de la vejiga a través de la uretra.

vena [vein]: Vaso sanguíneo a través del cual la sangre fluye hacia el corazón.

vitaminas [vitamins]: Grupo de sustancias orgánicas esenciales para el metabolismo de los organismos vivos. Se encuentran en cantidades muy pequeñas en los alimentos y algunas se producen en forma sintética.

vulva [vulva]: Órganos reproductores femeninos externos, incluyendo los labios genitales y el clítoris.

Credits

Unit 2

Unit 3

CHAPTER 9: Opener Shutterstock/Kushch Dmitry; **Cafeteria line** Shutterstock/ Fesus Robert; **9.1** BSCS by Carlye Calvin; **9.2** (recycling plastic, paper) BSCS by Bill Beaudin; **9.3** Comstock; **9.4** Corel; **9.7** (worm) Carlye Calvin, (worms and compost) BSCS by Bill Beaudin; **9.15** BSCS by Bill Beaudin; **9.16** (wheat in the field, grain harvest combine) Corel, (flour, tortillas) BSCS by Bill Beaudin; **9.17** (hen, raw whole chicken, cooked chicken) BSCS by Bill Beaudin; **9.18** BSCS by Bill Beaudin; **9.19** (a) Comstock, (c) PhotoDisc; **9.28** BSCS by Carlye Calvin; **9.29** BSCS by Bill Beaudin; **Finished compost** BSCS by Bill Beaudin; **9.31** USGS; **Cabin in the snow** BSCS by Wilber Fulker; **9.32** Corel.

EXPLAIN SECTION: Opener (bug collector in tree) Philippe Psaila/Photo Researchers, Inc., (woman looking into microscope) Shutterstock/Laurence Gough, (manatee researcher) Douglas Faulkner/Photo Researchers, Inc.; **Pregnant woman** PhotoDisc; **Ex.2** PhotoDisc.

Unit 4

Unit Opener (MRI brain scan) Shutterstock/Daisy Daisy, (MP3 player) Shutterstock/elen 418, (computer memory) Shutterstock/carroteater.

CHAPTER 10: Opener Eye of Science/Photo Researchers, Inc.; **Budding hydra** © Roland Birke/ Science Faction/Corbis; **Budding yeast** Dr. Dennis Kunkel/Visuals Unlimited; **Birds mating, Insects mating** Corel; **10.2** Comstock; **10.3** (a) M. Siegelman/Visuals Unlimited, (b) Cabisco/Visuals Unlimited, (c) James W. Richardson/Visuals Unlimited; **10.4** Corel; **10.5** Jason Pope/Colorado School for the Deaf and the Blind; **Lizards mating** Art Today/Painet, www.painetworks.com; **Puffball releasing spores** © Stephen Dalton/Photo Researchers; **10.6** The Roslin Institute, Edinburgh; **10.11** (b) Ed Reschke; **10.12** © Carolina Biological Supply Company, Used by permission. **10.14** Corel; **10.15** W. Perry Conway/Corbis; **10.17** Courtesy of the Lor Family; **10.18** PhotoDisc; **10.19** J. Terrence McCabe; **10.20** Kirsten Starcher.

CHAPTER 11: Opener (Navajo Code Talkers being honored) Paul Natonabah, The Navajo Times, (Navajos serving with Marine signal unit) Courtesy of Air Force News Archive, (Navajo Code Talkers in the field) © Corbis; **DNA model** Comstock; **11.3** Barbara McClintock Papers, American Philosophical Society; **11.5** Courtesy, Cold Spring Harbor Laboratory Archives; **11.8** BSCS by Robert F. Schwengel; **11.9** Adapted from art courtesy of National Human Genome Research Institute; **11.10** J. R. Paulsen, U. Laemmli, D. W. Fawcett/Visuals Unlimited; **11.18** (b) Dr. Stanley Flegler/Visuals Unlimited; **Hand holding corn kernels** Comstock; **11.31** (cotton plant) John Cunningham/Visuals Unlimited; **11.33** BSCS by Robert F. Schwengel; **11.35** Comstock; **11.36** U.S. Department of Energy Joint Genome Institute, http://www.jgi.doe.gov; **Human arm with DNA** PhotoDisc; **Geneticist** © Bob Handelman, All rights reserved.

CHAPTER 12: Opener © Kevin Dodge/Corbis; **Chromosomes and DNA** MedicalRF.com/Visuals Unlimited; **Father and baby** PhotoDisc; **12.1** © Jack Hollingsworth/Corbis; **Bunnies** (newborn and baby bunnies) Dee Wilkins, (adult bunnies) Lucinda Schirmer; **Heads side of a coin** Corel; **12.5** © Claude Edelmann/Photo Researchers; **12.8** © Biophoto Associates/Photo Researchers; **12.12** BSCS by Robert F. Schwengel; **12.16** March of Dimes Birth Defects Foundation; **12.20** (finch) Art Today; **Different types of beans** Corel; **12.22** BSCS by Carlye Calvin; **Romanov family** BSCS by Robert F. Schwengel; **12.31** Indigo Instruments, www.indigo.com; **12.33** Comstock.

Unit 5

Unit Opener (fetus) MedicalRF.com/Visuals Unlimited, (cell division) Greg Dale/National Geographic/Getty Images.

CHAPTER 13: Opener (glass frog and eggs) Thomas Marent/Visuals Unlimited, (horseshoe crab eggs) Gustav Verberber/Visuals Unlimited, (Cedar Waxwing chick embryo) Dr. John D. Cunningham/Visuals Unlimited, (salmon eggs) Natalie Fobes; **Boy with microscope** © Tim Pannell/Corbis; **13.2** Corel; **13.4** Courtesy of Wilber Fulker; **13.7** (left) Will Allgood/Media Design Associate, (middle) Cabisco/Visuals Unlimited, (right) John D. Cunningham/Visuals Unlimited; **13.8** Dr. Steven Scadding, Sandra J. Ackerley, Department of Zoology, University of Guelph, Ontario, Canada NIG 2W1; **13.13** BSCS by Carlye Calvin; **Students writing** EyeWire; **13.14** Media Design Associates; **13.15** Will Allgood, Mark Viner/Media Design Associates; **13.18** (a) Fred Hossler/Visuals Unlimited, (b) David M. Phillips/Visuals Unlimited, (c) John D. Cunningham/ Visuals Unlimited; **13.21** Craig Brunetti and Sean Carroll, HHMI, Dept. Molecular Biology, University of Wisconsin, Madison, USA; **13.22** (a) David Wrobel/Visuals Unlimited, (b) Jim Merli/ Visuals Unlimited; **13.23** (b) Michael Abbey/Visuals Unlimited; **13.25** Lochlean Macleay, M.D.; **13.28** (a) John Moss/Photo Researchers; **13.29** Courtesy of Phil and Ellen Goulding; **13.31** K. G.

Murti/Visuals Unlimited; **13.33** (left) PhotoDisc; **13.34** Ken Lucas/Visuals Unlimited; **13.36** (a) Dr. David Phillips/Visuals Unlimited, (b) Cabisco/Visuals Unlimited; **13.38** (a) Victor Hutchinson/ Visuals Unlimited, (b) Corel.

CHAPTER 14: Opener (family, mature woman) Ms. Lynn Peters Adler, National Centenarian Awareness Project, (centenarian) © William Clark; **Asian family** © 2010 Photos.com, a division of Getty Images. All rights reserved; **14.1** Courtesy of the Baena Family; **14.2** BSCS by Carlye Calvin; **Student writing in journal** BSCS by Carlye Calvin; **Children working on puzzle** EyeWire; **14.3** PhotoDisc; **Children** Comstock; **14.6** Courtesy of Jean and Mina Milani; **Senior with group of children** BSCS by Carlye Calvin; **Older Hispanic man** PhotoDisc; **Students debating** BSCS by Carlye Calvin; **African American father and child** BrandX Pictures; **14.15** BSCS by Carlye Calvin; **Teens from different ethnic backgrounds** Corel; **14.19** Bayard H. Brattstrom/Visuals Unlimited; **14.21** D. Long/Visuals Unlimited; **14.22** D. Long/Visuals Unlimited; **Amish at open market** Link/ Visuals Unlimited.

Unit 6

Unit Opener (riverbank) Shutterstock/Tony Ramos Photography, (logs and seagull) © Darren Greenwood/Design Pics/Corbis.

CHAPTER 15: Opener Shutterstock/Sascha Burkard; **People in waterfall** Rich Clarkson; **Spider with prey** Corel; **15.1** Comstock; **15.3** Carlye Calvin; **Stream** Corel; **Cows** Corel; **15.4** Eric Gaba; **15.5** Courtesy of Daryl O'Connor; **15.6** Corel; **15.9** Corel; **15.10** Corel; **15.11** BSCS by Carlye Calvin; **15.12** BSCS by Robert F. Schwengel; **Easter Island statues** Corel; **15.17** USDA Forest Service; **15.21** NOAA/National Climatic Data Center.

CHAPTER 16: Opener © NASA/Corbis; **Polar Bear** NOAA; **16.1** EyeWire; **Scientist taking notes** U.S. Geological Survey/Michael F. Diggles; **16.2** NASA; **16.3** Carlye Calvin; *Daphnia* Bruce J. Russell/BioMEDIA Associates, *Gammarus* John D. Cunningham/Visuals Unlimited; **Boys at edge of lake** EyeWire; **16.4** Ru Morrison; **16.6** PhotoDisc.

EVALUATE SECTION: Opener (biologists hunting eels) © Tony Kurdzuk/Star Ledger/Corbis, (students testing water samples) Martin Shields/Photo Researchers, Inc.; **Ev.4** Corel; **Ev.8** From S. E. Gabriel, K. N. Brigman, B. H. Koller, R. C. Boucher, and M. J. Stutts. (7 October 1994) Cystic fibrosis heterozygote resistance to cholera toxin in the cystic fibrosis mouse model. *Science, 266,* pp. 107–109; **Ev.9** Reiss, D., & Marino, L. (2001). Mirror self-recognition in the bottlenose dolphin: A case of cognitive convergence. *Proceedings of the National Academy of Sciences, 98*(10): 5937–5942. Copyright (2001) National Academy of Sciences, U.S.A.; **Ev.10** Adapted from "The relations of early whales (archaeocetes) to artiodactyls and the two extant groups, odontoceti and mysticeti. Tree by Felix G. Marx, University of Bristol. Images of cetacenas adapted from National Geographic's *The evolution of whales* by Douglas H. Chadwick, Shawn Gould and Robert Clark. Re-illustrated for public access distribution by Sharon Mooney ©2006. Open source license CC ASA 2.5", (Pakicetidae) Illustration by Carl Buell, (Ambulocetidae) Illustration by Arthur Weasley; **Ev.14** (a) Jack Bostrack/Visuals Unlimited, (b) Gary Robinson/Visuals Unlimited; **Big band dancers** The Bettmann Archive; **Wetlands** Carlye Calvin.

APPENDIX F: F1.1 Science VU/Visuals Unlimited; **F1.2** Courtesy of Bill Jacobi, Department of Agriculture Colorado State University; **F1.3** CDC, Photo by James Gathany; **F1.4** David M. Phillips/ Visuals Unlimited; **F1.5** (a) Science VU/Visuals Unlimited, (b) Hans Gerlderblon/Visuals Unlimited, (c) Cabisco/Visuals Unlimited; **F1.6** Science VU/Visuals Unlimited; **F1.8** (a) E. Couture-Tosi, The Electron Microspy, Group of Biozentrum Basel, Switzerland, (b) J. V. deu Brock, The Electron Microspy, Group of Biozentrum Basel, Switzerland; **F2 Opener** PhotoDisc; **F2.1** Jack Stein Grove/www.JSGrove.com; **F2.2** John D. Cunningham/Visuals Unlimited; **F2.4** Carlye Calvin; **F2.5** E. J. Cable/Tom Stack and Associates; **F2.6** (a) Doug Sokell/BSCS, (b) William S. Ormerod/Visuals Unlimited; **F2.8** Fred Hossler/Visuals Unlimited; **F2.11** (a) © Ripon Microslides. Used with permission from Carolina Biological Supply Company, Burlington, NC, (b) John D. Cunningham/ Visuals Unlimited; **F2.15** (a) Carlye Calvin, (b) John Shaw/Tom Stack and Associates, (c) Ken Davis/ Tom Stack and Associates; **F2.17** William S. Ormerod/Visuals Unlimited; **F2.18** (a) Greg Vaughn/Tom Stack and Associates, (b) Kevin Schafer Photography; **F2.20** © 2002 Steven J. Baskauf; **F2.21** (a) Hugh Spenser/BSCS, (b) Doug Sokell/BSCS; **F2.22** George Loun/Visuals Unlimited; **F2.23** (a) Doug Sokell/ BSCS, (c) John Cunningham/Visuals Unlimited; **F2.24** Doug Sokell/BSCS; **F2.26** Doug Sokell/BSCS; **F2.27** Carlye Calvin; **F2.28** Doug Sokell/BSCS; **F2.31** (a) Doug Sokell/BSCS; **F2.32** Jackie-Ott Rogers/ BSCS; **F3.1** Carolina Biological Supply/Phototake NYC; **F3.2** (epithelial tissue) Carolina Biological Supply/Phototake NYC, (connective tissue) Comstock, (nerve tissue, muscle tissue) Ed Reschke.

Index

Page numbers in bold print indicate item was in bold in the text; italics indicate a table, graph, illustration, or photograph.

Milankovitch cycles, 787
Miscarriage, **704**
Mitochondria, **389, 944**
Mitosis, **530, 684,** *685*
Modeling change, 97–101
Model of Earth history, 133–135
Molecules, **360,** 364–365, *416*; models of, 419–421; movement of, 233–235; source of energy in, 424–425
Moles, *384*
Monkeyflowers, reproductive isolation in, *176*
Monocots, **932,** *933*
Monogamy, **555**
Moss, *915*; life cycle, *915*
Motor cortex of brain, 49
Motor neurons, 259
Movement of molecules, 233–235
Mullis, Kary, 607, *607*
Multicellular organisms, 158, *390*
Multiple sclerosis (MS), 313
Muscles, *382,* 383, *385*; biceps, 383, *384*; cell, *694*; energy and, 389–390; exercise and, *400*; fatigue, 390; fibers of, *385*; filaments in, 385; glycogen levels in, *397–398*; mobility, 383–387; structures, 380–383, 389–390; tissue, *945*; in trachea, *692*; triceps, 383, *384*
Mutations, **582,** 583, 704; deletion, **582**; effects of, 614; insertion, **582**; preserving, *582*; spontaneous, 711; substitution, **582**
Myofibril, *385*

N

Nathans, Daniel, 601
National Collegiate Athletic Association (NCAA), 402
Natural defenses against disease, 309–313
Natural selection (Darwin), 112–114; population and, 110–111
Nature, exploring, 152
Nature Conservancy, 831
Nectar, **929**
Negative feedback systems, **263**
Nelkin, Dorothy, 612
Nephrons, **242**
Nerve cells, *694*
Nerve tissue, *945*
Nervous system, **261,** 273–276
Neurobiologists, **48**
Neurofibromatosis, 666

Neurons, **261,** *274*
Neurotransmitters, 273, **275**
Niacin, *901*
Nicotinamide adenine dinucleotide (NADH), 439
Nicotine, 404, 706, 711
Nimbus-7 satellite, 838
Nirenberg, Marshall, 599
Nitrates, 839–840, *840*
Nitrogen, 839; cycle, *487*
Nondisjunction, *639,* **639**
Nonspecific immunity, 310–311
Nostoc bacteria, *77*
Nucleic acids, *231,* 364, *365,* **577**
Nucleotides, **364, 577,** *578, 580*
Nucleus, **225, 944**
Nutrients, 353–355, 484; and energy, 360, *399*; positive and negative controls for, 358; tests, 356
Nutrition, 365–366

O

Observations, 37–38, *725,* 748; of cognitive growth, 726–727; of emotional growth, 728; guidelines for, 729–730; of physical development, 728; sample form, *731*; of social growth, 728
Olympic Training Center, Colorado Springs, Colorado, 405
Omnivores, *494*
Oncogenes, **710,** *710*
Onion skin specimen, *221*
On the Origin of Species (Darwin), 107–108
Orangutan, *64*
Organ, **944,** *945*
Organelles, **225, 944**
Organic molecules, **360**
Organisms: in ancient seas, 156; classifying, 189–191; complexity score for, 937; multicellular, 158
Organization: of diversity, 191–195; in living systems, 71; of phylum Arthropoda, 190; of phylum Chordata, 190, *192*
Organ systems, **239,** *946*; functions of, 946
Orgasm, **544**
Orrorin tugenensis, 131
Osmosis, **234,** *234,* 826
Ova, **529**
Ovarian cycle, *540,* **541**
Ovaries, **536,** *539*
Oviduct, **536**
Ovulation, **541**

Ovules, **916**
Ovum production, 539–541
Oxygen: accumulation in atmosphere, 157; transport of, *238, 690*

P

Paleobiologist, 118–119, **121**–122
Paleontologist, 925
Palmar prehension, *41*
Pang, Kevin, 184–185
Pangaea, 124
Pantothenic acid, *901*
Parfit, Michael, 812
Passive transport, **235**
Pastures, 769–771
Pathogens, 310, **317, 904**; eubacteria, 905; viruses, 907–909
PCR (polymerase chain reaction), **607,** *608,* 609
Pedigrees, 653–658, *655*
Penis, **538**
Pepsin, 378
Peptide bond, **595**
Peranema, 196, *197*
Performance and fitness, 351–353, 832–833; factors influencing, 401–405; muscles and, 380–383
Periodic table of elements, *900*
Peristalsis, 377
Permeable membrane, **231**
Personal glossary, 864–865, *865*
pH, 277, 801, 804; foods, *282*; information, 278; maintaining by buffers, 283; monitoring, 489–490; regulating, 278–283; small invertebrates and, 805
Pharmacogenics, 611
Phenotype, **647**–648
Phosphorous, *903*
Photosynthesis, **157,** 459–461; cell's view of, 454–458; measuring, 446–454
Photosynthetic bacteria, *157*
Phototrophic bacteria, *157*
Phyla, level of classification, 190, *192*
Physical activity, 349, *349*
Physical anthropologist, 119–120, **129**–130
Physical digestion, **376**
Physical fitness. *See* Fitness
Physiological processes, **261**
Physiological response, **258**
Phytoplanktons, 838
Piaget, Jean, 742
Pie graph, 893

Seeds, 91–92, 94–95, 156, 159, 926–932
Segregation, principle of, **636**
Selectively permeable membrane, **231**
Semen, **538**
Seminal vesicles, **538**
Seminiferous tubules, **542**
Senescence, **682**
Sensory cortex, **49**
Sensory neurons, **258**
Sepals, **916**
Sequoiadendron giganteum, 911
Sex-linked traits, 658–659
Sexual behavior, 548–550
Sexual intercourse, 544
Sexually transmitted diseases (STDs), *547,* **548**; prevention of, 335–336
Sexual reproduction, **529**–530, 914
Sexual selection, **552**
Shaken baby syndrome, 743
Sheep brains, 43, *43*
Shock, **302**
Sickle cell disease, 584, *587*; hemoglobin abnormalities in, 585–586, *586,* 596, *596*; red blood cell abnormalities in, 585–586, *586*
Single-celled organisms, 156
Skeleton, 65
Small intestine, 378, *379*
Smith, Hamilton, 601
Smoking, 324, 326, 404
Snails, 483, 488
Snakes, *182*
Social animals, 62
Social growth, 728, 743–745
Sodium, *903*
Solar energy, 455–456
Solar system model, 93
Solutes, **220,** *220,* 233
Solutions, **220,** *220*
Solvent, **220,** *220*
Sorting genes, 636–637
Space as limiting factor, 777
Speciation, **172,** *174,* 175–176
Species, 148, **172**
Specific immune response, **311**–313
Sperm, **529, 537,** 541–542, *542*
Sphagnum, 920
Spheric grasp, *41*
Spiders, *557*
Spontaneous abortion, 704
Spontaneous mutations, 711
Sporophyte, **915**
Stamens, **916**
Starch, **228,** 363; breakdown of,

369–370, *371,* 374; experimenting with, 370
Starfish, *699*
Stem cells, **700**–701
Stereum complicatum, 80
Stimulus, **274**
Stomach, 378
Stomata, **257, 914,** *914*
Strata, 121
Stratigraphy, **121,** 127, *127*
Streptococcus bacteria, 77, 318
Streptococcus mutans, 906
Stress, limits of homeostasis, 294–298
Stressors, 294, **296,** *325*
Stroma, **455**
Sturnus vulgaris, 195
Substitution mutation, **582**
Sulfolobus acidcaldarius, 196, *197*
Sulfur, *903*
Surface temperatures, 253–257
Sweating, 241, 246
Synapse, **275**
Systems analysis, **801**–803
Systolic blood pressure, **300**

T

Taieb, Maurice, 89
Tancredi, Laurence, 612
Tay-Sachs disease, 666
T4 bacteriophage, *907*
T cells, 317
Technology and fitness, 404–405
Telophase, *685,* **686**
Temperature: body, 253–257, **300**; measurement, 888; ranges of human body, *823*; regulation, 284–285; small invertebrates and, 806
Termites, 60, 62
Testes, **537**
Testosterone, 401, **542**
Thalidomide, 704, *707*
Thecamoeba cell, 72
Thermal energy, 417
Thermus aquaticus, 608
Thiamine, *901*
Think-share-advise-revise (TSAR) strategy, 38, 855–856, *856*
Thylakoids, **455**
Thymine, 579
Tiger salamander, 717–718, *718*
Tiktaalik, *138*
Till, James, 700
Tip prehension, *41*
Tissue, **944**
Tobacco, 404

Tobacco mosaic virus, *907*; in cabbage plant, *908*
Tocopherol, *901*
Toxic substances, 849
Toxins, **404,** 603
Trachea, *692*
Traits, human, 740, *740*
Transcription, **590,** *591, 594*
Transfer RNA (tRNA), **591,** *591,* 595
Transgenic organisms, **603**
Translation, 591–595, **592,** *594, 598*
Trash, 474–476
Tree of life, 160–161, 196
Triage, hospital. *See* Hospital triage
Triceps muscles, 383, *384*
Trichonympha protist, *81*
Tri-Lakes ecosystem (fictional lake system), 796, *796*; abiotic components of, 803; bass population in, 797, 799, 803, 807; biotic components of, 803; complexity of, 798–799; data packet, 800; identifying causes of change, 807–810; investigating, 803; limited system analysis of, 803; problems at, 797–798; and public policy, 815–817; study of, 798–799
Trobriand Islands, 749, *749*
Trophic level, **499**
Tropical rain forest, *482*
T-table, *857*
Tumors, 708
Turner syndrome, 640
Twins: fraternal, 740–741, *741*; identical, 740–741, *741*

U

Umbilical cord, **545,** 690
Uncontrollable risks, *326*
Unifying principles of biology, *22,* 516
Units of measurement, 887; area, 887; length, 887; mass, 888; temperature, 888; unit conversions, 888–891; volume, 888
Unity and diversity, 151
Urea, 483
Ureters, **241**
Urethra, **538**
Urinary system, 236, **239,** *241*
USDA food guide pyramid, *366*
Uterine cycle, *540,* **541**
Uterus, **536,** 704, *706*

V

Vaccines, **314, 904**; programs, 338
Vacuole, 235
Vagina, **537**
Variables in experiment, **217**
Variation and evolution, 641–644
Vascular plants, 912–913; adaptations, 914; root system, 914; seedless, 921–923; structure, 920, *921*
Vascular tissue, **912**
Vas deferens, **538**
Vasopressin, **262,** *263*
Veins, **239**
Venn diagrams, 859
Vermeij, Geerat, 925
Vestigial structures, **181,** *182*
Vibrio cholerae, 826
Virulence, **904**
Viruses: diseases, 907; pathogens, 907–909

Vital signs, 299–300, *301*
Vitamins, **365,** *901–902*
Volcanoes, 506–507, *507*
Volume measurement, 888
Volvox, *69*
Voyage of the HMS *Beagle, 107,* 107–108
Vulva, **537**
Vygotsky, Lev, 743

W

Wallace, Alfred Russel, 108, 110, *110,* 641
Wastes, 241–244
Water, 364–365; cycle, *485*; as limiting factor, 776, *777*; molecule, *420*
Watson, James, 570, *574*
Weather, 801, *801*
Web: credible information on, 867; searching, 866

Webb, Barbara, 835
Web of life, 491–492
Western gull, *288*
Whale, 830, *831*
White blood cells, **316,** *694, 700*
Wilkins, Maurice, 570
Windpipe, **692**
Windpollinated flowers, *929*
Wolves, *60*
Worms, 481–483

X

Xanthomonas campestris, 905
X-linked recessive trait, **659**

Z

Zebras, *148*; kinds of, 148–150; stripes of, 114–115
Zygote, **529,** 632